MICHAEL C FRAMPTON

INSTITUTE OF BASIC MEDICAL SCIENCES

OCTOBER 1980

Medical Physiology

9th EDITION

Review of Medical Physiology

WILLIAM F. GANONG, MD

Professor of Physiology

Chairman, Department of Physiology

University of California School of Medicine

San Francisco, California

Los Altos, California 94022

LANGE Medical Publications

International Standard Book Number: *0–87041–135–7*
Library of Congress Catalogue Card Number: *78–71798*

Review of Medical Physiology, 9th ed. $14.00

A Concise Medical Library for Practitioner and Student

Current Medical Diagnosis & Treatment 1979 (annual revision). Edited by M.A. Krupp and M.J. Chatton. 1130 pp. — 1979

Current Pediatric Diagnosis & Treatment, 5th ed. Edited by C.H. Kempe, H.K. Silver, and D. O'Brien. 1102 pp, *illus.* — 1978

Current Surgical Diagnosis & Treatment, 3rd ed. Edited by J.E. Dunphy and L.W. Way. 1139 pp, *illus.* — 1977

Current Obstetric & Gynecologic Diagnosis & Treatment, 2nd ed. Edited by R.C. Benson. 976 pp, *illus.* — 1978

Review of Physiological Chemistry, 17th ed. H.A. Harper, V.W. Rodwell, and P.A. Mayes. About 700 pp, *illus.* — 1979

Review of Medical Microbiology, 13th ed. E. Jawetz, J.L. Melnick, and E.A. Adelberg. 550 pp, *illus.* — 1978

Review of Medical Pharmacology, 6th ed. F.H. Meyers, E. Jawetz, and A. Goldfien. 762 pp, *illus.* — 1978

Basic & Clinical Immunology, 2nd ed. Edited by H.H. Fudenberg, D.P. Stites, J.L. Caldwell, and J.V. Wells. 758 pp, *illus.* — 1978

Basic Histology, 2nd ed. L.C. Junqueira, J. Carneiro, and A.N. Contopoulos. 468 pp, *illus.* — 1977

Clinical Cardiology. M. Sokolow and M.B. McIlroy. 659 pp, *illus.* — 1977

General Urology, 9th ed. D.R. Smith. 541 pp, *illus.* — 1978

General Ophthalmology, 8th ed. D. Vaughan and T. Asbury. 379 pp, *illus.* — 1977

Correlative Neuroanatomy & Functional Neurology, 17th ed. J.G. Chusid. 464 pp, *illus.* — 1979

Principles of Clinical Electrocardiography, 10th ed. M.J. Goldman. 415 pp, *illus.* — 1979

The Nervous System. W.F. Ganong. 226 pp, *illus.* — 1977

Handbook of Obstetrics & Gynecology, 6th ed. R.C. Benson. 772 pp, *illus.* — 1977

Physician's Handbook, 19th ed. M.A. Krupp, N.J. Sweet, E. Jawetz, E.G. Biglieri, R.L. Roe, and C.A. Camargo. 758 pp, *illus.* — 1979

Handbook of Pediatrics, 12th ed. H.K. Silver, C.H. Kempe, and H.B. Bruyn. 723 pp, *illus.* — 1977

Handbook of Poisoning: Diagnosis & Treatment, 9th ed. R.H. Dreisbach. 559 pp. — 1977

Table of Contents

SECTION III. FUNCTIONS OF THE NERVOUS SYSTEM

SECTION VIII. FORMATION & EXCRETION OF URINE

Preface

This book is designed to provide a concise summary of mammalian and, particularly, of human physiology which medical students and others can supplement with readings in current texts, monographs, and reviews. Pertinent aspects of general and comparative physiology are also included. Summaries of relevant anatomic considerations will be found in each section, but this book is written primarily for those who have some knowledge of anatomy, chemistry, and biochemistry.

Examples from clinical medicine are given where pertinent to illustrate physiologic points. Physicians desiring to use this book as a review will find short discussions of important symptoms produced by disordered function in several sections.

It has not been possible to be complete and concise without also being dogmatic. I believe, however, that the conclusions presented without a detailed discussion of the experimental data on which they are based are those supported by the bulk of the currently available evidence. Much of this evidence can be found in the papers cited in the credit lines of the illustrations. Further discussions of particular subjects and information on subjects not considered in detail in this book can be found in the references listed at the end of each section. Information about serial review publications which provide up-to-date discussions of various physiologic subjects is included in the note on general references in the appendix.

In the interest of brevity and clarity, I have in most instances omitted the names of the many investigators whose work made possible the view of physiology presented here. This is in no way intended to slight their contributions, but including their names and specific references to original papers would greatly increase the length of this book.

I am greatly indebted to many individuals who helped in the preparation of this book. Those whom I wish especially to thank for their help with the Ninth Edition include Drs. David Ramsay, Henry Keutmann, and Gordon Shepherd. I am also indebted to my wife, who labored long hours typing corrections, and to Annette Lowe and André Sala, who drew many of the illustrations. I also wish to thank all the students and others who took the time to write to me offering helpful criticisms and suggestions. Such comments are always welcome, and I solicit additional corrections and criticisms, which may be addressed to me at the Department of Physiology, University of California, San Francisco, California 94143, USA. Many associates and friends provided unpublished illustrative materials, and numerous authors and publishers generously granted permission to reproduce illustrations from other books and journals.

With the appearance of the ninth edition I am pleased to be able to announce that the following translations have been published: Portuguese (third edition), German (third edition), Italian (fifth edition), Spanish (sixth edition), Japanese (fifth edition), Polish, Czechoslovakian, Chinese, Greek, Serbo-Croatian, Turkish and French. Vietnamese and Indonesian translations are under way. The book has also been recorded on tape for use by the blind.

William F. Ganong

San Francisco
June, 1979

Physiologic Principles | 1

In unicellular organisms, all vital processes occur in a single cell. As the evolution of multicellular organisms has progressed, various cell groups have taken over particular functions. In higher animals and humans, the specialized cell groups include a gastrointestinal system to digest and absorb food, a respiratory system to take up O_2 and eliminate CO_2, a urinary system to remove wastes, a cardiovascular system to distribute food, O_2, and the products of metabolism, a reproductive system to perpetuate the species, and nervous and endocrine systems to coordinate and integrate the functions of the other systems. This book is concerned with the way these systems function and the way each contributes to the functions of the body as a whole.

CELLULAR STRUCTURE & FUNCTION

Revolutionary advances in the understanding of cell structure and function have been made through the use of electron microscopy, x-ray diffraction, and the other technics of modern cellular and molecular biology. The specialization of the cells in the various organs of higher animals is very great, and no cell can be called "typical" of all cells in the body. However, a number of structures, or **organelles,** are common to most cells. These structures are shown in Fig 1–1.

Cell Membrane
The membrane that surrounds the cell is a re-

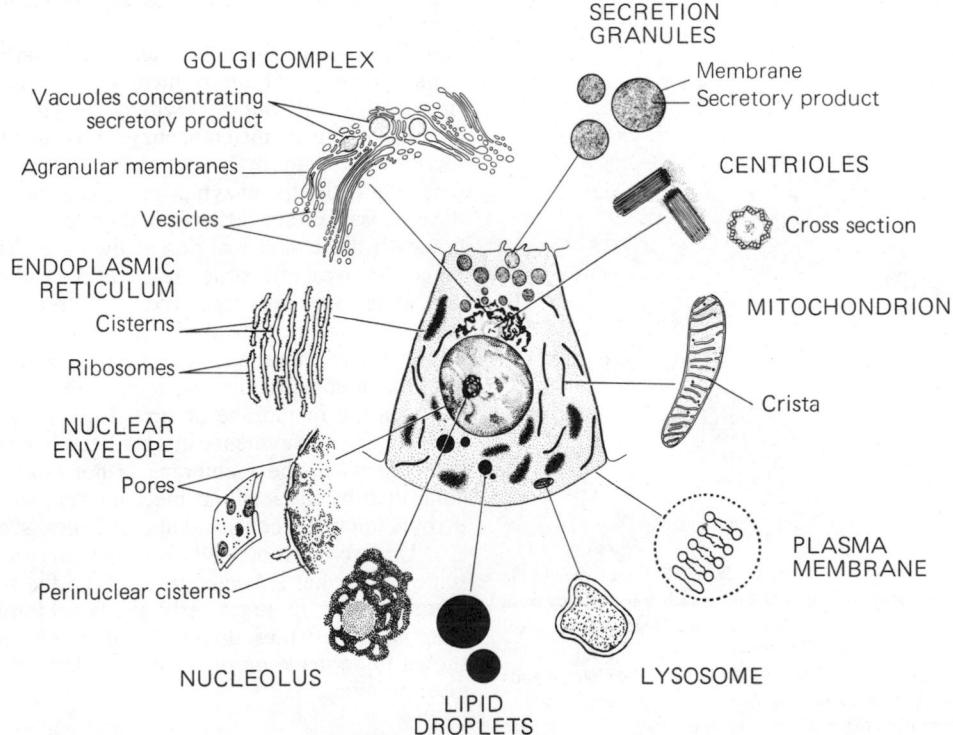

Figure 1–1. Ultrastructure of the common cell organelles and inclusions. The endoplasmic reticulum illustrated here is the granular type, with ribosomes attached to it. Some cells also contain tubes of membrane without ribosomes (agranular endoplasmic reticulum). The pores in the nuclear envelope are closed by a thin, homogeneous membrane. (Modified and reproduced, with permission, from Bloom W, Fawcett WD: *A Textbook of Histology,* 10th ed. Saunders, 1975.)

markable structure. It is not only semipermeable, allowing some substances to pass through it and excluding others, but its permeability can be varied. It is generally referred to as the **plasma membrane.** The nucleus is also surrounded by a membrane, and the organelles are surrounded by or made up of membrane.

Although the chemical structure of membranes and their properties vary considerably from one location to another, they have certain common features. They are generally about 7.5 nm (75 Angstrom units) thick. They are made up primarily of protein and lipids. The chemistry of proteins and lipids is discussed in Chapter 17. The major lipids are phospholipids such as phosphatidylcholine and phosphatidylethanolamine. The shape of the phospholipid molecule is roughly that of a clothespin (Fig 1–2). The head end of the molecule contains the phosphate portion, is positively charged, and is quite soluble in water (polar, or **hydrophilic**). The tails are quite insoluble (nonpolar, or **hydrophobic**). In the membrane, the hydrophilic ends are exposed to the aqueous environment that bathes the exterior of the cells and the aqueous cytoplasm; the hydrophobic ends meet in the

water-poor interior of the membrane. However, there is a degree of asymmetry in the distribution of lipid in the membrane; in human red cells, for example, there is more phosphatidylethanolamine and phosphatidylserine in the inner lamella and more lecithin and sphingomyelin in the outer lamella. The significance of this asymmetry is unknown. In **prokaryotes** (cells like bacteria in which there is no nucleus), phospholipids are the only membrane lipids, but in **eukaryotes** (cells containing nuclei), cell membranes also contain cholesterol (in animals) or other steroids (in plants). The cholesterol/phospholipid ratio in the membrane is inversely proportionate to the fluidity of the membrane.

There are many different proteins embedded in the membrane. They exist as separate globular units and stud the inside and outside of the membrane in a random array (Fig 1–2). Some are located in the inner surface of the membrane; some are located on the outer surface; and some extend through the membrane **(through and through proteins).** In general, the uncharged, hydrophobic portions of the protein molecules are located in the interior of the membrane and the charged, hydrophilic portions are located on the surfaces. Some of the proteins contain lipids (lipoproteins) and some contain carbohydrates (glycoproteins). Through and through glycoproteins with the carbohydrates attached to their outer ends function as receptors for hormones and neurotransmitters. Other proteins function as enzymes and probably as ion channels.

The protein structure—and particularly the enzyme content—of biologic membranes varies not only from cell to cell but also within the same cell. For example, there are different enzymes embedded in cell membranes than in mitochondrial membranes; in epithelial cells, the enzymes in the cell membrane on the mucosal surface differ from those in the cell membrane on the lateral margins of the cells. The membranes are dynamic structures, and their constituents are being constantly renewed at different rates. In addition, it is now clear that glycoproteins move laterally in the membrane. For example, membrane proteins that bind antibodies can aggregate in one or more spots on the membrane or spread diffusely over the surface. There is evidence that the lateral movement of components in the membrane is not random but is controlled by intracellular mechanisms that probably involve microfilaments and microtubules (see below).

Underlying most cells is a thin fuzzy layer plus some fibrils that collectively make up the **basement membrane** or, more properly, the **basal lamina.** The material that makes up the basal lamina has been shown to be made up of a collagen derivative plus 2 glycoproteins.

Intercellular Connections

Most cells stop dividing and moving when they come in contact with other cells. This **contact inhibition,** which is deficient in cancer cells, indicates that cells must communicate with each other. The mecha-

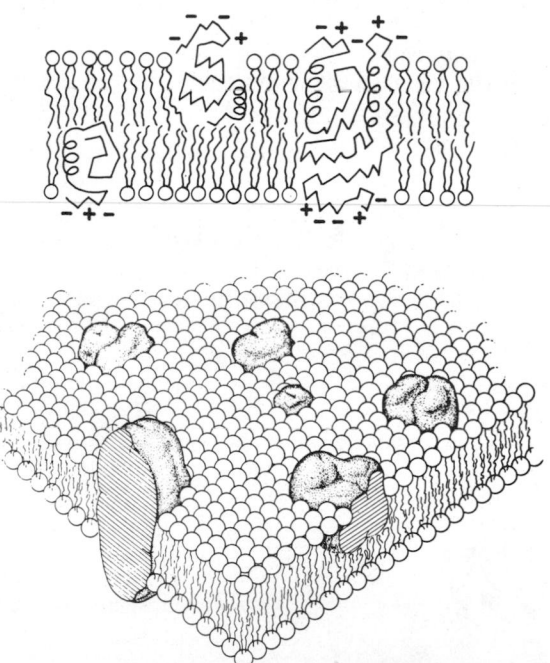

Figure 1–2. Biologic membrane. *Top:* Model of membrane structure. The phospholipid molecules each have 2 fatty acid chains (wavy lines) attached to a phosphate head (open circle). The proteins, indicated by the long lines, are partly in the α-helical configuration and partly folded, with the charged ends (+ and − signs) on the exterior or interior sides of the membrane. *Bottom:* Three-dimensional view of membrane. Proteins are shown as irregular shaded globules. (Reproduced, with permission, from Singer SJ, Nicolson GL: The fluid mosaic model of the structure of cell membranes. Science 175:720, 1972. Copyright 1972 by the American Association for the Advancement of Science.)

nisms responsible for this transfer of information are the subject of intensive research.

There are morphologically demonstrable connections between cells in tissues. Two types of connections are associated with cell-to-cell adhesion and maintenance of tissue strength and organization. One of these is the **tight junction,** in which the membranes of 2 cells become apposed and the outer layers of the membranes fuse. The other is the **adherens** type of junction, in which there are various forms of membrane specialization but the 2 membranes are separated by a 15–35 nm space. A third junction, the **gap junction** or **nexus,** permits the direct transfer of ions and other small molecules between cells without traversing the extracellular space. The gap junction is characterized by a 2 nm space between the opposing membranes. This gap is filled with densely packed particles through each of which there appears to be a channel that connects the 2 cells. Thus, the junction permits rapid propagation of electrical potential changes from one cell to another.

Nucleus & Related Structures

A nucleus is present in all animal cells that divide. If a cell is cut in half, the anucleate portion eventually dies without dividing. The nucleus is made up in large part of the **chromosomes,** the structures in the nucleus that carry a complete blueprint for all the heritable species and individual characteristics of the animal. During cell division, the pairs of chromosomes become visible, but between cell divisions the irregular clumps of the dark material called **chromatin** are the only evidence of their presence. Each chromosome is made up of supporting protein and a giant molecule of **deoxyribonucleic acid (DNA).** The ultimate units of heredity are the **genes** on the chromosomes, and each gene is a portion of the DNA molecule.

During normal cell division by **mitosis,** the chromosomes duplicate themselves and then divide in such a way that each daughter cell receives a full complement (**diploid number**) of chromosomes. During their final maturation, germ cells undergo a division in which half the chromosomes go to each daughter cell (see Chapter 23). This reduction division, or **meiosis,** is actually a 2-stage process; but the important consideration is that, as a result of it, mature sperms and ova contain half the normal number (the **haploid number**) of chromosomes. When a sperm and ovum unite, the resultant cell (**zygote**) has a full (diploid) complement of chromosomes, one-half from the female parent and one-half from the male. The chemistry of DNA and the splitting of its base chains during mitosis and meiosis are discussed in Chapter 17.

The nucleus of most cells contains a **nucleolus** (Fig 1–1), a patchwork of granules rich in **ribonucleic acid (RNA).** In some cells, the nucleus contains several of these structures. Nucleoli are most prominent and numerous in growing cells. The DNA in the nucleus serves as a template for the synthesis of RNA, which then moves to the cytoplasm, where it regulates the synthesis of proteins by the cell. The nucleolus is probably the site where the RNA found in the ribosomes (see below) is synthesized. Since the enzymes that control the metabolism of the cell are proteins, the synthesis of protein is the key to the control of the development of the cell. The chemistry of RNA and the subject of protein synthesis are discussed further in Chapter 17.

The nucleus is surrounded by a **nuclear membrane,** or **envelope** (Fig 1–1). This membrane is double, and the spaces between the 2 folds are called **perinuclear cisterns.** The nuclear membrane is apparently quite permeable, since it permits passage of molecules as large as RNA from the nucleus to the cytoplasm. There are areas of discontinuity in the nuclear membrane, but these ''pores'' are closed by a thin, homogeneous membrane.

Endoplasmic Reticulum

The endoplasmic reticulum is a complex series of tubules in the cytoplasm of the cell (Fig 1–1). The tubule walls are made up of membrane. In **granular** endoplasmic reticulum, granules called **ribosomes** are attached to the cytoplasmic side of the membrane, whereas in **agranular** endoplasmic reticulum the granules are absent. Free ribosomes are also found in the cytoplasm. The ribosomes are about 15 nm in diameter. Each is made up of a large and a small subunit called, on the basis of their rates of sedimentation in the centrifuge, the 50 S and the 30 S subunits, respectively. Sometimes, 3–5 ribosomes are clumped together, forming **polyribosomes (polysomes).** The ribosomes contain about 65% RNA and 35% protein. They are the sites of protein synthesis. The ribosomes attached to the endoplasmic reticulum synthesize proteins such as hormones secreted by the cell. The polypeptide chains are extruded into the endoplasmic reticulum. The free ribosomes synthesize cytoplasmic proteins such as hemoglobin (see Chapter 27).

The agranular endoplasmic reticulum is the site of steroid synthesis in steroid-secreting cells and the site of detoxification processes in other cells. As the sarcoplasmic reticulum (see Chapter 3), it plays an important role in skeletal and cardiac muscle.

Golgi Complex

The Golgi complex is a collection of membranous tubules and vesicles. It is usually located near the nucleus, and is particularly prominent in actively secreting gland cells. Hormones and enzymes are stored in protein-secreting cells as membrane-enclosed **secretion granules,** and these granules are produced in the Golgi complex. Thus, the Golgi complex ''packages'' proteins. The complex is also the site of formation of lysosomes (see below), and it adds certain carbohydrates to proteins to form glycoproteins (see Chapter 17). These carbohydrate-containing proteins on the cell surface play important roles in the association of cells to form tissues.

Mitochondria

Although their morphology varies somewhat

Figure 1–3. Cutaway drawing of a mitochondrion, showing the inner and outer membranes. The inner membrane is folded, forming shelves (cristae). The coiled structures represent possible arrangements of the mitochondrial DNA. Mitochondrial branching of the type shown here is not present in all cells. (Reproduced, with permission, from Nass MMK: Mitochondrial DNA: Advances, problems and goals. Science 165:25, 1969. Copyright 1969 by the American Association for the Advancement of Science.)

from cell to cell, each mitochondrion (Figs 1–1, 1–3) is in essence a sausage-shaped structure. It is made up of an outer membrane and an inner membrane that is folded to form shelves **(cristae).** The mitochondria are the power-generating units of the cell and are most plentiful and best developed in parts of cells where energy-requiring processes take place. The chemical reactions occurring in them are discussed in detail in Chapter 17. The outer membrane of each mitochondrion is studded with the enzymes concerned with biologic oxidations, providing raw materials for the reactions occurring inside the mitochondrion. The interior of the mitochondrion contains the enzymes concerned with the citric acid cycle and the respiratory chain enzymes by which the 2-carbon fragments produced by metabolism are burned to CO_2 and water (see Chapter 17). In this process, electrons are transferred along the respiratory enzyme chain. Coupled with the electron transfer is **oxidative phosphorylation,** the synthesis of the high-energy phosphate compound **adenosine triphosphate (ATP).** This ubiquitous molecule is the principal energy source for energy-requiring actions in animals and plants. The inner membrane of the mitochondrion appears to be made up of repeating units, each of which contains a basepiece, a stalk, and a spherical headpiece. The basepieces contain the enzymes of the electron transfer chain, and the stalks and headpieces contain adenosine triphosphatase and other enzymes concerned with the synthesis and metabolism of ATP.

The mitochondria contain DNA and can synthesize protein. It now appears that the mitochondrial DNA represents a second genetic system in the cell. However, the mitochondrial DNA alone does not contain enough genetic information to code for all mitochondrial components, and the nuclear and mitochondrial genetic systems apparently interact in the formation of the protein systems in the mitochondria.

Lysosomes

In the cytoplasm of the cell, there are large,

Table 1–1. Some of the enzymes found in lysosomes and the cell components which are their substrates.

Enzyme	Substrate
Ribonuclease	RNA
Deoxyribonuclease	DNA
Phosphatase	Phosphate esters
Glycosidases	Complex carbohydrates: glycosides and polysaccharides
Arylsulfatases	Sulfate esters
Collagenase	Proteins
Cathepsins	Proteins

somewhat irregular structures surrounded by membrane that may contain fragments of other cell structures. These organelles are the **lysosomes.** Some of the granules of the granulocytic white blood cells are lysosomes. Each lysosome contains a variety of enzymes (Table 1–1) that would cause the destruction of most cellular components if the enzymes were not separated from the rest of the cell by the membrane of the lysosome.

The lysosomes function as a form of digestive system for the cell. Exogenous substances such as bacteria that become engulfed by the cell end up in membrane-lined vacuoles. A vacuole of this type **(phagocytic vacuole)** may merge with a lysosome, permitting the contents of the vacuole and the lysosome to mix within a common membrane. Some of the products of the "digestion" of the engulfed material are absorbed through the walls of the vacuole, and the remnants are dumped from the cell (exocytosis; see below). The lysosomes also engulf worn out components of the cell in which they are located, forming **autophagic vacuoles.** When a cell dies, lysosomal enzymes cause autolysis of the remnants. In vitamin A intoxication and certain other conditions, lysosomal enzymes are released to the exterior of the cell with resultant breakdown of intercellular material. There is evidence that in gout, phagocytes ingest uric acid crystals, and that such ingestion triggers the release of lysosomal enzymes which contribute to the inflammatory response in the joints. When one of the lysosomal enzymes is congenitally absent, the lysosomes become engorged with one of the materials they normally degrade. This eventually disrupts the cells that contain the defective lysosomes and leads to one of the **lysosomal storage diseases.** More than 25 such diseases have been described. They are generally rare, but they include such widely known disorders as Tay-Sachs disease.

Centrioles

In the cytoplasm of most cells there are 2 short cylinders called **centrioles.** The centrioles are located near the nucleus, and they are arranged so that they are at right angles to each other. Tubules in groups of 3 run longitudinally in the walls of the centriole (Fig 1–1). There are 9 of these triplets spaced at regular intervals around the circumference. **Cilia,** the hairlike motile processes that in higher animals extend from various types of epithelial cells, also have an array of 9 tubular structures in their walls, but they have in addition a pair of tubules in the center and there are 2 rather than 3 tubules in each of the 9 circumferential structures. The **basal granule,** on the other hand, which is the structure to which a cilium is anchored, has 9 circumferential triplets, like a centriole.

The centrioles are concerned with the movement of the chromosomes during cell division. They duplicate themselves at the start of mitosis, and the pairs move apart to form the poles of the mitotic spindle. In multinucleate cells, there is a pair of centrioles near each nucleus.

Microtubules & Microfilaments

Many cells contain **microtubules,** long hollow structures about 25 nm in diameter, and **microfilaments,** solid fibers 4–6 nm in diameter. The microtubules and microfilaments are found in the mitotic spindles of dividing cells and are involved in the movement of the chromosomes. They are also involved in cell movement, in the processes that move secretion granules within cells, and in the movement of proteins within cell membranes. The structure of the microtubules is disrupted by the drug colchicine. The microtubules are made up of actin, the contractile protein in muscle (see Chapter 3), and the contractile protein myosin is also found in many kinds of cells. The function of the microfilaments is disrupted by cytochalasin, a compound secreted by certain fungi. Microtubules may make up the structures or "tracks" on which chromosomes and secretion granules move, and microfilaments may be responsible for the motion.

Secretion Granules

Secretion granules in cells that secrete proteins have been mentioned in the section on the Golgi complex. Typical examples include the granules of tropic hormones in the anterior lobe of the pituitary gland (see Chapter 22) and the granules of proteolytic enzyme precursors in the exocrine cells of the pancreas (see Chapter 26).

The proteins in these granules are synthesized in the endoplasmic reticulum, packaged into membrane-enclosed granules in the Golgi apparatus, and stored in the cytoplasm until they are extruded from the cell by exocytosis (see below).

Other Structures in Cells

If cells are homogenized and the resulting suspension is centrifuged, various cellular components can be isolated. The nuclei sediment first, followed by the mitochondria. High-speed centrifugation that generates forces of 100,000 times gravity or more causes a fraction made up of granules called the **microsomes** to sediment. This fraction includes the ribosomes, but it is not homogeneous and includes other granular material as well. The ribosomes and other components can be isolated from the microsomal fraction by further

ultracentrifugation or other technics. One particle fraction isolated in this way contains enzymes capable of reducing O_2 to hydrogen peroxide and then to water. These particles have been called **peroxisomes.**

BODY FLUID COMPARTMENTS

Organization of the Body

The cells that make up the bodies of all but the simplest multicellular animals, both aquatic and terrestrial, exist in an "internal sea" of **extracellular fluid (ECF)** enclosed within the integument of the animal. From this fluid, the cells take up O_2 and nutrients; into it, they discharge metabolic waste products. The ECF is more dilute than present-day seawater, but its composition closely resembles that of the

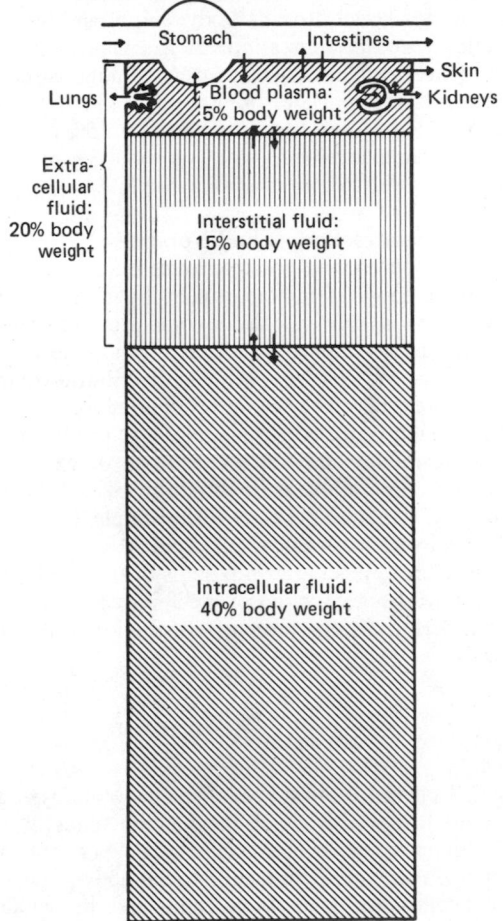

Figure 1–4. Body fluid compartments. Arrows represent fluid movement. Transcellular fluids, which constitute a very small percentage of total body fluids, are not shown. (Modified and reproduced, with permission, from Gamble JL: *Chemical Anatomy, Physiology, and Pathology of Extracellular Fluid,* 6th ed. Harvard Univ Press, 1954.)

primordial oceans in which, presumably, all life originated.

In animals with a closed vascular system, the ECF is divided into 2 components: the **interstitial fluid** and the circulating **blood plasma.** The plasma and the cellular elements of the blood, principally red blood cells, fill the vascular system, and together they constitute the **total blood volume.** The interstitial fluid is that part of the ECF which is outside the vascular system, bathing the cells. The special fluids lumped together as transcellular fluids are discussed below. About a third of the **total body water (TBW)** is extracellular; the remaining two-thirds are intracellular **(intracellular fluid).**

Size of the Fluid Compartments

In the average young adult male, 18% of the body weight is protein and related substances, 7% is mineral, and 15% is fat. The remaining 60% is water. The distribution of this water is shown in Fig 1–4.

The intracellular component of the body water accounts for about 40% of body weight and the extracellular component about 20%. Approximately 25% of the extracellular component is in the vascular system (plasma = 5% of body weight) and 75% outside the blood vessels (interstitial fluid = 15% of body weight). The total blood volume is about 8% of body weight.

Measurement of Body Fluid Volumes

It is theoretically possible to measure the size of each of the body fluid compartments by injecting substances that will stay in only one compartment and then calculating the volume of fluid in which the test substance is distributed (the **volume of distribution** of the injected material). The volume of distribution is equal to the amount injected (minus any that has been removed from the body by metabolism or excretion during the time allowed for mixing) divided by the concentration of the substance in the sample. *Example:* 150 mg of sucrose are injected into a 70 kg man. The plasma sucrose level after mixing is 0.01 mg/ml, and 10 mg have been excreted or metabolized during the mixing period. The volume of distribution of the sucrose is

$$\frac{150 \text{ mg} - 10 \text{ mg}}{0.01 \text{ mg/ml}} = 14,000 \text{ ml}$$

Since 14,000 ml is the space in which the sucrose was distributed, it is also called the **sucrose space.**

Volumes of distribution can be calculated for any substance that can be injected into the body provided the concentration in the body fluids and the amount removed by excretion and metabolism can be accurately measured.

Although the principle involved in such measurements is simple, there are a number of complicating factors that must be considered. The material injected must be nontoxic, must mix evenly throughout the compartment being measured, must have no effect of its own on the distribution of water or other substances in the body, and must be unchanged by the body during the mixing period. It also should be relatively easy to measure.

Plasma Volume, Total Blood Volume, & Red Cell Volume

Plasma volume has been measured by using dyes that become bound to plasma protein—particularly Evans blue (T-1824). Plasma volume can also be measured by injecting serum albumin labeled with radioactive iodine. Suitable aliquots of the injected solution and plasma samples obtained after injection are counted in a scintillation counter. An average value is 3500 ml (5% of the body weight of a 70 kg man, assuming unit density).

If the plasma volume and the hematocrit are known, **total blood volume** can be calculated by multiplying the plasma volume by

$$\frac{100}{100 - \text{hematocrit}}$$

Example: The hematocrit is 38 and the plasma volume 3500 ml. The total blood volume is

$$3500 \times \frac{100}{100 - 38} = 5645 \text{ ml}$$

The **red cell volume** (volume occupied by all the circulating red cells in the body) can be determined by subtracting the plasma volume from the total blood volume. It may also be measured independently, by injecting tagged red blood cells and, after mixing has occurred, measuring the fraction of the red cells that is tagged. A commonly used tag is ^{51}Cr, a radioactive isotope of chromium that is attached to the cells by incubating them in a suitable chromium solution. Isotopes of iron and phosphorus (^{59}Fe and ^{32}P) and antigenic tagging have also been employed.

Extracellular Fluid Volume

The ECF volume is difficult to measure because the limits of this space are ill defined and because few substances mix rapidly in all parts of the space while remaining exclusively extracellular. The lymph cannot be separated from the ECF, and is measured with it. Many substances enter the cerebrospinal fluid (CSF) slowly because of the blood-brain barrier (see Chapter 32). Equilibration is slow with joint fluid and aqueous humor and with the ECF in relatively avascular tissues such as dense connective tissue, cartilage, and some parts of bone. Substances that distribute in ECF appear in glandular secretions and in the contents of the gastrointestinal tract. Because they are not strictly part of the ECF, these fluids, as well as CSF, the fluids in the eye, and a few other special fluids, are called **transcellular fluids.** Their volume is relatively small.

Perhaps the most accurate measurement of ECF volume is that obtained by using inulin. Radioactive inulin has been prepared by substituting ^{14}C for one of the carbon atoms of the molecule; and when this material is used, inulin levels are easily determined by counting the samples with suitable radiation detectors. Mannitol and sucrose have also been used to measure ECF volume. Because chloride ions, for example, are largely extracellular in location, radioactive isotopes of chloride (^{36}Cl and ^{38}Cl) have been used for determination of ECF volume. However, some chloride is known to be intracellular. The same objection applies to ^{82}Br, which interchanges with chloride in the body. Other anions that have been used include sulfate, thiosulfate, thiocyanate, and ferrocyanide.

Careful measurement with each of these substances gives a range of values, indicating that each has a slightly different volume of distribution. A generally accepted value for ECF volume is 20% of the body weight, or about 14 liters in a 70 kg man (3.5 liters = plasma; 10.5 liters = interstitial fluid).

Interstitial Fluid Volume

The interstitial fluid space cannot be measured directly, since it is difficult to sample interstitial fluid and since substances that equilibrate in interstitial fluid also equilibrate in plasma. The volume of the interstitial fluid can be calculated by subtracting the plasma volume from the ECF volume. The ECF volume/intracellular fluid volume ratio is larger in infants and children than it is in adults, but the absolute volume of ECF in children is, of course, smaller than it is in adults. Therefore, dehydration develops more rapidly and is frequently more severe in children than in adults.

Intracellular Fluid Volume

The intracellular fluid volume cannot be measured directly, but it can be calculated by subtracting the ECF volume from the total body water (TBW). TBW can be measured by the same dilution principle used to measure the other body spaces. Deuterium oxide (D_2O, heavy water) is most frequently used. D_2O has properties that are slightly different from H_2O, but in equilibration experiments for measuring body water it gives accurate results. Tritium oxide and aminopyrine have also been used for this purpose.

The water content of lean body tissue is constant at 71–72 ml/100 g of tissue, but since fat is relatively free of water the ratio of TBW to body weight varies with the amount of fat present. In young men, water constitutes about 60% of body weight. The values for women are somewhat lower. In both sexes, the values tend to decrease with age (see Table 1–2).

UNITS FOR MEASURING CONCENTRATION OF SOLUTES

In considering the effects of various physiologically important substances and the interactions between them, the number of molecules, electrical charges, or particles of a substance per unit volume of a particular body fluid are often more meaningful than simply the weight of the substance per unit volume. For this reason, concentrations are frequently expressed in moles, equivalents, or osmoles.

Moles

The mole is defined as the gram-molecular weight of a substance, ie, the molecular weight of the substance in grams. Each mole (mol) consists of approximately 6×10^{23} molecules. The millimole (mmol) is 1/1000 of a mole, and the micromole (μmol) is 1/1,000,000 of a mole. Thus, 1 mol of NaCl = 23 + 35.5 g = 58.5 g, and 1 mmol = 58.5 mg. The mole is the standard unit for expressing the amount of substance in the SI unit system (see Appendix).

Equivalents

The concept of electrical equivalence is important in physiology because many of the important solutes in the body are in the form of charged particles. One equivalent (Eq) is 1 mol of an ionized substance divided by its valence. One mol of NaCl dissociates into 1 Eq of Na^+ and 1 Eq of Cl^-. One Eq of Na^+ = 23 g/l = 23 g; but 1 Eq of Ca^{2+} = 40 g/2 = 20 g. The milliequivalent (mEq) is 1/1000 of an equivalent.

Electrical equivalence is not necessarily the same as chemical equivalence. A gram equivalent is that weight of a substance which is chemically equivalent to 8.000 g of oxygen. The normality (N) of a solution is the number of gram equivalents in 1 liter. A 1 N solution of hydrochloric acid contains 1 + 35.5 g/L = 36.5 g/L.

Osmoles

When dealing with concentrations of osmotically active particles, the amounts of these particles are usually expressed in osmoles. One osmole (Osm) equals the molecular weight of the substance in grams divided by the number of freely moving particles each molecule liberates in solution. The milliosmole (mOsm) is 1/1000 of 1 osmole. Osmosis is discussed in detail in a later section of this chapter.

The **osmolal concentration** of a substance in a fluid is measured by the degree to which it depresses the freezing point, 1 mol/L of ideal solute depressing the freezing point 1.86 Celsius degrees. The number of mOsm/L in a solution equals the freezing point depres-

Table 1–2. TBW (as percentage of body weight) in relation to age and sex.*

Age	Male	Female
10–18	59%	57%
18–40	61%	51%
40–60	55%	47%
Over 60	52%	46%

*Modified and reproduced, with permission, from Edelman IS, Liebman J: Anatomy of body water and electrolytes. Am J Med 27:256, 1959.

sion divided by 0.00186. The **osmolarity** is the number of osmoles per liter of solution—eg, plasma—whereas the **osmolality** is the number of osmoles per kg of solvent. Therefore, osmolarity is affected by the volume of the various solutes in the solution and the temperature, while the osmolality is not. Osmotically active substances in the body are dissolved in water, and the density of water is 1, so osmolal concentrations can be expressed as Osm/L of water. In this book, osmolal (rather than osmolar) concentrations are considered, and osmolality is expressed in mOsm/L (of water).

COMPOSITION OF BODY FLUIDS

The distribution of electrolytes in the various compartments of the body fluid is shown in Fig 1–5. The figures for the intracellular phase ("cell fluid") are approximations. The composition of intracellular fluid varies somewhat depending upon the nature and function of the cell.

It is apparent from Fig 1–5 that electrolyte concentrations differ markedly in the various compartments. The most striking differences are the relatively low content of protein anions in interstitial fluid compared to intracellular fluid and plasma, and the fact that Na^+ and Cl^- are largely extracellular, whereas most of the K^+ is intracellular.

FORCES PRODUCING MOVEMENT OF SUBSTANCES BETWEEN COMPARTMENTS

The differences in composition of the various body fluid compartments are due in large part to the nature of the barriers separating them. The membranes of the cells separate the interstitial fluid and intracellular fluid, and the capillary wall separates the interstitial fluid from the plasma. The forces producing movement of water and other molecules across these barriers are diffusion, solvent drag, filtration, osmosis, active transport, and the processes of exocytosis and endocytosis.

It should be noted that next to biologic membranes in living animals, there is a layer of relatively unstirred water 100–400 μm thick. Solutes cross this **unstirred water layer** (UWL) by diffusion, and diffusion across it must be taken into account in considering transport across membranes. Its role is currently a matter of some debate, but in some instances, it represents a significant portion of the resistance to movement of a given solute across a membrane.

Diffusion

Diffusion is the process by which a gas or a substance in solution expands, because of the motion of its particles, to fill all of the available volume. The particles (molecules or ions) of a substance dissolved in a solvent are in continuous random movement. In regions where they are abundant, they frequently collide. They therefore tend to spread from areas of high concentration to areas of low concentration until the

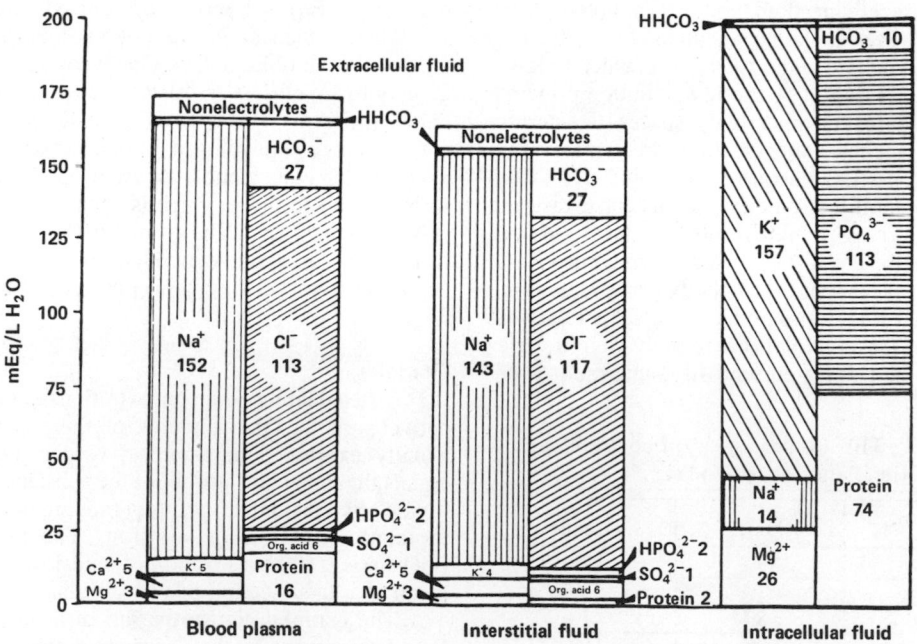

Figure 1–5. Electrolyte composition of human body fluids. Note that the values are in mEq/L of water, not of body fluid. (Reproduced, with permission, from Leaf A, Newburgh LH: *Significance of the Body Fluids in Clinical Medicine,* 2nd ed. Thomas, 1955.)

concentration is uniform throughout the solution. Solute particles are, of course, moving both into and out of the area of high concentration; however, since more molecules move out than in, there is a **net flux** of the molecular species to the area of low concentration. The magnitude of the diffusing tendency from one area to another is proportionate to the difference in concentration of the substance in the 2 areas (the **concentration, or chemical gradient**). Diffusion of ions is also affected by their electrical charge. Whenever there is a difference in potential between 2 areas, positively charged ions move along this **electrical gradient** to the more negatively charged area; negatively charged ions move in the opposite direction.

In the body, diffusion occurs not only within fluid compartments but also from one compartment to another provided the barrier between the compartments is permeable to the diffusing substances. The diffusion rate of most solutes across the barriers is much slower than the diffusion rate in water, but diffusion is still a major force affecting the distribution of water and solutes.

Donnan Effect

When there is an ion on one side of a membrane that cannot diffuse through the membrane, the distribution of other ions to which the membrane is permeable is affected in a predictable way. For example, the negative charge of a nondiffusible anion hinders diffusion of the diffusible cations and favors diffusion of the diffusible anions. Consider the following situation,

X		Y
	m	
K^+		K^+
Cl^-		Cl^-
$Prot^-$		

in which the membrane (m) between compartments X and Y is impermeable to $Prot^-$ but freely permeable to K^+ and Cl^-. Assume that the concentrations of the anions and of the cations on the 2 sides are initially equal. Cl^- tends to diffuse down its concentration gradient from Y to X and some K^+ moves with the negatively charged Cl^-. Therefore, at equilibrium,

$$[K^+_X] > [K^+_Y]$$

Furthermore,

$$[K^+_X] + [Cl^-_X] + [Prot^-_X] > [K^+_Y] + [Cl^-_Y]$$

ie, there are more osmotically active particles on side X than on side Y.

Donnan and Gibbs showed that in the presence of a nondiffusible ion, the diffusible ions distribute themselves so that, at equilibrium, their concentration ratios are equal:

$$\frac{[K^+_X]}{[K^+_Y]} = \frac{[Cl^-_Y]}{[Cl^-_X]}$$

In the case of single cations and anions of the same valence, the product of the concentration of the diffusible ions on one side equals that on the other side. Thus,

$$[K^+_X] \ [Cl^-_X] = [K^+_Y] \ [Cl^-_Y]$$

Electrochemical neutrality would require that the sum of the anions on each side of the membrane equal the sum of the cations on that side. Actually, there is a slight excess of cations on side Y and a slight excess of anions on side X at equilibrium, and therefore a difference in electrical potential exists between X and Y. However, it should be emphasized that the difference between the number of anions and the number of cations on either side of the membrane is extremely small relative to the total numbers of anions and cations present.

The **Donnan effect** on the distribution of diffusible ions is important in the body because of the presence in cells and in plasma, but not in interstitial fluid, of large quantities of nondiffusible protein anions (see Chapters 35 and 38).

Solvent Drag

When solvent is moving in one direction (**bulk flow**), the solvent tends to drag along some molecules of solute. This force is called **solvent drag.** In most situations in the body, its effects are very small.

Filtration

Filtration is the process by which fluid is forced through a membrane or other barrier due to a difference in hydrostatic pressure on the 2 sides. The amount of fluid filtered in a given interval is proportionate to the difference in pressure and the surface area of the membrane. Molecules that are smaller in diameter than the pores of the membrane pass through with the fluid, and larger molecules are retained. Filtration of small molecules across the capillary walls occurs when the hydrostatic pressure in the vessels is greater than that in the extravascular tissues.

Osmosis

Osmosis is the movement of **solvent** molecules across a membrane into an area in which there is a higher concentration of a **solute** to which the membrane is impermeable. It is an immensely important factor in physiologic processes. The tendency for movement of solvent molecules to a region of greater solute concentration can be prevented by applying pressure to the more concentrated solution. The pressure necessary to prevent solvent migration is the **effective osmotic pressure** of the solution.

Osmotic pressure, like vapor pressure lowering, freezing point depression, and boiling point elevation, depends upon the number rather than the type of particles in a solution, ie, it is a fundamental colligative property of solutions. In effect, it is due to a reduction in the **activity** of the solvent molecules in a solution. The activity of a substance is its effective concentra-

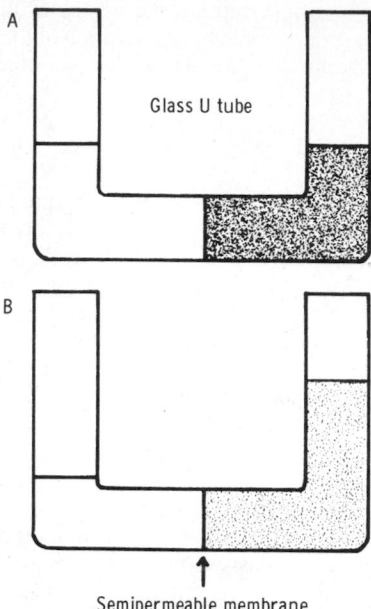

Figure 1-6. Demonstration of osmotic pressure. *A:* Immediately after adding a solution of glucose (shaded area) to the right arm of the U tube and an equal volume of water (clear space) to the other. *B:* After equilibration has taken place. The water has entered the glucose solution, which has increased in volume and decreased in concentration.

tion as evaluated by its behavior in solution. When a solute is dissolved in a solvent, the activity of the solvent molecules is decreased. A homogeneous solution of a single substance has an osmotic pressure, but this pressure can be expressed—ie, the solution has an effective osmotic pressure—only when the solution is in contact with a more dilute solution across a membrane permeable to the solvent but not to the solute. In this situation, solvent molecules will diffuse from the area in which their activity is greater (the **dilute** solution) to the area in which their activity is less (the **concentrated** solution). Thus, if a 10% aqueous solution of glucose is placed in contact with distilled water across a membrane permeable to water but not to glucose, the volume of the glucose solution increases and its glucose concentration decreases as water molecules move into it from the water compartment (see Fig 1-6).

Osmotic pressure (P) is related to temperature and volume in the same way as the pressure of a gas:

$$P = \frac{nRT}{V}$$

where n is the number of particles, R the gas constant, T the absolute temperature, and V the volume. If T is held constant, it is clear that the osmotic pressure is proportionate to the number of particles in solution per unit volume of solution. If the solute is a nonionizing compound such as glucose, the osmotic pressure is a function of the number of glucose molecules present. If the solute ionizes and forms an **ideal** solution, each ion is an osmotically active particle. For example, NaCl would dissociate into Na^+ and Cl^- ions, so that each mole in solution would supply 2 osmoles. One mole of Na_2SO_4 would dissociate into Na^+, Na^+, and SO_4^{2-}, supplying 3 osmoles. However, the body fluids are not ideal solutions, and although the dissociation of strong electrolytes is complete, the number of particles free to exert an osmotic effect is reduced due to interactions between the ions. Thus, it is actually the effective concentration, or activity in the body fluids, rather than the number of equivalents of an electrolyte in solution that determines its osmotic effect. This is why, for example, 1 mmol/L of NaCl in the body fluids contributes somewhat less than 2 mOsm/L of osmotically active particles.

Osmolal Concentration of Plasma: Tonicity

The freezing point of normal human plasma averages −0.54 C, which corresponds to an osmolal concentration in plasma of 290 mOsm/L. This is equivalent to an osmotic pressure of 7.3 atmospheres. The osmolality might be expected to be higher than this, because the sum of all the cation and anion equivalents in plasma is over 300. It is not this high because plasma is not an ideal solution, and ionic interactions reduce the number of particles free to exert an osmotic effect. Except when there has been insufficient time after a sudden change in composition for equilibration to occur, all fluid compartments of the body are apparently in or nearly in osmotic equilibrium. The term **tonicity** is used to describe the effective osmotic pressure of a solution relative to plasma. Solutions that have the same effective osmotic pressure as plasma are said to be **isotonic;** those with greater pressure are **hypertonic;** and those with lesser pressure are **hypotonic.** All solutions that are isosmotic with plasma—ie, have the same actual osmotic pressure or freezing point depression as plasma—would also be isotonic if it were not for the fact that some solutes diffuse into cells and others are metabolized. Thus, a 0.9% saline solution is isotonic because there is no net movement of the osmotically active particles in the solution into cells and the particles are not metabolized. However, urea diffuses rapidly into cells, so that the effective osmotic pressure drops when cells are suspended in an aqueous solution that initially contains 290 mOsm/L of urea. Similarly, a 5% glucose solution is isotonic when initially infused intravenously, but glucose is metabolized, so the net effect is that of infusing a hypotonic solution.

It is important to note the relative contributions of the various plasma components to the total osmolal concentration of plasma. All but 20 of the 290 mOsm in each liter are contributed by Na^+ and its accompanying anions, principally Cl^- and HCO_3^-. Other cations and anions make a small contribution. Glucose normally makes a much smaller contribution—about 5 mOsm—because it does not dissociate and has a molecular weight of 180. The plasma proteins have a high molecular weight, so that, even though they are present in large quantities, they make a very small contribution to the plasma osmolality. The osmolal concentration of protein derivatives (other than electrolytes) is about 0.33 times the blood urea nitrogen (BUN), or approximately 6 mOsm/L. Since plasma is not an ideal solution, the osmolality of the plasma can be estimated from the following formula:

$$\text{Osmolality} = 2\,[\text{Na}^+] + 0.05\,[\text{Glucose}] + 0.33\,[\text{BUN}]$$
$$(\text{mOsm/L}) \quad (\text{mEq/L}) \qquad (\text{mg/dl}) \qquad (\text{mg/dl})$$

This formula is useful in evaluating patients with fluid and electrolyte abnormalities as well as assessing the contributions of the various components to normal plasma osmolality. Hyperosmolality can cause coma (hyperosmolar coma; see Chapter 19).

Nonionic Diffusion

Some weak acids and bases are quite soluble in cell membranes in the undissociated form, whereas in the ionic form they cross membranes with difficulty. Consequently, molecules of the undissociated substance diffuse from one side of the membrane to the other and then dissociate, effectively moving ions from one side of the membrane to another. This phenomenon, which occurs in the gastrointestinal tract (see Chapter 25) and kidneys (see Chapter 38), is called **nonionic diffusion.**

Carrier-Mediated Transport

In addition to moving across cell membranes by diffusion, osmosis, and the processes described above, ions and larger nonionized molecules are transported by carrier molecules in the membranes. When such **carrier-mediated transport** is from an area of greater concentration of the transported molecules to an area of lesser concentration, energy is not required, and the process is called **facilitated diffusion.** In many instances, facilitated diffusion is regulated by hormones; eg, insulin increases the facilitated diffusion of glucose into muscle cells (see Chapter 19). When, on the other hand, the transport is from an area of lesser to an area of greater concentration and cannot be explained by movement down an electrical gradient (see below), the process requires energy and is referred to as **active transport.** The energy is supplied by the metabolism

of the cells, generally through adenosine triphosphate (ATP; see Chapter 17). Active transport is of major importance throughout the body.

Transport of Proteins & Other Large Molecules

In certain situations proteins enter cells, and a number of hormones secreted by endocrine cells are proteins or large peptides. Proteins and other large molecules enter cells by the process of endocytosis, and proteins and peptides are secreted by exocytosis. These processes provide an explanation of how large molecules can enter and leave cells without disrupting cell membranes.

In **exocytosis,** which has also been called **reverse pinocytosis,** or **emeiocytosis** (''cell vomiting''), the membrane around a vacuole or secretion granule fuses with the cell membrane and the region of fusion breaks down, leaving the contents of the vacuole or secretion granule outside the cell and the cell membrane intact (Fig 1–7). This requires Ca^{2+} and energy. The mechanism responsible for the breakdown of the membrane is unknown, but one theory holds that an anionic channel opens into the exocytotic vacuole, and that the influx of anions produces an increase in osmotic pressure that leads to dissolution of the area of membrane fusion (**chemiosmotic hypothesis).**

Endocytosis is the reverse process. One form of endocytosis, called **phagocytosis** (''cell eating''), is the process by which bacteria, dead tissue, or other bits of material visible under the microscope are engulfed by cells such as the polymorphonuclear leukocytes of the blood. The material makes contact with the cell membrane, which then invaginates. The invagination is pinched off, leaving the engulfed material in the membrane-enclosed vacuole and the cell membrane intact. **Pinocytosis** (''cell drinking'') is essentially the same process, the only difference being that the substances ingested are in solution and hence not visible under the microscope. In the cell, the membrane around a **pinocytic** or **phagocytic vacuole** may fuse with that of a lysosome, mixing the ''digestive'' enzymes in the lysosome with the contents of the vacuole. It has also been assumed that the membrane around vacuoles can be digested away, but the ultimate fate of the vacuoles is uncertain.

The rate of pinocytosis is greatly increased by

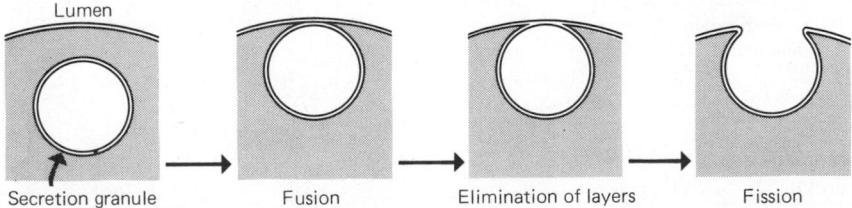

Lumen

Secretion granule   Fusion   Elimination of layers   Fission

Figure 1–7. Exocytosis. In this process, the secretion granule moves up to the cell membrane and its membrane fuses with the cell membrane. The area of fusion then breaks down, leaving the contents of the granule outside of the cell. (Modified from Palade G: Intracellular aspects of the process of protein synthesis. Science 189:347, 1975.)

substances called **inducers.** In mammalian cells, proteins such as albumins and globulins are potent inducers. Insulin apparently acts as an inducer in fat cells. There is evidence that pinocytosis and, presumably, phagocytosis are active processes that do not occur when the energy-producing processes in the cell are blocked.

It is apparent that exocytosis adds to the total amount of membrane in the cell, and, if membrane were not removed elsewhere at an equivalent rate, the cell would enlarge. However, removal of membrane occurs by endocytosis, and such exocytosis-endocytosis coupling maintains the cell at its normal size.

CELL MEMBRANE & RESTING MEMBRANE POTENTIALS

Ion Distribution Across Cell Membranes

The unique properties of the cell membranes are responsible for the differences in the composition of intracellular and interstitial fluid. Average values for the composition of intracellular fluid in humans are shown in Fig 1–5, and specific values for mammalian neurons are shown in Table 1–3.

Membrane Potentials

There is a potential difference across the membranes of most if not all cells, with the inside of the cells negative to the exterior. By convention, this **resting membrane potential** or **steady potential** is written with a minus sign, signifying that the inside is negative to the exterior. Its magnitude varies considerably from tissue to tissue, ranging from -9 to -100 mV.

Membrane Permeability

Cell membranes are practically impermeable to intracellular protein and other organic anions, which make up most of the intracellular anions and are usually represented by the symbol A^-. However, they are moderately permeable to Na^+ and Cl^- and rather freely

Table 1–4. Permeability coefficients (P) for cell membrane of frog skeletal muscle. Values are equivalents diffusing through 1 cm^2 of membrane under specified conditions and have the dimensions of cm/s. For purposes of comparison, P_{K^+} in water is 10.*

P_{A^-}	~ 0
P_{Na^+}	2×10^{-8}
P_{K^+}	2×10^{-6}
P_{Cl^-}	4×10^{-6}

*Data from Hodgkin AL, Horowicz P: The influence of potassium and chloride ions on the membrane potential of single muscle fibres. J Physiol 148:127, 1959.

permeable to K^+. K^+ permeability is 50–100 times greater than Na^+ permeability. The permeability values listed in Table 1–4 for the cell membrane of frog skeletal muscle are representative. It should be noted that permeability of these ions in the membrane, although appreciable, is a fraction of their permeability in water.

The way that ions move across cell membranes is still a matter of debate. Particle size is a relevant consideration (Table 1–5), and it should be noted that the ions in the body are hydrated. Thus, although the atomic weight of potassium (39) is greater than the atomic weight of sodium (23), the hydrated sodium ion—ie, Na^+ with its full complement of water—is larger than the hydrated potassium ion. However, it is clear that ions cross membranes via ion channels rather than simple pores, and the charge configurations around these channels and related variables make them relatively specific, ie, there are separate Na^+ channels, K^+ channels, and Cl^- channels. Differences in these channels account for the differences in permeability of the membranes to small ions.

Forces Acting on Ions

The forces acting across the cell membrane on

Table 1–3. Concentration of some ions inside and outside mammalian spinal motor neurons.*

	Concentration (mmol/L H_2O)		Equilibrium Potential (mV)
Ion	Inside Cell	Outside Cell	
Na^+	15.0	150.0	+60
K^+	150.0	5.5	−90
Cl^-	9.0	125.0	−70

Resting membrane potential = −70 mV

*Data from Mommaerts WFHM, in: *Essentials of Human Physiology.* Ross G (editor). Year Book, 1978.

Table 1–5. Size of hydrated ions and other substances of biologic interest.*

Substance	Atomic or Molecular Weight	Radius (nm)
Cl^-	35	0.12
K^+	39	0.12
H_2O	18	0.12
Ca^{2+}	40	0.15
Na^+	23	0.18
Urea	60	0.23
Li^+	7	0.24
Glucose	180	0.38
Sucrose	342	0.48
Inulin	5000	0.75
Albumin	69,000	7.50

*Data from Moore EW: *Physiology of Intestinal Water and Electrolyte Absorption.* American Gastroenterological Association, 1976.

each ion can be analyzed. Chloride ions are present in higher concentration in the ECF than in the cell interior, and they tend to diffuse along this **concentration gradient** into the cell. The interior of the cell is negative relative to the exterior, and chloride ions are pushed out of the cell along this **electrical gradient.** An equilibrium is reached at which Cl^- influx and Cl^- efflux are equal. The membrane potential at which this equilibrium exists is the **equilibrium potential.** Its magnitude can be calculated from the **Nernst equation,** as follows:

$$E_{Cl} = \frac{RT}{FZ_{Cl}} \ln \frac{[Cl_o^-]}{[Cl_i^-]}$$

Where E_{Cl} = equilibrium potential for Cl^-
R = gas constant
T = absolute temperature
F = the faraday (number of coulombs per mole of charge)
Z_{Cl} = valence of Cl^- (−1)
$[Cl_o^-]$ = Cl^- concentration outside the cell
$[Cl_i^-]$ = Cl^- concentration inside the cell

Converting from the natural log to the base 10 log and replacing some of the constants with numerical values, the equation becomes

$$E_{Cl} = 61.5 \log \frac{[Cl_i^-]}{[Cl_o^-]} \text{ at 37 C}$$

Note that in converting to the simplified expression, the concentration ratio is reversed because the minus 1 valence of Cl^- has been removed from the expression.

E_{Cl}, calculated from the values in Table 1–3, is −70 mV, a value identical to the measured resting membrane potential of −70 mV. Therefore, no forces other than those represented by the chemical and electrical gradients need be invoked to explain the distribution of Cl^- across the membrane.

A similar equilibrium potential can be calculated for K^+.

$$E_K = \frac{RT}{FZ_K} \ln \frac{[K_o^+]}{[K_i^+]} = 61.5 \log \frac{[K_o^+]}{[K_i^+]} \text{ at 37 C}$$

Where E_K = equilibrium potential for K^+
Z_K = valence of K^+ (+1)
$[K_o^+]$ = K^+ concentration outside the cell
$[K_i^+]$ = K^+ concentration inside the cell
R, T, and F as above

In this case, the concentration gradient is outward and the electrical gradient inward. In mammalian spinal motor neurons, E_K is −90 mV (Table 1–3). Since the resting membrane potential is −70 mV, there is somewhat more K^+ in the neurons than can be accounted for by the electrical and chemical gradients (see below).

The situation for Na^+ is quite different from that for K^+ and Cl^-. The direction of the chemical gradient for Na^+ is inward, to the area where it is in lesser concentration, and the electrical gradient is in the same direction. E_{Na} is +60 mV (Table 1–3). Experiments with radioactive sodium have established the fact that the membrane has a relatively low but definite permeability to Na^+ (Table 1–4) as well as K^+. Since neither E_K nor E_{Na} is at the membrane potential, one would expect the cell to gradually gain Na^+ and lose K^+ (Fig 1–8) if only passive electrical and chemical forces were acting across the membrane. However, the intracellular concentration of Na^+ and K^+ remains constant because there is active transport of Na^+ out of the cell against its electrical and concentration gradients, and this transport is coupled to active transport of K^+ into the cell. The passive and active fluxes across the membrane of a motor neuron at rest are summarized in Fig 1–9.

The situation in muscle and various other types of cells is similar. In muscle, for example, the resting membrane potential is about −90 mV. E_{Cl} is −86 mV, E_K is −100 mV, and E_{Na} is +55 mV. In red blood cells, on the other hand, the membrane potential is low (−9 mV) and near the Cl^- equilibrium potential, whereas both Na^+ and K^+ are actively transported across the cell membrane. Cl^- appears to be actively transported in some mammalian neurons and is actively transported in the kidney.

Ca^{2+} should also be mentioned in the present context. In mammals, ECF ionized calcium concentration is about 1.2 mmol/L, and the intracellular concentration is very low. Thus, both the electrical and chemical gradients are directed inward. The Ca^{2+} perme-

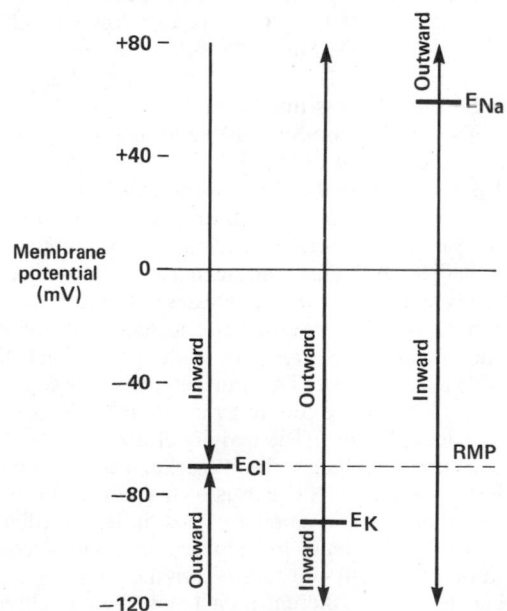

Figure 1–8. Summary of the net passive fluxes of ions across the membrane of mammalian motor neurons at various membrane potentials. RMP, resting membrane potential. (Courtesy of AM Thompson.)

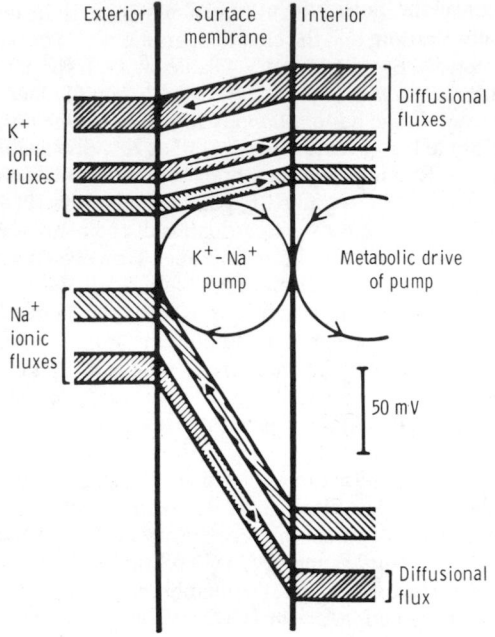

Figure 1–9. Na+ and K+ fluxes through the resting nerve cell membrane. The Na+ and K+ fluxes that are not labeled "diffusional fluxes" are due to active transport of these ions. The diffusional efflux of Na+, less than 1% of the influx, has been omitted. (Reproduced, with permission, from Eccles JC: *The Physiology of Nerve Cells.* Johns Hopkins Univ Press, 1957.)

ability of the nerve cell membrane is about 100 times less than the Na+ permeability, but some Ca^{2+} does enter. The intracellular Ca^{2+} is kept low by active transport of the ion out of the cell.

The Sodium-Potassium Pump

The mechanism responsible for the active transport of sodium out of the cell and potassium into the cell is a **sodium-potassium pump** that is sometimes referred to simply as the **sodium pump.** The pump is located in the membrane. The energy for pumping is provided by ATP, and an adequate supply of ATP depends on the metabolic processes in the cell. Application of ATP by micropipette to the inside of the membrane increases transport, while application to the outside has no effect. The transport of Na+ is coupled to that of K+, but the coupling ratio of Na+ to K+ varies from 1 to 4 or more. The activity of the pump is also directly proportional to the intracellular concentration of Na+. The rate of Na+ extrusion from the cell is thus proportionate to the amount of Na+ in it, a feedback arrangement that tends to keep the internal ionic composition of the cell constant. When the coupling ratio of Na+ to K+ is 1, there is no net movement of charge by the pump, and the pump is said to be nonelectrogenic. However, when more than 1 Na+ is transported out for each K+ transported into the cell, there is a net active flux of positive charge out of the cell with the production of hyperpolarization. Under these cir-

cumstances, the pump is **electrogenic.** The transport mechanism is inhibited by ouabain and related cardiac glycosides and by metabolic poisons that prevent the formation of ATP. The mechanism is markedly temperature dependent, as would be expected in view of its dependence on metabolic processes. When the temperature is reduced, Na+ efflux and K+ influx are reduced several times as much as the passive processes of Na+ influx and K+ efflux.

The details of the operation of the Na+ and K+ pump are the subject of intensive research. An enzyme that is intimately related to the pumping mechanism has been identified in red blood cells, brain cells, and the membranes of a great many other types of cells in a wide variety of species. This enzyme hydrolyzes ATP to adenosine diphosphate (ADP; see Chapter 17), and it is activated by Na+ and K+. It is therefore known as the **sodium-potassium–activated adenosine triphosphatase,** or **Na+-K+ ATPase.** Its concentration in cell membranes is proportionate to the rate of Na+ and K+ transport in the cells. It is a large lipoprotein with a molecular weight of 670,000 that requires Mg^{2+} for activity and is inhibited by ouabain. There is evidence that it extends through the membrane and that it contains 2 polypeptide units which form a channel through the membrane. It is postulated to exist in 2 conformational states. In one, it has a binding site for Na+ accessible only from the intracellular side of the membrane. Na+ binding activates a change to the other conformation, which leaves Na+ on the outside of the cell. In this second conformation, a K+ binding site is accessible only from the outside of the cell. K+ binding activates a change to the first configuration, and this leaves K+ inside the cell. It appears that Na+ binding is associated with phosphorylation of a component of the membrane and that K+ binding is associated with dephosphorylation.

Genesis of the Membrane Potential

The distribution of ions across the cell membrane and the nature of this membrane provide the explanation for the membrane potential. K+ diffuses out of the cell along its concentration gradient, while the nondiffusible anion component stays in the cell, creating a potential difference across the membrane. There is thus a slight excess of cations outside of the membrane and a slight excess of anions inside it. It should be emphasized, however, that the number of ions responsible for the membrane potential is a minute fraction of the total number present. Na+ influx does not compensate for the K+ efflux because the membrane at rest is much less permeable to Na+ than K+. Cl^- diffuses inward down its concentration gradient, but its movement is balanced by the electrical gradient. The sodium pump does not generate the membrane potential when the coupling ratio is 1, because it moves an equal number of cations in each direction. However, it maintains the concentration gradients on which the existence of the membrane potential depends. If the pump is shut off by the administration of metabolic inhibitors, Na+ enters the cell, K+ leaves it, and the membrane potential declines. The rate of this decline varies with the size of the cell. In large cells, it takes hours, but in nerve fibers with diameters of less than 1 μm, complete depolarization can occur in less than 4 minutes.

The magnitude of the membrane potential at any given time depends, of course, upon the distribution of Na$^+$, K$^+$, and Cl$^-$ and the permeability of the membrane to each of these ions. An equation that describes this relationship with considerable accuracy is the **Goldman constant-field equation:**

$$V = \frac{RT}{F} \ln \left(\frac{P_{K^+}[K_o^+] + P_{Na^+}[Na_o^+] + P_{Cl^-}[Cl_i^-]}{P_{K^+}[K_i^+] + P_{Na^+}[Na_i^+] + P_{Cl^-}[Cl_o^-]} \right)$$

where V is the membrane potential, R the gas constant, T the absolute temperature, F the faraday, and P_{K^+}, P_{Na^+}, and P_{Cl^-} the permeability of the membrane to K$^+$, Na$^+$, and Cl$^-$, respectively. The brackets signify concentration, and i and o refer to the inside and outside of the cell. Since P_{Na^+} is low relative to P_{K^+} in the resting cells, Na$^+$ contributes little to the value of V. As would be predicted from the Goldman equation, changes in external Na$^+$ produce little change in the resting membrane potential whereas increases in external K$^+$ decrease it.

Variations in Membrane Potential

If the resting membrane potential is decreased by the passage of a current through the membrane, the electrical gradient that keeps K$^+$ inside the cell is decreased, and there is an increase in K$^+$ diffusion out of the cell (Fig 1–8). This K$^+$ efflux and the simultaneous movement of Cl$^-$ into the cell result in a net movement of positive charge out of the cell, with consequent restoration of the resting membrane potential. When the membrane potential increases, these ions move in the opposite direction. These processes occur in all polarized cells, and tend to keep the resting membrane potential of the cells constant within narrow limits. However, in nerve and muscle cells, reduction of the membrane potential triggers a voltage-dependent increase in Na$^+$ permeability. This unique feature permits these cells to generate self-propagating impulses that are transmitted along their membranes for great distances. These impulses are considered in detail in Chapter 2.

Effects of the Sodium-Potassium Pump on Metabolic Rate

Active transport of Na$^+$ and K$^+$ is one of the major energy-using processes in the body, and probably accounts for a large part of the basal metabolism. Furthermore, there is a direct link between Na$^+$ and K$^+$ transport and metabolism; the greater the rate of pumping, the more ADP is formed, and the available supply of ADP determines the rate at which ATP is formed by oxidative phosphorylation (see Chapter 17).

Effects of the Sodium-Potassium Pump on Cell Volume

In animals, the maintenance of normal cell volume and pressure depend on Na$^+$ and K$^+$ pumping. In the absence of such pumping, Cl$^-$ and Na$^+$ would enter the cells down their concentration gradients, and water would follow along the osmotic gradient thus created, causing the cells to swell until the pressure inside them balanced the influx. This does not occur, and the osmolality of the cells remains the same as that of the interstitial fluid because Na$^+$ and K$^+$ are actively transported. The membrane potential is maintained, and [Cl$_i^-$] remains low.

THE CAPILLARY WALL

The structure of the capillary wall, the barrier between the plasma and the interstitial fluid, varies from one vascular bed to another (see Chapter 30). However, in skeletal muscle and many other organs, water and relatively small solutes are the only substances that cross the wall with ease. The apertures in the wall (probably the junctions between the endothelial cells) are too small to permit plasma proteins and other colloids to pass through in significant quantities. The colloids have a high molecular weight but are present in large amounts. The capillary wall therefore behaves like a membrane impermeable to colloids, which exert an osmotic pressure of about 25 mm Hg. The colloid osmotic pressure due to the plasma colloids is called the **oncotic pressure.** Filtration across the capillary membrane due to the hydrostatic pressure head in the vascular system is opposed by the oncotic pressure. The way the balance between the hydrostatic and oncotic pressures controls exchanges across the capillary wall is considered in detail in Chapter 30.

Moderate amounts of protein do cross the capillary walls and enter the lymph. The size and frequency of the pores necessary to explain this movement have been calculated, and studies with the electron microscope have failed to demonstrate pores of the necessary size. However, there are numerous vesicles in the capillary endothelium. Tagged protein molecules have been found in these vesicles, suggesting that proteins are transported out of capillaries across endothelial cells by endocytosis followed by exocytosis on the interstitial side of the cells. Transport by this putative mechanism has been called **vesicular transport** or **cytopempsis.**

SODIUM & POTASSIUM DISTRIBUTION & TOTAL BODY OSMOLALITY

The foregoing discussion of the various compartments of the body fluids and the barriers between them facilitates consideration of the total body stores of the principal cations, Na^+ and K^+.

Total Body Sodium

The total amount of exchangeable Na^+ in the body (Na_E)—as opposed to its concentration in any particular body fluid—can be determined by the same dilution principle used to measure the body fluid compartments. A radioactive isotope of sodium (usually ^{24}Na) is injected, and after equilibration, the fraction of the sodium in the body that is radioactive is determined. The fraction of a substance that is radioactive—ie, the concentration of radioactive molecules divided by the concentration of radioactive plus nonradioactive molecules—is the **specific activity** (SA) of the substance. The SA of sodium in plasma after the injection of ^{24}Na, for example, is

$$\frac{^{24}Na\ (counts/min/L)}{^{24}Na\ +\ nonradioactive\ Na\ (mEq/L)}$$

The total exchangeable body sodium (Na_E) =

$$\frac{^{24}Na\ injected\ -\ ^{24}Na\ excreted}{SA\ of\ plasma}$$

The average normal value for Na_E in healthy adults is 41 mEq/kg, whereas the total amount of Na^+ in the body is about 58 mEq/kg. Therefore, approximately 17 mEq/kg are not available for exchange. The vast majority of this nonexchangeable Na^+ is in the hydroxyapatite crystal lattice of bone. The amount of Na^+ in the various body compartments is summarized in Table 1–6.

Total Body Potassium

The total exchangeable body K^+ can be determined by measuring the dilution of radioactive potassium (^{42}K). The average value in young adult men is about 45 mEq/kg body weight. It is somewhat less in women, and declines slightly with advancing age. About 10% of the total body K^+ is bound, mostly in red blood cells, brain, and bone, and the remaining 90% is exchangeable (Fig 1–10).

Table 1–6. Distribution of sodium in the body in mEq/kg body weight and percentage of total body sodium.*

	mEq/kg	% of Total
Total	58	100
Exchangeable body sodium (Na_E)	41	70.7
Total intracellular	5.2	9.0
Total extracellular	52.8	91.0
Plasma	6.5	11.2
Interstitial fluid	16.8	29.0
Dense connective tissue and cartilage	6.8	11.7
Bone sodium		
Exchangeable	6.4	11.0
Nonexchangeable	14.8	25.5
Transcellular	1.5	2.6

*Data courtesy of IS Edelman.

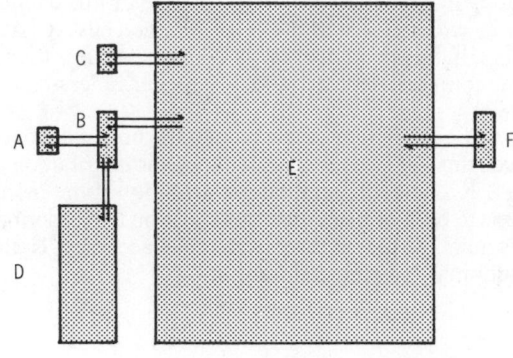

A: Plasma potassium, 0.4% of total body potassium
B: Interstitial lymph potassium, 1%
C: Dense connective tissue and cartilage potassium, 0.4%
D: Bone potassium, 7.6%
E: Intracellular potassium, 89.6%
F: Transcellular potassium, 1%

Figure 1–10. Body potassium distribution. Figures are percentages of total body potassium. (Data from Edelman IS, Liebman J: Am J Med 27:256, 1959.)

Interrelationships of Sodium & Potassium

Since the salts of sodium and potassium dissociate in the body to such a great extent, and since they are so plentiful, they determine in large part the osmolality of the body fluids. A change in the amount of electrolyte in one compartment is followed by predictable changes in the volume and electrolyte concentration in the others because the various compartments are in osmotic equilibrium. Fig 1–11 shows, for example, the changes in osmolal concentration and volume of the intracellular and extracellular fluid spaces that follow removal of 500 mOsm of extracellular electrolyte. Loss of electrolyte in excess of water from the ECF leads to hypotonicity of the ECF relative to the intracellular fluid. Consequently, water moves into the cells by osmosis until osmotic equilibrium between the ECF and the intracellular fluid is again attained. The net result is a decrease in ECF volume and an increase in intracellular fluid volume.

Total Body Osmolality

Since Na^+ is the principal cation of the plasma, the plasma osmotic pressure correlates well with the plasma Na^+ level. However, plasma Na^+ does not necessarily correlate well with Na_E. Total body osmolality reflects the electrolyte concentration in the body, ie, the total exchangeable body sodium plus the total exchangeable body potassium divided by the total body water:

$$\frac{Na_E\ +\ K_E}{TBW}$$

Because this latter figure has been found to correlate well with plasma Na^+, plasma Na^+ is a relatively

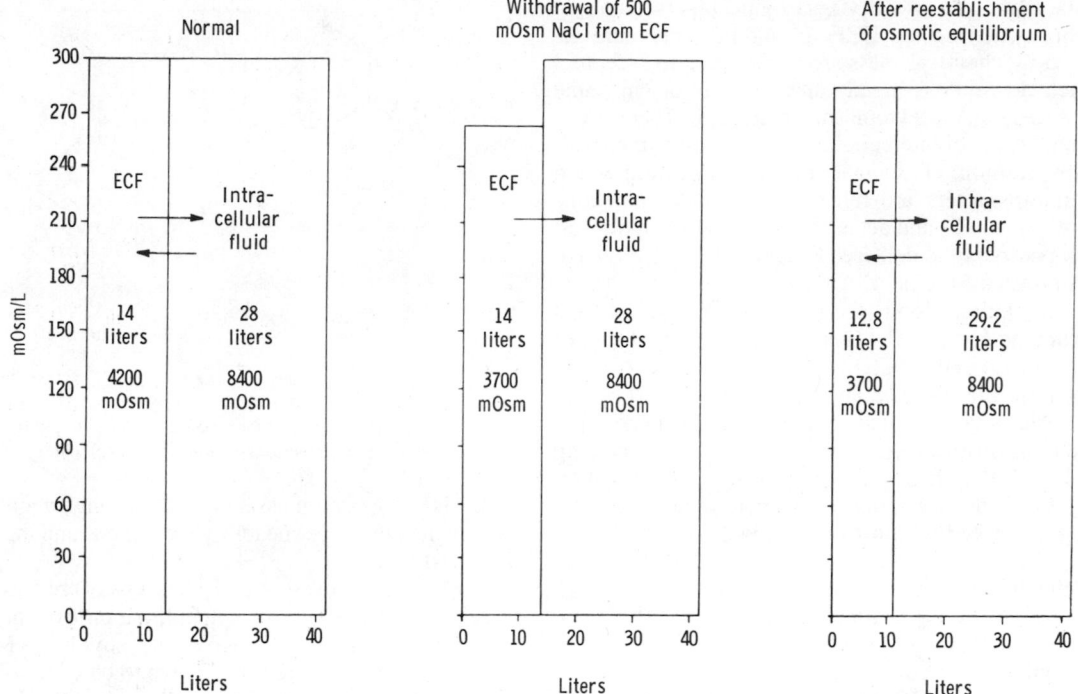

Figure 1–11. Response of body fluid to removal of 500 mOsm from ECF without change in total body water in a 70 kg man. The hypotonicity of the ECF causes water to enter cells until osmotic equilibrium is reestablished. Total mOsm in body after removal of 500 mOsm = $(14 \times 300) + (28 \times 300) - 500 = 12,100$ mOsm. New osmotic equilibrium = $12,100/(28 + 14) = 288$ mOsm/L. This means that the new volume of the ECF will be $(4200 - 500)/288 = 12.8$ L, and the new volume of the intracellular fluid will be $8400/288 = 29.2$ L. (After Darrow DC and Yannet H. Modified and reproduced, with permission, from Gamble JL: *Chemical Anatomy, Physiology, and Pathology of Extracellular Fluid*, 4th ed. Harvard Univ Press, 1942.)

accurate measure of total body osmolality. It is worth noting that plasma Na^+ can be affected by changes in any of 3 body components: Na_E itself, K_E, or TBW. A detailed discussion of the effects of disease on electrolyte and water balance is beyond the scope of this book, but the facts discussed above are basic to any consideration of pathologic water and electrolyte changes.

Plasma K^+ levels are not a good indicator of the total body K^+, since most of the K^+ is in the cells. There is a correlation between the K^+ and H^+ content of plasma, the 2 rising and falling together.

pH & BUFFERS

The maintenance of a stable pH in the body fluids is essential to life. The pH of a solution is the logarithm to the base 10 of the reciprocal of the H^+ concentration ($[H^+]$), ie, the negative logarithm of the $[H^+]$. The pH of water, in which H^+ and OH^- ions are present in equal numbers, is 7.0. For each pH unit less than 7.0, the $[H^+]$ is increased tenfold; for each pH unit above 7.0, it is decreased tenfold.

Buffers

The pH of the ECF is maintained at 7.40. In health, this value usually varies less than ±0.05 pH unit. Body pH is stabilized by the **buffering capacity** of the body fluids. A buffer is a substance that has the ability to bind or release H^+ in solution, thus maintaining the pH of the solution relatively constant despite the addition of considerable quantities of acid or base. One buffer in the body is carbonic acid, which is normally only slightly dissociated into H^+ and bicarbonate: $H_2CO_3 \rightleftharpoons H^+ + HCO_3^-$. If H^+ is added to a solution of carbonic acid, the equilibrium shifts and most of the added H^+ is removed from solution. If OH^- is added, H^+ and OH^- combine and more H_2CO_3 dissociates. Other buffers include the blood proteins and the proteins in cells. The quantitative aspects of buffering and the respiratory and renal adjustments that operate with the buffers to maintain a stable ECF pH of 7.40 are discussed in Chapters 35 and 40.

INTERCELLULAR COMMUNICATION

Cells communicate with each other via chemical messengers. Within a given tissue, some chemicals move from cell to cell via gap junctions (see above) without entering the ECF. In addition, cells are affected by chemical messengers that bind to receptors which are on the membranes of cells or, in some instances, in the cytoplasm or nucleus. There are 3 general types of intercellular communication mediated in this fashion: (1) **neural communication,** in which neurotransmitters are released at synaptic junctions from nerve cells and act across a narrow synaptic cleft on a postsynaptic cell (see Chapter 4), (2) **endocrine communication,** in which hormones reach cells via the circulating blood (see Chapters 18–24), and (3) **paracrine communication,** in which the products of cells diffuse in the ECF to affect neighboring cells that may be some distance away (see Chapter 19).

Although chemical messengers can exert their effects in various ways, most of them act by increasing cyclic AMP in their target cells or by inducing in their target cells the transcription of a portion of the genetic message stored within the DNA in the nucleus.

Cyclic AMP

In addition to its function in energy transfer, ATP is the precursor of cyclic adenosine-3',5'-monophosphate. This compound, the structure of which is shown in Fig 1–12, is also known as cyclic 3',5'-AMP, **cAMP,** or, most commonly, **cyclic AMP.**

Cyclic AMP serves as a key intracellular mediator for the effects of many hormones and other substances that modify cellular function. It is formed from ATP by the action of the enzyme **adenylate cyclase,** which is also known as **adenyl cyclase,** and sometimes as **adenylyl cyclase.** It is inactivated by conversion to 5'-AMP, a reaction catalyzed by the enzyme phosphodiesterase (Fig 1–13). Adenylate cyclase is located in cell membranes, and a specific receptor is associated with a part of the enzyme. Combination of the receptor with the hormone or other agent for which it is specific activates the adenylate cyclase, and cyclic AMP is released inside the cell. Thus, the hormone is a "first messenger" that remains outside the cell, and cyclic

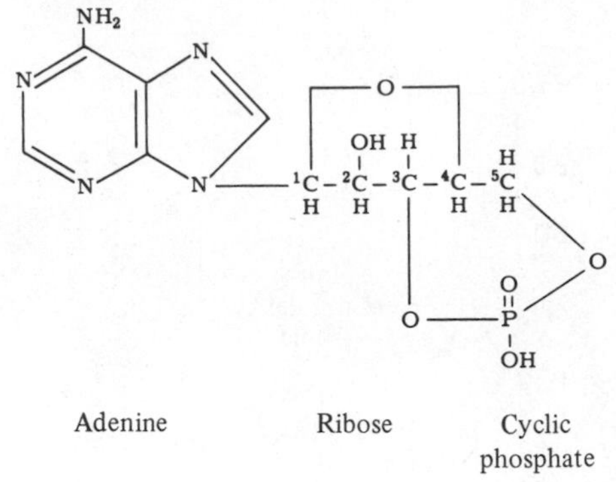

Figure 1–12. Cyclic adenosine-3',5'-monophosphate. The numbers indicate the positions in the ribose molecule.

AMP is a "second messenger" that brings about the actual changes in permeability, secretion, and the like (Fig 1–13).

Originally, cyclic AMP was discovered as the mediator of the effects of epinephrine on liver glycogen (see Chapter 17). However, cyclic AMP–mediated responses are now known to be exceedingly numerous and varied. Furthermore, cyclic AMP is found not only in mammals but throughout the animal kingdom, and it appears to have important functions in plants, slime molds, and bacteria. In mammals, it is responsible for the effects of many different chemical messengers.

It is worth noting that, although many different effects are mediated via cyclic AMP, the effects of the chemical messengers are specific. For example, ACTH stimulates adrenal corticoid secretion whereas TSH does not, and TSH stimulates thyroid hormone secretion whereas ACTH does not. The specificity of responses depends on the receptors associated with the adenylate cyclase; in each cell, the receptor is specific for the substance or substances that normally stimulate it. Some cyclic AMP does escape from cells upon

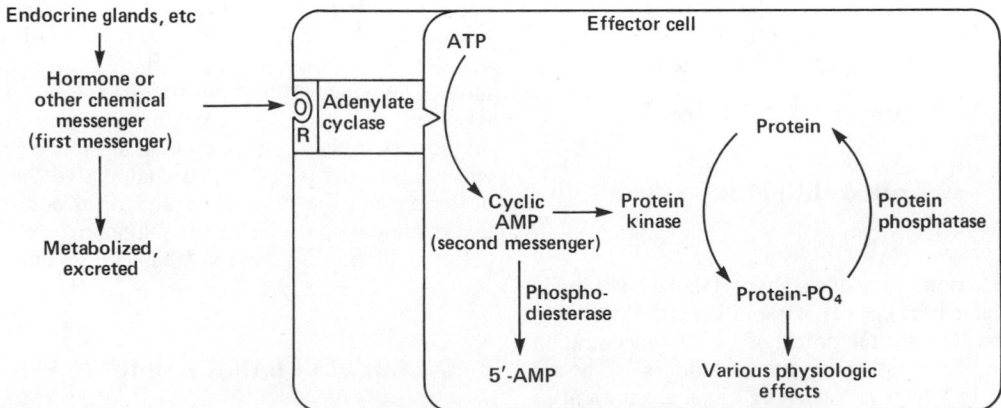

Figure 1–13. The role of cyclic AMP as a second messenger. R, receptor for first messenger. (Modified from Greengard P: Phosphorylated proteins as physiological effectors. Science 199:146, 1978.)

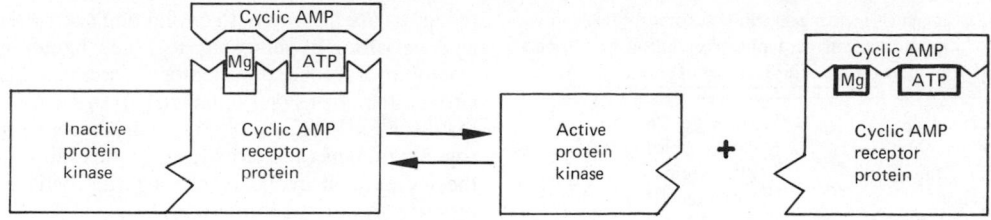

Figure 1–14. Interaction between protein kinase, cyclic AMP receptor protein, and cyclic AMP. Mg, magnesium ion. (Courtesy of J Roth.)

stimulation by certain hormones, but the amounts are small compared to the intracellular concentration, and only small amounts of extracellular cyclic AMP enter cells.

In a number of tissues, the effects of cyclic AMP have been shown to be exerted by activation of **protein kinases.** Protein kinases catalyze the transfer of phosphate from ATP to various enzymes (Fig 1–13), thus activating—or in some cases inactivating—the enzymes. An example of such mediation, the stimulation of phosphorylase in the liver by epinephrine, is discussed in Chapter 17. Observations on systems such as this have led to the general hypothesis that the effects of cyclic AMP are mediated via the protein kinases.

At least in some tissues, each protein kinase is associated with a cyclic AMP receptor protein, and when the receptor is unoccupied, the protein kinase is inactive. Cyclic AMP (plus ATP and Mg^{2+}) binds to this intracellular protein, and binding makes the kinase active (Fig 1–14). At the same time, intracellular binding protects the cyclic AMP from degradation. Thus, the intracellular concentration of active cyclic AMP depends on the equilibrium between the rate of its production by adenylate cyclase, the rate of its degradation by phosphodiesterase, and the amount of free receptor protein associated with protein kinase. Phosphodiesterase is inhibited by methyl xanthines such as caffeine and theophylline; consequently, these compounds augment hormonal and transmitter effects mediated via cyclic AMP.

Cyclic GMP

The cyclic derivative of guanosine, guanosine 3′,5′-monophosphate **(cyclic GMP),** is also present in cells of all living systems. Although its concentration is considerably less than that of cyclic AMP, it also mediates a variety of intracellular responses. For example, acetylcholine exerts at least some of its effects via cyclic GMP. There is evidence that in some systems cyclic AMP and cyclic GMP interact, one producing stimulation and the other inhibition. The enzyme that catalyzes cyclic GMP formation, **guanylate cyclase,** is a cell membrane enzyme like adenylate cyclase, and cyclic GMP acts, at least in part, via protein kinases.

Stimulation of Protein Synthesis

Unlike the other chemical messengers, steroid hormones act by inducing the synthesis of enzymes in their target cells. The process of protein synthesis is reviewed in Chapter 17. The steroids enter cells freely and bind to specific receptor proteins in the cytoplasm. The receptor protein–steroid complex then enters the nucleus, where it binds reversibly to DNA. In some way, this binding influences the gene to make more of the relevant mRNA, and the result is increased formation of specific protein molecules with enzyme activity. The steps involved are summarized in Fig 1–15, using adrenal glucocorticoids as the example. The actions of the individual steroid hormones are discussed in detail in Chapters 20, 21, and 23.

Thyroid hormones also stimulate enzyme synthesis, but they appear to bind directly to receptors in the nucleus rather than in the cytoplasm (see Chapter 18).

Other Substances Affecting Protein Phosphorylation

The phosphorylation of proteins that adjust cell function is affected not only by chemical messengers that affect cyclic AMP and cyclic GMP but also by hormones that act in other ways. For example, steroid hormones can affect phosphorylation by inducing the synthesis of substances that regulate the activity of protein kinases (Table 1–7). In addition, Ca^{2+} has pronounced effects on phosphorylation, and Ca^{2+} influx is increased by depolarization in excitable tissues

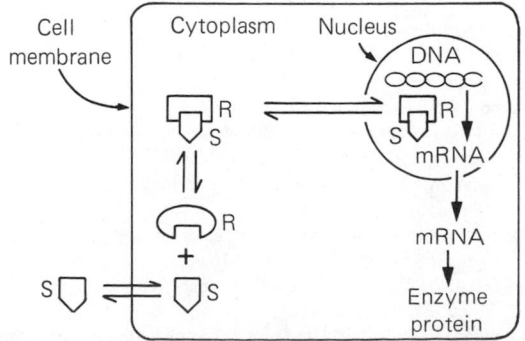

Figure 1–15. Events involved in glucocorticoid action. S, steroid; R, receptor. (Modified and reproduced, with permission, from Baxter J & others in: *Biochemistry of Gene Expression in Higher Organisms.* Australia and New Zealand Book Company, 1973.)

Table 1–7. Chemical messengers that apparently exert their effects via phosphorylation or dephosphorylation of proteins. a, β, H_1, H_2, and muscarinic refer to types of receptors.

By increasing cyclic AMP	By increasing cyclic GMP
Norepinephrine (β)	Norepinephrine (a)
Epinephrine (β)	Epinephrine (a)
Dopamine	Histamine (H_1)
Prostaglandin E_1	Acetylcholine (muscarinic)
Serotonin	Glutamate
Histamine (H_2)	**By inducing protein synthesis**
Peptide hormones	Steroid hormones
By decreasing cyclic AMP?	**By Ca^{2+}-dependent protein kinase?**
Insulin	Ca^{2+}

(see Chapters 2–4). Thus, phosphorylation of proteins is a ubiquitous mechanism for bringing about changes in cell function.

Receptors for Hormones & Neurotransmitters

Considerable progress has been made in the isolation, characterization, and study of the regulation of the receptors for chemical messengers. These proteins are not static components of the cell, but their numbers increase and decrease in response to various stimuli, and their properties change with changes in physiologic conditions. Current evidence suggests that when a hormone or neurotransmitter is present in excess, the number of active receptors decreases, whereas in the presence of a deficiency of the chemical messenger, there is an increase in the number of active receptors. There are also cross stimulation effects, one substance affecting the number or the affinity of receptors for other substances, or both. These effects on receptors are important in explaining such phenomena as denervation hypersensitivity (see Chapter 4), tolerance to morphine (see Chapter 7), and decreased sensitivity in diabetes (see Chapter 19). In several "receptor diseases" (eg, pseudohypoparathyroidism, nephrogenic diabetes insipidus), hormones fail to produce the increase in cyclic AMP in target cells that they produce in normal individuals.

HOMEOSTASIS

The actual environment of the cells of the body is the interstitial component of the ECF. Since normal cell function depends upon the constancy of this fluid, it is not surprising that in higher animals an immense number of regulatory mechanisms have evolved to maintain it. To describe "the various physiologic arrangements which serve to restore the normal state, once it has been disturbed," W.B. Cannon coined the term **homeostasis.** The buffering properties of the body fluids and the renal and respiratory adjustments to the presence of excess acid or alkali are examples of homeostatic mechanisms. There are countless other examples, and a large part of physiology is concerned with regulatory mechanisms that act to maintain the constancy of the internal environment. Many of these regulatory mechanisms operate on the principle of negative feedback; deviations from a given normal set point are detected by a sensor, and signals from the sensor trigger compensatory changes that continue until the set point is again reached.

References: Section I.
Introduction

Altman PL, Katz PD (editors): *Cell Biology.* Federation of American Societies of Experimental Biology, 1976.

Bennett MVL, Goodenough DA: Gap junctions, electrotonic coupling, and intracellular communication. Neurosci Res Prog Bull 16:375, 1978.

Bloom W, Fawcett DW: *A Textbook of Histology,* 10th ed. Saunders, 1975.

Cannon WB: *The Wisdom of the Body.* Norton, 1932.

Cohen SS: Are/were mitochondria and chloroplasts microorganisms? Am Sci 58:281, 1970.

Diamond JM: The epithelial junction: Bridge, gate, and fence. Physiologist 20:10, Feb 1977.

Edelman GM: Surface modulation in cell recognition and cell growth. Science 192:218, 1976.

Fawcett DW: What makes cilia and sperm tails beat? N Engl J Med 297:46, 1977.

Greengard P: Phosphorylated proteins as physiological effectors. Science 199:146, 1978.

Haggis GH & others: *Introduction to Molecular Biology,* 2nd ed. Wiley, 1973.

Jackson RL, Gotto AM Jr: Phospholipids in biology and medicine. N Engl J Med 290:24, 1974.

Jacobs S, Cuatrecasas P: Cell receptors in disease. N Engl J Med 297:1383, 1977.

Kolodny EH: Lysosomal storage diseases. N Engl J Med 294:1217, 1976.

Lodish HF, Rothman JE: The assembly of cell membranes. Sci Am 240:48, Jan 1979.

Loeb JN: The hyperosmolar state. N Engl J Med 290:1184, 1974.

Masters C, Holmes R: Peroxisomes: New aspects of cell physiology and biochemistry. Physiol Rev 57:816, 1977.

Palade G: Intracellular aspects of the process of protein synthesis. Science 189:347, 1975.

Schwartz A, Lindenmayer GE, Allen JC: The sodium-potassium adenosine triphosphatase: Pharmacological, physiological, and biochemical aspects. Pharmacol Rev 27:3, 1975.

Stephens RE, Edds KT: Microtubules: Structure, chemistry, and function. Physiol Rev 56:709, 1976.

Weissman G, Claiborne R (editors): *Cell Membranes: Biochemistry, Cell Biology and Pathology.* HP Publishing Co, 1975.

Wessells NK: How living cells change shape. Sci Am 225:76, Oct 1971.

Whaley WG, Dauwalder M, Kephart JE: Golgi apparatus: Influence on cell surfaces. Science 175:596, 1972.

Symposium: Membrane channels. Fed Proc 37:2626, 1978.

Section II. Physiology of Nerve & Muscle Cells

Excitable Tissue: Nerve | 2

The human nervous system contains more than 10 billion neurons. These basic building blocks of the nervous system have evolved from primitive neuroeffector cells that respond to various stimuli by contracting. In higher animals, contraction has become the specialized function of muscle cells, whereas transmission of nerve impulses has become the specialized function of neurons.

NERVE CELLS

Morphology

A typical spinal motor neuron such as that shown in Fig 2–1 has 5–7 processes called **dendrites** that extend out from the cell body and arborize extensively. It also has a long fibrous **axon** that originates from a somewhat thickened area of the cell body, the **axon hillock.** A short distance from its origin, the axon acquires a sheath of **myelin,** a protein-lipid complex made up of many layers of unit membrane (Fig 2–2). The myelin sheath envelops the axon except at its ending and at periodic constrictions about 1 mm apart called the **nodes of Ranvier.** The myelin plays an important role in neural functions. In multiple sclerosis, a crippling disease that appears to be related in some way to infection with measles virus, there is patchy destruction of myelin.

The axon ends in a number of **synaptic knobs,** which are also called **terminal buttons** or **axon telodendria.** These knobs contain granules or vesicles in which the synaptic transmitter secreted by the nerve is stored (see Chapter 4). Some mammalian neurons and most neurons in invertebrates are unmyelinated; the axons are invested in Schwann cells, but there has been no rotation of the axon to produce multiple layers of membrane (Fig 2–2).

The conventional terminology used above for the parts of a neuron works well enough for spinal motor neurons and interneurons, but it has obvious shortcomings in terms of "dendrites" and "axons" when it is applied to other types of neurons found in the nervous system (Fig 2–3). A terminology for the parts of neurons that generally harmonizes morphologic and functional considerations is shown in Fig 2–4. According to this terminology, the **dendritic zone** of the neuron is the receptor membrane of the neuron (see below and Chapters 4 and 5). The axon is the single, elongated cytoplasmic extension with the specialized function of conducting impulses away from the dendritic zone. The cell body is often located at the dendritic zone end of the axon, but it can be within the axon (eg, auditory neurons) or attached to the side of the axon (eg, cutaneous neurons). Its location makes no difference as far as the receptor function of the dendritic zone and the transmission function of the axon are concerned. It is worth pointing out, however,

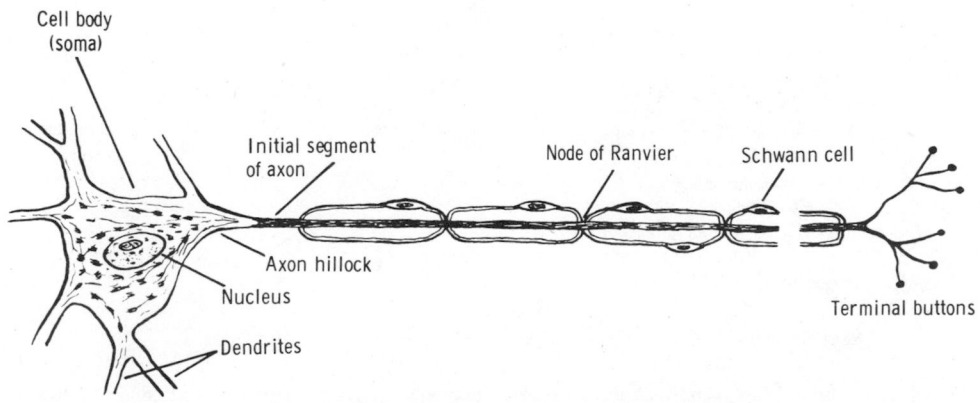

Figure 2–1. Motor neuron with myelinated axon.

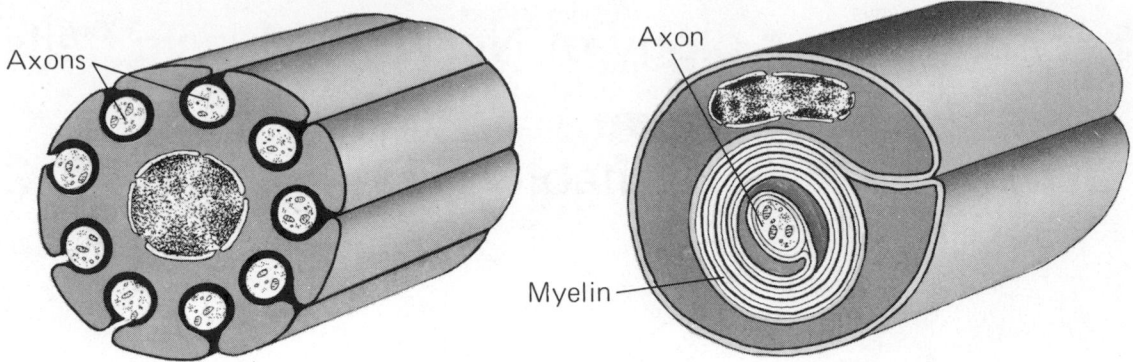

Figure 2–2. Diagrammatic representation of the relation of axons to Schwann cell in unmyelinated *(left)* and myelinated nerve *(right)*. In the former, the axons are simply buried in the cell. In the latter, the Schwann cell membrane is coiled many times around the axon, forming the multiple layers of membrane that make up myelin.

that some dendrites appear to be able to generate impulses as well as integrate activity. Indeed, transmission of impulses from one dendrite to another has been demonstrated in the CNS.

The size of the neurons and the length of their processes vary considerably in different parts of the nervous system. In some cases, the dimensions of the neurons are truly remarkable. In the case of spinal motor neurons supplying the muscles of the foot, for example, it has been calculated that if the cell body were the size of a tennis ball the dendrites of the cell would fill an average-sized living room and the axon

would be up to 1.6 km (almost a mile) long though only 13 mm (½ inch) in diameter.

Protein Synthesis & Axoplasmic Transport

Despite the extremely long axons of some neurons, it is the cell body that maintains the functional and anatomic integrity of the axon; if the axon is cut, the part distal to the cut degenerates (**wallerian degeneration**). The materials responsible for maintaining the axon, probably mostly proteins, are formed in the cell body and transported along the axon (**axoplasmic transport**). Proteins associated with synaptic trans-

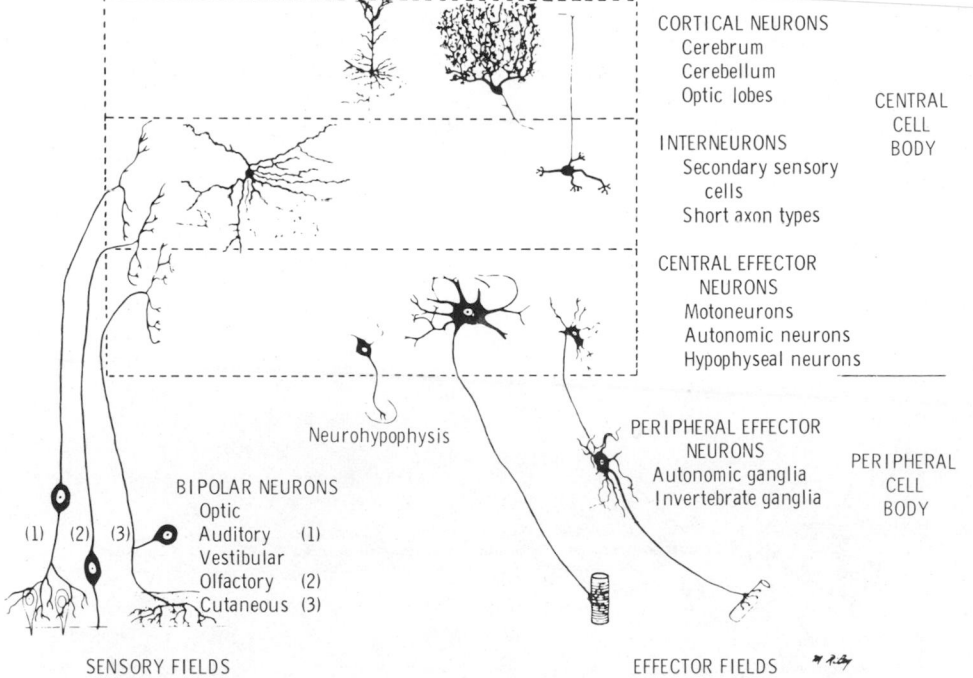

Figure 2–3. Types of neurons in the mammalian nervous system. (Reproduced, with permission, from Bodian D: Introductory survey of neurons. Cold Spring Harbor Symposium on Quantitative Biology 17:1, 1952.)

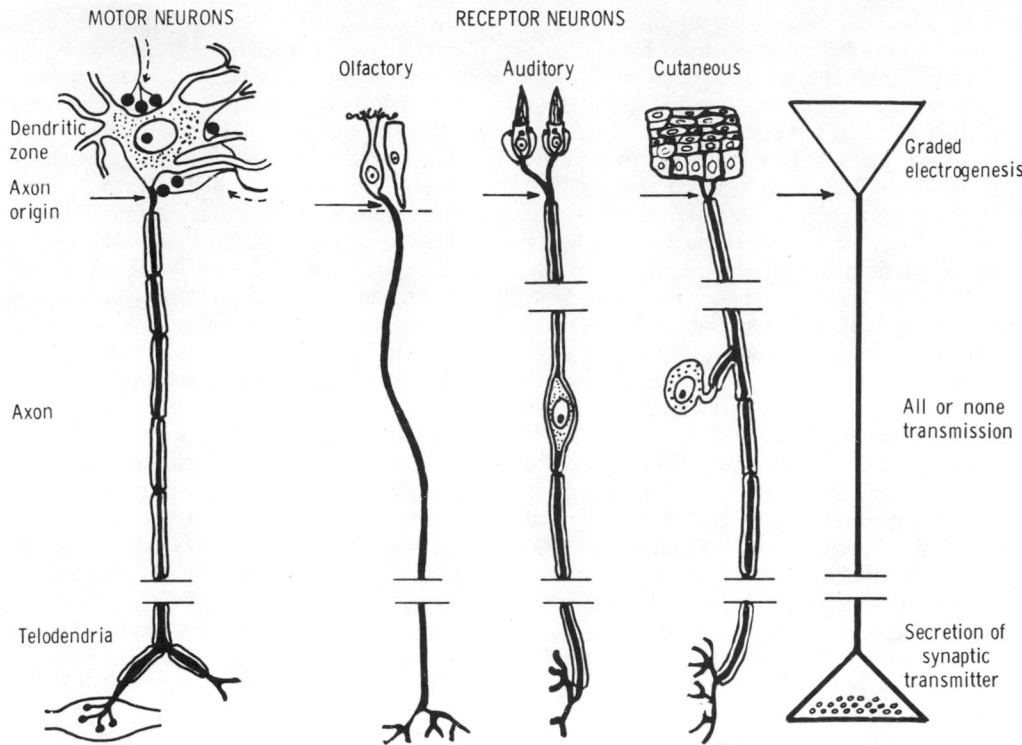

Figure 2–4. A variety of mammalian receptor and effector neurons. The neurons are arranged to illustrate the concept that impulse origin (indicated in each case by the arrow) rather than location of the cell body is the logical point of departure for analyzing neuronal structure in functional terms. Thus the dendritic zone, the area where the activity that generates the impulses occurs, may be dendrites or cell body. The axon conducts the impulses to the axon telodendria. The location of the cell body varies, and has no direct effect on impulse generation or transmission. (Modified after Grundfest and reproduced, with permission, from Bodian D: The generalized vertebrate neuron. Science 137:323, 1962. Copyright 1962 by the American Association for the Advancement of Science.)

mitters are also synthesized in the endoplasmic reticulum of the cell body and transported to the axon terminals. There is both fast (400 mm/d) and slow (approximately 200 mm/d) transport. Fast transport depends on the oxidative metabolism of the neuron and probably on ATP (see Chapter 17). Both forms of transport may depend on the microtubules. Since transport has some similarities to the contraction of muscle, the hypothesis has been advanced that the transported material is attached to filaments formed in the cell body and slides along the microtubules in a manner analogous to the way actin slides along myosin in skeletal muscle.

Excitation

Nerve cells have a low threshold for excitation. The stimulus may be electrical, chemical, or mechanical. Two types of physicochemical disturbances are produced: local, nonpropagated potentials called, depending on their location, **synaptic, generator,** or **electrotonic, potentials;** and propagated disturbances, the **nerve impulses.** These are the only responses of neurons and other excitable tissues, and they are the universal language of the nervous system.

The impulse is normally transmitted (or **con-**ducted) along the axon to its termination. Nerves are not "telephone wires" that transmit impulses passively; conduction of nerve impulses, although rapid, is much slower than that of electricity. Nerve tissue is in fact a relatively poor passive conductor, and it would take a potential of many volts to produce a signal of a fraction of 1 volt at the other end of a 1 meter axon in the absence of active processes in the nerve. Conduction is an active, self-propagating process that requires expenditure of energy by the nerve, and the impulse moves along the nerve at a constant amplitude and velocity. The process is often compared to what happens when a match is applied to one end of a train of gunpowder; by igniting the powder particles immediately in front of it, the flame moves steadily down the train to its end.

ELECTRICAL PHENOMENA IN NERVE CELLS

For over 100 years it has been known that there are electrical potential changes in a nerve when it conducts impulses, but it was not until suitable equipment was developed that these electrical events could be measured and studied in detail. Special instruments are necessary because the events are rapid, being measured in **milliseconds (ms);** and the potential changes are small, being measured in **millivolts (mV).** The principal advances that made detailed study of the electrical activity in nerves possible were the development of electronic amplifiers and the cathode-ray oscilloscope. Modern amplifiers magnify potential changes 1000 times or more, and the cathode-ray oscilloscope provides an almost inertialess and almost instantaneously responding "lever" for recording electrical events.

The Cathode-Ray Oscilloscope

The cathode-ray oscilloscope (CRO) is used to measure the electrical events in living tissue. A cathode emits electrons when a high voltage is applied across it and a suitable anode in a vacuum. In the CRO, the electrons are directed into a focused beam that strikes the face of the glass tube in which the cathode is located. The face is coated with one of a number of substances (phosphors) that emit light when struck by electrons. A vertical metal plate is placed on either side of the electron beam. When a voltage is applied across these plates, the negatively charged electrons are drawn toward the positively charged plate and repelled by the negatively charged plate. If the voltage applied to the vertical plates (X plates) is increased slowly and then reduced suddenly and increased again, the beam moves steadily toward the positive plate, snaps back to its former position, and moves toward the positive plate again. Application of a "saw-tooth voltage" of this type thus causes the beam to sweep across the face of the tube, and the speed of the sweep is proportionate to the rate of rise of the applied voltage.

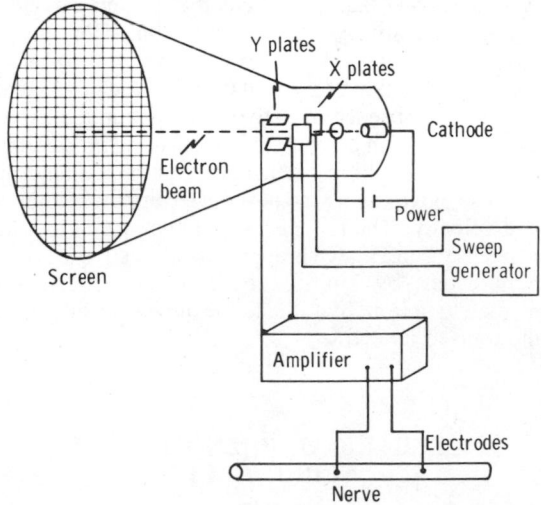

Figure 2–5. Cathode-ray oscilloscope. Simplified diagram of principal connections when arranged to record potential changes in nerve.

In the CRO (Fig 2–5), another set of plates (Y plates) is arranged horizontally, with one plate above and one below the beam. Voltages applied to these plates deflect the beam up and down as it sweeps across the face of the tube, the magnitude of the vertical deflection being proportionate to the potential difference between the horizontal plates at any given instant. In practice, electrodes placed on or in the nerve are connected through a suitable amplifier to the horizontal plates of the oscilloscope. Any changes in potential occurring in the nerve are thus recorded as vertical deflections of the beam as it moves across the tube. The tracing of the beam on the face of the oscilloscope may be photographed to make a permanent record.

Recording From Single Axons

With the CRO, the electrical events occurring in a piece of peripheral nerve dissected from a laboratory animal can be demonstrated. However, such preparations contain many axons, and it is important to be able to study the properties of a single axon. Mammalian axons are relatively small (20 μm or less in diameter) and are difficult to separate from other axons, but giant unmyelinated nerve cells exist in a number of invertebrate species. Such giant cells are found, for example, in crabs *(Carcinus)* and cuttlefish *(Sepia),* but the largest known axons are found in the squid *(Loligo).* The neck region of the muscular mantle of the squid contains single axons up to 1 mm in diameter. It appears that their fundamental properties are similar to those of mammalian axons.

Another important technical advance in neurophysiology has been the development of microelectrodes that can be inserted into nerve cells. These electrodes are made by drawing out glass capillary pipettes so that the diameter of the tip is very small. They are filled with a solution of electrolyte, usually potassium chloride. Electrodes with tip diameters of a few micrometers can be inserted into invertebrate giant axons, and ultramicroelectrodes with tip diameters of less than 1 μm can be inserted into mammalian nerve cells.

Resting Membrane Potential

When 2 electrodes are connected through a suitable amplifier to a CRO and placed on the surface of a single axon, no potential difference is observed. However, if one electrode is inserted into the interior of the cell, a constant potential difference is observed, with the inside negative relative to the outside of the cell at rest. This **resting membrane potential** is found in many different types of cells, and its genesis is discussed in Chapter 1. In neurons, it is usually about −70 mV.

Latent Period

If the axon is stimulated and a conducted impulse occurs, a characteristic series of potential changes is observed as the impulse passes the exterior electrode. When the stimulus is applied, there is a brief irregular deflection of the baseline, the **stimulus artifact.** This artifact is due to current leakage from the stimulating electrodes to the recording electrodes. It usually occurs despite careful shielding, but it is of value because it marks on the cathode-ray screen the point at which the stimulus was applied.

The stimulus artifact is followed by an isopotential interval or **latent period** that ends with the next potential change and corresponds to the time it takes the impulse to travel along the axon from the site of stimulation to the recording electrodes. Its duration is proportionate to the distance between the stimulating and recording electrodes and the speed of conduction of the axon. If the duration of the latent period and the distance between the electrodes are known, the speed of conduction in the axon can be calculated. For example, assume that the distance between the cathodal stimulating electrode and the exterior electrode in Fig 2–6 is 4 cm. The cathode is normally the stimulating electrode, as described below. If the latent period is 2 ms long, the speed of conduction is 4 cm/2 ms, or 20 m/s.

Action Potential

The first manifestation of the approaching impulse is a beginning depolarization of the membrane. After an initial 15 mV of depolarization, the rate of depolarization increases. The point at which this change in rate occurs is called the **firing level.** Thereafter, the tracing on the oscilloscope rapidly reaches and **overshoots** the isopotential (zero potential) line to approximately +35 mV. It then reverses and falls rapidly toward the resting level. When repolarization is about 70% completed, the rate of repolarization decreases and the tracing approaches the resting level

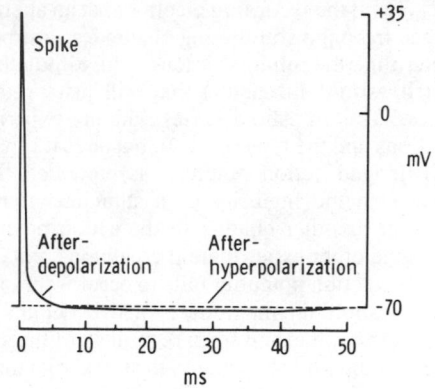

Figure 2–7. Diagram of complete action potential of large mammalian myelinated fiber, drawn without time or voltage distortion to show proportions of components.

more slowly. The sharp rise and rapid fall are the **spike potential** of the axon, and the slower fall at the end of the process is the **after-depolarization.** After reaching the previous resting level, the tracing overshoots slightly in the hyperpolarizing direction to form the small but prolonged **after-hyperpolarization.** The after-depolarization is sometimes called the **negative after-potential** and the after-hyperpolarization the **positive after-potential,** but the terms are now rarely used. The whole sequence of potential changes is called the **action potential.** It is a monophasic action potential because it is primarily in one direction. Before electrodes could be inserted in the axons, the response was approximated by recording between an electrode on intact membrane and an electrode on an area of nerve that had been damaged by crushing, destroying the integrity of the membrane. The potential difference between an intact area and such a damaged area is called a **demarcation potential.**

The proportions of the tracing in Fig 2–6 are intentionally distorted to illustrate these various components of the action potential. A tracing with the components plotted on exact temporal and magnitude scales for a mammalian neuron is shown in Fig 2–7. Note that the rise of the action potential is so rapid that it fails to show clearly the change in depolarization rate at the firing level, and also that the after-hyperpolarization is only about 1–2 mV in amplitude although it lasts about 40 ms. The duration of the after-depolarization is about 4 ms in this instance. It is shorter and less prominent in many other neurons. Changes may occur in the after-polarization without changes in the rest of the action potential. For example, if the nerve has been conducting repetitively for a long time, the after-hyperpolarization is usually quite large. These potentials represent recovery processes in the neuron rather than the events responsible for the spike portion of the action potential.

"All or None" Law

If an axon is arranged for recording as shown in

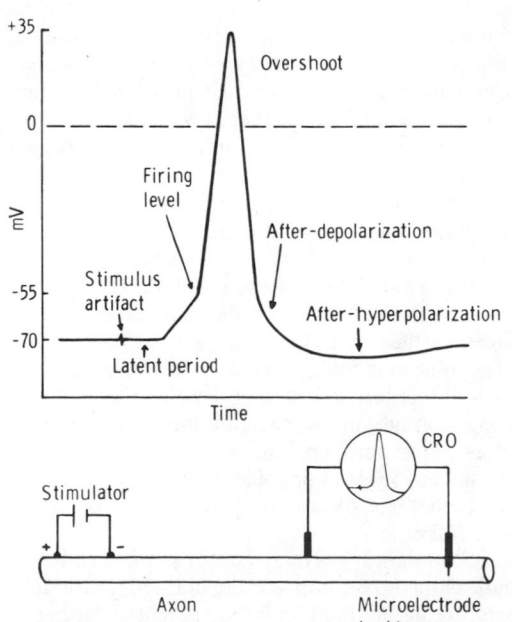

Figure 2–6. Action potential ("spike potential") recorded with one electrode inside cell.

Fig 2–6 with the recording electrodes at an appreciable distance from the stimulating electrodes, it is possible to determine the minimal intensity of stimulating current (**threshold intensity**) that will just produce an impulse. This threshold varies with the experimental conditions and the type of axon, but once it is reached, a full-fledged action potential is produced. Further increases in the intensity of a stimulus produce no increment or other change in the action potential as long as the other experimental conditions remain constant. The action potential fails to occur if the stimulus is subthreshold in magnitude, and it occurs with a constant amplitude and form regardless of the strength of the stimulus if the stimulus is at or above threshold intensity. The action potential is therefore "all or none" in character, and is said to obey the **"all or none" law.**

Strength-Duration Curve

In a preparation such as that in Fig 2–6, it is possible to determine experimentally the relationship between the strength of the stimulating current and the length of time it must be applied to the nerve to produce a response. Stimuli of extremely short duration will not excite the axon no matter how intense they may be. With stimuli of longer duration, threshold intensity is related to the duration of stimulus as shown in Fig 2–8. With weak stimuli, a point is reached where no response occurs no matter how long the stimulus is applied. The relationship shown in Fig 2–8 applies only to currents that rise to peak intensity rapidly. Slowly rising currents sometimes fail to fire the nerve because the nerve in some way adapts to the applied stimulus, a process called **accommodation.**

Classically, the magnitude of the current just sufficient to excite a given nerve or muscle is called the **rheobase** and the time for which it must be applied the **utilization time.** Another measurement is the **chronaxie,** ie, the length of time a current of twice rheobasic intensity must be applied to produce a response. Within limits, the chronaxie of any given excitable

tissue is constant for that tissue, and chronaxie values have been used to compare excitability of various tissues.

Electrotonic Potentials, Local Response, & Firing Level

Although subthreshold stimuli do not produce an action potential, they do have an effect on the membrane potential. This can be demonstrated by placing recording electrodes within a few millimeters of a stimulating electrode and applying subthreshold stimuli of fixed duration. Application of such currents with a cathode leads to a localized depolarizing potential change that rises sharply and decays exponentially with time. The magnitude of this response drops off rapidly as the distance between the stimulating and recording electrodes is increased. Conversely, an anodal current produces a hyperpolarizing potential change of similar duration. These potential changes are called **electrotonic potentials,** those produced at a cathode being **catelectrotonic** and those at an anode **anelectrotonic.** They are passive changes in membrane polarization caused by addition or subtraction of charge by the particular electrode. At low current intensities producing up to about 7 mV of depolarization or hyperpolarization, their size is proportionate to the magnitude of the stimulus. With stronger stimuli, this relationship remains constant for anelectrotonic responses but not for responses at the cathode. The cathodal responses are greater than would be expected from the magnitude of the applied current. Finally, when the cathodal stimulation is great enough to produce about 15 mV of depolarization, ie, at a membrane potential of −55 mV, the membrane potential suddenly begins to fall rapidly, and a propagated action potential occurs. The disproportionately greater response at the cathode to stimuli of sufficient strength to produce 7–15 mV of depolarization indicates active participation by the membrane in the process and is called the **local response** (Fig 2–9). The point at which a runaway spike potential is initiated is the **firing level.** Thus, cathodal currents that produce up to 7 mV of depolarization have a purely passive effect on the membrane caused by addition of negative charges. Those producing 7–15 mV of depolarization produce in addition a slight active change in the membrane, and this change contributes to the depolarizing process. However, the repolarizing forces are still stronger than the depolarizing forces, and the potential decays. At 15 mV of depolarization, the depolarizing forces are strong enough to overwhelm the repolarizing processes and an action potential results. These facts indicate that at 15 mV of depolarization some fundamental change that leads to runaway depolarization occurs in the membrane.

Stimulation normally occurs at the cathode because cathodal stimuli are depolarizing. Anodal currents, by taking the membrane potential farther away from the firing level, actually inhibit impulse formation. However, cessation of an anodal current may lead to an overshoot of the membrane potential in the de-

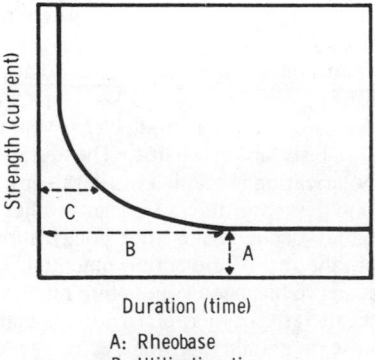

A: Rheobase
B: Utilization time
C: Chronaxie

Figure 2–8. Strength-duration curve. The curve relates the strength of a stimulus to the time for which it must be applied to an excitable tissue to produce a response.

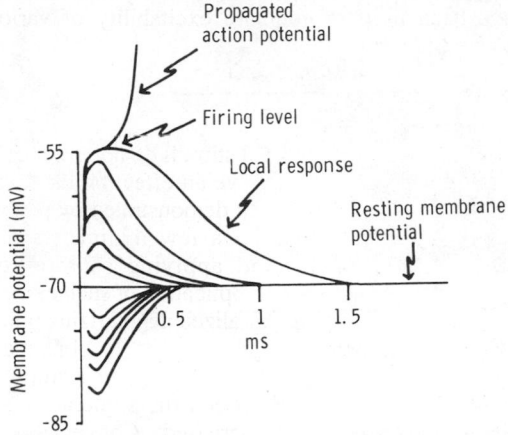

Figure 2–9. Electrotonic potentials and local response. The changes in the membrane potential of a neuron following application of stimuli of 0.2, 0.4, 0.6, 0.8, and 1.0 times threshold intensity are shown superimposed on the same time scale. The responses below the horizontal line are those recorded near the anode, and the responses above the line are those recorded near the cathode. The stimulus of threshold intensity was repeated twice. Once it caused a propagated action potential (top line), and once it did not. (Based on a diagram from Hodgkin AL: The subthreshold potentials in a crustacean nerve fibre. Proc Roy Soc London s.B 126:87, 1938.)

polarizing direction. This rebound is sometimes large enough to cause the nerve to fire at the end of an anodal stimulus.

Changes in Excitability During Electrotonic Potentials & the Action Potential

During the action potential as well as during catelectrotonic and anelectrotonic potentials and the local response, there are changes in the threshold of the neuron to stimulation. Hyperpolarizing anelectrotonic responses elevate the threshold and catelectrotonic potentials lower it as they move the membrane potential closer to the firing level. During the local response the threshold is also lowered, but during the rising and much of the falling phases of the spike potential the neuron is refractory to stimulation. This **refractory period** is divided into an **absolute refractory period,** corresponding to the period from the time the firing level is reached until repolarization is about one-third complete; and a **relative refractory period,** lasting from this point to the start of after-depolarization. During the absolute refractory period no stimulus, no matter how strong, will excite the nerve, but during the relative refractory period stronger than normal stimuli can cause excitation. During after-depolarization the threshold is again decreased, and during after-hyperpolarization it is increased. These changes in threshold are correlated with the phases of the action potential in Fig 2–10.

Electrogenesis of the Action Potential

The descriptive data discussed above may be formulated into a picture of the electrical events underlying the action potential. The nerve cell membrane is polarized at rest, with positive charges lined up along the outside of the membrane and negative charges along the inside. During the action potential, this polarity is abolished and for a brief period is actually reversed (Fig 2–11). Positive charges from the membrane ahead of and behind the action potential flow into the area of negativity represented by the action potential ("current sink"). By drawing off positive charges, this flow decreases the polarity of the membrane ahead of the action potential. Such electrotonic depolarization initiates a local response, and when the firing level is reached a propagated response occurs that in turn electrotonically depolarizes the membrane in front of it. This sequence of events moves regularly along an unmyelinated axon to its end. Thus, the self-propagating nature of the nerve impulse is due to circular current flow and successive electrotonic depolarizations to the firing level of the membrane ahead of the action potential. Once initiated, a moving impulse does not depolarize the area behind it to the firing level because this area is refractory.

The action potentials produced at synaptic junctions and sensory receptors also depend upon electrotonic depolarization of the nerve cell membrane to the firing level. The details of the process by which the nerve cell body and dendrites serve as a large current sink to draw off positive charges from the axon are described in Chapter 4.

Saltatory Conduction

Conduction in myelinated axons depends upon a similar pattern of circular current flow. However,

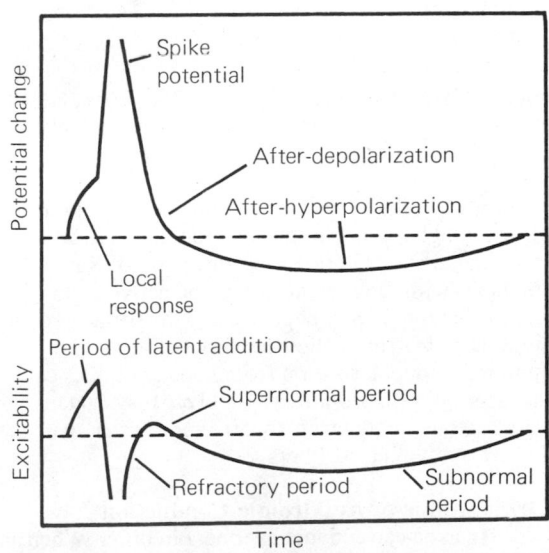

Figure 2–10. Relative changes in excitability of a nerve cell membrane during the passage of an impulse. Note that excitability is the reciprocal of threshold. (Modified and reproduced, with permission, from Morgan CT: *Physiological Psychology.* McGraw-Hill, 1943.)

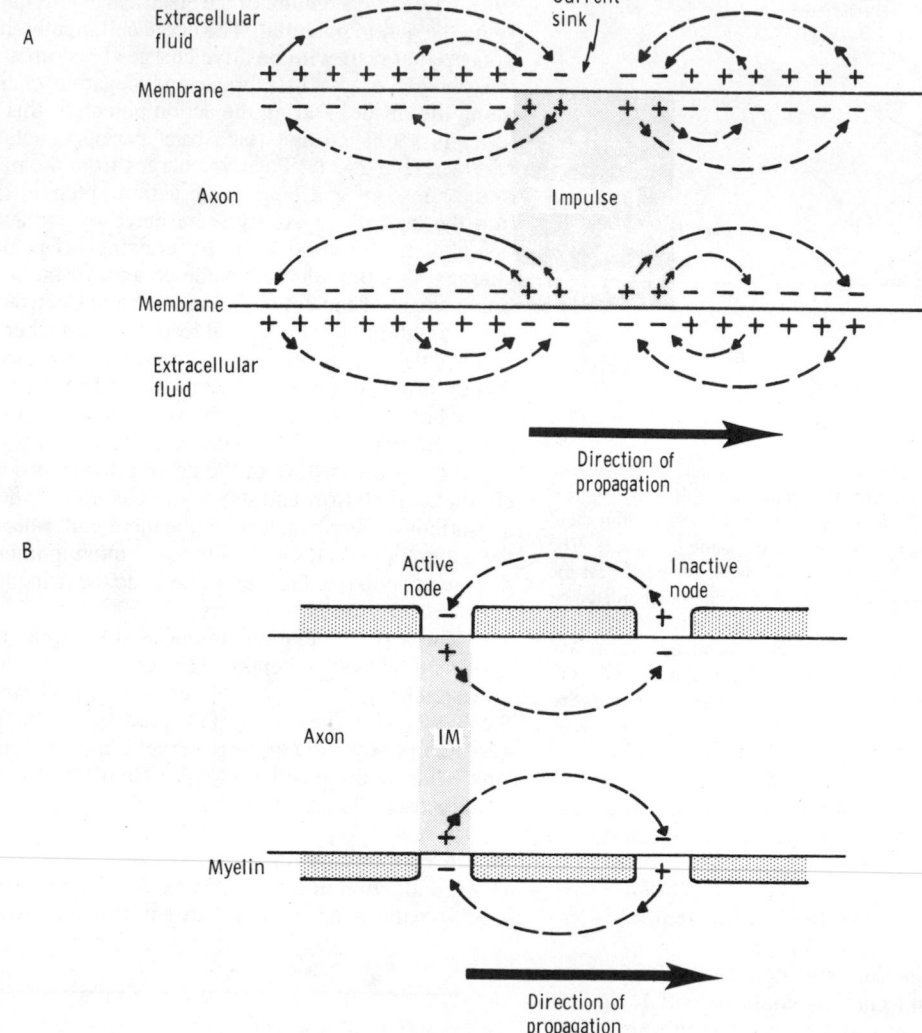

Figure 2–11. Local current flow around an impulse in an axon. Note that current flow is represented as movement of positive charges. *A* represents the situation in nonmyelinated nerves, *B* that in myelinated nerves (saltatory conduction). IM, impulse.

myelin is a relatively effective insulator, and current flow through it is negligible. Instead, depolarization in myelinated axons jumps from one node of Ranvier to the next, with the current sink at the active node serving to electrotonically depolarize to the firing level the node ahead of the action potential (Fig 2–11). This jumping of depolarization from node to node is called **saltatory conduction.** It is a rapid process, and myelinated axons conduct up to 50 times faster than the fastest unmyelinated fibers.

Orthodromic & Antidromic Conduction

An axon can conduct in either direction. When an action potential is initiated in the middle of it, 2 impulses traveling in opposite directions are set up by electrotonic depolarization on either side of the initial current sink.

In a living animal, impulses normally pass in one direction only, ie, from synaptic junctions or receptors along axons to their termination. Such conduction is called **orthodromic.** Conduction in the opposite direction is called **antidromic.** Since synapses, unlike axons, permit conduction in one direction only, any antidromic impulses that are set up fail to pass the first synapse they encounter (see Chapter 4) and die out at that point.

Biphasic Action Potentials

The descriptions of the resting membrane potential and action potential outlined above are based on recording with 2 electrodes, one on the surface of the axon and the other inside the axon. If both recording electrodes are placed on the surface of the axon, there is no potential difference between them at rest. When the nerve is stimulated and an impulse is conducted past the 2 electrodes, a characteristic sequence of po-

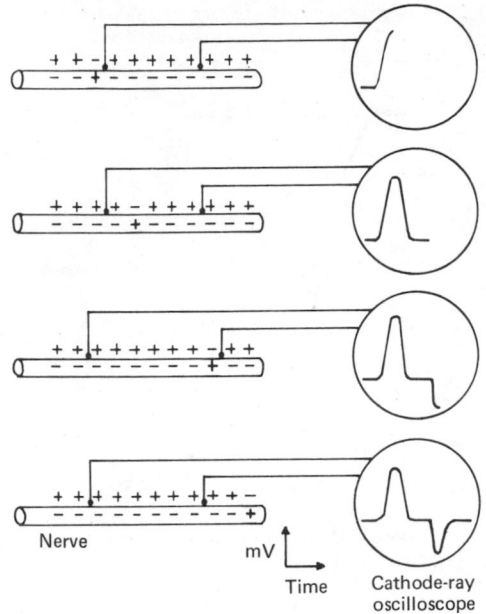

Figure 2–12. Biphasic action potential. Both recording electrodes are on the outside of the nerve membrane.

tential changes results. As the wave of depolarization reaches the electrode nearest the stimulator, this electrode becomes negative to the other electrode (Fig 2–12). When the impulse passes to the portion of the nerve between the 2 electrodes, the potential returns to zero and then, as it passes the second electrode, the first electrode becomes positive to the second. It is conventional to connect the leads in such a way that when the first electrode becomes negative to the second an upward deflection is recorded. Therefore, the record shows an upward deflection followed by an isoelectric interval and then a downward deflection. This sequence is called a **biphasic action potential** (Fig 2–12). The duration of the isoelectric interval is proportionate to the speed of conduction of the nerve and the distance between the 2 recording electrodes.

Conduction in a Volume Conductor

Because the body fluids contain large quantities of electrolytes, the nerves in the body function in a conducting medium that is often called a **volume conductor.** The monophasic and biphasic action potentials described above are those seen when an axon is stimulated in a nonconducting medium outside the body. The potential changes observed during extracellular recording in a volume conductor are basically similar to these action potentials, but they are complicated by the effects of current flow in the volume conductor. These effects are complex and are influenced by such factors as the orientation of the electrodes relative to the direction the action potential is moving and the distance between the recording electrode over active tissue and the indifferent electrode. In general, when an action potential is recorded in a

volume conductor, there are positive deflections before and after the negative spike. A simplified diagram of the genesis of these deflections is shown in Fig 2–13.

IONIC BASIS OF EXCITATION & CONDUCTION

Ionic Basis of Resting Membrane Potential

The ionic basis of the resting membrane potential has been discussed in Chapter 1. In nerves, as in other tissues, Na^+ is actively transported out of the cell and a small amount of K^+ is actively transported in. K^+ diffuses back out of the cell down its concentration gradient, and Na^+ diffuses back in, but since the permeability of the membrane to K^+ is much greater than it is to Na^+ at rest, the passive K^+ efflux is much greater than the passive Na^+ influx. Since the membrane is impermeable to most of the anions in the cell, the K^+ efflux is not accompanied by an equal flux of anions and the membrane is maintained in a polarized state with the outside positive to the inside. The ion fluxes across the nerve cell membrane at rest are summarized in Fig 1–9.

Ionic Fluxes During the Action Potential

In nerve, as in other tissues, a slight decrease in resting membrane potential leads to increased movement of K^+ out of and Cl^- into the cell, restoring the resting membrane potential. In nerve and muscle, however, there is a unique change in the cell membrane when depolarization exceeds 7 mV. This change is a voltage-dependent increase in membrane permeability to Na^+, so that the closer the membrane potential is to the firing level the greater the Na^+ permeability. The electrical and concentration gradients for Na^+ are both directed inward. During the local response, Na^+ permeability is slightly increased, but K^+ efflux is able to restore the potential to the resting value. When the firing level is reached, permeability is great enough so that Na^+ influx further lowers the membrane potential and Na^+ permeability is further increased. The consequent Na^+ influx swamps the repolarizing processes, and runaway depolarization results, producing the spike potential.

The equilibrium potential for Na^+ in mammalian neurons, calculated by using the Nernst equation, is about +60 mV. With the great increase in Na^+ permeability at the start of the action potential, the membrane potential approaches this value. It does not reach it, however, primarily because the change in Na^+ permeability is short-lived. Na^+ permeability starts to return to the resting value during the rising phase of the spike potential, and Na^+ conductance is decreased during repolarization. In addition, the direction of the electrical gradient for Na^+ is reversed during the overshoot because the membrane potential is reversed. These factors limit Na^+ influx and help bring about repolarization.

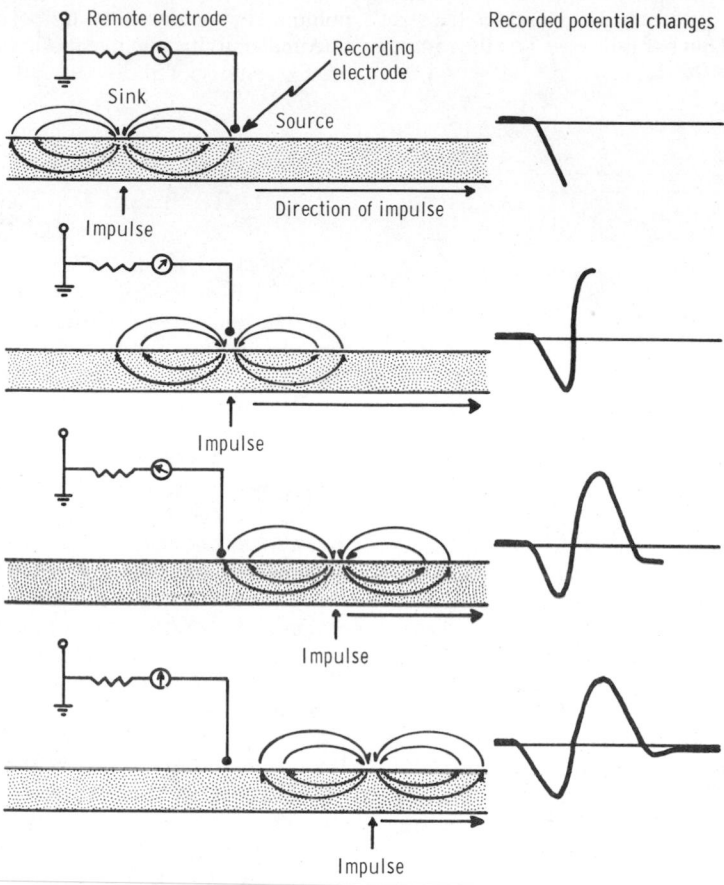

Figure 2–13. Potential changes recorded during passage of an impulse along an axon in a volume conductor. One electrode (recording electrode) is on the surface of the axon; the other (remote or indifferent electrode) is on inactive tissue at a distance in the conducting medium. (Reproduced, with permission, from Brazier M: *The Electrical Activity of the Nervous System,* 3rd ed. Pitman, 1968.)

Another important factor producing repolarization of the nerve membrane is the increase in K^+ permeability that accompanies the increase in Na^+ permeability. The change in K^+ permeability starts more slowly and reaches a peak during the falling phase of the action potential. The increase in permeability decreases the barrier to K^+ diffusion, and K^+ consequently leaves the cell. The resulting net transfer of positive charge out of the cell completes repolarization.

The changes in membrane permeability during the action potential have been documented in a number of ways, perhaps most clearly by the voltage clamp technic. This research technic, the details of which are beyond the scope of this book, has made it possible to measure changes in the **conductance** of the membrane for various ions. The conductance of an ion is the reciprocal of its electrical resistance in a membrane and is a measure of membrane permeability to that ion. The changes in Na^+ and K^+ conductance during the action potential are shown in Fig 2–14. There is no change in Cl^- conductance. Additional evidence that this ionic hypothesis of the basis of the action potential is correct is provided by the observation that decreas-

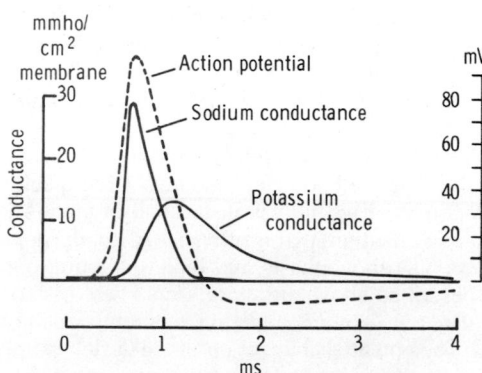

Figure 2–14. Changes in Na^+ and K^+ conductance during the action potential in giant squid axon. The dotted line represents the action potential superimposed on the same time coordinate. Note that the initial electrotonic depolarization initiates the change in Na^+ conductance, which in turn adds to the depolarization. (Redrawn and reproduced, with permission, from Hodgkin AL: Ionic movements and electrical activity in giant nerve fibres. Proc R Soc Lond [Biol] 148:1, 1958.)

ing the external Na^+ concentration decreases the size of the action potential but has little effect on the resting membrane potential. The lack of much effect on the resting membrane potential would be predicted from the Goldman equation (see Chapter 1), since the permeability of the membrane to Na^+ at rest is relatively low. Conversely, increasing the external K^+ concentration decreases the resting membrane potential. The way in which partial depolarization causes the change in membrane permeability to Na^+ has not been determined. However, it is clear that separate channels are involved in the transport of Na^+ and K^+. The Na^+ channels can be blocked by a poison called tetrodotoxin (TTX) without affecting the K^+ channels. Conversely, the K^+ channels can be blocked by tetraethylammonium (TEA) without any changes in Na^+ conductance.

Although Na^+ enters the nerve cell and K^+ leaves it during the action potential, the number of ions involved is not large relative to the total numbers present. The fact that the nerve gains Na^+ and loses K^+ during activity has been demonstrated experimentally, but significant differences in ion concentrations can be measured only after prolonged, repeated stimulation.

As noted above, the after-depolarization (negative after-potential) and the after-hyperpolarization (positive after-potential) represent restorative processes in the cell that are separate from those causing the action potential. Relatively little is known about their origin. The after-depolarization is reduced by agents that inhibit metabolism. The after-hyperpolarization is also reduced, and it now seems clear that it is due to the sodium pump acting in an electrogenic fashion. The net flux of Na^+ to the exterior hyperpolarizes the membrane.

A decrease in extracellular Ca^{2+} increases the excitability of nerve and muscle cells by decreasing the amount of depolarization necessary to initiate the changes in the Na^+ and K^+ conductance that produce the action potential. Conversely, an increase in extracellular Ca^{2+} "stabilizes the membrane" by decreasing excitability. The concentration and electrical gradients for Ca^{2+} are directed inward (Chapter 1), and Ca^{2+} enters neurons during the action potential. The early phase of Ca^{2+} entry is blocked by TTX, and it appears that even though Na^+ permeability is much greater than Ca^{2+} permeability, Ca^{2+} is entering via the Na^+ channels. An additional late phase of Ca^{2+} entry is unaffected by TTX and TEA and apparently occurs via a separate voltage-sensitive Ca^{2+} pathway. Ca^{2+} entering during the delayed phase plays an important role in the secretion of synaptic transmitters, a Ca^{2+}-dependent process (see Chapter 4). In addition, Ca^{2+} entry contributes to depolarization, and in some instances in invertebrates it is primarily responsible for the action potential.

Energy Sources & Metabolism of Nerve

The major part of the energy requirement of nerve is the portion used to maintain polarization of the membrane. The energy for the sodium-potassium pump is derived from the hydrolysis of ATP. During maximal activity, the metabolic rate of the nerve doubles; by comparison, that of skeletal muscle increases as much as 100-fold. Inhibition of lactic acid production does not influence nerve function.

Like muscle, nerve has a resting heat while inactive, an initial heat during the action potential, and a recovery heat that follows activity. However, in nerve, the recovery heat after a single impulse is about 30 times the initial heat. There is some evidence that the initial heat is produced during the after-depolarization rather than the spike. The metabolism of muscle is discussed in detail in Chapter 3.

PROPERTIES OF MIXED NERVES

Peripheral nerves in mammals are made up of many axons bound together in a fibrous envelope called the **epineurium.** Potential changes recorded from such nerves therefore represent an algebraic summation of the all or none action potentials of many axons. The thresholds of the individual axons in the nerve and their distance from the stimulating electrodes vary. With subthreshold stimuli, none of the axons are stimulated and no response occurs. When the stimuli are of threshold intensity, axons with low thresholds fire and a small potential change is observed. As the intensity of the stimulating current is increased, the axons with higher thresholds are also discharged. The electrical response increases proportionately until the stimulus is strong enough to excite all of the axons in the nerve. The stimulus that produces excitation of all the axons is the **maximal stimulus,** and further application of greater, **supramaximal** stimuli produces no further increase in the size of the observed potential.

Compound Action Potentials

Another property of mixed nerves, as opposed to single axons, is the appearance of multiple peaks in the action potential. The multi-peaked action potential is called a **compound action potential.** Its shape is due to the fact that a mixed nerve is made up of families of fibers with varying speeds of conduction. Therefore, when all the fibers are stimulated, the activity in fast-conducting fibers arrives at the recording electrodes sooner than the activity in slower fibers; and the farther away from the stimulating electrodes the action potential is recorded, the greater is the separation between the fast and slow fiber peaks. The number and size of the peaks vary with the types of fibers in the particular nerve being studied. If less than maximal stimuli are used, the shape of the compound action potential also depends upon the number and type of fibers stimulated.

Erlanger and Gasser have divided mammalian nerve fibers into A, B, and C groups, further subdividing the A group into α, β, γ, and δ fibers. The relative

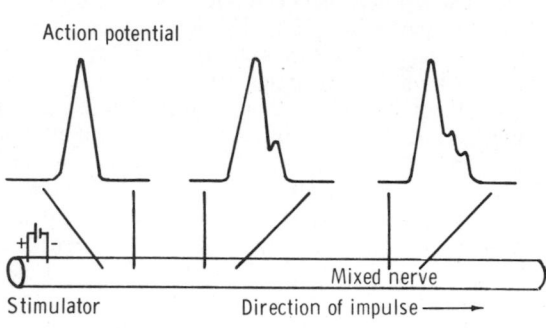
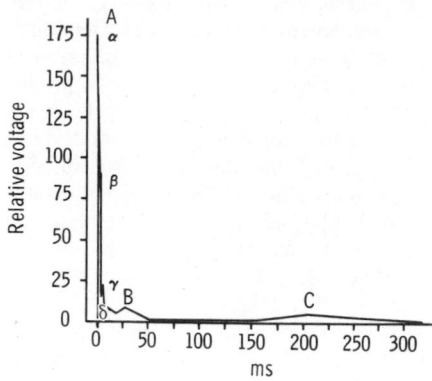

Figure 2–15. Compound action potential. *Left:* Record obtained with recording electrodes at various distances from the stimulating electrodes along a mixed nerve. *Right:* Reconstruction of a compound action potential to show relative sizes and time relationships of the components. (Redrawn and reproduced, with permission, from Erlanger J, Gasser HS: *Electrical Signs of Nervous Activity.* Univ of Pennsylvania Press, 1937.)

latencies of the electrical activity due to each of these components are shown in Fig 2–15. It should be emphasized that the drawing is not the compound action potential of any particular peripheral nerve; none of the peripheral nerves show all the components illustrated in this composite diagram because none contain all of the fiber types.

NERVE FIBER TYPES & FUNCTION

By comparing the neurologic deficits produced by careful dorsal root section and other nerve cutting experiments with the histologic changes in the nerves, the functions and histologic characteristics of each of the families of axons responsible for the various peaks of the compound action potential have been established. In general, the greater the diameter of a given nerve fiber, the greater its speed of conduction. The larger axons are concerned with proprioceptive sensation and somatic motor function, while the smaller axons subserve pain sensation and autonomic function. In Table 2–1, the various fiber types are listed

with their diameters, electrical characteristics, and functions. There is evidence that the dorsal root C fibers conduct impulses generated by touch and other cutaneous receptors in addition to pain receptors, but only the latter are relayed to consciousness. The other fibers presumably are concerned with reflex responses integrated in the spinal cord and brain stem.

Further research has shown that not all the classically described lettered components are homogeneous, and a numerical system (Ia, Ib, II, III, IV) has been used by some physiologists to classify sensory fibers. Unfortunately, this has led to some confusion. A comparison of the number system and the letter system is shown in Table 2–2.

In addition to variations in speed of conduction and fiber diameter, the various classes of fibers in peripheral nerves differ in their sensitivity to hypoxia and anesthetics (Table 2–3). This fact has clinical as well as physiologic significance. Local anesthetics depress transmission in the group C fibers before they affect the touch fibers in the A group. Conversely, pressure on a nerve can cause loss of conduction in motor, touch, and pressure fibers while pain sensation remains relatively intact. Patterns of this type are sometimes seen in individuals who sleep with their

Table 2–1. Nerve fiber types in mammalian nerve.

Fiber Type		Function	Fiber Diameter (μm)	Conduction Velocity (ms)	Spike Duration (ms)	Absolute Refractory Period (ms)
A	α	Proprioception; somatic motor	12–20	70–120		
	β	Touch, pressure	5–12	30–70	0.4–0.5	0.4–1
	γ	Motor to muscle spindles	3–6	15–30		
	δ	Pain, temperature, touch	2–5	12–30		
B		Preganglionic autonomic	<3	3–15	1.2	1.2
C	dorsal root	Pain, reflex responses	0.4–1.2	0.5–2	2	2
	sympathetic	Postganglionic sympathetics	0.3–1.3	0.7–2.3	2	2

Table 2—2. Numerical classification sometimes used for sensory neurons.

Number		Origin	Fiber Type
I	a	Muscle spindle, annulospiral ending	A α
	b	Golgi tendon organ	A α
II		Muscle spindle, flower-spray ending; touch, pressure	A β
III		Pain and temperature receptors; some touch receptors	A δ
IV		Pain and other receptors	Dorsal root C

Table 2—3. Relative susceptibility of mammalian A, B, and C nerve fibers to conduction block produced by various agents.

	Most Susceptible	Inter- mediate	Least Susceptible
Sensitivity to hypoxia	B	A	C
Sensitivity to pressure	A	B	C
Sensitivity to cocaine and local anes- thetics	C	B	A

Table 2—4. Types of fibers in peripheral and cranial nerves.

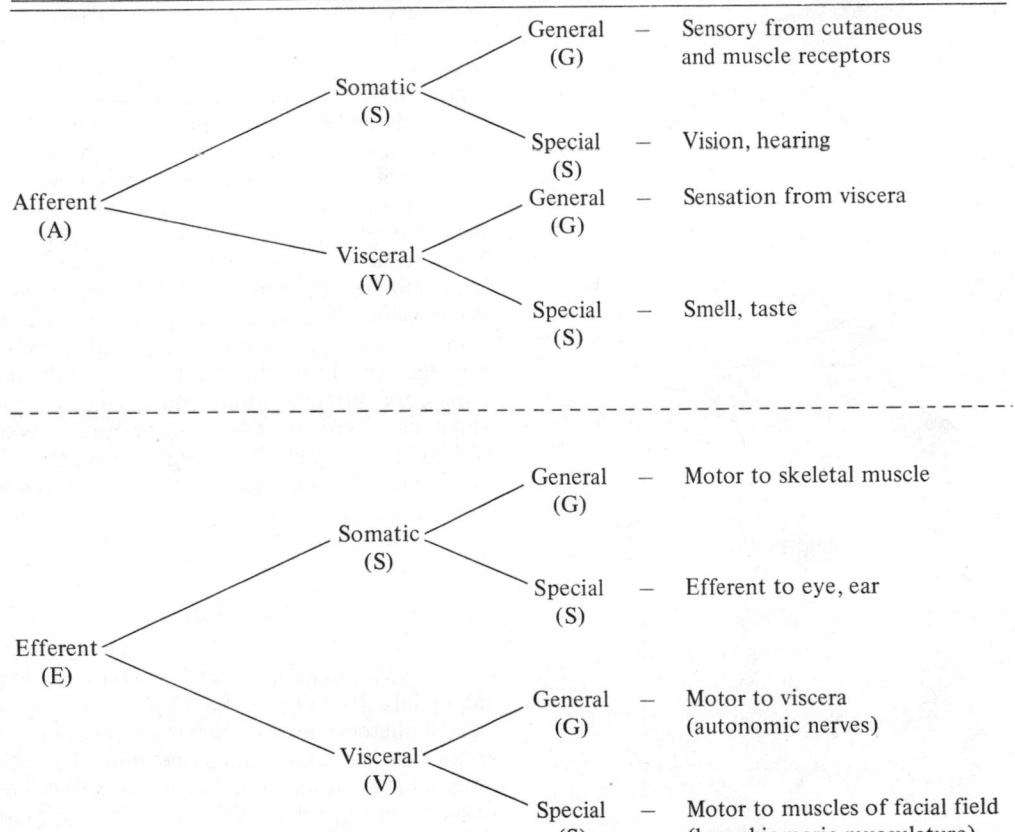

Thus, GVA = general visceral afferent; SVE = special visceral efferent; etc.

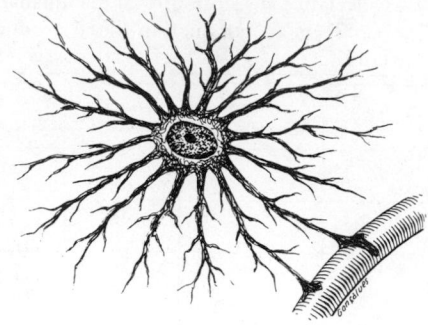

Protoplasmic astrocyte

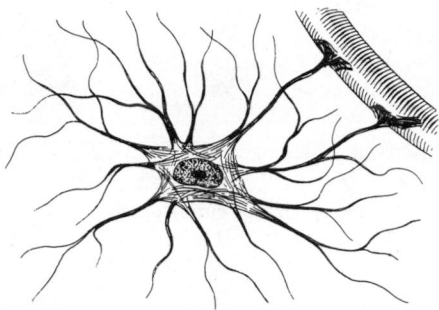

Fibrous astrocyte

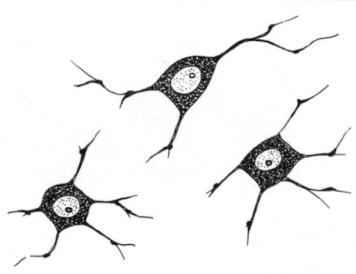

Oligodendrocytes

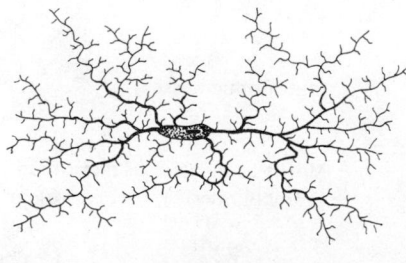

Microglia

Figure 2–16. Glial cells. (Reproduced, with permission, from Junqueira LC, Carneiro J, Contopoulos A: *Basic Histology,* 2nd ed. Lange, 1977.)

arms under their heads for long periods of time, causing compression of the nerves in the arms. Because of the association of deep sleep with alcoholic intoxication, the syndrome is common on weekends, and has acquired the interesting name Saturday night or Sunday morning paralysis.

Human peripheral nerve fibers are also classified on a physio-anatomic basis. This classification (Table 2–4) divides nerves into afferent and efferent categories, and further subdivides them according to whether they have somatic or visceral and general or special functions. The term special is applied to nerves that supply the organs of the special senses and the musculature which is branchiomeric in origin, ie, musculature arising from the branchial arches during embryonic development.

NERVE GROWTH FACTOR

Nerve growth factor (NGF) is a protein that is necessary for the growth and maintenance of sympathetic neurons and some sensory neurons. It is present in a broad spectrum of animal species, including humans, and is found in plasma and many different tissues. In male mice, there is a particularly high concentration in the salivary glands. The factor is a dimer made up of 2 peptides, each containing 118 amino acid residues. In mouse salivary glands, it exists in a complex with 4 other proteins. Antiserum against NGF has been prepared, and injection of this antiserum in newborn animals leads to near total destruction of the sympathetic ganglia; it thus produces an **immunosympathectomy.** The structure of NGF somewhat resembles that of insulin, and it appears to be one of a number of different hormonelike protein factors that stimulate the growth of various tissues in the body. It is picked up by neurons in the organs they innervate and is transported in retrograde fashion from the endings of the neurons to their cell bodies.

GLIA

In addition to neurons, the nervous system contains glial cells, or neuroglia (Fig 2–16). Glial cells are very numerous; indeed, there are approximately 10 times as many glial cells as neurons. The Schwann cells that invest axons in peripheral nerves are classified as glia. In the CNS, there are 3 types of glia. **Microglia** are scavenger cells that enter the nervous system from the blood vessels. The **oligodendroglia** are involved in myelin formation. The **astrocytes** are found throughout the brain, and many send end-feet to blood vessels (see Chapter 17). They have a membrane potential that varies with the external K^+ concentration but do not generate propagated potentials. Despite many theories, their function remains uncertain.

Excitable Tissue: Muscle | 3

Muscle cells, like neurons, can be excited chemically, electrically, and mechanically to produce an action potential that is transmitted along their cell membrane. They contain contractile proteins and, unlike neurons, they have a contractile mechanism that is activated by the action potential.

Muscle is generally divided into 3 types, **skeletal, cardiac,** and **smooth,** although smooth muscle is not a homogeneous single category. Skeletal muscle comprises the great mass of the somatic musculature. It has

well-developed cross-striations, does not normally contract in the absence of nervous stimulation, lacks anatomic and functional connections between individual muscle fibers, and is generally under voluntary control. Cardiac muscle also has cross-striations, but it is functionally syncytial in character and contracts rhythmically in the absence of external innervation due to the presence in the myocardium of pacemaker cells that discharge spontaneously. Smooth muscle lacks cross-striations. The type found in most hollow viscera

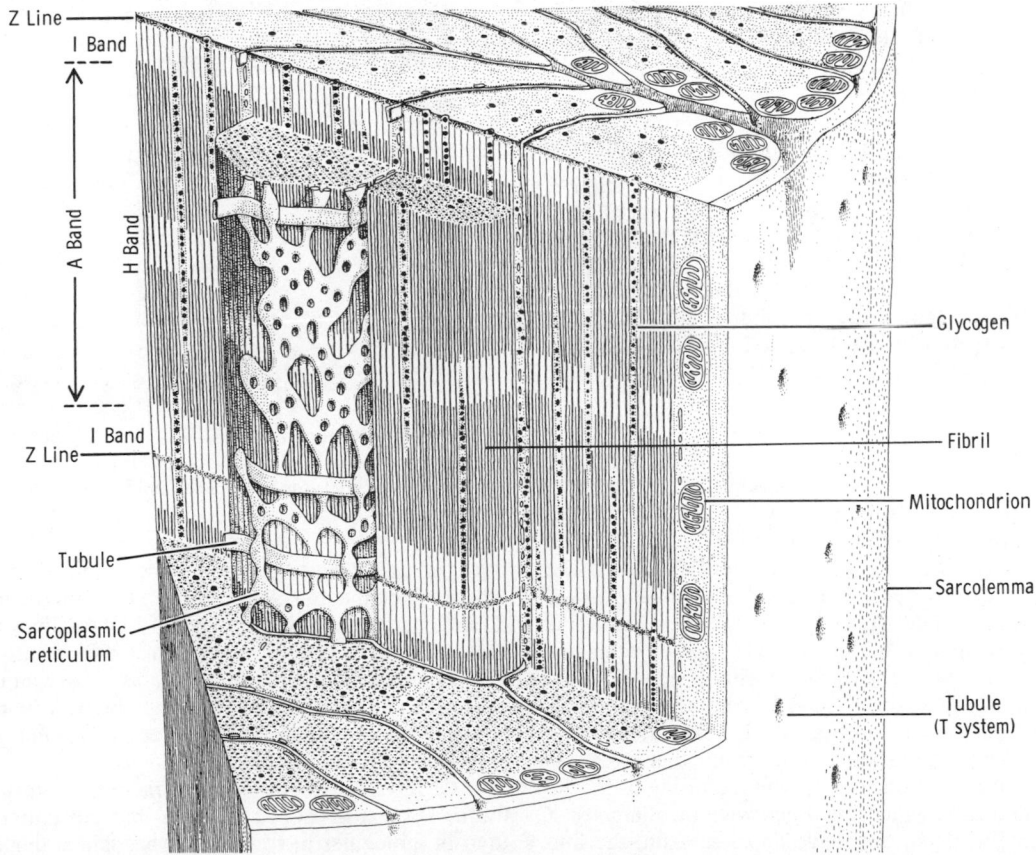

Figure 3–1. Structure of skeletal muscle fiber. The fiber is made up of a number of fibrils and surrounded by a membrane, the sarcolemma. Each fibril is surrounded by sarcoplasmic reticulum and by the T system of tubules, which opens to the exterior of the fiber. (Reproduced, with permission, from: How is muscle turned on and off? by Hoyle G. Scientific American 22:84 [April], 1970. Copyright © 1970 by Scientific American, Inc. All rights reserved.)

is functionally syncytial in character and contains pacemakers that discharge irregularly. The type found in the eye and in some other locations is not spontaneously active and resembles skeletal muscle. There are contractile proteins similar to those in muscle in many other cells and it appears that these proteins are responsible for cell motility, mitosis, and the movement of various components within cells (see Chapter 1).

SKELETAL MUSCLE

MORPHOLOGY

Organization

Skeletal muscle is made up of individual muscle fibers which are the "building blocks" of the muscular system in the same sense that the neurons are the building blocks of the nervous system. Most skeletal muscles begin and end in tendons, and the muscle fibers are arranged in parallel between the tendinous ends so that the force of contraction of the units is additive (Fig 3–1). Each muscle fiber is a single cell, multinucleated, long, and cylindrical in shape. There are no syncytial bridges between cells.

The muscle fibers are made up of fibrils, as shown in Fig 3–1, and the fibrils are divisible into individual filaments. The filaments are made up of the contractile proteins.

Muscle contains the proteins **myosin** (molecular weight about 500,000), **actin** (molecular weight about 45,000), **tropomyosin** (molecular weight about 70,000), and **troponin.** Troponin is made up of 3 subunits, **troponin I, troponin T,** and **troponin C.** The 3 subunits have molecular weights ranging from 18,000 to 35,000.

Striations

The cross-striations characteristic of skeletal muscle are due to differences in the refractive indexes of the various parts of the muscle fiber. The parts of the cross-striations are identified by letters (Fig 3–2). The light I band is divided by the dark Z line, and the dark A band has the lighter H band in its center. A transverse M line is seen in the middle of the H band, and this line plus the narrow light areas on either side of it are sometimes called the pseudo-H zone. The area between 2 adjacent Z lines is called a **sarcomere.** The arrangement of thick and thin filaments that is responsible for the striations is diagrammed in Fig 3–3. The thick filaments, which are about twice the diameter of the thin filaments, are made up of myosin; the thin filaments are made up of actin, tropomyosin, and troponin. The thick myosin filaments are lined up to form the A bands, whereas the array of thin actin filaments forms the less dense I bands. The lighter H

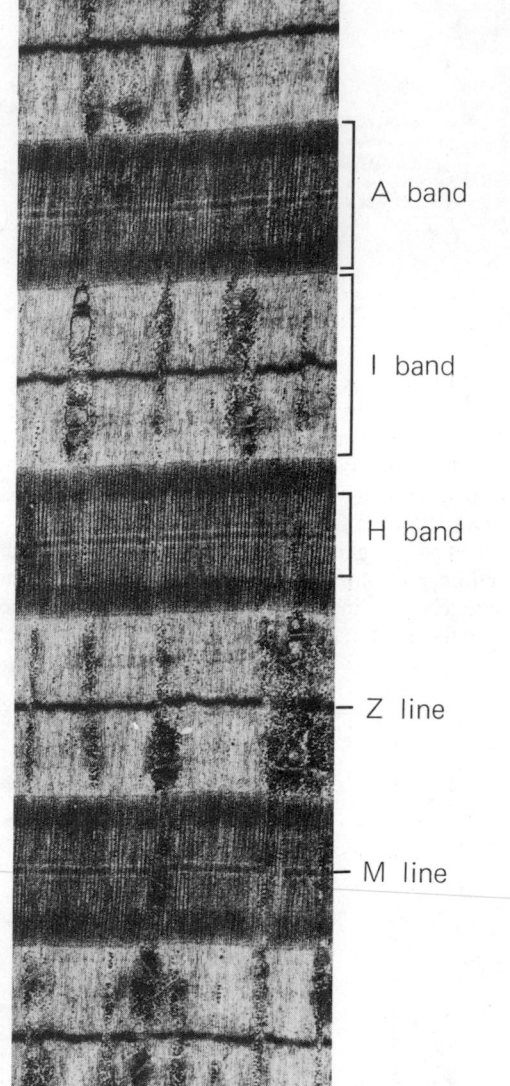

Figure 3–2. Electron micrograph of human gastrocnemius muscle. The various bands and lines are identified on the right. (× 13,500.) (Courtesy of SM Walker and GR Schrodt.)

bands in the center of the A bands are the regions where, when the muscle is relaxed, the actin filaments do not overlap the myosin filaments. The Z lines transect the fibrils and connect to the actin filaments. If a transverse section through the A band is examined under the electron microscope, each myosin filament is found to be surrounded by 6 actin filaments in a regular hexagonal pattern.

Observations with x-ray diffraction technics and the electron microscope indicate that the individual myosin molecules have enlarged heads and that they are arranged as shown in Fig 3–3. Cross-linkages form between the heads of the myosin molecules and the actin molecules. The myosin molecules are arranged symmetrically on either side of the center of the sarco-

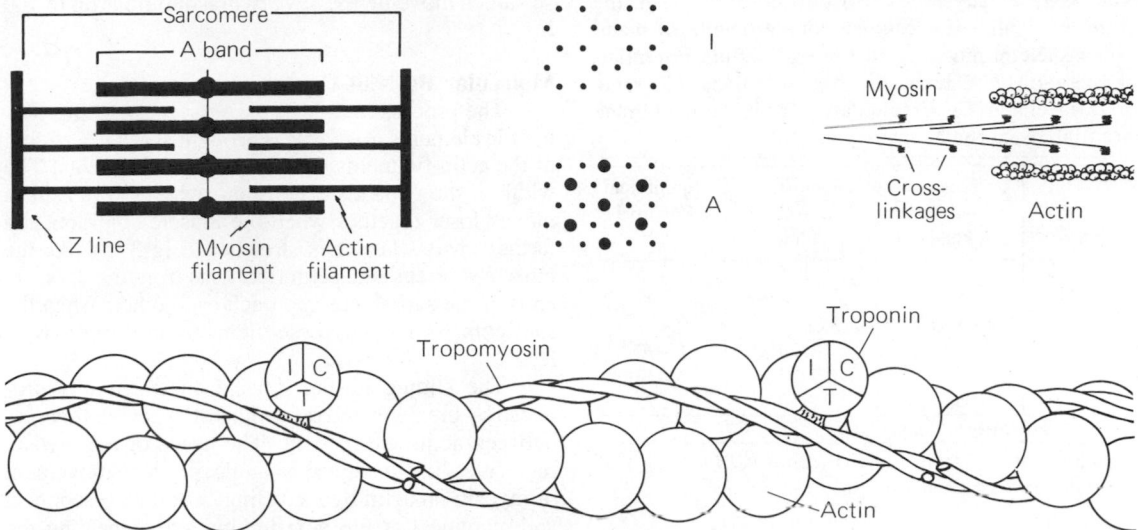

Figure 3–3. *Top left:* Arrangement of actin and myosin filaments in skeletal muscle. I and A represent a cross section through the I band and the lateral portion of the A band, respectively. *Top right:* Detail of structure of myosin and actin. *Bottom:* Diagrammatic representation of the arrangement of actin, tropomyosin, and the 3 subunits of troponin (see text).

mere, and it is this arrangement that creates the light areas in the pseudo-H zone. The M line is due to a central bulge in each of the thick filaments. At these points, there are slender cross-connections that hold the myosin filaments in proper array. There are several hundred myosin molecules in each thick segment.

The actin filaments are made up of 2 chains of globular units that form a long double helix. Tropomyosin molecules are long filaments located in the groove between the 2 chains in the actin (Fig 3–3). Each thin filament contains 300–400 actin molecules and 40–60 tropomyosin molecules. Troponin molecules are small globular units located at intervals along the tropomyosin molecules. Troponin T binds the other troponin components to tropomyosin, troponin I inhibits the interaction of myosin with actin (see below), and troponin C contains the binding sites for the Ca^{2+} that initiates contraction.

Sarcotubular System

The muscle fibrils are surrounded by structures made up of membrane that appear in electron photomicrographs as vesicles and tubules. These structures form the **sarcotubular system,** which is made up of a **T system** and a **sarcoplasmic reticulum.** The T system of transverse tubules, which is continuous with the membrane of the muscle fiber, forms a grid perforated by the individual muscle fibrils (Fig 3–1). The space between the 2 layers of the T system is an extension of the extracellular space. The sarcoplasmic reticulum forms an irregular curtain around each of the fibrils between its contacts with the T system, which in mammalian skeletal muscle is at the junction of the A and I bands. At these junctions, the arrangement of the central T system with sarcoplasmic reticulum on either

side has led to the use of the term **triads** to describe the system. The function of the T system is the rapid transmission of the action potential from the cell membrane to all the fibrils in the muscle. The sarcoplasmic reticulum is concerned with Ca^{2+} movement and muscle metabolism (see below).

ELECTRICAL PHENOMENA & IONIC FLUXES

Electrical Characteristics of Skeletal Muscle

The electrical events in skeletal muscle and the ionic fluxes underlying them are similar to those in nerve, although there are quantitative differences in timing and magnitude. The resting membrane potential of skeletal muscle is about −90 mV. The action potential lasts 2–4 ms, and is conducted along the muscle fiber at about 5 m/s. The absolute refractory period is 1–3 ms long and the after-polarizations, with their related changes in threshold to electrical stimulation, are relatively prolonged. The chronaxie of skeletal muscle is generally somewhat longer than that of nerve. The initiation of impulses at the myoneural junction is discussed in Chapter 4.

Although the electrical properties of the individual fibers in a muscle do not differ sufficiently to produce anything resembling a compound action potential, there are slight differences in the thresholds of the various fibers. Furthermore, in any stimulation experiment, some fibers are farther from the stimulating electrodes than others. Therefore, the size of the action potential recorded from a whole muscle preparation

Table 3–1. Steady-state distribution of ions in the intracellular and extracellular compartments of mammalian skeletal muscle, and the equilibrium potentials for these ions.* A⁻ represents organic anions. The value for intracellular Cl⁻ is calculated from the membrane potential, using the Nernst equation.

| Ion | Concentration, mmol/L | | Equilibrium Potential (mV) |
	Intracellular Fluid	Extracellular Fluid	
Na^+	12	145	+65
K^+	155	4	−95
H^+	13×10^{-5}	3.8×10^{-5}	−32
Cl^-	3.8	120	−90
HCO_3^-	8	27	−32
A^-	155	0	. . .
Membrane Potential = −90 mV			

*Data from Ruch TC, Patton HD (editors): *Physiology and Biophysics,* 19th ed. Saunders, 1965.

tion is proportionate to the intensity of the stimulating current between threshold and maximal current intensities.

Ion Distribution & Fluxes

The distribution of ions across the muscle fiber membrane is similar to that across the nerve cell membrane. The values for the various ions and their equilibrium potentials are shown in Table 3–1. As in nerve, depolarization is a manifestation of Na^+ influx, and repolarization is a manifestation of K^+ efflux (as described in Chapter 2 for nerve).

CONTRACTILE RESPONSES

It is important to distinguish between the electrical and mechanical events in muscle. Although one response does not normally occur without the other, their physiologic basis and characteristics are different. Muscle fiber membrane depolarization normally starts at the motor end-plate, the specialized structure under the motor nerve ending (see Chapter 4); the action potential is transmitted along the muscle fiber and initiates the contractile response.

The Muscle Twitch

A single action potential causes a brief contraction followed by relaxation. This response is called a **muscle twitch.** In Fig 3–4, the action potential and the twitch are plotted on the same time scale. The twitch starts about 2 ms after the start of depolarization of the membrane, before repolarization is complete. The duration of the twitch varies with the type of muscle being tested. "Fast" muscle fibers, primarily those concerned with fine, rapid, precise movement, have twitch durations as short as 7.5 ms. "Slow" muscle fibers, principally those involved in strong, gross,

sustained movements, have twitch durations up to 100 ms.

Molecular Basis of Contraction

The process by which the shortening of the contractile elements in muscle is brought about is a sliding of the actin filaments over the myosin filaments. The width of the A bands is constant, whereas the Z lines move closer together when the muscle contracts and farther apart when it is stretched (Fig 3–5). As the muscle shortens, the actin filaments from the opposite ends of the sarcomere approach each other; when the shortening is marked, these filaments apparently overlap.

The sliding during muscle contraction is produced by breaking and reforming of the cross-linkages between actin and myosin. The heads of the myosin molecules link to actin at an angle, produce movement of myosin on actin by swiveling, and then disconnect and reconnect at the next linking site, repeating the process in serial fashion (Fig 3–6). Each single cycle of attaching, swiveling, and detaching shortens the muscle 1%.

The immediate source of energy for muscle contraction is ATP (Fig 17–4). Hydrolysis of the bonds between the phosphate residues of this compound is associated with the release of a large amount of energy, and the bonds are therefore referred to as high-energy phosphate bonds. In muscle, the hydrolysis of ATP to adenosine diphosphate (ADP) is catalyzed by the contractile protein myosin; this **adenosine triphosphatase** activity is found in the heads of the myosin molecules, where they are in contact with actin.

The process by which depolarization of the muscle fiber initiates contraction is called **excitation-contraction coupling.** The action potential is transmitted to all the fibrils in the fiber via the T system. It

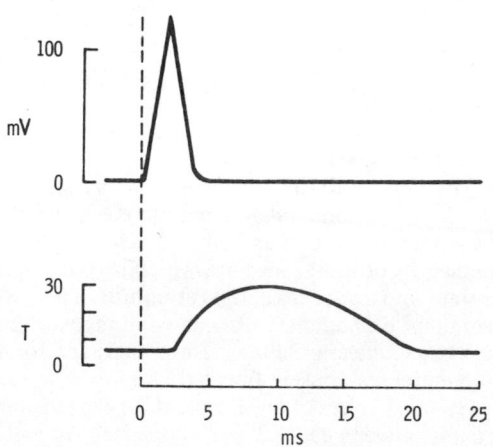

Figure 3–4. The electrical and mechanical responses of a mammalian skeletal muscle fiber to a single maximal stimulus. The electrical response (mV potential change) and the mechanical response (T, tension in arbitrary units) are plotted on the same abscissa (time).

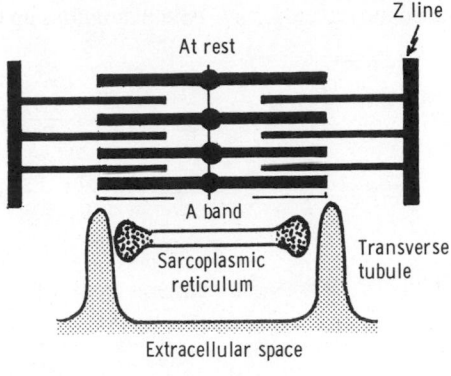

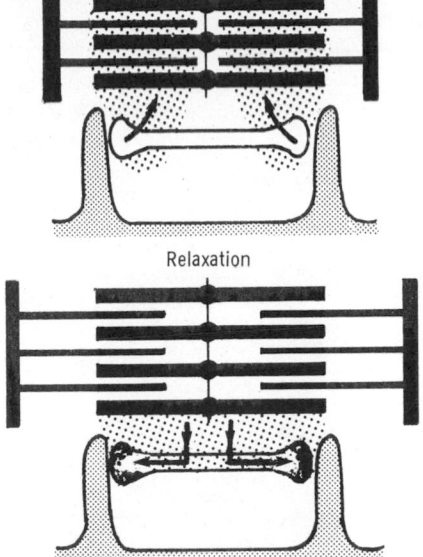

Figure 3–5. Muscle contraction. Calcium ions (represented by black dots) are normally stored in the cisterns of the sarcoplasmic reticulum. The action potential spreads via the transverse tubules and releases Ca^{2+}. The actin filaments (thin lines) slide on the myosin filaments, and the Z lines move closer together. Ca^{2+} is then pumped into the sarcoplasmic reticulum, and the muscle relaxes. (Modified from Layzer RB, Rowland LP: Cramps. N Engl J Med 285:31, 1971.)

triggers the release of calcium ions from the **terminal cisterns,** the lateral sacs of the sarcoplasmic reticulum next to the T system (Fig 3–5). The Ca^{2+} initiates contraction.

Ca^{2+} initiates contraction by binding to troponin C. In resting muscle, troponin I is tightly bound to actin, and tropomyosin covers the sites where myosin heads bind to actin. Thus, the troponin-tropomyosin complex constitutes a "relaxing protein" that inhibits the interaction between actin and myosin. When the Ca^{2+} released by the action potential binds to troponin C, the binding of troponin I to actin is presumably

weakened, and this permits the tropomyosin to move laterally (Fig 3–6). This movement uncovers binding sites for the myosin heads, so that ATP is split and contraction occurs. Seven myosin binding sites are uncovered for each molecule of troponin that binds a calcium ion.

Shortly after releasing Ca^{2+}, the sarcoplasmic reticulum begins to reaccumulate Ca^{2+}. The Ca^{2+} is actively pumped into longitudinal portions of the reticulum and diffuses from there to the cisterns, where it is stored (Fig 3–5). Once the Ca^{2+} concentration outside of the reticulum has been lowered sufficiently, chemical interaction between myosin and actin ceases and the muscle relaxes. If the active transport of Ca^{2+} is inhibited, relaxation does not occur even though there are no more action potentials; the resulting sustained contraction is called a **contracture.** It should be

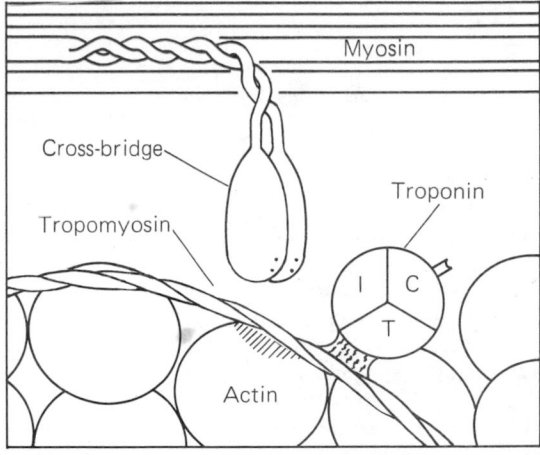

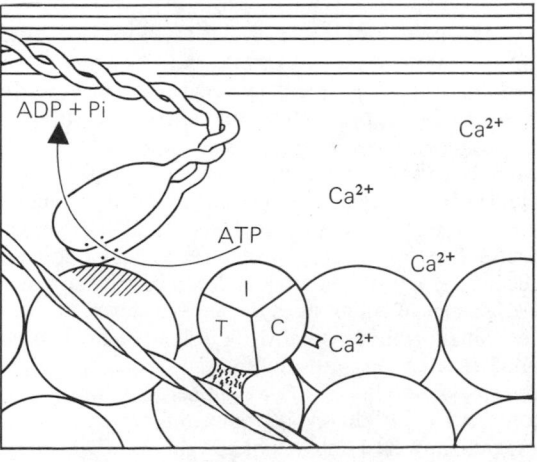

Figure 3–6. Initiation of muscle contraction by Ca^{2+}. The cross-bridges (heads of myosin molecules) attach to binding sites on actin (striped areas) and swivel when tropomyosin is displaced laterally by binding of Ca^{2+} to troponin C. (Modified from Katz AM: Congestive heart failure. N Engl J Med 293:1184, 1975.)

Table 3–2. Sequence of events in contraction and relaxation of skeletal muscle. (Steps 1–4 in contraction are discussed in Chapter 4.)

Steps in contraction
(1) Discharge of motor neuron.
(2) Release of transmitter (acetylcholine) at motor end-plate.
(3) Generation of end-plate potential.
(4) Generation of action potential in muscle fibers.
(5) Inward spread of depolarization along T tubules.
(6) Release of Ca^{2+} from lateral sacs of sarcoplasmic reticulum and diffusion to thick and thin filaments.
(7) Binding of Ca^{2+} to troponin C, uncovering myosin binding sites on actin.
(8) Formation of cross-linkages between actin and myosin and sliding of thin on thick filaments, producing shortening.

Steps in relaxation
(1) Ca^{2+} pumped back into sarcoplasmic reticulum.
(2) Release of Ca^{2+} from troponin.
(3) Cessation of interaction between actin and myosin.

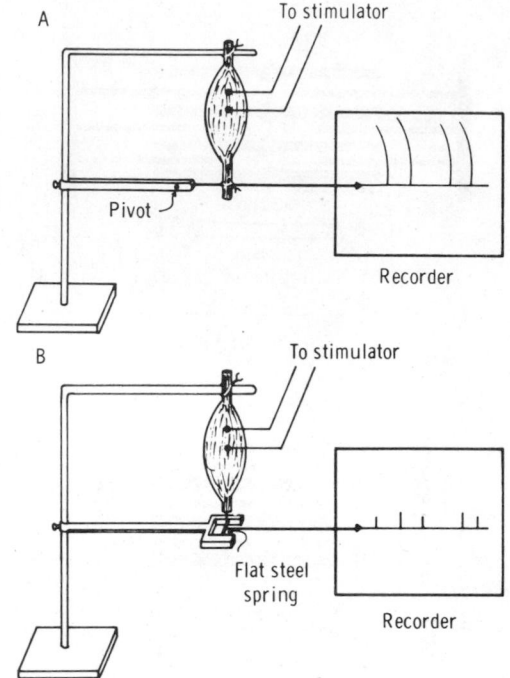

noted that ATP provides the energy for the active transport of Ca^{2+} into the sarcoplasmic reticulum. Thus, both contraction and relaxation of muscle require ATP.

The events involved in muscle contraction and relaxation are summarized in Table 3–2.

Figure 3–7. *A:* Muscle preparation arranged for recording isotonic contractions. *B:* Preparation arranged for recording isometric contractions. In A, the muscle is fastened to a writing lever that swings on a pivot. In B, it is attached to a steel spring to which is fastened a writing lever. Contraction deforms the spring and the slight motion is indicated by deflection of the writing lever.

Types of Contraction

Muscular contraction involves shortening of the contractile elements, but because muscles have elastic and viscous elements in series with the contractile mechanism, it is possible for contraction to occur without an appreciable decrease in the length of the whole muscle. Such a contraction is called **isometric** ("same measure" or length). Contraction against a constant load, with approximation of the ends of the muscle is **isotonic** ("same tension").

A whole muscle preparation arranged for recording isotonic contractions is shown in Fig 3–7A. The muscle lifts the lever, and the distance the lever moves indicates the degree of shortening. In this situation, the muscle does external work, since the lever is being moved a certain distance. The muscle preparation in Fig 3–7B is arranged for recording isometric contractions. It is attached to a strong metal spring, and contraction deforms the spring. The slight motion produced is proportionate to the tension developed. Since the product of force times distance in this situation is very small, little external work is done by the muscle. In other situations, it is possible for muscles to do no external work (Fig 3–8) or even negative work while contracting. This happens, for example, when a heavy weight is lowered onto a table. In this case, the biceps muscle actively resists the descent of the object, but the net effect of the effort is to lengthen the biceps muscle while it is contracting.

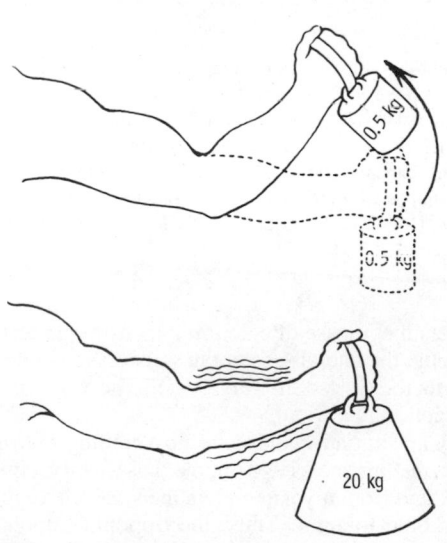

Figure 3–8. *Above:* Isotonic (free) contraction. Biceps shortens freely, weight is lifted. *Below:* Isometric contraction. Biceps generates force but cannot shorten and raise weight.

Summation of Contractions

The electrical response of a muscle fiber to re-

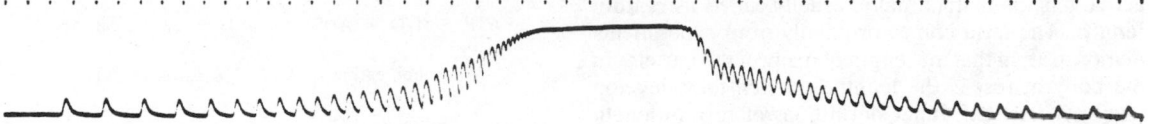

Figure 3–9. Tetanus. Isometric tension of a single muscle fiber during continuously increasing and decreasing stimulation frequency. Dots at top are at 0.2 s intervals. (Reproduced, with permission, from Buchthal F: Dan Biol Med 17:1, 1942.)

peated stimulation is like that of nerve. The fiber is electrically refractory only during the rising and part of the falling phase of the spike potential. At this time, the contraction initiated by the first stimulus is just beginning. However, because the contractile mechanism does not have a refractory period, repeated stimulation before relaxation has occurred produces additional activation of the contractile elements and a response that is added to the contraction already present. This phenomenon is known as **summation of contractions.** The tension developed during summation is considerably greater than that during the single muscle twitch. With rapidly repeated stimulation, activation of the contractile mechanism occurs repeatedly before any relaxation has occurred, and the individual responses fuse into one continuous contraction. Such a response is called a **tetanus,** or **tetanic contraction.** It is a **complete tetanus** when there is no relaxation between stimuli, and an **incomplete tetanus** when there are periods of incomplete relaxation between the summated stimuli. During a complete tetanus, the tension developed is about 4 times that developed by the individual twitch contractions. The development of an incomplete and a complete tetanus in response to stimuli of increasing frequency is shown in Fig 3–9.

The stimulation frequency at which summation of contractions will occur is determined by the twitch duration of the particular muscle being studied. For example, if the twitch duration is 10 ms, frequencies less than 1 per 10 ms (100/s) will cause discrete responses interrupted by complete relaxation, and frequencies greater than 100/s will cause summation.

Treppe

When a series of maximal stimuli are delivered to skeletal muscle at a frequency just below the tetanizing frequency, there is an increase in the tension developed during each twitch until, after several contractions, a uniform tension per contraction is reached. This phenomenon is known as **treppe,** or the "staircase" phenomenon (German *Treppe*, "staircase"). It also occurs in cardiac muscle. Treppe is believed to be due to increased availability of Ca^{2+} for binding to troponin C. It should not be confused with summation of contractions and tetanus.

Relation Between Muscle Length, Tension, & Velocity of Contraction

Both the tension that a muscle develops when stimulated to contract isometrically (the **total tension**), and the **passive tension** exerted by the unstimu-

lated muscle vary with the length of the muscle fiber. This relationship can be studied in a whole skeletal muscle preparation such as that shown in Fig 3–7B. The length of the muscle can be varied by changing the distance between the 2 rods to which it is attached. At each length, the passive tension is measured and the muscle then stimulated electrically and the total tension measured. The difference between the 2 values at any length is the amount of tension actually generated by the contractile process, the **active tension.** The records obtained by plotting passive tension and total tension against muscle length are shown in Fig 3–10. Similar curves are obtained when single muscle fibers are studied. Passive tension rises slowly at first, and then rapidly as the muscle is stretched. Rupture of the muscle occurs when it is stretched to about 3 times its **equilibrium length,** ie, the length of the relaxed muscle cut free from its bony attachments.

The total tension curve rises to a maximum and then declines until it reaches the passive tension curve, ie, until no additional tension is developed upon further stimulation. The length of the muscle at which the

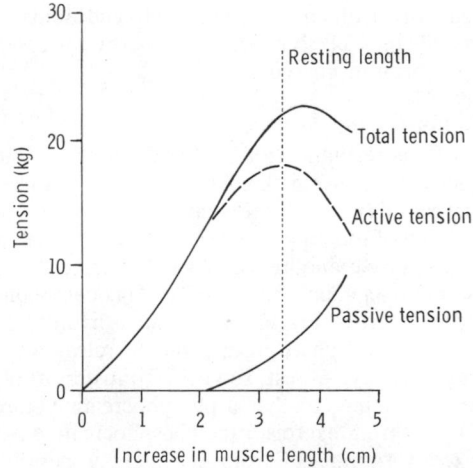

Figure 3–10. Length-tension diagram for skeletal muscle. The passive tension curve measures the tension exerted by the muscle at each length when it is not stimulated. The total tension curve represents the tension developed when the muscle contracts isometrically in response to a maximal stimulus. The active tension is the difference between the 2. (Drawn from data on human triceps muscle, with permission, from: *Report to the NRC, Committee on Artificial Limbs, on Fundamental Studies of Human Locomotion and Other Information Relating to Design of Artificial Limbs.* Univ of California [Berkeley], 1947, Vol 2.)

active tension is maximal is usually called its **resting length.** The term comes originally from experiments demonstrating that the length of many of the muscles in the body at rest is the length at which they develop maximal tension. Other definitions of resting length are sometimes used, but that given here is the most widely accepted and has the greatest physiologic validity.

The observed length-tension relation in skeletal muscle is explained by the sliding filament mechanism of muscle contraction. When the muscle fiber contracts isometrically, the tension developed is proportionate to the number of cross-linkages between the actin and the myosin molecules. When muscle is stretched, the overlap between actin and myosin is reduced and the number of cross-linkages is reduced. Conversely, when the muscle is shorter than resting length, the actin filaments overlap, and this also reduces the number of cross-linkages.

The velocity of muscle contraction varies inversely with the load on the muscle. At a given load, the velocity is maximal at the resting length and declines if the muscle is shorter or longer than this length.

ENERGY SOURCES & METABOLISM

Muscle contraction requires energy, and muscle has been called "a machine for converting chemical into mechanical energy." The immediate source of this energy is the energy-rich organic phosphate derivatives in muscle; the ultimate source is the intermediary metabolism of carbohydrate and lipids. The hydrolysis of ATP to provide the energy for contraction has been discussed above.

Phosphocreatine

ATP is resynthesized from ADP by the addition of a phosphate group. Under normal conditions, the energy for this endothermic reaction is supplied by the breakdown of glucose to CO_2 and H_2O, but there also exists in muscle another energy-rich phosphate compound that can supply this energy. This compound is **phosphocreatine** (Fig 17–24), which is hydrolyzed to creatine and phosphate groups with the release of considerable energy. At rest, some ATP transfers its phosphate to creatine, so that a phosphocreatine store is built up. During exercise, the phosphocreatine is hydrolyzed, forming ATP from ADP and thus permitting contraction to continue.

Carbohydrate Breakdown

Much of the energy for phosphocreatine and ATP resynthesis comes from the breakdown of glucose to CO_2 and H_2O. An outline of the major metabolic pathways involved is presented in Chapter 17. For the purposes of the present discussion, it is sufficient to point out that glucose in the bloodstream enters cells, where it is degraded through a series of chemical

$$ATP + H_2O \rightarrow ADP + H_3PO_4 + 12{,}000 \text{ calories}$$

$$\text{Phosphocreatine} + ADP \rightleftarrows \text{Creatine} + ATP$$

$$\text{Glucose} + 2 \text{ ATP (or glycogen} + 1 \text{ ATP)}$$
$$\xrightarrow[\text{Anaerobic}]{} 2 \text{ Lactic acid} + 4 \text{ ATP}$$

$$\text{Glucose} + 2 \text{ ATP (or glycogen} + 1 \text{ ATP)}$$
$$\xrightarrow[\text{Oxygen}]{} 6 \text{ CO}_2 + 6 \text{ H}_2\text{O} + 40 \text{ ATP}$$

$$\text{FFA} \xrightarrow{\text{Oxygen}} \text{CO}_2 + \text{H}_2\text{O} + \text{ATP}$$

Figure 3–11. Energy sources for muscle contraction. The amount of ATP formed per mole of free fatty acid (FFA) oxidized is large, but varies with the size of the FFA (see Chapter 17). For example, complete oxidation of 1 mol of palmitic acid generates 140 mol of ATP.

reactions to pyruvic acid. Another source of intracellular glucose, and consequently of pyruvic acid, is glycogen, the carbohydrate polymer that is especially abundant in liver and skeletal muscle. When adequate O_2 is present, pyruvic acid enters the citric acid cycle and is metabolized—through this cycle and the so-called respiratory enzyme pathway—to CO_2 and H_2O. This process is called **aerobic glycolysis.** The metabolism of glucose or glycogen to CO_2 and H_2O liberates sufficient energy to form large quantities of ATP from ADP. If O_2 supplies are insufficient, the pyruvic acid formed from glucose does not enter the tricarboxylic acid cycle but is reduced to lactic acid. This process of **anaerobic glycolysis** is associated with the net production of much smaller quantities of energy-rich phosphate bonds, but it does not require the presence of O_2. Skeletal muscle also takes up free fatty acids (FFA) from the blood and oxidizes them to CO_2 and H_2O. Indeed, FFA are probably the major substrates for muscle at rest and during recovery after contraction. The various reactions involved in supplying energy to skeletal muscle are summarized in Fig 3–11.

The Oxygen Debt Mechanism

During muscular exercise, the muscle blood vessels dilate and blood flow is increased so that the available O_2 supply is increased. Up to a point, the increase in O_2 consumption is proportionate to the energy expended, and all the energy needs are met by aerobic processes. However, when muscular exertion is very great, aerobic resynthesis of energy stores cannot keep pace with their utilization. Under these conditions, phosphocreatine is used to resynthesize ATP. Phosphocreatine resynthesis is accomplished by using the energy released by the anaerobic breakdown of glucose to lactic acid. This use of the anaerobic pathway is self-limiting, because in spite of rapid diffusion of lactic acid into the bloodstream, enough accumulates in the muscles to eventually exceed the capacity of the tissue buffers and produce an enzyme-inhibiting decline in pH. However, for short periods, the presence of an anaerobic pathway for glucose breakdown permits muscular exertion of a far greater magnitude than would be possible without it. Without this pathway, for example, walking or running at a slow jog would be possible but sprinting and all other forms of short-term, violent exertion would not.

After a period of exertion is over, extra O_2 is consumed to remove the excess lactic acid and replenish the ATP and phosphocreatine stores. The amount of extra O_2 consumed is proportionate to the extent to which the energy demands during exertion exceeded the capacity for the aerobic synthesis of energy stores, ie, the extent to which an **oxygen debt** was incurred. The O_2 debt is measured experimentally by determining O_2 consumption after exercise until a constant, basal consumption is reached and subtracting the basal consumption from the total. The amount of this debt may be 6 times the basal O_2 consumption, which indicates that the subject is capable of 6 times the exertion that would have been possible without it. Obviously, the maximal debt can be incurred rapidly or slowly; violent exertion is possible for only short periods of time, whereas less strenuous exercise can be carried on for longer periods of time.

Trained athletes are able to increase the O_2 consumption of their muscles to a greater degree than untrained individuals. Consequently, they are capable of greater exertion without increasing their lactic acid production, and they contract smaller oxygen debts for a given amount of exertion.

Heat Production in Muscle

Thermodynamically, the energy supplied to a muscle must equal its energy output. The energy output appears in work done by the muscle, in energy-rich phosphate bonds formed for later use, and in heat. The overall mechanical efficiency of skeletal muscle (work done/total energy expenditure) ranges up to 50% while lifting a weight during isotonic contraction and is essentially 0% during isometric contraction. Energy storage in phosphate bonds is a small factor. Consequently, heat production is considerable. The heat produced in muscle can be measured accurately with suitable thermocouples.

Resting heat, the heat given off at rest, is the external manifestation of basal metabolic processes. The heat produced in excess of resting heat during contraction is called the **initial heat.** This is made up of **activation heat,** the heat that muscle produces whenever it is contracting, and **shortening heat,** which is proportionate in amount to the distance the muscle shortens. Shortening heat is apparently due to some change in the structure of the muscle during shortening.

Following contraction, heat production in excess of resting heat continues for as long as 30 minutes. This **recovery heat** is the heat liberated by the metabolic processes that restore the muscle to its precontraction state. The recovery heat of muscle is approximately equal to the initial heat, ie, the heat produced during recovery is equal to the heat produced during contraction.

If a muscle that has contracted isotonically is restored to its previous length, extra heat in addition to recovery heat is produced (**relaxation heat**). External work must be done on the muscle to return it to its previous length, and relaxation heat is mainly a manifestation of this work.

PROPERTIES OF MUSCLES IN THE INTACT ORGANISM

Effects of Denervation

In the intact animal or human, healthy skeletal muscle does not contract except in response to stimulation of its motor nerve supply. Destruction of this nerve supply causes muscle atrophy. It also leads to abnormal excitability of the muscle and increases its sensitivity to circulating acetylcholine (denervation hypersensitivity; see Chapter 4). Fine, irregular contractions of individual fibers (**fibrillations**) appear. If the motor nerve regenerates, these disappear. Such contractions usually are not visible grossly and should not be confused with **fasciculations,** which are jerky, visible contractions of groups of muscle fibers due to pathologic discharge of spinal motor neurons.

The Motor Unit

Since the axons of the spinal motor neurons supplying skeletal muscle each branch to innervate several muscle fibers, the smallest possible amount of muscle that can contract in response to the excitation of a single motor neuron is not one muscle fiber but all the fibers supplied by the neuron. Each single motor neuron and the muscle fibers it innervates constitute a **motor unit.** The number of muscle fibers in a motor unit varies. In muscles such as those of the hand and those concerned with motion of the eye—ie, muscles concerned with fine, graded, precise movement—there are 3–6 muscle fibers per motor unit. On the other hand, values of 120–165 fibers per unit have been reported in cat leg muscles, and some of the large muscles of the back in humans probably contain even more.

Electromyography

Activation of motor units can be studied by **electromyography,** the process of recording the electrical activity of muscle on a cathode-ray oscilloscope. This may be done in unanesthetized humans by using small metal disks on the skin overlying the muscle as the pick-up electrodes, or by using hypodermic needle electrodes. The record obtained with such electrodes is the **electromyogram (EMG).** With needle electrodes, it is usually possible to pick up the activity of single muscle fibers. A typical EMG is shown in Fig 3–12.

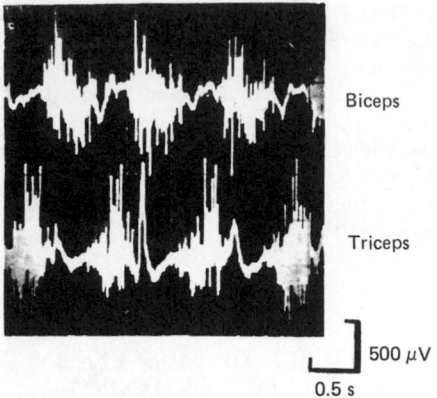

Biceps

Triceps

⌐ 500 μV

0.5 s

Figure 3–12. Electromyographic tracings from human biceps and triceps muscles during alternate flexion and extension of the elbow. (Courtesy of BC Garoutte.)

Factors Responsible for Grading of Muscular Activity

It has been shown by electromyography that there is little if any spontaneous activity in the skeletal muscles of normal individuals at rest. With minimal voluntary activity, a few motor units discharge, and with increasing voluntary effort more and more are brought into play. This process is sometimes called **recruitment of motor units.** Gradation of muscle response is therefore in part a function of the number of motor units activated. In addition, the frequency of discharge in the individual nerve fibers plays a role, the tension developed during a tetanic contraction being greater than that during individual twitches. The length of the muscle is also a factor. Finally, the motor units fire asynchronously, ie, out of phase with each other. This asynchronous firing causes the individual muscle fiber responses to merge into a smooth contraction of the whole muscle.

Muscle Types

The properties of muscles vary with the character of the muscle fibers they contain. Each spinal motor neuron innervates only one kind of muscle fiber, so that all of the muscle fibers in a motor unit are of the same type. Various classification schemes have been proposed for muscle, but classification on the basis of unit types seems most logical. On this basis, there are fast and slow units, based on the duration of their twitch contraction and the rate of conduction of their axons. Fast units are subdivided into 3 subtypes. The muscle fibers of slow units have low mitochondrial ATPase activity, and the muscle fibers of fast units have high ATPase activity. In general, the slow muscle units are innervated by small motor neurons and fast units by large motor neurons (**size principle**). In large limb muscles, the small, slow units are first recruited in most movements, are resistant to fatigue, and are the most used units. The fast units, which are more easily fatigued, are generally recruited with more forceful movements.

Most muscles contain a mixture of different kinds of muscle units. Those that contain many fast units are called **fast muscles** and, because they are pale, are also called **white muscles.** A few muscles are made up solely of **slow units,** and these **slow muscles** are also called **red muscles** because they are darker than other muscles. The red muscles, which respond slowly and have a long latency, are adapted for long, slow, posture-maintaining contractions. The long muscles of the back are red muscles. White muscles have short twitch durations and are specialized for fine, skilled movement. The extraocular muscles and some of the hand muscles are fast muscles.

The differences between types of muscle units are not inherent but are determined in part by their innervation. The nerves to fast and slow muscles have been crossed and allowed to regenerate. When regrowth was complete and the nerve that previously supplied the slow muscle innervated the fast one, the fast muscle became slow. The reverse change occurred in the previously slow muscle. There were also appropriate changes in ATPase content. There is evidence that substances can flow down neurons and enter muscle. However, the effect of the nerve on the chemistry of the muscle appears to be due to the pattern of discharge in the nerve rather than a trophic factor per se.

Denervation of skeletal muscle leads to atrophy and flaccid paralysis, with the appearance of fibrillations. These effects are the classical consequences of a **lower motor neuron lesion.** The muscle also becomes hypersensitive to acetylcholine (denervation hypersensitivity; see Chapter 4).

The Strength of Skeletal Muscles

Human skeletal muscle can exert 3–4 kg of tension per square centimeter of cross-sectional area. This figure is about the same as that obtained in a variety of experimental animals, and seems to be constant for all mammalian species. Since many of the muscles in humans have a relatively large cross-sectional area, the tension they can develop is quite large. The gastrocnemius, for example, not only supports the weight of the whole body during climbing but resists a force several times this great when the foot hits the ground during running or jumping. An even more striking example is the gluteus maximus, which can exert a tension of 1200 kg. The total tension that could be developed by all muscles in the body of an adult man is approximately 22,000 kg (nearly 25 tons).

Body Mechanics

Body movements are generally organized in such a way that they take maximal advantage of the physiologic principles outlined above. For example, the attachments of the muscles in the body are such that many of them are normally at or near their resting length when they start to contract. In the case of muscles that extend over more than one joint, movement at one joint may compensate for movement at another in such a way that relatively little shortening of the muscle occurs during contraction. Nearly isometric con-

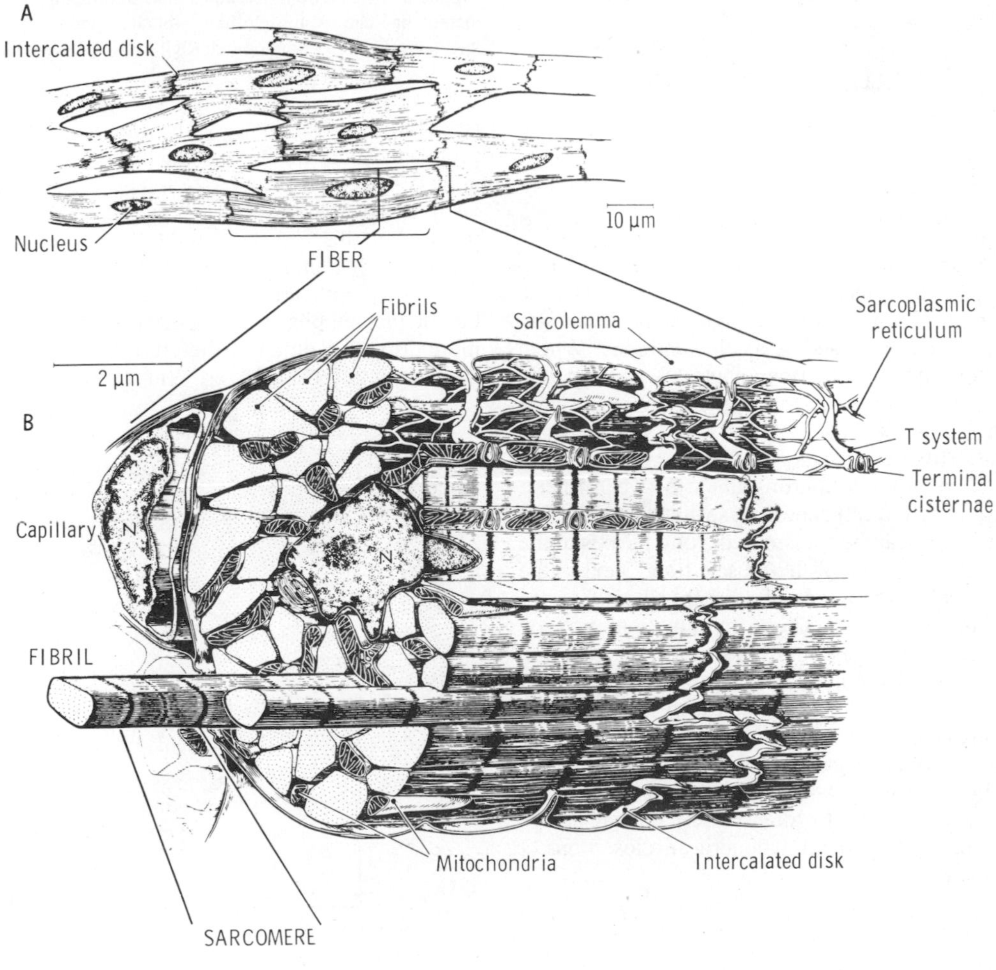

A

Intercalated disk

Nucleus

FIBER

10 μm

B

2 μm

Fibrils

Sarcolemma

Sarcoplasmic
reticulum

T system

Terminal
cisternae

Capillary

N

N

FIBRIL

Mitochondria

Intercalated disk

SARCOMERE

Figure 3–13. *Top:* Electron photomicrograph of cardiac muscle. The fuzzy thick lines are intercalated disks (× 12,000). (Reproduced, with permission, from Bloom W, Fawcett DW: *A Textbook of Histology,* 10th ed. Saunders, 1975.) *Bottom:* Diagram of cardiac muscle as seen under the light microscope *(A)* and the electron microscope *(B).* N, nucleus. (Reproduced, with permission, from Braunwald E; Ross J, Sonnenblick EH: Mechanisms of contraction of the normal and failing heart. N Engl J Med 277:794, 1967. Courtesy of Little, Brown, Inc.)

tractions of this type permit development of maximal tension per contraction. The hamstring muscles extend from the pelvis over the hip joint and the knee joint to the tibia and fibula. Hamstring contraction produces flexion of the leg on the thigh. If the thigh is flexed on the pelvis at the same time, the lengthening of the hamstrings across the hip joint tends to compensate for the shortening across the knee joint. In the course of walking and other activities, the body moves in a way that takes advantage of this.

Such factors as momentum and balance are integrated into body movement in ways that make possible maximal motion with minimal muscular exertion. In walking, for example, there is a brief burst of activity in the leg flexors at the start of each step, and then the leg is swung forward with little more active muscular contraction. Therefore, the muscles are active for only a fraction of each step, and walking for long periods of time causes relatively little fatigue.

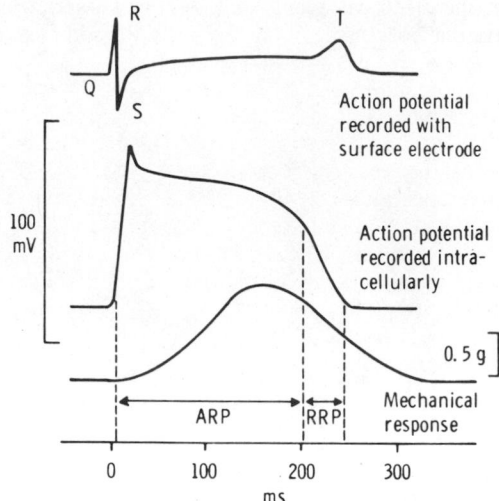

Figure 3–14. Action potentials and contractile response of mammalian cardiac muscle fiber plotted on the same time axis. ARP, absolute refractory period; RRP, relative refractory period.

CARDIAC MUSCLE

MORPHOLOGY

The striations in cardiac muscle are similar to those in skeletal muscle, and Z lines are present. The muscle fibers branch and interdigitate, but each is a complete unit surrounded by a cell membrane. Where the end of one muscle fiber abuts on another, the membranes of both fibers parallel each other through an extensive series of folds. These areas, which always occur at Z lines, are called **intercalated disks** (Fig 3–13). They provide a strong union between fibers, maintaining cell to cell cohesion, so that the pull of one contractile unit can be transmitted along its axis to the next. Along the sides of the muscle fibers next to the disks, the cell membranes of adjacent fibers fuse for considerable distances. These gap junctions provide low-resistance bridges for the spread of excitation from one fiber to another (see Chapter 1). They permit cardiac muscle to function as if it were a syncytium, even though there are no protoplasmic bridges between cells. The T system in cardiac muscle is located at the Z lines rather than at the A–I junction (as it is in mammalian skeletal muscle). Cardiac muscle contains large numbers of elongated mitochondria in close contact with the fibrils.

ELECTRICAL PROPERTIES

Resting Membrane & Action Potentials

The resting membrane potential of individual mammalian cardiac muscle cells is about −80 mV

(interior negative to exterior). Stimulation produces a propagated action potential that is responsible for initiating contraction. Depolarization proceeds rapidly and an overshoot is present, as in skeletal muscle and nerve, but this is followed by a plateau before the membrane potential returns to the baseline (Fig 3–14). In mammalian hearts, depolarization lasts about 2 ms, but the plateau phase and repolarization last 200 ms or more. Repolarization is therefore not complete until the contraction is half over. With extracellular record-

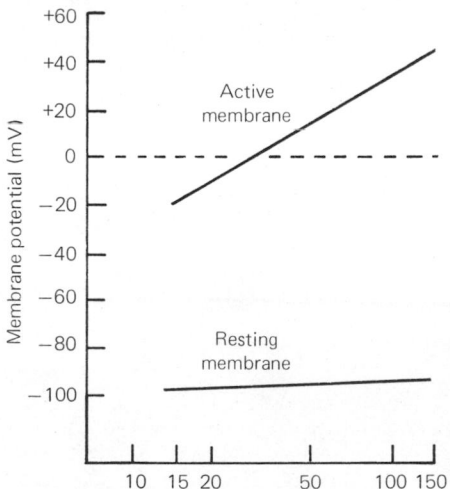

Figure 3–15. Effect of changes in the external concentration of Na^+ on the peak amplitude of the action potential (top curve) and the resting membrane potential (bottom curve) in cardiac muscle. (Modified from Weidmann S: *Elektrophysiologie der Herzmuskelfaser.* Verlag Hans Huber, 1956.)

ing, the electrical events include a spike and a later wave that bear a resemblance to the QRS complex and T wave of the electrocardiogram.

As in other excitable tissues, changes in the external K^+ concentration affect the resting membrane potential of cardiac muscle, whereas changes in the external Na^+ concentration affect the magnitude of the action potential (Fig 3–15). The initial rapid depolarization and the overshoot are due to a rapid increase in Na^+ permeability similar to that occurring in nerve and skeletal muscle, whereas the second plateau phase is due to a slower starting, less intense, and more prolonged increase in Ca^{2+} permeability. The third phase is the manifestation of a delayed increase in K^+ permeability. This increase produces the K^+ efflux that completes the repolarization process.

In cardiac muscle, the repolarization time decreases as the cardiac rate increases. At a cardiac rate of 75 beats per minute, the duration of the action potential (0.25 s) is almost 70% longer than it is at a cardiac rate of 200 beats per minute (0.15 s).

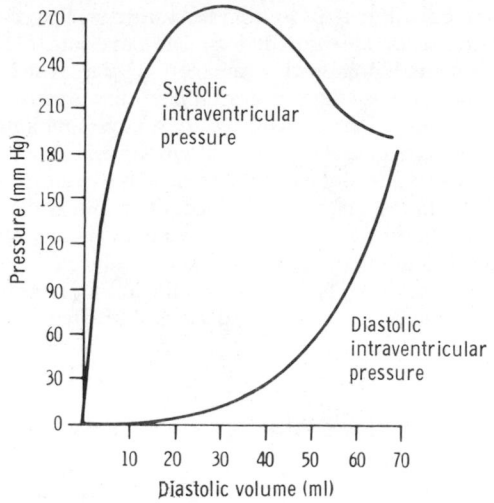

Figure 3–16. "Length-tension" relationship for cardiac muscle. The values are for dog heart.

MECHANICAL PROPERTIES

Response Characteristics

The contractile response of cardiac muscle begins just after the start of depolarization and lasts about 1½ times as long as the action potential (Fig 3–14). The role of Ca^{2+} in excitation-contraction coupling is similar to its role in skeletal muscle (see above), except that Ca^{2+} entering from the ECF as well as Ca^{2+} from the sarcoplasmic reticulum contributes to contraction. Responses of the muscle are all or none in character, ie, the muscle fibers contract fully if they respond at all. Since cardiac muscle is absolutely refractory during most of the action potential, the contractile response is more than half over by the time a second response can be initiated. Therefore, tetanus of the type seen in skeletal muscle cannot occur. Of course, tetanization of cardiac muscle for any length of time would have lethal consequences, and in this sense the fact that cardiac muscle cannot be tetanized is a safety feature. Ventricular muscle is said to be in the "vulnerable period" just at the end of the action potential, because stimulation at this time will sometimes initiate ventricular fibrillation.

Correlation Between Muscle Fiber
Length & Tension

The relation between initial fiber length and total tension in cardiac muscle is similar to that in skeletal muscle; there is a resting length at which the tension developed upon stimulation is maximal. In the body, the initial length of the fibers is determined by the degree of diastolic filling of the heart and the pressure developed in the ventricle is proportionate to the total tension developed. As the diastolic filling increases, the force of contraction of the ventricles is increased

(Fig 3–16). The homeostatic value of this response is discussed in Chapter 29.

The force of contraction of cardiac muscle is also increased by catecholamines (see Chapters 13 and 20), and this increase occurs without a change in muscle length. The increase, which is called the positively inotropic effect of catecholamines, is mediated via β-adrenergic receptors and cyclic AMP (see Chapter 17). Cyclic AMP in turn increases Ca^{2+} influx from the ECF, making more Ca^{2+} available to bind to troponin C. Cyclic AMP via a protein kinase also increases the active transport of Ca^{2+} to the sarcoplasmic reticulum, thus accelerating relaxation and consequently shortening systole. This is important when the cardiac rate is increased because it permits adequate diastolic filling (see Chapter 29). Digitalis glycosides increase cardiac contractions by inhibiting the Na^+-K^+ ATPase in cell membranes of the muscle fibers. The resultant increase in intracellular Na^+ acts via a poorly understood mechanism to increase the amount of intracellular Ca^{2+} available to the contractile mechanism.

METABOLISM

Although the general pattern of cardiac muscle metabolism resembles that of skeletal muscle, there are differences. Mammalian hearts have an abundant blood supply, numerous mitochondria, and a high content of myoglobin, a muscle pigment that may function as an O_2 storage mechanism (see Chapter 35). Normally, less than 1% of the total energy liberated is provided by anaerobic metabolism. During hypoxia, this figure may increase to nearly 10%; but under totally anaerobic conditions the energy liberated is inadequate to sustain ventricular contractions. Under basal conditions, 35% of the caloric needs of the human heart are provided by carbohydrate, 5% by ketones and amino acids, and 60% by fat. However, the proportions of substrates utilized vary greatly with the nutritional state. After feeding large amounts of glucose, more lactic acid and pyruvic acid are used; during prolonged starvation, more fat is used. Circulating free fatty acids normally account for almost 50% of the lipid utilized. In untreated diabetics, the carbohydrate utilization of cardiac muscle is reduced and that of fat increased. The factors affecting the O_2 consumption of the human heart are discussed in Chapter 29.

PACEMAKER TISSUE

The heart continues to beat after all nerves to it are sectioned; indeed, if the heart is cut into pieces, the pieces continue to beat. This is because of the presence in the heart of specialized pacemaker tissue that can initiate repetitive action potentials. The pacemaker tissue makes up the conduction system that normally spreads impulses throughout the heart (see Chapter 28).

Pacemaker tissue is characterized by an unstable membrane potential. Instead of a steady value between impulses, the membrane potential declines steadily after each action potential until the firing level is reached and another action potential is triggered. This slow depolarization between action potentials is called a **pacemaker potential** or **prepotential** (Figs 3–17, 28–2). The steeper its slope, the faster the rate at which the pacemaker fires. Some agents that modify the firing rate of pacemakers do so by changing the slope of the prepotential, although others act by altering the membrane potential and thus changing the amount of time required to reach the firing level. The prepotential has been shown to be due primarily to a slow decrease in K^+ permeability. This causes a progressive decline in K^+ efflux and a resultant reduction in membrane

potential. Prepotentials are not seen in atrial and ventricular muscle cells; and in these cells, K^+ permeability is constant during diastole.

SMOOTH MUSCLE

MORPHOLOGY

Smooth muscle is distinguished anatomically from skeletal and cardiac muscle because it lacks visible cross-striations. There is a sarcoplasmic reticulum, but it is poorly developed. The muscle contains actin and myosin, and there is debate about the arrangement of the filaments. In intestinal smooth muscle, there is evidence that the contractile units are made up of small bundles of interdigitating thick and thin filaments that are irregularly shaped and randomly arranged. When the muscle contracts, the thick and thin filaments are thought to slide on each other.

Types

There are various types of smooth muscle in the body. In general, smooth muscle can be divided into **visceral smooth muscle** and **multi-unit smooth muscle.** Visceral smooth muscle occurs in large sheets, has low-resistance bridges between individual muscle cells, and functions in a syncytial fashion. The bridges, like those in cardiac muscle, are junctions where the membranes of the 2 adjacent cells fuse to form a single membrane. Visceral smooth muscle is found primarily in the walls of hollow viscera. The musculature of the intestine, the uterus, and the ureters are examples. Multi-unit smooth muscle is made up of individual units without interconnecting bridges. It is found in structures such as the iris of the eye, in which fine, graded contractions occur. It is usually not under voluntary control, but it has many functional similarities to skeletal muscle.

VISCERAL SMOOTH MUSCLE

Electrical & Mechanical Activity

Visceral smooth muscle is characterized by the instability of its membrane potential and by the fact that it shows continuous, irregular contractions that are independent of its nerve supply. This maintained state of partial contraction is called **tonus,** or **tone.** The membrane potential has no true "resting" value, being relatively low when the tissue is active and higher when it is inhibited, but in periods of relative quiescence it averages about −50 mV. Superimposed on the membrane potential are waves of various types (Fig

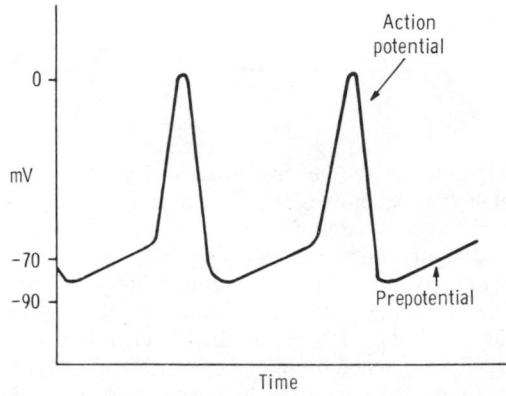

Figure 3–17. Diagram of the membrane potential of pacemaker tissue.

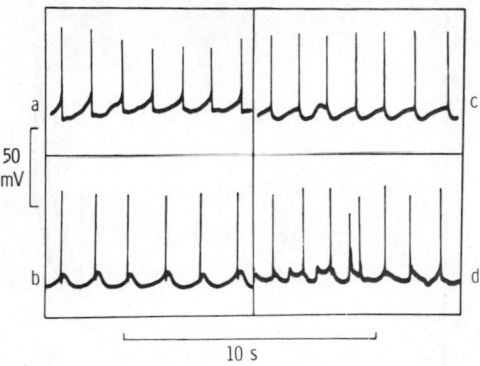

Figure 3–18. Spontaneous electrical activity in individual smooth muscle cells of teniae coli of guinea pig colon. *a:* Pacemaker type; *b:* sinusoidal waves with action potentials on the rising phases; *c:* sinusoidal waves with action potentials on the falling phases; *d:* mixture of pacemaker, oscillatory, and conducted action potentials. (Reproduced, with permission, from Bulbring E: Physiology and pharmacology of intestinal smooth muscle. Lectures on the Scientific Basis of Medicine 7:374, 1957.)

3–18). There are slow sine wave-like fluctuations a few millivolts in magnitude and spikes that sometimes overshoot the zero potential line and sometimes do not. In many tissues, the spikes have a duration of about 50 ms. However, in some tissues the action potentials have a prolonged plateau during repolarization, like the action potentials in cardiac muscle. The spikes may occur on the rising or falling phases of the sine wave oscillations. There are, in addition, pacemaker potentials similar to those found in the cardiac pacemakers. However, in visceral smooth muscle, these potentials are generated in multiple foci that shift from place to place. Spikes generated in the pacemaker foci are conducted for some distance in the muscle. Because of the continuous activity, it is difficult to study the relation between the electrical and mechanical events in visceral smooth muscle, but in some relatively inactive preparations, a single spike can be generated. The muscle starts to contract about 200 ms after the start of the spike and 150 ms after the spike is over. The peak contraction is reached as long as 500 ms after the spike. Thus, the excitation-contraction coupling in visceral smooth muscle is a very slow process compared to skeletal and cardiac muscle, in which the time from initial depolarization to initiation of contraction is less than 10 ms. Ca^{2+} is involved in the initiation of contraction of smooth muscle, as it is in skeletal muscle.

Visceral smooth muscle is unique in that, unlike other types of muscle, it contracts when stretched in the absence of any extrinsic innervation. Stretch is followed by a decline in membrane potential, an increase in the frequency of spikes, and a general increase in tone.

If epinephrine or norepinephrine is added to a preparation of intestinal smooth muscle arranged for recording of intracellular potentials in vitro, the mem-

brane potential usually becomes larger, the spikes decrease in frequency, and the muscle relaxes (Fig 3–19). Norepinephrine is the chemical mediator released at adrenergic nerve endings (see Chapter 13), and stimulation of the adrenergic nerves to the preparation produces inhibitory potentials (see Chapter 4). Stimulation of the adrenergic nerves to the intestine inhibits contractions in vivo. Norepinephrine exerts both α and β actions (see Chapter 13) on the muscle. The β action, reduced muscle tension in response to excitation, is mediated via cyclic AMP (see Chapter 1) and is probably due to increased intracellular binding of Ca^{2+}. The α action, which is also inhibition of contraction, is associated with increased Ca^{2+} efflux from the muscle cells.

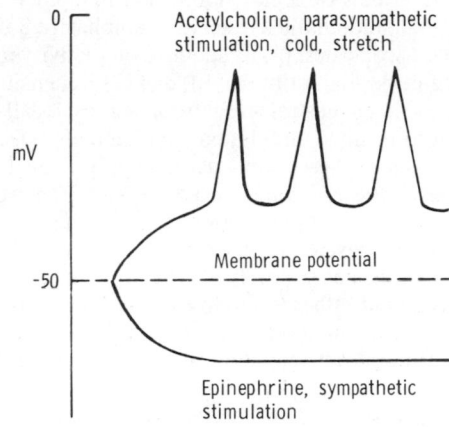

INTESTINAL SMOOTH MUSCLE

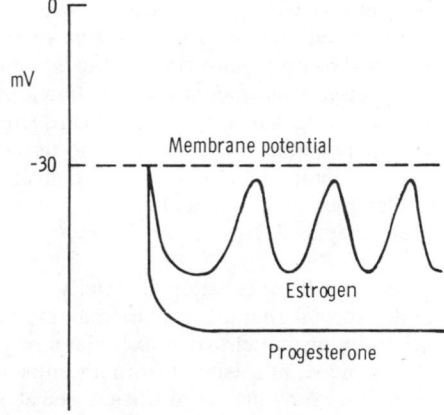

UTERINE SMOOTH MUSCLE

Figure 3–19. *Above:* Effects of various agents on the membrane potential of intestinal smooth muscle. *Below:* Effects of estrogens and of progesterone on the membrane potential of the uterus of the ovariectomized rabbit or rat. (Modified and reproduced, with permission, from Burnstock G, Halman ME, Prosser CL: Electrophysiology of smooth muscle. Physiol Rev 43:482, 1963.)

Acetylcholine has an effect opposite to that of norepinephrine on the membrane potential and contractile activity of intestinal smooth muscle. If acetylcholine is added to the fluid bathing a smooth muscle preparation in vitro, the membrane potential decreases and the spikes become more frequent (Fig 3–19). The muscle becomes more active, with an increase in tonic tension and the number of rhythmic contractions. The depolarization is apparently due to increases in Na^+ permeability and Ca^{2+} entry into the cell. In the intact animal, stimulation of cholinergic nerves causes release of acetylcholine, excitatory potentials (see Chapter 4), and increased intestinal contractions. In vitro, similar effects are produced by cold and stretch.

Function of the Nerve Supply to Smooth Muscle

The effects of acetylcholine and norepinephrine on visceral smooth muscle serve to emphasize 2 of its important properties: (1) its spontaneous activity in the absence of nervous stimulation, and (2) its sensitivity to chemical agents released from nerves locally or brought to it in the circulation. In mammals, visceral muscle usually has a dual nerve supply from the 2 divisions of the autonomic nervous system. The structure and function of the contacts between these nerves and smooth muscle are discussed in Chapter 4. The function of the nerve supply is not to initiate activity in the muscle but rather to modify it. Stimulation of one division of the autonomic nervous system usually increases smooth muscle activity, whereas stimulation of the other decreases it. However, in some organs, adrenergic stimulation increases and cholinergic stimulation decreases smooth muscle activity; in others, the reverse is true.

Other chemical agents also affect smooth muscle. An interesting example is the uterus. Uterine smooth muscle is relatively inexcitable during diestrus and in the ovariectomized animal. During estrus or in the estrogen-treated ovariectomized animal, excitability is enhanced, and tonus and spontaneous contractions occur. However, estrogen increases rather than decreases the membrane potential (Fig 3–19). Progesterone increases the membrane potential even further and inhibits the electrical and contractile activity of uterine muscle (see Chapter 23).

Relation of Length to Tension; Plasticity

Another special characteristic of smooth muscle is the variability of the tension it exerts at any given length. If a piece of visceral smooth muscle is stretched, it first exerts increased tension (see above). However, if the muscle is held at the greater length after stretching, the tension gradually decreases. Sometimes the tension falls to or below the level exerted before the muscle was stretched. It is consequently impossible to correlate length and developed tension accurately, and no resting length can be assigned. In some ways, therefore, smooth muscle behaves more like a viscous mass than a rigidly structured tissue, and it is this property which is referred to as the **plasticity** of smooth muscle.

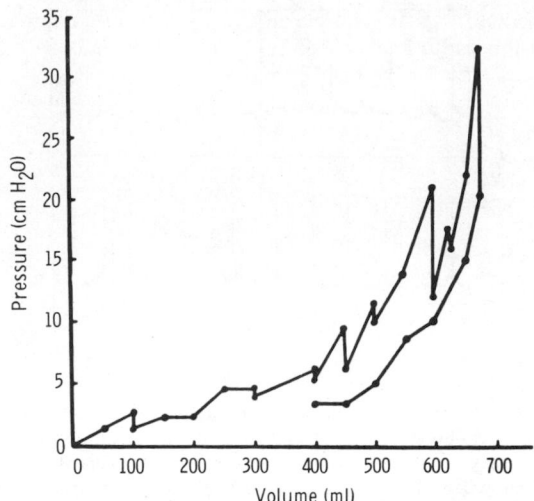

Figure 3–20. Change in pressure in the human bladder during filling and emptying. Water was instilled into the bladder by catheter 50 ml at a time, the inflow being stopped and the pressure measured after each increment (upper left curve). After 700 ml had been instilled, the bladder was allowed to empty 50 ml at a time (lower right curve). (Reproduced, with permission, from Denny-Brown D, Robertson EG: Physiology of micturition. Brain 56:149, 1933.)

The consequences of plasticity can be demonstrated in the intact animal. For example, the tension exerted by the smooth muscle walls of the bladder can be measured at varying degrees of distention. To obtain the data shown in Fig 3–20, a catheter was inserted into the empty bladder of an intact human and fluid introduced in 50 ml increments. After each addition of fluid, the tension was measured for a period of time. Immediately after each increment of fluid, the tension was higher; but after a short period of time, it decreased. Therefore, the filling curve in Fig 3–20 is not a smooth curve but a jagged line. After 700 ml had been infused into the bladder, the subject voided in 50 ml increments, and the tension was recorded after each increment. Plotting these tensions produced an emptying curve that was different from the filling curve, again due to the absence of any constant relationship between fiber length and tension.

MULTI–UNIT SMOOTH MUSCLE

Unlike visceral smooth muscle, multi-unit smooth muscle is nonsyncytial and contractions do not spread widely through it. Because of this, the contractions of multi-unit smooth muscle are more discrete, fine, and localized than those of visceral smooth muscle. Like visceral smooth muscle, multi-unit smooth muscle is very sensitive to circulating chemical substances and is normally activated by chemical mediators (acetylcholine and norepinephrine) released at the endings of its motor nerves. Especially in the case of norepinephrine, the mediator tends to persist and to cause repeated firing of the muscle after a single stimulus rather than a single action potential. There-fore, the contractile response produced is usually an irregular tetanus rather than a single twitch. When a single twitch response is obtained, it resembles the twitch contraction of skeletal muscle except that its duration is 10 times as long.

4 | Synaptic & Junctional Transmission

The all or none type of conduction seen in axons and skeletal muscle has been discussed in Chapters 2 and 3. Impulses are transmitted from one nerve cell to another at **synapses** (Fig 4–1). These are the junctions where the axon or some other portion of one cell (the **presynaptic cell**) terminates on the soma, the dendrites, or some other portion of another neuron (the **postsynaptic cell**). It is worth noting that dendrites as well as axons can be presynaptic or postsynaptic. Transmission at most of the junctions is chemical; the impulse in the presynaptic axon liberates a **chemical mediator.** The chemical mediator binds to receptors on the surface of the postsynaptic cell, and this triggers intracellular events that alter the permeability of the

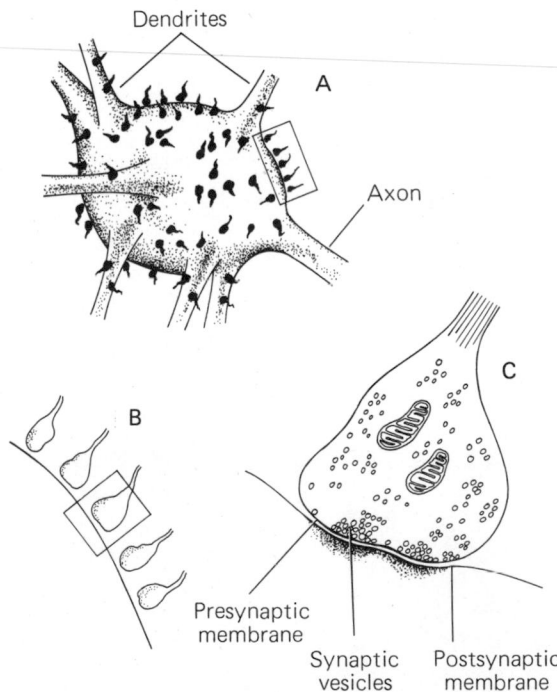

Figure 4–1. Synapses on a spinal motor neuron. *A:* Cell body of spinal motor neuron. The dark objects are synaptic knobs at the ends of the axons of presynaptic neurons. The area in the rectangle in *A* is enlarged in *B*, and the area in the rectangle in *B* is enlarged in *C*. (Modified from Junqueira LC, Carneiro J, Contopoulos AN: *Basic Histology,* 2nd ed. Lange, 1977.)

membrane of the postsynaptic neuron. At some of the junctions, however, transmission is **electrical,** and at a few **conjoint synapses** it is both electrical and chemical (Fig 4–2). In any case, impulses in the presynaptic fibers usually contribute to the initiation of conducted responses in the postsynaptic cell, but transmission is not a simple jumping of one action potential from the presynaptic to the postsynaptic neuron. It is a complex process that permits the grading and modulation of neural activity necessary for normal function.

In the case of electrical synapses, the membranes of the presynaptic and postsynaptic neurons come close together, forming a gap junction (see Chapter 1). Like the intercellular junctions in other tissues (see Chapter 1), these junctions form low-resistance bridges through which ions pass with relative ease. Electrical and conjoint synapses are being found with increasing frequency in mammals, and there is electrical coupling, for example, between some of the neurons in the lateral vestibular nucleus. However, most synaptic transmission is chemical. Consideration in this chapter is limited, unless otherwise specified, to chemical transmission.

Transmission from nerve to muscle resembles chemical synaptic transmission. The **myoneural junction,** the specialized area where a motor nerve terminates on a skeletal muscle fiber, is the site of a stereotyped transmission process. The contacts between autonomic neurons and smooth and cardiac muscle are less specialized, and transmission is a more diffuse process.

SYNAPTIC TRANSMISSION

SYNAPTIC ANATOMY

There is considerable variation in the anatomic structure of synapses in various parts of the mammalian nervous system. The ends of the presynaptic fibers are generally enlarged to form **terminal buttons,** or **synaptic knobs** (Figs 4–1, 4–2). Endings are com-

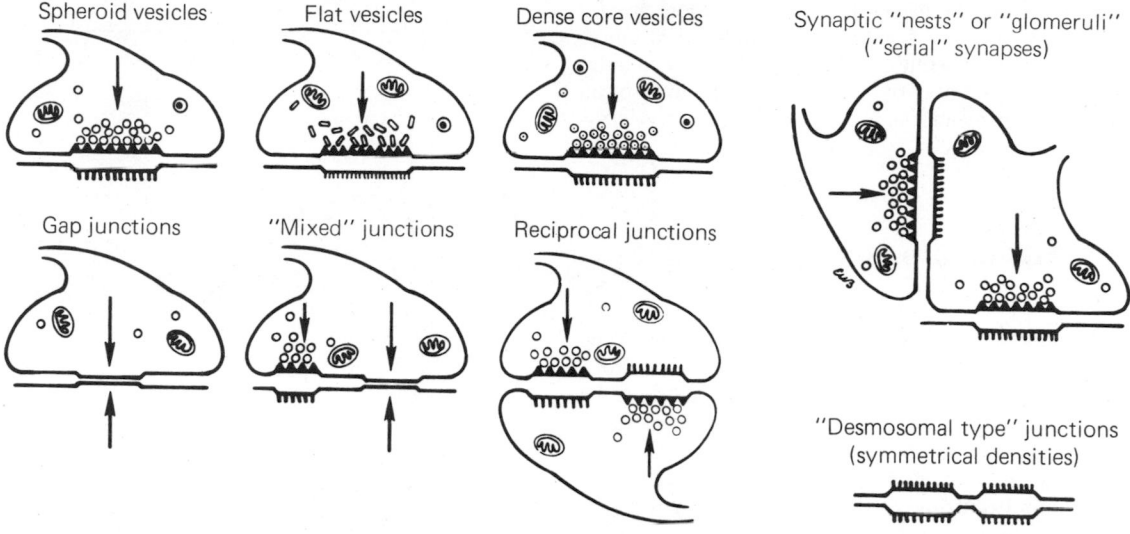

Figure 4–2. Major types of synaptic junctions. At synapses where there are vesicles, conduction is chemical, whereas conduction at gap junctions is electrical. Spheroid (clear) vesicles contain acetylcholine, flattened vesicles appear to contain inhibitory mediator, small dense core vesicles contain catecholamines or serotonin, and large core granules contain peptides. The "desmosomal type" junctions occur in sympathetic ganglia, but their function is unknown. (Reproduced, with permission, from Bodian D: Neuron junctions: A revolutionary decade. Anat Rec 174:73, 1973.)

monly located on **dendritic spines,** which are small knobs projecting from dendrites. In some instances, the terminal branches of the axon of the presynaptic neuron form a basket or net around the soma of the postsynaptic cell ("basket cells" of the cerebellum and autonomic ganglia). In other locations, they intertwine with the dendrites of the postsynaptic cell (climbing fibers of the cerebellum) or end on the dendrites directly (apical dendrites of cortical pyramids) or on the axons (axo-axonal endings). In the spinal cord, the presynaptic endings are closely applied to the soma and the proximal portions of the dendrites of the postsynaptic neuron. The number of synaptic knobs varies from one per postsynaptic cell (in the midbrain) to a very large number. The number of synaptic knobs applied to a single spinal motor neuron has been calculated to be about 5500; there are so many knobs that the neuron appears to be encrusted with them. The portion of the soma membrane covered by any single synaptic knob is small, but the synaptic knobs are so numerous that, in aggregate, the area covered by them all is often 40% of the total membrane area (Fig 4–1). There are even more endings on the dendrites. Indeed, in the cerebral cortex, it has been calculated that 98% of the synapses are on dendrites and only 2% are on cell bodies. In the human forebrain, the ratio of synapses to neurons has been calculated to be 4×10^4 to 1.

Synaptic Knobs

Under the electron microscope, the synaptic knobs at synapses where transmission is chemical are found to be separated from the soma of the postsynaptic cell by a definite **synaptic cleft** about 20 nm wide. The synaptic knob and the soma each have an intact

membrane. Inside the knob, there are many mitochondria and small vesicles or granules, the latter being especially numerous in the part of the knob closest to the synaptic cleft. The vesicles or granules contain small "packets" of the chemical transmitter responsible for synaptic transmission (see below). They vary in morphology depending on the particular transmitter they contain.

The transmitter is released from the synaptic knobs when action potentials pass along the axon to the endings. The membranes of the vesicles or granules fuse to the nerve cell membrane and the area of fusion breaks down, releasing the contents by the process of exocytosis (see Chapter 1). Ca^{2+} triggers this process, and the action potential increases the permeability of the nerve cell membrane to Ca^{2+}. The amount of transmitter released is proportionate to the Ca^{2+} influx.

Convergence & Divergence

Only a few of the synaptic knobs on a postsynaptic neuron are endings of any single presynaptic neuron. The inputs to the cell are multiple. In the case of spinal motor neurons, for example, some inputs come directly from the dorsal root, some from the long descending spinal tracts, and many from **interneurons,** the short interconnecting neurons of the spinal cord. Thus, many presynaptic neurons **converge** on any single postsynaptic neuron. Conversely, the axons of most presynaptic neurons divide into many branches that **diverge** to end on many postsynaptic neurons. Convergence and divergence are the anatomic substrates for facilitation, occlusion, and reverberation (see below). It has been calculated that there are approximately 10^{14} synapses in the human brain and that, on the average, each of the more than 10 billion neurons in the nervous system has 100 inputs converging on it while it in turn diverges to 100 other neurons. The number of possible paths an impulse can take through a neuron net of this complexity is astronomically large.

ELECTRICAL EVENTS AT SYNAPSES

Synaptic activity in the spinal cord has been studied in detail in cats by inserting a microelectrode into the soma of a motor neuron and recording the electrical events that follow stimulation of the excitatory and inhibitory inputs to these cells. Activity at other synapses has not been so well studied in mammals, but the events occurring at many of these synapses are apparently similar to those occurring at spinal synapses.

Penetration of an anterior horn cell is achieved by advancing a microelectrode through the ventral portion of the spinal cord. Puncture of a cell membrane is signalled by the appearance of a steady 70 mV potential difference between the microelectrode and an electrode outside the cell. The cell can be identified as a spinal motor neuron by stimulating the appropriate ventral root and observing the electrical activity of the cell. Such stimulation initiates an antidromic impulse (see Chapter 2) that is conducted to the soma and stops at this point. Therefore, the presence of an action potential in the cell after antidromic stimulation indicates that the cell which has been penetrated is a motor neuron rather than an interneuron. Activity in some of the presynaptic terminals impinging on the impaled spinal motor neuron (Fig 4–3) can be initiated by stimulating the dorsal roots.

Excitatory Postsynaptic Potentials

Single stimuli applied to the sensory nerves in the experimental situation described above characteristically do not lead to the formation of a propagated action potential in the postsynaptic neuron. Instead, the stimulation produces either a transient, partial depolarization or a transient hyperpolarization.

The depolarizing response produced by a single stimulus to the proper input begins about 0.5 ms after the afferent impulse enters the spinal cord. It reaches its peak 1–1.5 ms later, and then declines exponentially, with a **time constant** (time required for the response to decay to 1/e, or 1/2.718 of its maximum) of about 4 ms. During this potential, the excitability of the neuron to other stimuli is increased, and consequently the potential is called an **excitatory postsynaptic potential (EPSP).**

The EPSP is due to depolarization of the postsynaptic cell membrane immediately under the active synaptic knob. The area of inward current flow thus created is so small that it will not drain off enough positive charges to depolarize the whole membrane.

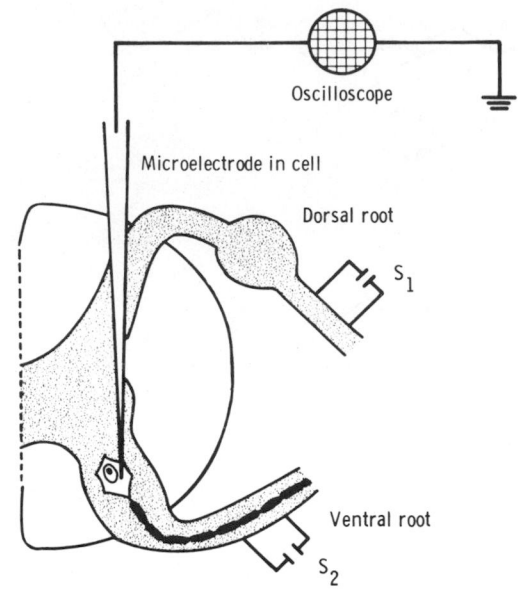

Figure 4–3. Arrangement of recording electrodes and stimulators for studying synaptic activity in spinal motor neurons in mammals. One stimulator (S_2) is used to produce antidromic impulses for identifying the cell; the other (S_1) is used to produce orthodromic stimulation via reflex pathways.

Instead, an EPSP is inscribed. The EPSP due to activity in one synaptic knob is small, but the depolarizations produced by each of the active knobs summate.

Summation may be **spatial** or **temporal.** When activity is present in more than one synaptic knob at the same time, spatial summation occurs and activity in one synaptic knob is said to **facilitate** activity in another to approach the firing level. Temporal summation occurs if repeated afferent stimuli cause new EPSPs before previous EPSPs have decayed. Spatial and temporal facilitation are illustrated in Fig 4–4. The EPSP is therefore not an all or none response but is proportionate in size to the strength of the afferent stimulus. If the EPSP is large enough to reach the firing level of the cell, a full-fledged action potential is produced.

Synaptic Delay

When an impulse reaches the presynaptic terminals, there is an interval of at least 0.5 ms, the **synaptic delay,** before a response is obtained in the postsynaptic neuron. The delay following maximal stimulation of the presynaptic neuron corresponds to the latency of the EPSP, and is due to the time it takes for the synaptic mediator to be released and to act on the membrane of the postsynaptic cell. Because of it, conduction along a chain of neurons is slower if there are many synapses in the chain than if there are only a few. This fact is important in comparing, for example, transmission in the lemniscal sensory pathways to the cerebral cortex and transmission in the reticular activating system (see Chapter 11). Since the minimum time for transmission

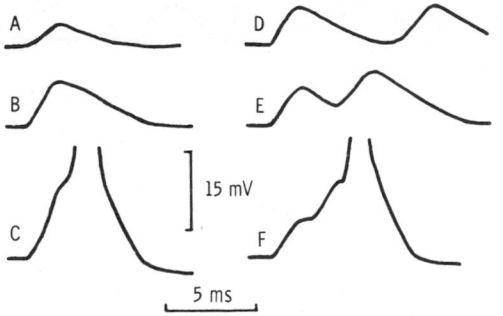

Figure 4–4. Spatial summation (A–C) and temporal summation (D–F) of EPSPs. Records are potential changes recorded with one electrode inside the postsynaptic cell. In A–C, afferent volleys of increasing strength were delivered. In C, the firing level was reached and an action potential generated. In D–F, 2 different volleys of the same strength were delivered, but the time interval between them was shortened. In F, the firing level was reached and an action potential generated.

across one synapse is 0.5 ms, it is also possible to determine whether a given reflex pathway is monosynaptic or polysynaptic (contains more than one synapse) by measuring the delay in transmission from the dorsal to the ventral root across the spinal cord.

Ionic Basis of EPSPs

The ionic events underlying excitatory synaptic activity have been worked out in considerable detail. Depolarization of the synaptic knob of an excitatory input is followed by an increase in the permeability of the soma membrane underlying it to Na^+. Consequently, Na^+ moves along its concentration and electrical gradients into the cell (see Chapter 2) and a depolarizing potential is produced. However, the area in which this influx occurs is so small that the repolarizing forces are able to overcome its influence, and runaway depolarization of the whole membrane does not result. If more excitatory synaptic knobs are active, more Na^+ enters and the depolarizing potential is greater. If Na^+ influx is great enough, the firing level is reached and a propagated action potential results.

Inhibitory Postsynaptic Potentials

An EPSP is usually produced by afferent stimulation, but stimulation of certain presynaptic fibers regularly initiates a hyperpolarizing response in spinal motor neurons. This response begins 1–1.25 ms after the afferent stimulus enters the cord, reaches its peak in 1.5–2 ms, and declines exponentially with a time constant of 3 ms. During this potential, the excitability of the neuron to other stimuli is decreased; consequently, it is called an **inhibitory postsynaptic potential (IPSP).** Spatial summation of IPSPs occurs, as shown by the increasing size of the response as the strength of an inhibitory afferent volley is increased (Fig 4–5). Temporal summation also occurs. This type of inhibition is called **postsynaptic** or **direct inhibition.**

Ionic Basis of IPSPs

At least in some neurons, the IPSP is apparently due to a localized increase in membrane permeability to Cl^- but not to Na^+. When an inhibitory synaptic knob becomes active, the area of the postsynaptic cell membrane under the knob permits increased Cl^- influx as the ions flow down their concentration gradients. The net effect is the transfer of negative charge into the cell, so that the membrane potential increases. However, the permeability change is short-lived, and resting conditions are rapidly restored. There is evidence that this restoration is due to active transport of Cl^- out of the cell.

The decreased excitability of the nerve cell during the IPSP is due in part to moving the membrane potential away from the firing level. Consequently, more excitatory (depolarizing) activity is necessary to reach the firing level. However, additional factors are involved; when the membrane potential is held at -80 mV, inhibitory stimulation still decreases excitability even though the membrane potential does not change. The actions of excitatory and inhibitory synaptic activity on the membrane of the postsynaptic cell are summarized in Fig 4–6.

Neurons Responsible for Postsynaptic Inhibition

Stimulation of certain sensory nerve fibers known to pass directly to motor neurons in the spinal cord produces EPSPs in these neurons and IPSPs in other neurons. If these afferent fibers also passed directly to the neurons in which IPSPs are produced, it would be necessary to postulate that a single presynaptic neuron has 2 kinds of endings, some excitatory and some inhibitory, or, alternatively, that the soma membrane of the postsynaptic cell is a patchwork of 2 kinds of membrane. However, evidence has accumulated that a single interneuron is inserted between afferent dorsal root fibers and inhibitory endings. This special inter-

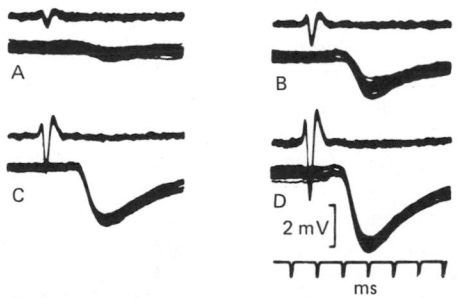

Figure 4–5. Inhibitory postsynaptic potentials. The lower tracing in each case is the intracellular response of a biceps semitendinosus motor neuron to stimulation of the nerve from the quadriceps. The upper tracing is the externally recorded response from the dorsal root. Note that the IPSPs increase in size as the stimulus strength is increased from A to D. All records were obtained by superimposing about 40 traces. (Reproduced, with permission, from Eccles JC, in: *Handbook of Physiology.* Field J, Magoun HW [editors]. Washington: American Physiological Society, 1959. Section 1, pages 59–74.)

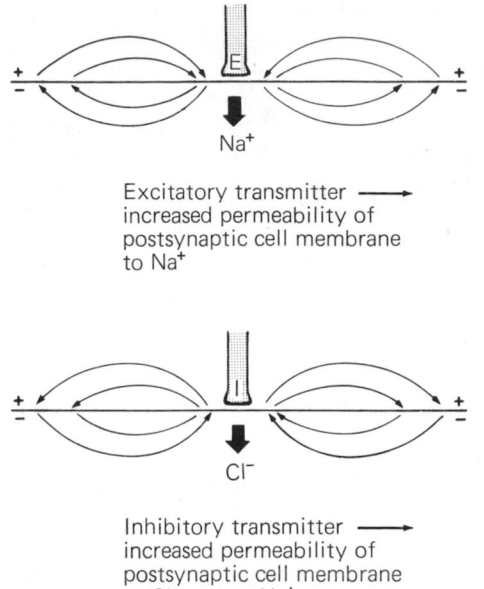

Excitatory transmitter ⟶
increased permeability of
postsynaptic cell membrane
to Na⁺

Inhibitory transmitter ⟶
increased permeability of
postsynaptic cell membrane
to Cl⁻, not to Na⁺

Figure 4–6. Summary of events occurring at synapses in mammals.

neuron, called a Golgi bottle neuron, is short and plump and has a thick axon. Discharge of the chemical mediator from the synaptic knobs of this neuron causes formation of an IPSP due to an increase in the permeability of the postsynaptic cell membrane to Cl^- but not to Na^+. In this way, excitatory input is "converted" into inhibitory input by interposing a single Golgi bottle neuron between the excitatory ending and the spinal motor neuron.

Generation of the Action Potential in the Postsynaptic Neuron

The constant interplay of excitatory and inhibitory activity on the postsynaptic neuron produces a fluctuating membrane potential that is the algebraic sum of the hyperpolarizing and depolarizing activity. The soma of the neuron thus acts as a sort of integrator. When the 10–15 mV of depolarization sufficient to reach the firing level is attained, a propagated spike results. However, the discharge of the neuron is slightly more complicated than this. In motor neurons, the portion of the cell with the lowest threshold for the production of a full-fledged action potential is the **initial segment,** the portion of the axon at and just beyond the axon hillock. This unmyelinated segment is depolarized or hyperpolarized electronically by the current sinks and sources under the excitatory and inhibitory synaptic knobs. It is the first part of the neuron to fire, and its discharge is propagated in 2 directions: down the axon and back into the soma. Retrograde firing of the soma in this fashion probably has value in "wiping the slate clean" for subsequent renewal of the interplay of excitatory and inhibitory activity on the cell.

Function of the Dendrites

Dendrites usually do not conduct like the axons. Action potentials are generated in some of the dendrites, but they are usually part of the "receptor membrane" of the neuron (see Chapter 2), the site of current sources or sinks that electrotonically change the membrane potential of the axon hillock region or other locus from which the action potentials are generated. In the CNS and the retina, there are in addition neurons with dendrites but no axons. These cells transmit action potentials or spread EPSPs and IPSPs from one neuron to another without a propagated action potential. In the olfactory bulb, for example, action potentials in mitral cells activate granule cell dendrites via dendrodendritic synapses. The dendrite then discharges an inhibitory transmitter on the same mitral cell, and as the electrical activity spreads in the granule cell, transmitter is released on other nearby mitral cells. Such microcircuits appear to be common in various parts of the brain.

When the dendritic tree of a neuron is extensive and has multiple presynaptic knobs ending on it, there is room for a great interplay of inhibitory and excitatory activity. Current flow to and from the dendrites in these situations waxes and wanes. The role of the dendrites in the genesis of the electroencephalogram is discussed in Chapter 11.

Electrical Transmission

At synaptic junctions where transmission is electrical, the impulse reaching the presynaptic terminal generates an EPSP in the postsynaptic cell that, because of the low-resistance bridge between the 2, has a much shorter latency than the EPSP at a synapse where transmission is chemical. In conjoint synapses, there is both a short latency response and a longer latency, chemically mediated, postsynaptic response.

CHEMICAL TRANSMISSION OF SYNAPTIC ACTIVITY

The nature of the chemical mediators at many of the synapses is not known. However, acetylcholine is the mediator at all synapses between preganglionic and postganglionic fibers of the autonomic nervous system, at the myoneural junction, and at all postganglionic parasympathetic and some postganglionic sympathetic endings. It is also a mediator in the CNS and the retina. The chemical and biophysical events occurring at synapses where it is a mediator are relatively well understood, and the mediator function of acetylcholine provides a good example of chemical mediation of synaptic activity. It should be emphasized, however, that acetylcholine is only one of the mediators in the nervous system.

Acetylcholine

The relatively simple structure of acetylcholine,

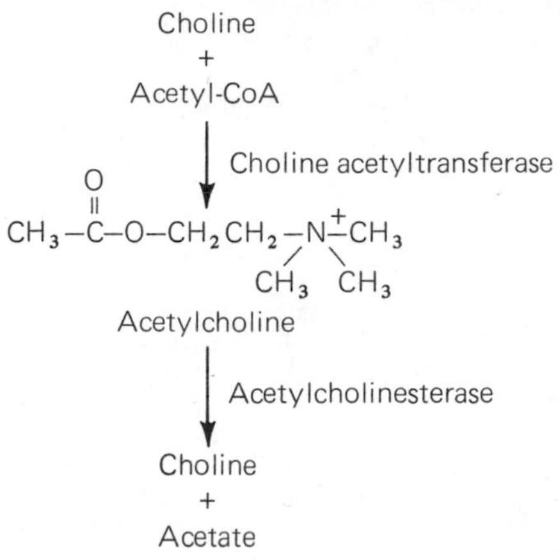

Choline
+
Acetyl-CoA

$\downarrow$ Choline acetyltransferase

$$CH_3-\overset{\overset{\displaystyle O}{\|}}{C}-O-CH_2CH_2-\overset{+}{\underset{\underset{\displaystyle CH_3\quad CH_3}{|}}{N}}CH_3$$

Acetylcholine

$\downarrow$ Acetylcholinesterase

Choline
+
Acetate

Figure 4–7. Biosynthesis and catabolism of acetylcholine.

which is the acetyl ester of choline, is shown in Fig 4–7. It exists, largely enclosed in clear synaptic vesicles, in high concentration in the terminal buttons of cholinergic neurons. Neurons that release acetylcholine are known as **cholinergic** neurons. The arrival of an impulse at a synaptic knob increases the Ca^{2+} permeability of the membrane, and the resultant Ca^{2+} influx causes liberation of acetylcholine into the synaptic cleft by the process of exocytosis. The transmitter crosses the cleft, and, at those synaptic junctions where acetylcholine is an excitatory mediator, it acts on receptors on the membrane of the postsynaptic cell to increase the permeability of the membrane to Na^+.

Cholinesterases

Acetylcholine must be rapidly removed from the synapse if repolarization is to occur. Some is taken up again by the presynaptic terminals, but most is hydrolyzed by a process catalyzed by the enzyme **acetylcholinesterase.** This enzyme is also called **true** or **specific cholinesterase.** It is present in high concentrations in the cell membranes at nerve terminals that are cholinergic, but it is also found in some other membranes, in red blood cells, and in the placenta. Its greatest affinity is for acetylcholine, but it also hydrolyzes other choline esters. There are a variety of esterases in the body. One found in plasma is capable of hydrolyzing acetylcholine but has different properties from acetylcholinesterase. It is therefore called **pseudocholinesterase** or **nonspecific cholinesterase.** The plasma moiety is partly under endocrine control and is affected by variations in liver function. On the other hand, the specific cholinesterase at nerve endings is highly localized. Hydrolysis of acetylcholine by this enzyme is rapid enough to explain the observed changes in Na^+ permeability and electrical activity during synaptic transmission.

Acetylcholine Synthesis

Synthesis of acetylcholine involves the reaction of choline with acetate. There is an active uptake of

choline into cholinergic neurons (Fig 13–4). The acetate is activated by the combination of acetate groups with reduced coenzyme A. The reaction between active acetate (acetyl-coenzyme A) and choline is catalyzed by the enzyme **choline acetyltransferase.** This enzyme is found in high concentration in the cytoplasm of cholinergic nerve endings; indeed, its localization is so specific that the presence of a high concentration in any given neural area has been taken as evidence that the synapses in that area are cholinergic.

Inhibitory Mediator

The chemical mediator released at the endings of the inhibitory interneurons in the spinal cord produces IPSPs in the postsynaptic neurons. This **inhibitory mediator** appears to be the amino acid **glycine.** Its action is inhibited, possibly competitively, by strychnine and tetanus toxin. Thus, the action of these 2 poisons is to inhibit inhibition, with consequent unopposed play of excitatory impulses. The clinical picture of convulsions and muscular hyperactivity produced by tetanus toxin and strychnine emphasizes the importance of postsynaptic inhibition in normal neural function.

Other Chemical Mediators

Norepinephrine is the mediator of activity at most postganglionic sympathetic endings in the autonomic nervous system. Its synthesis and metabolism are discussed in Chapter 13. Dopamine-secreting neurons that modulate the activity of norepinephrine-secreting neurons are found in sympathetic ganglia. Norepinephrine, dopamine, epinephrine, and 5-hydroxytryptamine (serotonin) are among the mediators found in the CNS. Neurons that secrete norepinephrine or epinephrine are called **adrenergic neurons.** Unlike acetylcholine, these amines are found in vesicles containing a dense core (granulated vesicles). Histamine, peptides such as "substance P" and somatostatin, and other agents may also be mediators in the brain (see Chapter 15).

One-Way Conduction

Synapses generally permit conduction of impulses in one direction only, from the presynaptic to the postsynaptic neurons. An impulse conducted antidromically up the axons of the ventral root dies out after depolarizing the cell bodies of the spinal motor neurons. Since axons will conduct in either direction with equal facility, the one-way gate at the synapses is necessary for orderly neural function. Chemical mediation at synaptic junctions explains one-way conduction. The mediator is located in the synaptic knobs of the presynaptic fibers, and very little if any is present in the postsynaptic membrane. Therefore, an impulse arriving at the postsynaptic membrane cannot liberate synaptic mediator. Progression of impulse traffic occurs only when the action potential arrives in the presynaptic terminals and causes liberation of stored chemical transmitter.

Pharmacologic Implications

The fact that transmission at most if not all synapses is chemical is of great pharmacologic importance. Transmission is also chemical at the endings of motor neurons on skeletal muscles, and at the points of contact between autonomic nerve fibers and smooth muscle (see below and Chapter 13). The biochemical events occurring at the synapse are much more sensitive than the events in the nerve fibers themselves to hypoxia and to drugs. For instance, polysynaptic pathways are more affected by anesthesia than those with few synapses, a factor that probably helps to explain the mechanism by which general anesthesia is produced (see Chapter 11). During deep anesthesia, synaptic transmission is blocked but long fibers still conduct impulses.

Nerve endings have been called biologic transducers that convert electrical energy into chemical energy. In broad terms, this conversion process involves the synthesis of the transmitter agents, their storage in the synaptic knobs, their release by the nerve impulses into the synaptic cleft, their action on the membrane of the postsynaptic cell, and their removal or their destruction, which is catalyzed by enzymes concentrated in the area around the endings. In theory, at least, all these processes can be inhibited or facilitated by drugs, with resultant changes in synaptic transmission. The synapses are thus a logical point for pharmacologic manipulation of neural function. Since transmission is chemical not only in the autonomic nervous system and at the myoneural junction but in the CNS as well, the pharmacologist can look forward to eventually regulating not only somatic and visceral motor activity but also emotions, behavior, and the other complex functions of the brain.

INHIBITION & FACILITATION AT SYNAPSES

Direct & Indirect Inhibition

Postsynaptic inhibition during the course of an IPSP is also called **direct inhibition** because it is not a consequence of previous discharges of the postsynaptic neuron. Various forms of **indirect inhibition,** inhibition due to the effects of previous postsynaptic neuron discharge, also occur. For example, the postsynaptic cell can be refractory to excitation because it has just fired and is in its refractory period. During after-hyperpolarization it is also less excitable; and in spinal neurons, especially after repeated firing, this after-hyperpolarization may be large and prolonged. In addition, there is evidence that with repeated stimulation of a given pathway the amount of transmitter released or the sensitivity of postsynaptic membrane to the transmitter decreases.

Postsynaptic Inhibition in the Spinal Cord

The various pathways in the nervous system that

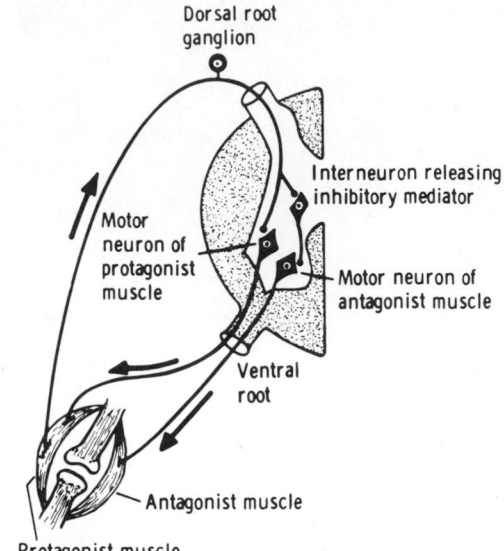

Figure 4–8. Diagram illustrating the probable anatomic connections responsible for inhibiting the antagonists to a muscle contracting in response to stretch. Activity is initiated in the spindle in the protagonist muscle. Impulses pass directly to the motor neurons supplying the same muscle and, via collaterals, to Golgi bottle neurons that end on the motor neurons of the antagonist muscle.

are known to mediate postsynaptic inhibition are discussed in Chapter 6, but one illustrative example will be presented here. Afferent fibers from the muscle spindles (stretch receptors) in skeletal muscle are known to pass directly to the spinal motor neurons of the motor units supplying the same muscle. Impulses in this afferent supply cause EPSPs and, with summation, propagated responses in the postsynaptic motor neurons. At the same time, IPSPs are produced in motor neurons supplying the antagonistic muscles. This latter response is probably mediated by collaterals of the afferent fibers that end on Golgi bottle neurons. These interneurons, in turn, end on the motor neurons that supply the antagonist (Fig 4–8) and secrete the inhibitory transmitter. Therefore, activity in the afferent fibers from the muscle spindles excites the motor neurons supplying the muscle from which the impulses come and inhibits those supplying its antagonists (**reciprocal innervation**).

Presynaptic Inhibition

Another type of inhibition occurring in the CNS is **presynaptic inhibition,** a process that reduces the amount of synaptic mediator liberated by action potentials arriving at excitatory synaptic knobs. It has been demonstrated that the amount of mediator liberated at a nerve ending is markedly reduced if the magnitude of the action potential reaching the ending is reduced. The neurons producing presynaptic inhibition end on the excitatory endings (Fig 4–9). When they discharge, they produce a partial depolarization of the

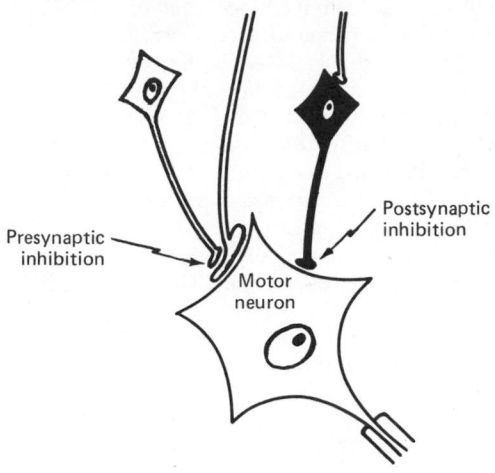

Figure 4–9. Arrangement of neurons producing presynaptic and postsynaptic inhibition. The neuron producing presynaptic inhibition is shown ending on an excitatory synaptic knob. Many of these neurons actually end higher up along the axon of the excitatory cell.

excitatory endings. Reducing the membrane potential of the excitatory endings to a level closer to the firing level makes the endings more excitable, but it also reduces the size of the action potentials reaching the ending by an amount equal to the amount of depolarization. Consequently, less mediator is released and there is less excitation of the postsynaptic cell. The neurons producing presynaptic inhibition often fire repetitively, and the partial depolarization may last 100 ms or more.

The chemical mediator released by the neurons responsible for presynaptic inhibition is antagonized by the convulsant drug picrotoxin, and there is reason to believe that it is γ-aminobutyric acid (GABA). It increases the permeability of the excitatory endings to Cl^-, but in this case, the membrane potential moves in a depolarizing rather than a hyperpolarizing direction because E_{Cl} is less negative than the resting membrane potential.

Organization of Inhibitory Systems

Presynaptic and postsynaptic inhibition are usually produced by stimulation of certain systems converging on a given postsynaptic neuron ("afferent inhibition"). Neurons may also inhibit themselves in a negative feedback fashion ("negative feedback inhibition"). For instance, spinal motor neurons regularly give off a recurrent collateral which synapses with an inhibitory interneuron that terminates on the cell body of the spinal neuron and other spinal motor neurons (Fig 4–10). This particular inhibitory neuron is sometimes called the Renshaw cell after its discoverer. Impulses generated in the motor neuron activate the inhibitory interneuron to liberate inhibitory mediator, and this slows or stops the discharge of the motor neuron. Similar inhibition via recurrent collaterals is

seen in the cerebral cortex and limbic system. Presynaptic inhibition appears to be in some cases a negative feedback inhibition in which cutaneous and other sensory neurons make connections that bring about presynaptic inhibition of their own terminals and surrounding terminals. In addition, fibers descending from the medulla in the pyramidal tract end on the excitatory endings of the afferent fibers from the muscle spindles. The muscle spindles are the receptors for the stretch reflex (see Chapter 6), and so impulses in the descending fibers presumably decrease stretch reflex activity.

Another type of inhibition is seen in the cerebellum. In this part of the brain, stimulation of basket cells produces IPSPs in the Purkinje cells. However, the basket cells and the Purkinje cells are excited by the same excitatory input. This arrangement, which has been called "feed-forward inhibition," presumably limits the duration of the excitation produced by any given afferent volley.

Summation & Occlusion

The interplay between excitatory and inhibitory influences at synaptic junctions in a nerve net illustrates the integrating and modulating activity of the nervous system.

In the hypothetical nerve net shown in Fig 4–11, neurons A and B converge on X, and neuron B diverges on X and Y. A stimulus applied to A or to B will set up an EPSP in X. If A and B are stimulated at the same time, 2 areas of depolarization will be produced in X and their actions will sum. The resultant EPSP in X will be twice as large as that produced by stimulation of A or B alone, and the membrane potential may well reach the firing level of X. The effect of the depolarization caused by the impulse in A is facilitated by that due to activity in B, and vice versa; spatial facilitation has taken place. In this case, Y has not fired, but its excitability has been increased, and it is easier for

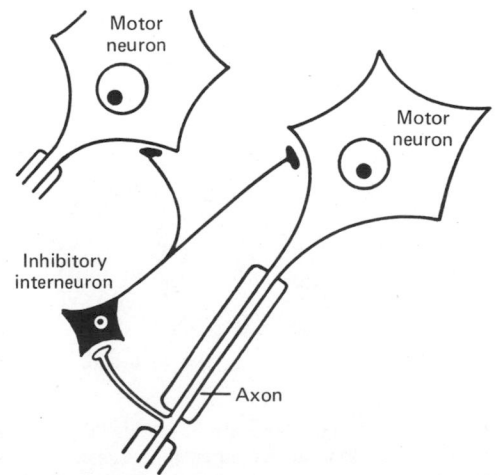

Figure 4–10. Negative feedback inhibition of a spinal motor neuron via an inhibitory interneuron (Renshaw cell).

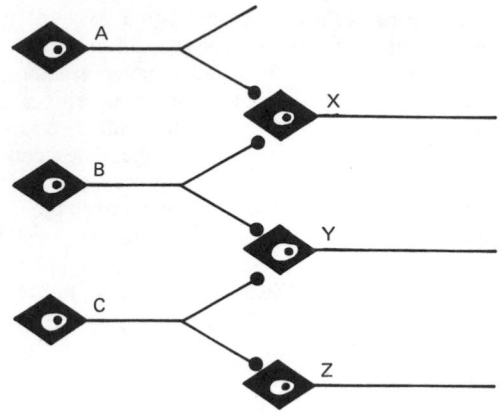

Figure 4–11. Simple nerve net. Neurons A, B, and C have excitatory endings on neurons X, Y, and Z.

activity in neuron C to fire it during the duration of the EPSP. Y is therefore said to be in the **subliminal fringe** of X. More generally stated, neurons are in the subliminal fringe if they are not discharged by an afferent volley (not in the **discharge zone**) but do have their excitability increased. The neurons that have few active knobs ending on them are in the subliminal fringe and those with many are in the discharge zone. However, this does not mean that with increasing strength of afferent stimulus the discharge zone becomes the same size as the subliminal fringe. In the case of stimulation of a dorsal root, the number of neurons discharged increases to a maximum with increasing strength of stimulation of the root, but so does the size of the subliminal fringe (Fig 4–12). Inhibitory

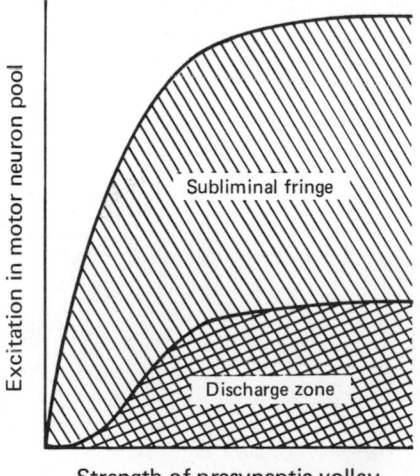

Figure 4–12. Relation of the size of the discharge zone and subliminal fringe to the strength of the presynaptic volley. (Redrawn and reproduced, with permission, from Lloyd DPC: Reflex action in relation to pattern and peripheral source of afferent stimulation. J Neurophysiol 6:111, 1943.)

impulses show similar temporal and spatial facilitation and subliminal fringe effects.

If neuron B in Fig 4–11 is stimulated repetitively, X and Y will discharge as a result of temporal summation of the EPSPs produced. If C is stimulated repetitively, Y and Z will discharge. If B and C are fired repetitively at the same time, X, Y, and Z will discharge. Thus, the response to stimulation of B and C together is not as great as the sum of responses to stimulation of B and C separately, because B and C both end on neuron Y. This decrease in expected response, due to presynaptic fibers sharing postsynaptic neurons, is called **occlusion.**

Excitatory and inhibitory subliminal effects and occlusive phenomena can have pronounced effects on transmission in any given pathway. Because of these effects, temporal patterns in peripheral nerves are usually altered as they pass through synapses on the way to the brain. These effects may also explain such important phenomena as referred pain (see Chapter 7).

POST–TETANIC POTENTIATION

The shifting patterns of facilitation and inhibition described above produce effects on neuronal excitability that are of relatively short duration. Another form of synaptic activity that has much more prolonged effects on excitability is the process of **post-tetanic potentiation.** This term refers to the decreased threshold for afferent stimulation of neurons in the CNS after their input has been subjected to prolonged repeated stimulation. It also occurs at autonomic ganglia and myoneural junctions. The potentiation may last several hours, and is localized to the afferent input that is stimulated. It does not spread to other afferent inputs. Inhibitory inputs also show post-tetanic potentiation, and the potentiation extends not only to the neurons directly fired but also to the subliminal fringe zone. This facilitation of transmission with repeated use of a pathway is in a sense an elementary form of learning. There is considerable evidence that the potentiation is due to an increase in transmitter release.

NEUROMUSCULAR TRANSMISSION

THE MYONEURAL JUNCTION

Anatomy

As the axon supplying a skeletal muscle fiber approaches its termination, it loses its myelin sheath and divides into a number of terminal buttons or end-

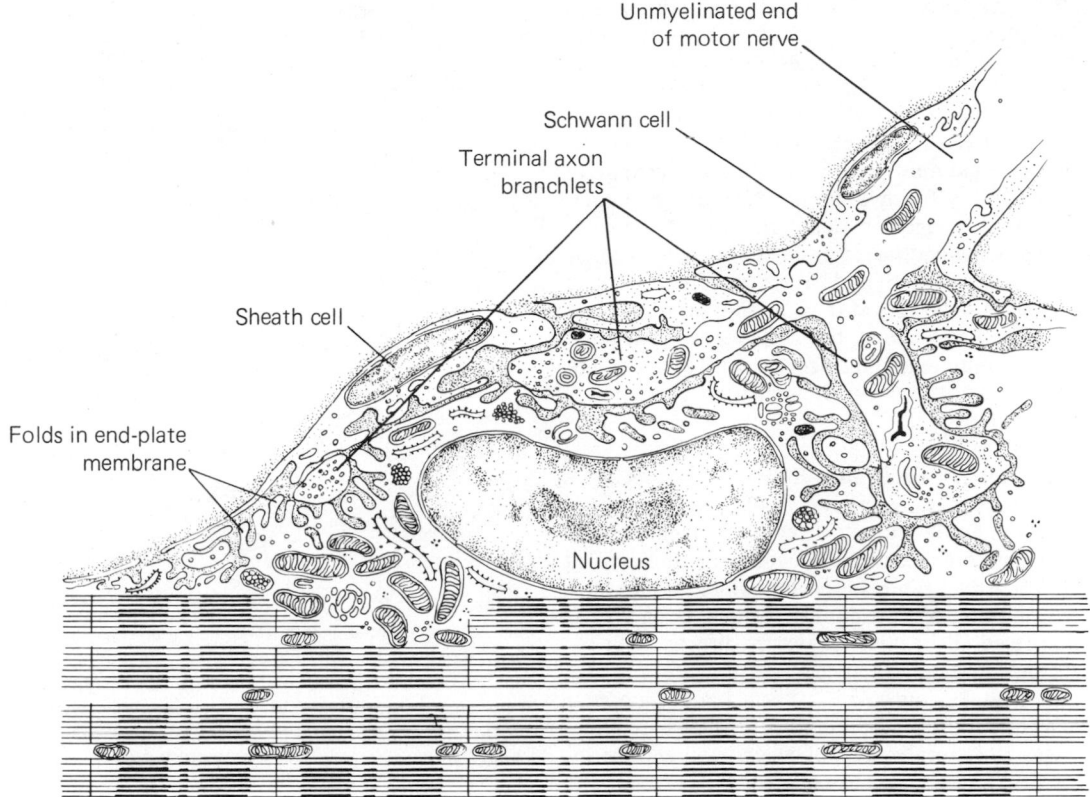

Figure 4–13. Myoneural junction. The drawing is based on electron micrographs of tissue from mice, and shows the terminal ends of a motor neuron axon buried in the end-plate cytoplasm, with the much folded end-plate membrane around them. (Modified and redrawn, with permission, from Anderson-Cedergren E: Ultrastructure of motor end plate and sarcoplasmic components of skeletal muscle fiber. J Ultrastruct Res, Suppl 1, 1959.)

feet (Fig 4–13). The end-feet contain many small clear vesicles that contain acetylcholine, the transmitter at these junctions. The endings fit into depressions in the **motor end-plate,** the thickened portion of the muscle membrane of the junction. Underneath the nerve ending, the muscle membrane of the end-plate is thrown into folds, the **palisades.** The space between the nerve and the thickened muscle membrane is comparable to the synaptic cleft at synapses. The whole structure is known as the **myoneural junction.** Only one nerve fiber ends on each end-plate, with no convergence of multiple inputs.

Sequence of Events During Transmission

The events occurring during transmission of impulses from the motor nerve to the muscle are somewhat similar to those occurring at synapses. The impulse arriving in the end of the motor neuron evokes liberation of acetylcholine from the vesicles in the nerve terminals. The acetylcholine increases the permeability of the underlying membrane, and Na^+ influx produces a depolarizing potential, the **end-plate potential.** The current sink created by this local potential depolarizes the adjacent muscle membrane to its firing level. Action potentials are generated on either side of

the end-plate and are conducted away from the end-plate in both directions along the muscle fiber. The muscle action potential, in turn, initiates muscle contraction, as described in Chapter 3.

End-Plate Potential

The end-plate potential is normally obscured by the propagated response initiated from the muscle fiber, but it can be seen if its magnitude is reduced to a size that is insufficient to fire the adjacent muscle membrane. Curare competes with acetylcholine for receptors on the end-plate membrane and forms a strong complex with the receptors. With small doses of curare, not all of the receptors are blocked, and acetylcholine acting at the unblocked receptors produces a small end-plate potential. The response is recorded only at the end-plate region and decreases exponentially away from it. Under these conditions, end-plate potentials can be shown to undergo temporal summation. Normally, however, the magnitude of the end-plate potential is sufficient to discharge the muscle membrane, and each impulse in the nerve ending produces a response in the muscle. Consequently, summation is not a usual phenomenon at the end-plate.

At the motor end-plate, it appears to be the complex formed by acetylcholine and the membrane receptor that induces the change in membrane permeability. There is a simultaneous increase in Na^+ and K^+ permeability, and the potential of the end-plate moves toward an equilibrium value of about -10 mV rather than the positive value reached during the action potential in nerve and muscle in which the peak increase in K^+ permeability follows the increase in Na^+ permeability. After triggering depolarization of the end-plate, the acetylcholine is probably bound to acetylcholinesterase, which hydrolyzes it. The end-plate membrane is depolarized if acetylcholine is dropped on it from a micropipette; but if the pipette is inserted through the muscle and the acetylcholine is applied to the underside of the end-plate membrane, no depolarization results.

Quantal Release of Transmitter

Small quanta, or "packets" of acetylcholine are released randomly from the nerve cell membrane at rest, each producing a minute depolarizing spike called a **miniature end-plate potential,** which is about 0.5 mV in amplitude. The number of quanta of acetylcholine released in this way varies directly with the Ca^{2+} concentration and inversely with the Mg^{2+} concentration at the end-plate. When a nerve impulse reaches the ending, the number of quanta released increases by several orders of magnitude, and the result is the large end-plate potential that exceeds the firing level of the muscle fiber. The nerve impulse increases the permeability of the ending to Ca^{2+} and the Ca^{2+} is responsible for the increased quantal release.

Quantal release of acetylcholine similar to that seen at the myoneural junction has been observed at other cholinergic synapses, and similar processes are presumably operating at adrenergic and other synaptic junctions.

NERVE ENDINGS IN SMOOTH & CARDIAC MUSCLE

Anatomy

The postganglionic neurons in the various smooth muscles that have been studied in detail branch extensively and come in close contact with the muscle cells. Some of these nerve fibers contain clear vesicles and are cholinergic, whereas others contain the characteristic dense-core granules within vesicles that are known to contain norepinephrine (see Chapter 13). There are no recognizable end-plates, and no discrete endings have been found; but the nerve fibers run along the membranes of the muscle cells and sometimes groove their surfaces. The adrenergic neurons have many branches and are beaded with enlargements or **varicosities** that contain adrenergic granules (Fig 4–14). The cholinergic neurons are probably similar. It has been suggested that transmitter is liberated at each

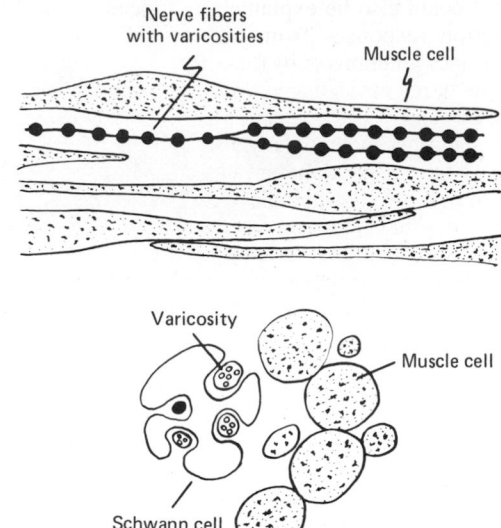

Figure 4–14. Relation of smooth muscle to autonomic nerve fibers. Longitudinal section *(top)* and transverse section *(bottom).* The Schwann cells that envelop the nerve fibers have been omitted from the top diagram. Note the areas of membrane fusion between muscle cells. (Modified from Bennett MR, Burnstock G, in: *Handbook of Physiology.* Code CF [editor]. Washington: The American Physiological Society, 1968. Section 6, pages 1709–1732.)

varicosity, ie, at many locations along each axon. This arrangement permits one neuron to innervate many effector cells. The type of contact in which a neuron grooves the surface of a smooth muscle cell and then passes on to make similar contacts with other cells has been called a **synapse en passant.**

In the heart, cholinergic and adrenergic nerve fibers end on the sinoatrial node, the atrioventricular node, and the bundle of His. Adrenergic fibers also innervate the ventricular muscle. The exact nature of the endings on nodal tissue is not known. In the ventricle, the contacts between the adrenergic fibers and the cardiac muscle fibers resemble those found in smooth muscle.

Electrical Responses

In smooth muscles in which adrenergic discharge is excitatory, stimulation of the adrenergic nerves produces discrete partial depolarizations that look like small end-plate potentials and are called **excitatory junction potentials (EJPs).** These potentials summate with repeated stimuli. Similar EJPs are seen in tissues excited by cholinergic discharges. In tissues inhibited by adrenergic stimuli, hyperpolarizing **inhibitory junction potentials (IJPs)** have been produced by stimulation of the adrenergic nerves.

These electrical responses are observed in many smooth muscle cells when a single nerve is stimulated, but their latency varies. This finding is consistent with the synapse en passant arrangement described above, but it could also be explained by transmission of the junction responses from cell to cell across low-resistance junctions or by diffusion of transmitter from its site of release to many smooth muscle cells. Miniature excitatory junction potentials similar to the miniature end-plate potentials in the skeletal muscle have been observed in some smooth muscle preparations, but they show considerable variation in size and duration. They may represent responses to single packets of transmitter, with the variation due to diffusion of the transmitter for variable distances.

DENERVATION HYPERSENSITIVITY

When the motor nerve to skeletal muscle is cut and allowed to degenerate, the muscle gradually becomes extremely sensitive to acetylcholine. This **denervation hypersensitivity** or **supersensitivity** is also seen in smooth muscle. Smooth muscle, unlike skeletal muscle, does not atrophy when denervated, but it becomes hyperresponsive to the chemical mediator that normally activates it. Denervated exocrine glands, except for sweat glands, also become hypersensitive. A good example of denervation hypersensitivity is the response of the denervated iris. If the postganglionic sympathetic nerves to one pupil are cut in an experimental animal and, after several weeks, norepinephrine is injected intravenously, the denervated pupil dilates widely. A much smaller, less prolonged response is observed on the intact side.

The reactions triggered by section of an axon are summarized in Fig 4–15. Hypersensitivity to the transmitter secreted at the receptor area, if previously innervated, is a general phenomenon, largely due to the synthesis or activation of more receptors. There is in addition orthograde degeneration (**wallerian degeneration;** see Chapter 2) and retrograde degeneration of the axon stump to the nearest collateral (**sustaining collateral**). A series of changes occur in the cell body that include a decrease in Nissl substance (chromatolysis). The nerve then starts to regrow, with multiple small branches projecting along the path the axon previously followed (regenerative sprouting).

When higher centers in the nervous system are destroyed, the activity of the lower centers they control is generally increased ("release phenomenon"). The increased activity may be due in part to denervation hypersensitivity of the lower centers. Indeed, one theory holds that many of the signs and symptoms of neurologic disease are due to denervation hypersensitivity of various groups of neurons in the brain.

Hypersensitivity is limited to the structures immediately innervated by the destroyed neurons, and fails to develop in neurons and muscle farther "downstream." Suprasegmental spinal cord lesions

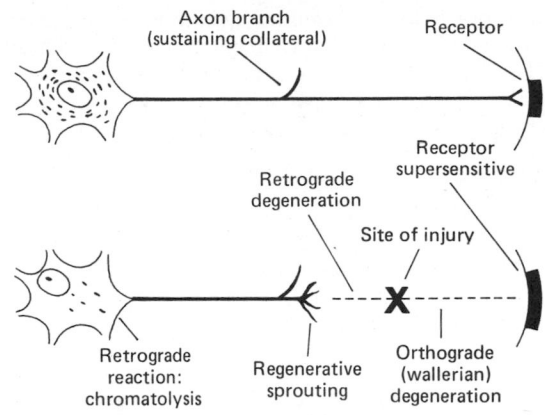

Figure 4–15. Summary of changes occurring in a neuron and the structure it innervates when its axon is crushed or cut at the point marked X. (Modified from D Ries.)

do not lead to hypersensitivity of the paralyzed skeletal muscles to acetylcholine, and destruction of the preganglionic autonomic nerves to visceral structures does not cause hypersensitivity of the denervated viscera. This fact has practical implications in the treatment of diseases due to spasm of the blood vessels in the extremities. For example, if the upper extremity is sympathectomized by removing the upper part of the ganglion chain and the stellate ganglion, the hypersensitive smooth muscle in the vessel walls is stimulated by circulating norepinephrine, and episodic vasospasm continues to occur. However, if preganglionic sympathectomy of the arm is performed by cutting the ganglion chain below the third ganglion (to interrupt ascending preganglionic fibers) and the white rami of the first 3 thoracic nerves, no hypersensitivity results.

The cause of denervation hypersensitivity is still obscure. As noted in Chapter 1, it appears to be a general rule that when there is a deficiency of a given neurotransmitter, there is an increase in the number of active receptors for the transmitter. In denervated skeletal muscle, there is an increase in the area of the muscle membrane sensitive to acetylcholine. Normally, only the end-plate region is depolarized by this mediator; after denervation, the sensitivity of the end-plate is no greater, but large portions of the muscle membrane respond. The sensitivity returns to normal if the nerve regrows. A similar spread of acetylcholine sensitivity has been demonstrated in denervated postganglionic cholinergic neurons. At endings where norepinephrine is normally secreted, another factor is lack of re-uptake of liberated catecholamines; the nerve endings in normal tissue take up large amounts of norepinephrine, and after they have degenerated, norepinephrine reaching the receptors from other sites has a greater effect than it otherwise would.

5 | Initiation of Impulses in Sense Organs

SENSE ORGANS & RECEPTORS

Information about the internal and external environment reaches the CNS via a variety of **sensory receptors.** These receptors are transducers that convert various forms of energy in the environment into action potentials in neurons. The sensory receptor may be part of a neuron or a specialized cell that generates action potentials in neurons. The receptor is often associated with nonneural cells that surround it, forming a **sense organ.** The forms of energy converted by the receptors include, for example, mechanical (touch-pressure), thermal (degrees of warmth), electromagnetic (light), and chemical energy (odor, taste, and O_2 content of blood). The receptors in each of the sense organs are adapted to respond to one particular form of energy at a much lower threshold than other receptors respond to this form of energy. The particular form of energy to which a receptor is most sensitive is called its **adequate stimulus.** The adequate stimulus for the rods and cones in the eye, for example, is light. Receptors do respond to forms of energy other than their adequate stimulus, but the threshold for these nonspecific responses is much higher. Pressure on the eyeball will stimulate the rods and cones, for example, but the threshold of these receptors to pressure is much higher than the threshold of the pressure receptors in the skin.

THE SENSES

Sensory Modalities

Because the sensory receptors are specialized to respond to one particular form of energy and because many variables in the environment are perceived, it follows that there must be many different types of receptors. We learn in elementary school that there are "5 senses," but the inadequacy of this dictum is apparent if we list the major sensory modalities and their receptors in humans. The list (Table 5–1) includes at least 11 conscious senses. There are, in addition, a large number of sensory receptors which relay information that does not reach consciousness. For example, the muscle spindles provide information about muscle length, and other receptors provide information about such variables as arterial blood pressure, the temperature of the blood in the head, and the pH of the cerebrospinal fluid. The existence of other receptors of this type is suspected, and future research will undoubtedly add to the list of "unconscious senses." Furthermore, any listing of the senses is bound to be arbitrary. The rods and cones, for example, respond maximally to light of different wavelengths, and there are different cones for each of the 3 primary colors. There are 4 different modalities of taste—sweet, salt, sour, and bitter—and each is subserved by a more or less distinct type of taste bud. Sounds of different pitches are heard primarily because different groups of hair cells in the organ of Corti are activated maximally by sound waves of different frequencies. Whether these various responses to light, taste, and sound should be considered separate senses is a semantic question that in the present context is largely academic.

Classifications of Sense Organs

Numerous attempts have been made to classify the senses into groups, but none have been entirely successful. Traditionally, the special senses are smell, vision, hearing, rotational and linear acceleration, and taste; the cutaneous senses are those with receptors in the skin; and the visceral senses are those concerned with perception of the internal environment. Pain from visceral structures is usually classified as a visceral sensation. Another classification of the various receptors divides them into (1) teleceptors ("distance receivers"), the receptors concerned with events at a distance; (2) exteroceptors, those concerned with the external environment near at hand; (3) interoceptors, those concerned with the internal environment; and (4) proprioceptors, those which provide information about the position of the body in space at any given instant. However, the conscious component of proprioception, or "body image," is actually synthesized from information coming not only from receptors in and around joints but from cutaneous touch and pressure receptors as well. Certain other special terms are sometimes used. Because pain fibers have connections that mediate strong and prepotent withdrawal reflexes (see Chapter 6), and because pain is initiated by potentially noxious or damaging stimuli, pain receptors are some-

Table 5–1. Principal sensory modalities. (The first 11 are conscious sensations.)

Sensory Modality	Receptor	Sense Organ
Vision	Rods and cones	Eye
Hearing	Hair cells	Ear (organ of Corti)
Smell	Olfactory neurons	Olfactory mucous membrane
Taste	Taste receptor cells	Taste bud
Rotational acceleration	Hair cells	Ear (semicircular canals)
Linear acceleration	Hair cells	Ear (utricle and saccule)
Touch-pressure	Nerve endings	Various*
Warmth	Nerve endings	Various*
Cold	Nerve endings	Various*
Pain	Naked nerve endings	. . .
Joint position and movement	Nerve endings	Various*
Muscle length	Nerve endings	Muscle spindle
Muscle tension	Nerve endings	Golgi tendon organ
Arterial blood pressure	Nerve endings	Stretch receptors in carotid sinus and aortic arch
Central venous pressure	Nerve endings	Stretch receptors in walls of great veins, atria
Inflation of lung	Nerve endings	Stretch receptors in lung parenchyma
Temperature of blood in head	Neurons in hypothalamus	. . .
Arterial P_{O_2}	Nerve endings?	Carotid and aortic bodies
pH of CSF	Receptors on ventral surface of medulla oblongata	. . .
Osmotic pressure of plasma	Cells in anterior hypothalamus	. . .
Arteriovenous blood glucose difference	Cells in hypothalamus (glucostats)	. . .

*See text.

times called **nociceptors.** The term **chemoreceptor** is used to refer to those receptors which are stimulated by a change in the chemical composition of the environment in which they are located. These include receptors for taste and smell as well as visceral receptors such as those sensitive to changes in the plasma level of O_2, pH, and osmolality.

Cutaneous Sense Organs

There are 4 cutaneous senses: touch-pressure (pressure is sustained touch), cold, warmth, and pain. The skin contains various types of sensory endings. These include naked nerve endings, expanded tips on sensory nerve terminals, and encapsulated endings. The expanded endings include Merkel's disks and Ruffini endings (Fig 5–1), whereas the encapsulated endings include pacinian corpuscles, Meissner's corpuscles, and Krause's end-bulbs. Ruffini endings and pacinian corpuscles are also found in deep fibrous tissues. In addition, sensory nerves end around hair follicles. However, none of the expanded or encapsulated endings appear to be necessary for cutaneous sensation. Their distribution varies in different regions of the body, and it has been repeatedly demonstrated that all 4 sensory modalities can be elicited from areas that on histologic examination contain only naked nerve endings. Where they are present, the expanded or encapsulated endings appear to function as mechanoreceptors that respond to tactile stimuli. The nerve endings around hair follicles mediate touch, and movements of hairs initiate tactile sensations. It should

be emphasized that although cutaneous sensory receptors lack histologic specificity, they are physiologically specific. Thus, any given ending signals one and only one kind of cutaneous sensation.

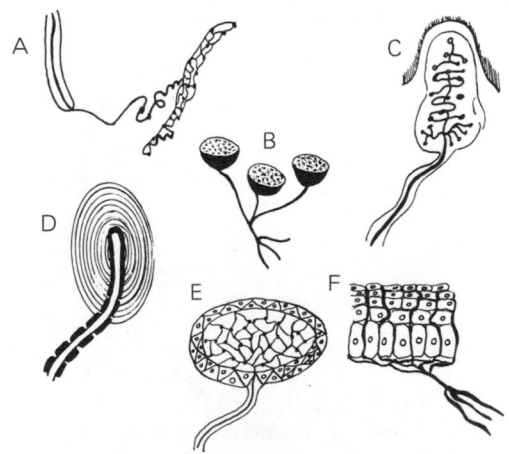

Figure 5–1. Sensory receptors in the skin. Ruffini endings (A) and Merkel's disks (B) are expanded ends of sensory nerve fibers. Meissner's corpuscles (C), pacinian corpuscles (D), and Krause's end-bulbs (E) are encapsulated endings. F, naked nerve endings.

ELECTRICAL & IONIC EVENTS IN RECEPTORS

Anatomic Relationships

The problem of how receptors convert energy into action potentials in the sensory nerves has been the subject of intensive study. In the complex sense organs such as those concerned with vision, hearing, equilibrium, and taste, there are separate receptor cells and synaptic junctions between receptors and afferent nerves. However, in most of the cutaneous sense organs, the receptors are specialized, histologically modified ends of sensory nerve fibers.

Pacinian corpuscles, which are touch receptors, have been studied in detail. Because of their relatively large size and accessibility in the mesentery of experimental animals, they can be isolated, studied with microelectrodes, and subjected to microdissection. Each capsule consists of the straight, unmyelinated ending of a sensory nerve fiber, 2 μm in diameter, surrounded by concentric lamellas of connective tissue that give the organ the appearance of a minute cocktail onion. The myelin sheath of the sensory nerve begins inside the corpuscle. The first node of Ranvier is also located inside, whereas the second is usually near the point at which the nerve fiber leaves the corpuscle (Fig 5–2).

Generator Potentials

Recording electrodes can be placed on the sensory nerve as it leaves a pacinian corpuscle and graded pressure applied to the corpuscle. When a small amount of pressure is applied, a nonpropagated depolarizing potential resembling an EPSP is recorded. This is called the **generator potential,** or **receptor potential.** As the pressure is increased, the magnitude of the receptor potential increases. When the magnitude of the generator potential is about 10 mV, an action potential is generated in the sensory nerve. As the pressure is further increased, the generator potential becomes even larger and the sensory nerve fires repetitively. Eventually, in the case of the pacinian corpuscle, the size of the generator potential reaches a maximum, but its rate of rise continues to increase as the magnitude of the applied pressure is increased.

Source of the Generator Potential

By microdissection technics, it has been shown that removal of the connective tissue lamellas from the unmyelinated nerve ending in a pacinian corpuscle does not abolish the generator potential. When the first node of Ranvier is blocked by pressure or narcotics, the generator potential is unaffected but conducted impulses are abolished (Fig 5–2). When the sensory nerve is sectioned and the nonmyelinated terminal is allowed to degenerate, no generator potential is formed. These and other experiments have established the fact that the generator potential is produced in the unmyelinated nerve terminal. This potential electrotonically depolarizes the first node of Ranvier. The receptor therefore converts mechanical energy into an electrical response, the magnitude of which is proportionate to the intensity of the stimulus. The generator potential in turn depolarizes the sensory nerve at the first node of Ranvier. Once the firing level is reached,

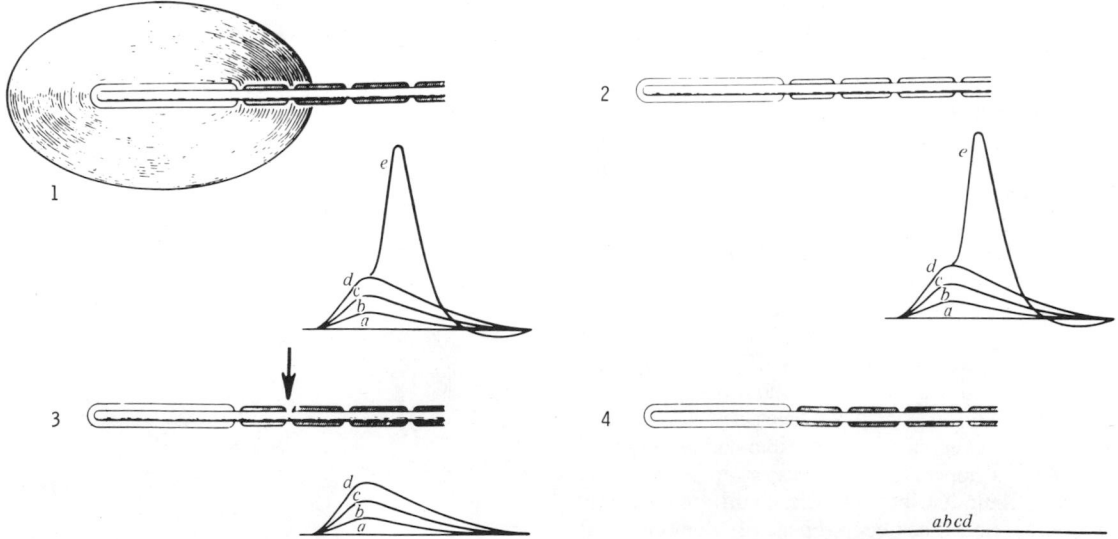

Figure 5–2. Demonstration that the generator potential in a pacinian corpuscle originates in the nonmyelinated nerve terminal. In 1, the electrical responses to a pressure of x (record a), 2 x (b), 3 x (c), and 4 x (d) were recorded. The strongest stimulus produced an action potential in the sensory nerve (e). In 2, the same responses persisted after removal of the connective tissue capsule. In 3, the generator responses persisted but the action potential was absent when the first node of Ranvier was blocked with pressure or narcotics (arrow). In 4, all responses disappeared when the sensory nerve was cut and allowed to degenerate before the experiment. (Reproduced, with permission, from Lowenstein W: Biological transducers. Scientific American 203:98, Aug 1960. Copyright © 1960 by Scientific American, Inc. All rights reserved.)

an action potential is produced and the membrane repolarizes. If the generator potential is great enough, the neuron fires again as soon as it repolarizes, and it continues to fire as long as the generator potential is large enough to bring the membrane potential of the node to the firing level. Thus, the node converts the graded response of the receptor into action potentials, the frequency of which is proportionate to the magnitude of the applied stimuli.

Similar generator potentials have been studied in the muscle spindle. The relationship between the stimulus intensity and the size of the generator potential and between the stimulus intensity and the frequency of the action potentials in the afferent nerve fiber from a spindle is shown in Fig 5–3. The frequency of the action potentials is generally related to the intensity of the stimulus by a power function (see below). Generator potentials have also been observed in the organ of Corti, the olfactory and taste organs, and other sense organs. Presumably, they are in most cases the mechanism by which sensory nerve fibers are activated.

Ionic Basis of Excitation

The biophysical events underlying the generator potential have not been completely clarified, but it is known that Na^+ depletion diminishes and eventually abolishes the generator potential in pacinian corpuscles. Presumably, the stimulus initiates an increase in the permeability of the membrane of the unmyelinated terminal to Na^+, the resultant influx of Na^+ produces the generator potential, and the magnitude of the permeability change is proportionate to the intensity of the stimulus. How the mechanical stimulus is converted into a change in membrane permeability is not known. It is possible that the change is due to stretching or distortion of the membrane, or it could be due to the release of some chemical mediator.

Adaptation

When a maintained stimulus of constant strength is applied to a receptor, the frequency of the action potentials in its sensory nerve declines over a period of time. This phenomenon is known as **adaptation.** The degree to which adaptation occurs varies with the type of sense organ (Fig 5–4). Touch adapts rapidly, and its receptors are called **phasic receptors.** Application of a maintained pressure to a pacinian corpuscle produces a generator potential that decays rapidly. On the other hand, the carotid sinus, the muscle spindles, and the organs for cold, pain, and lung inflation adapt very slowly and incompletely; the receptors involved are termed **tonic receptors.** This correlates with the fact that the generator potential of the muscle spindle is prolonged and decays very slowly when a steady stimulus is applied to it. Maintained pressure applied

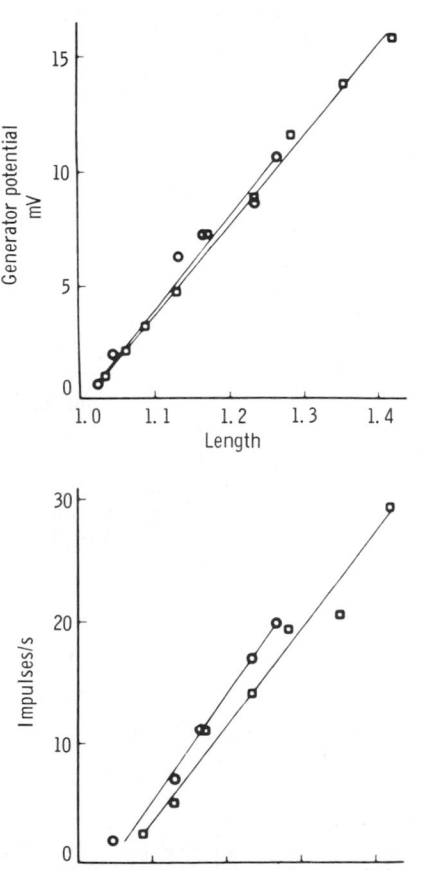

Figure 5–3. Relation between muscle length and size of generator potential *(above)* and impulse frequency *(below)* in crayfish stretch receptor. Squares and circles indicate values in 2 different preparations. (Reproduced, with permission, from Terzuolo CA, Washizu Y: Relation between stimulus strength, generator potential, and impulse frequency in stretch receptor of crustacea. J Neurophysiol 25:56, 1962.)

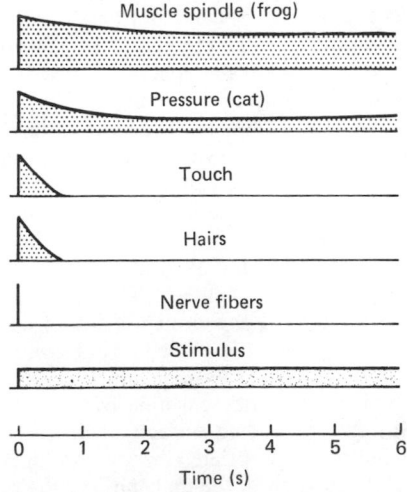

Figure 5–4. Adaptation. The height of the curve in each case indicates the frequency of the discharge in afferent nerve fibers at various times after beginning sustained stimulation. (Reproduced, with permission, from Adrian ED: *Basis of Sensation.* Christophers, 1928.)

to the outside of a pacinian corpuscle causes steady displacement in the outer lamellas, but the lamellas near the nerve fiber slip back to their original position, ending the distortion of the nerve ending and causing the generator potential to decline. However, this is not the only factor producing adaptation; there is still a slow decline in the number of action potentials generated over a period of time by a steady stimulus after removal of the outer lamellas from the pacinian corpuscle. This decline is due to accommodation of the sensory nerve fiber to the generator potential.

The slow, incomplete adaptation of the carotid sinus and the organs for muscle stretch, pain, and cold is of some value to the animal. Muscle stretch plays a role in prolonged postural adjustments. The sensations of pain and cold are initiated by potentially noxious stimuli, and they would lose some of their warning value if their receptors showed marked adaptation. Carotid and aortic receptors operate continuously in the regulation of blood pressure, and adaptation of these receptors would limit the precision with which the regulatory system operates.

"CODING" OF SENSORY INFORMATION

There are minor variations in the speed of conduction and other characteristics of sensory nerve fibers (see Chapter 2), but in general, action potentials are similar in all nerves. The action potentials in the nerve from a touch receptor, for example, are essentially identical to those in the nerve from a warmth receptor. This raises the question of why stimulation of a touch receptor causes a sensation of touch and not of warmth. It also raises the question of how it is possible to tell whether the touch is light or heavy.

Doctrine of Specific Nerve Energies

The sensation evoked by impulses generated in a receptor depends upon the specific part of the brain they ultimately activate. The specific sensory pathways are discrete from sense organ to cortex. Therefore, when the nerve pathways from a particular sense organ are stimulated, the sensation evoked is that for which the receptor is specialized no matter how or where along the pathway the activity is initiated. This principle, first enunciated by Müller, has been given the rather cumbersome name of the **doctrine of specific nerve energies.** For example, if the sensory nerve from a pacinian corpuscle in the hand is stimulated by pressure at the elbow or by irritation from a tumor in the brachial plexus, the sensation evoked is one of touch. Similarly, if a fine enough electrode could be inserted into the appropriate fibers of the dorsal columns of the spinal cord, the thalamus, or the postcentral gyrus of the cerebral cortex, the sensation produced by stimulation would be touch. This doctrine has been questioned from time to time, especially by those who claim that pain is produced by overstimulation of a variety of receptors. However, the overstimu-

lation hypothesis has been largely discredited, and the principle of specific nerve energies remains one of the cornerstones of sensory physiology.

Projection

No matter where a particular sensory pathway is stimulated along its course to the cortex, the conscious sensation produced is referred to the location of the receptor. This principle is called the **law of projection.** Cortical stimulation experiments during neurosurgical procedures on conscious patients illustrate this phenomenon. For example, when the cortical receiving area for impulses from the left hand is stimulated, the patient reports sensation in the left hand, not in the head. Another dramatic example is seen in amputees. These patients may complain, often bitterly, of pain and proprioceptive sensations in the absent limb ("phantom limb"). These sensations are due in part to pressure on the stump of the amputated limb. This pressure initiates impulses in nerve fibers that previously came from sense organs in the amputated limb, and the sensations evoked are projected to where the receptors used to be.

Intensity Discrimination

There are 2 ways in which information about intensity of stimuli is transmitted to the brain: by variation in the frequency of the action potentials generated by the activity in a given receptor, and by variation in the number of receptors activated. It has long been taught that the magnitude of the sensation felt is proportionate to the log of the intensity of the stimulus **(Weber-Fechner law).** It now appears, however, that a power function more accurately describes this relation. In other words, $R = KS^A$, where R is the sensation felt, S is the intensity of the stimulus, and, for any specific sensory modality, K and A are constants. The frequency of the action potentials a stimulus generates in a sensory nerve fiber is also related to the intensity of the initiating stimulus by a power function. An example of this relation is shown in Fig 5–3, in which the exponent is approximately 1.0. Another example is shown in Fig 5–5, in which the calculated exponent is 0.52. Current evidence indicates that in the CNS the relation between stimulus and sensation is linear; consequently, it appears that for any given sensory modality the relation between sensation and stimulus intensity is determined primarily by the properties of the peripheral receptors themselves.

Sensory Units

The term sensory unit is applied to a single sensory axon and all its peripheral branches. The number of these branches varies, but they may be numerous, especially in the case of the cutaneous senses. The **receptive field** of a sensory unit is the area from which a stimulus produces a response in that unit. In the cornea and adjacent sclera of the eye, the surface area supplied by a single sensory unit is 50–200 mm². Generally, the areas supplied by one unit overlap and interdigitate with the areas supplied by others.

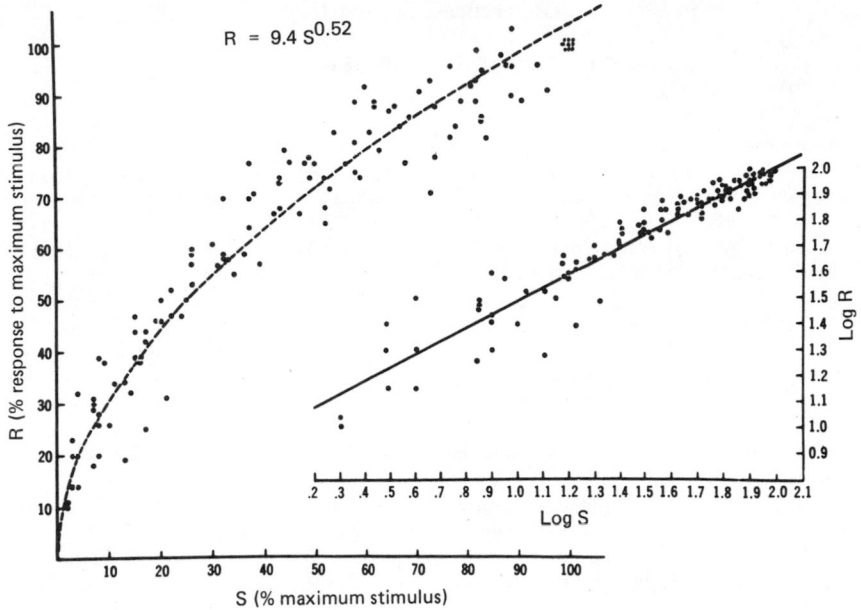

Figure 5–5. Relation between magnitude of touch stimulus (S) and frequency of action potentials in sensory nerve fibers (R). Dots are individual values from cats plotted on linear coordinates *(left)* and log-log coordinates *(right)*. The equation shows the calculated power function relationship between R and S. (Reproduced, with permission, from Werner G, Mountcastle VB: Neural activity in mechanoreceptive cutaneous afferents: Stimulus-response relations, Weber functions, and information transmission. J Neurophysiol 28:359, 1965.)

Recruitment of Sensory Units

As the strength of a stimulus is increased, it tends to spread over a large area and generally activates not only the sense organs immediately in contact with it but "recruits" those in the surrounding area as well. Furthermore, weak stimuli activate the receptors with the lowest thresholds, whereas stronger stimuli also activate those with higher thresholds. Some of the receptors activated are part of the same sensory unit, and impulse frequency in the unit therefore increases. Because of overlap and interdigitation of one unit with another, however, receptors of other units are also stimulated and consequently more units fire. In this way, more afferent pathways are activated, and this is interpreted in the brain as an increase in intensity of the sensation.

References: Section II.

Physiology of Nerve & Muscle Cells

Basmajian JV: Electromyography comes of age. Science 176:603, 1972.

Bradshaw RA: Nerve growth factor. Annu Rev Biochem 47:191, 1978.

Braunwald E, Ross J, Sonnenblick EH: *Mechanisms of Contraction of the Normal and Failing Heart,* 2nd ed. Little, Brown, 1976.

Bulbring E, Shuba MF (editors): *Physiology of Smooth Muscle.* Raven, 1975.

Burke RE: Motor units: Physiological/histochemical profiles, neural connectivity and functional specializations. Am Zool 18:127, 1978.

Cowan WM, Cuénod M (editors): *Use of Axonal Transport for Studies of Neuronal Connectivity.* Elsevier, 1975.

Fleming WW, McPhillips JJ, Westfall DP: Postjunctional supersensitivity and subsensitivity of excitable tissues to drugs. Ergeb Physiol 68:55, 1973.

Geffen LB, Livett BG: Synaptic vesicles in sympathetic neurons. Physiol Rev 51:98, 1971.

Hodgkin AL: The ionic basis of nervous conduction. Science 145:1148, 1964.

Hubbard JI: Microphysiology of vertebrate neuromuscular transmission. Physiol Rev 53:874, 1973.

Huxley AF: Excitation and conduction in nerve: Quantitative analysis. Science 145:1154, 1964.

Huxley AF: Muscular contraction. J Physiol 243:1, 1974.

Katz B: Quantal mechanism of neural transmitter release. Science 173:123, 1971.

Keynes RD: Ion channels in the nerve cell membrane. Sci Am 240:126, March 1979.

Llinás R: Electrical synaptic transmission in the mammalian central nervous system. In: *Golgi Centennial Symposium Proceedings.* Santini M (editor). Raven, 1975.

Lowenstein WR (editor): *Principles of Receptor Physiology.* In: *Handbook of Sensory Physiology.* Vol 1. Springer-Verlag, 1971.

Nathanson JA, Greengard P: "Second messengers" in the brain. Sci Am 237:108, Aug 1977.

Pappas GD, Purpura DP (editors): *Structure and Function of Synapses.* Raven, 1972.

Shepherd GM: Microcircuits in the nervous system. Sci Am 238:93, Feb 1978.

Watson WE: Physiology of neuroglia. Physiol Rev 54:245, 1974.

Symposium: Excitable junctions in smooth muscle cells. Fed Proc 36:243, 1977.

Symposium: The synapse. Cold Spring Harbor Symp Quant Biol 40:1, 1976.

Section III. Functions of the Nervous System

Reflexes | 6

THE REFLEX ARC

The basic unit of integrated neural activity is the reflex arc. This arc consists of a sense organ, an afferent neuron, one or more synapses in a central integrating station, an efferent neuron, and an effector. In mammals, the connection between afferent and efferent somatic neurons is in the brain or spinal cord. The afferent neurons enter via the dorsal roots or cranial nerves, and have their cell bodies in the dorsal root ganglia or in the homologous ganglia on the cranial nerves. The efferent fibers leave via the ventral roots or corresponding motor cranial nerves. The principle that in the spinal cord the dorsal roots are sensory and the ventral roots are motor is known as the **Bell-Magendie law.**

In previous chapters, the function of each of the components of the reflex arc has been considered in detail. As noted in Chapters 2 and 3, impulses generated in the axons of the afferent and efferent neurons and in muscle are "all or none" in character. On the other hand, there are 3 junctions or junctionlike areas in the reflex arc where responses are graded (Fig 6–1). These are the receptor–afferent neuron region, the synapse between the afferent and efferent neurons, and the myoneural junction. At each of these points, a nonpropagated potential proportionate in size to the magnitude of the incoming stimulus is generated. The graded potentials serve to electrotonically depolarize the adjacent nerve or muscle membrane and set up all or none responses. The number of action potentials in the afferent nerve is proportionate to the magnitude of the applied stimulus at the sense organ. There is also a rough correlation between the magnitude of the stimulus and the frequency of action potentials in the efferent nerve; however, since the connection between the afferent and efferent neurons is in the CNS, activity in the reflex arc is modified by the multiple inputs converging on the efferent neurons.

The simplest reflex arc is one with a single synapse between the afferent and efferent neurons. Such arcs are **monosynaptic,** and reflexes occurring in them are **monosynaptic reflexes.** Reflex arcs in which one or more interneurons are interposed between the afferent and efferent neurons are **polysynaptic,** the number of synapses in the arcs varying from 2 to many hundreds. In both types, but especially in polysynaptic reflex arcs, activity is modified by spatial and temporal facilitation, occlusion, and subliminal fringe effects.

MONOSYNAPTIC REFLEXES: THE STRETCH REFLEX

When a skeletal muscle with an intact nerve supply is stretched, it contracts. This response is called the

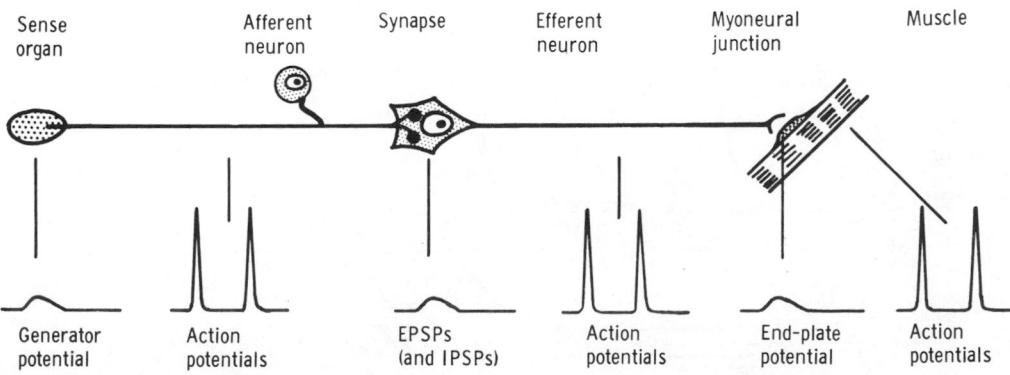

Figure 6–1. The reflex arc. Note that at the receptor and at each of the junctions in the arc there is a nonpropagated graded response that is proportionate to the magnitude of the stimulus, whereas in the portions of the arc specialized for transmission (axons, muscle membrane) the responses are all or none action potentials.

71

stretch reflex. The stimulus that initiates the reflex is stretch of the muscle, and the response is contraction of the muscle being stretched. The sense organ is the muscle spindle. The impulses originating in the spindle are conducted to the CNS by fast sensory fibers that pass directly to the motor neurons which supply the same muscle. Stretch reflexes are the only monosynaptic reflexes in the body.

Clinical Examples

Tapping the patellar tendon elicits the **knee jerk,** a stretch reflex of the quadriceps femoris muscle, because the tap on the tendon stretches the muscle. A similar contraction is observed if the quadriceps is stretched manually. Stretch reflexes can also be elicited from most of the large muscles of the body. Tapping on the tendon of the triceps brachii, for example, causes an extensor response at the elbow due to reflex contraction of the triceps; tapping on the Achilles tendon causes an ankle jerk due to reflex contraction of the gastrocnemius; and tapping on the side of the face causes a stretch reflex in the masseter. Other examples of stretch reflexes are listed in neurology textbooks.

Structure of Muscle Spindles

Each muscle spindle consists of 2–10 muscle fibers enclosed in a connective tissue capsule. These fibers arc more embryonal in character and have less distinct striations than the rest of the fibers in the muscle. They are called **intrafusal fibers** to distinguish them from the **extrafusal fibers,** the regular contractile units of the muscle. The intrafusal fibers are in parallel with the rest of the muscle fibers because the ends of the capsule of the spindle are attached to the tendons at either end of the muscle or to the sides of the extrafusal fibers.

There are 2 types of intrafusal fibers in mammalian muscle spindles. The first type contains many nuclei in a dilated central area and is therefore called a **nuclear bag fiber** (Fig 6–2). The second type, the **nuclear chain fiber,** is thinner and shorter and lacks a

definite bag. The ends of the nuclear chain fibers connect to the sides of the nuclear bag fibers. The ends of the intrafusal fibers are contractile, whereas central portions probably are not.

There are 2 kinds of sensory endings in each spindle. The **primary** or **annulospiral endings** are the terminations of rapidly conducting group Ia afferent fibers that wrap around the center of the nuclear bag and nuclear chain fibers. The **secondary** or **flower-spray endings** are terminations of group II sensory fibers and are located nearer the ends of the intrafusal fibers, probably only on nuclear chain fibers.

The spindles have a motor nerve supply of their own. These nerves are 3–6 μm in diameter, constitute about 30% of the fibers in the ventral roots, and belong in Erlanger and Gasser's A γ group. Because of their characteristic size, they are called the **gamma efferents of Leksell,** or the **small motor nerve system.** There also appears to be a sparse innervation of spindles by motor fibers of intermediate size. The function of this **beta innervation** is unknown.

The endings of the gamma efferent fibers are of 2 histologic types. There are motor end-plates (**plate endings**) on the nuclear bag fibers, and there are endings that form extensive networks (**trail endings**) primarily on the nuclear chain fibers. It is known that the spindles receive 2 functional types of innervation—dynamic gamma efferents and static gamma efferents (see below)—and it is reasonable to hypothesize that the dynamic gamma efferents terminate at the plate endings while the static gamma efferents terminate at the trail endings.

Central Connections of Afferent Fibers

It can be proved experimentally that the fibers from the primary endings end directly on motor neurons supplying the extrafusal fibers of the same muscle. The time between the application of the stimulus and the response in a reflex is the **reaction time.** In humans, the reaction time for a stretch reflex such as the knee jerk is 19–24 ms. Weak stimulation of

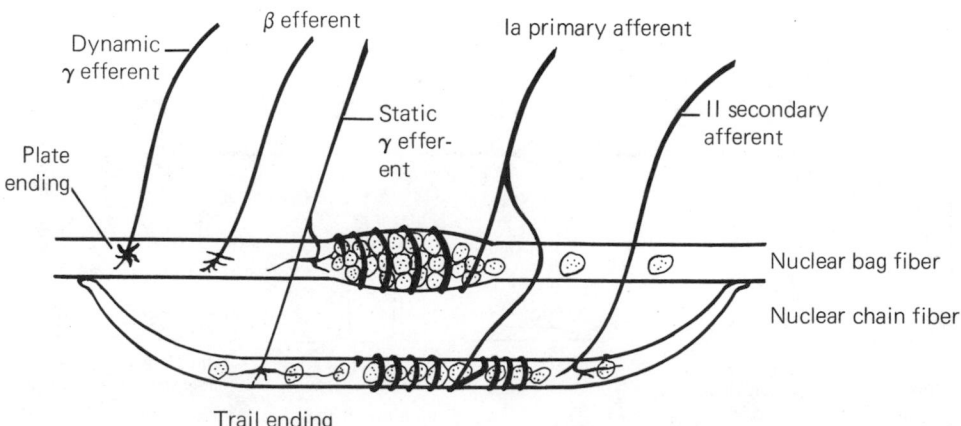

Figure 6–2. Diagram of muscle spindle. (Modified and reproduced, with permission, from Stein RB: Peripheral control of movement. Physiol Rev 54:215, 1974.)

the sensory nerve from the muscle, known to stimulate only Ia fibers, causes a contractile response with a similar latency. Since the conduction velocity of the afferent and efferent fiber types are known and the distance from the muscle to the spinal cord can be measured, it is possible to calculate how much of the reaction time was taken up by conduction to and from the spinal cord. When this value is subtracted from the reaction time, the remainder, called the **central delay,** is the time taken for the reflex activity to traverse the spinal cord. In humans, the central delay for the knee jerk is 0.6–0.9 ms, and figures of similar magnitude have been found in experimental animals. Since the minimal synaptic delay is 0.5 ms (see Chapter 4), only one synapse could have been traversed. It has been demonstrated that muscle spindles also make connections that cause muscle contraction via polysynaptic pathways.

The afferents from the secondary endings probably make connections that excite extensor muscles.

Function of Muscle Spindles

When the muscle spindle is stretched, the primary endings are distorted and receptor potentials are generated. These in turn set up action potentials in the sensory fibers at a frequency that is proportionate to the degree of stretching. The spindle is in parallel with the extrafusal fibers, and when the muscle is passively stretched, the spindles are also stretched. This initiates reflex contraction of the extrafusal fibers in the muscle. On the other hand, the spindle afferents characteristically stop firing when the muscle is made to contract by electrical stimulation of the nerve fibers to the extrafusal fibers because the muscle shortens while the spindle does not (Fig 6–3).

Thus, the spindle and its reflex connections constitute a feedback device that operates to maintain muscle length; if the muscle is stretched, spindle discharge increases and reflex shortening is produced, whereas, if the muscle is shortened without a change in gamma efferent discharge, spindle discharge decreases and the muscle relaxes.

Both primary and secondary endings are stimulated when the spindle is stretched, but the pattern of response differs. The nerve from a primary ending discharges most rapidly while the muscle is being stretched and less rapidly during sustained stretch (Fig 6–4). The nerve from a secondary ending discharges at an increased rate throughout the period when a muscle is stretched. Thus, the primary ending responds both to changes in length and changes in the rate of stretching, while the secondary ending responds primarily to length alone. In other words, the primary measures length plus velocity of stretch, and the secondary mea-

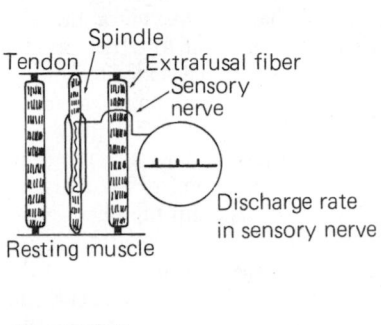

Spindle
Tendon / Extrafusal fiber
Sensory nerve
Discharge rate in sensory nerve
Resting muscle

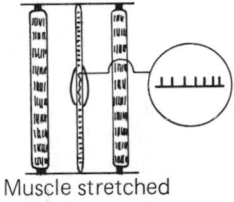

Muscle stretched

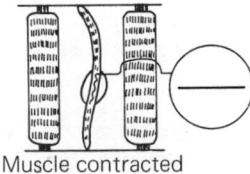

Muscle contracted

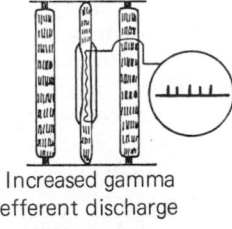

Increased gamma efferent discharge

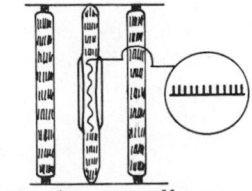

Increased gamma efferent discharge - muscle stretched

Figure 6–3. Effect of various conditions on muscle spindle discharge.

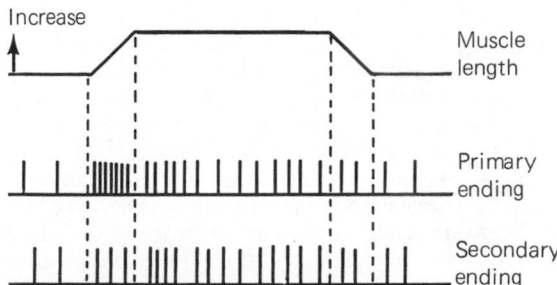

Figure 6–4. Response of spindle afferents to muscle stretch. The bottom 2 lines represent the number of discharges in afferent nerves from the primary and secondary endings as the muscle is stretched and then permitted to return to its original length.

sures mainly length. The response of the primary ending to the phasic as well as the tonic events in the muscle is important because the prompt, marked phasic response helps to dampen oscillation due to conduction delays in the feedback loop regulating muscle length. There is normally a small oscillation in this feedback loop: this is the physiologic tremor, which has a frequency of approximately 10 Hz. However, the tremor would be worse if it were not for the sensitivity of the spindle to velocity of stretch.

Effects of Gamma Efferent Discharge

Stimulation of the gamma efferent system produces a very different picture from that produced by stimulation of the extrafusal fibers. Such stimulation does not lead directly to detectable contraction of the muscles because the intrafusal fibers are not strong enough or plentiful enough to cause shortening. However, stimulation does cause the contractile ends of the intrafusal fibers to shorten and therefore stretches the nuclear bag portion of the spindles, deforming the annulospiral endings and initiating impulses in the Ia fibers. This in turn can lead to reflex contraction of the muscle. Thus, muscle can be made to contract via stimulation of the α motor neurons that innervate the extrafusal fibers, or the γ efferent neurons which initiate contraction indirectly via the stretch reflex. There is debate at present about how skilled and voluntary movements are brought about, and both α and γ mechanisms may be involved.

When the rate of gamma efferent discharge is increased, the intrafusal fibers are shorter than the extrafusal ones. If the whole muscle is stretched during stimulation of the gamma efferents, additional action potentials are generated owing to the additional stretch of the nuclear bag region, and the rate of discharge in the Ia fibers is further increased (Fig 6–3). Increased gamma efferent discharge thus increases spindle sensitivity, and the sensitivity of the spindles to stretch varies with the rate of gamma efferent discharge.

There is considerable evidence that there is increased gamma efferent discharge along with the increased discharge of the α motor neurons which initiates movements. Because of this ''alpha-gamma linkage,'' the spindle shortens with the muscle, and spindle discharge may continue throughout the contraction. In this way, the spindle remains capable of responding to stretch and reflexly adjusting motor neuron discharge throughout the contraction.

The existence of dynamic and static gamma efferents is mentioned above. Stimulation of the former, which may end via plate endings on nuclear bag fibers, increases spindle sensitivity to rate of change of stretch. Stimulation of the latter, possibly via trail endings on nuclear chain fibers, increases spindle sensitivity to steady, maintained stretch. It is thus possible to adjust separately the spindle responses to phasic and tonic events.

Control of Gamma Efferent Discharge

The motor neurons of the gamma efferent system are regulated to a large degree by descending tracts from a number of areas in the brain. Via these pathways, the sensitivity of the muscle spindles and hence the threshold of the stretch reflexes in various parts of the body can be adjusted and shifted to meet the needs of postural control (see Chapter 12).

Other factors also influence gamma efferent discharge. Anxiety causes an increased discharge, a fact that probably explains the hyperactive tendon reflexes sometimes seen in anxious patients. Stimulation of the skin, especially by noxious agents, increases gamma efferent discharge to ipsilateral flexor muscle spindles while decreasing that to extensors and produces the opposite pattern in the opposite limb. It is well known that trying to pull the hands apart when the flexed fingers are hooked together facilitates the knee jerk reflex (Jendrassik's maneuver), and this may also be due to increased gamma efferent discharge initiated by afferent impulses from the hands.

Reciprocal Innervation

When a stretch reflex occurs, the muscles that antagonize the action of the muscle involved (antagonists) relax. This phenomenon is said to be due to **reciprocal innervation.** Impulses in the Ia fibers from the muscle spindles of the protagonist muscle cause postsynaptic inhibition of the motor neurons to the antagonists. The pathway mediating this effect appears to be bisynaptic. A collateral from each Ia fiber passes in the spinal cord to an inhibitory interneuron (Golgi bottle neuron) that synapses directly on one of the motor neurons supplying the antagonist muscles. This example of postsynaptic inhibition is discussed in Chapter 4, and the pathway is illustrated in Fig 4–8.

Inverse Stretch Reflex

Up to a point, the harder a muscle is stretched, the stronger is the reflex contraction. However, when the tension becomes great enough, contraction suddenly ceases and the muscle relaxes. This relaxation in response to strong stretch is called the **inverse stretch reflex,** or **autogenic inhibition.**

The receptor for the inverse stretch reflex is in the **Golgi tendon organ** (Fig 6–5). This organ consists of a netlike collection of knobby nerve endings among the fascicles of a tendon. There are 3–25 muscle fibers per tendon organ. The fibers from the Golgi tendon organs make up the Ib group of myelinated, rapidly conducting sensory nerve fibers. Stimulation of these Ib fibers leads to the production of IPSPs on the motor neurons that supply the muscle from which the fibers arise. The Ib fibers apparently end in the spinal cord on inhibitory interneurons that, in turn, terminate directly on the motor neurons (Fig 6–6). They also make excitatory connections with motor neurons supplying antagonists to the muscle.

Since the Golgi tendon organs, unlike the spindles, are in series with the muscle fibers, they are stimulated by both passive stretch and active contraction of the muscle. The threshold of the Golgi tendon organs is low. The degree of stimulation by passive

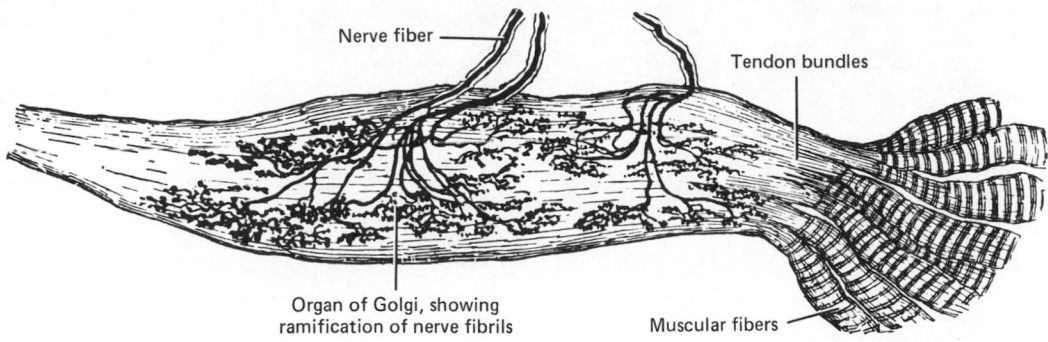

Figure 6–5. Golgi tendon organ. (Reproduced, with permission, from Goss CM [editor]: *Gray's Anatomy of the Human Body,* 29th ed. Lea & Febiger, 1973.)

stretch is not great because the more elastic muscle fibers take up much of the stretch, and this is why it takes a strong stretch to produce relaxation. However, discharge is regularly produced by contraction of the muscle, and the Golgi tendon organ thus functions as a transducer in a feedback circuit that regulates muscle force in a fashion analogous to the spindle feedback circuit which regulates muscle length.

The importance of the primary endings in the spindles, the secondary endings in the spindles, and the Golgi tendon organs in regulating the velocity of the muscle contraction, muscle length, and muscle

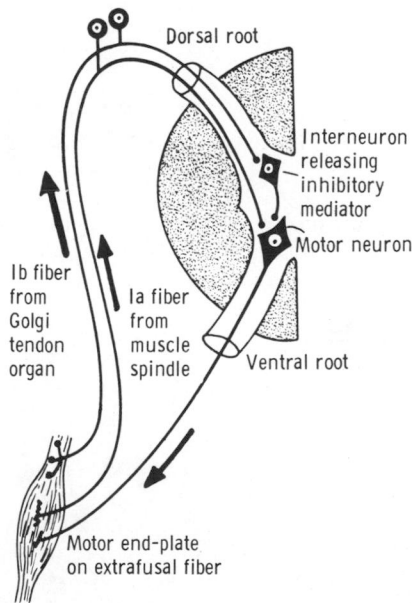

Figure 6–6. Diagram illustrating the pathways responsible for the stretch reflex and the inverse stretch reflex. Stretch stimulates the spindle, and impulses pass up the Ia fiber to excite the motor neuron. It also stimulates the Golgi tendon organ, and impulses passing up the Ib fiber activate the interneuron to release inhibitory mediator. With strong stretch, the resulting hyperpolarization of the motor neuron is so great that it stops discharging.

force, respectively, is illustrated by the fact that section of the afferent nerves to a limb causes the limb to hang loosely at the side in a semiparalyzed state. The organization of the system is shown in Fig 6–7, and the interaction of spindle discharge, tendon organ discharge, and reciprocal innervation in determining the rate of discharge of a motor neuron is shown in Fig 6–8.

Muscle Tone

The resistance of a muscle to stretch is often referred to as its **tone** or **tonus.** If the motor nerve to a muscle is cut, the muscle offers very little resistance and is said to be **flaccid.** A **hypertonic** or **spastic** muscle is one in which the resistance to stretch is high. Somewhere between the states of flaccidity and spasticity is the ill-defined area of normal tone. The muscles are generally **hypotonic** when the rate of gamma efferent discharge is low and hypertonic when it is high.

Lengthening Reaction

When the muscles are hypertonic, the sequence of moderate stretch → muscle contraction, strong stretch → muscle relaxation is clearly seen. Passive flexion of the elbow, for example, meets immediate resistance due to the stretch reflex in the triceps muscle. Further stretch activates the inverse stretch reflex. The resistance to flexion suddenly collapses, and the arm flexes. Continued passive flexion stretches the muscle again, and the sequence may be repeated. This sequence of resistance followed by give when a limb is moved passively is known clinically as the **clasp-knife effect** because of its resemblance to the closing of a pocket knife. The physiologic name for it is the **lengthening reaction** because it is the response of a spastic muscle (in the example cited, the triceps) to lengthening.

Clonus

Another finding characteristic of states in which increased gamma efferent discharge is present is **clonus.** This neurologic sign is the occurrence of regular, rhythmic contractions of a muscle subjected to

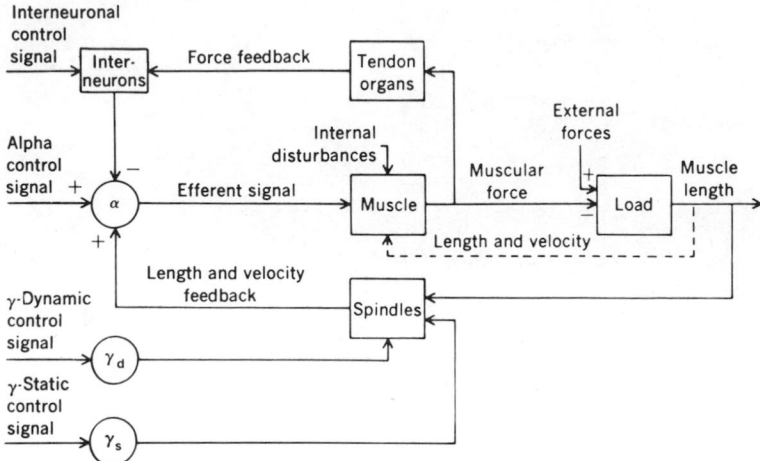

Figure 6–7. Block diagram of peripheral motor control system. The dashed line indicates the nonneural feedback from muscle that limits length and velocity via the inherent mechanical properties of muscle. γd, dynamic gamma motor neurons; γs, static gamma motor neurons. (Reproduced, with permission, from Houk J, in: *Medical Physiology,* 13th ed. Mountcastle VB [editor]. Mosby, 1974.)

sudden, maintained stretch. Ankle clonus is a typical example. This is initiated by brisk, maintained dorsiflexion of the foot, and the response is rhythmic plantar flexion at the ankle. The stretch reflex–inverse stretch reflex sequence described above may contribute to this response. However, it can occur on the basis of synchronized motor neuron discharge without Golgi tendon organ discharge. The spindles of the tested muscle are hyperactive, and the burst of impulses from them discharges all the motor neurons supplying the muscle at once. The consequent muscle contraction stops spindle discharge. However, the stretch has been maintained, and as soon as the muscle relaxes it is again stretched and the spindles stimulated.

POLYSYNAPTIC REFLEXES: THE WITHDRAWAL REFLEX

Polysynaptic reflex paths branch in a complex fashion (Fig 6–9). The number of synapses in each of

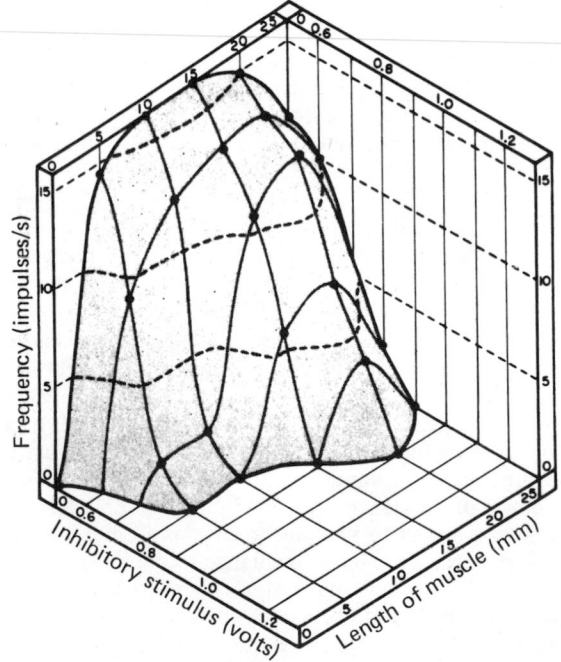

Figure 6–8. Discharge frequency of a motor neuron supplying a leg muscle in a cat. Discharge frequency is plotted against muscle length at various magnitudes of stimulation of the nerve from the antagonist to the muscle. (Reproduced, with permission, from Henneman E & others: Excitability and inhibitability of motor neurons of different sizes. J Neurophysiol 28:599, 1965.)

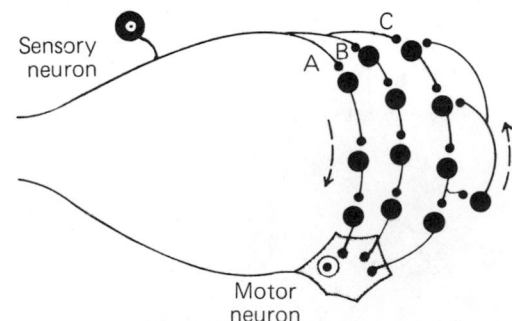

Figure 6–9. Diagram of polysynaptic connections between afferent and efferent neurons in the spinal cord. The dorsal root fiber activates pathway A with 3 interneurons, pathway B with 4 interneurons, and pathway C with 4 interneurons. Note that one of the interneurons in pathway C connects to a neuron which doubles back to other interneurons, forming reverberating circuits.

their branches is variable. Because of the synaptic delay incurred at each synapse, activity in the branches with fewer synapses reaches the motor neurons first, followed by activity in the longer pathways. This causes prolonged bombardment of the motor neurons from a single stimulus and consequently prolonged responses. Furthermore, as shown in Fig 6–9, at least some of the branch pathways turn back on themselves, permitting activity to reverberate until it becomes unable to cause a propagated transsynaptic response and dies out. Such **reverberating circuits** are common in the brain and spinal cord.

Withdrawal Reflex

The withdrawal reflex is a typical polysynaptic reflex that occurs in response to a noxious and usually painful stimulation of the skin or subcutaneous tissues and muscle. The response is flexor muscle contraction and inhibition of extensor muscles, so that the part stimulated is flexed and withdrawn from the stimulus. When a strong stimulus is applied to a limb, the response includes not only flexion and withdrawal of that limb but also extension of the opposite limb. This **crossed extensor response** is properly part of the withdrawal reflex. It can also be shown in experimental animals that strong stimuli generate activity in the interneuron pool which spreads to all 4 extremities. This is difficult to demonstrate in normal animals, but is easily demonstrated in an animal in which the modulating effects of impulses from the brain have been abolished by prior section of the spinal cord (**spinal animal**). For example, when the hind limb of a spinal cat is pinched, the stimulated limb is withdrawn, the opposite hind limb extended, the ipsilateral forelimb extended, and the contralateral forelimb flexed. This spread of excitatory impulses up and down the spinal cord to more and more motor neurons is called **irradiation of the stimulus,** and the increase in the number of active motor units is called **recruitment of motor units.**

Importance of the Withdrawal Reflex

Flexor responses can be produced by innocuous stimulation of the skin or by stretch of the muscle, but strong flexor responses with withdrawal are initiated only by stimuli that are noxious or at least potentially harmful to the animal. These stimuli are therefore called **nociceptive stimuli.** Sherrington pointed out the survival value of the withdrawal response. Flexion of the stimulated limb gets it away from the source of irritation, and extension of the other limb supports the body. The pattern assumed by all 4 extremities puts the animal in position to run away from the offending stimulus. Withdrawal reflexes are **prepotent,** ie, they preempt the spinal pathways from any other reflex activity taking place at the moment.

Many of the characteristics of polysynaptic reflexes can be demonstrated by studying the withdrawal reflex in the laboratory. A weak noxious stimulus to one foot evokes a minimal flexion response; stronger stimuli produce greater and greater flexion as the stimulus irradiates to more and more of the motor neuron pool supplying the muscles of the limb. Stronger stimuli also cause a more prolonged response. A weak stimulus causes one quick flexion movement; a strong stimulus causes prolonged flexion and sometimes a series of flexion movements. This prolonged response is due to prolonged, repeated firing of the motor neurons. The repeated firing is called **after-discharge,** and is due to continued bombardment of motor neurons by impulses arriving by complicated and circuitous polysynaptic paths.

As the strength of a noxious stimulus is increased, the reaction time is shortened. Spatial and temporal facilitation occur at the various synapses in the polysynaptic pathway. Stronger stimuli produce more action potentials per second in the active branches and cause more branches to become active; summation of the EPSPs to the firing level therefore occurs more rapidly.

Local Sign

The exact flexor pattern of the withdrawal reflex in a limb varies with the part of the limb that is stimulated. If the medial surface of the limb is stimulated, for example, the response will include some abduction, whereas stimulation of the lateral surface will produce some adduction with flexion. The reflex response in each case generally serves to effectively remove the limb from the irritating stimulus. This dependence of the exact response on the location of the stimulus is called **local sign.** The degree to which local sign determines the particular response pattern is illustrated in Fig 6–10.

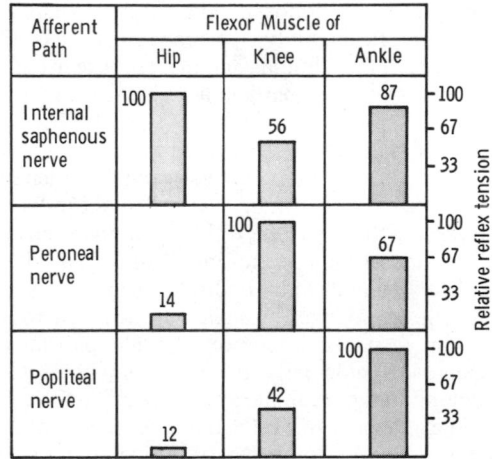

Figure 6–10. The importance of local sign in determining the character of the withdrawal response in a leg. When afferent fibers in each of the 3 nerves on the left were stimulated, hip, knee, and ankle flexors contracted but the relative tension developed in each case (shaded bars) varied. (Data from Creed RS, Sherrington C: Observations on concurrent contraction of flexor muscles in the flexion reflex. Proc R Soc Lond [Biol] 100:258, 1926.)

Fractionation & Occlusion

Another characteristic of the withdrawal response is the fact that supramaximal stimulation of any of the sensory nerves from a limb never produces as strong a contraction of the flexor muscles as that elicited by direct electrical stimulation of the muscles themselves. This indicates that the afferent inputs **fractionate** the motor neuron pool, ie, each input goes to only part of the motor neuron pool for the flexors of that particular extremity. On the other hand, if all the sensory inputs are dissected out and stimulated one after the other, the sum of the tension developed by stimulation of each is greater than that produced by direct electrical stimulation of the muscle or stimulation of all inputs at once. This fact indicates that the various afferent inputs share some of the motor neurons, and that occlusion (see Chapter 4) occurs when all inputs are stimulated at once.

Other Polysynaptic Reflexes

There are many polysynaptic reflexes in addition to the withdrawal reflex, all with similar properties. Such reflexes as the abdominal and cremasteric reflexes are forms of the withdrawal reflex. Others include visceral components. Numerous polysynaptic reflexes that relate to specific regulatory functions are described in other sections of this book, and comprehensive lists can be found in neurology textbooks.

GENERAL PROPERTIES OF REFLEXES

It is apparent from the preceding description of the properties of monosynaptic and polysynaptic reflexes that reflex activity is stereotyped and specific in terms of both the stimulus and the response; a particular stimulus elicits a particular response.

Adequate Stimulus

The stimulus that triggers a reflex is generally very precise. This stimulus is called the **adequate stimulus** for the particular reflex. A dramatic example is the scratch reflex in the dog. This spinal reflex is adequately stimulated by multiple linear touch stimuli such as those produced by an insect crawling across the skin. The response is vigorous scratching of the area stimulated. (Incidentally, the precision with which the scratching foot goes to the site of the irritant is a good example of local sign.) If the multiple touch stimuli are widely separated or are not in a line, the adequate stimulus is not produced and no scratching occurs.

Fleas crawl, but they also jump from place to place. This jumping separates the touch stimuli so that an adequate stimulus for the scratch reflex is not produced. It is doubtful if the flea population would long survive without the ability to jump.

Final Common Path

The motor neurons that supply the extrafusal fibers in skeletal muscles are the efferent side of the reflex arc. All neural influences affecting muscular contraction ultimately funnel through them to the muscles, and they are therefore called the **final common paths.** Numerous inputs converge on them. Indeed, the surface of the average motor neuron accommodates about 5500 synaptic knobs. There are at least 5 inputs from the same spinal segment to a typical spinal motor neuron. In addition to these, there are excitatory and inhibitory inputs, generally relayed via interneurons, from other levels of the spinal cord and multiple long descending tracts from the brain. All of these pathways converge on and determine the activity in the final common paths.

Central Excitatory & Inhibitory States

The spread up and down the spinal cord of subliminal fringe effects from excitatory stimulation has already been mentioned. Direct and presynaptic inhibitory effects can also be widespread. These effects are generally transient. However, the spinal cord also shows prolonged changes in excitability, possibly because of activity in reverberating circuits or prolonged effects of synaptic mediators. The terms **central excitatory state** and **central inhibitory state** have been used to describe prolonged states in which excitatory influences overbalance inhibitory influences and vice versa. When the central excitatory state is marked, excitatory impulses irradiate not only to many somatic areas of the spinal cord but also to autonomic areas and vice versa. In chronically paraplegic humans, for example, a mild noxious stimulus may cause, in addition to prolonged withdrawal-extension patterns in all 4 limbs, urination, defecation, sweating, and blood pressure fluctuations (**mass reflex**).

In view of the multiple, shifting, and often antagonistic influences that constantly bombard the final common paths, it is surprising that chaos does not result. Yet, as Mountcastle has expressed it, ''Order reigns. The end result of reflex action is always one of some functional meaning to the organism, and reflex actions occurring one after the other in time are coordinated in sequences of some purposeful character. Such coordination of neural activity into spatial and sequential patterns which serve a useful end is the essence of the integrative activity of the nervous system.''

Cutaneous, Deep, & Visceral Sensation | 7

PATHWAYS

The sense organs for mechanical stimulation (touch and pressure), warmth, cold, and pain have been discussed in Chapter 5, and the types of fibers that carry impulses generated in them to the CNS are listed in Chapter 2. These primary afferent fibers end on interneurons that make polysynaptic reflex connections to motor neurons at many levels in the spinal cord as well as on the neurons of ascending pathways which relay impulses to the cerebral cortex. There is considerable evidence that the transmitter released by at least some of the primary afferents is substance P. Somatostatin (see Chapter 14) is also produced by primary afferent neurons in tissue culture, but its function in these neurons is unknown.

The principal direct pathways to the cerebral cortex for these senses are shown in Fig 7–1. Upon entering the spinal cord, the dorsal root fibers become segregated according to function. Fibers mediating fine touch, pressure, and proprioception ascend in the dorsal columns to the medulla, where they synapse in the gracile and cuneate nuclei. The second order neurons from the gracile and cuneate nuclei cross the midline and ascend in the medial lemniscus to end in the specific sensory relay nuclei of the thalamus. This ascending system is frequently called the **dorsal column** or **lemniscal system.**

Other touch fibers, along with those mediating temperature and pain, synapse on neurons in the dorsal horn, and particularly in the **substantia gelatinosa,** a lightly staining area at the top of each dorsal horn. The axons from these neurons cross the midline and ascend in the anterolateral quadrant of the spinal cord, where they form the **anterolateral system** of ascending fibers. In general, touch is associated with the ventral spinothalamic tract whereas pain and temperature are associated with the lateral spinothalamic tract, but there is no rigid localization of function. Some of the fibers of the anterolateral system end in the specific relay nuclei of the thalamus; others project to the midline and intralaminar nonspecific projection nuclei. There is a major input from the anterolateral systems into the mesencephalic reticular formation. Thus, sensory input activates the reticular activating system, which in turn maintains the cortex in the alert state (see Chapter 11).

Collaterals from the fibers that enter the dorsal columns pass to the substantia gelatinosa. These collaterals may modify the input into other cutaneous sensory systems, including the pain system. The dorsal horn represents a ''gate'' in which impulses in the sensory nerve fibers are translated into impulses in ascending tracts, and it now appears that passage through this gate is dependent on the nature and pattern

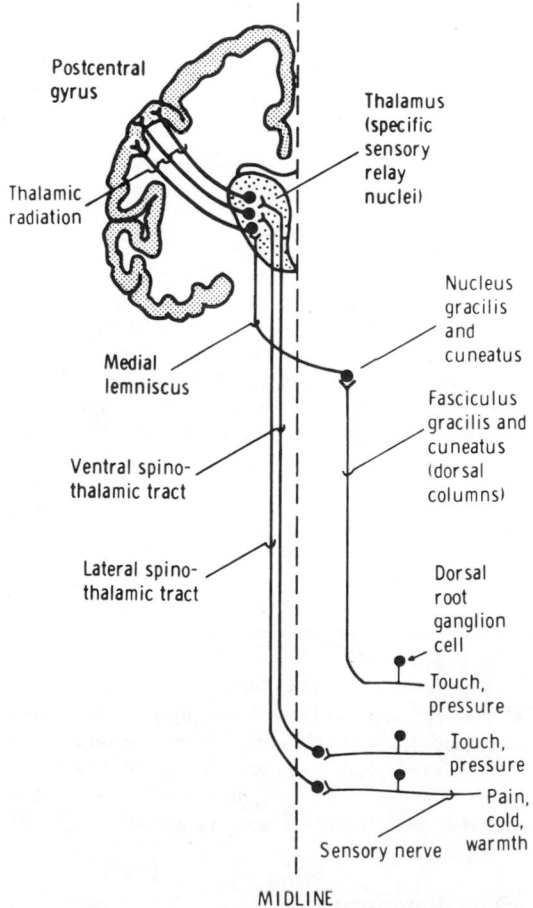

Figure 7–1. Touch, pressure, pain, and temperature pathways from the trunk and limbs. The anterolateral system (ventral and lateral spinothalamic tracts) also projects to the mesencephalic reticular formation and the nonspecific thalamic nuclei.

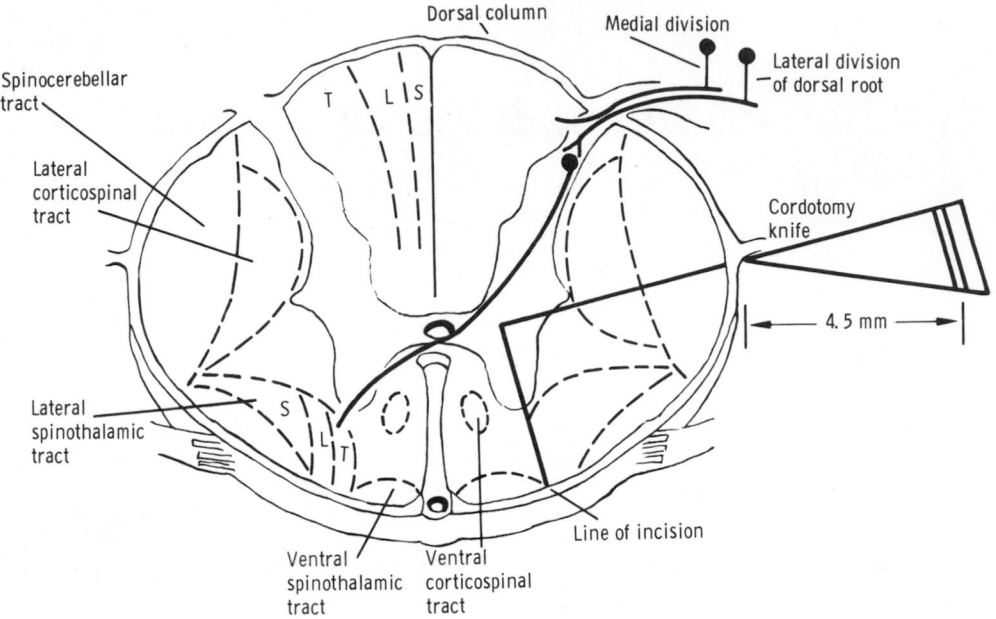

Figure 7–2. Major spinal pathways. The solid line on the right represents the line of incision in performing an anterolateral cordotomy. Note the lamination of the tracts. S, sacral; L, lumbar; T, thoracic.

of impulses reaching the substantia gelatinosa. This gate is also affected by impulses in descending tracts from the brain, and in particular from the periaqueductal gray and raphe nuclei.

Axons of the spinothalamic tracts from sacral and lumbar segments of the body are pushed laterally by axons crossing the midline at successively higher levels. On the other hand, sacral and lumbar dorsal column fibers are pushed medially by fibers from higher segments (Fig 7–2). Consequently, both of these ascending systems are laminated, with cervical to sacral segments represented from medial to lateral in the anterolateral pathways and sacral to cervical segments from medial to lateral in the dorsal columns. Because of this lamination, tumors arising outside the spinal cord first compress the spinothalamic fibers from sacral and lumbar areas, causing the early symptom of loss of pain and temperature sensation in the sacral region. Intraspinal tumors cause anesthesia first in higher segments.

The fibers within the lemniscal and anterolateral systems are joined in the brain stem by fibers mediating sensation from the head. Pain and temperature impulses are relayed via the spinal nucleus of the trigeminal nerve, and touch, pressure, and proprioception mostly via the main sensory and mesencephalic nuclei of this nerve.

Cortical Representation

From the specific sensory nuclei of the thalamus, neurons project in a highly specific way to the 2 somatic sensory areas of the cortex: somatic sensory area I (SI) in the postcentral gyrus and somatic sensory area II (SII) in the wall of the sylvian fissure (lateral cerebral sulcus).

The arrangement of the thalamic fibers to SI is such that the parts of the body are represented in order along the postcentral gyrus, with the legs on top and the head at the foot of the gyrus (Fig 7–3). Not only is there detailed localization of the fibers from the various parts of the body in the postcentral gyrus, but the size of the cortical receiving area for impulses from a particular part of the body is proportionate to the number of receptors in the part. The relative sizes of the cortical receiving areas are shown dramatically in

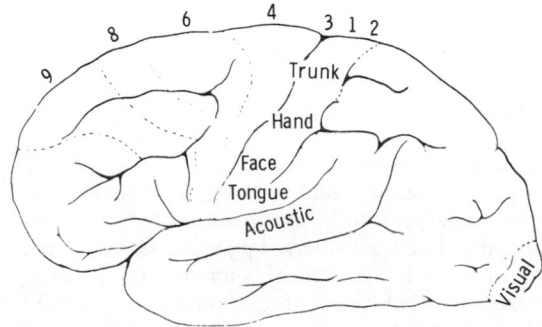

Figure 7–3. Some of the cortical receiving areas for various sensory modalities in the human brain. The numbers are those of Brodmann's cortical areas. The auditory (acoustic) area is actually located in the fissure on the top of the superior temporal gyrus and is not normally visible. (Reproduced, with permission, from Brazier MAB: *The Electrical Activity of the Nervous System,* 3rd ed. Pitman, 1968.)

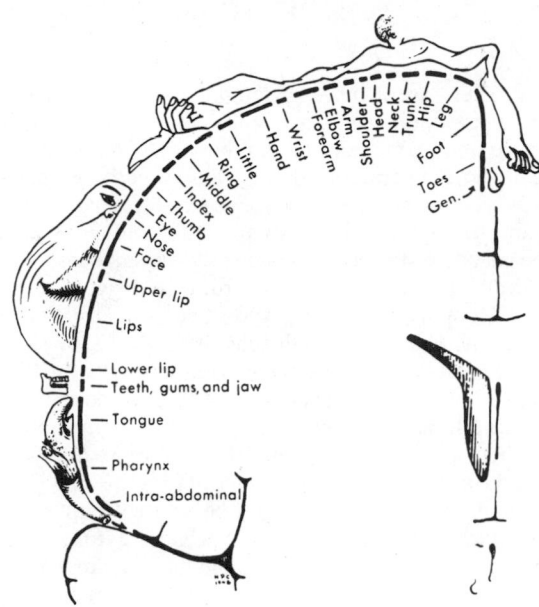

Figure 7–4. Sensory homunculus, drawn overlying a coronal section through the postcentral gyrus. Gen., genitalia. (Reproduced, with permission, from Penfield W, Rasmussen G: *The Cerebral Cortex of Man*. Macmillan, 1950.)

Fig 7–4, in which the proportions of the homunculus have been distorted to correspond to the size of the cortical receiving areas for each. Note that the cortical areas for sensation from the trunk and back are small, whereas very large areas are concerned with impulses from the hand and the parts of the mouth concerned with speech.

Studies of the sensory receiving area emphasize the very discrete nature of the point-for-point localization of peripheral areas in the cortex and provide further evidence for the validity of the doctrine of specific nerve energies (see Chapter 5). Stimulation of the various parts of the postcentral gyrus gives rise to sensations projected to appropriate parts of the body. The sensations produced are usually those of numbness, tingling, or a sense of movement, but with fine enough electrodes it has been possible to produce relatively pure sensations of touch, warmth, cold, and pain. The cells in the postcentral gyrus appear to be organized in vertical columns, like cells in the visual cortex (see Chapter 8). The cells in a given column are all activated by afferents from a given part of the body, and all respond to the same sensory modality.

Somatic sensory area II is located in the superior wall of the sylvian fissure. The head is represented at the inferior end of the postcentral gyrus, and the feet at the bottom of the sylvian fissure. The representation of the body parts is not as complete or detailed as it is in the postcentral gyrus. The function of SII is not known, although it may play a role in the perception of pain. Its ablation in animals does not cause any detectable deficit in other sensory modalities.

Effects of Cortical Lesions

In experimental animals and humans, lesions of the postcentral gyrus decrease but do not entirely abolish sensation. Proprioception and fine touch are most affected by cortical lesions. Temperature sensibility is less affected, and pain sensibility is only slightly affected. This suggests that a certain degree of perception is possible in the absence of the cortex. Upon recovery, pain sensibility returns first, followed by temperature sense and, finally, proprioception and fine touch.

Principles of Sensory Physiology

The important general principles that relate to the physiology of sensory systems have been discussed in detail in Chapter 5. Each sense organ is specialized to convert one particular form of energy into action potentials in the sensory nerves. Each modality has a discrete pathway to the brain, and the sensation perceived as well as the part of the body to which it is localized is determined by the particular part of the brain activated. Differences in intensity of a given sensation are signaled in 2 ways: by changes in the frequency of action potentials in the sensory nerves, and by changes in the number of receptors activated. An increase in the intensity of stimulation of a sense organ has very little (if any) effect on the quality of the sensation produced.

Another principle that applies to cutaneous sensation is that of punctate representation. If the skin is carefully mapped, millimeter by millimeter, with a fine hair, a sensation of touch is evoked from spots overlying touch receptors. None is evoked from the intervening areas. Similarly, pain and temperature sensations are produced by stimulation of the skin only over the spots where the sense organs for these modalities are located.

TOUCH

Touch receptor organs adapt rapidly. They are most numerous in the skin of the fingers and lips and relatively scarce in the skin of the trunk. There are many receptors around hair follicles in addition to those in the subcutaneous tissues of hairless areas. When a hair is moved, it acts as a lever with its fulcrum at the edge of the follicle so that slight movements of the hairs are magnified into relatively potent stimuli to the nerve endings around the follicles. The stiff vibrissae on the snouts of some animals are highly developed examples of hairs that act as levers to magnify tactile stimuli. The pacinian corpuscles, which are also touch receptors, are found in the subcutaneous tissues, muscles, and joints. They also abound in the mesentery, where their function is not known.

The group II sensory fibers that transmit impulses from touch receptors to the CNS are 5–12 μm in diameter and have conduction velocities of 30–70 m/s.

Some touch impulses are also conducted via C fibers.

Touch information is transmitted in both the lemniscal and anterolateral pathways, so that only very extensive lesions completely interrupt touch sensation. However, there are differences in the type of touch information transmitted in the 2 systems. When the dorsal columns are destroyed, vibratory sensation and proprioception are lost, the touch threshold is elevated, and the number of touch-sensitive areas in the skin is decreased. In addition, localization of touch sensation is impaired. An increase in touch threshold and a decrease in the number of touch spots in the skin are also observed after interrupting the spinothalamic tracts, but the touch deficit is slight and touch localization remains normal. The information carried in the lemniscal system is concerned with the detailed localization, spatial form, and temporal pattern of tactile stimuli. The information carried in the spinothalamic tracts, on the other hand, is concerned with poorly localized, gross tactile sensations.

While lesions limited to the postcentral gyrus produce loss of fine touch discrimination on the opposite side of the body, lesions of the parietal lobe in the representational hemisphere produce contralateral disorders of spatial orientation, and lesions of the parietal lobe in the categorical hemisphere produce agnosias. These abnormalities are discussed in Chapter 16.

PROPRIOCEPTION

Proprioceptive information is transmitted up the spinal cord in the dorsal columns. A good deal of the proprioceptive input goes to the cerebellum, but some passes via the medial lemnisci and thalamic radiations to the cortex. Diseases of the dorsal columns produce ataxia because of the interruption of proprioceptive input to the cerebellum.

There is some evidence that proprioceptive information passes to consciousness in the anterolateral columns of the spinal cord. Since stimulation of group I fibers produces no electrical response in the cerebral cortex, impulses initiated in the muscle spindles and Golgi tendon organs apparently do not reach consciousness. Conscious awareness of the position of the various parts of the body in space depends instead upon impulses from sense organs in and around the joints. The organs involved are slowly adapting ''spray'' endings, structures that resemble Golgi tendon organs, and probably pacinian corpuscles in the synovia and ligaments. Impulses from these organs and those from touch receptors in other tissue are synthesized in the cortex into a conscious picture of the position of the body in space. Microelectrode studies indicate that many of the neurons in the sensory cortex respond to particular movements, not just to touch or static position. In this regard, the sensory cortex is organized like the visual cortex (see Chapter 8).

TEMPERATURE

There are 2 types of temperature sense organs: those responding maximally to temperatures slightly above body temperature, and those responding maximally to temperatures slightly below body temperature. The former are the sense organs for what we call warmth, and the latter for what we call cold. However, the adequate stimuli are actually 2 different degrees of warmth, since cold is not a form of energy.

Mapping experiments show that there are discrete cold-sensitive and warmth-sensitive spots in the skin. There are 4–10 times as many cold spots as warm. The temperature sense organs are naked nerve endings that respond to absolute temperature, not the temperature gradient across the skin. The afferents are small myelinated fibers 2–5 μm in diameter in Erlanger and Gasser's A δ group (group III fibers; see Chapter 2). Impulses in them pass to the postcentral gyrus via the lateral spinothalamic tract and the thalamic radiation.

Because the sense organs are located subepithelially, it is the temperature of the subcutaneous tissues that determines the responses. Cool metal objects feel colder than wooden objects of the same temperature because the metal conducts heat away from the skin more rapidly, cooling the subcutaneous tissues to a greater degree. Below a skin temperature of 20 C and above 40 C, there is no adaptation, but between 20 and 40 C there is adaptation, so that the sensation produced by a temperature change gradually fades to one of thermal neutrality. In humans, the intensities of warm or cold sensations are related by a power function to the temperature of the stimulus (see Chapter 5). Above 45 C, tissue damage begins to occur, and the sensation becomes one of pain.

PAIN

The sense organs for pain are the naked nerve endings found in almost every tissue of the body. Pain impulses are transmitted to the CNS by 2 fiber systems. One system is made up of small myelinated A δ fibers, 2–5 μm in diameter, which conduct at rates of 12–30 m/s. The other consists of unmyelinated C fibers, 0.4–1.2 μm in diameter. These latter fibers are found in the lateral division of the dorsal roots, and are often called dorsal root C fibers. They conduct at the slow rate of 0.5–2 m/s. Both fiber groups end on the lateral spinothalamic tract neurons, and pain impulses ascend via this tract to the ventral posteromedial and posterolateral nuclei of the thalamus. From there, they relay to the postcentral gyri of the cerebral cortex.

Although there are no pain fibers in the dorsal columns, section of the dorsal column fibers may make painful stimuli more severe and unpleasant (see below).

Fast & Slow Pain

The presence of 2 pain pathways, one slow and one fast, explains the physiologic observation that there are 2 kinds of pain. A painful stimulus causes a "bright," sharp, localized sensation followed by a dull, aching, diffuse, and unpleasant feeling. These 2 sensations are variously called fast and slow pain or first and second pain. The farther from the brain the stimulus is applied, the greater the temporal separation of the 2 components. This and other evidence make it clear that fast pain is due to activity in the A δ pain fibers, while slow pain is due to activity in the C pain fibers.

Subcortical Perception & Affect

There is considerable evidence that sensory stimuli are perceived in the absence of the cerebral cortex, and this is especially true of pain. The cortical receiving areas are apparently concerned with the discriminative, exact, and meaningful interpretation of pain, but perception alone does not require the cortex.

Pain was called by Sherrington the "psychical adjunct of an imperative protective reflex." Stimuli that are painful generally initiate potent withdrawal and avoidance responses. Furthermore, pain is peculiar among the senses in that it is associated with a strong emotional component. Information transmitted via the special senses may secondarily evoke pleasant or unpleasant emotions, depending largely upon past experience, but pain alone has a "built-in" unpleasant affect. Present evidence indicates that this affective response depends upon connections of the pain pathways in the thalamus. Damage to the thalamus may be associated with a peculiar over-reaction to painful stimuli known as the **thalamic syndrome.** In this condition, usually due to blockage of the thalamogeniculate branch of the posterior cerebral artery with consequent damage to the posterior thalamic nuclei, minor stimuli lead to prolonged, severe, and very unpleasant pain. Such bouts of pain may occur spontaneously, or at least without evident external stimuli. Another interesting fact is that at least in some cases pain can be dissociated from its unpleasant subjective affect by cutting the deep connections between the frontal lobes and the rest of the brain (**prefrontal lobotomy**). After this operation patients report that they feel pain but that it "doesn't bother" them. The operation is sometimes useful in the treatment of intractable pain caused by terminal cancer.

Lobotomy is, of course, only one of the many neurosurgical procedures employed to relieve intractable pain in terminal cancer patients, and it produces extensive personality changes (see Chapter 16). Other operations are summarized in Fig 7–5. One of the most extensively used is **anterolateral cordotomy.** In this procedure, a knife is inserted into the lateral aspect of the spinal cord and swept anteriorly and laterally as shown in Fig 7–2. When properly performed, this procedure cuts the lateral spinothalamic pain fibers while leaving some of the ventral spinothalamic touch fibers intact. Even if there is extensive damage to the

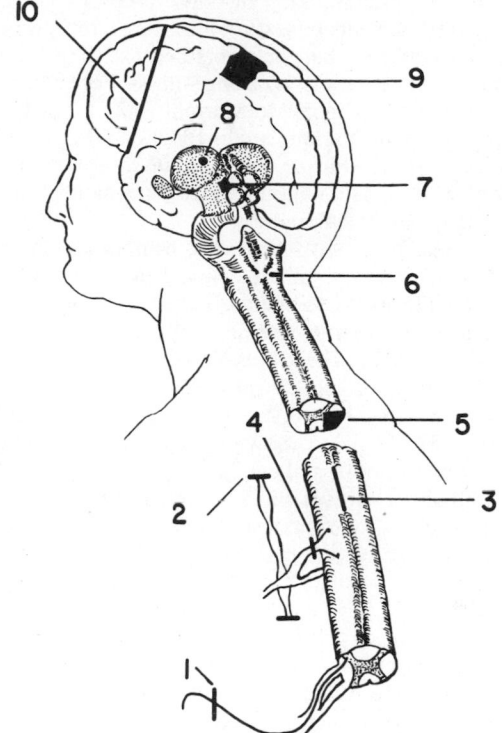

Figure 7–5. Diagram of various surgical procedures designed to alleviate pain. 1, nerve section; 2, sympathectomy (for visceral pain); 3, myelotomy to section spinothalamic fibers in anterior white commissure; 4, posterior rhizotomy; 5, anterolateral cordotomy; 6, medullary tractotomy; 7, mesencephalic tractotomy; 8, thalamotomy; 9, gyrectomy; 10, prefrontal lobotomy. (Modified from MacCarty CS, Drake LR: Neurosurgical procedures for the control of pain. Proc Staff Meet Mayo Clin 31:208, 1956.)

touch fibers in the anterolateral quadrants, touch is very little impaired because the dorsal column touch system is intact.

Deep Pain

The main difference between superficial and deep sensibility is the different nature of the pain evoked by noxious stimuli. Unlike superficial pain, deep pain is poorly localized, nauseating, and frequently associated with sweating and changes in blood pressure. Pain can be elicited experimentally from the periosteum and ligaments by injecting hypertonic saline into them. The pain produced in this fashion initiates reflex contraction of nearby skeletal muscles. This reflex contraction is similar to the muscle spasm associated with injuries to bones, tendons, and joints. The steadily contracting muscles become ischemic, and ischemia stimulates the pain receptors in the muscles (see below). The pain in turn initiates more spasm, and a vicious cycle is set up.

Adequate Stimulus

Pain receptors are specific, and pain is not produced by overstimulation of other receptors. On the other hand, the adequate stimulus for pain receptors is not as specific as that for others because they can be stimulated by a variety of strong stimuli. For example, pain receptors respond to warmth, but it has been calculated that their threshold for thermal energy is over 100 times that of the warmth receptors. Pain receptors also respond to electrical, mechanical, and, especially, chemical energy.

It has been suggested that pain is chemically mediated, and that stimuli which provoke it have in common the ability to liberate a chemical agent which stimulates the nerve endings. The chemical agent might be a kinin. The kinins are polypeptides that are liberated from proteins by proteolytic enzymes. Their formation and metabolism are discussed in detail in Chapter 31. They are known to be liberated in tissues by noxious stimuli, and they are capable of producing severe pain. However, the pain produced by injected kinins is usually transient. Histamine also causes pain on local injection and may be a chemical mediator of pain.

Muscle Pain

If a muscle contracts rhythmically in the presence of an adequate blood supply, pain does not usually result. However, if the blood supply to a muscle is occluded, contraction soon causes pain. The pain persists after the contraction until blood flow is reestablished. If a muscle with a normal blood supply is made to contract continuously without periods of relaxation, it also begins to ache because the maintained contraction compresses the blood vessels supplying the muscle.

These observations are difficult to interpret except in terms of the release during contraction of a chemical agent (Lewis' "P factor") that causes pain when its local concentration is high enough. When the blood supply is restored, the material is washed out or metabolized. The identity of the P factor is not settled, but it could be K^+ or possibly a kinin.

Clinically, the substernal pain that develops when the myocardium becomes ischemic during exertion (angina pectoris) is a classic example of the accumulation of P factor in a muscle. Angina is relieved by rest because this decreases the myocardial O_2 requirement and permits the blood supply to remove the factor. Intermittent claudication, the pain produced in the leg muscles of persons with occlusive vascular disease, is another example. It characteristically comes on while the patient is walking and disappears upon resting.

Hyperalgesia

In pathologic conditions, the sensitivity of the pain receptors is altered. There are 2 important types of alteration, primary and secondary hyperalgesia. In the area surrounding an inflamed or injured area, the threshold for pain is lowered so that trivial stimuli cause pain. This phenomenon, **primary hyperalgesia,** is seen in the area of the **flare,** the region of vasodilatation around the injury. In the area of actual

tissue damage, the vasodilatation and, presumably, the pain are due to substances liberated from injured cells, but the flare in surrounding undamaged tissue is due to substance P liberated by antidromic impulses in primary afferent fibers (see Chapter 32).

Another aberration of sensation following injury is **secondary hyperalgesia.** In the area affected, the threshold for pain is actually elevated but the pain produced is unpleasant, prolonged, and severe. The area from which this response is obtained extends well beyond the site of injury, and the condition does not last as long as primary hyperalgesia. It is probably due to some sort of central facilitation by impulses from the injured area of the pathways responsible for the unpleasant affect component of pain. Such facilitation or alteration of pathways may be a spinal subliminal fringe effect, or it may occur at the thalamic or even the cortical level.

DIFFERENCES BETWEEN SOMATIC & VISCERAL SENSORY MECHANISMS

The autonomic nervous system, like the somatic, has afferent components, central integrating stations, and effector pathways. The visceral afferent mechanisms play a major role in homeostatic adjustments. In the viscera, there are a number of special receptors— osmoreceptors, baroreceptors, chemoreceptors, etc—that respond to changes in the internal environment. The afferent nerves from these receptors make reflex connections that are intimately concerned with regulating the function of the various systems with which they are associated, and their physiology is discussed in the chapters on these systems.

The receptors for pain and the other sensory modalities present in the viscera are similar to those in skin, but there are marked differences in their distribution. There are no proprioceptors in the viscera, and few temperature and touch sense organs. If the abdominal wall is infiltrated with a local anesthetic, the abdomen can be opened and the intestines can be handled, cut, and even burned without eliciting any discomfort. Pain receptors are present in the viscera, however, and although they are more sparsely distributed than in somatic structures, certain types of stimuli cause severe pain. There are many pacinian corpuscles in the mesentery, but their function in this location is not known.

Afferent fibers from visceral structures reach the CNS via sympathetic and parasympathetic pathways. Their cell bodies are located in the dorsal roots and the homologous cranial nerve ganglia. Specifically, there are visceral afferents in the facial, glossopharyngeal, and vagus nerves, in the thoracic and upper lumbar dorsal roots, and in the sacral roots (Fig 7–6). There may also be visceral afferent fibers from the eye in the trigeminal nerve. There are A β and A δ afferent fibers in the splanchnic nerves, but only A δ fibers in the

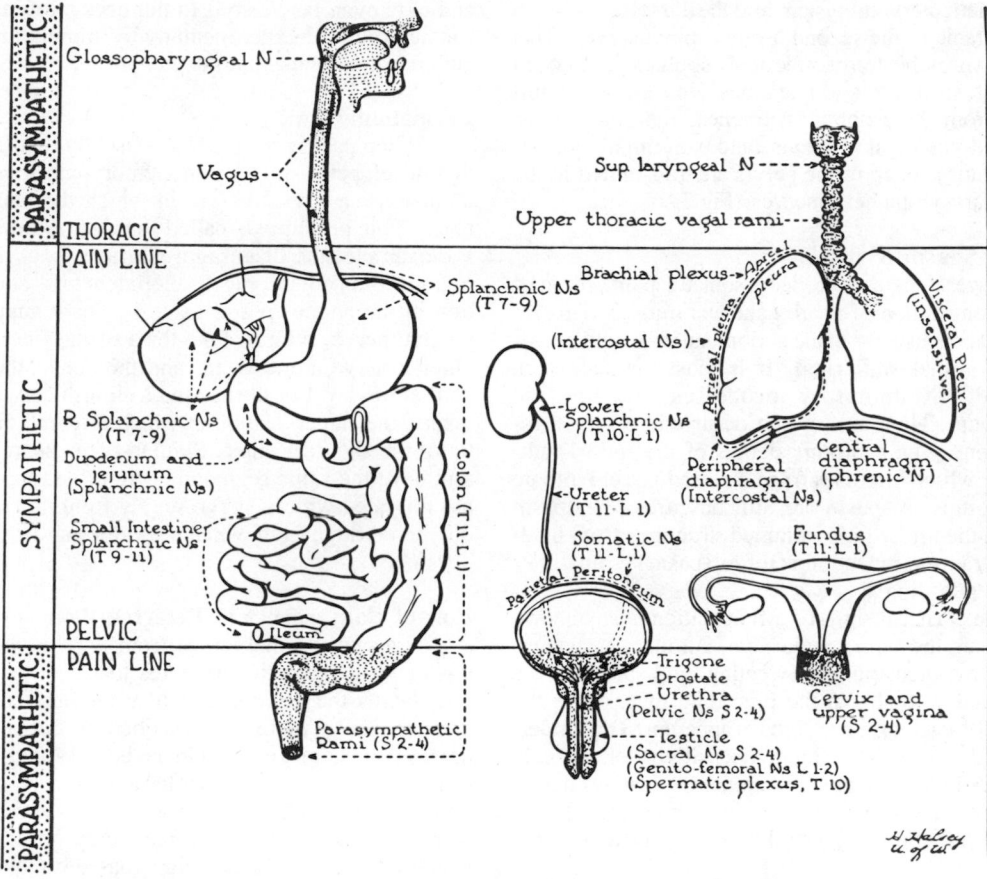

Figure 7–6. Pain innervation of the viscera. Pain afferents from structures above the thoracic pain line and below the pelvic pain line traverse parasympathetic pathways. (After White JC. Reproduced, with permission, from Ruch TC, in: *Physiology and Biophysics,* 19th ed. Ruch TC, Patton HD [editors]. Saunders, 1965.)

pelvic and vagus nerves. Visceral sensation travels along the same pathways as somatic sensation in the spinothalamic tracts and thalamic radiations, and the cortical receiving areas for visceral sensation are intermixed with the somatic receiving areas in the postcentral gyri.

VISCERAL PAIN

Pain from visceral structures is poorly localized, unpleasant, associated with nausea and autonomic symptoms, and often radiates or is referred to other areas.

Stimulation of Pain Fibers

Because there are relatively few pain receptors in the viscera, visceral pain is poorly localized. However, as almost everyone knows from personal experience, visceral pain can be very severe. The receptors in the walls of the hollow viscera are especially sensitive to distention of these organs. Such distention can be produced experimentally in the gastrointestinal tract by inflation of a swallowed balloon attached to a tube. This produces pain which waxes and wanes (intestinal colic) as the intestine contracts and relaxes on the balloon. Similar colic is produced in intestinal obstruction by the contractions of the dilated intestine above the obstruction. When a viscus is inflamed or hyperemic, relatively minor stimuli cause severe pain. This is probably a form of primary hyperalgesia similar to that which occurs in somatic structures. Traction on the mesentery is also claimed to be painful, but the significance of this observation in the production of visceral pain is not clear. Visceral pain is particularly unpleasant not only because of the affective component it has in common with all pain but also because so many visceral afferents excited by the same process that causes the pain have reflex connections that initiate nausea, vomiting, and other autonomic effects.

Pathways

Pain impulses from the thoracic and abdominal viscera are almost exclusively conducted through the sympathetic nervous system and the dorsal roots of the first thoracic to the second lumbar spinal nerves. This is why sympathectomy effectively abolishes pain from the heart, stomach, and intestines. However, pain impulses from the esophagus, trachea, and pharynx are mediated via vagal afferents, and pain impulses from the structures deep in the pelvis are transmitted in the sacral parasympathetic nerves (Fig 7–6).

Muscle Spasm & Rigidity

Visceral pain, like deep somatic pain, initiates reflex contraction of nearby skeletal muscle. This reflex spasm is usually in the abdominal wall, and makes the abdominal wall rigid. It is most marked when visceral inflammatory processes involve the peritoneum. However, it can occur without such involvement. The anatomic details of the reflex pathways by which impulses from diseased viscera initiate skeletal muscle spasm are still obscure. The spasm protects the underlying inflamed structures from inadvertent trauma. Indeed, this reflex spasm is sometimes called "guarding."

The classical signs of inflammation in an abdominal viscus are pain, tenderness, autonomic changes such as hypotension and sweating, and spasm of the abdominal wall. From the preceding discussion, the genesis of each of these signs is apparent. The tenderness is due to the heightened sensitivity of the pain receptors in the viscus, the autonomic changes due to activation of visceral reflexes, and the spasm due to reflex contraction of skeletal muscle in the abdominal wall.

REFERRAL & INHIBITION OF PAIN

Referred Pain

Irritation of a viscus frequently produces pain which is felt not in the viscus but in some somatic structure that may be a considerable distance away. Such pain is said to be **referred** to the somatic structure. Deep somatic pain may also be referred, but superficial pain is not. When visceral pain is both local and referred, it sometimes seems to spread or **radiate** from the local to the distant site.

Obviously, a knowledge of referred pain and the common sites of pain referral from each of the viscera is of great importance to the physician. Perhaps the best-known example is referral of cardiac pain to the inner aspect of the left arm. Other dramatic examples include pain in the tip of the shoulder due to irritation of the central portion of the diaphragm and pain in the testicle due to distention of the ureter. Additional instances abound in the practice of medicine, surgery, and dentistry. However, sites of reference are not stereotyped, and unusual reference sites occur with considerable frequency. Heart pain, for instance, may be purely abdominal, may be referred to the right arm,

and may even be referred to the neck. Referred pain can be produced experimentally by stimulation of the cut end of a splanchnic nerve.

Dermatomal Rule

When pain is referred, it is usually to a structure that developed from the same embryonic segment or dermatome as the structure in which the pain originates. This principle is called the **dermatomal rule**. For example, the diaphragm migrates from the neck region during embryonic development to its adult location in the abdomen and takes its nerve supply, the phrenic nerve, with it. One-third of the fibers in the phrenic nerve are afferent, and they enter the spinal cord at the level of the second to fourth cervical segments, the same location at which afferents from the tip of the shoulder enter. Similarly, the heart and the arm have the same segmental origin, and the testicle has migrated with its nerve supply from the primitive urogenital ridge from which the kidney and ureter also developed.

Role of Convergence in Referred Pain

Not only do the nerves from the visceral structures and the somatic structures to which pain is referred enter the nervous system at the same level, but there are many more sensory fibers in the peripheral nerves than there are axons in the lateral spinothalamic tracts. Therefore, a considerable degree of convergence of peripheral sensory fibers on the spinothalamic neurons must occur. One theory of the mechanism underlying referred pain is based on this fact. It holds that somatic and visceral afferents converge on the same spinothalamic neurons (Fig 7–7). Since somatic pain is much more common than visceral pain,

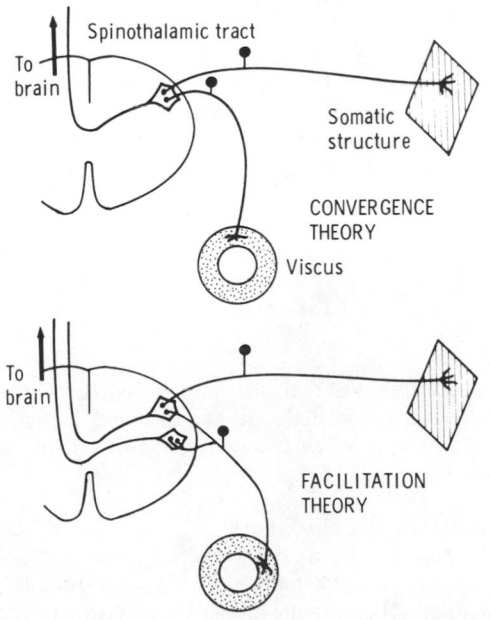

Figure 7–7. Diagram of convergence and facilitation theories of referred pain.

the brain has "learned" that activity arriving in a given pathway is due to a pain stimulus in a particular somatic area. When the same pathway is stimulated by activity in visceral afferents, the signal reaching the brain is no different and the pain is projected to the somatic area.

Past experience does play an important role in referred pain. Although pain originating in an inflamed abdominal viscus is usually referred to the midline, in patients who have had previous abdominal surgery the pain of abdominal disease is frequently referred to their surgical scars. Pain originating in the maxillary sinus is usually referred to nearby teeth, but in patients with a history of traumatic dental work such pain is regularly referred to the previously traumatized teeth. This is true even when the teeth are a considerable distance away from the sinus.

Facilitation Effects

Another theory of the origin of referred pain holds that, owing to subliminal fringe effects, incoming impulses from visceral structures lower the threshold of spinothalamic neurons receiving afferents from somatic areas, so that minor activity in the pain pathways from the somatic areas—activity which would normally die out in the spinal cord—passes on to the brain.

If convergence alone were the explanation for referred pain, anesthetizing the somatic area of reference with procaine should have no effect on the pain, whereas if subliminal fringe effects were responsible the pain should disappear. The effects of local anesthesia in the area of reference vary. When the pain is severe, it is usually unaffected, but when the pain is mild it may be completely abolished. Therefore, it appears that both convergence and facilitation play a role in the pathogenesis of referred pain.

Central Inhibition & Counterirritants

It is of course well known that soldiers wounded in the heat of battle may feel no pain until the battle is over. Many people have learned from practical experience that touching or shaking an injured area decreases the pain of the injury. Acupuncture has been used for 4000 years to prevent or relieve pain, and, using this technic, it is possible in some instances to perform major surgery without any other type of anesthesia. These and other observations make it clear that pain transmission and perception are subject to inhibition or modification. Experimental evidence for the modifiability of pain transmission is provided by the observation that the potentials evoked in the cerebral cortex by stimulation of the splanchnic nerves disappear if the stimulation is preceded or accompanied by stimulation of somatic afferents.

Inhibition in central sensory pathways may explain the efficacy of counterirritants. Stimulation of the skin over an area of visceral inflammation produces some relief of the pain due to the visceral disease. The old-fashioned mustard plaster works on this principle. Some similar mechanism may explain the "anes-

thesia" produced in dental patients by loud sound, although much of this effect is admittedly due to suggestion.

Gating in the Substantia Gelatinosa

One site of inhibition of pain transmission is the substantia gelatinosa, the "gate" through which pain impulses reach the lateral spinothalamic system. Stimulation of large fiber afferents from an area from which pain is being initiated reduces the pain. Collateral fibers from the dorsal column touch fibers enter the substantia gelatinosa, and it has been postulated that impulses in these collaterals or interneurons on which they end inhibit transmission from the dorsal root pain fibers to the spinothalamic neurons. The mechanism involved appears to be presynaptic inhibition (see Chapter 4) at the endings of the primary afferents that transmit pain impulses. Chronic stimulation of the dorsal columns with implanted stimulators has been used clinically as a method of relieving intractable pain. The pain relief is presumably due to antidromic rather than orthodromic conduction with impulses passing via the collaterals to the "gate," since section of the dorsal columns enhances rather than reduces responses to noxious stimuli.

Action of Morphine & Enkephalins

Morphine relieves pain and produces euphoria. There are receptors to which morphine binds in the brain, spinal cord, and gastrointestinal tract, and it has now been demonstrated that a variety of naturally occurring peptides also bind to these receptors. The larger peptides are called endorphins; the smaller ones are called enkephalins (see Chapter 15). There are enkephalin-containing neurons in the substantia gelatinosa that presumably terminate presynaptically on pain-mediating primary afferent fibers, and enkephalins reduce the release of substance P, the transmitter released by these afferents. Thus, part of the action of morphine is probably due to binding to enkephalin receptors on primary afferent neurons, with a resultant decrease in the release of their transmitter. However, morphine also acts at the level of the periaqueductal gray matter to activate descending pathways that produce inhibition of primary afferent transmission in the substantia gelatinosa. There is some evidence that acupuncture exerts its analgesic effect by causing release of enkephalins. Prolonged exposure of receptors to the neurotransmitter that normally binds to them decreases the number of receptors (see Chapter 1), and the development of tolerance to morphine may be due to a decrease in the number of enkephalin receptors.

OTHER SENSATIONS

Itch & Tickle

Itching is probably produced by repetitive low-frequency stimulation of C fibers. Very mild stimulation of this system, especially if produced by something that moves across the skin, produces tickle. Itch spots can be identified on the skin by careful mapping; like the pain spots, they are in regions in which there are many naked endings of unmyelinated fibers. Itch persists along with burning pain in nerve block experiments when only C fibers are conducting, and itch, like pain, is abolished by section of the spinothalamic tracts. However, the distribution of itch and pain are different; itching occurs only in the skin, the eyes, and certain mucous membranes, and not in the deep tissues or viscera. Furthermore, low-frequency stimulation of pain fibers generally produces pain, not itch, and high-frequency stimulation of itch spots on the skin may merely increase the intensity of the itching without producing pain. These observations suggest that the C fiber system responsible for itching is not the same as that responsible for pain. It is interesting that a tickling sensation is usually regarded as pleasurable, whereas itching is at least annoying, and pain is unpleasant.

Itching can be produced not only by repeated local mechanical stimulation of the skin but by a variety of chemical agents. Histamine produces intense itching, and various injuries cause its liberation in the skin. However, in most instances of itching, histamine does not appear to be the responsible agent; doses of histamine that are too small to produce itching still produce redness and swelling on injection into the skin, and severe itching frequently occurs without any visible change in the skin. The kinins cause severe itching, and it may be that they are the chemical mediators responsible for the sensation. It is interesting in this regard that itch powder, which is made up of the spicules from the pods of the tropical plant cowhage, contains a proteolytic enzyme, and the powder presumably acts by liberating itch-producing peptides.

"Synthetic Senses"

The cutaneous senses for which separate receptors exist are touch, warmth, cold, pain, and possibly itching. Combinations of these sensations plus, in some cases, cortical components are synthesized into the sensations of vibratory sensation, 2-point discrimination, and stereognosis.

Vibratory Sensibility

When a vibrating tuning fork is applied to the skin, a buzzing or thrill is felt. The sensation is most marked over bones, but it can be felt when the tuning fork is placed in other locations. The receptors involved are the pressure receptors, but a time factor is also necessary. A pattern of rhythmic pressure stimuli is interpreted as vibration. The impulses responsible for the vibrating sensation are carried in the dorsal columns. Degeneration of this part of the spinal cord occurs in poorly controlled diabetes, pernicious anemia, some vitamin deficiencies, and occasionally in other conditions; depression of the threshold for vibratory stimuli is an early symptom of this degeneration. Vibratory sensation and proprioception are closely related; when one is depressed, so is the other.

Two-Point Discrimination

The minimal distance by which 2 touch stimuli must be separated to be perceived as separate is called the **2-point threshold.** It depends upon touch plus the cortical component of identifying 1 rather than 2 stimuli. Its magnitude varies from place to place on the body, and is smallest where the touch receptors are most abundant. Points on the back, for instance, must be separated by 65 mm or more before they can be distinguished as separate points, whereas on the fingers 2 stimuli can be resolved if they are separated by as little as 3 mm. On the hands, the magnitude of the 2-point threshold is approximately the diameter of the area of skin supplied by a single sensory unit. However, the peripheral neural basis of discriminating 2 points is not completely understood, and in view of the extensive interdigitation and overlapping of the sensory units, it is probably complex.

Stereognosis

The ability to identify objects by handling them without looking at them is called **stereognosis.** Normal persons can readily identify objects such as keys and coins of various denominations. This ability obviously depends upon relatively intact touch and pressure sensation, but it also has a large cortical component. Impaired stereognosis is an early sign of damage to the cerebral cortex, and sometimes occurs in the absence of any defect in touch and pressure sensation when there is a lesion in the parietal lobe posterior to the postcentral gyrus.

ANATOMIC CONSIDERATIONS

The eyes are complex sense organs that have evolved from primitive light-sensitive spots on the surface of invertebrates. Within its protective casing, each eye has a layer of receptors, a lens system for focusing light on these receptors, and a system of nerves for conducting impulses from the receptors to the brain. The principal structures are shown in Fig 8–1. The outer protective layer of the eyeball, the **sclera,** is modified anteriorly to form the transparent **cornea,** through which light rays enter the eye. Inside the sclera is the **choroid,** a pigmented layer that contains many of the blood vessels which nourish the structures in the eyeball. Lining the posterior two-thirds of the choroid is the **retina,** the neural tissue containing the receptor cells.

The **crystalline lens** is a transparent structure held in place by a circular **lens ligament,** or **zonule.** The zonule is attached to the thickened anterior part of the choroid, the **ciliary body.** The ciliary body con-

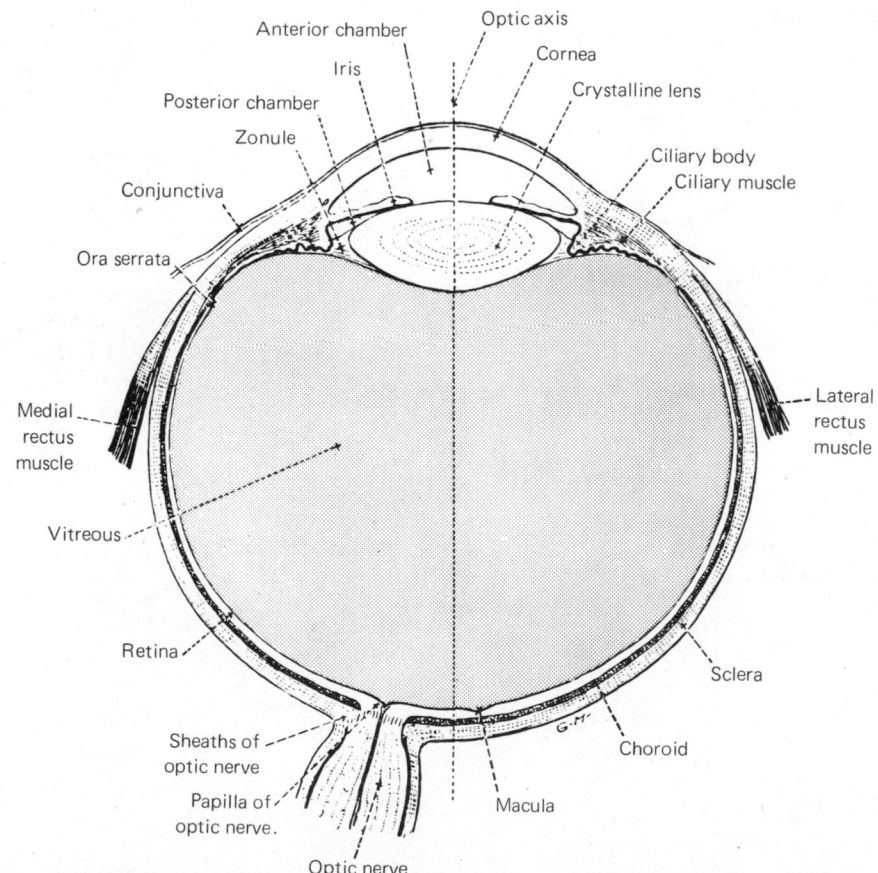

Figure 8–1. Section through right eye in horizontal plane magnified about 4 times. (After Eycleshymer AC and Jones TS. Reproduced, with permission, from Jones T, Shepard WC: *A Manual of Surgical Anatomy.* Saunders, 1945.)

tains circular muscle fibers and longitudinal fibers that attach near the corneoscleral junction. In front of the lens is the pigmented and opaque **iris,** the colored portion of the eye. The iris contains circular muscle fibers which constrict and radial fibers which dilate the **pupil.** Variations in the diameter of the pupil can produce up to 5-fold changes in the amount of light reaching the retina.

The space between the lens and the retina is filled primarily with a clear gelatinous material called the **vitreous (vitreous humor). Aqueous humor,** a clear liquid, is produced in the ciliary body by diffusion and active transport and flows through the pupil to fill the anterior chamber of the eye. It is normally reabsorbed through a network of trabeculae into the **canal of Schlemm,** a venous channel at the junction between the iris and the cornea (anterior chamber angle). Obstruction of this outlet leads to increased intraocular pressure and the serious eye disease **glaucoma.** One cause is decreased permeability through the trabeculae **(open-angle glaucoma)** and another is forward movement of the iris, obliterating the angle **(angle-closure glaucoma).**

Retina

The retina extends anteriorly almost to the ciliary body. It is organized in 10 layers and contains the rods and cones, which are the visual receptors, plus 4 types of neurons: **bipolar cells, ganglion cells, horizontal cells,** and **amacrine cells** (Fig 8–2). The rods and cones, which are next to the choroid, synapse with bipolar cells, and the bipolar cells synapse with ganglion cells. The axons of the ganglion cells converge and leave the eye as the optic nerve. Horizontal cells connect receptor cells to other receptor cells in the outer plexiform layer. Amacrine cells connect ganglion cells to one another in the inner plexiform layer and in some instances may be inserted between bipolar cells and ganglion cells. They have no axons, and their processes make both pre- and postsynaptic connections with neighboring neural elements. There is considerable overall convergence of receptors on bipolar cells and bipolar cells on ganglion cells (see below). Since the receptor layer of the retina is apposed to the choroid, light rays must pass through the ganglion cell and bipolar cell layers to reach the rods and cones. The pigmented layer of choroid next to the retina absorbs

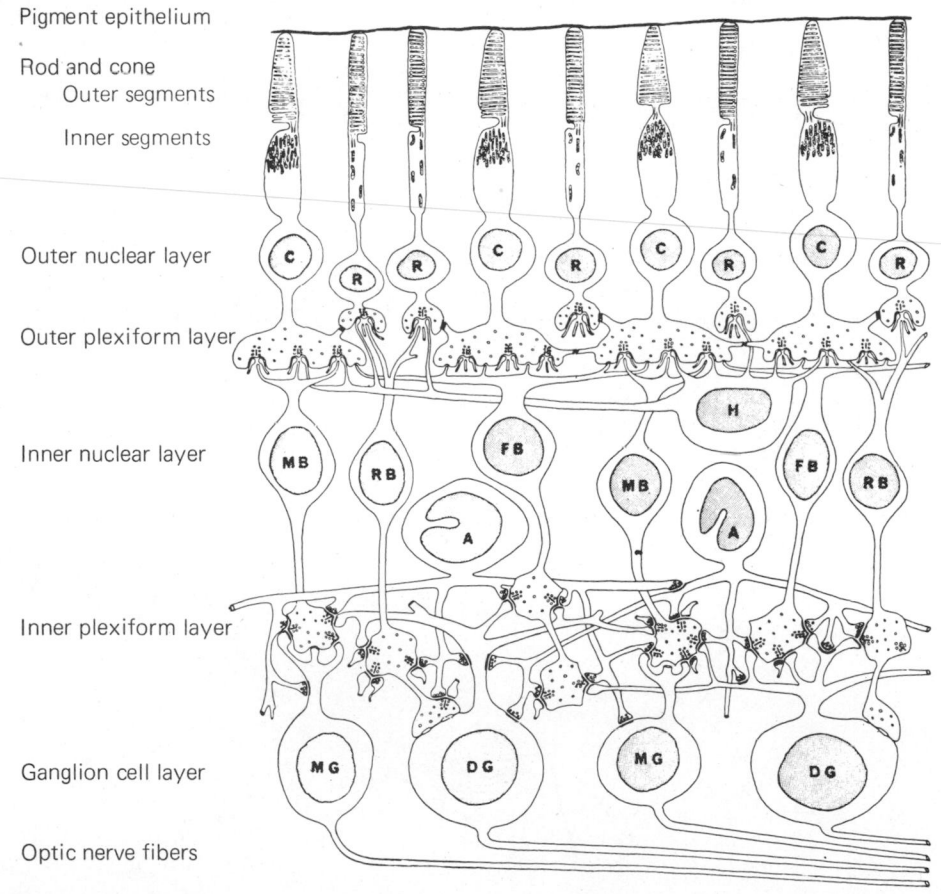

Pigment epithelium

Rod and cone
　Outer segments
　Inner segments

Outer nuclear layer

Outer plexiform layer

Inner nuclear layer

Inner plexiform layer

Ganglion cell layer

Optic nerve fibers

Figure 8–2. Neural components of the retina. C, cone; R, rod; MB, RB, and FB, midget, rod, and flat bipolar cells; DG and MG, diffuse and midget ganglion cells; H, horizontal cells; A, amacrine cells. (Reproduced, with permission, from Dowling JE, Boycott BB: Organization of the primate retina: Electron microscopy. Proc R Soc Lond [Biol] 166:80, 1966.)

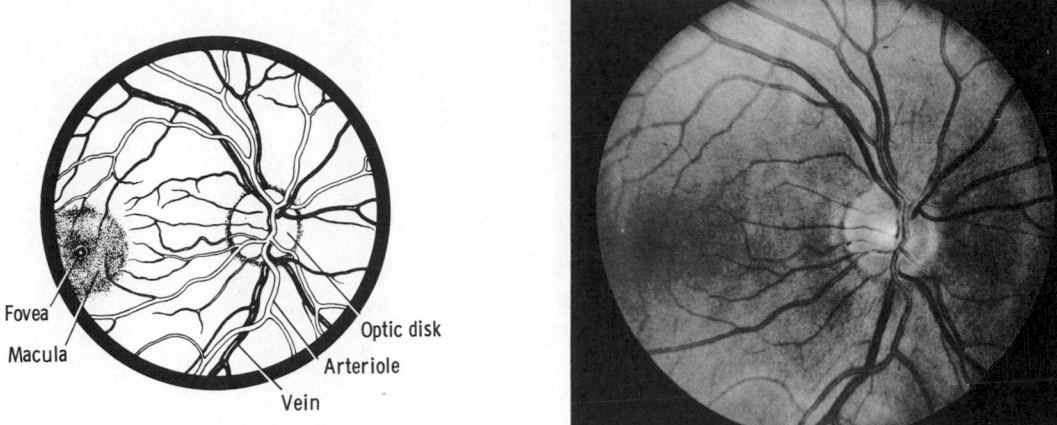

Figure 8–3. Retina seen through the ophthalmoscope in a normal human. Diagram at left identifies the landmarks in the photograph on the right. (Reproduced, with permission, from Vaughan D, Asbury T: *General Ophthalmology,* 8th ed. Lange, 1977.)

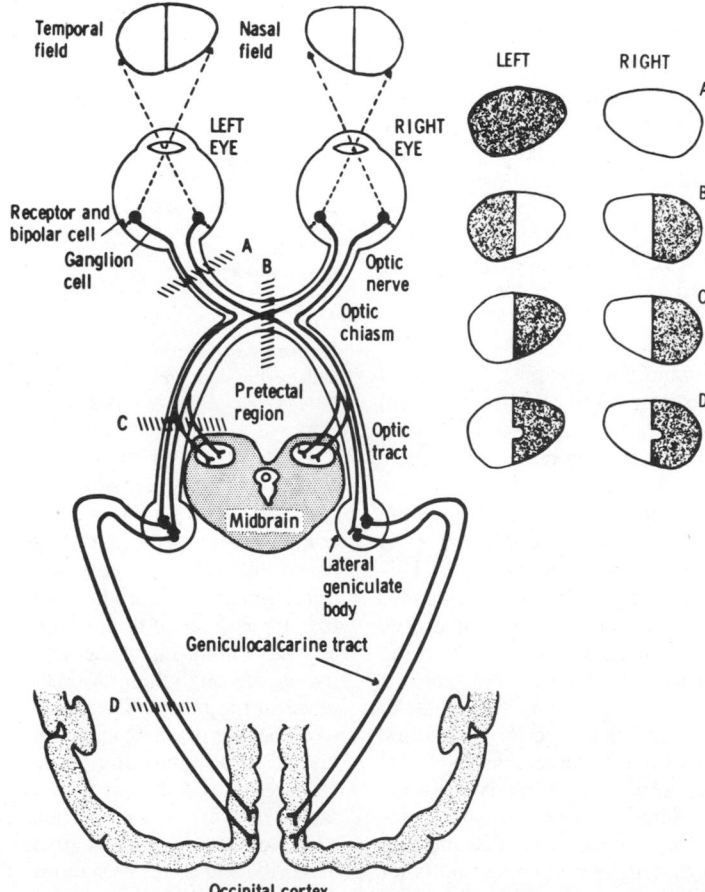

Figure 8–4. Visual pathways. Lesions at the points marked by the letters cause the visual field defects shown in the diagrams on the right (see text). Occipital lesions may spare the fibers from the macula (as in D) because of the separation in the brain of these fibers from the others subserving vision.

light rays, preventing the reflection of rays back through the retina. Such reflection would produce blurring of the visual images.

The neural elements of the retina are bound together by glial cells called Müller cells. The processes of these cells form an internal limiting membrane on the inner surface of the retina and an external limiting membrane in the receptor layer.

The optic nerve leaves the eye and the retinal blood vessels enter it at a point 3 mm medial to and slightly above the posterior pole of the globe. This region is visible through the ophthalmoscope as the **optic disk** (Fig 8–3). There are no visual receptors overlying the disk, and consequently this spot is blind (the **blind spot**). At the posterior pole of the eye, there is a yellowish pigmented spot, the **macula lutea.** This marks the location of the **fovea centralis,** a thinned-out, rod-free portion of the retina where the cones are densely packed and there are very few cells and no blood vessels overlying the receptors. The fovea is highly developed in humans. It is the point where visual acuity is greatest. When attention is attracted to or fixed on an object, the eyes are normally moved so that light rays coming from the object fall on the fovea.

The arteries, arterioles, and veins in the superficial layers of the retina near its vitreous surface can be seen through the ophthalmoscope. Since this is the one place in the body where arterioles are readily visible, ophthalmoscopic examination is of great value in the diagnosis and evaluation of diabetes mellitus, hypertension, and other diseases that affect the blood vessels. The retinal vessels supply the bipolar and ganglion cells, but the receptors are nourished for the most part by the capillary plexus in the choroid. This is why retinal detachment is so damaging to the receptor cells.

Neural Pathways

The axons of the ganglion cells pass caudally in the **optic nerve** and **optic tract** to end in the **lateral geniculate body,** a part of the thalamus. The fibers from each nasal hemiretina decussate in the **optic chiasm.** In the geniculate body, the fibers from the nasal half of one retina and the temporal half of the other synapse in a highly specific fashion on the cells whose axons form the **geniculocalcarine tract.** This tract passes to the occipital lobe of the cerebral cortex. The primary visual receiving area, or **visual cortex** (Brodmann's area 17), is located principally on the sides of the calcarine fissure. Branches of the ganglion cell axons pass from the optic tract to the pretectal region of the midbrain and the superior colliculus, where they form connections that mediate visual reflexes (Fig 8–4). Other axons pass directly from the optic chiasm to the suprachiasmatic nuclei in the hypothalamus, where they form connections that mediate light entrainment of a variety of endocrine and other circadian rhythms (see Chapters 14 and 20).

Receptors

Each rod and cone is divided into an inner and an outer segment, a nuclear region, and a synaptic zone

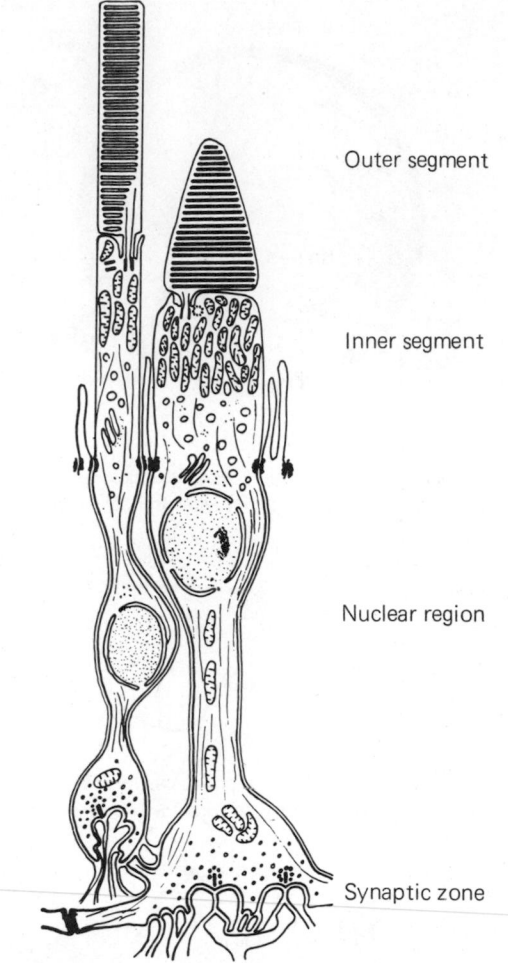

Figure 8–5. Human rod *(left)* and cone *(right)*. (Reproduced, with permission, from Missotten L: *The Ultrastructure of the Human Retina.* Editions Arscia, 1965.)

(Fig 8–5). The outer segments are modified cilia, and are made up of regular stacks of flattened saccules composed of membrane. These saccules contain the photosensitive pigment. The inner segments are rich in mitochondria. The rods are named for the thin, rod-like appearance of their outer segments. Cones generally have thick inner segments and conical outer segments, although their morphology varies from place to place in the retina. There are tight junctions between rods, between cones, and from rods to cones. In cones, the saccules in the outer segments are infoldings of the cell membrane, but in rods, most saccules are separated from the cell membrane.

Rod outer segments are being constantly renewed by formation of new saccules at the inner edge of the segment and phagocytosis of old saccules from the outer tip by cells of the pigment epithelium. In the disease retinitis pigmentosa, the phagocytic process is defective, and a layer of debris accumulates between the receptors and the pigment epithelium. Cone re-

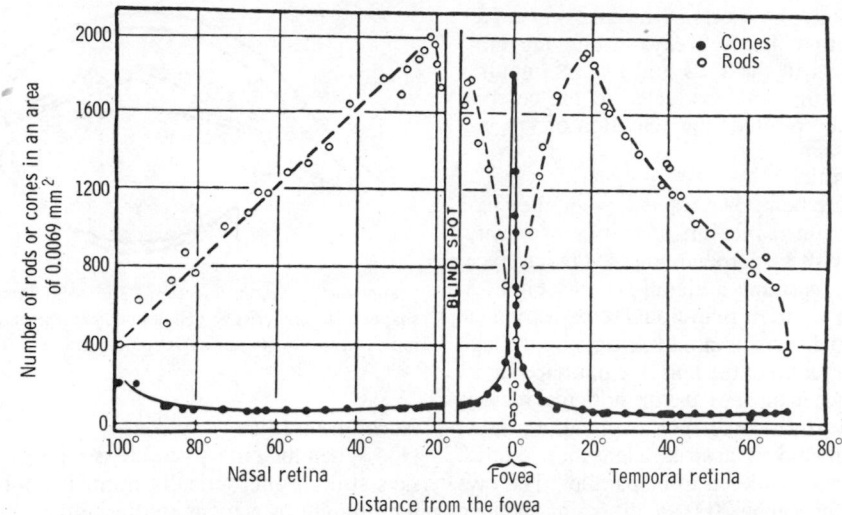

Figure 8–6. Rod and cone density along the horizontal meridian through the human retina. A plot of the relative acuity of vision in the various parts of the light-adapted eye would parallel the cone density curve; a similar plot of relative acuity of the dark-adapted eye would parallel the rod density curve. (Modified and reproduced, with permission, from Østerberg G: Topography of the layer of rods and cones in the human retina. Acta Ophthalmol [Kbh] Vol 13, Suppl 6, 1935.)

newal is a more diffuse process and appears to occur at multiple sites in the outer segments.

The fovea contains no rods, and each foveal cone has a single midget bipolar cell connecting it to a single ganglion cell, so that each foveal cone is connected to a single fiber in the optic nerve. In other portions of the retina, rods predominate (Fig 8–6), and there is a good deal of convergence. Flat bipolar cells (Fig 8–2) make synaptic contact with several cones, and rod bipolar cells make synaptic contact with several rods. Since there are approximately 6 million cones and 120 million rods in each human eye, but only 1.2 million nerve fibers in each optic nerve, the overall convergence of receptors through bipolar cells on ganglion cells is about 105:1.

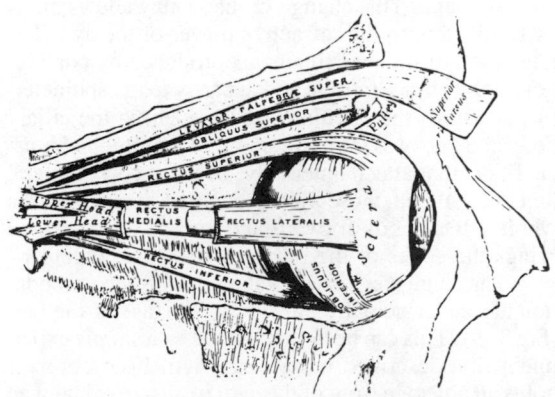

Figure 8–7. Muscles of the right orbit. The 6 muscles that move the eyeball and the levator palpebrae superioris, which raises the upper lid, are shown. (Reproduced, with permission, from: *Gray's Anatomy of the Human Body*, 29th ed. Goss CM [editor]. Lea & Febiger, 1973.)

The rods are extremely sensitive to light and are the receptors for night vision **(scotopic vision).** The scotopic visual apparatus is not capable of resolving the details and boundaries of objects or determining their color. The cones have a much higher threshold, but the cone system has a much greater acuity and is the system responsible for vision in bright light **(photopic vision)** and for color vision. There are thus 2 kinds of inputs to the CNS from the eye: input from the rods and input from the cones. The existence of these 2 kinds of inputs, each working maximally under different conditions of illumination, is called the **duplicity theory.**

Eye Muscles

The eye is moved within the orbit by 6 ocular muscles (Fig 8–7). These are innervated by the oculomotor, trochlear, and abducens nerves. The muscles and the directions in which they move the eyeball are discussed at the end of this chapter.

Protection

The eye is well protected from injury by the bony walls of the orbit. The cornea is moistened and kept clear by tears that course from the **lacrimal gland** in the upper portion of each orbit across the surface of the eye to empty via the **lacrimal duct** into the nose. Blinking helps keep the cornea moist.

THE IMAGE–FORMING MECHANISM

The eyes convert energy in the visible spectrum into action potentials in the optic nerve. The wavelengths of visible light are approximately 397–

723 nm. The images of objects in the environment are focused on the retina. The light rays striking the retina generate potentials in the rods and cones. Impulses initiated in the retina are conducted to the cerebral cortex, where they produce the sensation of vision.

Principles of Optics

Light rays are bent, or refracted, when they pass from one medium into a medium of a different density, except when they strike perpendicular to the interface. Parallel light rays striking a biconvex lens (Fig 8–8) are refracted to a point, or **principal focus,** behind the lens. The principal focus is on a line passing through the centers of curvature of the lens, the **principal axis.** The distance between the lens and the principal focus is the **principal focal distance.** For practical purposes, light rays from an object that strike a lens more than 20 ft (6 m) away are considered to be parallel. The rays from an object closer than 20 ft are diverging, and are therefore brought to a focus farther back on the principal axis than the principal focus (Fig 8–8). Biconcave lenses cause light rays to diverge.

The greater the curvature of a lens, the greater its refractive power. The refractive power of a lens is conveniently measured in **diopters,** the number of diopters being the reciprocal of the principal focal distance in meters. For example, a lens with a principal focal distance of 0.25 m has a refractive power of 1/0.25, or 4 diopters. The human eye has a refractive power of approximately 66.7 diopters at rest.

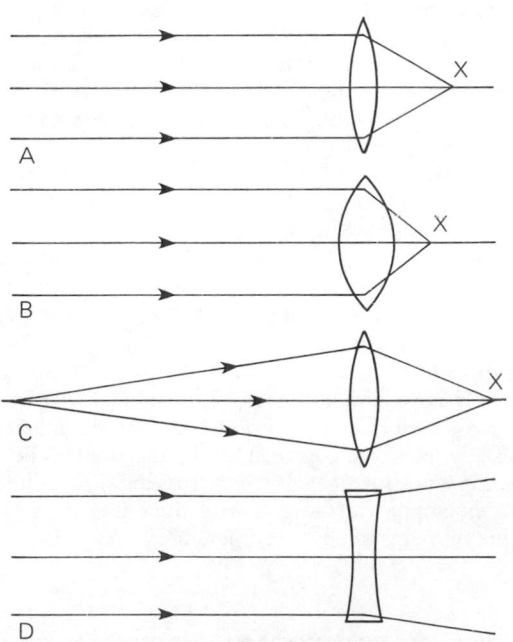

Figure 8–8. Refraction of light rays by lenses. *A:* Biconvex lens. *B:* Biconvex lens of greater strength than *A. C:* Same lens as *A,* showing effect on light rays from a near point. *D:* Biconcave lens. The center line in each case is the principal axis. X is the principal focus.

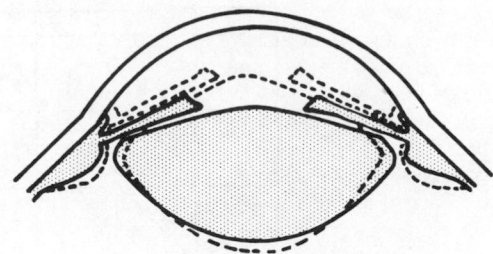

Figure 8–9. Accommodation. The solid lines represent the shape of the lens, iris, and ciliary body at rest, and the dotted lines represent the shape during accommodation.

Accommodation

When the ciliary muscle is relaxed, parallel light rays striking the optically normal **(emmetropic)** eye are brought to a focus on the retina. As long as this relaxation is maintained, rays from objects closer to the observer are brought to a focus behind the retina, and consequently the objects appear blurred. The problem of bringing diverging rays from objects closer than 6 m to a focus on the retina can be solved by increasing the distance between the lens and the retina or by increasing the curvature or refractive power of the lens. In bony fish, the problem is solved by increasing the length of the eyeball, a solution analogous to the manner in which the images of objects closer than 6 m are focused on the film of a camera by moving the lens away from the film. In mammals, the problem is solved by increasing the curvature of the lens.

The process by which the curvature of the lens is increased is called **accommodation.** At rest, the lens is held under tension by the lens ligaments. Because the lens substance is malleable and the lens capsule has considerable elasticity, the lens is pulled into a flattened shape. When the gaze is directed at a near object, the ciliary muscle contracts. This decreases the distance between the edges of the ciliary body and relaxes the lens ligaments, so that the lens springs into a more convex shape. This change in shape may add as many as 12 diopters to the refractive power of the eye. The relaxation of the lens ligaments produced by contraction of the ciliary muscle is due partly to the sphincter-like action of the circular muscle fibers in the ciliary body and partly to the contraction of longitudinal muscle fibers that attach anteriorly, near the corneoscleral junction. When these fibers contract, they pull the whole ciliary body forward and inward. This motion brings the edges of the ciliary body closer together.

The change in lens curvature during accommodation affects principally the anterior surface of the lens (Fig 8–9). This can be demonstrated by a simple experiment first described many years ago. If an observer holds an object in front of the eyes of an individual who is looking into the distance, 3 reflections of the object are visible in the subject's eye. A clear, small upright image is reflected from the cornea; a larger, fainter upright image is reflected from the anterior surface of the lens; and a small inverted image is reflected from the posterior surface of the lens. If the subject then focuses on an object nearby, the large, faint upright image becomes smaller and moves toward the other upright image whereas the other 2 images change very little. The change in size of the image is due to the increase in curvature of the reflecting surface, the anterior surface of the lens (Fig 8–9). The fact that the small upright image does not change and the inverted image changes very little shows that the corneal curvature is unchanged and that the curvature of the posterior lens surface is changed very little by accommodation.

Near Point

Accommodation is an active process, requiring muscular effort, and can therefore be tiring. Indeed, the ciliary muscle is one of the most used muscles in the body. The degree to which the lens curvature can be increased is, of course, limited, and light rays from an object very near the individual cannot be brought to a focus on the retina even with the greatest effort. The nearest point to the eye at which an object can be brought into clear focus by accommodation is called the **near point of vision.** The near point recedes throughout life, slowly at first and then rapidly with advancing age. For example, at age 8 the average normal near point is 8.6 cm from the eye and at age 20 it is 10.4 cm from the eye; but at age 60 it is 83.3 cm from the eye. This recession of the near point is due principally to increasing hardness of the lens substance, with a resulting steady decrease in the degree to which the curvature of the lens can be increased. By the time the normal individual reaches the age of 40–45, the near point often recedes far enough so that reading and close work become difficult. This condition, which is known as **presbyopia,** can be corrected by wearing glasses with convex lenses (see below).

The Near Response

In addition to accommodation, the visual axes converge and the pupil constricts when an individual looks at a near object. This 3-part response— accommodation, convergence, and pupillary constriction—is called the **near response.**

Other Pupillary Reflexes

When light is directed into one eye, the pupil constricts (**pupillary light reflex**). The pupil of the other eye also constricts (**consensual light reflex**). The optic nerve fibers that carry the impulses initiating pupillary responses end in the pretectal region and the superior colliculi. The pathway for the light reflex, which presumably passes from the pretectal region to the oculomotor nuclei (Edinger-Westphal nuclei) bilaterally, is different from that for accommodation. In some pathologic conditions, notably neurosyphilis, the pupillary response to light may be absent while the response to accommodation remains intact. This phenomenon, the so-called **Argyll Robertson pupil,** is said to be due to a destructive lesion in the tectal region.

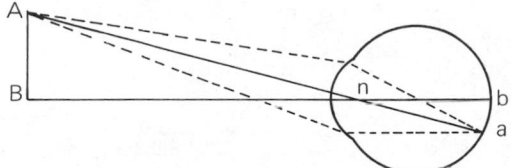

Figure 8–10. Reduced eye. n, nodal point. AnB and anb are similar triangles. In this reduced eye, the nodal point is 15 mm from the retina. All refraction is assumed to take place at the surface of the cornea, 5 mm from the nodal point, between a medium of density 1.000 (air) and a medium of density 1.333 (water). The dotted lines represent rays of light diverging from A and refracted at the cornea so that they are focused on the retina at a.

Retinal Image

In the eye, light is actually refracted at the anterior surface of the cornea and at the anterior and posterior surfaces of the lens. The process of refraction can be represented diagrammatically, however, without introducing any appreciable error, by drawing the rays of light as if all refraction occurs at the anterior surface of the cornea. Fig 8–10 is a diagram of such a "reduced" or "schematic" eye. In this diagram, the **nodal point** or optical center of the eye coincides with the junction of the middle and posterior third of the lens, 15 mm from the retina. This is the point through which the light rays from an object pass without refraction. All other rays entering the pupil from each point on the object are refracted and brought to a focus on the retina. If the height of the object (**AB**), and its distance from the observer (**Bn**) are known, the size of its retinal image can be calculated because **AnB** and **anb** in Fig 8–10 are similar triangles. The angle AnB is the **visual angle** subtended by object AB. It should be noted that the retinal image is inverted. The connections of the retinal receptors are such that from birth any inverted image on the retina is viewed right side up and projected to the visual field on the side opposite to the retinal area stimulated. This perception is innate. It is present in infants and when vision is restored in previously blind individuals who have had congenital cataracts removed surgically. If retinal images are turned right side up by means of special lenses, the objects viewed look as if they were upside down.

Common Defects of the Image-Forming Mechanism

In some individuals, the eyeball is shorter than normal and parallel rays of light are brought to a focus behind the retina. This abnormality is called **hyperopia,** or farsightedness (Fig 8–11). Sustained accommodation, even when viewing distant objects, can partially compensate for the defect, but the prolonged muscular effort is tiring and may cause headaches and blurring of vision. The prolonged convergence of the visual axes associated with the accommodation may lead eventually to squint, or

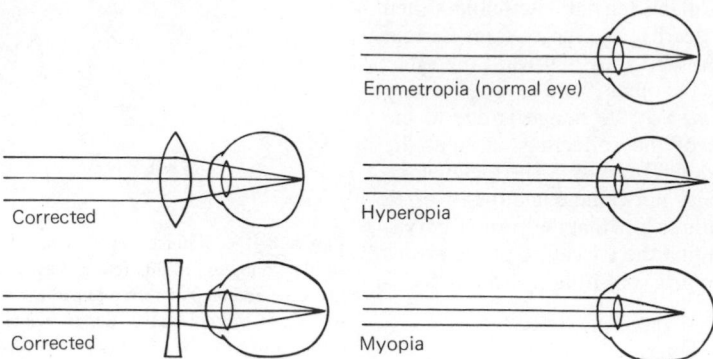

Figure 8–11. Common defects of the optical system of the eye. In hyperopia, the eyeball is too short, and light rays come to a focus behind the retina. A biconvex lens corrects this by adding to the refractive power of the lens of the eye. In myopia, the eyeball is too long, and light rays focus in front of the retina. Placing a biconcave lens in front of the eye causes the light rays to diverge slightly before striking the eye, so that they are brought to a focus on the retina.

strabismus (see below). The use of glasses with convex lenses to aid the refractive power of the eye in shortening the focal distance corrects the defect.

In **myopia,** or nearsightedness, the anteroposterior diameter of the eyeball is too long. This defect can be corrected by the use of glasses with biconcave lenses so that parallel light rays are made to diverge slightly before they strike the eye.

Astigmatism is a common condition in which the curvature of the cornea is not uniform. When the curvature in one meridian is different from that in others, light rays in that meridian are refracted to a different focus so that part of the retinal image is blurred. A similar defect may be produced if the lens is pushed out of alignment or the curvature of the lens is

not uniform, but these conditions are rare. Astigmatism can usually be corrected with cylindric lenses placed in such a way that they equalize the refraction in all meridians. **Presbyopia** has been mentioned above.

THE PHOTORECEPTOR MECHANISM: GENESIS OF ACTION POTENTIALS

The potential changes that initiate action potentials in the retina are generated by the action of light on photosensitive compounds in the rods and cones. When light is absorbed by these substances, their struc-

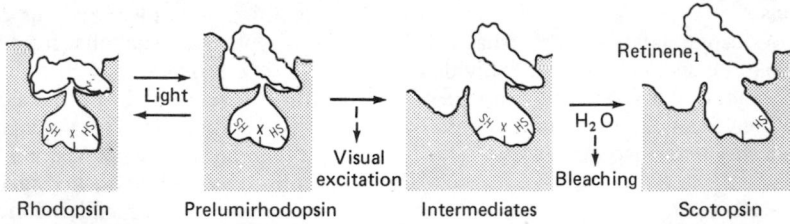

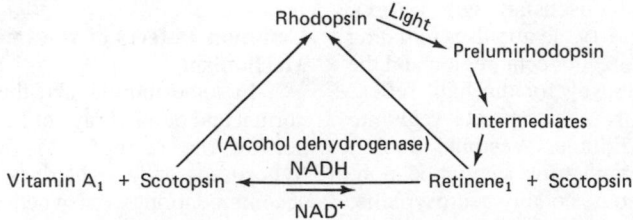

Figure 8–12. *Top:* Diagrammatic representation of events believed to occur in rods. Light converts retinene from the cis to the trans isomer, straightening out the molecule and permitting the opsin to open up. SH, HS, and X represent hypothetical active groups in the opsin that are exposed by the straightening of the retinene molecule. *Bottom:* Rhodopsin cycle in humans. The iodopsin cycle is presumably similar. (Modified from Brown KT in: *Medical Physiology,* 14th ed. Mountcastle VB [editor]. Mosby, 1979 [in press].)

ture changes, and this change is responsible for initiating neural activity.

The photosensitive compounds in the eyes of humans and most other mammals are made up of a protein, called an **opsin,** and **retinene₁**, the aldehyde of vitamin A₁. The term retinene₁ is used to distinguish this compound from retinene₂, which is found in the eyes of some animal species. Since the retinenes are aldehydes, they are also called **retinals.** The A vitamins themselves are alcohols and are therefore called **retinols.**

Rhodopsin

The photosensitive pigment in the rods is called **rhodopsin,** or **visual purple.** Its opsin is called **scotopsin.** Light bleaches rhodopsin by breaking the retinene-scotopsin bond, the reaction proceeding through a series of short-lived intermediates to retinene and scotopsin.

The mechanism of action of light on rhodopsin is shown diagrammatically in Fig 8–12. The retinene in rhodopsin is in the form of the 11-cis isomer. The only action of light is conversion of the retinene to the all-trans isomer, forming **prelumirhodopsin.** This straightens out the retinene and permits the spontaneous occurrence of the next step, a change in the shape of the opsin. The opening up of the opsin may expose reactive groups that catalyze the reactions leading to the potential change. The last step in the sequence of reactions is the bleaching proper, the separation of the retinene from the opsin by hydrolysis. Some of the rhodopsin is regenerated directly, while some of the retinene₁ is reduced by the enzyme alcohol dehydrogenase in the presence of NADH to vitamin A₁, and this in turn reacts with scotopsin to form rhodopsin.

All of these reactions except the formation of prelumirhodopsin are independent of light, proceeding equally well in light or darkness. The amount of rhodopsin in the receptors therefore varies inversely with the incident light.

In vitro, solutions of rhodopsin absorb light maximally at a wavelength of 505 nm (Fig 8–13). The curve relating the sensitivity in dim light of the intact eye to light of different wavelengths also reaches a maximum at 505 nm. The fact that this **scotopic visibility curve** and the absorption curve of rhodopsin in vitro coincide is strong evidence that the rod pigment responsible for dim light vision is indeed rhodopsin.

Cone Pigments

There are 3 different types of cones in primates (see below), and there are 3 different cone pigments. One cone pigment, **iodopsin,** has been isolated. It is found in human cones and appears to be the pigment most sensitive to red light. It is made up of retinene₁ and **photopsin,** a protein different from scotopsin. The other cone pigments also contain retinene₁ and the differences between them are due to differences in the structures of the opsins. The **photopic visibility curve** (Fig 8–13) is the composite curve of the 3 cone systems.

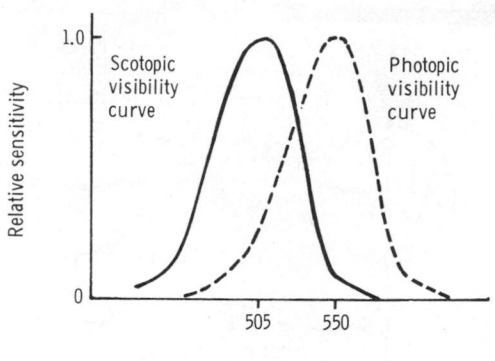

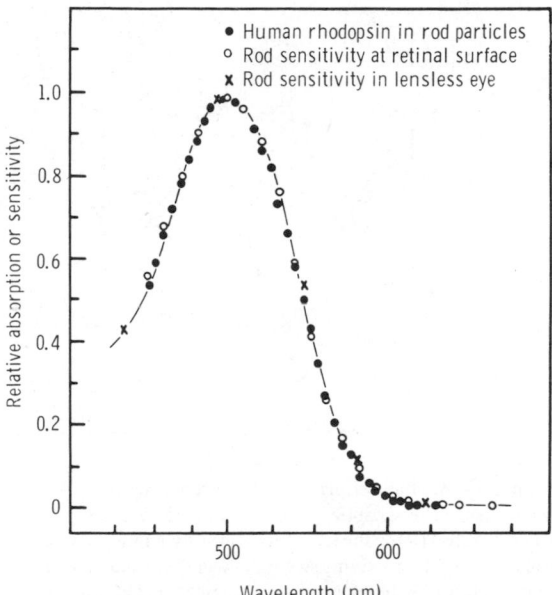

Figure 8–13. *Top:* Scotopic and photopic visibility curves. Both curves are adjusted so that at peak sensitivity they have a relative sensitivity value of 1.0. In terms of absolute values, rod (scotopic) sensitivity is, of course, much greater than cone (photopic) sensitivity. *Bottom:* Correspondence between absorption of human rhodopsin and rod sensitivity. The rod sensitivity curves have been plotted with and without the lens. (Reproduced, with permission, from Wald G, Brown PK: Human rhodopsin. Science 127:222, 1958.)

Potentials

The receptor potentials of rods and cones are preceded by an earlier biphasic electrical response. This response has a very short latency and has been named the **early receptor potential.** It is closely associated with rapid molecular events that follow the absorption of light by the photopigment. It provides a convenient method for recording these rapid events, but it is not part of the direct sequence of excitatory events in retinal photoreceptors.

The eye is unique in that the receptor potentials of the photoreceptors and the electrical responses of most

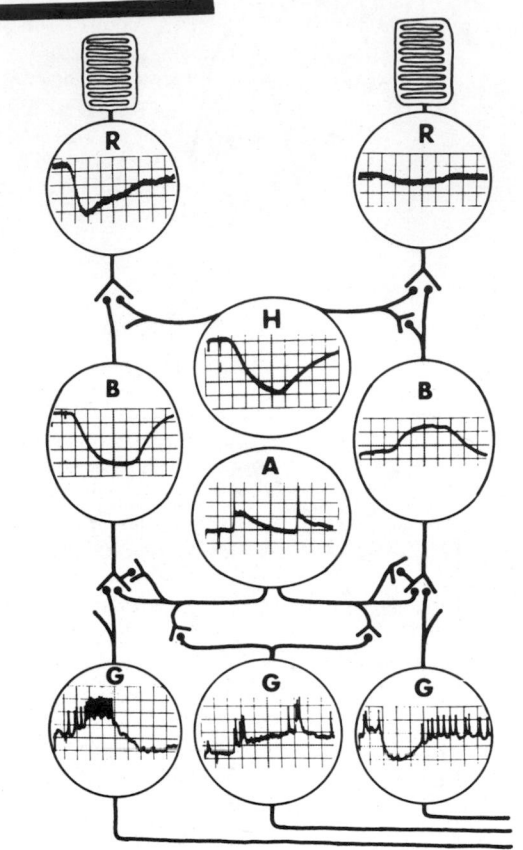

Figure 8–14. Intracellularly recorded responses of cells in retina to light. The synaptic connections of the cells are also indicated. The rod (R) on the left is receiving a light flash, whereas the rod on the right is receiving steady, low-intensity illumination. H, horizontal cell; B, bipolar cell; A, amacrine cell; G, ganglion cell. (Reproduced, with permission, from Dowling JE: Organization of vertebrate retinas. Invest Ophthalmol 9:655, 1970.)

of the other natural elements in the retina are local, graded potentials, and it is only in the ganglion cells that all or none action potentials transmitted over appreciable distances are generated. The responses of the rods, cones, and horizontal cells are hyperpolarizing (Fig 8–14), and the responses of the bipolar cells are either hyperpolarizing or depolarizing, whereas amacrine cells produce depolarizing potentials and spikes that may act as generator potentials for the propagated spikes produced in the ganglion cells.

Genesis of Photoreceptor Responses

It is now established that in the dark there is a steady current flow from the outer portion of the inner segments of the rods and cones to their outer segments. This current flow is due to the operation of an electrogenic Na^+-K^+ pump in the portion of the inner segments that is rich in mitochondria. Light causes a sharp decrease in Na^+ conductance in the outer segments, causing a decrease in the dark current and

hyperpolarizing the receptor. The hyperpolarization, which is proportionate to the amount of light striking the receptor, initiates the electrical events in the other neural elements. Current evidence indicates that there is steady release of transmitter from the photoreceptors in the dark and that the light-induced hyperpolarization decreases transmitter release.

The cone receptor potential has a sharp onset and offset, whereas the rod receptor potential has a sharp onset and slow offset. The cone response range shifts with background illumination, whereas the rod response range does not. For this reason, cones generate good responses to changes in light intensity above background but do not represent absolute illumination well, whereas rods detect absolute illumination.

The mechanism by which the action of light on visual pigment leads to a decrease in the Na^+ conductance of the cell membrane of photoreceptors is still unknown. The pigments are embedded in the membranes forming the saccules in the outer segments, and the change in the configuration of retinene presumably opens channels through which a substance passes to the inside of the membrane that surrounds the cell. There it acts to decrease conductance through Na^+ channels. In the case of rods, the substance must diffuse from one membrane to another, since most of the saccule membranes are separated from the cell membrane. In the case of cones, the substance presumably passes from ECF into the cell, since cone saccules are invaginations of the cell membrane. There is considerable evidence that the substance involved is Ca^{2+}, but additional research is needed to settle the issue.

Image Formation

In a sense, the processing of visual information in the retina involves the formation of three images. The first image formed by the action of light on the photoreceptors is changed to a second image in the bipolar cells, and this in turn is converted to a third image in the ganglion cells. In the formation of the second image, the signal is altered by the horizontal cells, and in the formation of the third, it is altered by the amacrine cells. There is little change in the impulse pattern in the lateral geniculate bodies, so the third image reaches the occipital cortex.

The electrical responses of the bipolar cells are graded, slow potential changes. One type of bipolar cell depolarizes on steady illumination of the retina with a spot of light whereas another type hyperpolarizes. In each case, addition of an annulus of light around the central spot (surround illumination) reduces the response to the central spot. The decrease is probably due to inhibitory feedback from one photoreceptor to another mediated via horizontal cells. Thus, activation of nearby photoreceptors by addition of the annulus triggers horizontal cell hyperpolarization, which in turn inhibits the response of the centrally activated photoreceptors. The inhibition of the response to central illumination by an increase in surrounding illumination is an example of **lateral** or **afferent inhibition**—that form of inhibition in which activation of a particular neural unit is associated with inhibition of the activity of nearby units. It is a general phenomenon in mammalian sensory systems and helps to sharpen the edges of a stimulus and improve discrimination.

The ganglion cells, which produce propagated spikes, are of 2 types: a tonic, or "on," type and a phasic, or "off," type. The "on" type produces a steady discharge of spikes in response to central illumination, and its rate of discharge is suppressed by surround illumination. The "off" type produces a burst of action potentials at the onset and the termination of illumination and is silent between. The responses of the "on" cells resemble the responses of the bipolar cells, and they appear to signal the relative level of illumination in the center of their receptive fields (see Chapter 4). Their sensitivity is controlled by the level of surrounding illumination. The responses of the "off" cells resemble those of the amacrine cells, which depolarize when a stimulus is turned on and when it is turned off. It seems likely that the "off" ganglion cells detect movement or change in the visual field.

Electroretinogram

The electrical activity of the eye has been studied by recording fluctuations in the potential difference between an electrode in the eye and another on the back of the eye. At rest, there is a 6 mV potential difference between the front and the back of the eye, with the front positive. When light strikes the eye, a characteristic sequence of potential changes follows. The record of this sequence is known as the **electroretinogram (ERG).** Turning on the light stimulus elicits the **a** and **b waves,** as shown in Fig 8–15, and also the **c wave,** which is so slow that with short stimuli its peak occurs after the stimulus. When the stimulus is turned off, a negative off-deflection occurs.

Through careful analysis of the effects of drugs and records obtained with microelectrodes inserted to varying depths in the retina, the ERG has been re-

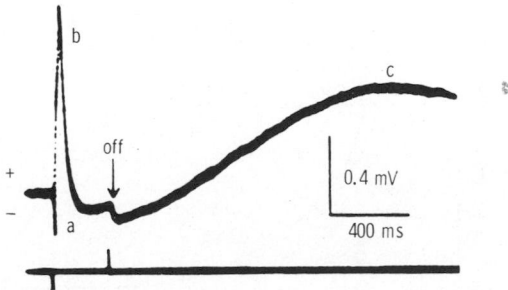

Figure 8–15. Electroretinogram recorded with an electrode in the vitreous humor of a cat. Note that, by convention in electroretinography, positive deflections are upward. The onset and termination of the stimulus are indicated by the vertical lines in the lower record. (Reproduced, with permission, from Brown KT: The electroretinogram: Its components and their origins. Vision Res 8:633, 1968.)

solved into its components. The c wave is generated in the pigment epithelium. The neural components summate to give the other deflections of the ERG.

Electroretinograms can be recorded in humans with one electrode on the cornea and the other on the skin of the head. Electroretinographic records are helpful in the diagnosis of certain ophthalmologic disorders, but most of these diseases are more readily diagnosed by simpler methods.

Synaptic Mediators in the Retina

There is evidence that acetylcholine is a transmitter at some of the synaptic junctions in the retina. The retina also contains relatively large amounts of dopamine, 5-hydroxytryptamine, gamma-aminobutyric acid (GABA), and substance P, a polypeptide. The evidence that most of these substances are synaptic mediators in the brain is discussed in Chapter 15. Evidence that GABA is an important transmitter in the eye includes the observation that injection of the GABA antagonist picrotoxin into the blood supply of the eye abolishes the directional sensitivity of ganglion cells that normally respond to changes in the direction of a stimulus. The presence of dopamine in some of the amacrine cells has been established by histochemical technics. It has been reported that one of the drugs which inhibits monoamine oxidase impairs red-green color discrimination. Monoamine oxidase is the enzyme that catalyzes the oxidation of 5-hydroxytryptamine and dopamine (see Chapter 15).

RESPONSES IN THE VISUAL CORTEX

The ganglion cell axons project an accurate spatial representation of the retina on the lateral geniculate body, and the body projects a similar point for point representation on the visual cortex. There appear to be about twice as many fibers projecting from the lateral geniculate body to the visual cortex as there are reaching the body. In the visual cortex, there are many nerve cells associated with each fiber.

The receptive fields of the neurons in the lateral geniculate body are similar to those of the ganglion cells except that they respond more to the peripheral portions of their fields. In the visual cortex, however, single cells respond to lines and edges in their receptive fields rather than to circular spots. On the basis of the characteristics of their responses, the cells have been classified as simple, complex, or hypercomplex.

The **simple cells** respond maximally to slits of light, dark lines, or edges, but a particular cell responds only when the stimulus has a particular orientation. The farther the stimulating line is turned from the optimal orientation, the less the discharge it creates (Fig 8–16), and discharge is minimal when it is perpendicular to the optimal orientation. Like the ganglion cells, the simple cells show patterns of on-off

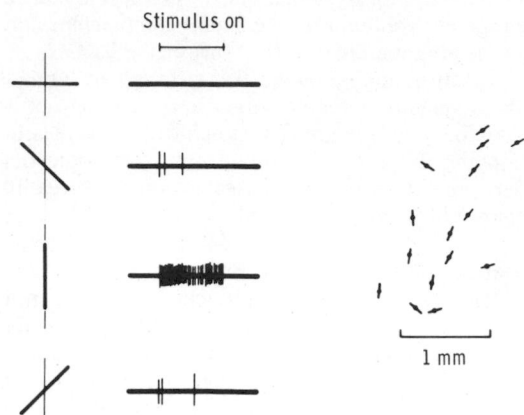

Figure 8–16. *Left:* Diagrammatic representation of the response of a single neuron in the occipital cortex to a linear visual stimulus with various orientations. The records show the number of action potentials generated when the eye was stimulated. Discharge was maximal when the orientation of the stimulus was vertical, as indicated on the left, and nil when it was horizontal. (Data from Hubel D, Wiesel T: Receptive fields of single neurons in the cat's striate cortex. J Physiol [Lond] 148:574, 1959.) *Right:* Receptive field orientation of superficial neurons in a small portion of the occipital cortex. The locations of the neurons are indicated by the dots on this map of the cortical surface, and the orientation of the stimulus to which each neuron responded maximally is indicated by the line through the dot. (Data from Hubel D, Wiesel T: Shape and arrangement of columns in cat's striate cortex. J Physiol [Lond] 165:559, 1963.)

interaction in their receptive fields. Typically, a long narrow "on" area is sandwiched between 2 "off" areas. Other patterns are also found, but the organization is always linear. Simple cells respond to movement of the stimulus, but with only a transient burst of activity.

The **complex cells** also respond to edges and lines in a particular orientation, but they discharge in a sustained fashion when the stimulus is moved. An appreciable number of the neurons in the visual cortex are directionally sensitive in this fashion. **Hypercomplex cells** resemble complex cells, but their response is dependent on the length of the edge or line. Simple cells are stellate neurons, whereas complex and hypercomplex cells are larger pyramidal neurons. Since these various types of cells in the visual cortex respond to one or another of the features of the stimulus, they have been called **feature detectors.** Feature detectors are also found in the cortical areas for other sensory modalities.

The visual cortex, like the other primary sensory areas in the cortex, is organized in vertically oriented columns of cells. Many simple cells project onto each complex cell. Presumably, among the many millions of neurons in the visual cortex there are simple cells with maximum rates of discharge for all the possible orientations in all the portions of the visual field. The complex cells integrate the discharges of the simple cells and the output of the complex cells is in turn elaborated by as yet unknown mechanisms into the sensation of vision.

OTHER ASPECTS OF VISUAL FUNCTION

Dark Adaptation

If a person spends a considerable period of time in brightly lighted surroundings and then moves to a dimly lighted environment, the retinas slowly become more sensitive to light as the individual becomes "accustomed to the dark." This decline in visual threshold is known as **dark adaptation.** It is nearly maximal in about 20 minutes, although there is some further decline over longer periods. On the other hand, when one passes suddenly from a dim to a brightly lighted environment, the light seems intensely and even uncomfortably bright until the eyes adapt to the increased illumination and the visual threshold rises. This adaptation occurs over a period of about 5 minutes and is called **light adaptation,** although, strictly speaking, it is merely the disappearance of dark adaptation.

There are actually 2 components to the dark adaptation response (Fig 8–17). The first drop in visual threshold, rapid but small in magnitude, is known to be due to dark adaptation of the cones because when only the foveal, rod-free portion of the retina is tested the decline proceeds no further. In the peripheral portions of the retina, a further drop occurs due to adaptation of the rods. The total change in threshold between the light-adapted and the fully dark-adapted eye is very great.

Radiologists, aircraft pilots, and others who need maximal visual sensitivity in dim light can avoid having to wait 20 minutes in the dark to become dark-

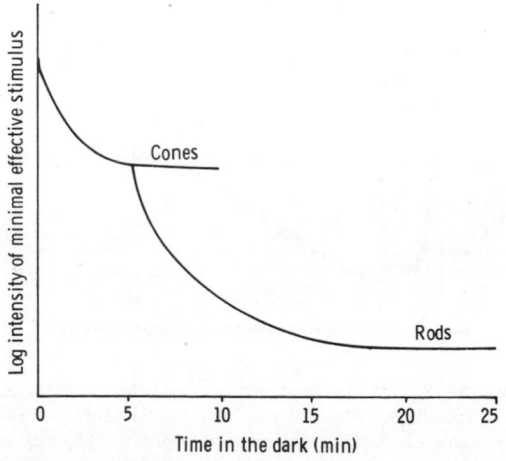

Figure 8–17. Dark adaptation. The curve shows the change in the intensity of a stimulus necessary to just excite the retina in dim light as a function of the time the observer has been in the dark.

adapted if they wear red goggles when in bright light. Light wavelengths in the red end of the spectrum stimulate the rods to only a slight degree while permitting the cones to function reasonably well (Fig 8–13). Therefore, a person wearing red glasses can see in bright light during the time it takes for the rods to become dark-adapted.

The time required for dark adaptation is determined in part by the time required to build up the rhodopsin stores. In bright light, much of the pigment is continuously being broken down, and some time is required in dim light for accumulation of the amounts necessary for optimal rod function. However, dark adaptation also occurs in the cones, and additional factors are undoubtedly involved.

Effect of Vitamin Deficiencies on the Eye

In view of the importance of vitamin A in the synthesis of rhodopsin and iodopsin, it is not surprising that avitaminosis A produces visual abnormalities. Among these, one of the earliest is night blindness, or **nyctalopia.** This fact first called attention to the role of vitamin A in rod function, but it is now clear that concomitant cone degeneration occurs as vitamin A deficiency develops, which happens with reduced dietary intake or impaired intestinal absorption of this fat-soluble vitamin. Prolonged deficiency is associated with anatomic changes in the rods and cones followed by degeneration of the neural layers of the retina. Treatment with vitamin A can restore retinal function if given before the receptors are destroyed.

Other vitamins, especially those of the B complex, are necessary for the normal functioning of the retina and other neural tissues. Nicotinamide is part of the nicotinamide adenine dinucleotide (NAD^+) molecule, and this coenzyme plays a role in the interconversion of retinene and vitamin A in the rhodopsin cycle.

Physiologic Nystagmus

Even when a subject stares fixedly at a stationary object, the eyeballs are not still; there are continuous jerky motions and other movements. This **physiologic nystagmus** appears to have an important function. Although individual visual receptors do not adapt rapidly to constant illumination, their neural connections do. Indeed, it has been shown that if, by means of an optical lever system, the image of an object is fixed so that it falls steadily on the same spot in the retina, the object disappears from view. Continuous visualization of objects apparently requires that the retinal images be continuously and rapidly shifted from one receptor to another.

Visual Acuity

Physiologic nystagmus is one of the many factors that determine **visual acuity.** This parameter of vision should not be confused with **visual threshold.** Visual threshold is the minimal amount of light that elicits a sensation of light; visual acuity is the degree to which the details and contours of objects are perceived. Al-

though there is evidence that other measures are more accurate, visual acuity is usually defined in terms of the **minimum separable**—ie, the shortest distance by which 2 lines can be separated and still be perceived as 2 lines. Clinically, visual acuity is often determined by use of the familiar Snellen letter charts viewed at a distance of 20 ft (6 m). The individual being tested reads aloud the smallest line distinguishable. The results are expressed as a fraction. The numerator of the fraction is 20, the distance at which the subject reads the chart. The denominator is the greatest distance from the chart at which a normal individual can read the smallest line the subject can read. Normal visual acuity is 20/20; a subject with 20/15 visual acuity has better than normal vision (not farsightedness); and one with 20/100 visual acuity has subnormal vision. The Snellen charts are designed so that the height of the letters in the smallest line a normal individual can read at 20 ft subtends a visual angle of 5 min. Each line in the letters subtends 1 min of arc, and the lines in the letters are separated by 1 min of arc. Thus, the minimum separable in a normal individual corresponds to a visual angle of about 1 min.

Visual acuity is a complex phenomenon, and is influenced by a large variety of factors. These include optical factors such as the state of the image-forming mechanisms of the eye, retinal factors such as the state of the cones, and stimulus factors including the illumination, brightness of the stimulus, contrast between the stimulus and background, and the length of time the subject is exposed to the stimulus.

Critical Fusion Frequency

The time-resolving ability of the eye is determined by measuring the **critical fusion frequency (CFF),** the rate at which stimuli can be presented and still be perceived as separate stimuli. Stimuli presented at a more rapid rate than the CFF are perceived as a continuous stimulus. Motion pictures move because the frames are presented at a rate above the CFF. Consequently, movies begin to flicker when the projector slows down.

Visual Fields & Binocular Vision

The visual field of each eye is the portion of the external world visible out of that eye. Theoretically it should be circular, but actually it is cut off medially by the nose and superiorly by the roof of the orbit (Fig 8–18). Mapping the visual fields is important in neurologic diagnosis. The peripheral portions of the visual fields are mapped with an instrument called a **perimeter,** and the process is referred to as **perimetry.** One eye is covered while the other is fixed on a central point. A small target is moved toward this central point along selected meridians, and, along each, the location where it first becomes visible is plotted in degrees of arc away from the central point (Fig 8–18). The central visual fields are mapped with a **tangent screen,** a black felt screen across which a white target is moved. By noting the locations where the target disappears and reappears, the blind spot and

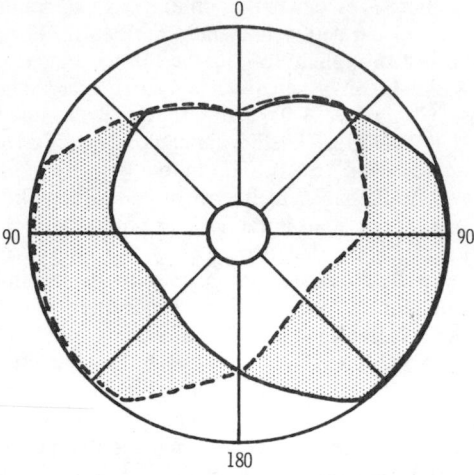

Figure 8–18. Monocular and binocular visual fields. The dotted line encloses the visual field of the left eye; the solid line that of the right eye. The common area (heart-shaped clear zone in the center) is viewed with binocular vision. The shaded areas are viewed with monocular vision.

any **objective scotomas** (blind spots due to disease) can be outlined.

The central parts of the visual fields of the 2 eyes coincide; therefore, anything in this portion of the field is viewed with **binocular vision.** The impulses set up in the 2 retinas by light rays from an object are fused at the cortical level into a single image **(fusion).** The points on the retina on which the image of an object must fall if it is to be seen binocularly as a single object are called **corresponding points.** If one eye is gently pushed out of line while staring fixedly at an object in the center of the visual field, double vision **(diplopia)** results; the image on the retina of the eye that is displaced no longer falls on the corresponding point. When visual images chronically fall on noncorresponding points in the 2 retinas in children under the age of 6, one is eventually suppressed **(suppression scotoma)** and diplopia disappears. This suppression is a cortical phenomenon, and it usually does not develop in adults.

Binocular vision is often assigned an important role in the perception of depth. Actually, depth perception is to a large degree monocular, depending upon the relative sizes of objects, their shadows, and, in the case of moving objects, their movement relative to one another (movement parallax). However, binocular vision does add some appreciation of depth and proportion.

Effect of Lesions in the Optic Pathways

The anatomy of the pathways from the eyes to the brain is shown in Fig 8–4. Lesions along these pathways can be localized with a high degree of accuracy by the effects they produce in the visual fields.

The fibers from the nasal half of each retina decussate in the optic chiasm, so that the fibers in the optic tracts are those from the temporal half of one retina and the nasal half of the other. In other words, each optic tract subserves half of the field of vision. Therefore, a lesion that interrupts one optic nerve causes blindness in that eye, but a lesion in one optic tract causes blindness in half of the visual field (Fig 8–4). This defect is classified as a **homonymous** (same side of both visual fields) **hemianopsia** (half-blindness). Lesions affecting the optic chiasm, such as pituitary tumors expanding out of the sella turcica, cause destruction of the fibers from both nasal hemiretinas, and produce a **heteronymous** (opposite sides of the visual fields) **hemianopsia.** Since the fibers from the maculas are located posteriorly in the optic chiasm, hemianopsic scotomas develop before there is complete loss of vision in the 2 hemiretinas. Selective visual field defects are further classified as bitemporal, binasal, and right or left.

The optic nerve fibers from the upper retinal quadrants subserving vision in the lower half of the visual field terminate in the medial half of the lateral geniculate body, while the fibers from the lower retinal quadrants terminate in the lateral half. The geniculocalcarine fibers from the medial half of the lateral geniculate terminate on the superior lip of the calcarine fissure, while those from the lateral half terminate on the inferior lip. Furthermore, the fibers from the lateral geniculate body that subserve macular vision separate from those which subserve peripheral vision and end more posteriorly on the lips of the calcarine fissure (Fig 8–19). Because of this anatomic arrangement, occipital lobe lesions may produce discrete quadrantic visual field defects (upper and lower quadrants of each half visual field). **Macular sparing,** ie, loss of peripheral vision with intact macular vision, is also common with occipital lesions (Fig 8–4) because the macular representation is separate from that of the peripheral fields and very large relative to that of the peripheral fields. Therefore, occipital lesions must extend considerable distances to destroy macular as well as peripheral vision.

Bilateral destruction of the occipital cortex in humans causes essentially complete blindness, although in lower mammals considerable vision (especially rod vision) remains. The primary visual receiving area, Brodmann's area 17, also plays a role in visual discrimination. Areas 18 and 19, the so-called visual association areas, are apparently concerned with visual orientation, depth perception, and the relay of information from the visual cortex to other parts of the brain.

The fibers subserving the reflex pupillary constriction produced by shining a light into the eye leave the optic tracts in front of the geniculate bodies to enter the pretectal region. Therefore, blindness with preservation of the pupillary light reflex is almost invariably due to a lesion behind the optic tracts.

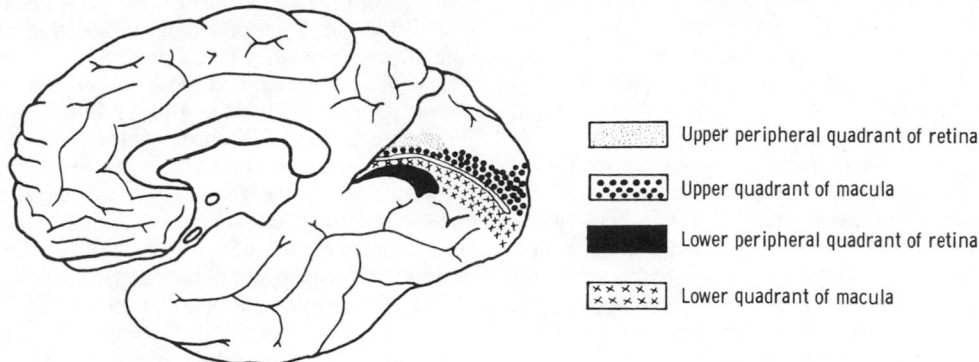

Upper peripheral quadrant of retina

Upper quadrant of macula

Lower peripheral quadrant of retina

Lower quadrant of macula

Figure 8–19. Medial view of human cerebral hemisphere showing projection of the retina on the calcarine fissure. (Redrawn and reproduced, with permission, from Brouwer H: Projection of the retina on the cortex in man. Res Publ Assoc Res Nerv Ment Dis 13:529, 1934.)

COLOR VISION

Characteristics of Color

Colors have 3 attributes: **hue, intensity,** and **saturation,** or degree of freedom from dilution with white. For any color there is a **complementary color** that, when properly mixed with it, produces a sensation of white. Black is the sensation produced by the absence of light, but it is probably a positive sensation because the blind eye does not "see black"; it "sees nothing." Such phenomena as successive and simultaneous contrasts, optical tricks that produce a sensation of color in the absence of color, negative and positive after-images, and various psychologic aspects of color vision are also pertinent. Detailed discussion of these phenomena can be found in textbooks of physiologic optics.

Another observation of basic importance is the demonstration that the sensation of any spectral color, white, and even the extraspectral color, purple, can be produced by mixing various proportions of red light (wavelength 723–647 nm), green light (575–492 nm), and blue light (492–450 nm). Red, green, and blue are therefore called the **primary colors.**

Retinal Mechanisms

Before the turn of the century, color vision was believed to be subserved by 3 types of cones, each type containing a different photosensitive substance and being maximally sensitive to one of the 3 primary colors. This view, generally called the **Young-Helmholtz theory,** also held that the sensation of any given color was determined by the relative frequency of the impulses reaching the brain from each of the 3 cone systems.

The existence of 3 types of cones in the eyes of fish, monkeys, and humans has been proved by measuring the absorption spectrums of individual cones (Fig 8–20). One type of human cone absorbs light maximally in the blue-violet portion of the spec-

trum; the second absorbs maximally in the green portion; and the third absorbs maximally in the yellow portion. Blue, green, and red are the primary colors, but the cones with their maximal sensitivity in the yellow portion of the spectrum are sensitive enough in the red portion to respond to red light at a lower threshold than green. This is all the Young-Helmholtz theory requires. Thus, the 3-receptor theory of color vision is established.

On the other hand, current evidence does not support the view that there are separate pathways from each of the cone systems to the brain. There is instead a coding process in the retina that converts color information into "on" and "off" responses in individual ganglion cells. In fish retinas, certain horizontal cells receive a depolarizing input from red and a hyperpolarizing input from green cells. Thus, the size and polarity of the potential in each of these horizontal cells depends on the degree of simultaneous stimulation of the red and green cones to which it is connected. Other horizontal cells are depolarized by yellow light and hyperpolarized by blue light. They are attached to red

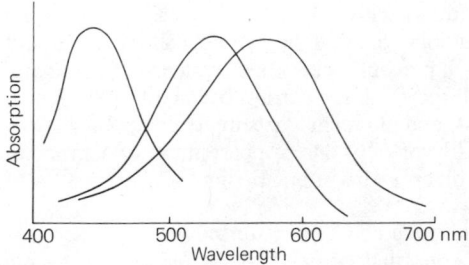

Figure 8–20. Absorption spectrums of the 3 cone pigments in the human retina. The pigment that peaks at 445 nm senses blue and the pigment that peaks at 535 nm senses green. The remaining pigment peaks in the yellow portion of the spectrum, at 570 nm, but its spectrum extends far enough into the long wavelengths to sense red. (Reproduced, with permission, from Michael CR: Color vision. N Engl J Med 288:724, 1973.)

and green cones, both of which are stimulated by yellow light, and to blue cones. Their response depends on the relative proportions of yellow and blue light striking the receptor field. Thus, color is coded in terms of the magnitude and polarity of the horizontal cell potentials along a yellow-blue spectrum and red-green spectrum. Responses in the human retina are presumably similar. Such an arrangement would explain the fact that the 4 main subjective hues of the spectrum are yellow, red, green, and blue. It would also explain the fact that red and green are **complementary colors** which, when mixed in appropriate amounts, lead to cancellation of color sensation. Similarly, yellow and blue are complementary colors. The way these graded horizontal cell potentials are coded in ganglion cell action potentials is not settled, but the effect appears to be an on-off code. Thus, certain ganglion cells appear to be red-on, green-off cells whereas others are green-on, red-off cells; etc.

Color Blindness

There are numerous tests for detecting color blindness. The most commonly used routine tests are the yarn matching test and the Ishihara charts. In the former test, the subject is presented with a skein of yarn and asked to pick out the ones that match it from a pile of variously colored skeins. The Ishihara charts and similar polychromatic plates are plates on which are printed figures made up of colored spots on a background of similarly shaped colored spots. The figures are intentionally made up of colors that are liable to look the same as the background to an individual who is color blind.

The most common classification of the types of color blindness is based on the 3-receptor theory. Some individuals are unable to distinguish certain colors, whereas others have only a color weakness. The suffix -anomaly denotes color weakness and the suffix -anopia color blindness. The prefixes prot-, deuter-, and trit- refer to defects of the red, green, and blue cone systems, respectively. Individuals with normal color vision and those with protanomaly, deuteranomaly, and tritanomaly are called **trichromats;** they have all 3 cone systems, but one may be weak. **Dichromats** are individuals with only 2 cone systems; they may have protanopia, deuteranopia, or tritanopia. **Monochromats** have only one cone system. Dichromats can match their color spectrum by mixing only 2 primary colors, and monochromats match theirs by varying the intensity of only one. Apparently monochromats see only black and white and shades of gray.

Inheritance of Color Blindness

Abnormal color vision is present in the human population in about 8% of males and 0.4% of females. Some cases arise as a complication of various eye diseases, but most are inherited. Deuteranomaly is the most common form, followed by deuteranopia, protanopia, and protanomaly. These abnormalities are inherited as recessive and X-linked characteristics, ie, they are due to a mutant gene on the X chromosome.

Since all of the male's cells except germ cells contain one X and one Y chromosome in addition to the 44 somatic chromosomes (see Chapter 23), color blindness is present in males if the X chromosome has the abnormal gene. On the other hand, the normal female's cells have 2 X chromosomes, one from each parent, and since color blindness is recessive, females show the defect only when both X chromosomes contain the abnormal gene. However, female children of a color blind male are carriers of color blindness, and pass the defect on to half of their sons. Therefore, color blindness skips generations and appears in males of every second generation. Hemophilia, Duchenne muscular dystrophy, and a variety of other inherited disorders are caused by mutant genes on the X chromosome.

EYE MOVEMENTS

The direction in which each of the eye muscles moves the eye and the definitions of the terms used in describing eye movements are summarized in Table 8–1. Since the oblique muscles pull medially (Fig 8–7), their actions vary with the position of the eye. When the eye is turned nasally, the obliques elevate and depress it, whereas the superior and inferior recti rotate it; when the eye is turned temporally, the superior and inferior recti elevate and depress it and the obliques rotate it.

Since much of the visual field is binocular, it is clear that a very high order of coordination of the movements of the 2 eyes is necessary if visual images are to fall at all times on corresponding points in the 2 retinas and diplopia is to be avoided.

There are 4 types of eye movements, each controlled by a different neural system but sharing the same final common path, the motor neurons that sup-

Table 8–1. Actions of the external ocular muscles.*

Muscle	Primary Action	Secondary Action
Lateral rectus	Abduction	None
Medial rectus	Adduction	None
Superior rectus	Elevation	Adduction, intorsion
Inferior rectus	Depression	Adduction, extorsion
Superior oblique	Depression	Intorsion, abduction
Inferior oblique	Elevation	Extorsion, abduction

*Abduction and adduction refer to rotation of the eyeball around the vertical axis with the pupil moving away from or toward the midline, respectively; elevation and depression refer to rotation around the transverse horizontal axis, with the pupil moving up or down; and torsion refers to rotation around the anteroposterior horizontal axis with the top of the pupil moving toward the nose (intorsion) or away from the nose (extorsion). (Reproduced, with permission, from Vaughan D, Asbury T: *General Ophthalmology,* 8th ed. Lange, 1977.)

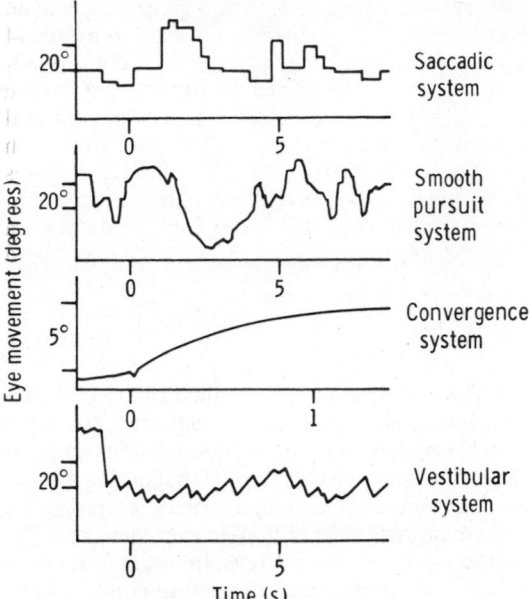

Figure 8–21. Types of eye movements. (Modified and reproduced, with permission, from Robinson DA: Eye movement control in primates. Science 161 [No. 3847]:1219–1224, 1968. Copyright 1968 by the American Association for the Advancement of Science.)

ply the external ocular muscles (Fig 8–21). **Saccades,** sudden jerky movements, occur as the gaze shifts from one object to another. **Smooth pursuit movements** are tracking movements of the eyes as they follow moving objects. **Vestibular movements,** adjustments that occur in response to stimuli initiated in the semicircular canals, maintain visual fixation as the head moves. **Convergence movements** bring the visual axes toward each other as attention is focused on objects near the observer. The similarity to a man-made tracking system on an unstable platform such as a ship is apparent; saccadic movements seek out visual targets, pursuit movements follow them as they move about, and vestibular movements stabilize the tracking device as the platform on which the device is mounted (ie, the head) moves about.

Strabismus

Abnormalities of the coordinating mechanisms can be due to a variety of causes. When the visual axes no longer are maintained in a position that keeps the visual images on corresponding retinal points, **strabismus** or squint is said to be present. Successful treatment of some types of strabismus is possible by careful surgical shortening of some of the eye muscles, by eye muscle training exercises, and by the use of glasses with prisms that bend the light rays sufficiently to compensate for the abnormal position of the eyeball.

9 | Functions of the Ear

ANATOMIC CONSIDERATIONS

Receptors for 2 sensory modalities, hearing and equilibrium, are housed in the ear. The external ear, the middle ear, and the cochlea of the inner ear are concerned with hearing. The semicircular canals, the utricle, and probably the saccule of the inner ear are concerned with equilibrium.

EXTERNAL & MIDDLE EAR

The external ear funnels sound waves into the **external auditory meatus.** In some animals, the ears can be moved like radar antennas to seek out sound. From the meatus, the **external auditory canal** passes inward to the **tympanic membrane,** or eardrum (Fig 9–1).

The middle ear is an air-filled cavity in the temporal bone that opens via the auditory tube into the nasopharynx and through the nasopharynx to the exterior. The tube is usually closed, but during swallowing, chewing, and yawning it opens, keeping the air pressure on the 2 sides of the eardrum equalized. The 3 **auditory ossicles,** the **malleus, incus,** and **stapes,** are located in the middle ear. The **manubrium,** or handle of the malleus, is attached to the back of the tympanic membrane. Its head is attached to the wall of the middle ear and its short process is attached to the incus, which in turn articulates with the head of the stapes. The stapes is named for its resemblance to a stirrup. Its **foot plate** is attached by an annular ligament to the walls of the **oval window** (Fig 9–2). Two small skeletal muscles, the **tensor tympani** and the **stapedius,** are also located in the middle ear. Contraction of the former pulls the manubrium of the malleus medially and decreases the vibrations of the tympanic membrane; contraction of the latter pulls the foot plate of the stapes out of the oval window.

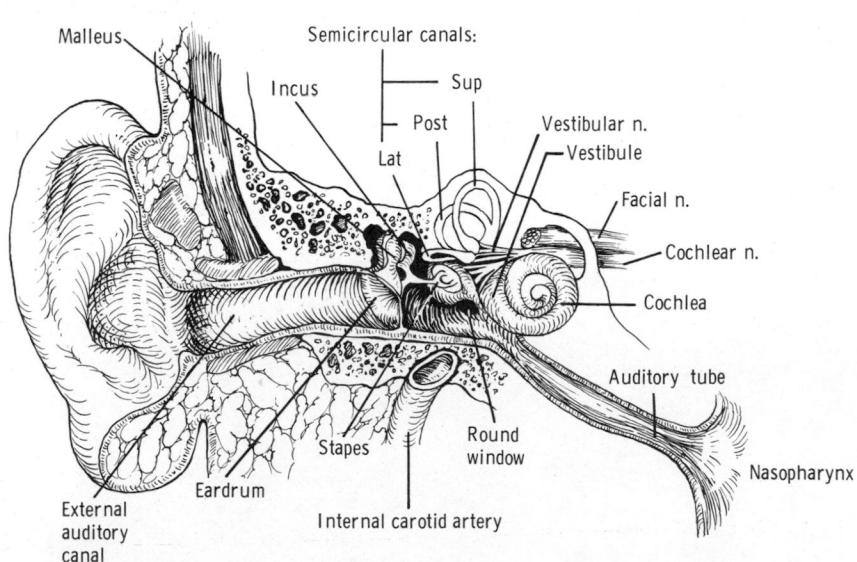

Figure 9–1. The human ear. To make the relationships clear, the cochlea has been turned slightly and the middle ear muscles have been omitted. Sup, superior; Post, posterior; Lat, lateral. (Modified and redrawn from Brödel M: *Three Unpublished Drawings of The Anatomy of The Human Ear.* Saunders, 1946.)

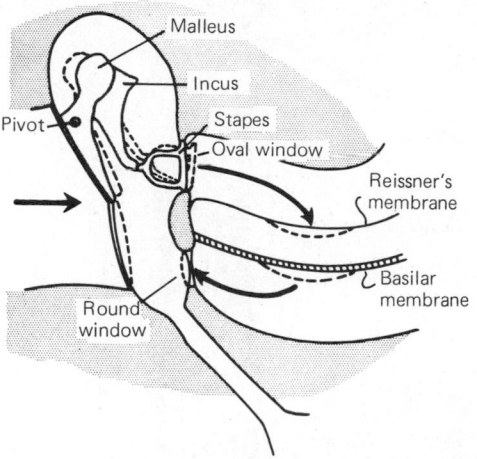

Figure 9–2. Schematic representation of the auditory ossicles and the way their movement translates movements of the tympanic membrane into a wave in the fluid of the inner ear. The wave is dissipated at the round window. The movements of the ossicles, the membranous labyrinth, and the round window are indicated by dashed lines. (Redrawn and reproduced, with permission, from an original by Netter FH in Ciba Clinical Symposia. Copyright © Ciba Pharmaceutical Co., 1962.)

INNER EAR

The inner ear, or **labyrinth,** is made up of 2 parts, one within the other. The **bony labyrinth** is a series of channels in the petrous portion of the temporal bone. Inside these channels, surrounded by a fluid called **perilymph,** is the **membranous labyrinth.** The membranous labyrinth more or less duplicates the

shape of the bony channels (Fig 9–3). It is filled with a fluid called **endolymph,** and there is no communication between the spaces filled with endolymph and those filled with perilymph.

Cochlea

The cochlear portion of the labyrinth is a coiled tube, 35 mm long, which in humans makes 2¾ turns. Throughout its length, the basilar membrane and Reissner's membrane divide it into 3 chambers, or **scalae** (Fig 9–4). The upper **scala vestibuli** and the lower **scala tympani** contain perilymph and communicate with each other at the apex of the cochlea through a small opening called the **helicotrema.** At the base of the cochlea, the scala vestibuli ends at the oval window, which is closed by the foot plate of the stapes. The scala tympani ends at the **round window,** a foramen on the medial wall of the middle ear that is closed by the flexible **secondary tympanic membrane.** The **scala media,** the middle cochlear chamber, is continuous with the membranous labyrinth and does not communicate with the other 2 scalae. It contains endolymph (Figs 9–3 and 9–4).

Organ of Corti

Located on the basilar membrane is the organ of Corti, the structure that contains the auditory receptor cells. This organ extends from the apex to the base of the cochlea and consequently has a spiral shape. The auditory receptors are hair cells arranged in 2 rows (Fig 9–4), with their processes piercing the tough, membranelike **reticular lamina.** There are 3500 inner and 20,000 outer hair cells in each human cochlea. The reticular lamina is supported by the **rods of Corti.** Covering the rows of hair cells is a thin, viscous but elastic **tectorial membrane** in which the tips of the

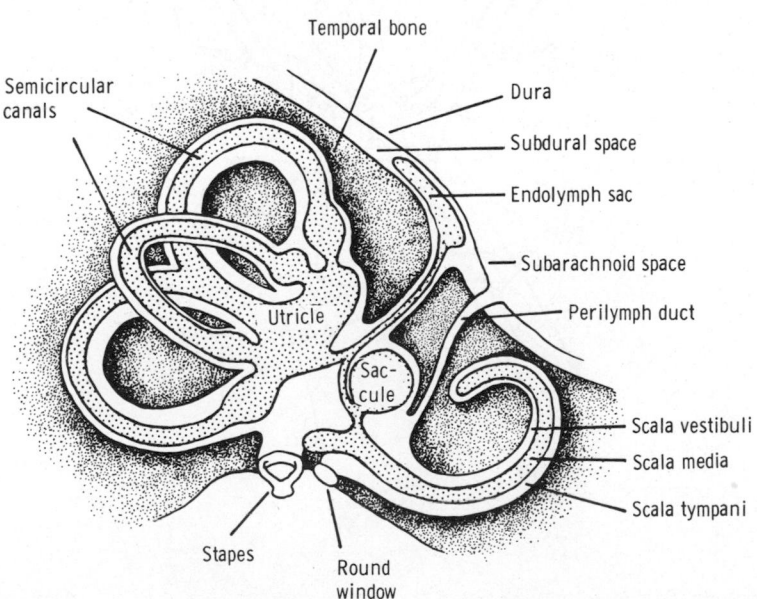

Figure 9–3. Relationship between the membranous and osseous labyrinths (diagrammatic).

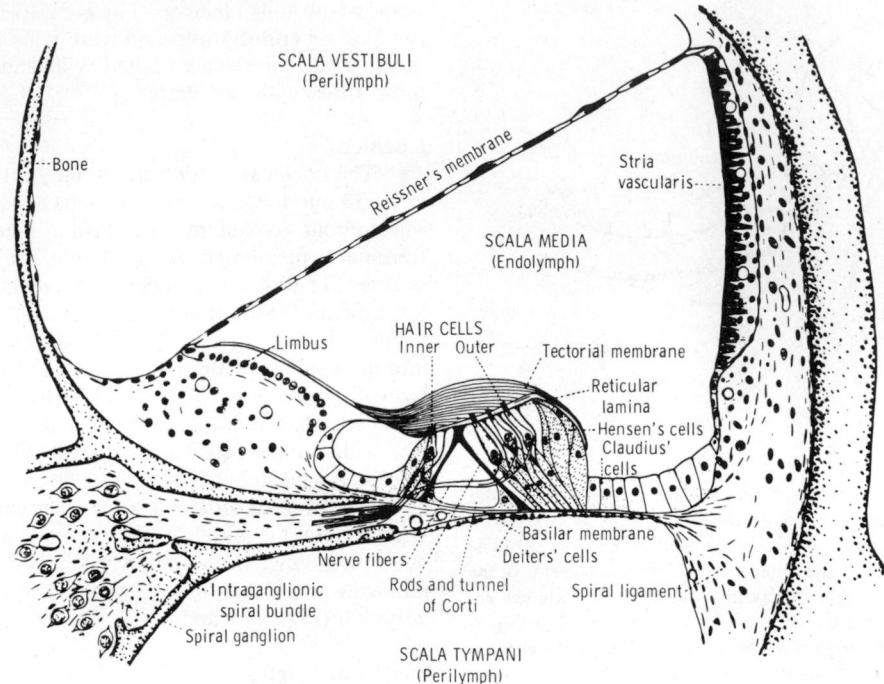

Figure 9–4. Cross section of one turn of the cochlea of a guinea pig. (Reproduced, with permission, from Davis H & others: Acoustic trauma in the guinea pig. J Acoust Soc Am 25:1180, 1953.)

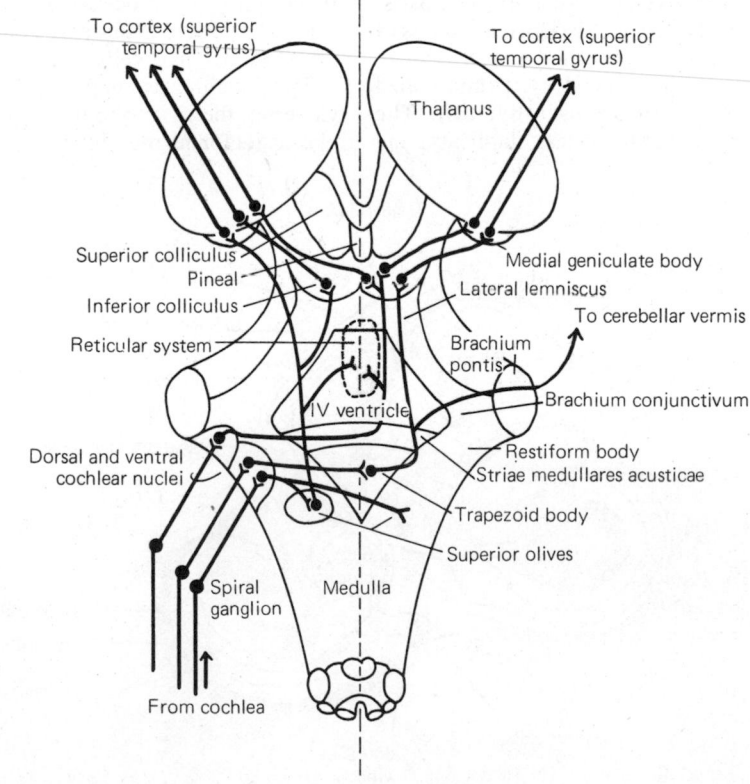

Figure 9–5. Simplified diagram of main auditory pathways superimposed on a dorsal view of the brain stem. Cerebellum and cerebral cortex removed.

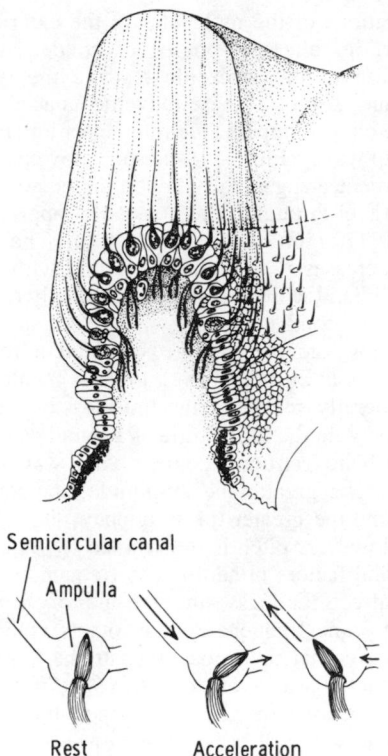

Semicircular canal

Ampulla

Rest   Acceleration

Figure 9–6. Ampullar crista. *Above:* Schematic 3-dimensional drawing of a cross section of an ampullar crista. *Below:* Movements of cupula in ampullary crista during rotational acceleration. Arrows indicate direction of fluid movement. (Redrawn and reproduced, with permission, from Wersäll J: Studies on the structure and innervation of the sensory epithelium of the cristae ampullares in the guinea pig. Acta Otolaryngol [Stockh] Suppl 126:1, 1956.)

hair cell processes are embedded. The cell bodies of the afferent neurons that arborize extensively around the hair cells are located in the **spiral ganglion** within the **modiolus,** the bony core around which the cochlea is wound. Their axons form the auditory division of the acoustic nerve and terminate in the **dorsal** and **ventral cochlear nuclei** of the medulla oblongata. There are approximately 28,000 fibers in each auditory nerve, and so there is no net convergence of receptors on first order neurons; most of the fibers, however, supply more than one cell, and conversely, most cells are supplied by more than one fiber.

Central Auditory Pathways

From the cochlear nuclei, axons carrying auditory impulses pass via a variety of pathways to the **inferior colliculi,** the centers for auditory reflexes; and via the **medial geniculate body** in the thalamus to the **auditory cortex.** Others enter the reticular formation (Fig 9–5). Information from both ears converges on each superior olive, and at all higher levels most of the neurons respond to inputs from both sides. In humans, the primary auditory cortex, Brodmann's area 41, is

located in the superior portion of the temporal lobe, buried in the floor of the lateral cerebral fissure (Fig 7–3). There is reason to believe that there are several additional auditory receiving areas, just as there is a secondary receiving area for cutaneous sensation (see Chapter 7). The auditory association areas adjacent to the primary auditory receiving area are widespread, extending onto the insula. The **olivocochlear bundle** is a prominent bundle of efferent fibers in each auditory nerve that arises in the olivary nucleus of the opposite side and ends around the bases of the hair cells of the organ of Corti.

Semicircular Canals

On each side of the head, the semicircular canals are perpendicular to each other so that they are oriented in the 3 planes of space. Inside the bony canals, the membranous canals are suspended in perilymph. A receptor structure, the **crista ampullaris,** is located in the expanded end or **ampulla** of each of the membranous canals. Each crista consists of hair cells and sustentacular cells surmounted by a gelatinous partition, or **cupula,** that closes off the ampulla like a swinging door (Fig 9–6). Endings of the afferent fibers of the vestibular division of the acoustic nerve are in close contact with the hair cells.

Utricle & Saccule

Within each membranous labyrinth, on the floor of the utricle, there is an **otolithic organ** or **macula.** Another macula is located on the wall of the saccule, tilted 30 degrees from the vertical plane. The maculas contain sustentacular cells and hair cells, surmounted by a membrane in which are embedded crystals of calcium carbonate, the **otoliths** (Fig 9–7). In the maculas and cristae, there are hair cells surrounded by nerve fibers (type I) and hair cells with nerve fibers only at the base (type II). However, the functional difference between the 2 types is uncertain. The nerve fibers from the hair cells join those from the cristae.

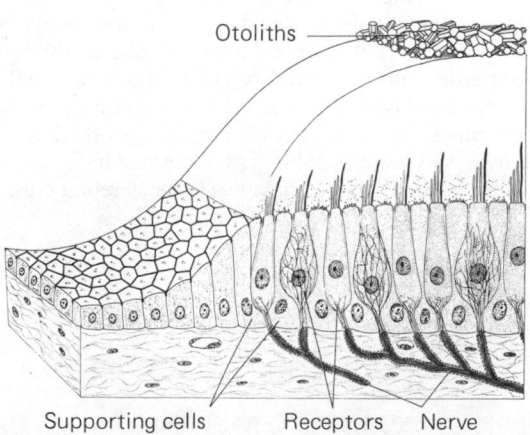

Otoliths

Supporting cells   Receptors   Nerve

Figure 9–7. Otolithic organ. (Reproduced, with permission, from Junqueira LC, Carneiro J, Contopoulos A: *Basic Histology,* 2nd ed. Lange, 1977.)

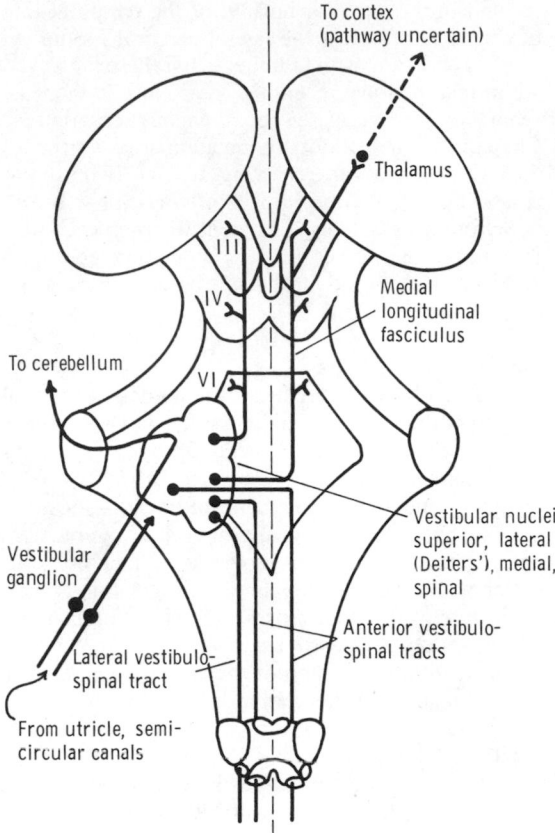

Figure 9–8. Principal vestibular pathways superimposed on a dorsal view of the brain stem. Cerebellum and cerebral cortex removed.

nal vibrations of the molecules in the external environment, ie, alternate phases of condensation and rarefaction of the molecules, strike the tympanic membrane. A plot of these movements as changes in pressure on the tympanic membrane per unit of time is a series of waves (Fig 9–9), and such movements in the environment are generally called sound waves. The waves travel through air at a speed of approximately 344 m/s (770 mi/h) at 20 C at sea level. The speed of sound increases with temperature and with altitude. Other media in which humans occasionally find themselves also conduct sound waves, but at different speeds. For example, the speed of sound in fresh water is 1450 m/s at 20 C and even greater in salt water.

Generally speaking, the **loudness** of a sound is correlated with the **amplitude** of a sound wave and its **pitch** with the **frequency,** or number of waves per unit of time. The greater the amplitude, the louder the sound; and the greater the frequency, the higher the pitch. However, pitch is determined by other poorly understood factors in addition to frequency, and frequency affects loudness, since the auditory threshold is lower at some frequencies than others (see below). Sound waves that have repeating patterns, even though the individual waves are complex, are perceived as musical sounds; aperiodic nonrepeating vibrations cause a sensation of noise. Most musical sounds are made up of a wave with a primary frequency that determines its pitch plus a number of harmonic vibrations, or **overtones,** which give the sound its characteristic **timbre** or quality. Variations in timbre permit us to identify the sounds of the various musical instruments even though they are playing notes of the same pitch.

Neural Pathways

The cell bodies of the 19,000 neurons supplying the cristae and maculas on each side are located in the vestibular ganglion. Each vestibular nerve terminates in the ipsilateral 4-part vestibular nucleus and in the flocculonodular lobe of the cerebellum. Second order neurons pass down the spinal cord from the vestibular nuclei in the vestibulospinal tracts and ascend through the **medial longitudinal fasciculi** to the motor nuclei of the cranial nerves concerned with the control of eye movement. There are also anatomically poorly defined pathways by which impulses from the vestibular receptors are relayed via the thalamus to the cerebral cortex (Fig 9–8).

HEARING

AUDITORY RESPONSES

Sound Waves

Sound is the sensation produced when longitudi-

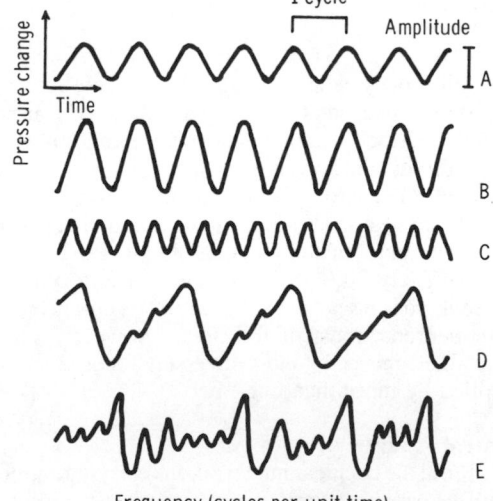

Figure 9–9. Characteristics of sound waves. *A* is the record of a pure tone. *B* has a greater amplitude and is louder than A. *C* has the same amplitude as A but a greater frequency, and its pitch is higher. *D* is a complex wave form that is regularly repeated. Such patterns are perceived as musical sounds, whereas waves like that shown in *E,* which have no regular pattern, are perceived as noise.

The amplitude of a sound wave can be expressed in terms of the maximum pressure change or the root mean square pressure at the eardrum, but a relative scale is more convenient. The **decibel scale** is such a scale. The intensity of a sound in **bels** is the logarithm of the ratio of the intensities of that sound and a standard sound:

$$\text{bel} = \log \frac{\text{intensity of sound}}{\text{intensity of standard sound}}$$

The intensity is proportionate to the square of the sound pressure. Therefore,

$$\text{bel} = 2 \log \frac{\text{pressure of sound}}{\text{pressure of standard sound}}$$

A decibel is 0.1 bel. The standard sound reference level adopted by the Acoustical Society of America corresponds to 0 decibels at a pressure level of 0.000204 dyne/cm², a value that is just at the auditory threshold for the average human. In Fig 9–10, the decibel levels of various common sounds are compared. It is important to remember that the decibel scale is a log scale. Therefore, a value of 0 decibels does not mean the absence of sound but a sound level of an intensity equal to that of the standard. Furthermore, the 0–140 decibel range from threshold intensity to an intensity that is potentially damaging to the organ of Corti actually represents a 10^{14} (100 trillion)-fold variation in sound intensity.

The sound frequencies audible to the human range from about 20 to a maximum of 20,000 cycles per second (cps or Hz). In other animals, notably bats and dogs, much higher frequencies are audible. The

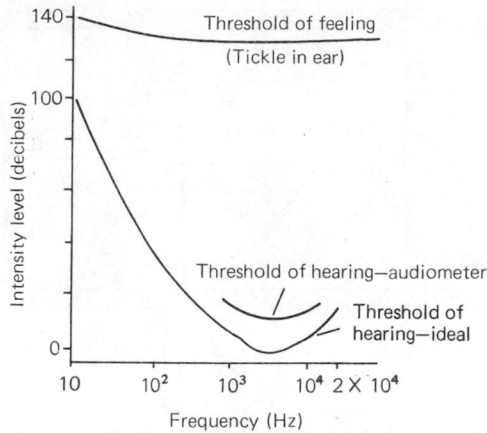

Figure 9–11. Human audibility curve. The middle curve is that obtained by audiometry under the usual conditions. The lower curve is that obtained under ideal conditions. At about 140 decibels (top curve), sounds are felt as well as heard. (Redrawn and reproduced, with permission, from Licklider JCR in: *Handbook of Experimental Psychology.* Stevens SS [editor]. Wiley, 1951.)

threshold of the human ear varies with the pitch of the sound (Fig 9–11), the greatest sensitivity being in the 1000–4000 Hz range. The pitch of the average male voice in conversation is about 120 Hz and that of the average female voice about 250 Hz. The number of pitches that can be distinguished by an average individual is about 2000, but trained musicians can improve on this figure considerably. Pitch discrimination is best in the 1000–3000 Hz range and is poor at high and low pitches.

Masking

It is common knowledge that the presence of one sound decreases an individual's ability to hear other sounds. This phenomenon is known as **masking.** It is believed to be due to the relative or absolute refractoriness of previously stimulated auditory receptors and nerve fibers to other stimuli. The degree to which a given tone masks other tones is related to its pitch. The masking effect of the background noise in all but the most carefully soundproofed environments raises the auditory threshold a definite and measurable amount.

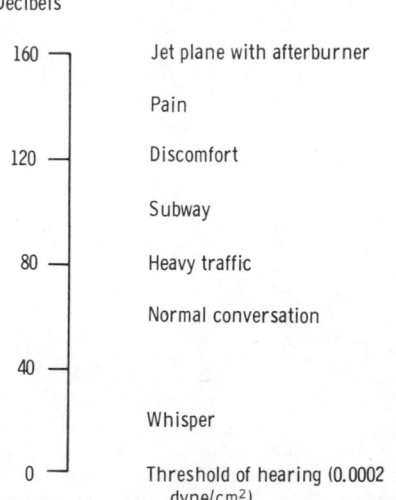

Figure 9–10. Decibel scale for common sounds. The reference standard is that adopted by the Acoustical Society of America, 10^{-16} watt/cm². (Modified from Stevens SS: Some similarities between hearing and seeing. Laryngoscope 68:512, 1958.)

SOUND TRANSMISSION

The ear converts sound waves in the external environment into action potentials in the auditory nerves. The waves are transformed by the eardrum and auditory ossicles into movements of the foot plate of the stapes. These movements set up waves in the fluid of the inner ear. The action of the waves on the organ of Corti generates action potentials in the nerve fibers.

Functions of the Tympanic Membrane & Ossicles

In response to the pressure changes produced by

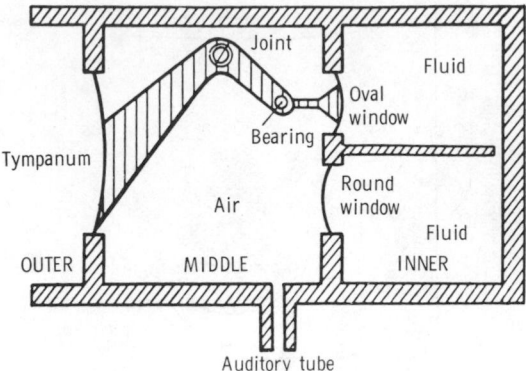

Figure 9–12. Diagrammatic representation of the transmission of vibrations from the outer to the inner ear. (Reproduced, with permission, from Lippold OCJ, Winton FR: *Human Physiology*, 6th ed. Churchill, 1972.)

sound waves on its external surface, the tympanic membrane moves in and out. The membrane therefore functions as a **resonator** that reproduces the vibrations of the sound source. It stops vibrating almost immediately when the sound wave stops, ie, it is very nearly **critically damped.** The motions of the tympanic membrane are imparted to the manubrium of the malleus. The malleus rocks on an axis through the junction of its long and short processes, so that the short process transmits the vibrations of the manubrium to the incus. The incus moves in such a way that the vibrations are transmitted to the head of the stapes. Movements of the head of the stapes swing its foot plate to and fro like a door hinged at the posterior edge of the oval window. The auditory ossicles thus function as a lever system that converts the resonant vibrations of the tympanic membrane into movements of the stapes against the perilymph-filled scala vestibuli of the cochlea (Figs 9–2 and 9–12). This system increases the sound pressure that arrives at the oval window because the lever action of the malleus and incus multiplies the force 1.3 times and the area of the tympanic membrane is much greater than the area of the foot plate of the stapes. There are losses of sound energy due to resistance, but it has been calculated that, at frequencies below 3000 Hz, 60% of the sound energy incident on the tympanic membrane is transmitted to the fluid in the cochlea.

Tympanic Reflex

When the middle ear muscles—the tensor tympani and the stapedius—contract, they pull the manubrium of the malleus inward and the foot plate of the stapes outward. This decreases sound transmission. Loud sounds initiate a reflex contraction of these muscles generally called the **tympanic reflex.** Its function is protective, preventing strong sound waves from causing excessive stimulation of the auditory receptors. However, the reaction time for the reflex is 40–160 ms, so it does not protect against brief intense stimulation such as that produced by gunshots.

Bone & Air Conduction

Conduction of sound waves to the fluid of the inner ear via the tympanic membrane and the auditory ossicles is called **ossicular conduction.** Sound waves also initiate vibrations of the secondary tympanic membrane that closes the round window. This process, unimportant in normal hearing, is called **air conduction.** A third type of conduction, **bone conduction,** is the transmission of vibrations of the bones of the skull to the fluid of the inner ear. When tuning forks or other vibrating bodies are applied directly to the skull, considerable conduction occurs in this fashion, and this route also plays some role in the transmission of extremely loud sounds.

Traveling Waves

The movements of the foot plate of the stapes set up a series of traveling waves in the perilymph of the scala vestibuli. A diagram of such a wave is shown in Fig 9–13. As the wave moves up the cochlea, its height increases to a maximum and then drops off rapidly. The distance from the stapes to this point of maximum height varies with the frequency of the vibrations initiating the wave. High-pitched sounds generate waves that reach maximum height near the base of the cochlea; low-pitched sounds generate waves that peak near the apex. The bony walls of the scala vestibuli are rigid, but Reissner's membrane is flexible. The basilar membrane is not under tension, and it also is readily depressed into the scala tympani by the peaks of waves in the scala vestibuli. Displacements of the fluid in the scala tympani are dissipated into air at the round window. Therefore, sound produces distortion of the basilar membrane, and the site at which this distortion is maximal is determined by the frequency of the sound wave. The tops of the hair cells in the organ of Corti are

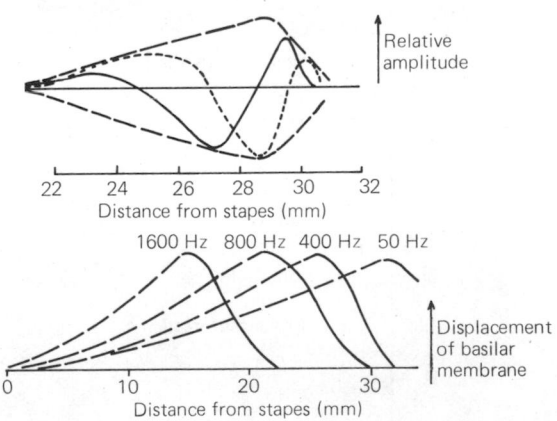

Figure 9–13. Traveling waves. *Above:* The solid and the short-dashed lines represent the wave at 2 instants of time. The long-dashed line shows the "envelope" of the wave formed by connecting the wave peaks at successive instants. *Below:* Displacement of the basilar membrane by the waves generated by stapes vibration of the frequencies shown at the top of each curve. (Data from von Békésy G, Rosenblith WA, in: *Handbook of Experimental Psychology.* Stevens SS [editor]. Wiley, 1951.)

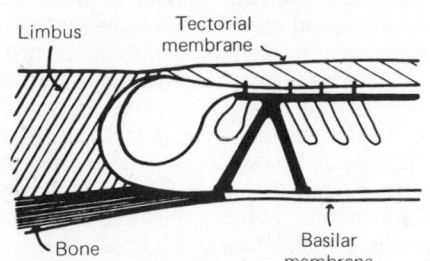 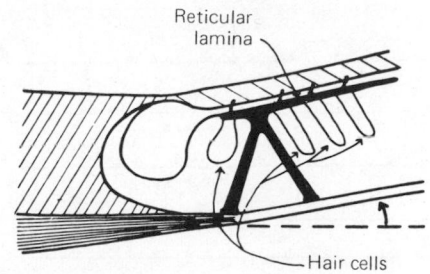

Figure 9–14. Effect of movement on the organ of Corti. The shearing action between 2 stiff structures, the tectorial membrane and the reticular lamina, bends the processes of the hair cells. (Reproduced, with permission, from Davis H in: *Physiological Triggers and Discontinuous Rate Processes.* Bullock TH [editor]. American Physiological Society, 1957.)

held rigid by the reticular lamina, and their hairs are embedded in the tectorial membrane (Figs 9–4 and 9–14). When the basilar membrane is depressed, the motion of the tectorial membrane relative to the reticular lamina bends the hairs. This bending in some way generates action potentials in the auditory nerves.

ELECTRICAL PHENOMENA

Endocochlear Potential

At rest, there is a steady 80 mV potential difference, the **endocochlear potential,** between the endolymph of the scala media and the perilymph. The endolymph is positive to the perilymph, whereas the interiors of the large cells of the organ of Corti, including the hair cells, are 65–75 mV negative to the perilymph. The total potential difference between the cells and the endolymph is therefore 150 mV. The boundaries of the space from which the endocochlear potential can be recorded are shown in Fig 9–15. The tunnel of Corti and the bases of the hair cells, which are bathed in perilymph, are outside this space. The ionic compositions of endolymph and perilymph are very different, endolymph being the only ECF in the body with a high K^+ content (Table 9–1). The significance of this fact in terms of potential differences is unsettled; the difference in ionic composition exists not only in the cochlea, where the potential difference between endolymph and perilymph is 80 mV, but in the utricle,

where the potential difference between the 2 is only 5 mV. However, it seems clear that the endocochlear potential is generated by and depends upon an ion pump in the stria vascularis. A sodium-potassium–activated adenosine triphosphatase system (see Chapter 1) has been demonstrated in this structure.

Cochlear Microphonic & Summating Potentials

One of the electrical responses of the cochlea to sound is the **cochlear microphonic,** a potential fluctuation that can be recorded between an electrode on or near the cochlea and an indifferent electrode. It is generated by deformation of the processes of the hair cells, and is linearly proportionate to the magnitude of the basement membrane displacement. Consequently, it reproduces the wave form of the sound stimulus. Indeed, the reproduction of the frequency and amplitude of the sound is so faithful that if music is played into an experimental animal's ear, a faithful rendition of the song can be produced by simply feeding the

Table 9–1. Composition of endolymph, perilymph, and spinal fluid.*

	Endolymph	Perilymph	Spinal Fluid
K^+	144.8	4.8	4.2
Na^+	15.8	150.3	150.0
Cl^-	107.1	121.5	122.4
Protein	15.0	50.0	21.0

*Data from Smith CA & others: Electrolytes of the labyrinthine fluids. Laryngoscope 64:141, 1954. K^+, Na^+, Cl^-, mEq/L; protein, mg/dl.

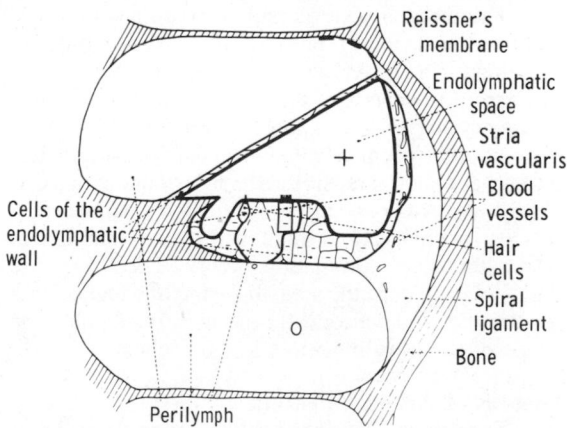

Figure 9–15. Distribution of the positive endocochlear potential (the area within the heavy black line). This potential is positive ($+$) relative to the perilymph (0). The minus signs inside the cells indicate that they are negative relative to the perilymph. (Reproduced, with permission, from Tasaki I, Davis H, Eldridge DH: Exploration of cochlear potentials in guinea pig with a microelectrode. J Acoust Soc Am 26:765, 1954.)

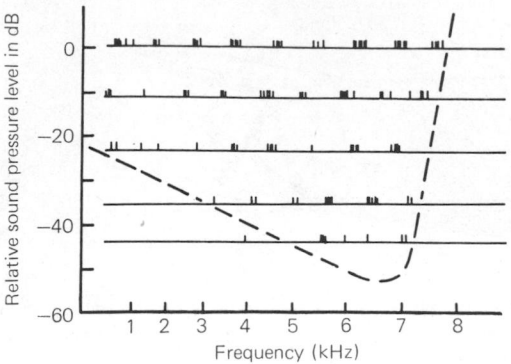

Figure 9–16. Responses (vertical lines) of a guinea pig single auditory nerve fiber to tones of different frequencies and intensities. The sound intensity is expressed in decibels below an arbitrary standard. The dotted line encloses the "response area" of this fiber. Note the sharp cut-off at higher frequencies and the relatively greater response spectrum at higher sound intensities on the low-frequency side. (Reproduced, with permission, from Tasaki I: Nerve impulses in individual auditory nerve fibers of guinea pig. J Neurophysiol 17:97, 1954.)

The major determinant of the pitch perceived when a sound wave strikes the ear is the place in the organ of Corti that is maximally stimulated. The traveling wave set up by a tone produces peak depression of the basilar membrane, and consequently maximal receptor stimulation, at one point. The distance between this point and the stapes is inversely related to the pitch of the sound, low tones producing maximal stimulation at the apex of the cochlea and high tones producing maximal stimulation at the base. The pathways from the various parts of the cochlea to the brain are distinct. An additional factor involved in pitch perception at sound frequencies of less than 2000 Hz may be the pattern of the action potentials in the auditory nerve. When the frequency is low enough, the nerve fibers begin to respond with an impulse to each cycle of a sound wave. The importance of this **volley effect,** however, is limited; the frequency of the action potentials in a given auditory nerve fiber determines principally the loudness, rather than the pitch, of a sound.

BRAIN MECHANISMS

Auditory Responses of Neurons in the Medulla Oblongata

The responses of individual second order neurons in the cochlear nuclei to sound stimuli are like those of the individual auditory nerve fibers. The frequency at which sounds of lowest intensity evoke a response varies from unit to unit; with increased sound intensities, the band of frequencies to which a response occurs becomes wider. The major difference between the responses of the first and second order neurons is the presence of a sharper "cut-off" on the low-frequency side in the medullary neurons (Fig 9–17).

cochlear microphonic into an audio amplifier. The microphonic can be recorded from the auditory nerve close to the cochlea, and it is probably produced by mechanical distortion **(piezoelectric effect)** affecting the hair cells or some other structure in the cochlea. Two additional potentials, the **negative** and **positive summating potentials,** are generated when sound strikes the ear. They are principally direct current baseline shifts on which the cochlear microphonic is superimposed.

Action Potentials in Auditory Nerve Fibers

The frequency of the action potentials in single auditory nerve fibers is proportionate to the loudness of the sound stimuli. At low sound intensities, each axon discharges to sounds of only one frequency, and this frequency varies from axon to axon depending upon the part of the cochlea from which the fiber originates. At higher sound intensities, the individual axons discharge to a wider spectrum of sound frequencies (Fig 9–16)—particularly to frequencies lower than that at which threshold stimulation occurs. The "response area" of each unit, the area above the line that defines its threshold at various frequencies, resembles the shape of the traveling wave in the cochlea.

Genesis of Action Potentials

The way the various cochlear potentials are interrelated in the genesis of action potentials in the afferent nerves is still unsettled. Apparently the cochlear microphonic, possibly in association with the negative summating potential, serves as the generator potential. The endocochlear potential probably keeps the receptors in a ready state by maintaining the potential difference between the hair cells and their processes.

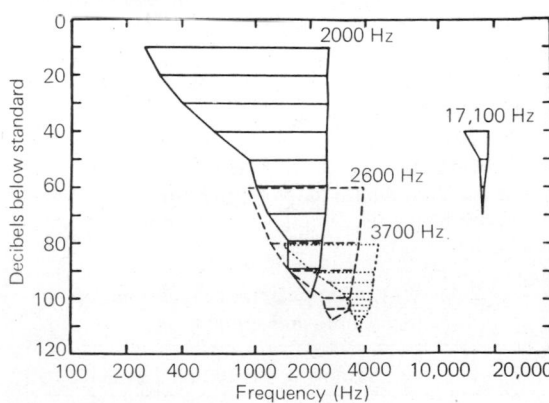

Figure 9–17. "Response areas" of 4 second order auditory neurons in the cochlear nuclei of the cat. The sound intensity is expressed in decibels below an arbitrary standard. Compare with Fig 9–16. (Reproduced, with permission, from Galambos R, Davis H: The response of single auditory nerve fibers to acoustic stimulation. J Neurophysiol 6:39, 1943.)

This greater specificity of the second order neurons is probably due to some sort of inhibitory process in the brain stem, but how it is achieved is not known.

Although the pitch of a sound depends primarily on the frequency of the sound wave, loudness also plays a part; low tones (below 500 Hz) seem lower, and high tones (above 4000 Hz) seem higher as their loudness increases. Duration also affects pitch to a minor degree. The pitch of a tone cannot be perceived unless it lasts for more than 0.01 s, and with durations between 0.01 and 0.1 s pitch rises as duration increases.

Auditory Cortex

The pathways from the cochlea to the auditory cortex are described in the first section of this chapter. Impulses ascend from the dorsal and ventral cochlear nuclei through complex paths that are both crossed and uncrossed. In animals, there is an organized pattern of tonal localization in the primary auditory cortex, as if the cochlea had been unrolled upon it. In humans, low tones are represented anterolaterally and high tones posteromedially in the auditory cortex. However, individual neurons in the auditory cortex respond to such parameters as the onset, duration, and repetition rate of an auditory stimulus and particularly to the direction from which it came. In this way, they are analogous to some of the neurons in the visual cortex (see Chapter 8). Many animal species have better hearing than humans in the absence of any auditory cortex. In the common laboratory mammals, destruction of the auditory cortex not only fails to cause deafness but also fails to obliterate established conditioned responses to sound of a given frequency. On the other hand, responses to a given sequence of 3 or more tones are absent. All of this suggests that the auditory cortex is concerned with recognition of tonal patterns, with analysis of properties of sounds, and with sound localization.

Sound Localization

Determination of the direction from which a sound emanates depends upon detecting the difference in time between the arrival of the stimulus in the 2 ears and the consequent difference in phase of the sound waves on the 2 sides, as well as upon the fact that the sound is louder on the side closest to the source. The time difference is said to be the most important factor at frequencies below 3000 Hz, and the loudness difference the most important at frequencies above 3000 Hz. Many neurons in the auditory cortex receive input from both ears, and they respond maximally or minimally when the time of arrival of a stimulus at one ear is delayed by a fixed time period relative to the time of arrival at the other ear. This fixed time period varies from neuron to neuron. Sounds coming from directly in front of the individual presumably differ in quality from those coming from behind, because the external ears are turned slightly forward. Sound localization is markedly disrupted by lesions of the auditory cortex in experimental animals and humans.

Inhibitory Mechanisms

Stimulation of the efferent olivocochlear bundle in the auditory nerve decreases the neural response to auditory stimuli, by liberating a hyperpolarizing mediator, possibly acetylcholine, from the endings of the olivocochlear fibers. Other mechanisms inhibit transmission at the synaptic relays in the brain stem. These and similar mechanisms that operate as "volume controls" in all the specific sensory systems are discussed in detail in Chapter 11.

DEAFNESS

Clinical deafness may be due to impaired sound transmission in the external or middle ear (**conduction deafness**) or to damage to the neural pathways (**nerve deafness**). Among the causes of conduction deafness are plugging of the external auditory canals with wax or foreign bodies, destruction of the auditory ossicles, thickening of the eardrum following repeated middle ear infections, and abnormal rigidity of the attachments of the stapes to the oval window. Causes of nerve deafness include toxic degeneration of the acoustic nerve produced by streptomycin, tumors of the acoustic nerve and cerebellopontine angle, and vascular damage in the medulla.

Conduction and nerve deafness can be distinguished by a number of simple tests with a tuning fork. Three of these tests, named for the men who developed them, are outlined in Table 9–2. The Weber and Schwabach tests demonstrate the important masking effect of environmental noise on the auditory threshold.

Audiometry

Auditory acuity is commonly measured with an **audiometer.** This device presents the subject with pure tones of various frequencies through earphones. At each frequency, the threshold intensity is determined and plotted on a graph as a percentage of normal hearing. This provides an objective measurement of the degree of deafness and a picture of the tonal range most affected.

Fenestration Procedures

A common form of conduction deafness is that due to **otosclerosis,** a disease in which the attachments of the foot plate of the stapes to the oval window become abnormally rigid. In patients with this disease, air conduction (see above) can be utilized to bring about some restoration of hearing. A membrane-covered outlet from the bony labyrinth is created so that waves set up by vibrations of the secondary tympanic membrane can be dissipated. In the "fenestration operation," an outlet is created by drilling a hole in the horizontal semicircular canal and covering it with skin.

Table 9–2. Common tests with a tuning fork to distinguish between
nerve and conduction deafness.

	Weber	Rinne	Schwabach
Method	Base of vibrating tuning fork placed on vertex of skull.	Base of vibrating tuning fork placed on mastoid process until subject no longer hears it, then held in air next to ear.	Bone conduction of patient compared to that of normal subject.
Normal	Hears equally on both sides.	Hears vibration in air after bone conduction is over.	
Conduction deafness (one ear)	Sound louder in diseased ear because masking effect of environmental noise is absent on diseased side.	Does not hear vibrations in air after bone conduction is over.	Bone conduction better than normal (conduction defect excludes masking noise).
Nerve deafness (one ear)	Sound louder in normal ear.	Hears vibration in air after bone conduction is over.	Bone conduction less than normal.

VESTIBULAR FUNCTION

RESPONSES TO ROTATIONAL & LINEAR ACCELERATION

Semicircular Canals

Rotational acceleration in the plane of a given semicircular canal stimulates its crista. The endolymph, because of its inertia, is displaced in a direction opposite to the direction of rotation. The fluid pushes on the cupula and swings it like a door (Fig 9–6), bending the processes of the hair cells. When a constant speed of rotation is reached, the fluid spins at the same rate as the body and the cupula swings back into the upright position. When rotation is stopped, deceleration produces displacement of the endolymph in the direction of the rotation, and the cupula swings in a direction opposite to that during acceleration. It returns to midposition in 25–30 s. Movement of the cupula in one direction commonly causes increased impulse traffic in single nerve fibers from its crista, whereas movement in the opposite direction commonly inhibits neural activity (Fig 9–18).

Rotation causes maximal stimulation of the semicircular canals most nearly in the plane of rotation. Since the canals on one side of the head are a mirror image of those on the other side, the endolymph is displaced toward the ampulla on one side and away from it on the other. The pattern of stimulation reaching the brain therefore varies with the direction as well as the plane of rotation. Linear acceleration probably fails to displace the cupula and therefore does not stimulate the cristae. However, there is considerable evidence that when one part of the labyrinth is destroyed other parts take over its functions. Experimental localization of labyrinthine functions is therefore difficult.

The tracts that descend from the vestibular nuclei

into the spinal cord are concerned primarily with postural adjustments (see Chapter 12); the ascending connections to cranial nerve nuclei are largely concerned with eye movements.

Nystagmus

The characteristic jerky movement of the eye observed at the start and end of a period of rotation is called **nystagmus.** It is actually a reflex that maintains visual fixation on stationary points while the body rotates, although it is not initiated by visual impulses and is present in blind individuals. When rotation starts, the eyes move slowly in a direction opposite to the direction of rotation. When the limit of this movement is reached, the eyes quickly snap back to a new fixation point and then again move slowly in the other direction. The slow component is initiated by impulses from the labyrinths; the quick component is triggered by a center in the brain stem. Nystagmus is frequently horizontal, ie, the eyes move in the horizontal plane;

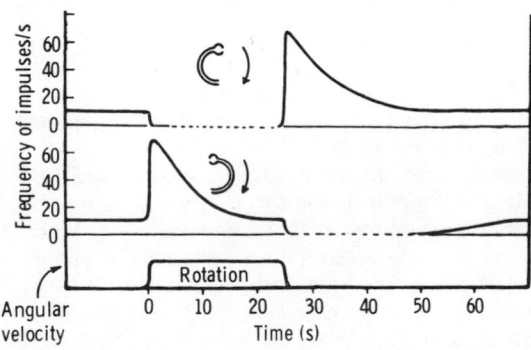

Figure 9–18. Ampullary responses to rotation. Average time course of impulse discharge from ampulla of 2 semicircular canals during rotational acceleration, steady rotation, and deceleration. (Reproduced, with permission, from Adrian ED: Discharges from vestibular receptors in the cat. J Physiol [Lond] 101:389, 1943.)

but it can also be vertical, when the head is tipped sidewise during rotation, or rotatory, when the head is tipped forward. By convention, the direction of eye movement in nystagmus is identified by the direction of the quick component. The direction of the quick component during rotation is the same as that of the rotation, but the **postrotatory nystagmus** that occurs due to displacement of the cupula when rotation is stopped is in the opposite direction.

Macular Responses

In mammals, the utricular and saccular maculas respond to linear acceleration. The otoliths are more dense than the endolymph, and acceleration in any direction causes them to be displaced in the opposite direction, distorting the hair cells and generating activity in the nerve fibers. The maculas also discharge tonically in the absence of head movement, because of the pull of gravity on the otoliths. The impulses generated from these receptors are partly responsible for reflex righting of the head and other important postural adjustments discussed in Chapter 12.

Although most of the responses to stimulation of the maculas are reflex in nature, vestibular impulses also reach the cerebral cortex. These impulses are presumably responsible for conscious perception of motion and supply part of the information necessary for orientation in space. The nausea, blood pressure changes, sweating, pallor, and vomiting that are the well-known accompaniments of excessive vestibular stimulation are probably due to reflexes mediated via vestibular connections in the brain stem. **Vertigo** is the sensation of rotation in the absence of actual rotation.

Caloric Stimulation

The semicircular canals can be stimulated by instilling water that is hotter or colder than body temperature into the external auditory meatus. The temperature difference sets up convection currents in the endolymph, with consequent motion of the cupula. This technic of **caloric stimulation,** which is sometimes used diagnostically, causes some nystagmus, vertigo, and nausea. To avoid these symptoms when irrigating the ear canals in the treatment of ear infections, it is important to be sure that the fluid used is at body temperature.

ORIENTATION IN SPACE

Orientation in space depends in large part upon input from the vestibular receptors, but visual cues are also important. When the horizon is manipulated so that the vestibular and visual cues are conflicting, women are said to place more reliance on their visual sensations and men on their vestibular. Pertinent information is also supplied by impulses from proprioceptors in joint capsules, which supply data about the relative position of the various parts of the body, and impulses from cutaneous exteroceptors, especially touch and pressure receptors. These 4 inputs are synthesized at a cortical level into a continuous picture of the individual's orientation in space.

EFFECTS OF LABYRINTHECTOMY

The effects of unilateral labyrinthectomy are presumably due to unbalanced discharge from the remaining normal side. They vary from species to species and with the speed at which the labyrinth is destroyed. Rats develop abnormal body postures and roll over and over as they continuously attempt to right themselves. Postural changes are less marked in humans, but the symptoms are distressing. Motion aggravates the symptoms, but efforts to minimize stimulation by lying absolutely still are constantly thwarted by waves of nausea, vomiting, and even diarrhea. Fortunately, compensation for the loss occurs, and after 1–2 months the symptoms disappear completely.

Symptoms of this type are absent after bilateral destruction of the labyrinths, but defects in orientation are present. For this reason, diving is hazardous for persons who lack vestibular function. The only means these individuals have of finding the surface is vision, because in the water the pressure sensed by the cutaneous exteroceptors is equal all over the body. If for any reason vision is obscured, a person whose vestibular apparatus is impaired has no mechanism for self-orientation. It is therefore possible to swim away from rather than toward the surface and, consequently, to drown.

10 | Smell & Taste

Smell and taste are generally classified as visceral senses because of their close association with gastrointestinal function. Physiologically, they are related to each other. The flavors of various foods are in large part a combination of their taste and smell. Consequently, foods may taste ''different'' if one has a cold that depresses the sense of smell. Both taste and smell receptors are chemoreceptors that are stimulated by molecules in solution in the fluids of the nose and mouth. However, these 2 senses are anatomically quite different. The smell receptors are distance receptors (teleceptors); the smell pathways have no relay in the thalamus; and there is no neocortical projection area for olfaction. The taste pathways pass up the brain stem to the thalamus and project to the postcentral gyrus along with those for touch and pressure sensibility from the mouth.

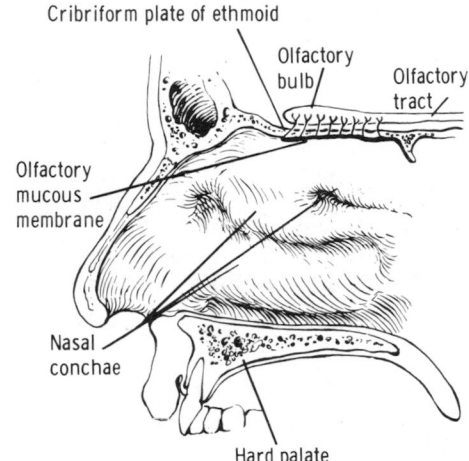

Figure 10–1. Olfactory mucous membrane. (Reproduced, with permission, from Chusid JG: *Correlative Neuroanatomy & Functional Neurology,* 17th ed. Lange, 1979.)

SMELL

RECEPTORS & PATHWAYS

Olfactory Mucous Membrane

The olfactory receptors are located in a specialized portion of the nasal mucosa, the yellowish-pigmented **olfactory mucous membrane.** In dogs and other animals in which the sense of smell is highly developed (macrosmatic animals), the area covered by this membrane is large; in microsmatic animals such as humans, it is small, covering an area of 5 cm² in the roof of the nasal cavity near the septum (Fig 10–1). The supporting cells secrete the layer of mucus that constantly overlies the epithelium and send many microvilli into this mucus. Interspersed among the supporting cells of this mucous membrane are 10–20 million receptor cells. Each olfactory receptor is a neuron, and the olfactory mucous membrane is said to be the place in the body where the nervous system is closest to the external world. The neurons have short, thick dendrites with expanded ends called olfactory rods (Fig 10–2). From these rods, cilia project to the surface of the mucus. The cilia are unmyelinated pro-

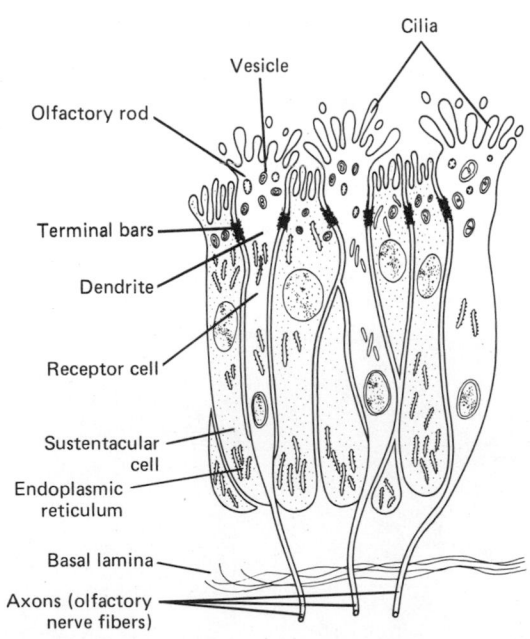

Figure 10–2. Structure of the olfactory mucous membrane. (Modified from de Lorenzo AJD, in: *Olfaction and Taste.* Zotterman Y [editor]. Macmillan, 1963.)

cesses, about 2 μm long and 0.1 μm in diameter. There are 10–20 cilia per receptor neuron. The axons of the olfactory receptor neurons pierce the cribriform plate of the ethmoid bone and enter the olfactory bulbs.

Olfactory Bulbs

In the olfactory bulbs, the axons of the receptors terminate among the dendrites of the **mitral** and **tufted cells** (Figs 10–3, 10–4) to form the complex globular synapses called **olfactory glomeruli.** An average of 26,000 receptor cell axons converge on each glomerulus. The axons of the mitral and tufted cells pass posteriorly through the **intermediate olfactory stria** to end in the **anterior perforated substance** and the **area of the diagonal band.** Impulses concerned with olfactory reflexes pass from this region to the rest of the limbic system and hypothalamus. Another band of fibers, mostly axons of mitral cells, passes from the glomeruli through the **lateral olfactory stria** to the cortical and medial portions of the ipsilateral **amygdaloid nucleus** and to the prepiriform and periamygdaloid cortex. There are no direct connections to the hippocampal formation or the hippocampal gyrus, and the **cortical olfactory area** is in the prepiriform and periamygdaloid cortex (Fig 10–3). Evoked potentials have been recorded in the amygdaloid nuclei in re-

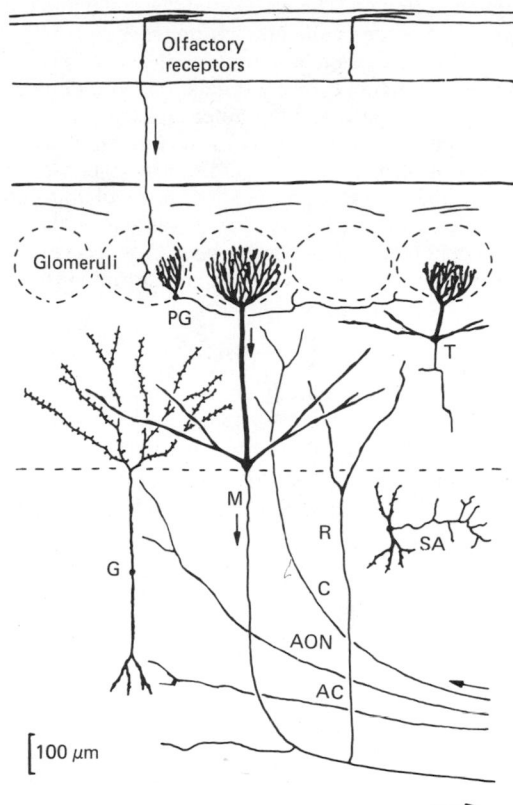

Figure 10–4. Neural elements in the olfactory bulb. In addition to olfactory nerve fibers, inputs include centrifugal fibers (C) from the nucleus of the diagonal band; ipsilateral fibers from the anterior olfactory nucleus (AON); and contralateral fibers from the anterior commissure (AC). Neurons include mitral cells (M) with recurrent collaterals (R), tufted cells (T), granule cells (G), periglomerular short-axon cells (PG), and deep short-axon cells (SA). (Reproduced, with permission, from Shepherd GM: *The Synaptic Organization of the Brain.* Oxford, 1974.)

sponse to olfactory stimuli in humans.

There are 3 inputs from other parts of the brain into the olfactory bulb in addition to the extrinsic input from the olfactory mucous membrane via the olfactory nerves. The terminations of these fibers are shown in Figure 10–4. One of the central inputs arises from the nucleus of the horizontal limb of the diagonal band (centrifugal fibers). Another arises from the ipsilateral anterior olfactory nucleus just posterior to the bulb, and the third arises from the contralateral anterior olfactory nucleus, reaching the olfactory bulb via the anterior commissure. The functional significance of this peculiar fiber arrangement is not known. In experimental animals, section of the anterior commissure apparently produces considerable olfactory deficit, but destruction of one olfactory bulb produces only unilateral loss of olfaction (**anosmia**).

Limbic System

The inferior frontal and perihilar portions of the

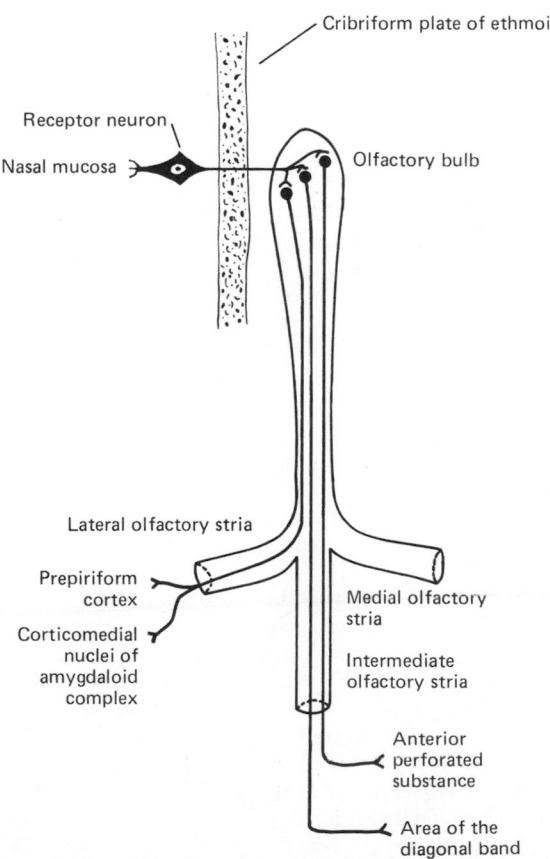

Figure 10–3. Diagram of olfactory pathways.

cerebral cortex and the associated deep nuclei in these regions have been called the **rhinencephalon** because this part of the brain was presumed to subserve only olfactory functions. In mammals, including humans, only a small part of the rhinencephalon is directly concerned with olfaction. The rest of the rhinencephalon is concerned with the emotional responses, instincts, and complex neuroendocrine regulatory functions discussed in Chapter 15. For this reason, the term rhinencephalon has generally been dropped, and this part of the brain is now called the **limbic system** or **limbic lobe** (Fig 15–1).

Inhibitory Pathways

There are efferent fibers in the olfactory striae, and stimulation of these fibers decreases the electrical activity of the olfactory bulbs. Presumably, therefore, inhibitory mechanisms analogous to those in the eye, ear, and other sensory systems exist in the olfactory system.

PHYSIOLOGY OF OLFACTION

Stimulation of Receptors

Olfactory receptors respond only to substances that are in contact with the olfactory epithelium and are dissolved in the thin layer of mucus that covers it. The olfactory thresholds for the representative substances shown in Table 10–1 illustrate the remarkable sensitivity of the olfactory receptors to some substances. For example, methyl mercaptan, the substance that gives garlic its characteristic odor, can be smelled at a concentration of less than one-millionth of a milligram per liter of air. On the other hand, discrimination of differences in the intensity of any given odor is poor. The concentration of an odor-producing substance must be changed by about 30% before a difference can be detected. The comparable visual discrimination threshold is a 1% change in light intensity.

When odoriferous molecules react with a receptor, they generate a receptor potential; but the mechanism by which the molecules generate the potential is

Table 10–1. Some olfactory thresholds.*

Substance	mg/L of Air
Ethyl ether	5.83
Chloroform	3.30
Pyridine	0.03
Oil of peppermint	0.02
Iodoform	0.02
Butyric acid	0.009
Propyl mercaptan	0.006
Artificial musk	0.00004
Methyl mercaptan	0.0000004

*Data from Allison VC, Katz SH: J Ind Chem 11:336, 1919.

not known. Odor-producing molecules are generally those containing from 3–4 up to 18–20 carbon atoms, and molecules with the same number of carbon atoms but different structural configurations have different odors. Relatively high water and lipid solubility are characteristic of substances with strong odors. One theory holds that odoriferous molecules inactivate enzyme systems in the epithelium, altering its chemical reactions. Another theory holds that the molecules alter the surface of the receptor cells, thus changing their electrical state. A third theory holds that the molecules simply alter the Na^+ permeability of the receptor membrane.

Discrimination of Different Odors

Humans can distinguish between 2000 and 4000 different odors. The physiologic basis of this olfactory discrimination is not known. A number of attempts have been made to divide olfactory receptors into different fundamental types, but they have not been very successful. There is some evidence that odor discrimination depends on the spatial pattern of receptors stimulated in the mucous membrane. The direction from which a smell comes appears to be indicated by the slight difference in the time of arrival of odoriferous molecules in the 2 nostrils.

There is a close relationship between smell and sexual function in many species of animals, and the perfume ads are ample evidence that a similar relationship exists in humans. The sense of smell is generally more acute in women than in men, and in women it is most acute at the time of ovulation. Olfaction and taste are both hypersensitive in patients with adrenal insufficiency (see Chapter 20).

Sniffing

The portion of the nasal cavity containing the olfactory receptors is poorly ventilated. Most of the air normally moves quietly through the lower part of the nose with each respiratory cycle, although eddy currents, probably set up by convection as cool air strikes the warm mucosal surfaces, pass some air over the olfactory mucous membrane. The amount of air reaching this region is greatly increased by sniffing, an action that includes contraction of the lower part of the nares on the septum to help deflect the airstream upward. Sniffing is a semireflex response that usually occurs when a new odor attracts attention.

Role of Pain Fibers in the Nose

Naked endings of many trigeminal pain fibers are found in the olfactory mucous membrane. They are stimulated by irritating substances, and an irritative, trigeminally mediated component is part of the characteristic "odor" of such substances as peppermint, menthol, and chlorine. These endings are also responsible for initiating sneezing, lacrimation, respiratory inhibition, and other reflex responses to nasal irritants.

Adaptation

It is common knowledge that when one is continuously exposed to even the most disagreeable odor, perception of the odor decreases and eventually ceases. This sometimes beneficent phenomenon is due to the fairly rapid adaptation that occurs in the olfactory system. It is specific for the particular odor being smelled, and the threshold for other odors is unchanged. Olfactory adaptation is in part a central phenomenon, but it is also due to a change in the receptors.

TASTE

RECEPTOR ORGANS & PATHWAYS

Taste Buds

The taste buds, the sense organs for taste, are ovoid bodies measuring 50–70 μm. Each taste bud is made up of supporting cells and 5–18 hair cells, the **gustatory receptors.** The receptor cells each have a number of hairs projecting into the **taste pore,** the opening at the epithelial surface of the taste bud (Fig 10–5). The unmyelinated ends of the sensory nerve fibers are wrapped around the receptor cells in intimate fashion. Each taste bud is innervated by about 50 nerve fibers, and conversely, each nerve fiber receives input from an average of 5 taste buds. If the sensory nerve is cut, the taste buds it innervates degenerate and eventually disappear. However, if the nerve regenerates, the cells in the neighborhood become organized into new taste buds, presumably as a result of some sort of chemical inductive effect from the regenerating fiber.

The taste buds are located in the mucosa of the epiglottis, palate, and pharynx and in the walls of the **fungiform** and **vallate papillae** of the tongue. The fungiform papillae are rounded structures most numerous near the tip of the tongue; the vallate papillae are prominent structures arranged in a V on the back of the tongue. There are up to 5 taste buds per fungiform papilla, and they are usually located at the top of the papilla. The larger vallate papillae each contain up to 100 taste buds, usually located along the sides of the papillae. The small conical **filiform papillae** that cover the dorsum of the tongue do not usually contain taste buds. There are a total of about 10,000 taste buds in humans.

Taste Pathways

The sensory nerve fibers from the taste buds on the anterior two-thirds of the tongue travel in the chorda tympani branch of the facial nerve. The fibers from the posterior third of the tongue reach the brain stem via the glossopharyngeal nerve. The fibers from areas other than the tongue reach the brain stem via the vagus nerve. On each side, the myelinated but relatively slow-conducting taste fibers in these 3 nerves unite in the medulla oblongata to form the **tractus solitarius** (Fig 10–6). The second order neurons are located in the nucleus of this tract, and their axons cross the midline and join the medial lemniscus, ending with the fibers for touch, pain, and temperature sensibility in the specific sensory relay nuclei of the

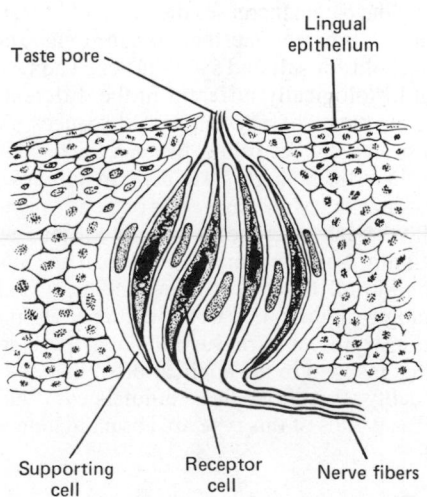

Figure 10–5. Taste bud.

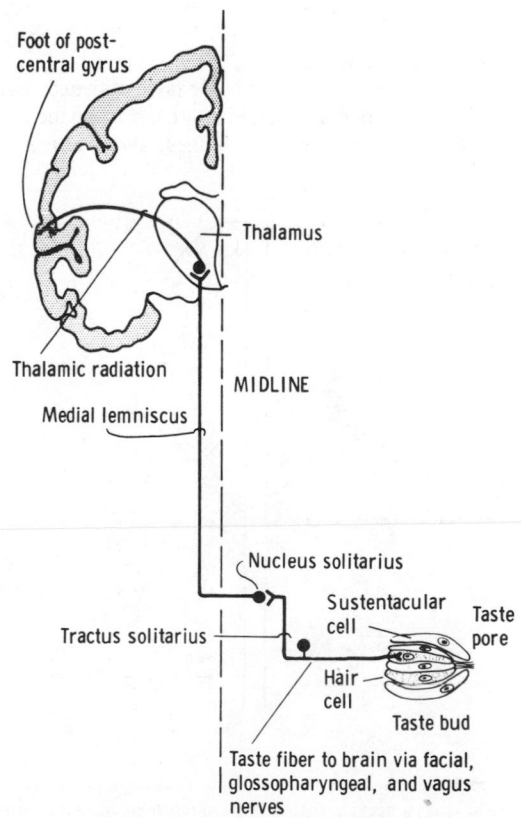

Figure 10–6. Diagram of taste pathways.

thalamus. Impulses are relayed from there to the taste projection area in the cerebral cortex at the foot of the postcentral gyrus. Taste does not have a separate cortical projection area, but is represented in the portion of the postcentral gyrus that subserves cutaneous sensation from the face.

PHYSIOLOGY OF TASTE

Receptor Stimulation

Taste receptors are chemoreceptors that respond to substances dissolved in the oral fluids bathing them. These substances appear to evoke generator potentials, but how molecules in solution interact with receptor cells to produce these potentials is not known. There is evidence that taste-producing molecules act on the membranes of the receptor cells or their processes. One theory is based on the hypothesis that the receptor hairs have a polyelectrolyte surface film. According to this theory, binding of ions to this film causes a distortion in the spatial arrangement of the film with a consequent change in the distribution of charge density. There is also evidence that taste-provoking molecules bind to specific proteins in taste buds. The binding of substances to the receptors must be weak because it usually takes relatively little washing with water to abolish a taste.

Basic Taste Modalities

In humans there are 4 basic tastes: sweet, sour, bitter, and salt. Bitter substances are tasted on the back of the tongue, sour along the edges, sweet at the tip,

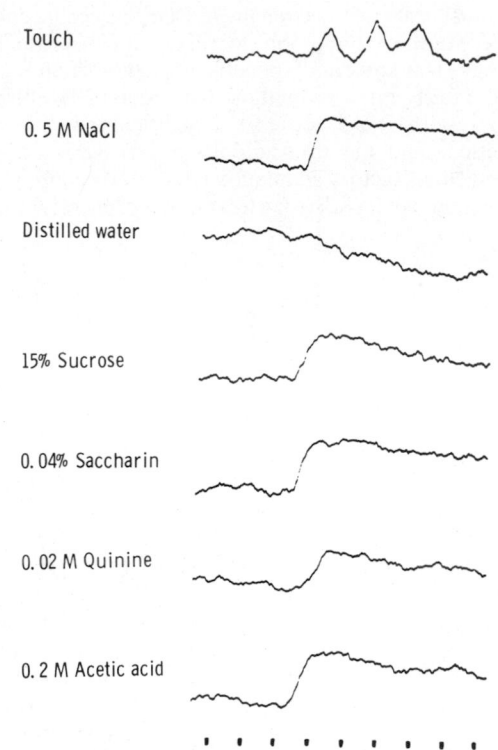

Figure 10–8. Integrated responses of the whole human chorda tympani to various solutions poured over the tongue. The height of each curve is proportionate to the firing rate. The dots at the bottom are at 1-second intervals. (Reproduced, with permission, from Zotterman Y: The nervous mechanism of taste. Ann NY Acad Sci 81:358, 1959.)

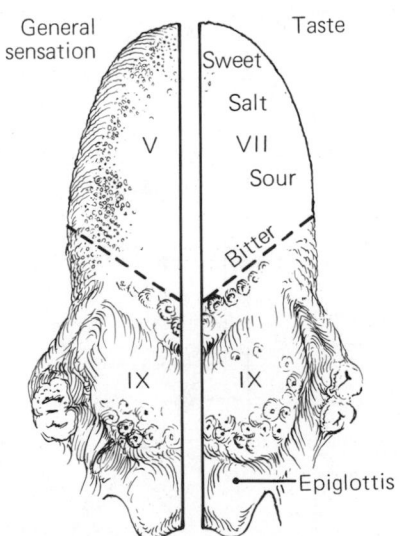

Figure 10–7. Sensory innervation of the tongue. The numbers refer to cranial nerves. (Modified and reproduced, with permission, from Chusid JG: *Correlative Neuroanatomy & Functional Neurology,* 17th ed. Lange, 1979.)

and salt on the dorsum anteriorly (Fig 10–7). Sour and bitter substances are also tasted on the palate along with some sensitivity to sweet and salt. All 4 modalities can be sensed on the pharynx and epiglottis. Anesthetizing the palate increases the threshold for sour and bitter tastes, whereas anesthetizing the tongue elevates the threshold for salt and sweet tastes. The taste buds are not histologically different in the different areas, but the existence of physiologic differences has been demonstrated by recording the electrical activity of nerve fibers from single taste buds in animals. These studies show that some taste buds respond only to bitter stimuli whereas others respond only to salt, sweet, or sour stimuli. Some respond to more than one modality, but none to all four. A curious finding of unknown physiologic significance is the demonstration that in cats, dogs, pigs, and rhesus monkeys there are taste buds that respond to the application of distilled water. Presumably, therefore, these animals can "taste water." Taste buds of this type are absent in humans (Fig 10–8).

Taste Thresholds & Intensity Discriminations

The ability of humans to discriminate differences in the intensity of tastes, like intensity discrimination

Table 10–2. Some taste thresholds.

Substance	Taste	Threshold Concentration (mol/L)
Hydrochloric acid	Sour	0.0001
Sodium chloride	Salt	0.02
Strychnine hydrochloride	Bitter	0.0000016
Glucose	Sweet	0.08
Sucrose	Sweet	0.01
Saccharin	Sweet	0.000023

in olfaction, is relatively crude. A 30% change in the concentration of the substance being tasted is necessary before an intensity difference can be detected. The threshold concentrations of substances to which the taste buds respond vary with the particular substance (Table 10–2). These thresholds are lowered in patients with adrenal insufficiency (see Chapter 20).

Substances Evoking Primary Taste Sensations

Acids taste **sour.** The H^+, rather than the associated anion, stimulates the receptors. For any given acid, sourness is generally proportionate to the H^+ concentration, but organic acids are often more sour for a given H^+ concentration than are mineral acids. This is probably because they penetrate cells more rapidly than the mineral acids.

A **salty** taste is produced by the anion of inorganic salts. The halogens are particularly effective, but some organic compounds also taste salty.

The substance usually used to test the **bitter** taste is quinine sulfate. This compound can be detected in a concentration of 0.000008 mol/L, although the threshold for strychnine hydrochloride is even lower (Table 10–2). Other organic compounds, especially morphine, nicotine, caffeine, and urea, taste bitter. Inorganic salts of magnesium, ammonium, and calcium also taste bitter. The taste is due to the cation. Thus, there is no apparent common feature of the molecular structure of substances that taste bitter.

Most **sweet** substances are organic. Sucrose, maltose, lactose, and glucose are the most familiar examples, but polysaccharides, glycerol, some of the

alcohols and ketones, and a number of compounds with no apparent relation to any of these, such as chloroform, beryllium salts, and various amides of aspartic acid also taste sweet. So do some proteins, including 2 that are 100,000 times as sweet as sucrose. Saccharin is in demand as a sweetening agent in reducing diets because it produces satisfactory sweetening in an amount that is a minute fraction of the amount of calorie-rich sucrose required for the same purpose. Lead salts also taste sweet.

Flavor

The almost infinite variety of tastes so dear to the gourmet are mostly synthesized from the 4 basic taste components. In some cases, a desirable taste includes an element of pain stimulation (eg, "hot" sauces). In addition, smell plays an important role in the overall sensation produced by food, and the consistency (or texture) and temperature of foods also contribute to their "flavor."

Taste Variation & After-Effects

There is considerable variation in the distribution of the 4 basic taste buds in various species and, within a given species, from individual to individual. In humans, there is an interesting variation in ability to taste **phenylthiocarbamide (PTC).** In dilute solution, PTC tastes sour to about 70% of the Caucasian population but is tasteless to the other 30%. Inability to taste PTC is inherited as an autosomal recessive trait. Testing for this trait is of considerable value in studies of human genetics.

Taste exhibits after-reactions and contrast phenomena that are similar in some ways to visual after-images and contrasts. Some of these are chemical "tricks," but others may be true central phenomena. A taste modifier protein, **miraculin,** has been discovered in a plant. When applied to the tongue, this protein makes acids taste sweet.

Animals, including humans, form particularly strong aversions to novel foods if eating the food is followed by illness. The survival value of such aversions is apparent in terms of avoiding poisons. The facility with which this type of learning occurs is so great that it has led some investigators to argue that its occurrence is reason to challenge classical learning theory.

11 | The Reticular Activating System, Sleep & the Electrical Activity of the Brain

THE RETICULAR FORMATION & THE RETICULAR ACTIVATING SYSTEM

The various sensory pathways described in Chapters 7–10 relay impulses from sense organs via 3- and 4-neuron chains to particular loci in the cerebral cortex. The impulses are responsible for perception and localization of individual sensations. Impulses in these systems also relay via collaterals to the **reticular activating system (RAS)** in the brain stem reticular formation. Activity in this system produces the conscious, alert state that makes perception possible.

The **reticular formation,** the phylogenetically old reticular core of the brain, occupies the midventral portion of the medulla and midbrain. It is made up of myriads of small neurons arranged in complex, intertwining nets. Located within it are centers that regulate respiration, blood pressure, heart rate, and other vegetative functions. In addition, it contains ascending and descending components that play important roles in the adjustment of endocrine secretion, the formation of conditioned reflexes, and the regulation of sensory input, learning, and consciousness. The components concerned with consciousness and the modulation of sensory input are discussed in this chapter. The vegetative functions of the reticular core are considered in the chapters on the endocrine, gastrointestinal, cardiovascular, and respiratory systems. The functions related to learning are discussed in Chapter 16, ''Higher Functions of the Nervous System.''

The reticular activating system is a complex polysynaptic pathway. Collaterals funnel into it not only from the long ascending sensory tracts but also from the trigeminal, auditory, and visual systems and the olfactory system. The complexity of the neuron net and the degree of convergence in it abolish modality specificity, and most reticular neurons are activated with equal facility by different sensory stimuli. The system is therefore **nonspecific,** whereas the classical sensory pathways are **specific** in that the fibers in them are activated only by one type of sensory stimulation. Part of the RAS bypasses the thalamus to project diffusely to the cortex. Another part of the RAS ends in the intralaminar and related thalamic nuclei, and from them is projected diffusely and nonspecifically to the whole neocortex (Fig 11–1). The RAS is intimately concerned with the electrical activity of the cortex.

THE THALAMUS & THE CEREBRAL CORTEX

Thalamic Nuclei

On developmental and topographic grounds, the thalamus can be divided into 3 parts: the epithalamus, the dorsal thalamus, and the ventral thalamus. The **epithalamus** has connections to the olfactory system, and the projections and functions of the **ventral thalamus** are undetermined. The **dorsal thalamus** can be divided into nuclei which project diffusely to the whole neocortex and nuclei which project to specific discrete portions of the neocortex and limbic system. The nuclei that project to all parts of the neocortex are the midline and intralaminar nuclei. They are called collectively the **nonspecific projection nuclei.** They receive input from the reticular activating system. Impulses responsible for the diffuse secondary response and the alerting effect of reticular activation (see below) are relayed through them. The nuclei of the dorsal thalamus that project to specific areas can be divided into 3 groups: the specific sensory relay nuclei, the nuclei concerned with efferent control mechanisms, and the nuclei concerned with complex integrative

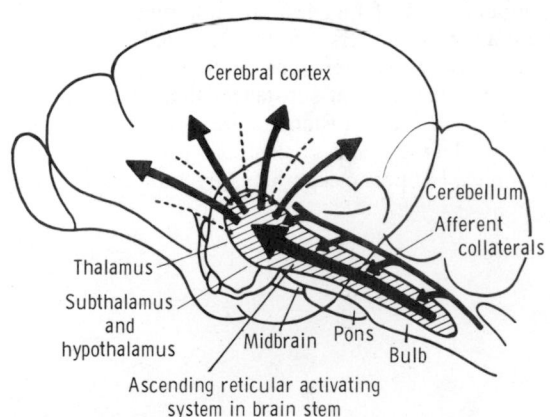

Figure 11–1. Diagram of ascending reticular system projected on a sagittal section of the cat brain. (Reproduced, with permission, from Starzl TE, Taylor CW, Magoun HW: Collateral afferent excitation of reticular formation of brain stem. J Neurophysiol 14:479, 1951.)

functions. The **specific sensory relay nuclei** include the medial and lateral geniculate bodies, which relay auditory and visual impulses to the auditory and visual cortices, and the ventrobasal group of nuclei that relay somathesthetic information to the postcentral gyrus. The **nuclei concerned with efferent control mechanisms** include several nuclei that are concerned with motor function. They receive input from the basal ganglia and the cerebellum and project to the motor cortex. Also included in this group are the anterior nuclei, which receive afferents from the mammillary bodies and project to the limbic cortex. This is part of the limbic circuit, which appears to be concerned with recent memory and emotion (see Chapters 15 and 16). The **nuclei concerned with complex integrative functions** are the dorsolateral nuclei that project to the cortical association areas and are concerned primarily with functions such as language.

Cortical Organization

The neocortex is generally arranged in 6 layers (Fig 11–2). The neurons are mostly pyramidal cells with extensive vertical dendritic trees (Figs 11–2, 11–3) that may reach to the cortical surface. The axons of these cells usually give off recurrent collaterals that turn back and synapse on the superficial portions of the dendritic trees. Afferents from the specific nuclei of the thalamus terminate primarily in cortical layer IV, whereas the nonspecific afferents are distributed to all cortical layers.

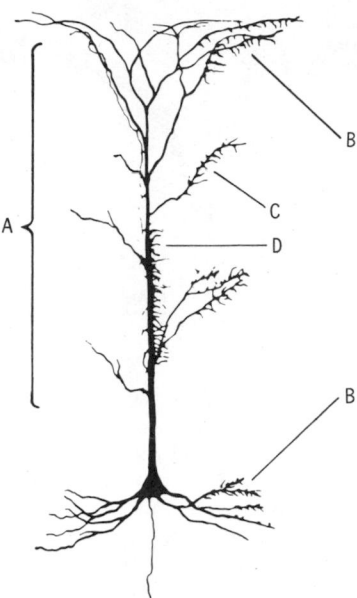

Figure 11–3. Cortical pyramidal cell, showing the distribution of presynaptic terminals. *A,* nonspecific afferents from the reticular formation and the thalamus; *B,* recurrent collaterals of pyramidal cell axons; *C,* commissural fibers from mirror image sites in contralateral hemisphere; *D,* specific afferents from thalamic sensory relay nuclei. (Reproduced, with permission, from Chow KL, Leiman AL: The structural and functional organization of the neocortex. Neurosci Res Program Bull 8:157, 1970.)

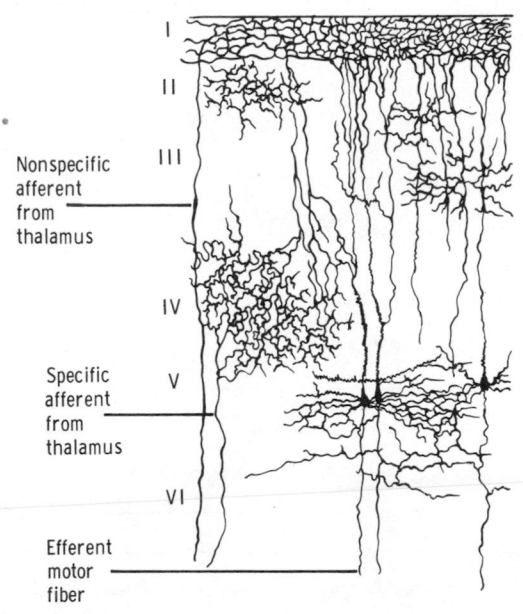

Figure 11–2. Neuronal connections in the neocortex. On the left are afferent fibers from the thalamus. The numbers identify the cortical layers. Note the extensive dendritic processes of the cells, especially those in the deep layers. (Based on drawing of Lorente de No R, in Fulton JF: *Physiology of the Nervous System,* 2nd ed. Oxford Univ Press, 1943.)

EVOKED CORTICAL POTENTIALS

The electrical events that occur in the cortex after stimulation of a sense organ can be monitored with an exploring electrode connected to another electrode at an indifferent point some distance away. A characteristic response is seen in animals under barbiturate anesthesia. If the exploring electrode is over the primary receiving area for the particular sense, a surface-positive wave appears with a latency of 5–12 ms. This is followed by a small negative wave and then by a larger, more prolonged positive deflection with a latency of 20–80 ms. This sequence of potential changes is illustrated in Fig 11–4. The first positive-negative wave sequence is the **primary evoked potential;** the second is the **diffuse secondary response.**

Primary Evoked Potential

The primary evoked potential is highly specific in its location and can be observed only where the pathways from a particular sense organ end. Indeed, it is so discrete that it has been used to map the specific cortical sensory areas. It was thought at one time that the primary response was due to activity ascending to the cortex in the thalamic radiations. However, an electrode on the pial surface of the cortex samples activity to a depth of only 0.3-0.6 mm. The primary response is negative rather than positive when it is recorded with a

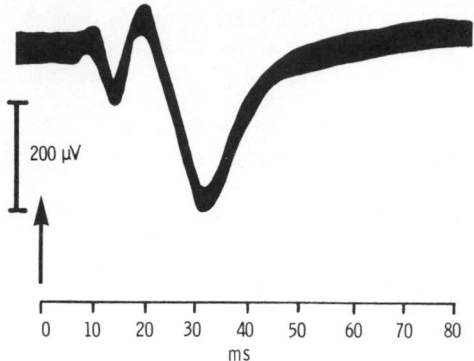

Figure 11–4. Response evoked in the contralateral sensory cortex by stimulation (at the arrow) of the sciatic nerve in a cat under barbiturate anesthesia. Upward deflection is surface-negative. (Modified from Forbes A, Morison BR: Cortical response to sensory stimulation under deep barbiturate narcosis. J Neurophysiol 2:112, 1939.)

microelectrode inserted in layers 2–6 of the underlying cortex, and the negative wave within the cortex is followed by a positive wave. This indicates depolarization on the dendrites and somas of the cells in the cortex, followed by hyperpolarization. The positive-negative wave sequence recorded from the surface of the cortex is due to the fact that the superficial cortical layers are positive relative to the initial negativity, then negative to the deep hyperpolarization. In unanesthetized animals, the primary evoked potential is largely obscured by the spontaneous activity of the brain, but it can be demonstrated with special technics. It is somewhat more diffuse in unanesthetized animals, but still well localized compared to the diffuse secondary response.

Diffuse Secondary Response

The surface-positive diffuse secondary response is sometimes followed by a negative wave or series of waves. Unlike the primary response, the secondary response is not highly localized. It appears at the same time over most of the cortex and in many other parts of the brain. The uniform latency in different parts of the cortex and the fact that it is not affected by a circular cut through the cortical gray matter that isolates an area from all lateral connections indicates that the secondary response cannot be due to lateral spread of the primary evoked response. It therefore must be due to activity ascending from below the cortex. The pathway involved appears to be the nonspecific thalamic projection system from the midline and related thalamic nuclei.

The diffuse secondary response is present in unanesthetized animals and in them is influenced by a variety of emotional and motivational factors. When the animal is presented with a stimulus to which it has become accustomed, the diffuse secondary response produced by it is small and inconspicuous. However, if the stimulus is followed a number of times by an electric shock, the diffuse secondary response to the same stimulus is large and is present not only in all parts of the cortex but in a variety of subcortical loci as well.

THE ELECTROENCEPHALOGRAM

The background electrical activity of the brain in unanesthetized animals was described in the 19th century, but it was first analyzed in a systematic fashion by the German psychiatrist Hans Berger, who introduced the term **electroencephalogram (EEG)** to denote the record of the variations in potential recorded from the brain. The EEG can be recorded with scalp electrodes through the unopened skull, or with electrodes on or in the brain. The term **electrocorticogram (ECoG)** is sometimes used to refer to the record obtained with electrodes on the pial surface of the cortex.

EEG records may be **bipolar** or **unipolar.** The former is the record of potential fluctuations between 2 cortical electrodes; the latter is the record of potential differences between a cortical electrode and a theoretically indifferent electrode on some part of the body distant from the cortex.

Alpha Rhythm

In an adult human at rest with mind wandering and eyes closed, the most prominent component of the EEG is a fairly regular pattern of waves at a frequency of 8–12/s and an amplitude of about 50 μV when recorded from the scalp. This pattern is the **alpha rhythm.** It is most marked in the parieto-occipital area, although it is sometimes observed in other locations. A similar rhythm has been observed in a wide variety of mammalian species (Fig 11–5). In the cat, it

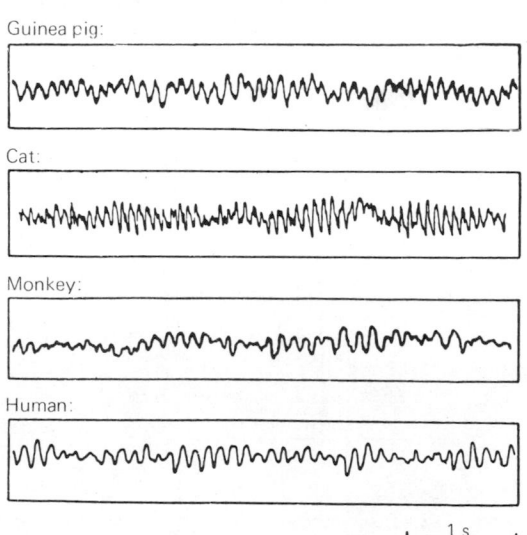

Figure 11–5. EEG records showing alpha rhythm from 4 different species. (Reproduced, with permission, from Brazier MAB: *Electrical Activity of the Nervous System,* 2nd ed. Pitman, 1960.)

is slightly more rapid than in the human, and there are other minor variations from species to species, but in all mammals the pattern is remarkably similar.

Other Rhythms

In addition to the dominant alpha rhythm, 18–30/s patterns of lower voltage are sometimes seen over the frontal regions. This rhythm, the **beta rhythm,** may be a harmonic of the alpha. A pattern of large, regular 4–7/s waves called the **theta rhythm** occurs in normal children and is generated in the hippocampus in experimental animals (see below). Large, slow waves with a frequency of less than 4/s are sometimes called **delta waves.**

Variations in the EEG

In humans, the frequency of the dominant EEG rhythm at rest varies with age. In infants, there is fast, betalike activity, but the occipital rhythm is a slow 0.5–2/s pattern. During childhood this latter rhythm speeds up, and the adult alpha pattern gradually appears during adolescence. The frequency of the alpha rhythm is decreased by a low blood glucose level, a low body temperature, a low level of adrenal glucocorticoid hormones, and a high arterial partial pressure of CO_2 (P_{CO_2}). It is increased by the reverse conditions. Forced overbreathing to lower the arterial P_{CO_2} is sometimes used clinically to bring out latent EEG abnormalities.

Alpha Block

When the eyes are opened, the alpha rhythm is replaced by fast, irregular low-voltage activity with no dominant frequency. This phenomenon is called **alpha block.** A breakup of the alpha pattern is also produced by any form of sensory stimulation (Fig 11–6) or mental concentration such as solving arithmetic problems. A common term for this replacement of the regular alpha rhythm with irregular low-voltage activity is **desynchronization,** because it represents a breaking up of the synchronized activity of neural elements responsible for the wave pattern. Because desynchronization is produced by sensory stimulation and is correlated with the aroused, alert state, it is also called the **arousal** or **alerting response.**

Sleep Patterns

When an individual in a relaxed, inattentive state becomes drowsy and falls asleep, the alpha rhythm is replaced by slower, larger waves. In deep sleep (slow wave sleep), very large, somewhat irregular delta waves at a frequency of less than 4/s are observed. Interspersed with these waves during moderately deep sleep are bursts of alphalike, 10–14/s, 50 μV

waves—the **sleep spindles.** However, there is a special form of sleep in which there is rapid, irregular cortical activity (REM sleep; see below). The alpha rhythm and the patterns of the drowsy and sleeping individual are **synchronized,** in contrast to the desynchronized, irregular activity seen in the alert state and REM sleep.

PHYSIOLOGIC BASIS OF THE EEG & CONSCIOUSNESS

The presence of rhythmic waves in the alpha and slow wave sleep patterns indicates a priori that neural components of some sort are discharging rhythmically, since random discharges of individual units would cancel out and no waves would be produced. The main questions to be answered are which units are discharging synchronously, and what mechanisms are responsible for desynchronization and synchronization.

Source of the EEG

EEG waves were originally thought to be the summed action potentials of cortical cells discharging in a volume conductor. However, the activity recorded in the EEG is mostly that of the most superficial layers of the cortical gray substance, and there are relatively few cell bodies in these layers. Present evidence indicates that the potential changes in the cortical EEG are due to current flow in the fluctuating dipoles formed on the dendrites of the cortical cells and the cell bodies. The dendrites of the cortical cells are a forest of similarly oriented, densely packed units in the superficial layers of the cerebral cortex (Fig 11–2). As pointed out in Chapter 4, dendrites may be conducting processes, but they generally do not produce propagated all or none spikes; rather, they are the site of nonpropagated hypopolarizing and hyperpolarizing local potential changes. As excitatory and inhibitory endings on the dendrites of each cell become active, current flows into and out of these current sinks and sources from the rest of the dendritic processes and the cell body. The cell-dendrite relationship is therefore that of a constantly shifting dipole. Current flow in this dipole would be expected to produce wavelike potential fluctuations in a volume conductor (Fig 11–7). When the sum of the dendritic activity is negative relative to the cell, the cell is hypopolarized and hyperexcitable; when it is positive, the cell is hyperpolarized and less excitable. It also seems that information can be transmitted electrotonically from one dendrite to another (see Chapter 4).

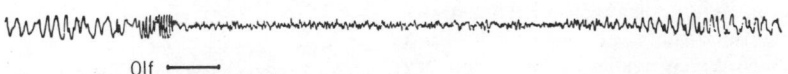

Olf ——▶

Figure 11–6. Desynchronization of the cortical EEG of a rabbit by an olfactory stimulus (indicated by the line after Olf). (Reproduced, with permission, from Green JD, Arduini A: Hippocampal electrical activity during arousal. J Neurophysiol 17:533, 1954.)

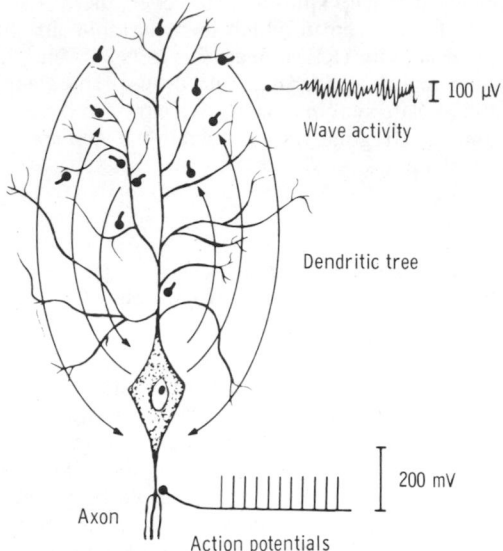

I 100 µV

Wave activity

Dendritic tree

I 200 mV

Axon

Action potentials

Figure 11–7. Diagrammatic comparison of the electrical responses of the axon and the dendrites of a large cortical neuron. Current flow to and from active synaptic knobs on the dendrites produces wave activity, while all or none action potentials are transmitted down the axon. (Modified and redrawn, with permission, from Bickford RG: Computational aspects of brain function. Institute of Radio Engineers, Medical Electronics Series [IRE,ME] 6:164, 1959.)

The cerebellar cortex and the hippocampus are 2 other parts of the CNS where many complex, parallel dendritic processes are located subpially over a layer of cells. In both areas, there is a characteristic rhythmic fluctuation in surface potential similar to that observed in the cortical EEG.

Desynchronizing Mechanisms

Desynchronization, the replacement of a rhythmic EEG pattern with irregular low-voltage activity, is produced by stimulation of the specific sensory systems up to the level of the midbrain, but stimulation of these systems above the midbrain, stimulation of the specific sensory relay nuclei of the thalamus, or stimulation of the cortical receiving areas themselves does not produce desynchronization. On the other hand, high-frequency stimulation of the reticular formation in the midbrain tegmentum and of the nonspecific projection nuclei of the thalamus desynchronizes the EEG and arouses a sleeping animal. Large lesions of the lateral and superior portions of the midbrain that interrupt the medial lemnisci and other ascending specific sensory systems fail to prevent the desynchronization produced by sensory stimulation, but lesions in the midbrain tegmentum which disrupt the RAS without damaging the specific systems are associated with a synchronized pattern which is unaffected by sensory stimulation (Fig 11–8). Animals with the former type of lesion are awake; those with the latter type are comatose for long periods. It therefore appears that the

ascending activity responsible for desynchronization following sensory stimulation passes up the specific sensory systems to the midbrain, enters the RAS via collaterals, and continues through the thalamus and the nonspecific thalamic projection system to the cortex. On the other hand, sensory input is not absolutely essential for desynchronization. In animals in which the brain stem has been sectioned rostral to the trigeminal input but caudal to the dorsal border of the pons, section of the olfactory and optic nerves does not prevent desynchronization. Thus, it may be that the reticular formation has an additional intrinsic capacity to produce desynchronization and, possibly, the waking state.

Generalized & Localized Cortical Arousal

There is some evidence for localization of function within the RAS. The hypothesis has been advanced that the lower part of the reticular system is responsible for relatively crude sleep-wakefulness changes, whereas the thalamic portions of the system mediate shifting, localized alerting of the various parts of the cortex in response to the panorama of highly specific stimuli demanding attention in any active individual. The ways in which selected parts of the brain can be alerted under certain conditions, and the relationship of these responses to conditioned learning, are discussed in Chapter 16.

It should be pointed out that although arousal and EEG desynchronization generally occur together, they do not always coexist. The presence of desynchronization in paradoxical sleep has been mentioned above and is discussed in detail below. In addition, strong nociceptive peripheral stimulation can produce arousal without desynchronization in animals with lesions of the midbrain tegmentum and desynchronization without arousal in animals with lesions in the posterior hypothalamus. Thus, different components of the reticular formation appear to mediate desynchronization and arousal.

Effect of RAS Stimulation on Cortical Neurons

It is not known how impulses ascending in the

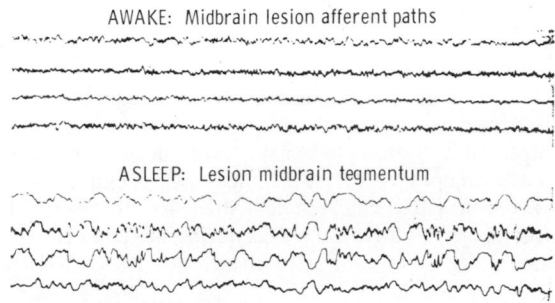

AWAKE: Midbrain lesion afferent paths

ASLEEP: Lesion midbrain tegmentum

Figure 11–8. Typical EEG records of cat with lesion of lemniscal pathways (*above*) and cat with lesion of midbrain tegmentum (*below*). (Reproduced, with permission, from Lindsley DB & others: Behavioral and EEG changes following chronic brain stem lesions in the cat. Electroencephalogr Clin Neurophysiol 2:483, 1950.)

RAS break up synchronized cortical activity or produce arousal. Stimulation of the RAS inhibits burst activity, the recruiting response (see below), and the cortical waves produced by the application of strychnine to certain parts of the brain. Since RAS stimulation arouses and alerts the animal, one might expect it to produce a heightened rather than a depressed excitability of cortical neurons. However, some of the neurons in the cortical sensory projection areas fire randomly during sleep whereas they discharge only in response to specific stimuli when the animal is awake. It is possible that RAS activity abolishes this random firing by producing some degree of cortical inhibition, leaving these neurons free to respond only to specific sensory signals. The net effect of RAS activity, therefore, might be an increase in the "signal/noise ratio" at the expense of a slight decrease in absolute excitability.

Arousal Following Cortical Stimulation

Electrical stimulation of certain portions of the cerebral cortex causes increased reticular activity and EEG arousal. The most effective cortical loci in the monkey are the superior temporal gyrus and the orbital surface of the frontal lobe. Stimulation of these regions wakes a sleeping animal but causes no movements and has few visible effects in the conscious animal. Stimulation of other cortical areas, even with strong currents, does not produce electrical or behavioral arousal. These observations indicate that a system of **corticofugal fibers** passes from the cortex to the reticular formation, providing a pathway by which intracortical events can initiate arousal. The system may be responsible for the alerting responses to emotions and related psychic phenomena that occur in the absence of any apparent external stimulus.

Alerting Effects of Epinephrine & Related Compounds

An interesting pharmacologic effect on the RAS is the arousal response produced by agents that mimic the action of the sympathetic nervous system. Epinephrine, norepinephrine, and amphetamine produce EEG arousal and behavioral alerting by lowering the threshold of reticular neurons in the brain stem. Epinephrine and norepinephrine secreted from the adrenal medulla in the stressed individual have the same effect. Therefore, one of the effects of the mass adrenergic discharge in emergency situations (see Chapter 13) is reinforcement of the alert, attentive state necessary for effective action.

It was originally thought that the alerting effect was due to a direct action of pressor agents on the neurons in the midbrain, but it has been demonstrated that any increase in blood pressure increases the excitability of the reticular formation. Apparently there are blood pressure–sensitive neurons in the midbrain, because pressor agents produce EEG arousal in animals in which the brain has been transected at the top of the pons but not in animals in which transection has been carried out at higher levels.

Clinical Correlates

Patients with tumors or other lesions that interrupt the RAS are generally comatose. This system is especially vulnerable at the top of the midbrain and in the posterior hypothalamus, where it is pushed medially by other fiber systems. Relatively small lesions in this location may cause prolonged coma while producing very few other symptoms. In animals it has been demonstrated that concussion depresses activity in the RAS and produces a sleep pattern in the EEG which persists as long as the unconsciousness lasts.

The RAS & General Anesthesia

The ability of general anesthetics to produce unconsciousness appears to be due, at least in part, to their action in depressing conduction in the RAS. The effect of ether on the response of the reticular formation and the medial lemnisci to a sensory stimulus is shown in Fig 11–9. Similar blocking effects are produced by anesthetic doses of barbiturates. These effects may be simply a manifestation of general synaptic depression by these drugs. There are hundreds of synapses in the reticular pathways, whereas the specific systems have only 2–4. At each synapse, the EPSPs must build up until the firing level of the postsynaptic neurons is reached (see Chapter 4). Any agent that has a moderate depressant effect on this process will block conduction in multisynaptic paths before blocking it in those with only a few synapses.

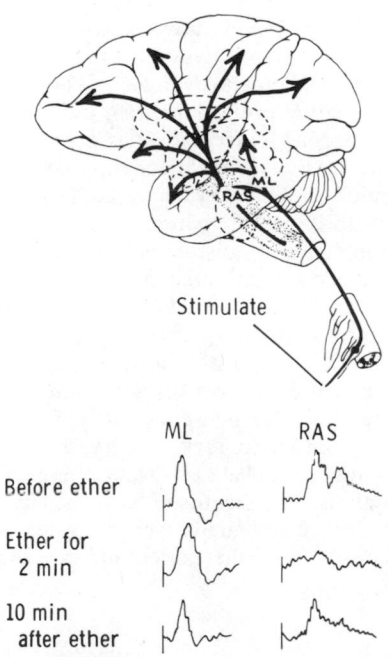

Figure 11–9. Effect of ether anesthesia on lemniscal (ML) and reticular (RAS) response to stimulation of the sciatic nerve. (Redrawn and reproduced, with permission, from French JD, King EE: Mechanisms involved in the anesthetic state. Surgery 38:228, 1955.)

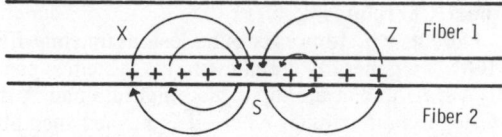

Figure 11–10. Effect of activity in one nerve fiber on the activity of a neighboring fiber in a volume conductor. Current flows into the area of depolarization (S) on fiber 2 from the surrounding membrane. At X and Z on the membrane of fiber 1, positive charges pile up, hyperpolarizing the membrane; at Y, positive charges are pulled off, partly depolarizing it.

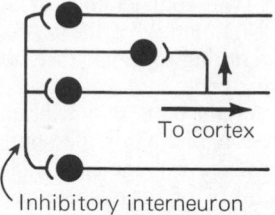

Figure 11–12. Postulated circuit in thalamus that generates rhythmic discharge to cortex. Arrows indicate direction of action potentials when neuron in center discharges.

Synchronizing Mechanisms

The wave pattern of the alpha rhythm indicates that the activity of many of the dendritic units is synchronized. Two factors contribute to this synchronization: the synchronizing effect on each unit of activity in neighboring parallel fibers, and rhythmic discharge of impulses from the thalamus.

If 2 nerve fibers are placed side by side in a volume conductor, depolarization of one of them rarely if ever causes a propagated discharge in the other but does influence its excitability. This is because external current flow into the area of depolarization in the active fiber hyperpolarizes the membrane of the neighboring fiber at 2 points and partially depolarizes it at another. Current flow in the opposite direction creates areas of positivity in fibers adjacent to sites where inhibitory endings are active (Fig 11–10). In a large population of similarly oriented neural processes, this formation of current sinks and sources in neighboring fibers tends to synchronize current flow.

The dendritic potentials of the cerebral cortex are also influenced by projections from the thalamus. A circular cut around a piece of cortex does not alter its synchronized activity if the blood supply is intact, but the rhythmicity is markedly decreased if the deep connections of the cortical "button" are severed. Large lesions of the thalamus disrupt the EEG synchrony on the side of the lesion. Stimulation of thalamic nuclei at a frequency of about 8/s produces a characteristic 8/s response throughout most of the ipsilateral cortex. Because the amplitude of this response waxes and wanes, it is called the **recruiting response** (Fig 11–11). The recruiting response has many similarities to the alpha rhythm and to **burst activity,** the occurrence of short trains of alphalike waves superimposed on slower rhythms. The records of burst activity such as sleep spindles are essentially identical when recorded simultaneously from the cortex and the thalamus.

Figure 11–11. Recruiting response in cortex produced by 8/s stimulation of intralaminar thalamic region. (Based on recordings of Morison RS, Dempsey EW: A study of thalamo-cortical relations. Am J Physiol 135:281, 1942.)

These observations point to activity projected from the thalamus or reverberating activity between the thalamus and the cortex as being of importance in the genesis of the synchronized EEG rhythm. A current theory holds that synchrony is produced by a thalamic circuit which includes a pathway for **recurrent collateral inhibition.** The proposed pathway is shown in Fig 11–12. Each time the central neuron discharges, it activates via a collateral branch an inhibitory interneuron that produces IPSPs in the discharging neuron and its neighbors. The thalamic neurons are also postulated to be hyperexcitable after a period of inhibition and to discharge spontaneously during the rebound **(postinhibitory rebound excitation).** Therefore, they discharge rhythmically.

EEG synchrony and slow wave sleep (see below) can be produced by stimulation of at least 3 subcortical regions. The region discussed in the preceding paragraph is the **diencephalic sleep zone** in the posterior hypothalamus and the nearby intralaminar and anterior thalamic nuclei. The stimulus frequency must be about 8/s; faster stimuli produce arousal. This finding need not be confusing; the important point is that low-frequency stimulation produces one response, whereas high-frequency stimulation produces another. The second zone is the **medullary synchronizing zone** in the reticular formation of the medulla oblongata at the level of the nucleus of the tractus solitarius. Stimulation of this zone, like stimulation of the diencephalic sleep zone, produces synchrony and sleep if the frequency is slow but arousal if the frequency is fast. The mechanism by which synchrony is produced is not known, but it presumably involves pathways that ascend to the thalamus. The third synchronizing region is the **basal forebrain sleep zone.** This zone includes the preoptic area and the diagonal band of Broca. It differs from the other 2 zones in that stimulation of the basal forebrain zone produces synchrony and sleep whether the stimulating frequency is fast or slow. There is some evidence that its effects are mediated by descending pathways which inhibit neurons in the ascending reticular formation.

Clinical Uses of the EEG

The EEG is sometimes of value in localizing pathologic processes. When a collection of fluid overlies a portion of the cortex, activity over this area may

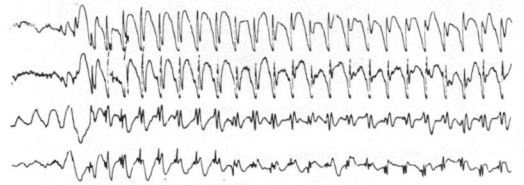

Figure 11–13. Petit mal epilepsy. Record of 4 cortical EEG leads from a 6-year-old boy who during the recording had one of his "blank spells" in which he was transiently unaware of his surroundings and blinked his eyelids. (Reproduced, with permission, from Chusid JG: *Correlative Neuroanatomy & Functional Neurology,* 17th ed. Lange, 1979.)

be damped. This fact may aid in diagnosing and localizing conditions such as subdural hematomas. Lesions in the cortex cause local formation of irregular or slow waves that can be picked up in the EEG leads. Epileptogenic foci sometimes generate high-voltage waves that can be localized.

The waves recorded from corresponding anatomic loci on the 2 hemispheres are normally remarkably similar in timing and shape. This is presumably due to a central subcortical "pacemaker" that keeps the activity of both hemispheres in phase. A lesion in one hemisphere distorts the pattern; consequently, if records from homologous points on the 2 hemispheres are out of phase with each other, focal cortical damage is indicated.

In epileptics, there are characteristic EEG patterns during seizures; between attacks, however, abnormalities are often difficult to demonstrate. **Grand mal** seizures, epileptic attacks in which an aura precedes a generalized convulsion with tonic muscular contraction and clonic jerks, have a characteristic EEG pattern. There is fast activity during the tonic phase. Slow waves, each preceded by a spike, occur at the time of each clonic jerk. For a while after the attack, slow waves are present. Similar changes are seen in experimental animals during convulsions produced by electric shocks. **Petit mal** epileptic attacks, seizures characterized by a momentary loss of responsiveness, are associated with 3/s doublets, each consisting of a typical spike and rounded wave (Fig 11–13). **Psychomotor seizures,** attacks in which emotional lability and stereotyped behavior are seen due to discharge from a temporal lobe focus, are not associated with any typical EEG changes. During the various types of diencephalic seizures that originate in the brain stem, there are also no characteristic EEG abnormalities.

SLEEP

Sleep Stages

There are 2 different kinds of sleep: **rapid eye movement (REM) sleep** and **non-REM (NREM)** or **slow wave sleep.** NREM sleep is divided into 4 stages.

A person falling asleep first enters stage 1, which is characterized by low amplitude, fast frequency EEG activity (Fig 11–14). Stage 2 is marked by the appearance of sleep spindles (see above). In stage 3, the pattern is one of slower frequency and increased amplitude of the EEG waves. Maximum slowing with large waves is seen in stage 4. Thus, the characteristic of deep sleep is a pattern of synchronized slow waves.

REM Sleep

The high-amplitude slow waves seen in the EEG during sleep are sometimes replaced by rapid, low-voltage, irregular EEG activity which resembles that seen in alert animals and humans. However, sleep is not interrupted; indeed, the threshold for arousal by sensory stimuli and by stimulation of the reticular formation is elevated. The condition has been called **paradoxical sleep.** There are rapid, roving movements of the eyes during paradoxical sleep, and for this reason it is also called REM sleep. There are no such movements in slow-wave sleep, and consequently it is often called NREM sleep. Another characteristic of REM sleep is the occurrence of large phasic potentials, occurring in groups of 3–5, that originate in the pons and pass rapidly to the lateral geniculate body and thence to the occipital cortex. For this reason, they are called **ponto-geniculo-occipital (PGO) spikes.** There is a marked reduction in skeletal muscle tone during REM sleep (Fig 11–14) despite the rapid eye movements and PGO spikes. The hypotonia is due to increased activity of the reticular inhibiting area in the medulla (see Chapter 12), which brings about decreases in stretch and polysynaptic reflexes by way of both pre- and postsynaptic inhibition.

Humans aroused at a time when they show the EEG characteristics of REM sleep generally report that they were dreaming, whereas individuals wakened from slow wave sleep do not. This observation and other evidence indicate that REM sleep and dreaming are closely associated. The teeth-grinding (**bruxism**) that occurs in some individuals is also associated with dreaming. REM sleep is found in all species of mammals and birds that have been studied, but it probably does not occur in other classes of animals.

If humans are awakened every time they show REM sleep, they become somewhat anxious and irritable. If they are then permitted to sleep without interruption, they show a great deal more than the normal amount of paradoxical sleep for a few nights. The same "rebound" effect is seen in animals treated the same way. These observations have led some investigators to conclude that dreaming is necessary to maintain mental health. However, it is now established that prolonged REM deprivation does not have any adverse psychologic effects.

Distribution of Stages

In a typical night of sleep, a young adult passes through stages 1 and 2 and spends 70–100 minutes in stages 3 and 4. Sleep then lightens, and a REM period follows. This cycle is repeated at intervals of about 90

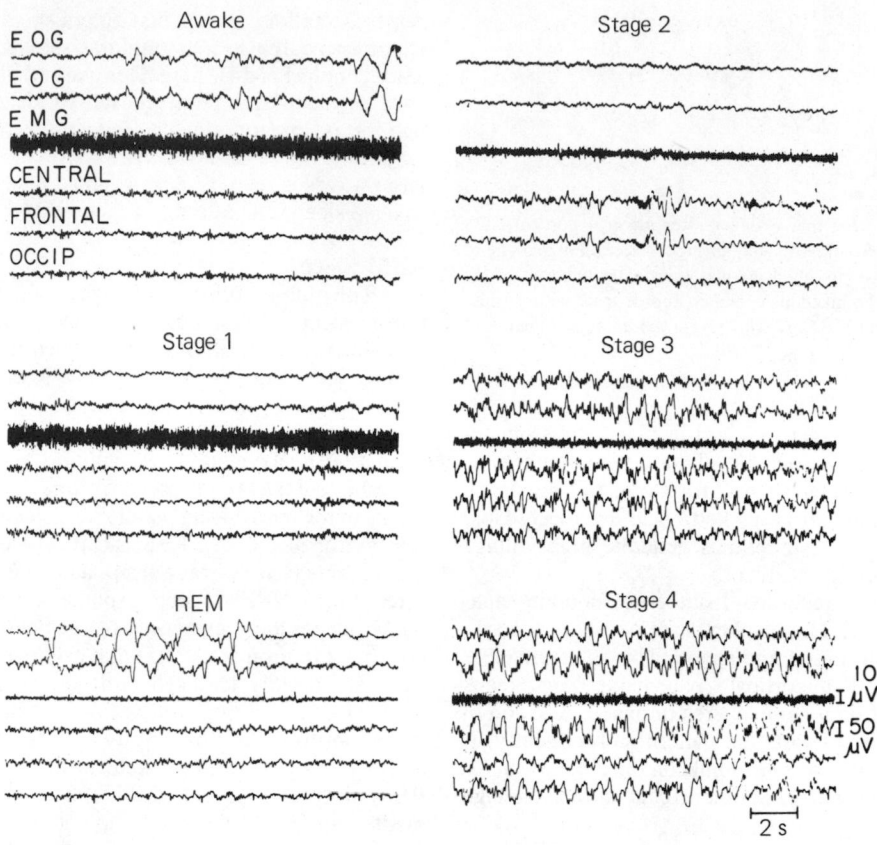

Figure 11–14. Sleep stages. EOG, electrooculogram registering eye movements; EMG, electromyogram registering skeletal muscle activity; central, frontal, occip, 3 EEG leads. Note the low muscle tone with extensive eye movements in REM. (Reproduced, with permission, from Kales A & others: Sleep and dreams: Recent research on clinical aspects. Ann Intern Med 68:1078, 1968.)

minutes throughout the night (Fig 11–15). The cycles are similar, although there is less stage 3 and 4 sleep and more REM sleep toward morning. Thus, there are 4–6 REM periods per night. At all ages, REM sleep constitutes about 25% of total sleep time. Children have more stage 3 and 4 sleep than young adults, and old people have much less.

Genesis of Slow Wave Sleep

Slow wave sleep is produced in part by the absence of desynchronizing activity transmitted via the ascending reticular system. However, it is actively produced as well by the synchronizing zone. The synchronizing activity of the thalamus is apparently influenced by ascending activity from the pons and hindbrain, since stimulation of the medullary sleep zone produces synchrony and sleep (see above). The role of the basal forebrain zone in the production of normal sleep is unknown. Stimulation of afferents from mechanoreceptors in the skin at rates of 10/s or less also produces sleep in animals, apparently via the brain stem, and it is of course common knowledge that regularly repeated monotonous stimuli put humans to sleep. The relationship of these observations, if any, to the production of **electrosleep** or **electric anesthesia** is

not known. These terms refer to the unconscious state produced in some humans by the application of small amounts of current to the head in the form of pulses at a frequency of 20–40 Hz. However, sleep and insensibility to pain are not produced by the current in all individuals.

There is evidence that discharge of serotonin-secreting neurons is involved in the production of slow wave sleep, and the serotonergic neurons that project to the limbic system and other rostral areas have their cell bodies in the raphe nuclei located in the hindbrain. The role of serotonin as a synaptic mediator in the CNS is discussed in Chapter 15. Parachlorophenylalanine, a drug that depletes brain serotonin, causes insomnia in cats, and this effect is overcome by administration of 5-hydroxtryptophan, which restores the serotonin content of the neurons to normal.

Genesis of REM Sleep

The mechanism that triggers REM sleep is located in the pontine reticular formation. Lesions of the oral and caudal pontine reticular nuclei abolish the desynchronized EEG activity, usually without affecting slow wave sleep or arousal. Other evidence also indicates that the desynchronization is brought about

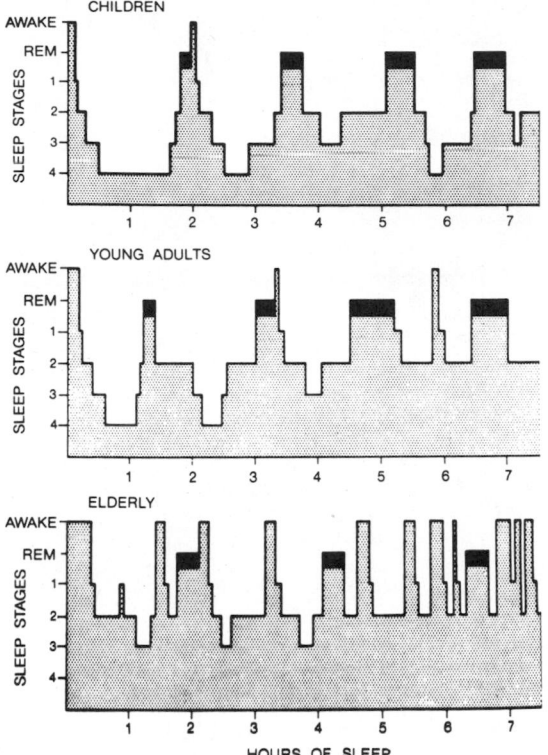

Figure 11–15. Normal sleep cycles at various ages. REM sleep is indicated by the dark areas. (Reproduced, with permission, from Kales AM, Kales JD: Sleep disorders. N Engl J Med 290:487, 1974.)

by pathways which are different from those mediating desynchronization during the aroused waking state. The rapid eye movements are mediated via the vestibular nuclei. The structures that activate the medullary reticular inhibitory area to produce hypotonia are located in the mediolateral pontine tegmentum, and include the locus ceruleus. PGO spikes originate in the lateral pontine tegmentum.

PGO spikes herald the onset of REM sleep, but it is not known what initiates the discharges from the pons. The available evidence indicates that no single synaptic transmitter is responsible for REM sleep but that the locus ceruleus and the norepinephrine-secreting neurons which emanate from it play an important role in the phenomenon.

REM sleep is suppressed by brain stem lesions that deplete the forebrain of norepinephrine. However, drugs that inhibit monoamine oxidase increase brain norepinephrine and decrease REM sleep. Reserpine, which depletes serotonin and catecholamines, blocks slow wave sleep and the hypotonia and EEG desynchronization characteristic of REM sleep but increases PGO spike activity. Drugs that block muscarinic cholinergic synapses (see Chapter 13) also decrease the hypotonia and EEG desynchronization but do not affect PGO spike activity. Barbiturates also decrease the amount of REM sleep.

Sleep Disorders

Sleepwalking (**somnambulism**) and bed-wetting (**nocturnal enuresis**) have been shown to occur during slow wave sleep or, more specifically, during arousal from slow wave sleep. They are not associated with REM sleep. Episodes of sleepwalking are more common in children than adults and occur predominantly in males. They may last several minutes. Somnambulists walk with their eyes open and avoid obstacles, but when awakened they cannot recall the episodes.

Narcolepsy is a not uncommon disease of unknown cause in which there is an eventually irresistible urge to sleep during daytime activities. In some cases, it has been shown to start with the sudden onset of REM sleep. REM sleep almost never occurs without previous slow wave sleep in normal individuals.

MODULATION OF SENSORY INPUT

The first evidence that the brain regulates the generation of sensory impulses or their transmission in the specific sensory systems was the observation that stimulation of the bulbar reticular formation inhibited transmission at the first synapse in the lemniscal and spinothalamic systems and the trigeminal nuclei. Inhibitory effects on transmission in the cochlear nucleus have also been observed. It has been claimed that some of the inhibitory effects in the auditory system are due to contraction of the stapedius and tensor tympani muscles (see Chapter 9). However, efferent fibers in the auditory nerve pass all the way to the cochlea, and stimulation of these efferent fibers inhibits the initiation of impulses in the organ of Corti. There are efferent fibers in the optic nerve that when stimulated either inhibit or augment retinal activity. These observations establish the existence of brain mechanisms which can turn up or down the volume of afferent input by effects on the specific sensory pathways or the sense organs themselves. Some of these mechanisms are reticular, but others are not. Stimulation of the sensory cortex produces presynaptic inhibition at synaptic junctions in the gracile and cuneate nuclei. There are other inhibitory mechanisms that affect transmission in the dorsal horns (see Chapter 7), the specific thalamic nuclei, and in the cortex itself.

Some of these modulating mechanisms are brought into play when the individual's attention is focused on a particular object. In the experiment illustrated in Fig 11–16, electrodes were implanted in the cochlear nucleus of a cat. After the animal recovered, the electrical activity of the cochlear nucleus was recorded while a clicker was sounded at regular intervals. While the cat sat quietly in its cage, a spike was observed with each click. However, when the animal's attention was focused on a pair of mice placed in front of it, the click response in the cochlear nucleus practically disappeared. It returned when the mice were removed, but disappeared again when the cat's atten-

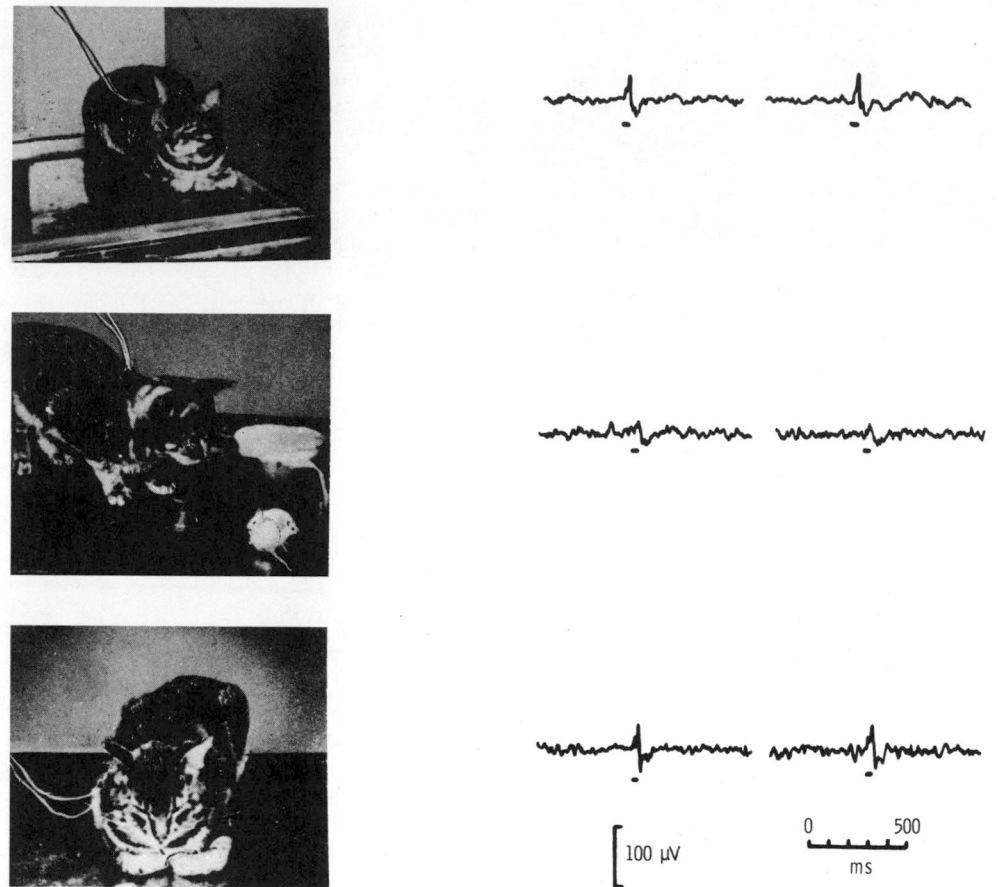

Figure 11–16. Changes in response of cochlear nucleus to repeated click stimuli (at dashes) before *(top)*, during *(middle)*, and after *(bottom)* attention is fixed on mice in a bell jar. (Reproduced, with permission, from Hernández Peón R, Scherrer H, Jouvet M: Modification of electrical activity in cochlear nucleus during "attention." Science 123:331, 1956.)

tion was attracted by the smell of fish. These observations indicate that—contrary to some theories—part of the narrowing of the field of awareness during focused attention is due to "turning off" some of the incoming stimuli before they reach the cerebral cortex.

Another example of central control of sensory input is the regulatory effect of brain centers on muscle spindle sensitivity. The effect of changes in the rate of gamma efferent discharge on the sensitivity of the spindles is described in Chapter 6. The gamma efferent neurons are subjected to both facilitatory and inhibitory influences via descending tracts in the lateral funiculus of the spinal cord. Stimulation of one part of the brain stem reticular formation facilitates gamma efferent discharge, whereas stimulation of another portion inhibits it. There are also inhibitory centers in the cerebellum, basal ganglia, and motor cortex. Their function in the regulation of body posture is discussed in the next chapter.

Somatic motor activity depends ultimately upon the pattern and rate of discharge of the spinal motor neurons and homologous neurons in the motor nuclei of the cranial nerves. These neurons, the final common paths to skeletal muscle, are bombarded by impulses from an immense array of pathways. There are many inputs to each spinal motor neuron from the same spinal segment (see Chapter 6). Numerous suprasegmental inputs also converge on these cells, in part via interneurons and in part via the neurons of the gamma efferent system to the muscle spindles and back through the Ia afferent fibers to the spinal cord. It is the integrated activity of these multiple inputs from spinal, medullary, midbrain, and cortical levels that regulates the posture of the body and makes coordinated movement possible.

The inputs converging on the motor neurons subserve 3 semidistinct functions: they bring about skilled, voluntary activity; they adjust body posture to provide a stable background for movement; and they coordinate the action of the various muscles to make movements smooth and precise. Current evidence indicates that patterns of voluntary activity are planned within the brain and the commands are sent to the muscles via the **pyramidal** and **extrapyramidal systems.** The first of these is concerned with skilled, fine movement; the second with grosser movements and posture. The **cerebellum** and its connections are concerned with coordinating and smoothing movement. There is also some evidence that portions of the extrapyramidal system, the basal ganglia, are concerned with the generation of slow, steady movements (ramp movements) whereas the cerebellum generates rapid, ballistic movements (saccadic movements).

Encephalization

In species in which the cerebral cortex is highly developed, the process of **encephalization,** ie, the relatively greater role of the cerebral cortex in various functions, is an important phenomenon. For this reason, the effects of cortical ablation in primates are generally more severe and sometimes quite different from those in cats, dogs, and other laboratory animals. Because this chapter is concerned primarily with motor function in humans, pathologic and clinical observations in humans and experiments in laboratory primates are emphasized.

Upper & Lower Motor Neurons

The motor system is commonly divided into **upper** and **lower motor neurons.** Lesions of the lower motor neurons—the spinal and cranial motor neurons that directly innervate the muscles—are associated with flaccid paralysis, muscular atrophy, and absence of reflex responses. The syndrome of spastic paralysis and hyperactive stretch reflexes in the absence of muscle atrophy is said to be due to destruction of the "upper motor neurons," the neurons in the brain and spinal cord that activate the motor neurons. However, there are 3 types of "upper motor neurons" to consider. Lesions in the extrapyramidal posture-regulating pathways do cause spastic paralysis, but lesions limited to the pyramidal tracts produce weakness **(paresis)** rather than paralysis, and the affected musculature is generally hypotonic, whereas cerebellar lesions produce incoordination. The unmodified term upper motor neuron is therefore confusing and should not be used.

PYRAMIDAL SYSTEM

ANATOMY

Tracts

The nerve fibers that form the pyramids in the medulla and hence are called the pyramidal system descend in the internal capsule from the cerebral cortex. About 80% of them cross the midline in the pyramidal decussation to form the **lateral corticospinal tract;** the remainder descend as the **anterior corticospinal tract,** decussating just before their termination (Fig 12–1). Additional uncrossed corticospinal fibers may exist. In most animals, the corticospinal axons end on interneurons rather than motor neurons. In humans, however, at least 10% of the axons make direct synaptic connections with the motor neurons. Ninety percent of the fibers in the pyramidal system are small, and 50% are unmyelinated.

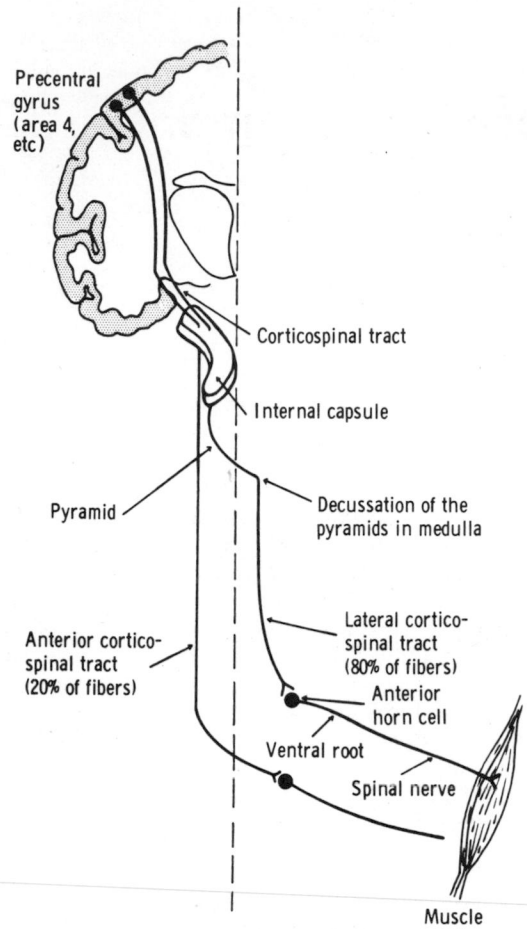

Figure 12–1. The corticospinal tracts.

Cortical Motor Areas

The cortical areas from which the pyramidal system originates are generally held to be those where stimulation produces prompt discrete movement. There are 4 such areas in the cortex. The best known is the **motor cortex** in the precentral gyrus (Fig 12–2). However, there is a **supplementary motor area** of unknown function on and above the superior bank of the cingulate sulcus on the medial side of the hemisphere (Fig 12–3). Motor responses are also produced by stimulation of somatic sensory area I in the post-

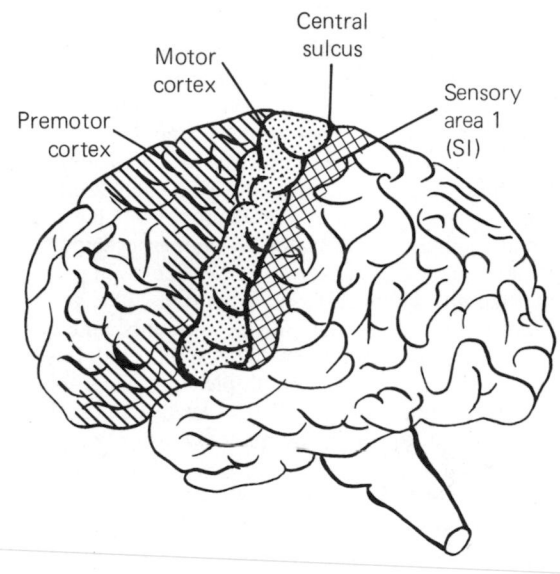

Figure 12–2. Diagram showing classical cortical motor areas.

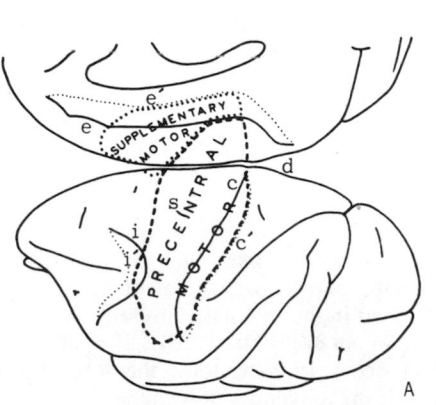

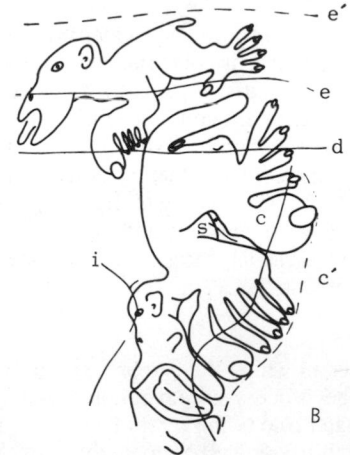

Figure 12–3. Motor "simiusculi," showing the cortical localization of motor function in the monkey represented in the same way as it is in Fig 12–4. *B* is an enlarged view of *A*, the various lines representing the sulci and medial edge of the hemisphere as indicated in *A*. c, central sulcus; c′, bottom of central sulcus; d, medial edge of hemisphere; e, sulcus cinguli; e′, bottom of sulcus cinguli; i, inferior precentral sulcus; i′, bottom of inferior precentral sulcus; s, superior precentral sulcus. (Reproduced, with permission, from Woolsey CN & others: Patterns of localization in pre-central and "supplementary" motor areas and their relation to the concept of a premotor area. Res Publ Assoc Res Nerv Ment Dis 30:238, 1950.)

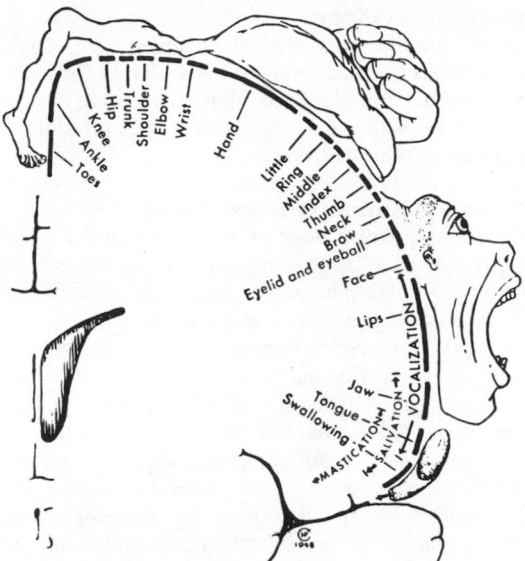

Figure 12–4. Motor homunculus. The figure represents, on a coronal section of the precentral gyrus, the location of the cortical representation of the various parts. The size of the various parts is proportionate to the amount of cortical area devoted to them. (Reproduced, with permission, from Penfield W, Rasmussen G: *The Cerebral Cortex of Man: A Clinical Study of Localization of Function.* Macmillan, 1950.)

central gyrus and by stimulation of somatic sensory area II in the wall of the sylvian fissure (see Chapter 7). It is probable that all of these areas contribute fibers to the pyramidal system and to the extrapyramidal system as well. About 60% of the pyramidal fibers arise from the precentral gyrus, but only 2% come from the large Betz cells in area 4.

By means of stimulation experiments in patients undergoing craniotomy under local anesthesia, it has been possible to outline most of the motor projection from the precentral gyrus (Fig 12–4). The various parts of the body are represented in the precentral gyrus, with the feet at the top of the gyrus and the face at the bottom. The facial area is represented bilaterally, but the rest of the representation is unilateral, the cortical motor area controlling the musculature on the opposite side of the body. The cortical representation of each body part is proportionate in size to the skill with which the part is used in fine, voluntary movement. The muscles involved in speech and hand movements are especially well represented in the cortex; use of the pharynx, lips, and tongue to form words, and the fingers and opposable thumbs to manipulate the environment are activities in which humans are especially skilled.

The conditions under which these human studies were performed precluded stimulation of the banks of the sulci and other inaccessible areas. In monkeys, meticulous study has shown that the hand area is not interposed between the trunk and face areas. Instead, there is a regular representation of the body, with the axial musculature and the proximal portions of the limbs represented along the anterior edge of the precentral gyrus and the distal part of the limbs along the posterior edge (Fig 12–3). The cells in the cortical motor areas are arranged in columns. The cells in each column receive fairly extensive sensory input from the peripheral area in which they produce movement.

Premotor Cortex

Brodmann's area 6, the region anterior to the precentral gyrus, has traditionally been called the **premotor cortex** or **premotor area** (Fig 12–2). Under certain conditions, stimulation in this region produces **adversive movements,** ie, gross rotation of the eyes, head, and trunk to the opposite side. These movements may be due to stimulation of extrapyramidal pathways, but they may also be due to intracortical spread of the stimuli to the pyramidal system. On this basis, the existence of the premotor area as a separate entity has been questioned.

Other Areas

Stimulation of the frontal cortex anterior to and below area 6 causes eye movements in primates. The most common response is movement of both eyes in the same direction (**conjugate deviation**), but pupillary dilatation and nystagmus have also been observed. It is probable that this **frontal eye field** is a center concerned with integration of eye movements, but the details of the way it functions are not known. Stimulation of the occipital lobe near the visual cortex also causes conjugate deviation of the eyes to the opposite side. Stimulation of an area adjacent to the auditory cortex causes movement of the ears.

FUNCTION

Role in Movement

The pyramidal system appears to be concerned with skilled, fine movement. This does not mean that movement—even skilled movement—is impossible without it. Nonmammalian vertebrates have essentially no pyramidal system, but they move with great agility. Cats and dogs stand, walk, run, and even eat if food is presented to them after complete destruction of the pyramidal system.

In primates, it is difficult to produce selective disruption of pyramidal function, and this fact is responsible for much of the confusion about the role of the pyramidal system in humans. Even the most circumscribed lesions in the cortical motor area destroy cells concerned with extrapyramidal and cerebellar functions. Careful surgical section of the pyramids in the medulla is probably the most selective experimental approach, but even this procedure damages other fibers.

After section of one pyramid in a monkey, the limbs on the opposite side of the body hang limply

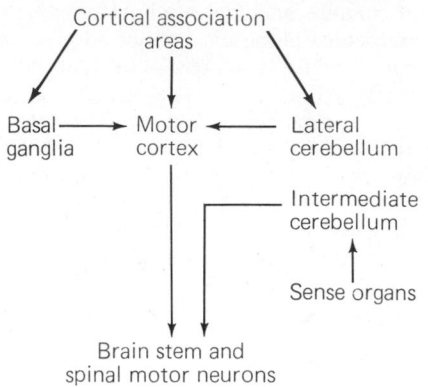

Figure 12–5. Role of the motor cortex and other structures in the control of movement.

much of the time. However, they are not paralyzed. The hopping and placing postural reactions are defective (see below), but otherwise the monkey uses its limbs to maintain its posture and to right itself in the normal fashion. Furthermore, if use of the normal arm is prevented, the monkey will occasionally reach for food and other objects with the affected arm, especially when motivation is strong. The motions lack precision; there is a loss of accuracy in the use of the digits, and a particular inability to maneuver objects into the palm of the hand, so that the grasp is clumsy. The main defects produced by destruction of the pyramidal system are therefore weakness and clumsiness.

What, then, is the role of the precentral motor cortex in skilled movement? It appears reasonable, on the basis of present information, to hypothesize that ideas or commands for fine movements arise in the association areas of the cortex (Fig 12–5). It also seems probable that movement patterns are generated in structures such as the basal ganglia and the cerebellum; that the patterns are modulated in the cortex in terms of the somatosensory input provided by afferents from the periphery; and that the pyramidal system is a final common path for these patterns to the spinal motor neurons. The fact that movements (such as those of the fingers) which require the most somatosensory input are most compromised by pyramidal lesions supports this hypothesis.

Effects on Stretch Reflexes

Section of the pyramids in monkeys produces prolonged hypotonia and flaccidity rather than spasticity. The anatomic arrangements in humans are such that disease processes rarely, if ever, damage the pyramidal system anywhere along its course without also destroying extrapyramidal posture-regulating pathways. When spasticity is present, it is probably due to damage to these latter pathways rather than to the pyramidal system itself.

Damage to the pyramidal tract in humans produces the **Babinski sign:** dorsiflexion of the great toe and fanning of the other toes when the lateral aspect of the sole of the foot is scratched. In normal individuals, the response to this stimulation is a plantar flexion of all the toes. The Babinski sign is valuable for the localization of disease processes, but its physiologic significance is unknown.

Relation of Movement to Perception

If the apparent position of objects in the visual field is displaced by looking at them through prisms, an individual at first has trouble reaching for them. The misreaching is gradually corrected, but correction is not simply a result of recognizing the error and correcting it. The correction and that of other experimentally produced visual and auditory displacements have been shown to be independent of their recognition and dependent on the active movements made by the individual. Without movements, no correction occurs, and passive movements fail to provide the necessary information input to the perceptual apparatus; only active movements by the subject will suffice.

There is other evidence of the close connection between sensory input and motor output. If a limb is deafferented by section of the dorsal roots of the spinal nerves that supply it, it is severely paralyzed. Indeed, the paralysis is more severe than that which follows section of the pyramids. This illustrates the importance of reflexes and sensory input in the regulation of movement. However, the paralysis does not last, and motor function gradually returns. After a period of time, the deafferented animal can move its limb relatively well even when visual and other external cues are eliminated. Thus, there must be, in addition to sensory input, a central programming mechanism of some sort that can be made to work independently of peripheral sensation.

EXTRAPYRAMIDAL MECHANISMS

By definition, the extrapyramidal system is made up of those areas in the CNS other than the pyramidal and cerebellar systems that are concerned with movement. It includes a whole series of nuclei and portions of many structures, including the cerebral cortex, the basal ganglia, the midbrain, the medulla, and the spinal cord. It is concerned with the programming and initiation of movement and with posture.

Integration

The extrapyramidal mechanisms concerned with posture are integrated at various levels all the way from the spinal cord to the cerebral cortex. At the spinal cord level, afferent impulses produce simple reflex responses. At higher levels in the nervous system, neural connections of increasing complexity mediate increas-

Table 12–1. Summary of levels involved in various neural functions.*

Functions	Preparation						Level of Integration
	Normal	Decorticate	Midbrain	Hindbrain (Decerebrate)	Spinal	Decerebellate	
Initiative, memory, etc	+	0	0	0	0	+	Cerebral cortex required
Conditioned reflexes	+	++†	0	0	0	+	Cerebral cortex required
Emotional responses	+	++	0	0	0	+	Hypothalamus, limbic system
Locomotor reflexes	+	++	+	0	0	Incoordinate	Midbrain, thalamus
Righting reflexes	+	+	++	0	0	Incoordinate	Midbrain
Antigravity reflexes	+	+	+	++	0	Incoordinate	Medulla
Respiration	+	+	+	+	0	+	Lower medulla
Spinal reflexes‡	+	+	+	+	++	+	Spinal cord

Legend: 0 = absent; + = present; ++ = accentuated.
*Modified from Cobb S: *Foundations of Neuropsychiatry,* 6th ed. Williams & Wilkins, 1958.
†Conditioned reflexes can be established in decorticate animals but special technics are required.
‡Other than stretch reflexes.

ingly complicated motor responses. This principle of levels of motor integration is illustrated in Table 12–1. In the intact animal, the individual motor responses are fitted into or "submerged" in the total pattern of motor activity. When the neural axis is transected, the activities integrated below the section are cut off or **released** from the "control of higher brain centers," and often appear to be accentuated. Release of this type, long a cardinal principle in neurology, may in some situations be due to removal of an inhibitory control by higher neural centers. A more important

cause of the apparent hyperactivity is loss of differentiation of the reaction, so that it no longer fits into the broader pattern of motor activity. An additional factor may be denervation hypersensitivity of the centers below the transection, but the role of this component remains to be determined.

Postural Control

It is impossible to separate postural adjustments from voluntary movement in any rigid way, but it is possible to differentiate a series of postural reflexes

Table 12–2. Principal postural reflexes.

Reflex	Stimulus	Response	Receptor	Integrated In
Stretch reflexes	Stretch	Contraction of muscle	Muscle spindles	Spinal cord, medulla
Positive supporting (magnet) reaction	Contact with sole or palm	Foot extended to support body	Proprioceptors in distal flexors	Spinal cord
Negative supporting reaction	Stretch	Release of positive supporting reaction	Proprioceptors in extensors	Spinal cord
Tonic labyrinthine reflexes	Gravity	Extensor rigidity	Otolithic organs	Medulla
Tonic neck reflexes	Head turned: (1) To side (2) Up (3) Down	Change in pattern of rigidity (1) Extension of limbs on side to which head is turned (2) Hind legs flex (3) Forelegs flex	Neck proprioceptors	Medulla
Labyrinthine righting reflexes	Gravity	Head kept level	Otolithic organs	Midbrain
Neck righting reflexes	Stretch of neck muscles	Righting of thorax and shoulders, then pelvis	Muscle spindles	Midbrain
Body on head righting reflexes	Pressure on side of body	Righting of head	Exteroceptors	Midbrain
Body on body righting reflexes	Pressure on side of body	Righting of body even when head held sideways	Exteroceptors	Midbrain
Optical righting reflexes	Visual cues	Righting of head	Eyes	Cerebral cortex
Placing reactions	Various visual, exteroceptive, and proprioceptive cues	Foot placed on supporting surface in position to support body	Various	Cerebral cortex
Hopping reactions	Lateral displacement while standing	Hops, maintaining limbs in position to support body	Muscle spindles	Cerebral cortex

(Table 12–2) that not only maintain the body in an upright, balanced position but also provide the constant adjustments necessary to maintain a stable postural background for voluntary activity. These adjustments include maintained **static** reflexes and dynamic, short-term **phasic** reflexes. The former involve sustained contraction of the musculature, whereas the latter involve transient movements. Both are integrated at various levels in the CNS from the spinal cord to the cerebral cortex, and are effected largely through extrapyramidal motor pathways. A major factor in postural control is variation in the threshold of the spinal stretch reflexes caused in turn by changes in the excitability of motor neurons and, indirectly, by changes in the rate of discharge in the small motor nerve system.

SPINAL INTEGRATION

The responses of animals and humans after spinal cord transection in the cervical region illustrate the integration of reflexes at the spinal level. The individual spinal reflexes are discussed in detail in Chapter 6.

Spinal Shock
In all vertebrates, transection of the spinal cord is followed by a period of **spinal shock** during which all spinal reflex responses are profoundly depressed. During it, the resting membrane potential of the spinal motor neurons is 2–6 mV greater than normal. Subsequently, reflex responses return and become relatively hyperactive. The duration of spinal shock is proportionate to the degree of encephalization of motor function in the various species. In frogs it lasts for minutes, in dogs and cats it lasts for 1–2 hours, in monkeys it lasts for days, and in humans it usually lasts for a minimum of 2 weeks.

The cause of spinal shock is uncertain. Cessation of tonic bombardment of spinal neurons by excitatory impulses in descending pathways undoubtedly plays a role, but the subsequent return of reflexes and their eventual hyperactivity also need to be explained. The recovery of reflex excitability may possibly be due to the development of denervation hypersensitivity to the mediators released by the remaining spinal excitatory endings. Another possibility for which there is some evidence is the sprouting of collaterals from existing neurons with the formation of additional excitatory endings on interneurons and motor neurons.

The first reflex response to reappear as spinal shock wears off in humans is frequently a slight contraction of the leg flexors and adductors in response to a noxious stimulus. In some patients, the knee jerks come back first. The interval between cord transection and the beginning return of reflex activity is about 2 weeks in the absence of any complications, but if complications are present it is much longer. It is not known why infection, malnutrition, and other compli-

cations of cord transection inhibit spinal reflex activity.

Complications of Cord Transection
The problems in the management of paraplegic and quadriplegic humans are complex. Like all immobilized patients, they develop a negative nitrogen balance and catabolize large amounts of body protein. The weight of the body compresses the circulation to the skin over bony prominences, so that unless the patient is moved frequently the skin breaks down at these points and **decubitus ulcers** form. The ulcers heal poorly and are prone to infection because of body protein depletion. The tissues broken down include the protein matrix of bone, and calcium is liberated in large amounts. The hypercalcemia leads to hypercalciuria, and calcium stones often form in the urinary tract. The stones and the paralysis of bladder function both cause urinary stasis, which predisposes to urinary infection. Therefore, the prognosis in patients with transected spinal cords used to be very poor, and death from septicemia, uremia, or inanition was the rule. Since World War II, however, the use of antibiotics and meticulous attention to nutrition, fluid balance, skin care, bladder function, and general nursing care have made it possible for many of these patients to survive.

Responses in Chronic Spinal Animals & Humans
Once the spinal reflexes begin to reappear after spinal shock, their threshold steadily drops. In chronically quadriplegic humans, the threshold of the withdrawal reflex is especially low. Even minor noxious stimuli may cause not only prolonged withdrawal of one extremity but marked flexion-extension patterns in the other 3 limbs. Repeated flexion movements may occur for prolonged periods, and contractures of the flexor muscles develop. Stretch reflexes are also hyperactive, as are more complex reactions based on this reflex as well. For example, if a finger is placed on the sole of the foot of an animal after the spinal cord has been transected (**spinal animal**), the limb usually extends, following the examining finger. This **magnet reaction** or **positive supporting reaction** involves proprioceptive as well as tactile afferents and transforms the limb into a rigid pillar to resist gravity and support the animal. Its disappearance is also in part an active phenomenon (**negative supporting reaction**) initiated by stretch of the extensor muscles. On the basis of the positive supporting reaction, spinal cats and dogs can be made to stand, albeit awkwardly, for as long as 2–3 minutes.

Autonomic Reflexes
Reflex contractions of the full bladder and rectum occur in spinal animals and humans, although the bladder is rarely emptied completely. Hyperactive bladder reflexes can keep the bladder in a shrunken state long enough for hypertrophy and fibrosis of its wall to occur. Blood pressure is generally normal at

rest, but the precise feedback regulation normally supplied by the baroreceptor reflexes is absent and wide swings in pressure are common. Bouts of sweating and blanching of the skin also occur.

The intermediolateral gray columns of the spinal cord are relatively rich in norepinephrine and serotonin. Seven days after cord section in rabbits, when the autonomic reflexes are hyperactive, the norepinephrine and serotonin content of the spinal cord below the transection is markedly reduced. These observations suggest that norepinephrine and serotonin are mediators in descending pathways which normally inhibit autonomic function.

Sexual Reflexes

Other reflex responses are present in the spinal animal, but in general they are only fragments of patterns that are integrated in the normal animal into purposeful sequences. The sexual reflexes are an example. Coordinated sexual activity depends upon a series of reflexes integrated at many neural levels, and is absent after cord transection. However, genital manipulation in the male spinal animal and human produces erection and even ejaculation. In the female spinal dog, vaginal stimulation causes tail deviation and movement of the pelvis into the copulatory position.

Mass Reflex

In chronic spinal animals, afferent stimuli irradiate from one reflex center to another. When even a relatively minor noxious stimulus is applied to the skin, it may irradiate to autonomic centers and produce evacuation of the bladder and rectum, sweating, pallor, and blood pressure swings in addition to the withdrawal response. This distressing **mass reflex** can sometimes be used to give paraplegic patients a degree of bladder and bowel control. They can be trained to initiate urination and defecation by stroking or pinching their thighs, thus producing an intentional mild mass reflex.

MEDULLARY COMPONENTS

In experimental animals in which the hindbrain and spinal cord are isolated from the rest of the brain by transection of the brain stem at the superior border of the pons, the most prominent finding is marked spasticity of the body musculature. The operative procedure is called **decerebration,** and the resulting pattern of spasticity is called **decerebrate rigidity.** Decerebration produces no phenomenon akin to spinal shock, and the rigidity develops as soon as the brain stem is transected. Flexor and extensor muscles are both involved, but in the dog and cat, the spasticity is most prominent in the extensor muscles. This produces the characteristic posture of decerebration: neck and limbs extended, back arched, and tail elevated.

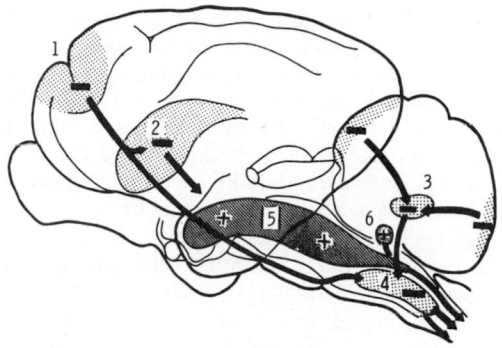

Figure 12–6. Areas in the cat brain where stimulation produces facilitation (plus signs) or inhibition (minus signs) of stretch reflexes. *1,* motor cortex; *2,* basal ganglia; *3,* cerebellum; *4,* reticular inhibitory area; *5,* reticular facilitatory area; *6,* vestibular nuclei. (Reproduced, with permission, from Lindsley DB, Schreiner LH, Magoun HW: An electromyographic study of spasticity. J Neurophysiol 12:197, 1949.)

Mechanism of Decerebrate Rigidity

On analysis, decerebrate rigidity is found to be due to a diffuse facilitation of stretch reflexes. The facilitation is due to 2 factors: increased general excitability of the motor neuron pool and increase in the rate of discharge in the gamma efferent neurons.

Supraspinal Regulation of Stretch Reflexes

The brain areas that facilitate and inhibit stretch reflexes are shown in Fig 12–6. Except for the vestibular nuclei, these areas act by increasing or decreasing spindle sensitivity (Fig 12–7). The large facilitatory area in the brain stem reticular formation discharges spontaneously, possibly in response to afferent input like the reticular activating system. However, the smaller brain stem area that inhibits gamma efferent

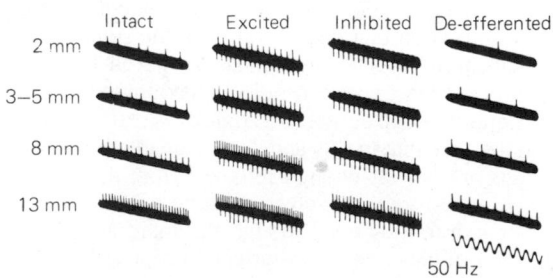

Figure 12–7. Response of single afferent fiber from muscle spindle to various degrees of muscle stretch. Figures at left indicate amount of stretch. The upward deflections are action potentials; the downward deflections are stimulus artifacts. Records were obtained before brain stimulation (first column), during stimulation of brain areas facilitating (second column) and inhibiting (third column) stretch reflexes, and after section of the motor nerve (fourth column). (Reproduced, with permission, from Eldred E, Granit R, Merton PA: Supraspinal control of muscle spindles. J Physiol [Lond] 122:498, 1953.)

discharge does not discharge spontaneously but is driven instead by fibers from the cerebral cortex and the cerebellum. The inhibitory area in the basal ganglia may act through descending connections, as shown in Fig 12–6, or by stimulating the cortical inhibitory center. From the reticular inhibitory and facilitatory areas, impulses descend in the lateral funiculus of the spinal cord. When the brain stem is transected at the level of the top of the pons, 2 of the 3 inhibitory areas that drive the reticular inhibitory center are removed. Discharge of the facilitatory area continues, but that of the inhibitory area is decreased. Consequently, the balance of facilitatory and inhibitory impulses converging on the gamma efferent neurons shifts toward facilitation. Gamma efferent discharge is increased, and stretch reflexes become hyperactive. The cerebellar inhibitory area is still present, and, in decerebrate animals, removal of the cerebellum increases the rigidity. The influence of the cerebellum is complex, however, and destruction of the cerebellum in humans produces hypotonia rather than spasticity.

The vestibulospinal pathways are also facilitatory to stretch reflexes and promote rigidity. Unlike the reticular pathways, they pass primarily in the anterior funiculus of the spinal cord, and the rigidity due to increased discharge in them is not abolished by deafferentation of the muscles. This indicates that this rigidity is due to a direct action on the motor neurons rather than an effect mediated through the small motor nerve system which would, of course, be blocked by deafferentation.

Significance of Decerebrate Rigidity

Sherrington pointed out that the extensor muscles are those with which the cat and dog resist gravity; the decerebrate posture in these animals is, as he put it, "a caricature of the normal standing position." What has been uncovered by decerebration, then, are the tonic, static postural reflex mechanisms that support the animal against gravity. Additional evidence that this is the correct interpretation of the phenomenon comes from the observation that decerebration in the sloth, an arboreal animal which hangs upside down from branches most of the time, causes rigidity in flexion. In humans, the pattern in true decerebrate rigidity is extensor in all 4 limbs, like that in cats and dogs. Apparently, human beings are not far enough removed from their quadruped ancestors to have changed the pattern in their upper extremities even though the main antigravity muscles of the arms in the upright position are flexors. However, decerebrate rigidity is rare in disease states, and the defects that produce it are usually incompatible with life. The more common pattern of extensor rigidity in the legs and moderate flexion in the arms is actually **decorticate rigidity** due to lesions of the cerebral cortex, with most of the brain stem intact (Fig 12–8).

Tonic Labyrinthine Reflexes

In the decerebrate animal, the pattern of rigidity in the limbs varies with the position. No righting re-

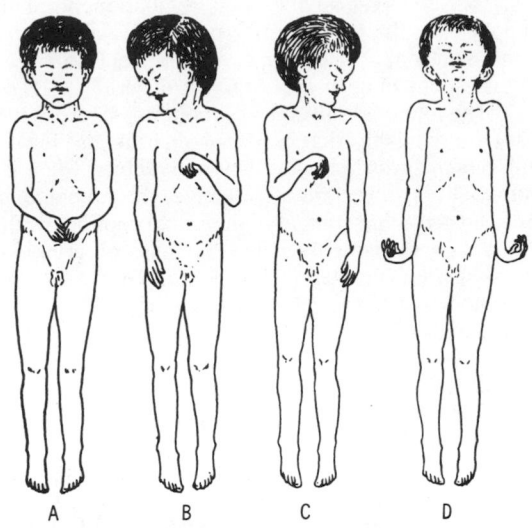

Figure 12–8. Human decorticate rigidity *(A–C)* and true decerebrate rigidity *(D)*. In *A* the patient is lying supine with head unturned. In *B* and *C*, the tonic neck reflex patterns produced by turning of the head to the right or left are shown. (Reproduced, with permission, from *Textbook of Physiology*, 17th ed. Fulton JF [editor]. Saunders, 1955.)

sponses are present, and the animal stays in the position in which it is put. If the animal is placed on its back, the extension of all 4 limbs is maximal. As the animal is turned to either side, the rigidity decreases, and when it is prone, the rigidity is minimal though still present. These changes in rigidity, the **tonic labyrinthine reflexes,** are initiated by the action of gravity on the otolithic organs and are effected via the vestibulospinal tracts. They are rather surprising in view of the role of rigidity in standing, and their exact physiologic significance remains obscure.

Tonic Neck Reflexes

If the head of a decerebrate animal is moved relative to the body, changes in the pattern of rigidity occur. If the head is turned to one side, the limbs on that side ("jaw limbs") become more rigidly extended while the contralateral limbs become less so. This is the position often assumed by a normal animal looking to one side. Flexion of the head causes flexion of the forelimbs and continued extension of the hindlimbs: the posture of an animal looking into a hole in the ground. Extension of the head causes flexion of the hindlimbs and extension of the forelimbs: the posture of an animal looking over an obstacle. These responses are the **tonic neck reflexes.** They are initiated by stretch of the proprioceptors in the upper part of the neck, and they can be sustained for long periods of time.

MIDBRAIN COMPONENTS

After section of the neural axis at the superior border of the midbrain (**midbrain animal**), extensor rigidity like that seen in the decerebrate animal is present only when the animal lies quietly on its back. In the decerebrate animal, the rigidity, which is a static postural reflex, is prominent because there are no modifying phasic postural reflexes. Chronic midbrain preparations can rise to the standing position, walk, and right themselves. While the animals are engaged in these phasic activities, the static phenomenon of rigidity is not seen.

Righting Reflexes

All higher animals have righting reflexes that operate to maintain their normal standing position and keep their heads upright. These reflexes are a series of responses integrated for the most part in the nuclei of the midbrain.

When a midbrain animal is held by its body and tipped from side to side, the head stays level in response to the **labyrinthine righting reflexes.** The stimulus is tilting of the head, which stimulates the otolithic organs; the response is compensatory contraction of the neck muscles to keep the head level. If the animal is laid on its side, the pressure on that side of the body initiates reflex righting of the head even if the labyrinths have been destroyed. This is the **body on head righting reflex.** If the head is righted by either of these mechanisms and the body remains tilted, the neck muscles are stretched. Their contraction rights the thorax and initiates a wave of similar stretch reflexes that pass down the body, righting the abdomen and the hind quarters (**neck righting reflexes**). Pressure on the side of the body may cause body righting even if the head is prevented from righting (**body on body righting reflex**).

In cats, dogs, and primates, visual cues can initiate **optical righting reflexes** that right the animal in the absence of labyrinthine or body stimulation. Unlike the other righting reflexes, these responses depend upon an intact cerebral cortex.

Grasp Reflex

When a primate in which the brain tissue above the thalamus has been removed lies on its side, the limbs next to the supporting surface are extended. The upper limbs are flexed, and the hand on the upper side grasps firmly any object brought in contact with it (**grasp reflex**). This whole response is probably a supporting reaction that steadies the animal and aids in pulling it upright.

Other Midbrain Responses

Animals with intact midbrains show pupillary light reflexes if the optic nerves are also intact. Nystagmus, the reflex response to rotational acceleration described in Chapter 9, is also present. If a blindfolded animal is lowered rapidly, its forelegs extend and its toes spread. This response to linear acceleration is a **vestibular placing reaction** that prepares the animal to land on the floor.

CORTICAL COMPONENTS

Effects of Decortication

Removal of the cerebral cortex (**decortication**) produces little motor deficit in many species of mammals. In primates, the deficit is more severe, but a great deal of movement is still possible. Decorticate animals have all the reflex patterns of midbrain animals, and the responses generally are present in the immediate postoperative period, whereas in midbrain preparations they take 2–3 weeks to appear. This suggests that centers between the top of the midbrain and the cerebral cortex facilitate brain stem reflexes. In addition, decorticate animals are easier to maintain than midbrain animals because temperature regulation and other visceral homeostatic mechanisms integrated in the hypothalamus (see Chapter 14) are present. The most striking defect is inability to react in terms of past experience. With certain special types of training, conditioned reflexes can be established in the absence of the cerebral cortex, but under normal laboratory conditions, there is no evidence that learning or conditioning occurs.

Decorticate Rigidity

Moderate rigidity is present in the decorticate animal as a result of the loss of the cortical area that inhibits gamma efferent discharge via the reticular formation. Like the rigidity present after transection of the neural axis anywhere above the top of the midbrain, this **decorticate rigidity** is obscured by phasic postural reflexes and is only seen when the animal is at rest. Decorticate rigidity is seen on the hemiplegic side in humans after hemorrhages or thromboses in the internal capsule. Probably because of their anatomy, the small arteries in the internal capsule are especially prone to rupture or thrombotic obstruction, so this type of decorticate rigidity is common.

Suppressor Areas

The exact site of origin in the cerebral cortex of the fibers that inhibit stretch reflexes is a subject of debate. Under certain experimental conditions, stimulation of the anterior edge of the precentral gyrus is said to cause inhibition of stretch reflexes and cortically evoked movements. This region, which also projects to the basal ganglia, has been named area 4s, or the **suppressor strip.** Four other suppressor regions (Brodmann's areas 2, 8, 19, and 24) have also been described. However, the stimulation experiments on which the hypothesis of discrete suppressor areas is based have not been uniformly confirmed. Ablation of area 4s does cause spasticity in the trunk and proximal limb muscles of the contralateral side of the body, but destruction of the caudal part of area 4 produces spasticity in the distal limb muscles. Mapping experiments show that the musculature of the trunk and proximal portions of the limbs is represented in the anterior portion of the precentral gyrus, whereas that of the distal portions is represented posteriorly. It is therefore probable that the inhibitory fibers originate with the pyramidal fibers from all of the precentral motor area and that the distribution of the spasticity produced by lesions in this area depends upon the particular portion of the motor cortex destroyed.

Placing & Hopping Reactions

Two types of postural reactions are seriously disrupted by decortication, the **hopping** and **placing reactions.** The former are the hopping movements that keep the limbs in position to support the body when a standing animal is pushed laterally. The latter are the reactions that place the foot firmly on a supporting surface. They can be initiated in a blindfolded animal held suspended in the air by touching the supporting surface with any part of the foot. Similarly, when the snout or vibrissae of a suspended animal touch a table, the animal immediately places both forepaws on the table; and if one limb of a standing animal is pulled out from under it, the limb is promptly replaced on the supporting surface. The vestibular placing reaction has already been mentioned. In cats, dogs, and primates, the limbs are extended to support the body when the animal is lowered toward a surface it can see. These various placing reactions are abolished on one side by unilateral decortication, but some of them reappear after subsequent removal of the other hemisphere. This

casts doubt on the claim that they are entirely dependent upon an intact motor cortex, but this portion of the brain is certainly important in their regulation.

BASAL GANGLIA

Anatomic Considerations

The term **basal ganglia** is generally applied to the **caudate nucleus, putamen,** and **globus pallidus**—the 3 large nuclear masses underlying the cortical mantle (Fig 12–9)—and the functionally related **subthalamic nucleus** (body of Luys), **substantia nigra,** and **red nucleus** on each side. Parts of the thalamus are intimately related to this system, but the claustrum and the amygdala probably are not properly included although they have been in some classifications. The caudate nucleus and the putamen are sometimes called the **striatum;** the putamen and the globus pallidus are sometimes called the **lenticular nucleus** (Table 12–3).

The interconnections of these nuclei are complex (Fig 12–10). On each side, the caudate nucleus projects in part to the putamen, the putamen to the globus pallidus, and the globus pallidus via the **ansa lenticularis,** the major efferent pathway from the lenticular nucleus, to the thalamus, subthalamic nuclei, red nuclei, and other structures. There is considerable evidence for a feedback circuit that projects from the motor cortex to the caudate nucleus and from there back to the cortex via the lenticular nucleus, the ansa

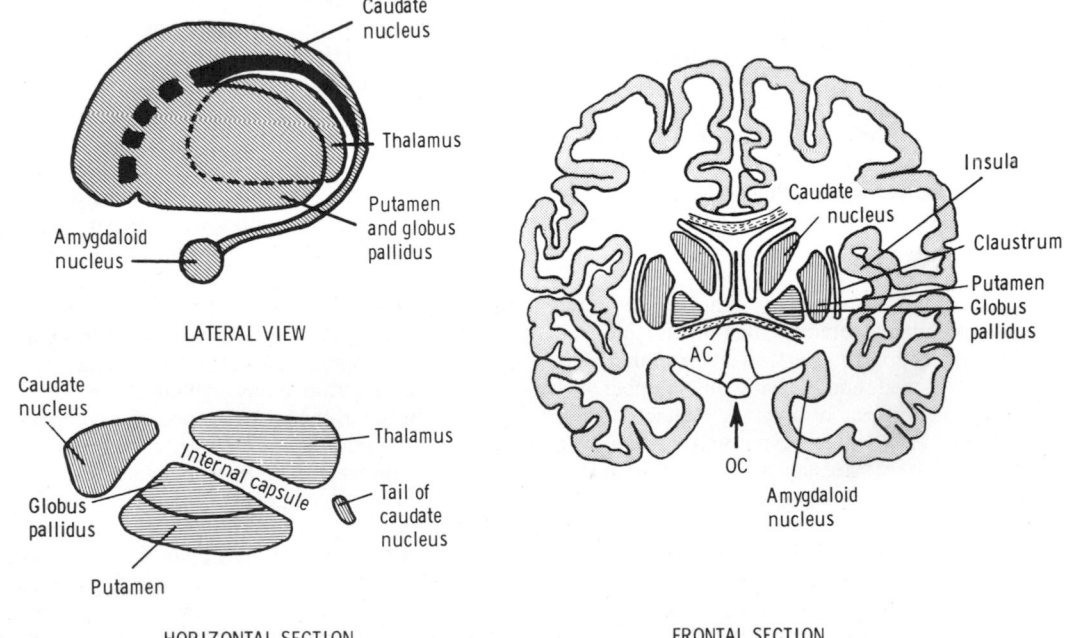

Figure 12–9. The basal ganglia. AC, anterior commissure; OC, optic chiasm.

Table 12–3. The basal ganglia.

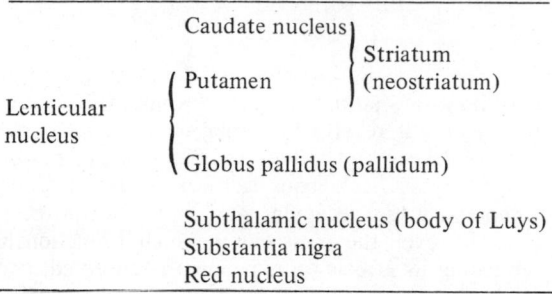

Lenticular nucleus	Caudate nucleus	Striatum (neostriatum)
	Putamen	
	Globus pallidus (pallidum)	

Subthalamic nucleus (body of Luys)
Substantia nigra
Red nucleus

lenticularis, and the ventrolateral nuclei of the thalamus.

There is a prominent system of dopaminergic neurons, the **nigrostriatal dopaminergic system,** with cell bodies in the substantia nigra and axonal endings in the caudate nucleus (see Chapter 15). The dopamine released at these endings appears to inhibit cells in the caudate, whereas acetylcholine released from other cells excites them. A feedback circuit from the caudate to the substantia nigra is made up of neurons that secrete GABA (see Chapter 15).

Metabolic Considerations

The metabolism of the basal ganglia is unique in a number of ways. These structures have an O_2 consumption per gram of tissue which in dogs exceeds that of the cerebral cortex (see Chapter 32). The copper content of the substantia nigra and the nearby locus

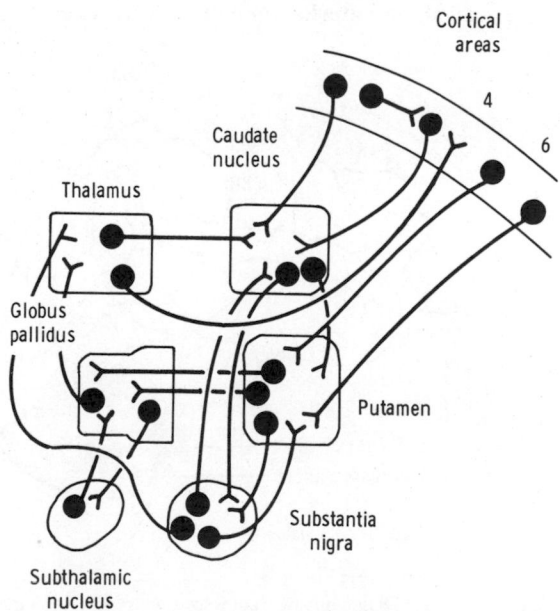

Figure 12–10. Some of the interconnections of the cerebral cortex and basal ganglia. (Modified from Carman JB: Anatomic basis of surgical treatment of Parkinson's disease. N Engl J Med 279:919, 1968. Courtesy of Little, Brown, Inc.)

ceruleus is particularly high. In Wilson's disease, a familial disorder of copper metabolism in which the plasma copper-binding protein, **ceruloplasmin,** is usually low, there is severe degeneration of the lenticular nucleus. However, the exact nature of the defect in copper metabolism in this disease is not known.

Function

The precise functions of the basal ganglia are an enigma. In birds, reptiles, and other animals in which the motor cortex is rudimentary or absent, these nuclear masses are prominent and take the place of a motor cortex. Removal of the striatum and pallidum in decorticate animals does not produce any additional gross impairment in motor function. Stimulation studies in animals have generally produced negative results, although stimulation of the caudate nucleus inhibits stretch reflexes. This inhibition is probably mediated by activation of the cortical inhibitory areas through the thalamocortical feedback pathways. Stimulation of the globus pallidus and caudate nucleus also inhibits movements evoked by cortical stimulation.

More recently, it has been shown that many neurons in the basal ganglia fire throughout slow, steady ramp movements and are silent during rapid saccadic movements. Like the motor cortex and the cerebellum, they begin to discharge before the movements begin. Thus, it appears that the basal ganglia are involved in the planning and programming of movement. The abnormalities in humans with basal ganglion disease also support this hypothesis.

Diseases of the Basal Ganglia in Humans

Disorders of movement associated with diseases of the basal ganglia in humans are of 2 general types: **hyperkinetic** and **hypokinetic.** The hyperkinetic conditions, those in which there is excessive and abnormal movement, include chorea, athetosis, and ballism. In Parkinson's disease, there are both hyperkinetic and hypokinetic features.

Hyperkinetic Disorders

Chorea is associated with degeneration of the caudate nucleus. It is characterized by rapid, involuntary "dancing" movements that may be a mixture of unrelated or conflicting cortical automatisms. **Athetosis** is due to lesions in the lenticular nucleus and is characterized by continuous slow, writhing movements that may be tonic avoiding or grasping reactions. In **ballism,** the involuntary movements are flailing, intense, and violent. They appear when the subthalamic nuclei are damaged, and a sudden onset of the movements on one side of the body (**hemiballism**) due to hemorrhage in the contralateral subthalamic nucleus is one of the most dramatic syndromes in clinical medicine.

Parkinson's Disease (Paralysis Agitans)

In the syndrome originally described by James Parkinson and named for him, the nigrostriatal system of dopaminergic neurons is damaged. Parkinsonism was a common late complication of the type of influenza that was epidemic during World War I, and it occurs in elderly individuals possibly because of the development of cerebral arteriosclerosis. It is also seen as a complication of treatment with the phenothiazine group of tranquilizer drugs. These drugs block dopamine receptors. The hallmarks of parkinsonism are **akinesia** or **poverty of movement** (a hypokinetic feature) and the hyperkinetic features **rigidity** and **tremor.** The absence of motor activity can be quite striking. There is difficulty in initiating voluntary movements, and there is also a decrease in **associated movements,** the normal, unconscious movements such as swinging of the arms during walking, the panorama of facial expressions related to the emotional content of thought and speech, and the multiple "fidgety" actions and gestures that occur in all of us. The rigidity is different from spasticity because there is increased motor neuron discharge to both the agonist and antagonist muscles. Passive motion of an extremity meets with a plastic, dead-feeling resistance that has been likened to bending a lead pipe and is therefore called **lead-pipe rigidity.** Sometimes there is a series of "catches" during passive motion (**cogwheel rigidity),** but the sudden loss of resistance seen in a spastic extremity is absent. The tremor, which is present at rest and disappears with activity, is due to regular, alternating, 8/s contractions of antagonistic muscles.

It has been difficult to reproduce parkinsonism by means of lesions in laboratory animals. An interesting feature of the syndrome in humans is the fact that even though it is due to lesions in parts of the basal ganglia, further destruction of these nuclei and other motor systems sometimes brings about clinical improvement. Ablation of the motor cortex, section of the cerebral peduncles, posterolateral spinal cordotomy, destruction of the medial part of the globus pallidus, interruption of the ansa lenticularis, and lesions of the ventrolateral nucleus of the thalamus produced by electrocoagulation or the injection of alcohol (chemopallidectomy, etc) have all been used to diminish the rigidity and the tremor.

These treatments have been superseded by the use of L-dopa, which produces dramatic improvement in many patients. Unlike dopamine, this dopamine precursor crosses the blood-brain barrier (see Chapter 15) and remedies the dopamine deficiency. A number of synthetic dopamine agonists that penetrate brain tissue have also proved to be of value. In addition, some improvement is produced by decreasing the cholinergic influence with anticholinergic drugs.

Conclusion

The experimental and clinical data described above suggest that the basal ganglia function in some way in the programming of movement, in part by preventing oscillation and after-discharge in motor systems. Except for these necessarily vague speculations, however, the functions of the basal ganglia remain unclear.

CEREBELLUM

The cerebellum is concerned primarily with the coordination, adjustment, and smoothing out of movement. It receives information from the motor areas of the cerebral cortex and afferent impulses from proprioceptors, cutaneous tactile receptors, auditory receptors, visual receptors, and even visceral receptors. However, the exact way in which it functions in producing its effects on movement is unsettled.

ANATOMIC & FUNCTIONAL ORGANIZATION

Orientation

The cerebellum sits astride the main sensory and motor systems in the brain stem (Fig 12–11). It is connected to the brain stem on each side by a **superior peduncle** (brachium conjunctivum), **middle peduncle** (brachium pontis), and **inferior peduncle** (restiform body). The medial **vermis** and lateral **cerebellar hemispheres** are more extensively folded and fissured than the cerebral cortex; the cerebellum weighs only 10% as much as the cerebral cortex, but its surface area is about 75% of that of the cerebral cortex. There are 10 primary lobules in the vermis, numbered I–X from superior to inferior. These lobules are identified by name and number in Fig 12–12. Folia I–V and the corresponding portions of the hemispheres are sometimes called the **anterior lobe** of the cerebellum.

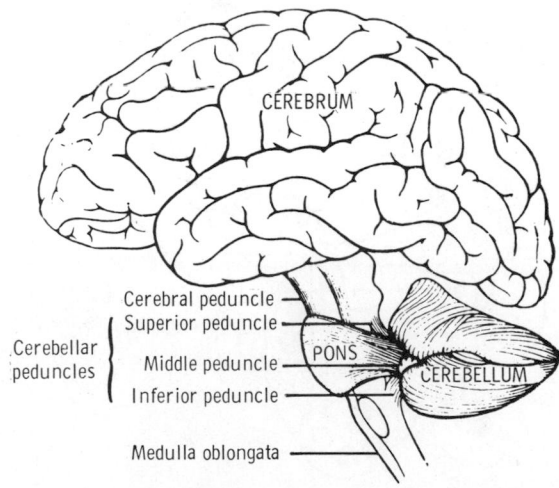

Figure 12–11. Diagrammatic representation of the principal parts of the brain. The parts are distorted to show the cerebellar peduncles and the way the cerebellum, pons, and middle peduncle form a napkin ring around the brain stem. (Reproduced, with permission, from Goss CM [editor]: *Gray's Anatomy of the Human Body,* 27th ed. Lea & Febiger, 1959.)

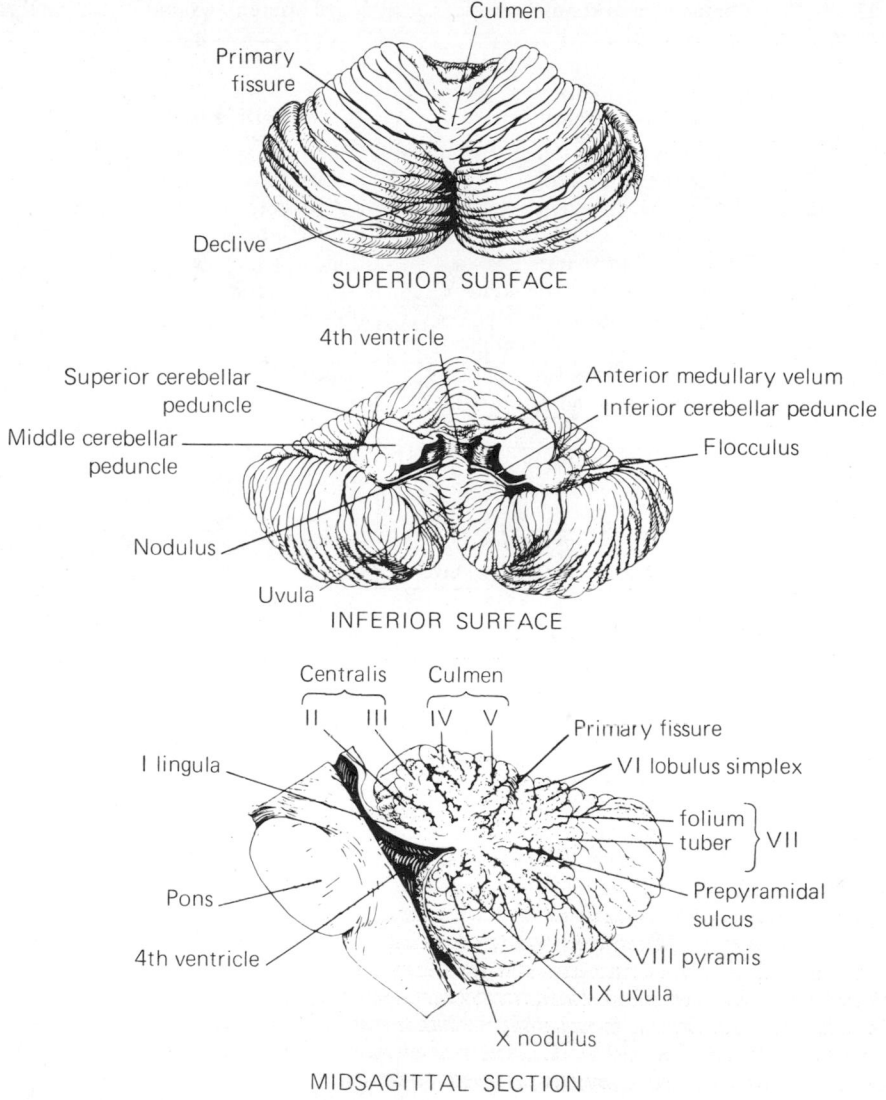

Figure 12–12. Superior and inferior views and sagittal section of the human cerebellum. The 10 principal lobules are identified by name and by number (I–X) on the basis of comparative studies of the mammalian cerebellum. (Modified from Chusid JG: *Correlative Neuroanatomy & Functional Neurology,* 17th ed. Lange, 1979.)

Afferent and Efferent Connections

The cerebellum has an external **cerebellar cortex** separated by white matter from deep **cerebellar nuclei.** Its afferent input goes to the cortex and, via collaterals, to the deep nuclei. The cortex projects to the deep nuclei, and the deep nuclei project on each side to the red nucleus, the ventrolateral nucleus of the thalamus, the vestibular nuclei, and the reticular formation.

The afferent pathways to the cerebellum are summarized in Table 12–4. They transmit proprioceptive and sensory information from all parts of the body. One portion of the proprioceptive input is relayed via the inferior olive, and the olivocerebellar fibers form the excitatory climbing fiber input (see below). In addition, information is relayed to the cerebellum from all the motor areas in the cerebral cortex via the pontine nuclei.

The cerebellar cortex contains 3 layers (Fig 12–13): an external molecular layer, a Purkinje cell layer that is only 1 cell thick, and an internal granular layer. The Purkinje cells are among the biggest neurons in the body. They have very extensive dendritic arbors that extend throughout the molecular layer. Their axons, which are the only output from the cerebellar cortex, pass to the deep nuclei: the **fastigial, globose, emboliform,** and **dentate nuclei.** The fastigial nuclei receive axons from the vermis; the globose, emboliform, and dentate nuclei receive axons from the lateral portions of the hemispheres. The cerebellar

Table 12–4. Function and major terminations of the principal afferent systems to the cerebellum.*

Afferent Tracts	Transmits	Distribution	Peduncle by Which Enters Cerebellum
Dorsal spinocerebellar	Proprioceptive and exteroceptive impulses from body	Folia I–VI, pyramis and para-median lobule	Inferior
Ventral spinocerebellar	Proprioceptive and exteroceptive impulses from body	Folia I–VI, pyramis and para-median lobule	Superior
Cuneocerebellar	Proprioceptive impulses, especially from head and neck	Folia I–VI, pyramis and para-median lobule	Inferior
Tectocerebellar	Auditory and visual impulses via inferior and superior colliculi	Folium, tuber, ansiform lobule	Superior
Vestibulocerebellar	Vestibular impulses from labyrinths direct and via vestibular nuclei	Principally flocculonodular lobe	Inferior
Pontocerebellar	Impulses from motor and other parts of cerebral cortex via pontine nuclei	All cerebellar cortex except flocculonodular lobe	Middle
Olivocerebellar	Proprioceptive input from whole body via relay in inferior olive	All cerebellar cortex and deep nuclei	Inferior

*Several other pathways transmit impulses from nuclei in the brain stem to the cerebellar cortex and to the deep nuclei.

cortex also contains **granule cells,** which receive input from the mossy fibers (see below) and innervate the Purkinje cells. The granule cells have their cell bodies in the granular layer. Each sends an axon to the molecular layer, where the axon bifurcates to form a T. The branches of the T are straight and run long distances. Consequently, they are called **parallel fibers.** The dendritic trees of the Purkinje cells are markedly flattened (Fig 12–13) and oriented at right angles to the parallel fibers. The parallel fibers thus make synaptic

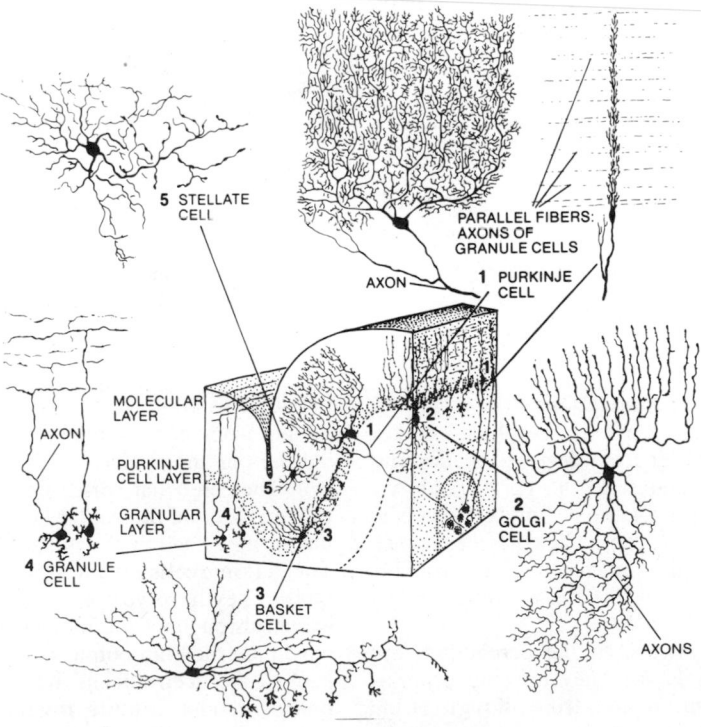

Figure 12–13. Location and structure of neurons in the cerebellar cortex. (Reproduced, with permission, from Kuffler SW, Nicholls JG: *From Neuron to Brain.* Sinauer Associates, 1976.)

contact with the dendrites of many Purkinje cells, and the parallel fibers and Purkinje dendritic trees form a grid of remarkably regular proportions.

The other 3 types of neurons in the cerebellar cortex are in effect inhibitory interneurons. The **basket cells** (Fig 12–13) are located in the molecular layer. They receive input from the parallel fibers, and each projects to many Purkinje cells. Their axons form a basket around the cell body and axon hillock of each Purkinje cell they innervate. The **stellate cells** are similar to the basket cells but more superficial in location. The **Golgi cells** are located in the granular layer. Their dendrites, which project into the molecular layer, receive input from the parallel fibers and their cell bodies receive input via collaterals from the incoming climbing fibers (see below) and the Purkinje cells. Their axons project to the dendrites of the granule cells.

There are 2 main sources of input to the cerebellar cortex: **climbing fibers** and **mossy fibers.** The climbing fibers come from the inferior olivary nuclei, and each projects to the primary dendrites of the Purkinje cell, around which it entwines like a climbing plant. The mossy fibers constitute most of the other incoming fibers. They end on the dendrites of granule cells in complex synaptic junctions called **glomeruli.** The glomeruli also contain the inhibitory endings of the Golgi cells mentioned above.

The fundamental circuits of the cerebellar cortex are thus relatively simple (Fig 12–14). Climbing fiber inputs exert a strong excitatory effect on single Purkinje cells, whereas mossy fiber inputs exert a weak

excitatory effect on many Purkinje cells via the granule cells. The basket and stellate cells are also excited by granule cells via the parallel fibers, and their output inhibits Purkinje cell discharge. Golgi cells are excited by the mossy fiber collaterals, Purkinje cell collaterals, and parallel fibers, and they inhibit transmission from mossy fibers to granule cells.

The output of the Purkinje cells is in turn inhibitory to the deep cerebellar nuclei. These nuclei also receive excitatory inputs via collaterals from the mossy and climbing fibers, and they may also receive other excitatory inputs. It is interesting, in view of their inhibitory Purkinje cell input, that the output of the deep cerebellar nuclei to the brain stem and thalamus is always excitatory. Thus, the entire cerebellar circuitry seems to be concerned solely with modulating, or possibly with timing, the excitatory output of the deep cerebellar nuclei to the brain stem and thalamus.

PHYSIOLOGY

Flocculonodular Lobe

The phylogenetically oldest part of the cerebellum, the **flocculonodular lobe,** consists of the central **nodule** and lateral **flocculus** on either side. Its connections are essentially all vestibular. Animals in which it has been destroyed walk in a staggering fashion on a broad base. They tend to fall and are reluctant to move without support. Similar defects are seen in children as the earliest signs of a midline cerebellar tumor called a medulloblastoma. This malignant tumor arises from cell rests in the nodule and early in its course produces damage that is generally localized to the flocculonodular lobe.

Motion Sickness

Selective ablation of the flocculonodular lobe in dogs abolishes the syndrome of **motion sickness,** whereas extensive lesions in other parts of the cerebellum and the rest of the brain fail to affect it. This "disease," a ubiquitous if minor complication of modern travel, is a consequence of excessive and repetitive labyrinthine stimulation due to the motion of a vehicle. In humans, it can of course be controlled by a number of antiemetic tranquilizing drugs without recourse to surgery.

Uvula & Paraflocculus

According to some authors, the uvula and paraflocculus are part of the cerebellar area coordinating movement. Although the uvula is a constant anatomic feature throughout the phylogenetic scale, the paraflocculus is variable in size. It is rudimentary or absent in humans and most terrestrial animals, but it is large in aquatic diving mammals. It may play some role in the extensive reflex adjustments necessary for diving.

Folium, Tuber, & Ansiform Lobules

Auditory and visual stimuli evoke electrical re-

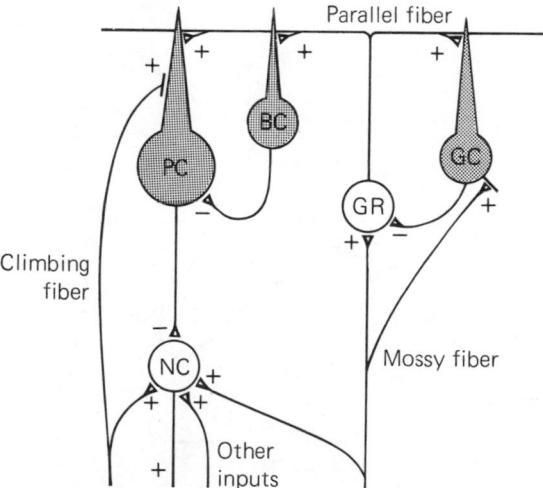

Figure 12–14. Diagram of neural connections in the cerebellum. Shaded neurons are inhibitory and + and − signs indicate whether endings are excitatory or inhibitory. BC, basket cell; GC, Golgi cell; GR, granule cell; NC, nuclear cell; PC, Purkinje cell. The connections of the stellate cells are similar to those of the basket cells, except that they end for the most part on Purkinje cell dendrites. (Modified from Eccles JC, Itoh M, Szentágothai J: *The Cerebellum as a Neuronal Machine.* Springer, 1967.)

sponses in the folium, tuber, and ansiform lobules and often in the adjoining portion of the lobulus simplex. The size of this portion of the cerebellum parallels the growth of the cerebral cortex. It is very large in primates, and the ansiform lobules make up a large part of the cerebellar hemispheres in humans. The auditory and visual impulses reach the cerebellum via the tectocerebellar tract from the inferior and superior colliculi. Each stimulus causes a response in 2 areas: one in the tuber (area II in Fig 12–15) and another in the folium and adjacent areas (area I in Fig 12–15). The significance of this elaborate projection is far from clear. Stimulation of the region produces turning of the head and eyes to the ipsilateral side. Localized lesions of the region generally have little effect, although it has been reported that monkeys with such lesions crash into walls while running in spite of excellent vision and good coordination. Purkinje cells in folia VI and VII discharge in advance of eye movements, and the rate of discharge is inversely proportionate to the magnitude of the eye movement (Fig 12–16).

Folia I–VI, Pyramis, & Paramedian Lobules

The portions of the cerebellum that may be most concerned with the adjustment of posture and movement are folia I–VI of the vermis and their associated areas in the hemispheres, plus the pyramis and the paramedian lobules. These areas receive impulses from the motor cortex via the pons. They also receive proprioceptive input from the entire body, as well as tactile and other sensory impulses. In both the superior (folia I–VI) and inferior (paramedian) areas, there is a point-for-point projection of peripheral sensory receptors, so that homunculi can be plotted on the cerebellar surface (Fig 12–15).

Effects on Stretch Reflexes

Stimulation of the cerebellar areas that receive proprioceptive input sometimes inhibits and sometimes facilitates movements evoked by stimulation of the cerebral cortex. In resting animals, cerebellar stimulation leads to changes in muscle tone through variations in the rate of gamma efferent discharge. Stretch reflexes are usually inhibited, especially if the site of stimulation is near the midline. However, more lateral stimuli may augment spasticity, and the response also varies with the parameters of stimulation. Lesions in folia I–VI and the paramedian areas in experimental animals cause spasticity localized to the part of the body that is represented in the part of the cerebellum destroyed. However, hypotonia is characteristic of cerebellar destruction in humans.

Effects on Movement

Except for the changes in stretch reflexes, animals with cerebellar lesions show no abnormalities as long as they are at rest. However, pronounced abnormalities are apparent when they move. There is no

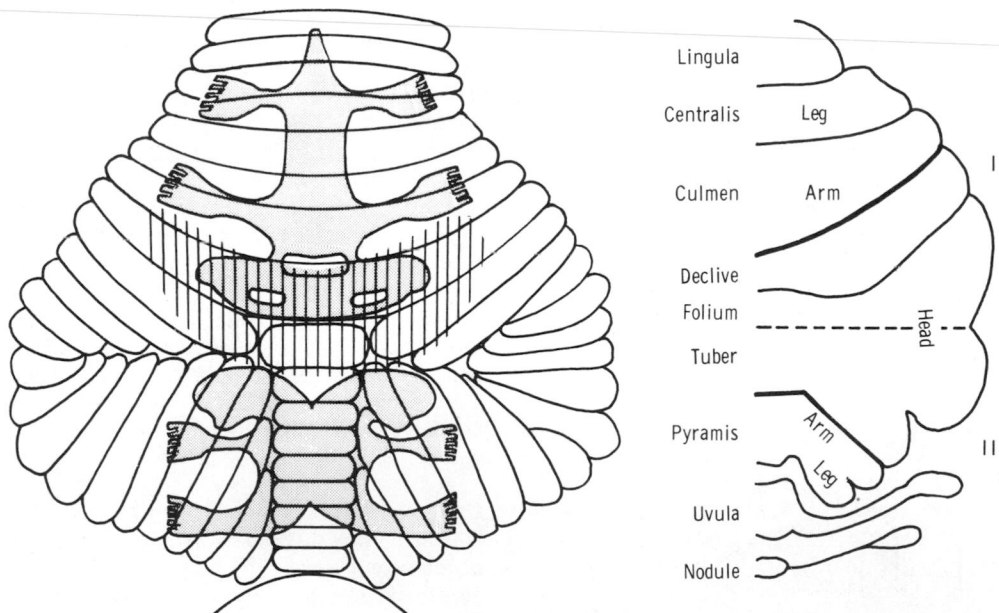

Figure 12–15. *Left:* Cerebellar homunculi. Proprioceptive and tactile stimuli are projected as shown in the figure above and the split figure below. The striped area represents the region from which evoked responses to auditory and visual stimuli are observed. (Redrawn and reproduced, with permission, from Snider RS: The cerebellum. Scientific American 199:84 [Aug], 1958. Copyright © 1958 by Scientific American, Inc. All rights reserved.) *Right:* Projection of the body on the cerebellum. Areas I and II (above and below the dashed line) are the 2 areas where auditory and visual stimuli are projected. (Redrawn and reproduced, with permission, from Hampson JL & others: Cerebro-cerebellar projections and the somatotopic localization of motor function in the cerebellum. Res Publ Assoc Res Nerv Ment Dis 30:299, 1950.)

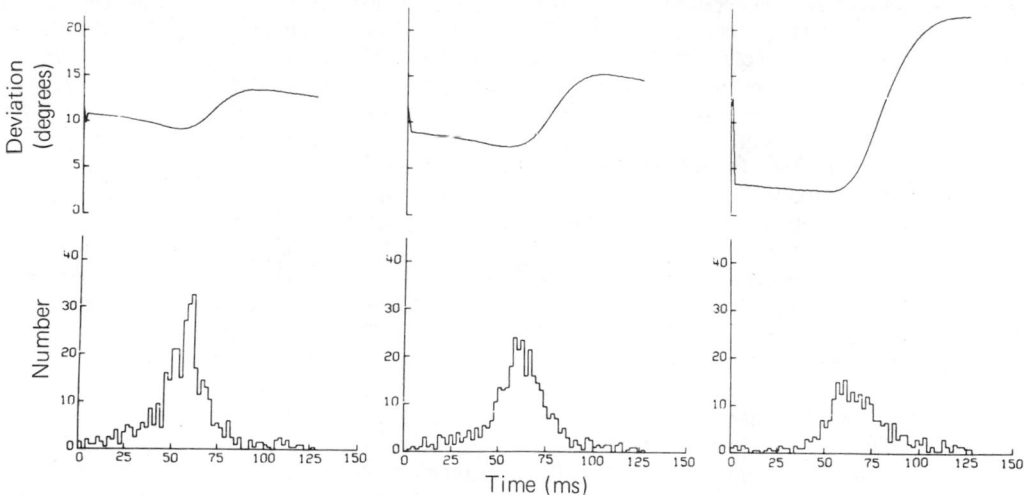

Figure 12–16. Relation between eye movement and discharge of a Purkinje cell. Deviation of the eyes of a monkey recorded in degrees on the top and the number of spikes per 2 ms from the Purkinje cell at the bottom. Note that the larger the saccadic eye movement, the smaller the number of spikes in the Purkinje cell before the movement started. (Reproduced, with permission, from Llinás RR: Motor aspects of cerebellar control. Physiologist 17:19, 1974.)

paralysis and no sensory deficit, but all movements are characterized by a marked **ataxia,** a defect defined as incoordination due to errors in the rate, range, force, and direction of movement. With circumscribed lesions in animals and humans, the ataxia may be localized to one part of the body. If only the cortex of the cerebellum is involved, the movement abnormalities gradually disappear as **compensation** occurs. Lesions of the cerebellar nuclei produce more generalized defects, and the abnormalities are permanent. For this reason, care should be taken to avoid damaging the nuclei when surgical removal of parts of the cerebellum is necessary.

Defects Produced by Cerebellar Lesions in Humans

The signs of cerebellar deficit in humans provide additional illustrations of the importance of the cerebellar mechanisms in the control of movement. The hypotonia and the early symptoms of relatively selective destruction of the flocculonodular lobe have been mentioned above. The common denominator of most cerebellar signs is inappropriate rate, range, force, and direction of movement. Ataxia is manifest not only in the wide-based, unsteady, "drunken" gait of patients but also in defects of the skilled movements involved in the production of speech, so that slurred or **scanning speech** results. Other voluntary movements are also highly abnormal. For example, attempting to touch an object with a finger results in overshooting to one side or the other. This **dysmetria,** or **past-pointing,** promptly initiates a gross corrective action, but the correction overshoots to the other side. Consequently, the finger oscillates back and forth, and the farther it travels the greater the excursions become. This oscillation is the **intention tremor** of cerebellar disease.

Unlike the resting tremor of parkinsonism, it is absent at rest; however, it appears whenever the patient attempts to perform some voluntary action. Another characteristic of cerebellar disease is inability to "put on the brakes," to stop movement promptly. Normally, for example, flexion of the forearm against resistance is quickly checked when the resistance force is suddenly broken off. The patient with cerebellar diseases cannot brake the movement of the limb, and the forearm flies backward in a wide arc. This abnormal response is known as the **rebound phenomenon,** and similar impairment is detectable in other motor activities. This is one of the important reasons these patients show **adiadochokinesia,** the inability to perform rapidly alternating opposite movements such as repeated pronation and supination of the hands. Finally, patients with cerebellar disease have difficulty performing actions that involve simultaneous motion at more than one joint. They dissect such movements and carry them out one joint at a time, a phenomenon known as **decomposition of movement.**

Nature of Cerebellar Control

Movement depends not only on the coordinated activity of the muscles primarily responsible for the movement (**agonists** or **protagonists**) but also on that of **antagonistic** muscles, **synergistic** muscles, and muscles that anchor various parts of the body to form a base for movement (**fixation** muscles). Phasic reflex responses as well as skilled voluntary motion require a delicately adjusted interaction of all these muscles. Organizing this "cooperation in movement" has generally been regarded to be the function of the cerebellum.

In general terms, the motor cortex projects to the cerebellum and the cerebellum in turn projects to the cerebral cortex via the ventrolateral nucleus of the thalamus. The basal ganglia, the cerebral cortex, and the cerebellum project to the skeletal muscles via the motor neurons of the spinal cord and the brain stem (Fig 12–5). The cerebral cortex and the cerebellum receive input from the sense organs. It now appears that the cerebellum functions in the regulation of movement both before and during movement. The lateral portions of the cerebellar cortex appear to be involved in the generation of rapid, ballistic movements (saccadic movements), and these movements, unlike slow ramp movements, are not subject to feedback control. Instead, the Purkinje cells discharge before the movement starts (Fig 12–16). Thus, the function of part of the cerebellar cortex may be to convert the energies needed for different movements into the requisite different durations of action potential trains to the motor neurons. This interesting concept—that the cerebellar cortex functions as a clock preprogramming the duration of fast movements—should stimulate additional research into the problem of how the cerebellum exerts its effects on movement.

The intermediate portion of the cerebellar cortex receives a massive input from proprioceptors throughout the body and appears to regulate movement that is under way. Thus, it functions as a feedback, stabilizing comparator circuit that, by continuous comparison of the motor program to the actual performance, adjusts motion so that it is smooth and precise (Fig 12–5).

The relation of the electrical events in the cerebellum to its function in motor control is another interesting problem. The cerebellar cortex has a basic, 150–300/s, 200 μV electrical rhythm and, superimposed on this, a 1000–2000/s component of smaller amplitude. The frequency of the basic rhythm is thus more than 10 times as great as that of the similarly recorded cerebral cortical EEG, and the amplitude is considerably less. Incoming stimuli generally alter the amplitude of the cerebellar rhythm, like a broadcast signal modulating a carrier frequency in radio transmission. However, the significance of these electrical phenomena in terms of cerebellar function is not known.

Efferent Pathways to Visceral Effectors | 13

The autonomic nervous system, like the somatic nervous system, is organized on the basis of the reflex arc. Impulses initiated in visceral receptors are relayed via afferent autonomic pathways to the CNS, integrated within it at various levels, and transmitted via efferent pathways to visceral effectors. This organization deserves emphasis because the functionally important afferent components have often been ignored. The visceral receptors and afferent pathways have been considered in Chapters 5 and 7 and the major autonomic effector, smooth muscle, in Chapter 3. The efferent pathways to the viscera are the subject of this chapter. Autonomic integration in the CNS is considered in Chapter 14.

ANATOMIC ORGANIZATION OF AUTONOMIC OUTFLOW

The peripheral motor portions of the autonomic nervous system are made up of **preganglionic** and **postganglionic neurons** (Figs 13–1 and 13–2). The cell bodies of the preganglionic neurons are located in the visceral efferent (lateral gray) column of the spinal cord or the homologous motor nuclei of the cranial nerves. Their axons are mostly myelinated, relatively slow-conducting B fibers. The axons synapse on the cell bodies of postganglionic neurons that are located in all cases outside the CNS. Each preganglionic axon diverges to an average of 8–9 postganglionic neurons. In this way, autonomic output is diffused. The axons of the postganglionic neurons, mostly unmyelinated C fibers, end on the visceral effectors.

Anatomically, the autonomic outflow is divided into 2 components: the **sympathetic** and **parasympathetic** divisions of the autonomic nervous system.

Sympathetic Division

The axons of the sympathetic preganglionic neurons leave the spinal cord with the ventral roots of the first thoracic to the third or fourth lumbar spinal nerves. They pass via the **white rami communicantes** to the **paravertebral sympathetic ganglion chain,**

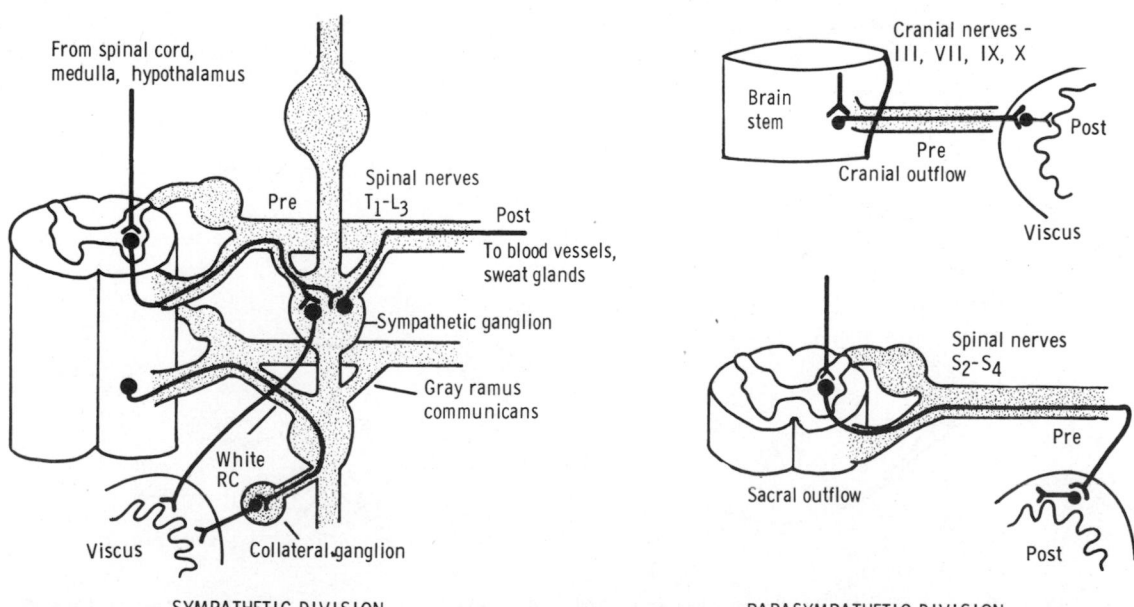

SYMPATHETIC DIVISION

PARASYMPATHETIC DIVISION

Figure 13–1. Autonomic nervous system. Pre, preganglionic neuron; Post, postganglionic neuron; RC, ramus communicans.

where most of them end on the cell bodies of the postganglionic neurons. The axons of some of the postganglionic neurons pass to the viscera in the various sympathetic nerves. Others reenter the spinal nerves via the **gray rami communicantes** from the chain ganglia and are distributed to autonomic effectors in the areas supplied by these spinal nerves. The postganglionic sympathetic nerves to the head originate in the **superior, middle,** and **stellate** ganglia in the cranial extension of the sympathetic ganglion chain

and travel to the effectors with the blood vessels. Some preganglionic neurons pass through the paravertebral ganglion chain and end on postganglionic neurons located in **collateral ganglia** close to the viscera. The myometrium of the uterus, unlike the rest of the organ, is innervated by a special system of **short adrenergic neurons** (not shown in Fig 13–2) with cell bodies in the uterus, and the preganglionic fibers to these postganglionic neurons presumably go all the way to the uterus.

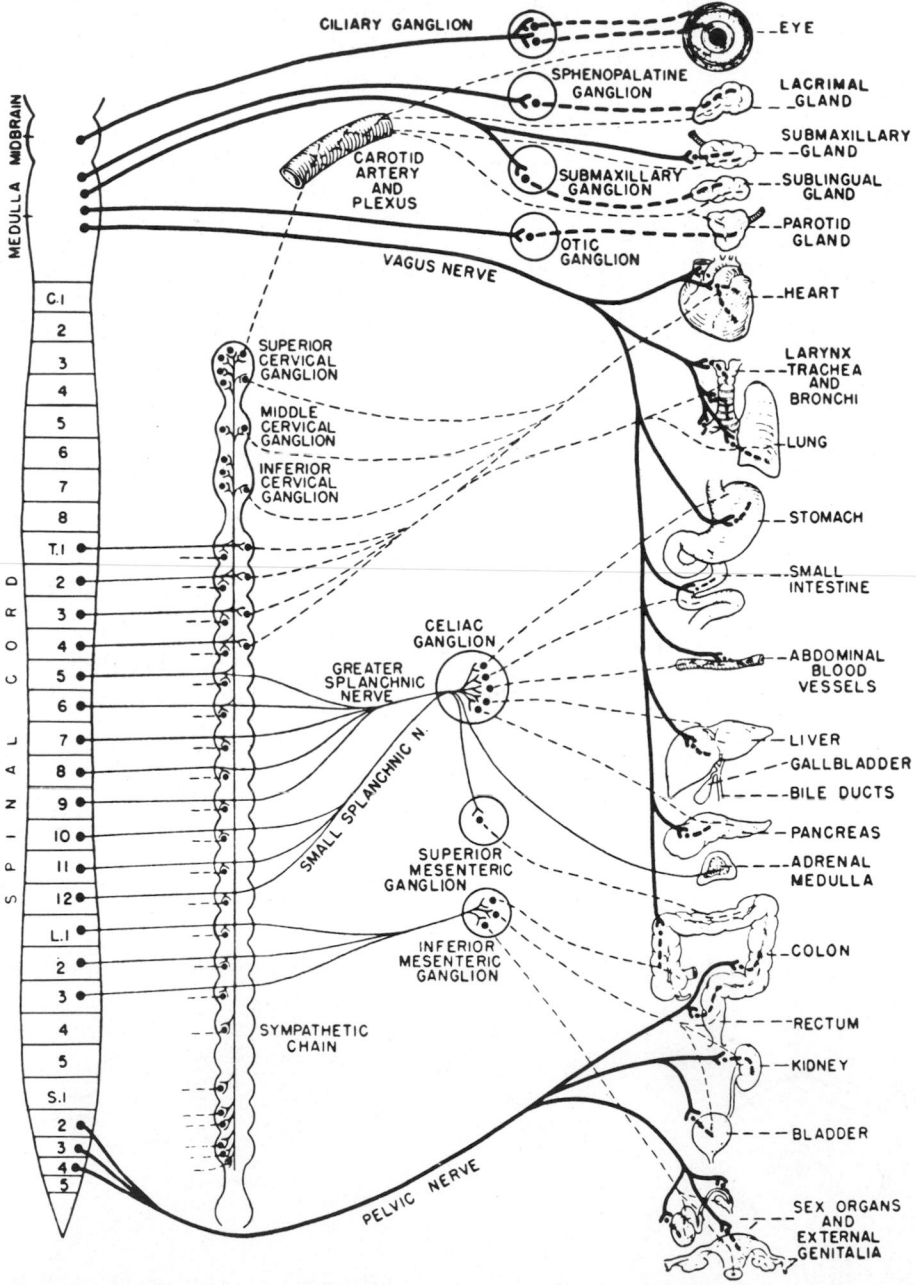

Figure 13–2. Diagram of the efferent autonomic pathways. Preganglionic neurons are shown as solid lines, postganglionic neurons as dashed lines. The heavy lines are parasympathetic fibers; the light lines are sympathetic. (Reproduced, with permission, from Youmans W: *Fundamentals of Human Physiology,* 2nd ed. Year Book, 1962.)

Parasympathetic Division

The **cranial outflow** of the parasympathetic division supplies the visceral structures in the head via the oculomotor, facial, and glossopharyngeal nerves, and those in the thorax and upper abdomen via the vagus nerves. The **sacral outflow** supplies the pelvic viscera via the pelvic branches of the second to fourth sacral spinal nerves. The preganglionic fibers in both outflows end on short postganglionic neurons located on or near the visceral structures (Fig 13–2).

CHEMICAL TRANSMISSION AT AUTONOMIC JUNCTIONS

Transmission at the synaptic junctions between pre- and postganglionic neurons and between the postganglionic neurons and the autonomic effectors is chemically mediated. The principal transmitter agents involved are **acetylcholine** and **norepinephrine,** although **dopamine** is also secreted by interneurons in the sympathetic ganglia.

Acetylcholine

The mediator liberated at all preganglionic endings and at anatomically parasympathetic postganglionic endings is acetylcholine. The biosynthesis and metabolism of this transmitter and its mechanism of action are described in detail in Chapter 4. It is stored in clear vesicles in the synaptic terminals of cholinergic neurons. It is released from the terminals by the nerve impulses. The secreted acetylcholine is in turn hydrolyzed. The enzyme that catalyzes this reaction is acetylcholinesterase, and choline acetyltransferase catalyzes the synthesis of acetylcholine from choline and active acetate. There are a number of esterases in the body, including a pseudocholinesterase in plasma that is capable of hydrolyzing acetylcholine, but only acetylcholinesterase is found in high concentration in cholinergic nerve endings.

Although the same transmitter is released by preganglionic and by postganglionic cholinergic neurons, the properties of the receptors on which the acetylcholine acts are different in the 2 locations. Muscarine, the alkaloid responsible for the toxicity of toadstools, has little effect on autonomic ganglia but mimics the stimulatory action of acetylcholine on smooth muscle and glands. These actions of acetylcholine are therefore called **muscarinic actions,** and the receptors involved are **muscarinic receptors.** Muscarinic receptors are blocked by the drug atropine, and there is evidence that the effects of stimulating muscarinic receptors are mediated via intracellular liberation of cyclic GMP (see Chapter 17). In sympathetic ganglia, small amounts of acetylcholine stimulate postganglionic neurons and large amounts block transmission of impulses from pre- to postganglionic neurons. These actions are unaffected by atropine but mimicked by nicotine. Consequently, these actions of acetyl-

choline are **nicotinic actions** and the receptors are **nicotinic receptors.** The receptors in the motor endplates of skeletal muscle are also nicotinic but are not identical to those in sympathetic ganglia, since they respond differently to certain drugs.

Norepinephrine

The chemical transmitter at most sympathetic postganglionic endings is norepinephrine (levarterenol). It is stored in the synaptic knobs of adrenergic neurons in characteristic vesicles that have a dense core (granulated vesicles). Norepinephrine and its methyl derivative, epinephrine, are secreted by the adrenal medulla (see Chapter 20), but epinephrine is not a mediator at postganglionic sympathetic endings. The endings of sympathetic postganglionic neurons in smooth muscle are discussed in Chapter 4; each neuron has multiple varicosities along its course, and each of these varicosities appears to be a site at which norepinephrine is liberated. There are also norepinephrine-secreting, dopamine-secreting, and epinephrine-secreting neurons in the brain (see Chapter 15).

Biosynthesis & Release of Catecholamines

The principal **catecholamines** found in the body—norepinephrine, epinephrine, and dopamine—are formed by hydroxylation and decarboxylation of the amino acids phenylalanine and tyrosine (Fig 13–3). Phenylalanine hydroxylase is found primarily in the liver. Tyrosine is transported into adrenergic nerve endings by a concentrating mechanism. It is converted to dopa and then to dopamine in the cytoplasm of the neurons by tyrosine hydroxylase and dopa decarboxylase. The decarboxylase, which is also called aromatic L-amino acid decarboxylase, is very similar but probably not identical to 5-hydroxytryptophan decarboxylase. The dopamine then enters the granulated vesicles, within which it is converted to norepinephrine by dopamine β-hydroxylase. L-Dopa is the isomer involved, and it is the L isomer of norepinephrine that is produced. The rate-limiting step in synthesis is the conversion of tyrosine to dopa. Tyrosine hydroxylase, which catalyzes this step, is subject to feedback inhibition by dopamine and norepinephrine, thus providing internal control of the synthetic process. The cofactor for tyrosine hydroxylase is tetrahydrobiopterin, which is converted to dihydrobiopterin when tyrosine is converted to dopa.

Synthesis of catecholamines in adrenal medullary cells is presumably similar to synthesis in neurons; however, unlike the postganglionic adrenergic endings, the granules in some of the adrenal medullary cells also contain the enzyme phenylethanolamine-N-methyltransferase (PNMT). This enzyme catalyzes the conversion of norepinephrine to epinephrine. In the granulated vesicles, norepinephrine and epinephrine are bound to ATP and a binding protein called chromogranin. The amines are held in the granulated vesicles by an active transport system, and the action of this transport system is inhibited by the drug reserpine.

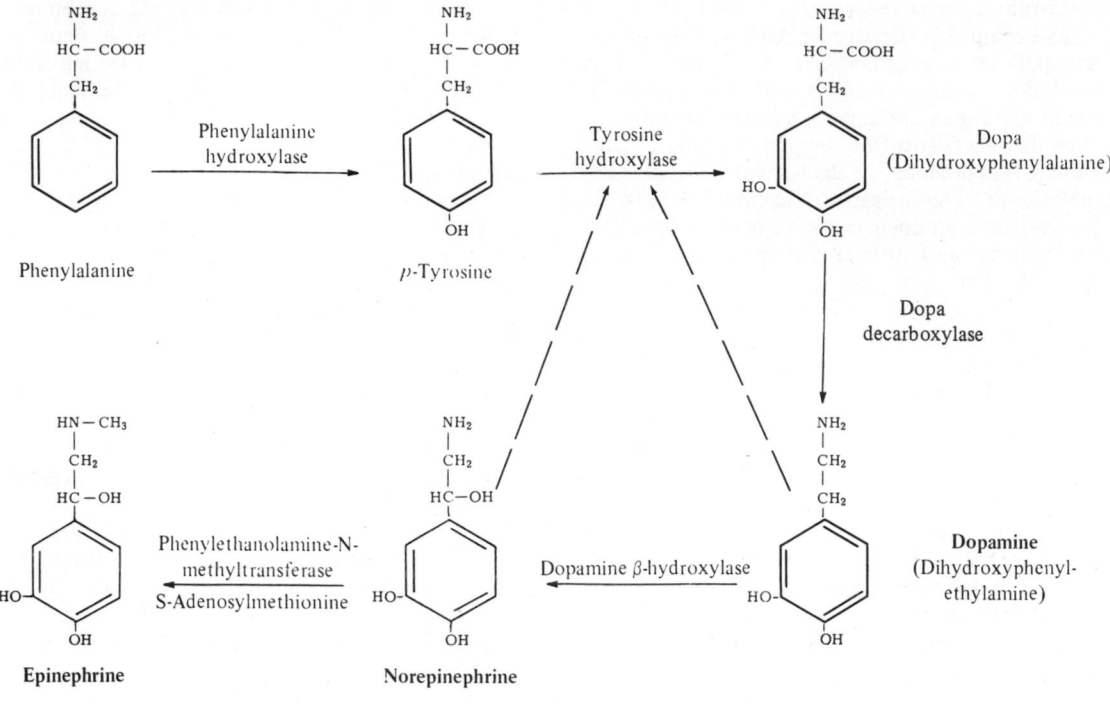

Figure 13–3. Biosynthesis of catecholamines.

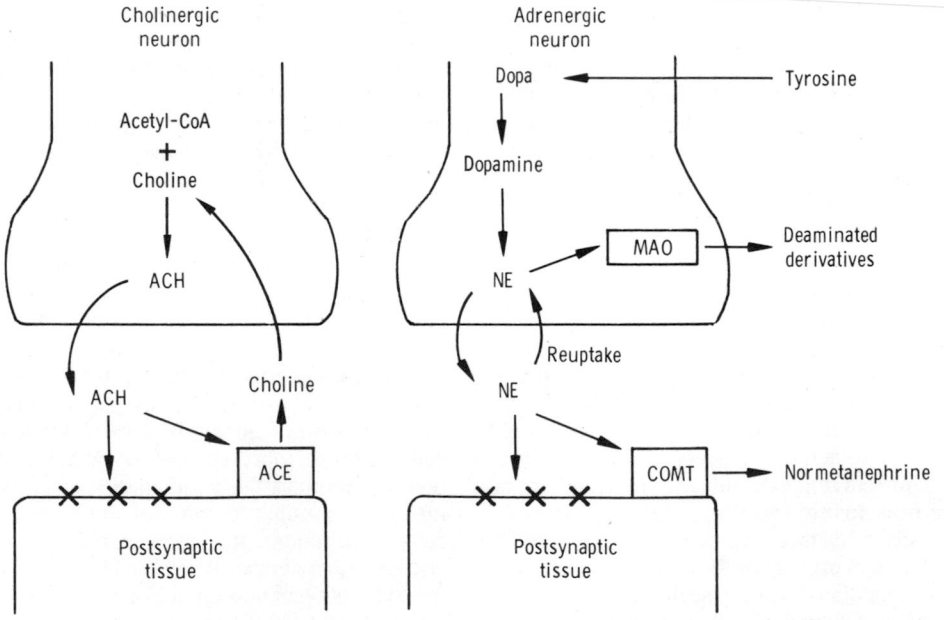

Figure 13–4. Comparison of the biochemical events at cholinergic endings with those at adrenergic endings. ACH, acetylcholine; ACE, acetylcholinesterase; NE, norepinephrine; X, receptor. Note that monoamine oxidase (MAO) is intracellular, so that some norepinephrine is being constantly deaminated in adrenergic endings. Catechol-O-methyltransferase (COMT) acts on norepinephrine after it is secreted.

Catecholamines are released from autonomic neurons and adrenal medullary cells by exocytosis (see Chapter 1). ATP, chromogranin, and dopamine β-hydroxylase are therefore released with norepinephrine and epinephrine in the same proportions as they exist in the granulated vesicles. Circulating levels of dopamine β-hydroxylase were originally thought to be a good index of sympathetic activity. However, the half-life of circulating dopamine β-hydroxylase is much longer than that of the catecholamines, and circulating levels are affected by genetic and other factors in addition to the rate of sympathetic activity.

Some of the norepinephrine in nerve endings is manufactured there, but some is also norepinephrine that has been secreted and then taken up again into the adrenergic neurons. An active **reuptake mechanism** is characteristic of adrenergic neurons. Circulating norepinephrine and epinephrine are also picked up in small amounts by adrenergic neurons in the autonomic nervous system. In this regard, adrenergic neurons differ from cholinergic neurons. Acetylcholine is not taken up to any appreciable degree, but the choline formed by the action of acetylcholinesterase is actively taken up and recycled (Fig 13–4).

The pathways involved in the metabolism of phenylalanine are of considerable clinical importance because they are the site of several **inborn errors of metabolism,** diseases caused by congenital absence of various specific enzymes. Each of these diseases is believed to be due to inheritance from both parents of a particular mutant gene that fails to perform its normal function of initiating the synthesis of a particular enzyme or enzyme subunit. **Phenylpyruvic oligophrenia,** a disorder characterized by severe mental deficiency and the accumulation in the blood and tissues of large amounts of phenylalanine and its keto acid derivatives, is due to congenital absence of phenylalanine hydroxylase (Fig 13–3). The mental deficiency must be secondary to the accumulation of phenylalanine derivatives; if the condition is diagnosed at birth and a low-phenylalanine diet is instituted immediately, the mental retardation is often at least partially prevented. There is evidence that high phenylalanine levels in the blood inhibit protein synthesis in the brain. There is also a deficiency of brain catecholamines and serotonin (see Chapter 15) in this disease, and some investigators believe that the serotonin deficiency is a major factor in the production of the mental abnormality. Ingested tyrosine presumably makes up for the deficiency in the formation of tyrosine from phenylalanine, but it appears that the formation of catecholamines from tyrosine is inhibited, possibly because tyrosine hydroxylase is inhibited by the excess phenylalanine.

Catabolism of Catecholamines

Epinephrine and norepinephrine are metabolized to biologically inactive products by oxidation and methylation. The former reaction is catalyzed by **monoamine oxidase (MAO)** and the latter by **catechol-O-methyltransferase (COMT)** (Figs 13–4,

13–5). MAO is found in the mitochondria. It is widely distributed, being particularly plentiful in the brain, liver, and kidneys, and large amounts are found in the mitochondria of the adrenergic nerve endings. COMT is also widely distributed, with high concentrations in the liver and kidneys, but it is not found in adrenergic nerve endings. Consequently, there are 2 different patterns of catecholamine metabolism.

Circulating epinephrine and norepinephrine are for the most part O-methylated, and measurement of the O-methylated derivatives normetanephrine and metanephrine in the urine is a good index of the rate of secretion of norepinephrine and epinephrine. The O-methylated derivatives that are not excreted are largely oxidized, and VMA (Fig 13–5) is the most plentiful catecholamine metabolite in the urine.

In the adrenergic nerve endings, on the other hand, some of the norepinephrine is being constantly converted by MAO to the physiologically inactive deaminated derivatives 3,4-dihydroxymandelic acid (DOMA) and its corresponding glycol (DOPEG). These compounds enter the circulation and may subsequently be converted to their corresponding O-methyl derivatives (Fig 13–5).

The reuptake of released norepinephrine mentioned above is a major mechanism by which norepinephrine is removed from the vicinity of autonomic endings. The hypersensitivity of the sympathetically denervated structures (see Chapter 4) is probably explained in part on this basis. After the adrenergic neurons are cut, their endings degenerate; consequently, there is no reuptake, and more of a given dose of norepinephrine is available to stimulate the receptors of the autonomic effectors.

Chemical Divisions of the Autonomic Nervous System

On the basis of the chemical mediator released, the autonomic nervous system can be divided into cholinergic and adrenergic divisions. The neurons that are cholinergic are (1) all preganglionic neurons; (2) the anatomically parasympathetic postganglionic neurons; (3) the anatomically sympathetic postganglionic neurons which innervate sweat glands; and (4) the anatomically sympathetic neurons which end on blood vessels in skeletal muscles and produce vasodilatation when stimulated (sympathetic vasodilator nerves; see Chapter 31). The remaining postganglionic sympathetic neurons are adrenergic. The adrenal medulla is essentially a sympathetic ganglion in which the postganglionic cells have lost their axons and become specialized for secretion directly into the bloodstream. The cholinergic preganglionic neurons to these cells have consequently become the secretomotor nerve supply of this gland.

Transmission in Sympathetic Ganglia

The responses produced in postganglionic neurons by stimulation of their preganglionic innervation include not only a rapid depolarization (**fast EPSP**) that generates action potentials (Fig 13–6) but

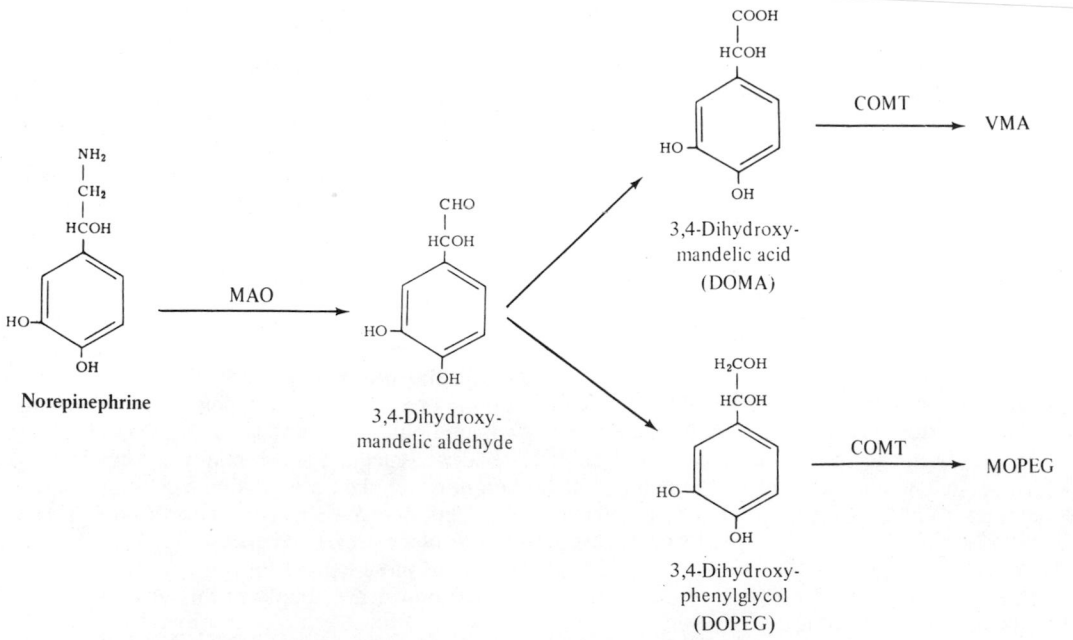

Figure 13–5. *Top:* Catabolism of circulating epinephrine and norepinephrine. The main site of catabolism is the liver. The conjugates are mostly glucuronides and sulfates. ***Bottom:*** Catabolism of norepinephrine in adrenergic nerve endings. The acid and the glycol enter the circulation, and may be subsequently O-methylated to VMA and MOPEG. Epinephrine in nerve endings is presumably catabolized in the same way. MAO, monoamine oxidase; COMT, catechol-O-methyltransferase.

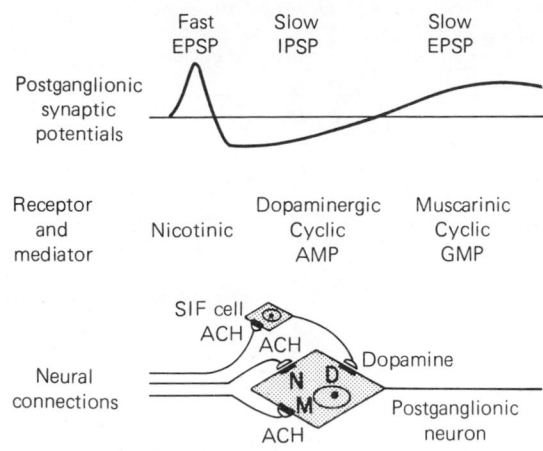

Figure 13–6. Synaptic potentials in postganglionic neurons. The neural connections are those presumed to underlie the potentials. ACH, acetylcholine; N, D, M, nicotinic, dopaminergic, and muscarinic receptors. The receptor on the SIF cell is muscarinic. (Modified from Greengard P, Kebabian JW: Role of cyclic AMP in synaptic transmission in the mammalian peripheral nervous system. Fed Proc 33:1059, 1974.)

also a prolonged inhibitory postsynaptic potential **(slow IPSP)** and a prolonged excitatory postsynaptic potential **(slow EPSP).** These latter 2 responses apparently modulate and regulate transmission through the sympathetic ganglia. The initial depolarization is produced by acetylcholine via a nicotinic receptor. The slow IPSP is produced by dopamine, which is secreted by an interneuron within the ganglion. The interneuron is excited by activation of a muscarinic receptor. The interneurons that secrete dopamine are the small, intensely fluorescent cells **(SIF cells)** in the ganglia. The slow EPSP is produced by acetylcholine acting on a muscarinic receptor on the membrane of the postganglionic neuron. There is evidence that the effects of activating the dopamine receptor are mediated intracellularly by cyclic AMP, and the effects of activating the muscarinic receptor are mediated via cyclic GMP (see Chapter 17).

RESPONSES OF EFFECTOR ORGANS TO AUTONOMIC NERVE IMPULSES

General Principles

The effects of stimulation of the adrenergic and cholinergic postganglionic nerve fibers to the viscera are listed in Table 13–1. The smooth muscle in the walls of the hollow viscera is generally innervated by both adrenergic and cholinergic fibers, and activity in one of these systems increases the intrinsic activity of the smooth muscle whereas activity in the other decreases it. However, there is no uniform rule about which system stimulates and which inhibits. In the case of sphincter muscles, both adrenergic and cholinergic innervations are excitatory, but one supplies the constrictor component of the sphincter and the other the dilator.

There is usually no acetylcholine in the circulating blood, and the effects of localized cholinergic discharge are generally discrete and of short duration because of the high concentration of acetylcholinesterase at cholinergic nerve endings. Norepinephrine spreads farther and has a more prolonged action than acetylcholine. The normal plasma norepinephrine concentration is about 300 pg/ml (1.8 nmol/L). Plasma dopamine is about 200 pg/ml (1.3 nmol/L), and plasma epinephrine is about 30 pg/ml (0.16 nmol/L). The epinephrine and some of the dopamine come from the adrenal medulla, but much of the norepinephrine diffuses into the bloodstream from adrenergic nerve endings.

Cholinergic Discharge

In a general way, the functions promoted by activity in the cholinergic division of the autonomic nervous system are those concerned with the vegetative aspects of day-to-day living. For example, cholinergic action favors digestion and absorption of food by increasing the activity of the intestinal musculature, increasing gastric secretion, and relaxing the pyloric sphincter. For this reason, and to contrast it with the "catabolic" adrenergic division, the cholinergic division is sometimes called the **anabolic nervous system.**

Adrenergic Discharge

The adrenergic division discharges as a unit in emergency situations. The effects of this discharge are of considerable value in preparing the individual to cope with the emergency, although it is important to avoid the teleologic fallacy involved in the statement that the system discharges in order to do this. For example, adrenergic discharge relaxes accommodation and dilates the pupil (letting more light into the eye), accelerates the heartbeat and raises the blood pressure (providing better perfusion of the vital organs and muscles), and constricts the blood vessels of the skin (which limits bleeding if wounded). Adrenergic discharge also leads to lower thresholds in the reticular formation (reinforcing the alert, aroused state) and elevated blood glucose and free fatty acid levels (supplying more energy). On the basis of effects like these, Cannon called the emergency-induced discharge of the adrenergic nervous system the "preparation for flight or fight."

The emphasis on mass discharge in stressful situations should not obscure the fact that the adrenergic autonomic fibers also subserve other functions. For example, tonic adrenergic discharge to the arterioles maintains arterial pressure, and variations in this tonic discharge are the mechanism by which the carotid sinus feedback regulation of blood pressure is effected. In addition, sympathetic discharge is decreased in fasting animals and increased when fasted animals are refed. These changes may explain the decrease in

Table 13–1. Responses of effector organs to autonomic nerve impulses and circulating catecholamines.*

Effector Organs	Cholinergic Impulses Response	Adrenergic Impulses Receptor Type	Adrenergic Impulses Response
Eye			
Radial muscle of iris	...	α	Contraction (mydriasis)
Sphincter muscle of iris	Contraction (miosis)		...
Ciliary muscle	Contraction for near vision	β	Relaxation for far vision
Heart			
S-A node	Decrease in heart rate; vagal arrest	β†	Increase in heart rate
Atria	Decrease in contractility and (usually) increase in conduction velocity	β†	Increase in contractility and conduction velocity
A-V node and conduction system	Decrease in conduction velocity; A-V block	β†	Increase in conduction velocity
Ventricles	...	β†	Increase in contractility and conduction velocity
Blood vessels			
Coronary	Dilatation	α	Constriction
		β	Dilatation
Skin and mucosa	...	α	Constriction
Skeletal muscle	Dilatation	α	Constriction
		β	Dilatation
Cerebral	...	α	Constriction (slight)
Pulmonary	...	α	Constriction
Abdominal viscera	...	α	Constriction
		β	Dilatation
Renal	...	α	Constriction
Salivary glands	Dilatation	α	Constriction
Lung			
Bronchial muscle	Contraction	β	Relaxation
Bronchial glands	Stimulation		Inhibition (?)
Stomach			
Motility and tone	Increase	β	Decrease (usually)
Sphincters	Relaxation (usually)	α	Contraction (usually)
Secretion	Stimulation		Inhibition (?)
Intestine			
Motility and tone	Increase	α, β	Decrease
Sphincters	Relaxation (usually)	α	Contraction (usually)
Secretion	Stimulation		Inhibition (?)
Gallbladder and ducts	Contraction		Relaxation
Urinary bladder			
Detrusor	Contraction	β	Relaxation (usually)
Trigone and sphincter	Relaxation	α	Contraction
Ureter			
Motility and tone	Increase (?)		Increase (usually)
Uterus	Variable‡	α, β	Variable‡
Male sex organs	Erection		Ejaculation
Skin			
Pilomotor muscles	...	α	Contraction
Sweat glands	Generalized secretion	α	Slight, localized secretion§
Spleen capsule	...	α	Contraction
Adrenal medulla	Secretion of epinephrine and norepinephrine		...
Liver	...	β	Glycogenolysis
Pancreas			
Acini	Secretion		Decreased secretion
Islets	Insulin and glucagon secretion	α	Inhibition of insulin and glucagon secretion
		β	Insulin and glucagon secretion
Salivary glands	Profuse, watery secretion	α	Thick, viscous secretion
Lacrimal glands	Secretion		...
Nasopharyngeal glands	Secretion		...
Adipose tissue	...	β	Lipolysis
Juxtaglomerular cells	...	β	Renin secretion
Pineal gland	...	β	Melatonin synthesis and secretion

*Modified from Goodman LS, Gilman A: *The Pharmacological Basis of Therapeutics,* 5th ed. Macmillan, 1975.
†The β receptors of the heart and adipose tissue are β_1 receptors, and most other β receptors are β_2 receptors.
‡Depends on stage of menstrual cycle, amount of circulating estrogen and progesterone, pregnancy, and other factors.
§On palms of hands and in some other locations ("adrenergic sweating").

Table 13–2. Relative sensitivities of α- and β-adrenergic receptors to epinephrine (E), norepinephrine (NE), and the sympathomimetic amines phenylephrine (PE) and isoproterenol (ISO).

Receptor	Response
α	E > NE > PE > ISO
β_1	ISO > E = NE > PE
β_2	ISO >> E > NE > PE

blood pressure and metabolic rate produced by fasting and the opposite changes produced by feeding.

Alpha & Beta Receptors

The effectors on which epinephrine and norepinephrine act can be separated into 2 categories on the basis of their different sensitivities to certain drugs. These differences are in turn due to the existence of 2 types of catecholamine receptors, the α and β receptors, in the effector organs. The α receptors mediate vasoconstriction, whereas the β receptors mediate such actions as increases in cardiac rate and strength of cardiac contraction (see Chapters 20 and 29). Beta

receptors are now subdivided into 2 types: β_1 and β_2 receptors. The β_1 receptors are the β receptors in the heart, whereas most other receptors are β_2 receptors. The relative sensitivities of the receptors to catecholamines are summarized in Table 13–2, and drugs affecting them are listed in Table 13–3. The effects of β receptor stimulation are brought about by activation of adenylate cyclase with a consequent increase in intracellular cyclic AMP (see Chapter 17). There is some evidence that α receptor activation stimulates guanylate cyclase, increasing intracellular cyclic GMP; however, the mechanisms by which α receptors exert their effects remains unsettled.

Presynaptic Receptors

The α and β adrenergic receptors described above are located on postsynaptic muscle fibers and are thus **postsynaptic receptors.** They can also occur on neurons. On noradrenergic neurons, there are in addition **presynaptic α-adrenergic receptors** which when activated decrease norepinephrine release (Fig 13–7). Some of the norepinephrine released at the synaptic junction diffuses to the presynaptic receptor, preventing excessive or prolonged discharge. The postsynaptic receptors are now called α_1 receptors and the pre-

Table 13–3. Some drugs that affect sympathetic activity. Only the principal actions of the drugs are listed. Note that guanethidine is believed to have 2 principal actions.

Site of Action	Drugs Which Augment Sympathetic Activity	Drugs Which Depress Sympathetic Activity
Sympathetic ganglia	**Stimulate postganglionic neurons** Acetylcholine Nicotine Dimethphenylpiperazinium **Inhibit acetylcholinesterase** DFP (diisopropyl fluorophosphate) Physostigmine (eserine) Neostigmine (Prostigmin) Parathion	**Block conduction** Chlorisondamine (Ecolid) Hexamethonium (Bistrium, C-6) Mecamylamine (Inversine) Pentolinium (Ansolysen) Tetraethylammonium (Etamon, TEA) Trimethaphan (Arfonad) High concentrations of acetylcholine, anticholinesterase drugs
Endings of postganglionic neurons	**Release norepinephrine** Tyramine Ephedrine Amphetamine	**Block norepinephrine synthesis** α-Methyl-p-tyrosine **Interfere with norepinephrine storage** Reserpine Guanethidine (Ismelin) **Prevent norepinephrine release** Bretylium tosylate (Darenthin) Guanethidine (Ismelin) **Form false transmitters** α-Methyldopa (Aldomet)
α Receptors	**Stimulate α receptors** Norepinephrine (levarterenol; Levophed) Epinephrine Metaraminol (Aramine) Methoxamine (Vasoxyl) Phenylephrine (Neo-Synephrine)	**Block α receptors** Phenoxybenzamine (Dibenzyline) Phentolamine (Regitine) Ergot alkaloids
β Receptors	**Stimulate β receptors** Isoproterenol (Isuprel) Epinephrine Norepinephrine	**Block β receptors** Propranolol (Inderol) Practolol (blocks β_1) Butoxamine (blocks β_2)

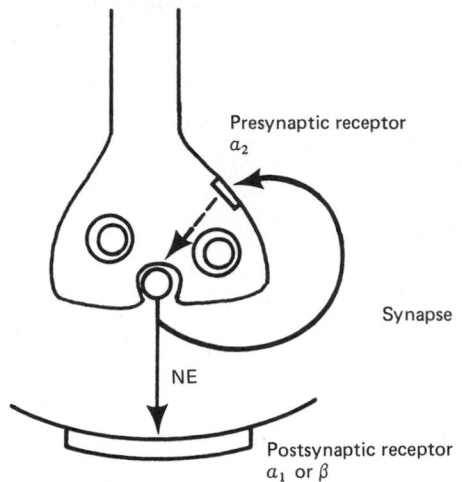

Figure 13–7. Presynaptic (α_2) adrenergic receptor. Some of the norepinephrine released at the ending acts on the postsynaptic (α_1) receptor to inhibit norepinephrine release (dashed arrow).

synaptic α_2 receptors. There are presynaptic adrenergic receptors on noradrenergic neurons in the brain as well (see Chapter 15). In addition, there is evidence for adrenergic presynaptic receptors that increase norepinephrine release, and presynaptic receptors of various types are probably a general phenomenon in the nervous system.

Autonomic Pharmacology

The junctions in the peripheral autonomic motor pathways are a logical site for pharmacologic manipulation of visceral function because transmission across them is chemical. The transmitter agents are synthe-sized, stored in the nerve endings, and released near the neurons, muscle cells, or gland cells on which they act. They bind to receptors on these cells, thus initiating their characteristic actions, and they are then removed from the area by reuptake or metabolism. Each of these steps can be stimulated or inhibited, with predictable consequences. In adrenergic endings, certain drugs also cause the formation of compounds that replace norepinephrine in the granules, and these weak or inactive "false transmitters" are released instead of norepinephrine by the action potentials reaching the endings.

Drugs with muscarinic actions include congeners of acetylcholine and drugs that inhibit acetylcholinesterase. Among the latter are diisopropyl fluorophosphate (DFP) and a number of other derivatives of the so-called nerve gases, which kill by producing massive inhibition of acetylcholinesterase. Atropine, scopolamine, and other natural and synthetic belladonna-like drugs block muscarinic receptors.

A list of some of the commonly used drugs that affect sympathetic activity and the mechanisms by which they produce their effects are summarized in Table 13–3. The drugs that block the effects of norepinephrine on visceral effectors are referred to as adrenergic blocking agents, peripheral sympathetic blocking agents, adrenolytic agents, or sympatholytic agents. Monoamine oxidase inhibitors increase the catecholamine content of the brain but do not affect circulating levels of these amines. When COMT is inhibited, there is a slight prolongation of the physiologic effects of catecholamines; but even when both MAO and COMT are inhibited, the metabolism of epinephrine and norepinephrine is still rapid. Presumably, the catecholamines are being inactivated via the other pathways (Fig 13–5) that normally account for only a small portion of their metabolism.

Neural Centers Regulating Visceral Function | 14

The levels of autonomic integration within the CNS are arranged, like their somatic counterparts, in a hierarchy. Simple reflexes such as contraction of the full bladder are integrated in the spinal cord (see Chapter 12). More complex reflexes that regulate respiration and blood pressure are integrated in the medulla oblongata. Those that control pupillary responses to light and accommodation are integrated in the midbrain. The complex autonomic mechanisms that maintain the chemical constancy and temperature of the internal environment are integrated in the hypothalamus. The brain stem and diencephalic visceral regulatory centers are the subject of this chapter. The hypothalamus also functions with the limbic system as a unit that regulates emotional and instinctual behavior, and these aspects of hypothalamic function are discussed in the next chapter.

MEDULLA OBLONGATA

Control of Respiration, Heart Rate, & Blood Pressure

The medullary centers for the autonomic reflex control of the circulation, heart, and lungs are called the **vital centers** because damage to them is usually fatal. The afferent fibers to these centers originate in a number of instances in highly specialized visceral receptors. The specialized receptors include not only those of the carotid and aortic sinuses and bodies, but also receptor cells that are apparently located in the medulla itself. The motor responses are graded and delicately adjusted and include somatic as well as visceral components. The details of the reflexes themselves are discussed in the chapters on the regulation of the circulation and respiration.

Other Medullary Autonomic Reflexes

Swallowing, coughing, sneezing, gagging, and vomiting are also reflex responses integrated in the medulla oblongata. The swallowing reflex is initiated by the voluntary act of propelling the oral contents toward the back of the pharynx (see Chapter 26). Coughing is initiated by irritation of the lining of the respiratory passages. The glottis closes and strong contraction of the respiratory muscles builds up intrapulmonary pressure, whereupon the glottis suddenly opens, causing an explosive discharge of air (see Chapter 36). Sneezing is a somewhat similar response to irritation of the nasal epithelium. It is initiated by stimulation of pain fibers in the trigeminal nerves.

Vomiting

Vomiting is another example of the way visceral reflexes integrated in the medulla include coordinated and carefully timed somatic as well as visceral components. Vomiting starts with salivation and the sensation of nausea. The glottis closes, preventing aspiration of vomitus into the trachea. The breath is held in midinspiration. The muscles of the abdominal wall contract, and because the chest is held in a fixed position, the contraction increases intra-abdominal pressure. The esophagus and gastric cardiac sphincter relax, reverse peristalsis begins, and the gastric contents are ejected.

The "vomiting center" in the reticular formation of the medulla at the level of the olivary nuclei controls these activities (Fig 14–1).

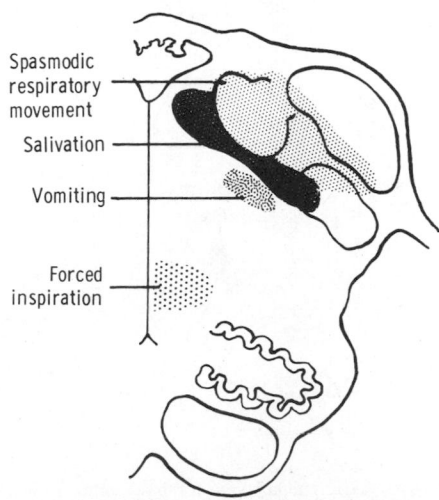

Figure 14–1. Cross section of the medulla oblongata, showing approximate location of areas concerned with components of the vomiting reflex. (Reproduced, with permission, from: *Research in the Service of Medicine*, Vol 44, Searle & Co, 1956.)

Afferents

Irritation of the mucosa of the upper gastrointestinal tract causes vomiting. Impulses are relayed from the mucosa to the vomiting center over visceral afferent pathways in the sympathetic nerves and vagi. Other afferents presumably reach the vomiting center from the diencephalon and limbic system, because emetic responses to emotionally charged stimuli also occur. Thus, we speak of "nauseating smells" and "sickening sights."

It has been claimed that there are chemoreceptor cells in the medulla that initiate vomiting when they are stimulated by circulating chemical agents. The **chemoreceptor trigger zone** in which these cells are located (Fig 14–2) is in or near the **area postrema,** a V-shaped band of tissue on the lateral walls of the fourth ventricle near the obex. This structure is one of the circumventricular organs (see Chapter 32) and is more permeable to many substances than the underlying medulla. Lesions of the area postrema have little effect on the vomiting response to gastrointestinal irritation but abolish the vomiting that follows injection of apomorphine and a number of other emetic drugs. Such lesions also decrease vomiting in uremia and radiation sickness, both of which may be associated with endogenous production of circulating emetic substances. A chemoreceptor mechanism stimulated by circulating toxins would explain vomiting in many clinical disorders.

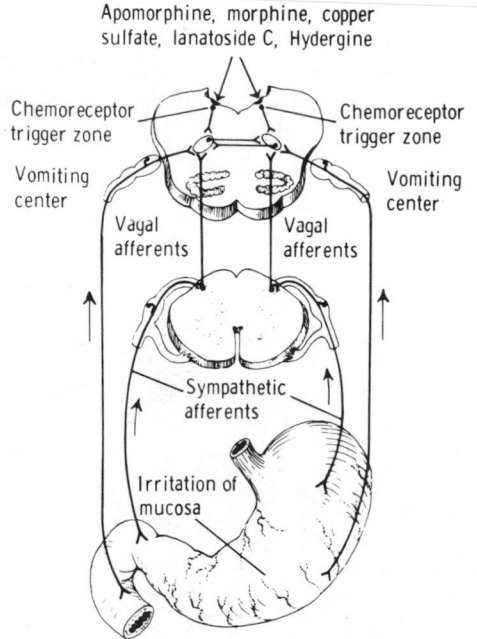

Figure 14–2. Afferent pathways for the vomiting reflex, showing the chemoreceptor trigger zone in the medulla. (Redrawn and reproduced, with permission, from: *Research in the Service of Medicine*, Vol 44. Searle & Co, 1956.)

HYPOTHALAMUS

ANATOMIC CONSIDERATIONS

The hypothalamus is that portion of the anterior end of the diencephalon which lies below the hypothalamic sulcus and in front of the interpeduncular nuclei. It is divided into a variety of nuclei and nuclear areas (Fig 14–3). The supraoptic, the paraventricular, and, in some species, the ventromedial nuclei are clearly delineated, but most of the other nuclei and areas are rather ill-defined collections of small cells.

Relation to the Pituitary Gland

There are neural connections between the hypothalamus and the posterior lobe of the pituitary gland and vascular connections between the hypothalamus and the anterior lobe. The detailed anatomy of the pituitary and the adjacent ventral hypothalamus is shown in Fig 14–4. Embryologically, the posterior pituitary arises as an evagination of the floor of the third ventricle. In the adult, it retains its essentially neural character. It receives an abundant supply of nerve fibers, the **hypothalamohypophyseal tract,** from the supraoptic and paraventricular nuclei. Most of the supraoptic fibers end in the posterior lobe itself, whereas many of the paraventricular fibers end in the pituitary stalk. The anterior and intermediate lobes of the pituitary arise in the embryo from Rathke's pouch, an evagination from the roof of the pharynx (Fig 22–1). Sympathetic nerve fibers reach the anterior lobe from its capsule, and parasympathetic fibers reach it from the petrosal nerves, but very few nerve fibers pass to it from the hypothalamus. However, the **portal hypophyseal vessels** form a direct vascular link between the hypothalamus and the anterior pituitary. Arterial twigs from the carotid arteries and circle of Willis form a network of fenestrated capillaries called the primary plexus on the ventral surface of the hypothalamus (Fig 14–4). Capillary loops also penetrate into the median eminence. The capillaries drain into the sinusoidal portal hypophyseal vessels that carry blood down the pituitary stalk to the capillaries of the anterior pituitary. This system begins and ends in capillaries without going through the heart and is therefore a true portal system. In birds and some mammals, including humans, there is no other anterior hypophyseal arterial supply except capsular vessels and anastomotic connections from the capillaries of the posterior pituitary. In other mammals, some blood reaches the anterior lobe through a separate set of anterior hypophyseal arteries; but in all vertebrates, a large fraction of the anterior lobe blood supply is carried by the portal vessels. The **median eminence** is generally defined as the portion of the ventral hypothalamus from which the portal vessels arise. This region is "outside the blood-brain barrier" (see Chapter 32).

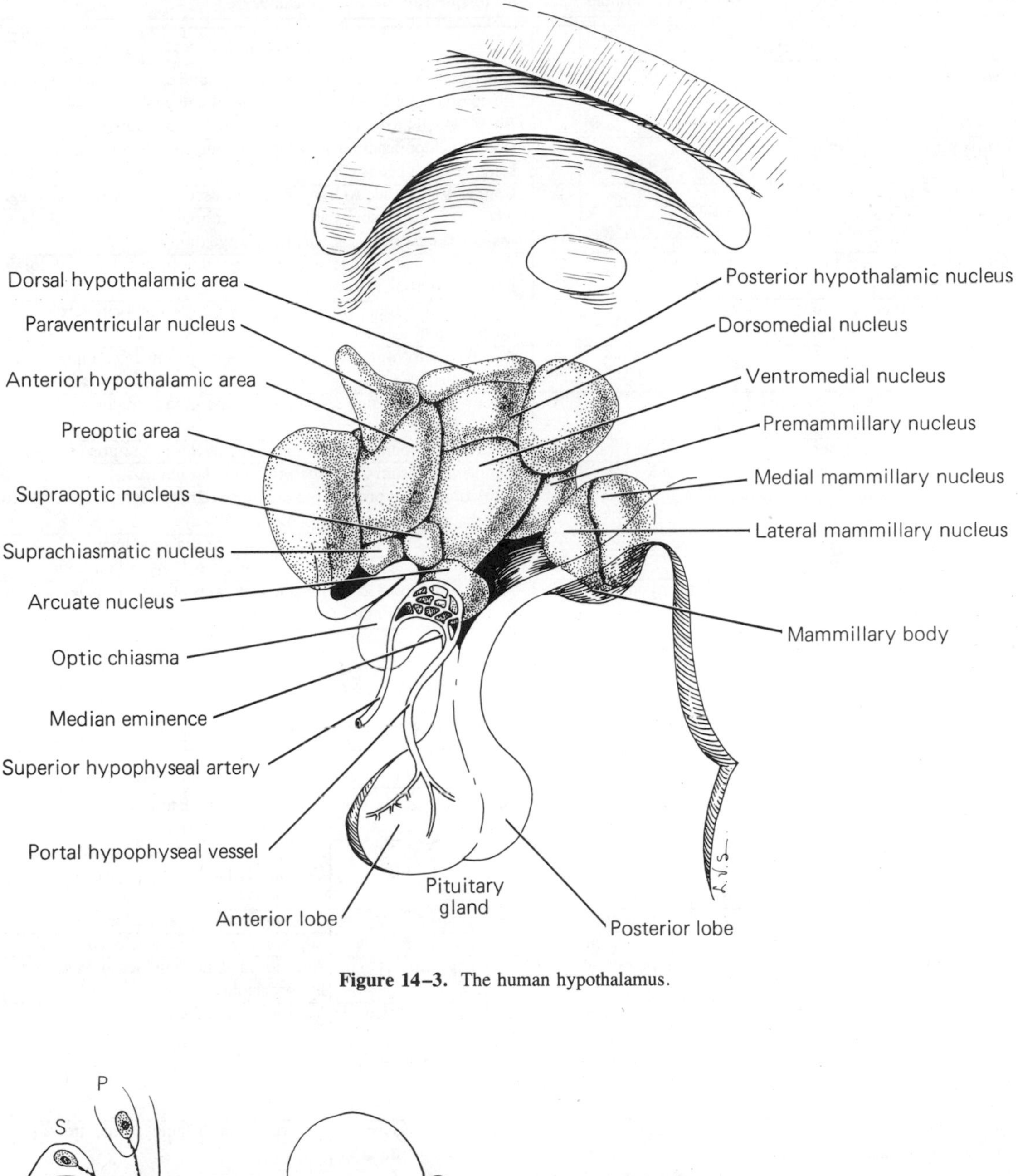

Dorsal hypothalamic area

Paraventricular nucleus

Anterior hypothalamic area

Preoptic area

Supraoptic nucleus

Suprachiasmatic nucleus

Arcuate nucleus

Optic chiasma

Median eminence

Superior hypophyseal artery

Portal hypophyseal vessel

Posterior hypothalamic nucleus

Dorsomedial nucleus

Ventromedial nucleus

Premammillary nucleus

Medial mammillary nucleus

Lateral mammillary nucleus

Mammillary body

Pituitary gland

Anterior lobe

Posterior lobe

Figure 14–3. The human hypothalamus.

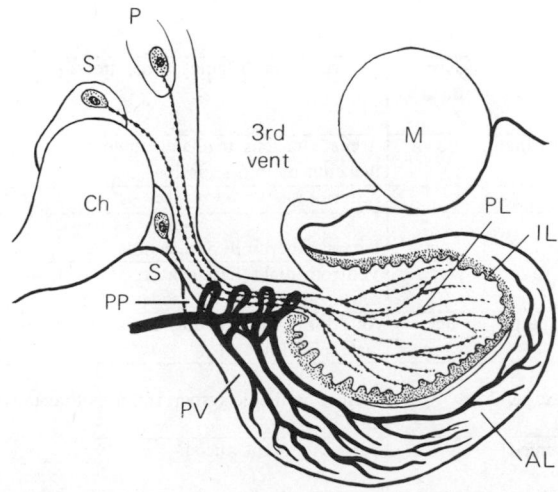

Figure 14–4. Diagram of the connections between the hypothalamus and pituitary in mammals. The capillary loops and capillaries on the ventral surface of the median eminence of the hypothalamus (primary plexus; PP) drain into the portal hypophyseal vessels (PV). Ch, chiasm; S, supraoptic nucleus; P, paraventricular nucleus; M, mammillary body; 3rd vent, third ventricle; AL, anterior lobe; IL, intermediate lobe; PL, posterior lobe.

Table 14–1. Principal pathways to and from the hypothalamus.

Tract		Description
Medial forebrain bundle	A,E	Connects limbic lobe and midbrain via lateral hypothalamus, where fibers enter and leave it; includes direct amygdalohypothalamic fibers, which are sometimes referred to as a separate pathway.
Fornix	A	Connects hippocampus to hypothalamus, mostly mammillary bodies; some efferent fibers (?).
Stria terminalis	A	Connects amygdala to hypothalamus, especially ventromedial region.
Mammillary peduncle	A	Diverges from sensory pathways in midbrain to enter hypothalamus; may be the pathway by which sensory stimuli enter.
Ventral noradrenergic bundle	A	Axons of noradrenergic neurons projecting from various hindbrain nuclei to ventral hypothalamus.
Dorsal noradrenergic bundle	A	Axons of noradrenergic neurons projecting from locus ceruleus to dorsal hypothalamus.
Serotonergic fibers	A	Axons of serotonin-secreting neurons projecting from raphe nuclei to hypothalamus.
Epinephrinergic fibers	A	Axons of epinephrine-secreting neurons from medulla to ventral hypothalamus.
Retinohypothalamic fibers	A	Optic nerve fibers to suprachiasmatic nuclei from optic chiasm.
Thalamohypothalamic and pallidohypothalamic fibers	A	Connections from thalamus and lenticular nucleus.
Periventricular system (including dorsal longitudinal fasciculus of Schütz)	A, E	Interconnects hypothalamus and midbrain; efferent projections to spinal cord, afferent from sensory pathways.
Mammillothalamic tract of Vicq d'Azyr	E	Connects mammillary nuclei to anterior thalamic nuclei.
Mammillotegmental tract	E	Connects hypothalamus with reticular portions of midbrain.
Hypothalamohypophyseal tract (supraopticohypophyseal and paraventriculohypophyseal tracts)	E	Axons of neurons in supraoptic and paraventricular nuclei that end in pituitary stalk and posterior pituitary.

A = principally afferent; E = principally efferent.

Table 14–2. Summary of hypothalamic regulatory mechanisms.

Function	Afferents From	Integrating Areas
Temperature regulation	Cutaneous cold receptors; temperature-sensitive cells in hypothalamus	Anterior hypothalamus, response to heat; posterior hypothalamus, response to cold
Neuroendocrine control of:		
Catecholamines	Emotional stimuli, probably via limbic system	Dorsomedial and posterior hypothalamus
Vasopressin	Osmoreceptors, "volume receptors," others	Supraoptic and paraventricular nuclei
Oxytocin	Touch receptors in breast, uterus, genitalia	Supraoptic and paraventricular nuclei
Thyroid-stimulating hormone (TSH)	Temperature receptors, perhaps others (?)	Anterior median eminence and anterior hypothalamus
Adrenocorticotropic hormone (ACTH)	Limbic system (emotional stimuli); reticular formation ("systemic" stimuli); hypothalamic or anterior pituitary cells sensitive to circulating blood cortisol level; others (?)	Ventral hypothalamus
Follicle-stimulating hormone (FSH) and luteinizing hormone (LH)	Hypothalamic cells sensitive to estrogens; eyes, touch receptors in skin and genitalia of reflex ovulating species	Anterior hypothalamus, other areas
Prolactin	Touch receptors in breasts, other unknown receptors	Arcuate nucleus, median eminence (hypothalamus inhibits secretion)
Growth hormone	Unknown receptors	Anterior median eminence
"Appetitive" behavior		
Thirst	Osmoreceptors	Lateral superior hypothalamus
Hunger	"Glucostat" cells sensitive to rate of glucose utilization	Ventromedial satiety center, lateral hunger center, also limbic components
Sexual behavior	Cells sensitive to circulating estrogen and androgen, others	Anterior ventral hypothalamus, plus, in the male, piriform cortex
Defensive reactions		
Fear, rage	Sense organs and neocortex, paths unknown	Diffuse, in limbic system and hypothalamus
Control of various endocrine and activity rhythms	Retina via retinohypothalamic fibers	Suprachiasmatic nuclei

Afferent & Efferent Connections
of the Hypothalamus

The principal afferent and efferent neural pathways to and from the hypothalamus are listed in Table 14–1. Most of the fibers are unmyelinated. Many connect the hypothalamus to the limbic system. There are also important connections between the hypothalamus and nuclei in the midbrain tegmentum, pons, and hindbrain.

Norepinephrine-secreting neurons with their cell bodies in the hindbrain end in the supraoptic and paraventricular nuclei, the periventricular area, and the median eminence. A few neurons that appear to secrete epinephrine have their cell bodies in the hindbrain and end in the ventral hypothalamus. There is an intrahypothalamic system of dopamine-secreting neurons which have their cell bodies in the arcuate nucleus and end on or near the capillaries that form the portal vessels in the median eminence (Fig 15–11). Serotonin-secreting neurons project to the hypothalamus from the raphe nuclei.

HYPOTHALAMIC FUNCTION

The major functions of the hypothalamus are summarized in Table 14–2. Some are fairly clear-cut visceral reflexes, and others include complex behavioral and emotional reactions; but all involve a particular response to a particular stimulus. It is important to keep this pattern of stimulus-integration-response in mind in considering hypothalamic function.

RELATION OF HYPOTHALAMUS TO AUTONOMIC FUNCTION

Many years ago, Sherrington called the hypothalamus "the head ganglion of the autonomic system." Stimulation of the hypothalamus does produce autonomic responses, but there is little evidence that the hypothalamus is concerned with the regulation of visceral function per se. Rather, the autonomic responses triggered in the hypothalamus are part of more complex phenomena such as rage and other emotions.

"Parasympathetic Center"

Stimulation of the superior anterior hypothalamus occasionally causes contraction of the urinary bladder, a parasympathetic response. Largely on this basis, the statement is often made that there is a "parasympathetic center" in the anterior hypothalamus. However, bladder contraction can also be elicited by stimulation of other parts of the hypothalamus, and hypothalamic stimulation causes very few other parasympathetic responses. Thus, there is very little evidence that a localized "parasympathetic center" exists. Stimulation

of the hypothalamus can cause cardiac arrhythmias, and there is reason to believe that these are due to simultaneous activation of vagal and sympathetic nerves to the heart (see Chapter 28).

Sympathetic Responses

Stimulation of various parts of the hypothalamus, especially the lateral areas, produces a rise in blood pressure, pupillary dilatation, piloerection, and other signs of diffuse adrenergic discharge. The stimuli that trigger this pattern of responses in the intact animal are not regulatory impulses from the viscera but emotional stimuli, especially rage and fear. Adrenergic responses are also triggered as part of the reactions that conserve heat (see below).

Low-voltage electrical stimulation of the middorsal portion of the hypothalamus causes vasodilatation in muscle. Associated vasoconstriction in the skin and elsewhere maintains blood pressure at a fairly constant level. This observation and other evidence support the conclusion that the hypothalamus is a way station on the so-called cholinergic sympathetic vasodilator system which originates in the cerebral cortex. It may be this system which is responsible for the dilatation of muscle blood vessels at the start of exercise (see Chapter 31).

Stimulation of the dorsomedial nuclei and posterior hypothalamic areas produces increased secretion of epinephrine and norepinephrine from the adrenal medulla (Fig 14–5). Increased adrenal medullary secretion is one of the physical changes associated with rage and fear, and may occur when the cholinergic

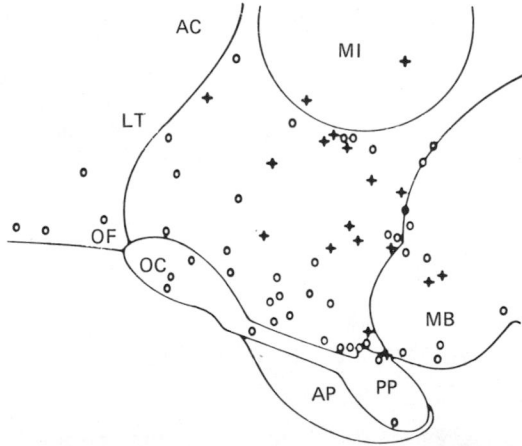

Figure 14–5. Points in the hypothalamus where low-intensity stimulation produces increased catecholamine secretion from the adrenal medulla of dogs. +, catecholamine output increased; 0, catecholamine output unchanged. Points are projected on a midsagittal view of the hypothalamus. MI, massa intermedia; OC, optic chiasm; AP, anterior pituitary; PP, posterior pituitary; MB, mammillary body; OF, orbital surface of the frontal lobe; AC, anterior commissure; LT, lamina terminalis. (Reproduced, with permission, from Goldfien A, Ganong WF: The adrenal medullary and adrenal cortical response to stimulation of the diencephalon. Am J Physiol 202:205, 1962.)

sympathetic vasodilator system is activated. It has been claimed that there are separate hypothalamic centers for the control of epinephrine and norepinephrine secretion. Differential secretion of one or the other of these adrenal medullary catecholamines does occur in certain situations (see Chapter 20), but the selective increases are small.

RELATION TO SLEEP

Lesions of the posterior hypothalamus cause prolonged sleep, and stimulation of the dorsal hypothalamus in conscious animals causes them to go to sleep. These observations have led to considerable speculation about the existence of "sleep centers" and "wakefulness centers" in the hypothalamus, but study of the functions of the RAS and nonspecific projection nuclei of the thalamus (see Chapter 11) has provided alternative explanations.

The posterior hypothalamic lesions that cause coma involve fibers of the RAS as they pass to the thalamus and cortex. The sleep-producing effects of posterior hypothalamic lesions are therefore probably explicable on the basis of damage to the RAS rather than destruction of a hypothetical hypothalamic "wakefulness center."

The hypothalamic loci where stimulation produces sleep are close to the nonspecific projection nuclei of the thalamus. The stimulating frequency that produces sleep is approximately 8/s. Stimulation at greater frequencies arouses rather than depresses the animal. As noted in Chapter 11, stimulation of the thalamus, the orbital surface of the frontal lobe, and some parts of the brain stem at a frequency of 8/s produces sleep. It therefore seems likely that the reported effects of hypothalamic stimulation are actually due to stimulation of a diffuse system, the slow frequency stimulation of which produces sleep. On the basis of these considerations, it seems unlikely that the hypothalamus plays any direct or unique role in the regulation of sleep.

RELATION TO CYCLIC PHENOMENA

Lesions of the suprachiasmatic nuclei disrupt the circadian rhythm in the secretion of ACTH (see Chapter 20) and melatonin (see Chapter 24). In addition, these lesions interrupt estrous cycles and activity patterns in laboratory animals. The suprachiasmatic nuclei receive an important input from the eyes via the retinohypothalamic fibers, and it appears that they normally function to entrain various body rhythms to the 24-hour light-dark cycle. There is a prominent serotonergic input from the raphe nuclei to the suprachiasmatic nuclei (see Chapter 15), but the exact relation of this input to their function is not known.

HUNGER

Feeding & Satiety Centers

Hypothalamic regulation of the appetite for food depends primarily upon the interaction of 2 areas: a lateral **"feeding center"** in the bed nucleus of the medial forebrain bundle at its junction with the pallidohypothalamic fibers, and a medial **"satiety center"** in the ventromedial nucleus. Stimulation of the feeding center evokes eating behavior in conscious animals, and its destruction causes severe, fatal anorexia in otherwise healthy animals. Stimulation of the ventromedial nucleus causes cessation of eating, whereas lesions in this region cause hyperphagia and, if the food supply is abundant, the syndrome of **hypothalamic obesity** (Fig 14–6). Destruction of the feeding center in rats with lesions of the satiety center causes anorexia, which indicates that the satiety center functions by inhibiting the feeding center (Fig 14–7). It appears that the feeding center is chronically active and that its activity is transiently inhibited by activity in the satiety center after the ingestion of food. However, it is not certain that the feeding center and the satiety center simply control the desire for food. For example, rats with ventromedial lesions gain weight for a while, but their food intake then levels off (Fig 14–8). After their intake reaches a plateau, their appetite mechanism operates to maintain their new, higher weight. If they are made more obese by force feeding, their spontaneous food intake drops until their weight falls, and if they are starved, their spontaneous intake increases until they regain the weight they had lost. One theory that has been advanced to explain these observations is that it is the set point for body weight rather than food intake per se which is regulated by the hypothalamic centers.

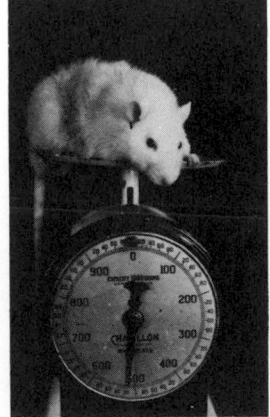

Figure 14–6. Hypothalamic obesity. The animal on the right, in which bilateral lesions have been placed in the ventromedial nuclei 4 months previously, weighs 1080 g. The control animal on the left weighs 520 g. (Reproduced, with permission, from Stevenson JAF, in: *The Hypothalamus.* Haymaker W, Anderson E, Nauta WJH [editors]. Thomas, 1969.)

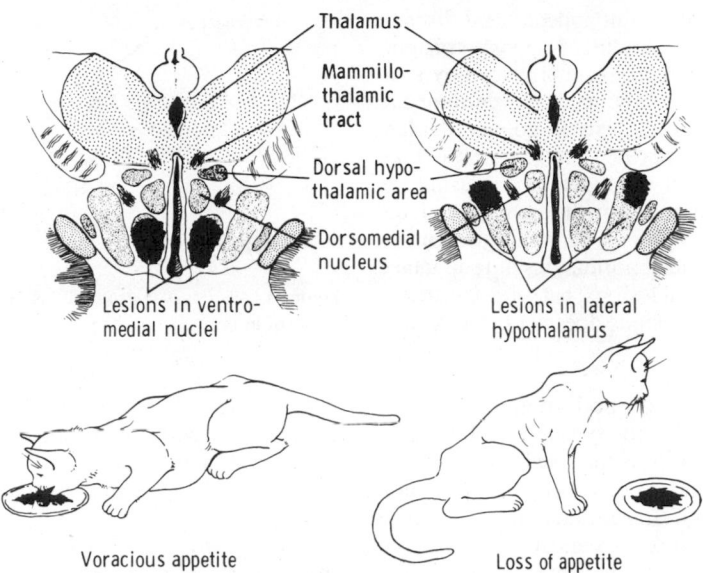

Figure 14–7. Diagrammatic summary of the effects of hypothalamic lesions on feeding. (Redrawn from an original by Netter FH in: Ciba Clinical Symposia. Copyright © 1956, Ciba Pharmaceutical Co. Reproduced with permission.)

Afferent Mechanisms

There is considerable debate about the signals that are sensed by the satiety and feeding center to regulate food intake. The activity of the satiety center is probably governed in part by the level of glucose utilization of cells within the center. These cells have therefore been called **glucostats.** It has been postulated that when their glucose utilization is low—and consequently when the arteriovenous blood glucose difference across them is low—their activity is decreased. Under these conditions, the activity of the

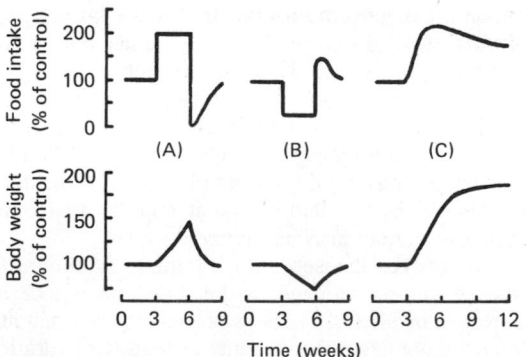

Figure 14–8. Effects of changes in food intake and ventromedial hypothalamic lesions on spontaneous food intake and body weight. In A, rats were force fed for weeks 3–6, then permitted free access to food. In B, rats were partially starved for weeks 3–6, then permitted free access to food. In C, bilateral ventromedial hypothalamic lesions were produced at 3 weeks and the rats allowed free access to food throughout. (Reproduced, with permission, from Stricker E: Hyperphagia. N Engl J Med 298:1010, 1978.)

feeding center is unchecked, and the individual is hungry. When utilization is high, the activity of the glucostats is increased, the feeding center is inhibited, and the individual feels sated. This **glucostatic hypothesis** of appetite regulation is supported by an appreciable body of experimental data. Other factors undoubtedly affect appetite, but the glucostatic hypothesis has the merit of explaining the increased appetite in diabetes, in which the blood sugar is high but the glucose utilization of the cells is low because of the insulin deficiency. The objection has been raised that most neural tissue does not require insulin to metabolize glucose. However, the region of the ventromedial nucleus has been shown to be different from the rest of the brain in that its rate of glucose utilization does vary with the amount of insulin in the circulation.

Relatively large amounts of radioactive glucose are taken up by cells of the ventromedial nuclei. This affinity for glucose probably explains why injections of gold thioglucose produce obesity in the mice. The ventromedial cells presumably take up the toxic gold-substituted glucose molecules, which destroy the cells and thus prevent inhibition of the lateral feeding center. Animals that have received gold thioglucose injections and have become obese have demonstrable lesions in the ventromedial nuclei.

The limbic system is also involved in the neural regulation of appetite. Lesions of the amygdaloid nuclei produce moderate hyperphagia. However, unlike animals with ventromedial hypothalamic lesions, animals with amygdaloid lesions will eat adulterated or tainted food. They are omniphagic and attempt to eat all sorts of objects (see Chapter 15). This suggests that fundamentally different mechanisms underlie the hyperphagia.

The ascending noradrenergic fibers in the ventral

bundle (see Chapter 15) inhibit appetite, and discrete bilateral lesions in the bundle cause hyperphagia. However, the type of hyperphagia produced by such lesions differs from that produced by ventromedial lesions, and ventromedial lesions do not deplete hypothalamic norepinephrine. Amphetamine may exert its inhibitory effect on appetite by causing the release of norepinephrine from the terminals of the ascending noradrenergic fibers. Serotonergic neurons may mediate some of the abnormalities in food intake produced by ventromedial lesions, but serotonin depletion produced by raphe lesions does not produce obesity.

Other Factors Regulating Food Intake

There is evidence that the size of body fat depots is sensed by either neural or hormonal signals to the brain, and that appetite is controlled in this fashion **(lipostatic hypothesis).** In addition, there is some evidence that protein intake is regulated independent of body weight. A cold environment stimulates and a hot environment depresses appetite. Distention of the gastrointestinal tract inhibits and contractions of the empty stomach **(hunger contractions)** stimulate appetite, but denervation of the stomach and intestines does not affect the amount of food eaten. In animals with esophageal fistulas, chewing and swallowing food docs cause some satiety even though the food never reaches the stomach. Especially in humans, cultural factors, environment, and past experiences relative to the sight, smell, and taste of food also affect food intake.

The net effect of all the appetite-regulating mechanisms in normal adult animals and humans is an adjustment of food intake to the point where caloric intake balances energy expenditures, with the result that body weight is maintained. In hyperthyroidism and diabetes mellitus, hunger increases as energy output increases. However, the link between energy needs and food intake is indirect, and in some situations, intake is not correlated with immediate energy expenditure. For example, animals that gain weight because of force feeding subsequently eat less until they regain their normal weight (Fig 14–8). Conversely, animals that lose weight because they are starved subsequently eat increased amounts until they regain their normal weight. During growth, after exercise, and during recovery from debilitating illnesses, food intake is increased. How these long-term adjustments are brought about is not known.

THIRST

Another appetitive mechanism that is under hypothalamic control is thirst. Appropriately placed hypothalamic lesions diminish or abolish fluid intake, in some instances without any change in food intake, and electrical stimulation of the hypothalamus causes

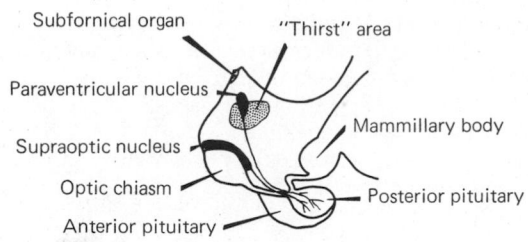

Figure 14–9. Hypothalamic areas concerned with water metabolism in dogs.

drinking. In the rat, the area concerned with thirst is in the lateral hypothalamus posterior to the feeding center; in dogs and goats it is in the dorsal hypothalamus lateral and posterior to the paraventricular nuclei (Fig 14–9).

Drinking is increased by increased effective osmotic pressure of the plasma, by decreases in ECF volume, and by psychologic and other factors. Injection of hypertonic saline into the anterior hypothalamus causes drinking in conscious animals. This observation suggests that in the hypothalamus there are **osmoreceptors,** cells which are stimulated by an increased osmotic pressure of the body fluids to initiate thirst and drinking.

Decreases in ECF volume also stimulate thirst, and hemorrhage causes increased drinking even though there is no change in the osmolality of the plasma. The effect of ECF volume depletion on thirst is mediated in part via the renin-angiotensin system (see Chapter 24). Renin secretion is increased by hypovolemia, and there is a resultant increase in circulating angiotensin II. The angiotensin II acts on the **subfornical organ,** a specialized receptor area in the diencephalon (Fig 14–9), to stimulate the neural areas concerned with thirst. There is some evidence that it acts on the **organum vasculosum of the lamina terminalis (OVLT)** as well. These areas are highly permeable, and are 2 of the circumventricular organs located "outside the blood-brain barrier" (see Chapter 32). The link from the subfornical organ to the neural areas may be cholinergic. Drugs which block the action of angiotensin II do not completely block the thirst response to hypovolemia, and it appears that other mechanisms may also be involved.

Whenever the sensation of thirst is obtunded, either by direct damage to the diencephalon or by depressed or altered states of consciousness, patients stop drinking adequate amounts of fluid. Dehydration results if appropriate measures are not instituted to maintain water balance. If the protein intake is high, the products of protein metabolism cause an osmotic diuresis (see Chapter 38), and the amounts of water required to maintain hydration are large. Most cases of hypernatremia are actually due to simple dehydration in patients with psychoses or cerebral disease who do not or cannot increase their water intake when their thirst mechanism is stimulated.

Other Factors Regulating Water Intake

A number of other well-established factors contribute to the regulation of water intake. Psychologic and social factors are important. Dryness of the pharyngeal mucous membrane causes a sensation of thirst. Patients in whom fluid intake must be restricted sometimes get appreciable relief of thirst by sucking ice chips or a wet cloth. Rats with lesions in their thirst areas will drink small amounts of water when their throats become dry even though they do not respond to dehydration per se.

Dehydrated dogs, cats, camels, and some other animals rapidly drink just enough water to make up their water deficit. They stop drinking before the water is absorbed (while their plasma is still hypertonic), so some kind of pharyngeal or gastrointestinal "metering" must be involved. In humans, this ability to drink just the right amount of water is not so well developed, and deficits are usually made up more slowly.

CONTROL OF POSTERIOR PITUITARY SECRETION

Posterior Pituitary Hormones

The 2 hormones of the posterior pituitary gland are synthesized in the cell bodies of neurons in the supraoptic and paraventricular nuclei and transported down their axons to the posterior pituitary. In all mammals studied except members of the pig family, the hormones are **oxytocin** and **arginine vasopressin.** In pigs and hippopotamuses, arginine in the vasopressin molecule is replaced by lysine to form **lysine vasopressin.** The posterior pituitaries of some African warthogs and peccaries contain a mixture of arginine and lysine vasopressin. The posterior lobe hormones are nonapeptides (considering each half cystine as a single amino acid) with a disulfide ring at one end (Fig 14–10). Synthetic peptides more active than the naturally occurring substances have been produced

```
  ┌─ S ───────── S ┐
Cys-Tyr-Phe-Gln-Asn-Cys-Pro-Arg-Gly-NH₂
 1   2   3   4   5   6   7   8   9
```

Arginine vasopressin

```
  ┌─ S ───────── S ┐
Cys-Tyr-Ile-Gln-Asn-Cys-Pro-Leu-Gly-NH₂
 1   2   3   4   5   6   7   8   9
```

Oxytocin

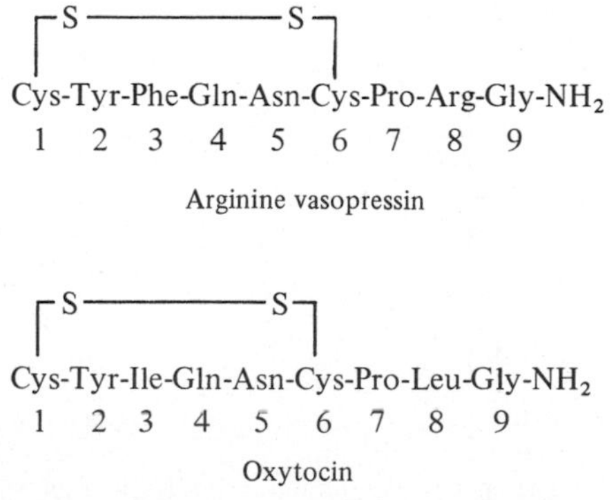

Figure 14–10. Arginine vasopressin and oxytocin. In pigs and hippopotamuses, lysine is substituted for arginine in position 8 of the vasopressin molecule.

by altering the amino acid residues. For example, 1-deamine-8D-arginine vasopressin (DDAVP) has very high antidiuretic activity with little pressor activity, making it potentially valuable for the treatment of vasopressin deficiency (see below).

In the posterior pituitary, oxytocin and vasopressin are stored bound to polypeptides called **neurophysins.** The neurophysins contain approximately 95 amino acid residues, and it seems likely that in humans, as in experimental animals, there is one neurophysin for oxytocin and another for vasopressin. The storage granules contain oxytocin or vasopressin, ATP, and neurophysin. Release is by exocytosis, and when the posterior lobe is stimulated, all 3 are secreted. Consequently, neurophysins are present in the peripheral blood, where they can be measured by immunoassay.

Effects of Vasopressin

Because its principal physiologic effect is the retention of water by the kidney, vasopressin is often called the antidiuretic hormone (ADH). It increases the permeability of the collecting ducts of the kidney, so that water enters the hypertonic interstitium of the renal pyramids (see Chapter 38). The urine becomes concentrated and its volume decreases. The overall effect is therefore retention of water in excess of solute; consequently, the effective osmotic pressure of the body fluids is decreased. In the absence of vasopressin, the urine is hypotonic to plasma, urine volume is increased, and there is a net water loss. Consequently, the osmolality of the body fluids rises. Vasopressin also increases the permeability of the collecting ducts to urea and decreases blood flow in the renal medulla. In addition, it increases the permeability of the bladder of toads and the skin of frogs to water.

In large doses, vasopressin elevates arterial blood pressure by an action on the smooth muscle of the arterioles. However, it is doubtful if enough endogenous vasopressin is ever secreted to exert any appreciable effect on blood pressure homeostasis. Hemorrhage is a potent stimulus to vasopressin secretion, but the blood pressure fall after hemorrhage is not significantly greater or more prolonged in the absence of the posterior pituitary than when it is present.

Circulating vasopressin is rapidly inactivated, principally in the liver and kidneys. It has a **biologic half-life** (time required for inactivation of half a given amount) of about 18 minutes in humans. Its effects on the kidney develop rapidly but are of short duration.

Mechanism of Action

Vasopressin binds to receptors on the blood side of responsive renal tubular cells, activating adenylate cyclase and thus causing the formation of additional cyclic AMP in the cells. The role of cyclic AMP in mediating the action of hormones is discussed in Chapter 1. In the renal tubular cells, the cyclic AMP produces a striking increase in the permeability of the membrane on the luminal side of the cells to water, urea, and some other solutes. The effect may be

Table 14–3. Summary of stimuli affecting vasopressin secretion.

Vasopressin Secretion Increased	Vasopressin Secretion Decreased
Increased effective osmotic pressure of plasma	Decreased effective osmotic pressure of plasma
Decreased extracellular fluid volume	Increased extracellular fluid volume
Pain, emotion, "stress," exercise	Alcohol
Morphine, nicotine, barbiturates	Butorphanol, oxilorphan
Chlorpropamide, clofibrate, carbamazepine	

mediated via a protein kinase or increased formation of microtubules and microfilaments or both. It is known that vasopressin causes aggregation of particles in the cell membrane, but the relation of this latent movement of proteins to the changes in permeability is unsettled.

Control of Vasopressin Secretion: Osmotic Stimuli

Vasopressin is stored in the posterior pituitary and released into the bloodstream by impulses in the nerve fibers that contain the hormone. There are cell bodies of vasopressin-secreting neurons in both the supraoptic and paraventricular nuclei. When the effective osmotic pressure of the plasma is increased, the rate of discharge of these neurons increases; when the effective osmotic pressure is decreased, discharge is inhibited (Table 14–3, Fig 14–11). The changes are mediated via **osmoreceptor** cells sensitive to changes in the osmotic pressure of the plasma. These cells are located in the anterior hypothalamus. They may be the supraoptic and paraventricular neurons themselves, or they may be separate cells located in the perinuclear zone. It is not known if they are the same osmoreceptors that regulate water intake (see above).

Vasopressin secretion is thus controlled by a delicate feedback mechanism that operates continuously to defend the osmolality of the plasma. There is a steady,

moderate level of vasopressin secretion when the plasma osmolality is normal, and the normal plasma vasopressin level is maintained at about 2 pg/ml (Fig 14–12). Whenever the effective osmotic pressure of plasma is increased, vasopressin secretion is increased; whenever plasma osmolality is decreased, vasopressin secretion is decreased. Significant changes in secretion occur when osmolality is changed as little as 2%. In this way, the osmolality of the plasma in normal individuals is maintained very close to 290 mOsm/L.

Volume Effects

ECF volume also affects vasopressin secretion. Vasopressin secretion is increased when ECF volume is low and decreased when ECF volume is high (Table 14–3). There is an inverse relationship between the rate of vasopressin secretion and the rate of discharge in afferents from stretch receptors in the low- and high-pressure portions of the vascular system. The low-pressure receptors are those in the great veins, right and left atria, and pulmonary vessels; the high-pressure receptors are those in the carotid sinuses and aortic arch (see Chapter 31). The low-pressure receptors monitor the fullness of the vascular system. Moderate decreases in ECF volume and, consequently, in blood volume increase vasopressin secretion without causing any change in arterial blood pressure; it therefore appears that the low-pressure receptors are the

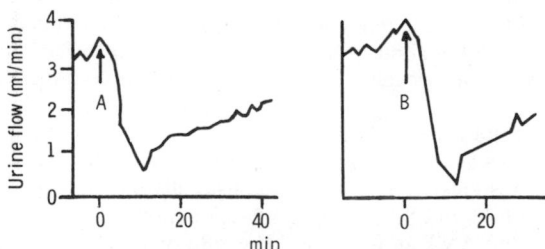

Figure 14–11. Inhibition of water diuresis in a dog by injection of 10.5 ml of 1.5% NaCl (at A) and 11 ml of 1.5% NaCl (at B) into the carotid artery. (Redrawn and reproduced, with permission, from Verney EB: The antidiuretic hormone and the factors which determine its release. Proc R Soc Lond [Biol] 135:25, 1947.)

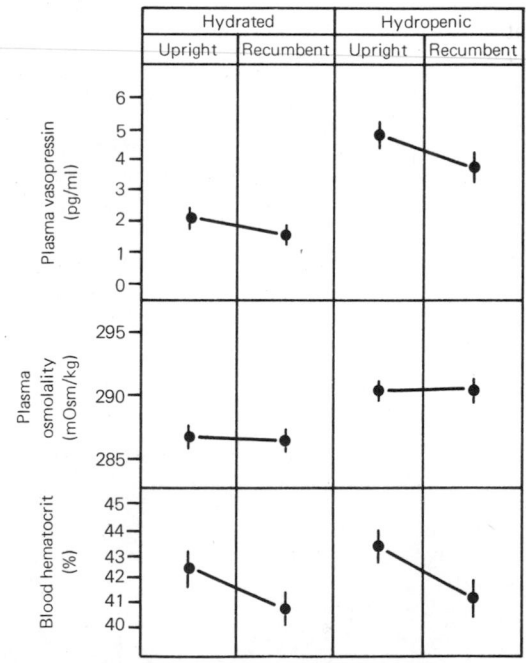

Figure 14–12. Effect of posture and hydropenia on plasma vasopressin in normal humans. Hydrated subjects drank fluids ad libitum. Hydropenic subjects had been deprived of fluids for 17–25 hours. (Modified from Robertson GL, Athar S: The interaction of blood osmolality and blood volume in regulating plasma vasopressin in man. J Clin Endocrinol Metab 42:613, 1976.)

primary mediators of volume effects on vasopressin secretion. However, when the volume changes are large enough to produce changes in blood pressure, the carotid and aortic receptors also play a role. It has also been established that angiotensin II acts on the brain to increase vasopressin secretion.

There is a statistically significant increase in vasopressin secretion upon rising from the recumbent to the upright position (Fig 14–12) because blood pools in the legs. Hemorrhage causes a greater response. It releases much greater amounts of vasopressin than plasma hyperosmolality, and hypovolemia causes vasopressin secretion even if the plasma is hypotonic.

Other Stimuli Affecting Vasopressin Secretion

A variety of stimuli in addition to osmotic pressure changes and ECF volume aberrations increase vasopressin secretion. These include pain, surgical stress, some emotions, and a number of drugs (Table 14–3), including morphine, nicotine, and large doses of barbiturates. Alcohol and the opiate antagonists butorphanol and oxilorphan decrease vasopressin secretion.

Clinical Implications

In various clinical conditions, volume and other nonosmotic stimuli override the osmotic control of vasopressin secretion, producing water retention and a decrease in plasma osmolality. In patients with such hypersecretion, a high fluid intake can cause water intoxication. The water retention and hyponatremia seen after surgery are partly explained on this basis. Water retention occurs in addition to salt retention in patients with edema due to congestive heart failure, cirrhosis of the liver, and nephrosis. It has been argued that the water retention is due to diminished removal of vasopressin from the plasma by the liver and kidney, prolonging the half-life of the hormone. This may be a factor, but water retention does not occur unless there is abnormal posterior pituitary secretion as well. If the osmoreceptor mechanism were normal, the decreased plasma osmolality would inhibit posterior pituitary secretion and the defect would correct itself. The cause of excess vasopressin secretion in diseases of the heart, liver, and kidneys is not known with certainty, but it is probably due to abnormal activity of the "volume-sensing" mechanism described above.

An "inappropriate" hypersecretion of vasopressin is believed to be responsible for the hyponatremia that occurs with high levels of salt excretion in some patients with cerebral or pulmonary disease. In these cases of "cerebral salt wasting" and "pulmonary salt wasting," water retention is sufficient to expand ECF volume. This inhibits the secretion of aldosterone by the adrenal cortex (see Chapter 20), and salt is lost in the urine. The syndrome is different from that seen in patients with edema because the latter retain salt and usually have a high level of aldosterone secretion. Hypersecretion of vasopressin in patients with pulmonary diseases such as lung cancer may be due in part to the interruption of inhibitory impulses in vagal afferents from the stretch receptors in the atria and great veins. However, a significant number of lung tumors and some other malignancies secrete a substance with antidiuretic activity that appears to be vasopressin. Patients with inappropriate hypersecretion of vasopressin have been successfully treated with demeclocycline, an antibiotic that reduces the renal response to vasopressin. If the increased amounts of vasopressin do not come from a tumor, secretion can be reduced by treatment with the butorphanol and oxilorphan. It is not known why these opiate antagonists inhibit the release of vasopressin from supraoptic and paraventricular neurons.

Diabetes insipidus is the syndrome that results when vasopressin deficiency develops due to disease processes in the supraoptic and paraventricular nuclei, the hypothalamohypophyseal tract, or the posterior pituitary gland. It also develops after surgical removal of the posterior lobe of the pituitary. It may be temporary if only the distal ends of the supraoptic and paraventricular fibers are damaged, because the fibers recover and begin again to secrete vasopressin. The symptoms are passage of large amounts of dilute urine (**polyuria**) and the drinking of large amounts of fluid (**polydipsia**), provided the thirst mechanism is intact. It is the polydipsia that keeps these patients healthy. If their sense of thirst is depressed for any reason and their intake of dilute fluid decreases, they develop dehydration that can be fatal. In patients who have an incomplete rather than total vasopressin deficiency, treatment with drugs that increase vasopressin secretion such as chlorpropamide and clofibrate has proved to be of value. Chlorpropamide also increases the renal response to vasopressin.

Another cause of diabetes insipidus is inability of the kidneys to respond to vasopressin. In this condition, which is known as **nephrogenic diabetes insipidus,** vasopressin fails to increase renal cyclic AMP.

The amelioration of diabetes insipidus produced by the development of concomitant anterior pituitary insufficiency is discussed in Chapter 22.

Oxytocin

In mammals, the principal physiologic effect of oxytocin is on the **myoepithelial cells,** smooth muscle–like cells that line the ducts of the breast. The hormone makes these cells contract, squeezing the milk out of the alveoli of the lactating breast into the large ducts (sinuses), and thence out the nipple (**milk ejection**). Many hormones acting in concert are responsible for breast growth and the secretion of milk into the ducts (see Chapter 23), but milk ejection in most species requires oxytocin.

The Milk Ejection Reflex

Milk ejection is normally initiated by a neuroendocrine reflex. The receptors involved are the touch receptors, which are plentiful in the breast — especially around the nipple. Impulses generated in these receptors are relayed from the somatic touch pathways via the bundle of Schütz and mammillary peduncle to the supraoptic and paraventricular nuclei. Discharge of the oxytocin-containing neurons causes liberation of oxytocin from the posterior pituitary. The infant suckling at the breast stimulates the touch receptors, the nuclei are stimulated, oxytocin is released, and the milk is expressed into the sinuses, ready to flow into the mouth of the waiting infant. In lactating women, genital stimulation and emotional stimuli also produce oxytocin secretion, sometimes causing milk to spurt from the breasts.

Other Actions of Oxytocin

Oxytocin causes contraction of the smooth muscle of the uterus. The sensitivity of the uterine musculature to oxytocin varies. It is enhanced by estrogen and inhibited by progesterone. In late pregnancy, the uterus becomes very sensitive to oxytocin, and oxytocin secretion is increased during labor. After dilatation of the cervix, descent of the fetus down the birth canal probably initiates impulses in the afferent nerves that are relayed to the supraoptic and paraventricular nuclei, causing secretion of sufficient oxytocin to enhance labor. Oxytocin may also play some role in initiating labor. However, the mechanisms controlling the onset of labor are immensely complex, and neuroendocrine reflexes are certainly not the only mechanisms responsible for delivery.

Oxytocin may also act on the nonpregnant uterus to facilitate sperm transport. The passage of sperm up the female genital tract to the uterine tubes, where fertilization normally takes place, depends not only on the motile powers of the sperm but, at least in some species, on uterine contractions as well. The genital stimulation involved in coitus releases oxytocin, but it has not been proved that it is oxytocin which initiates the rather specialized uterine contractions which transport the sperm. The secretion of oxytocin, like that of vasopressin, is inhibited by alcohol.

Site of Origin of Posterior Pituitary Hormones

When the hypothalamus and pituitary are treated with the Gomori stain or a number of other special stains, large granules made up of posterior lobe hormones bound to neurophysins (Herring bodies) are seen in nerve endings in the posterior pituitary. There are similar granules along the axons of the supraoptic and paraventricular neurons and in their cell bodies. The granules in both locations are depleted by stimuli known to increase the secretion of posterior pituitary hormones. After section of the pituitary stalk, they disappear below the section and pile up above it. These observations and considerable additional evidence make it clear that vasopressin and oxytocin and their respective neurophysins are manufactured in the cell bodies of the supraoptic and paraventricular neurons and transported down their axons to the endings in the posterior pituitary. There they are stored until released to the ECF by exocytosis in response to action potentials in the neurons. Although it has not been proved,

the posterior pituitary hormone–neurophysin complexes may well be formed in the cell bodies as single molecules and consequently represent examples of prohormones (see Chapter 19). The peptides are then split from the neurophysins before secretion.

Neurosecretion

Neurons which contain granules that stain with the Gomori stain are generally called neurosecretory neurons, and the secretion of chemical substances at their endings is called "neurosecretion." The supraoptic and paraventricular neurons are the only neurons that normally contain abundant Gomori-positive granules in mammals. However, all neurons appear to liberate chemical agents. Most neurons secrete transmitter substances (see Chapter 4) that cross the synaptic clefts and act on the membranes of the postsynaptic cells. Others secrete substances that pass through the bloodstream to affect distant organs. Some of these neurons contain Gomori-positive neurosecretory granules, but others do not. To avoid confusion, it seems wise to abandon the term **neurosecretion** or at least to redefine it as the secretion into the circulating body fluids by the endings of a neuron of chemical substances that act on other cells some distance away, whether or not the neuron contains Gomori-positive granules.

CONTROL OF ANTERIOR PITUITARY SECRETION

Anterior Pituitary Hormones

The anterior pituitary secretes 6 hormones: **adrenocorticotropic hormone** (corticotropin, ACTH), **thyroid-stimulating hormone** (thyrotropin, TSH), **growth hormone, follicle-stimulating hormone** (FSH), **luteinizing hormone** (LH), and **prolactin** (luteotropic hormone, LTH). The actions of these hormones are summarized in Fig 14–13, and other synonyms and abbreviations for them are listed in Table 22–1. Five of the hormones are **tropic hormones,** ie, they stimulate the secretion of substances from other glands. Prolactin promotes the formation of milk in the breast. The hormones are discussed in detail in the chapters on the endocrine system. An additional peptide, β-lipotropin (β-LPH) is secreted with ACTH, but its physiologic role is unknown. The hypothalamus plays an important stimulatory role in regulating the secretion of ACTH, TSH, growth hormone, FSH, and LH. It also regulates prolactin secretion, but its effect is predominantly inhibitory rather than stimulatory.

Nature of Hypothalamic Control

There may be a few nerve fibers that pass directly from the brain to the anterior pituitary, but they do not control anterior pituitary function. Instead, anterior pituitary secretion is controlled by chemical agents

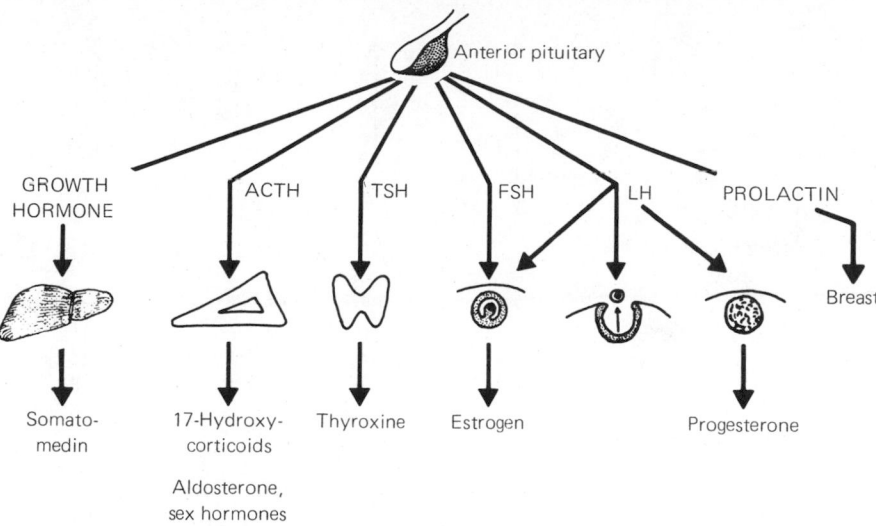

Figure 14–13. Anterior pituitary hormones. In women, FSH and LH act in sequence on the ovary to produce growth of the ovarian follicle, which secretes estrogen; ovulation; and formation and maintenance of the corpus luteum, which secretes estrogen and progesterone. In men, FSH and LH control the functions of the testes (see Chapter 23). Prolactin stimulates lactation.

carried in the portal hypophyseal vessels from the hypothalamus to the pituitary. These substances have generally been referred to as releasing and inhibiting factors, but they are now commonly called hormones. The latter term seems appropriate, since they are secreted into the bloodstream and act at a distance from their site of origin. Furthermore, several of them have been synthesized, and the synthetic factors used clinically are called hormones. Consequently, the term hormone is used in this book. There are 7 relatively well established hypothalamic releasing and inhibiting hormones: **corticotropin-releasing hormone (CRH); thyrotropin-releasing hormone (TRH); growth hormone–releasing hormone (GRH); growth hormone–inhibiting hormone (GIH;** also called **somatostatin); luteinizing hormone–releasing hormone (LRH); prolactin-releasing hormone (PRH);** and **prolactin-inhibiting hormone (PIH).** LRH stimulates the secretion of FSH as well as LH, and it is uncertain whether or not there is a separate **follicle-stimulating hormone–releasing hormone (FRH).** The proponents of a single gonadotropin-regulating hormone refer to LRH as GnRH (**gonadotropin-releasing hormone).**

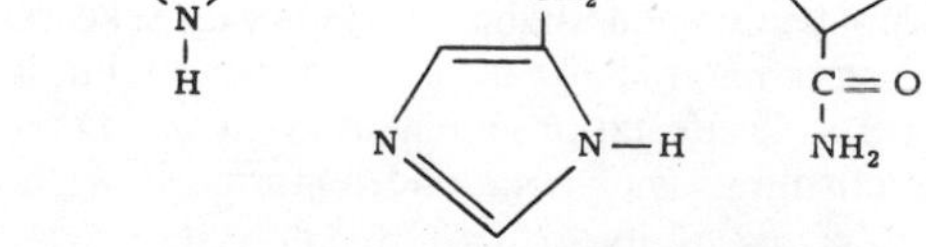

TRH is a tripeptide (Fig 14–14); LRH is a decapeptide (Fig 14–15); and somatostatin (Table 26–1) is a tetradecapeptide that contains a disulfide bridge. PIH is almost certainly the catecholamine dopamine (see Chapters 15 and 23). The structures of the other hormones are not yet known, although they are probably peptides.

The area from which the hypothalamic releasing and inhibiting hormones are secreted is the median eminence of the hypothalamus (Fig 14–4). This region contains few nerve cell bodies, but there are many nerve endings in close proximity to the capillary loops from which the portal vessels originate. The hormones are secreted from these endings. Their release is therefore an example of neurosecretion as defined above. This type of neuroendocrine regulation is intermediate between that in the adrenal medulla, where nerve fibers stimulate gland cells, and that in the posterior pituitary, where substances secreted by neurons pass into the general circulation (Fig 14–16).

In rats and other experimental animals, the cell bodies of the LRH-secreting neurons are located in the preoptic areas and neighboring portions of the anterior hypothalamus. The neurons end in the external layer of the median eminence in the infundibular region. The cell bodies of the tuberoinfundibular neurons that secrete dopamine into the portal hypophyseal vessels have their cell bodies in the arcuate nuclei (Fig 15–11) and their endings in the same region as the LRH-secreting neurons. The cell bodies of the TRH-secreting neurons are located in the dorsomedial nu-

Figure 14–14. Structure of human, porcine, and bovine TRH.

(pyro)Glu-His-Pro-NH$_2$

(pyro)Glu-His-Trp-Ser-Tyr-Gly-Leu-Arg-Pro-Gly-NH$_2$

 1   2   3   4   5   6   7   8   9   10

Figure 14–15. Porcine LRH

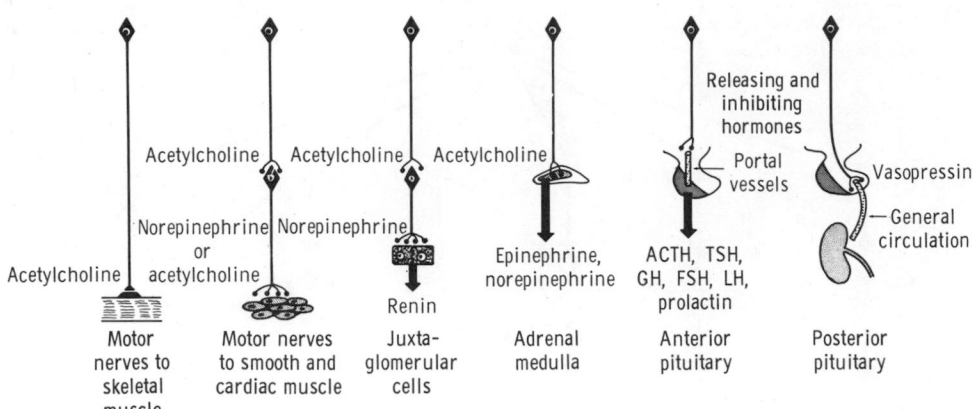

Figure 14–16. Diagrammatic representation of 6 situations in which humoral substances are released by neurons. The last 2 are examples of neurosecretion as this term is defined in the text.

cleus and adjacent areas, and their endings are located in the anterior portion of the median eminence. The cell bodies of the somatostatin-secreting neurons are located anteriorly, above the optic chiasm, and their endings are distributed to the anterior and middle portions of the median eminence. The cells that secrete CRH and the other hypothalamic releasing hormones have not been identified, but in dogs, it appears that CRH is secreted in the midportion of the median eminence (Fig 14–17). A similar hypothalamic localization in humans has not been proved, but there is circumstantial evidence that the arrangement is similar to that in dogs.

There is evidence that anterior pituitary hormones and, in the case of the gonadotropins, gonadal steroids feed back on the hypothalamus to inhibit the secretion of the hypothalamic hormones. The hypothalamic hormone–secreting neurons receive multiple neural inputs, and the transmitters secreted by these converg-

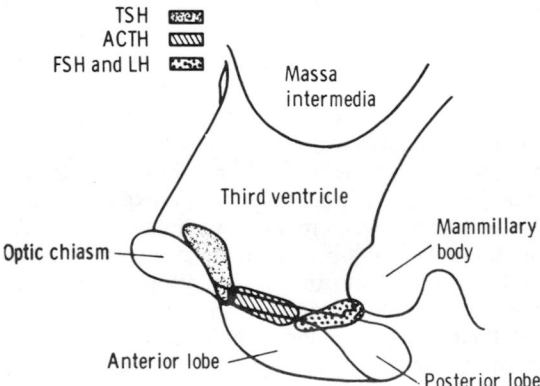

Figure 14–17. Areas involved in the control of anterior pituitary secretion in dogs. The sites were determined by the localization of lesions that produced selective blockade of tropic hormone secretion. (Redrawn and reproduced, with permission, from Ganong WF, in: *Comparative Endocrinology.* Gorbman A [editor]. Wiley, 1959.)

ing afferent fibers probably include norepinephrine and serotonin (see Chapter 15).

Significance & Clinical Implications

The research delineating the multiple neuroendocrine regulatory functions of the hypothalamus is important because it explains how endocrine secretion is made appropriate to the demands of a changing environment. The nervous system receives information about changes in the internal and external environment from the sense organs. We now know that it brings about adjustments to these changes through effector mechanisms that include not only somatic movement but also changes in the rate at which hormones are secreted. There are many examples of the operation of the neuroendocrine effector pathways. In birds and many mammals, the increasing number of daylight hours in the spring stimulates gonadotropin secretion, activating the quiescent gonads and starting the breeding season. In some avian species, the sight of a member of the opposite sex in a mating dance apparently produces the gonadotropin secretion necessary to cause ovulation. It has been claimed that Eskimo women cease to ovulate during the long winter night and that regular menstrual cycles and sexual vigor return in the spring. In more temperate climates, menstruation in women is a year-round phenomenon, but its regularity can be markedly affected by somatic and emotional stimuli. The disappearance of regular periods when young girls move away from home (sometimes called "boarding school amenorrhea") and the inhibition of menstruation that can be produced by fear of pregnancy are examples of the many ways in which psychic phenomena affect endocrine secretion.

Hypothalamic disease is not common, but it does occur. Its manifestations are neurologic defects, endocrine changes, and metabolic abnormalities such as hyperphagia and hyperthermia. The relative frequencies of the signs and symptoms of hypothalamic disease in one large series of cases are shown in Table 14–4. The possibility of hypothalamic pathology

Table 14–4. Symptoms and signs in 60 autopsied cases of hypothalamic disease.*

	Percentage of Cases
Endocrine and metabolic findings	
Precocious puberty	40
Hypogonadism	32
Diabetes insipidus	35
Obesity	25
Abnormalities of temperature regulation	22
Emaciation	18
Bulimia	8
Anorexia	7
Neurologic findings	
Eye signs	78
Pyramidal and sensory deficits	75
Headache	65
Extrapyramidal signs	62
Vomiting	40
Psychic disturbances, rage attacks, etc	35
Somnolence	30
Convulsions	15

*Data from Bauer HG: Endocrine and other clinical manifestations of hypothalamic disease. J Clin Endocrinol 14:13, 1954. See also Kahana L & others: Endocrine manifestations of intracranial extrasellar lesions. J Clin Endocrinol 22:304, 1962.

should be kept in mind in evaluating all patients with pituitary dysfunction, especially those with isolated deficiencies of single pituitary tropic hormones. Many of these deficiencies are proving to be due to hypothalamic rather than primary pituitary disease.

Other Actions of Hypothalamic Hormones

It is worth noting that the hypothalamic hormones which have been synthesized affect the secretion of more than one anterior pituitary hormone. The FSH-stimulating activity of LRH has been mentioned above. TRH stimulates the secretion of prolactin as well as TSH. Somatostatin inhibits the secretion of TSH as well as growth hormone. It does not normally inhibit the secretion of the other anterior pituitary hormones, but it does inhibit the abnormally elevated secretion of ACTH in patients with Nelson's syndrome (see Chapter 22).

Appreciable quantities of LRH and somatostatin are found not only in the median eminence but also in other circumventricular organs (see Chapter 32). Their function in these locations is unknown. Somatostatin and TRH are also found in neural tissue in other parts of the brain, and somatostatin is present in small diameter primary afferent neurons in the dorsal horn region of the spinal cord. These observations indicate that hypothalamic hormones probably function as synaptic transmitters as well as regulators of anterior pituitary secretion.

Somatostatin has been found to be present in the pancreas and the gastric and intestinal mucosa as well

as the brain. In addition to its action on anterior pituitary secretion, it inhibits the secretion of insulin and glucagon (see Chapter 19) and the gastrointestinal hormones gastrin, secretin, VIP, GIP, and motilin (see Chapter 26). It also inhibits gastric acid secretion and motility and the exocrine secretion of the pancreas. Thus, it is clear that this hypothalamic hormone has very widespread effects in the body.

TEMPERATURE REGULATION

In the body, heat is produced by muscular exercise, assimilation of food, and all the vital processes that contribute to the basal metabolic rate (see Chapter 17). It is lost from the body by radiation, conduction, and vaporization of water in the respiratory passages and on the skin. Small amounts of heat are also removed in the urine and feces. The balance between heat production and heat loss determines the body temperature. Because the speed of chemical reactions varies with the temperature and because the enzyme systems of the body have narrow temperature ranges in which their function is optimal, normal body function depends upon a relatively constant body temperature.

Invertebrates generally cannot adjust their body temperatures and so are at the mercy of the environment. In vertebrates, mechanisms for maintaining body temperature by adjusting heat production and heat loss have evolved. In reptiles, amphibia, and fish, the adjusting mechanisms are relatively rudimentary, and these species are called "cold-blooded" or **poikilothermic** because their body temperature fluctuates over a considerable range. In birds and mammals, the "warm-blooded" or **homeothermic** animals, a group of reflex responses that are primarily integrated in the hypothalamus operate to maintain body temperature within a narrow range in spite of wide fluctuations in environmental temperature. The hibernating mammals are a partial exception. While awake, they are homeothermic, but during hibernation, their body temperature falls.

Normal Body Temperature

In homeothermic animals, the actual temperature at which the body is maintained varies from species to species and, to a lesser degree, from individual to individual. In humans, the traditional normal value for the oral temperature is 37 C (98.6 F), but in one large series of normal young adults, the morning oral temperature averaged 36.7 C, with a standard deviation of 0.2 degree. Therefore, 95% of all young adults would be expected to have a morning oral temperature of 36.3–37.1 C, or 97.3–98.8 F (mean ±1.96 standard deviations; see Appendix). Various parts of the body are at different temperatures, and the magnitude of the temperature difference between the parts varies with the environmental temperature (Fig 14–18). The extremities are generally cooler than the rest of the body.

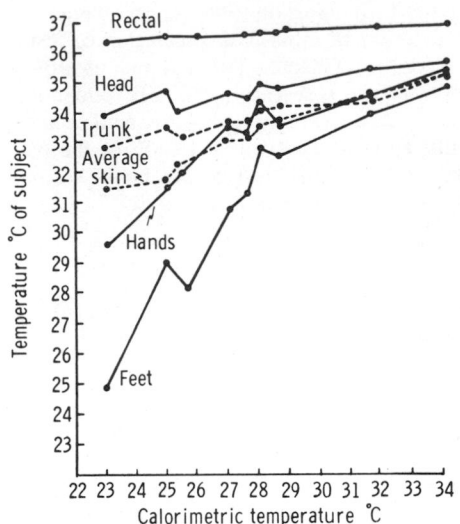

Figure 14–18. Temperature of various parts of the body of a naked subject at various ambient temperatures in a calorimeter. (Redrawn and reproduced, with permission, from Hardy JD, DuBois EF: Basal metabolism, radiation, convection and vaporization at temperatures of 22–35° C. J Nutr 15:477, 1938.)

The rectal temperature is representative of the temperature at the core of the body and varies least with changes in environmental temperature. Oral temperature is normally 0.5 C lower than the rectal temperature, but it is affected by many factors, including ingestion of hot or cold fluids, gum-chewing, smoking, and mouth breathing.

The normal human core temperature undergoes a regular circadian fluctuation of 0.5–0.7 C. In individuals who sleep at night and are awake during the day (even when hospitalized at bed rest), it is lowest at about 6:00 AM and highest in the evenings (Fig 14–19). It is lowest during sleep, slightly higher in the awake but relaxed state, and rises with activity. In women, there is an additional monthly cycle of temperature variation characterized by a rise in basal temperature at

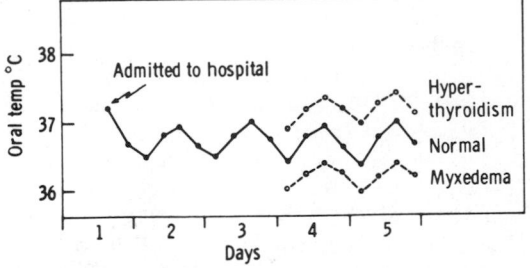

Figure 14–19. Typical temperature chart of a hospitalized patient who does not have a febrile disease. Note the slight rise in temperature, due to excitement and apprehension, at the time of admission to the hospital, and the regular circadian temperature cycle.

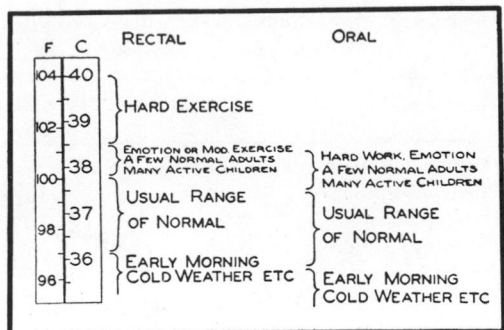

Figure 14–20. Ranges in rectal and oral temperatures seen in normal humans. (Reproduced, with permission, from DuBois EF: *Fever and the Regulation of Body Temperature.* Thomas, 1948.)

the time of ovulation (see Chapter 23, Fig 23–28). Temperature regulation is less precise in young children, and they may normally have a temperature that is 0.5 C or so above the established norm for adults.

During exercise, the heat produced by muscular contraction accumulates in the body, and rectal temperature normally rises as high as 40 C (104 F). This rise is due in part to the inability of the heat-dissipating mechanisms to handle the greatly increased amount of heat which is produced, but there is evidence that in addition there is an elevation of the body temperature at which the heat-dissipating mechanisms are activated during exercise. Body temperature also rises slightly during emotional excitement, probably due to unconscious tensing of the muscles (Figs 14–19 and 14–20). It is chronically elevated by as much as 0.5 C when the metabolic rate is high, as in hyperthyroidism, and lowered when the metabolic rate is low, as in myxedema. Some apparently normal adults chronically have a temperature above the normal range (constitutional hyperthermia).

Heat Production

Heat production and energy balance are discussed in Chapter 17. A variety of basic chemical reactions contribute to body heat production at all times. Ingestion of food increases heat production because of the specific dynamic action of the food (see Chapter 17), but the major source of heat is the contraction of skeletal muscle (Table 14–5). Heat production can be varied in the absence of food intake or muscular exertion by endocrine mechanisms. Epinephrine and norepinephrine produce a rapid but short-lived increase in heat production; thyroid hormones produce a slowly developing but prolonged increase. Furthermore, sympathetic discharge is decreased during fasting and increased by feeding (see Chapter 13).

A source of considerable heat in human infants is a special type of fat, **brown fat,** that is located between and around the scapulas. This fat has a high rate of metabolism, and its function has been likened to that of

Table 14–5. Body heat production and heat loss.

Body heat is produced by:
  Basic metabolic processes
  Food intake (specific dynamic action)
  Muscular activity

Body heat is lost by:	Percentage of Heat Lost at 21 C
Radiation and conduction	70
Vaporization of sweat	27
Respiration	2
Urination and defecation	1

an electric blanket. Brown fat is also found in a variety of animals, but unlike ordinary white fat, it is not found in adult humans.

Heat Loss

The processes by which heat is lost from the body when the environmental temperature is below body temperature are listed in Table 14–5. **Radiation** is the transfer of heat from one object to another with which it is not in contact. **Conduction** is heat exchange between objects at different temperatures that are in contact with one another. The amount of heat transferred by conduction is proportionate to the temperature difference between the 2 objects (**thermal gradient**). **Convection,** the movement of the molecules of a gas or a liquid at one temperature to another location which is at a different temperature, aids conduction. When an individual is in a cold environment, heat is lost by conduction to the surrounding air and by radiation to cool objects in the vicinity. When in a hot environment, heat is transferred to the individual by these processes and adds to the heat load. Thus, in a sense, radiation and conduction work against the maintenance of body temperature. On a cold but sunny day, the heat of the sun reflected off bright objects exerts an appreciable warming effect. It is the heat reflected from the snow, for example, that makes it possible to ski in fairly light clothes even though the air temperature is below freezing.

Since conduction occurs from the surface of one object to the surface of another, the temperature of the skin determines to a large extent the degree to which body heat is lost or gained. The amount of heat reaching the skin from the deep tissues can be varied by changing the blood flow to the skin. When the cutaneous vessels are dilated, warm blood wells up into the skin, whereas in the maximally vasoconstricted state, heat is held centrally in the body. The rate at which heat is transferred from the deep tissues to the skin is called the **tissue conductance.** Birds have a layer of feathers next to the skin, and most mammals have a significant layer of hair or fur. Heat is conducted from the skin to the air trapped in this layer, and from the trapped air to the exterior. When the thickness of the trapped layer is increased by fluffing the feathers or erection of the hairs (**horripilation**), heat transfer

across the layer is reduced and heat losses (or, in a hot environment, heat gains) are decreased. ''Goose pimples'' are the result of horripilation in humans; they are the visible manifestation of cold-induced contraction of the piloerector muscles attached to the rather meager hair supply. Humans usually supplement this layer of hair with a layer of clothes. Heat is conducted from the skin to the layer of air trapped by the clothes, from the inside of the clothes to the outside, and from the outside of the clothes to the exterior. The magnitude of the heat transfer across the clothing, a function of its texture and thickness, is the most important determinant of how warm or cool the clothes feel, but other factors, especially the size of the trapped layer of warm air, are important also. Dark clothes absorb radiated heat, and light-colored clothes reflect it back to the exterior.

The other major process transferring heat from the body in humans and those animals that sweat is vaporization of water on the skin and mucous membranes of the mouth and respiratory passages. Vaporization of 1 g of water removes about 0.6 kcal of heat. A certain amount of water is vaporized at all times. This **insensible water loss** amounts to 50 ml/h in humans. When sweat secretion is increased, the degree to which the sweat vaporizes depends upon the humidity of the environment. It is common knowledge that one feels hotter on a humid day. This is due in part to the decreased vaporization of sweat, but even under conditions in which vaporization of sweat is complete, an individual in a humid environment feels warmer than an individual in a dry environment. The reason for this difference is not known, but it seems related to the fact that in the humid environment sweat spreads over a greater area of skin before it evaporates. During muscular exertion in a hot environment, sweat secretion reaches values as high as 1600 ml/h, and in a dry atmosphere, most of this sweat is vaporized. Heat loss by vaporization of water therefore varies from 30 to over 900 kcal/h.

Some mammals lose heat by **panting.** This rapid, shallow breathing greatly increases the amount of water vaporized in the mouth and respiratory passages, and therefore the amount of heat lost. Because the breathing is shallow, it produces relatively little change in the composition of alveolar air (Chapter 34).

The relative contribution of each of the processes that transfer heat away from the body (Table 14–5) varies with the environmental temperature. At 21 C, vaporization is a minor component in humans at rest. As the environmental temperature approaches body temperature, radiation losses decline and vaporization losses increase.

Temperature-Regulating Mechanisms

The reflex and semireflex thermoregulatory responses are listed in Table 14–6. They include autonomic, somatic, endocrine, and behavioral changes. One group of responses increases heat loss and decreases heat production; the other decreases heat loss and increases heat production.

Table 14–6. Temperature-regulating mechanisms.

Mechanisms activated by cold:	
Shivering	
Hunger	Increase
Increased voluntary activity	heat
Increased secretion of norepi-	production
nephrine and epinephrine	
Cutaneous vasoconstriction	Decrease
Curling up	heat
Horripilation	loss
Mechanisms activated by heat:	
Cutaneous vasodilatation	Increase
Sweating	heat
Increased respiration	loss
Anorexia	Decrease
Apathy and inertia	heat
	production

Curling up "in a ball" is a common reaction to cold in animals and has a counterpart in the position some people assume on climbing into a cold bed. Curling up decreases the body surface exposed to the environment. Shivering is an involuntary response of the skeletal muscles, but cold also causes a semiconscious general increase in motor activity. Examples include foot stamping and dancing up and down on a cold day. Increased catecholamine secretion is an important endocrine response to cold; adrenal medullectomized rats die faster than normal controls when exposed to cold. TSH secretion is increased by cold and decreased by heat in laboratory animals, but the change in TSH secretion produced by cold in adult humans is small and of questionable significance. It is common knowledge that activity is decreased in hot weather—the "it's too hot to move" reaction.

The reflex responses activated by cold are controlled from the posterior hypothalamus. Those activated by warmth are primarily controlled from the anterior hypothalamus, although some thermoregulation against heat still occurs after decerebration at the level of the rostral midbrain. Stimulation of the anterior hypothalamus causes cutaneous vasodilatation and sweating, and lesions in this region cause hyperthermia, with rectal temperatures sometimes reaching 43 C (109.4 F). Posterior hypothalamic stimulation causes shivering, and the body temperature of animals with posterior hypothalamic lesions falls toward that of the environment.

There is some evidence that in primates and humans serotonin is a synaptic mediator in the centers controlling the mechanisms activated by cold, and norepinephrine plays a similar role in those activated by heat. However, there are marked species variations in the temperature responses to these amines, and the details of the central synaptic connections concerned with thermoregulation are still unknown.

Afferents

The signals that activate the hypothalamic temperature-regulating centers come from 2 sources: temperature-sensitive cells in the anterior hypothalamus, and cutaneous temperature receptors, especially cold receptors. Present evidence indicates that the stimuli which activate the defenses against high temperatures in humans come mainly from the temperature-sensitive cells in the hypothalamus. This conclusion grew out of research in which the temperature of the back of the nasal cavity and the interior of the ear, near the hypothalamus, was correlated with thermoregulatory responses to changing environmental temperatures (Fig 14–21). This "head temperature" does not always correlate with rectal "body core" temperature, a fact that was often overlooked in previous research. The response of body heat production to cooling is modified by interactions between cutaneous and central stimuli. Heat production is increased when head temperature falls below a given threshold value, but the threshold for the response is lower and its magnitude decreased when the skin temperature is increased.

Fever

Fever is perhaps the oldest and most universally known hallmark of disease. It occurs not only in mammals but also in birds, reptiles, amphibia, and

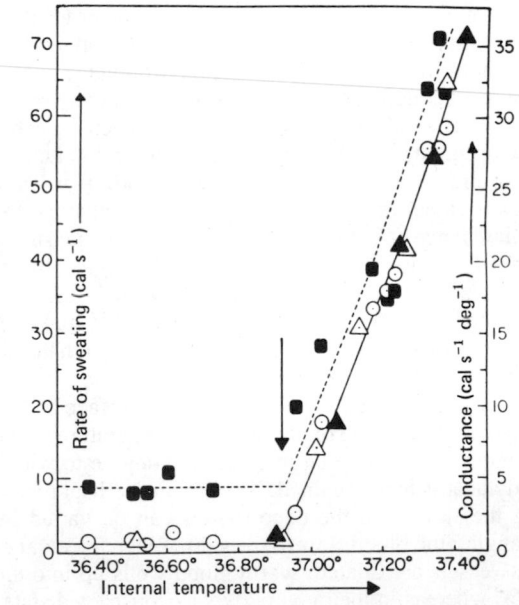

Figure 14–21. Quantitative relations in humans between the temperature of the interior of the head (internal temperature) and cutaneous blood flow (squares, scale at the right), and sweating (circles and triangles, scale at the left). The arrow points to the sharp threshold at which these parameters start to rise. In this subject, the threshold was at 36.9 C. (Reproduced, with permission, from Benzinger TH: Receptor organs and quantitative mechanisms of human temperature control in a warm environment. Fed Proc 19:32, 1960.)

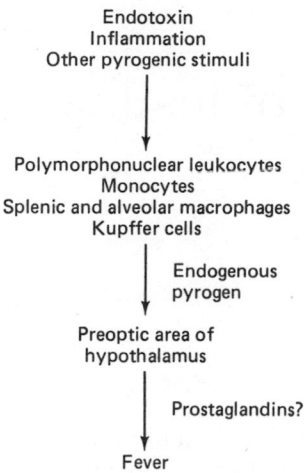

Endotoxin
Inflammation
Other pyrogenic stimuli

↓

Polymorphonuclear leukocytes
Monocytes
Splenic and alveolar macrophages
Kupffer cells

↓ Endogenous pyrogen

Preoptic area of
hypothalamus

↓ Prostaglandins?

Fever

Figure 14–22. Pathogenesis of fever.

fish. When it occurs in homeothermic animals, the thermoregulatory mechanisms behave as if they were adjusted to maintain body temperature at a higher than normal level, ie, "as if the thermostat had been reset" to a new point above 37 C. The temperature receptors then signal that the actual temperature is below the new set point, and temperature-raising mechanisms are activated. This usually produces chilly sensations due to cutaneous vasoconstriction and occasionally enough shivering to produce a shaking chill. However, the nature of the response depends on the ambient temperature. The temperature rise in experimental animals injected with a pyrogen is due mostly to increased heat production if they are in a cold environment and mostly to decreased heat loss if they are in a warm environment.

The pathogenesis of fever is summarized in Fig 14–22. Toxins from bacteria such as endotoxin act on bone marrow–produced phagocytic cells—polymorphonuclear leukocytes, monocytes, macrophages, and Kupffer cells—to produce **endogenous pyrogen (EP).** Diverse other agents, including the steroid etiocholanolone, a metabolite of testosterone (see Chapter 23), also cause these cells to produce the pyrogen. EP is a protein, or family of proteins, with a molecular weight of 10,000–20,000. Its synthesis is blocked by antibodies that prevent transcription of DNA (see Chapter 17). EP enters the brain and acts directly on the preoptic area of the hypothalamus. The

resulting fever may be due to local release of prostaglandins. Injection of prostaglandins into the hypothalamus produces fever. In addition, the antipyretic effect of aspirin is exerted directly on the hypothalamus, and aspirin inhibits prostaglandin synthesis. However, there is some evidence that the prostaglandins are not involved, and the question of their role in the production of fever is currently a matter of much debate.

The benefit of fever to the organism is unknown, although it is presumably beneficial in some way because it has evolved and persisted as a response to infections and other diseases. Before the advent of antibiotics, fevers were artificially induced for the treatment of neurosyphilis. However, it is uncertain whether fever helps to kill the microorganisms that cause other infectious diseases. Very high temperatures are harmful. When the rectal temperature is over 41 C (106 F) for prolonged periods, some permanent brain damage results. When it is over 43 C, heat stroke develops, and death is common.

Hypothermia

In hibernating mammals, body temperature drops to low levels without causing any ill effects that are demonstrable upon subsequent arousal. This observation led to experiments on induced hypothermia. When the skin or the blood is cooled enough to lower the body temperature in nonhibernating animals and in humans, metabolic and physiologic processes slow down. Respiration and heart rate are very slow, blood pressure is low, and consciousness is lost. At rectal temperatures of about 28 C, ability to spontaneously return the temperature to normal is lost, but the individual continues to survive and, if rewarmed with external heat, returns to a normal state. If care is taken to prevent the formation of ice crystals in the tissues, the body temperature of experimental animals can be lowered to subfreezing levels without producing any damage that is detectable after subsequent rewarming.

Humans tolerate body temperatures of 21–24 C (70–75 F) without permanent ill effects, and induced hypothermia has been used extensively in surgery. In hypothermic patients, the circulation can be stopped for relatively long periods because the O_2 needs of the tissues are greatly reduced. Blood pressure is low, and bleeding is minimal. It is possible under hypothermia to stop and open the heart and to perform other procedures, especially brain operations, that would have been impossible without cooling.

15 | Neurophysiologic Basis of Instinctual Behavior & Emotions

Emotions have both mental and physical components. They involve **cognition,** an awareness of the sensation and usually its cause; **affect,** the feeling itself; **conation,** the urge to take action; and **physical changes** such as hypertension, tachycardia, and sweating. Physiologists have been concerned for some time with the physical manifestations of emotional states, while psychologists have been concerned with emotions themselves. However, their interests merge in the hypothalamus and limbic systems, since these parts of the brain are now known to be intimately concerned not only with emotional expression but with the genesis of emotions as well.

ANATOMIC CONSIDERATIONS

The term **limbic lobe** or **limbic system** is now generally applied to the part of the brain formerly called the rhinencephalon because it has become clear that only a small portion of this part of the brain is directly concerned with smell. Each limbic lobe consists of a rim of cortical tissue around the hilus of the cerebral hemisphere and a group of associated deep structures—the amygdala, the hippocampus, and the septal nuclei (Figs 15–1 and 15–2).

Histology

The limbic cortex is phylogenetically the oldest part of the cerebral cortex. Histologically, it is made up of a primitive type of cortical tissue called **allocortex,** surrounding the hilus of the hemisphere, and a second ring of a transitional type of cortex called **juxtallocortex** between the allocortex and the rest of the cerebral hemisphere. The cortical tissue of the remaining nonlimbic portions of the hemisphere is called **neocortex.** The neocortex is the most highly developed type, and is characteristically 6-layered. The actual extent of the allocortical and juxtallocortical areas has changed little

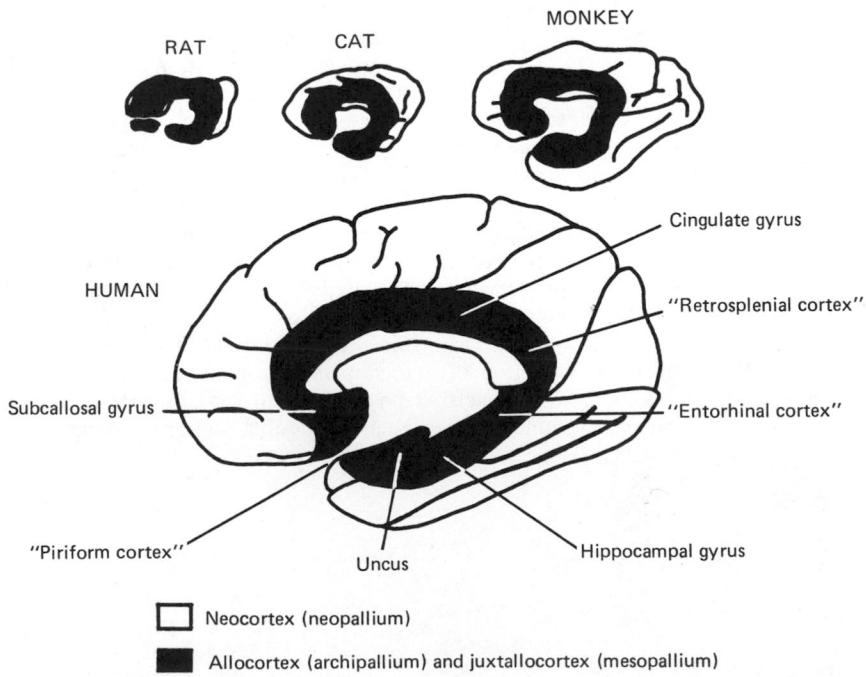

Figure 15–1. Relation of the limbic cortex in rats, cats, monkeys, and humans. (Redrawn and reproduced, with permission, from MacLean P: The limbic system and its hippocampal formation. J Neurosurg 11:29, 1954.)

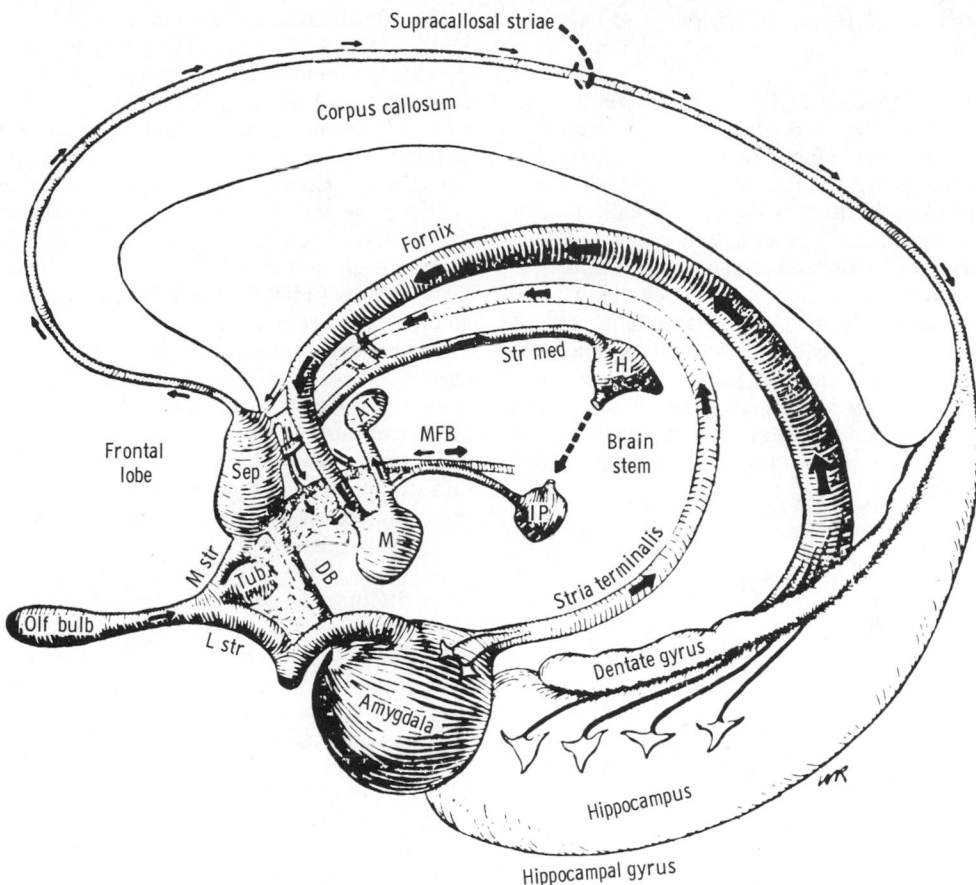

Figure 15–2. Diagram of the principal connections of the limbic system. M str, L str, medial and lateral olfactory striae; Str med, stria medullaris; Tub, olfactory tubercle; DB, diagonal band of Broca; Sep, septum; AT, anterior nucleus of the thalamus; M, mammillary body; H, habenula; IP, interpeduncular nucleus; MFB, medial forebrain bundle. (After Krieg WJS. Reproduced, with permission, from MacLean PD: Psychosomatic disease and the visceral brain. Psychosom Med 11:338, 1949.)

as mammals have evolved, but these regions have been overshadowed by the immense growth of the neocortex, which reaches its greatest development in humans (Fig 15–1).

Afferent & Efferent Connections

The major connections of the limbic system are shown in Fig 15–2. The fornix connects the hippocampus to the mammillary bodies, which are in turn connected to the anterior nuclei of the thalamus by the mammillothalamic tract of Vicq d'Azyr. The anterior nuclei of the thalamus project to the cingulate cortex, and from the cingulate cortex there are connections to the hippocampus, completing a complex closed circuit. This circuit was originally described by Papez, and has been called the Papez circuit.

Correlations Between Structure & Function

One characteristic of the limbic system is the paucity of the connections between it and the neocortex. Nauta has aptly stated that "the neocortex sits astride the limbic system like a rider on a horse without

reins." Actually, there are a few reins; there are fibers from the frontal lobe to adjacent limbic structures and probably some indirect connections via the thalamus. From a functional point of view, neocortical activity does modify emotional behavior and vice versa. However, one of the characteristics of emotion is that it cannot be turned on and off at will.

Another characteristic of limbic circuits is their prolonged after-discharge following stimulation. This may explain in part the fact that emotional responses are generally prolonged rather than evanescent and outlast the stimuli that initiate them.

LIMBIC FUNCTIONS

Stimulation and ablation experiments indicate that in addition to its role in olfaction (Chapter 10), the limbic system is concerned with feeding behavior. Along with the hypothalamus, it is also concerned with sexual behavior, the emotions of rage and fear, and motivation.

Autonomic Responses & Feeding Behavior

Limbic stimulation produces autonomic effects, particularly changes in blood pressure and respiration. These responses are elicited from many limbic structures, and there is little evidence of localization of autonomic responses. This suggests that the autonomic effects are part of more complex phenomena, particularly emotional and behavioral responses. Stimulation of the amygdaloid nuclei causes movements such as chewing and licking and other activities related to feeding. Lesions in the amygdala cause moderate hyperphagia, with indiscriminate ingestion of all kinds of food. The relation of this type of omniphagia to the hypothalamic mechanisms regulating appetite is discussed in Chapter 14.

SEXUAL BEHAVIOR

Mating is a basic but complex phenomenon in which many parts of the nervous system are involved. Copulation itself is made up of a series of reflexes integrated in spinal and lower brain stem centers, but the behavioral components that accompany it, the urge to copulate, and the coordinated sequence of events in the male and female that lead to pregnancy are regulated to a large degree in the limbic system and hypothalamus. Learning plays a part in the development of mating behavior, particularly in primates and humans, but in lower animals, courtship and successful mating can occur with no previous sexual experience. The basic responses are therefore innate and are undoubtedly present in all mammals. However, in humans, the sexual functions have become extensively encephalized and conditioned by social and psychic factors. The basic physiologic mechanisms of sexual behavior in animals are therefore considered first and then compared to the responses in humans.

Relation to Endocrine Function

In animals other than humans, removal of the gonads leads eventually to decreased or absent sexual activity in both the male and the female—although the loss is slow to develop in the males of some species. Injections of gonadal hormones in castrate animals revive sexual activity. Testosterone in the male and estrogen in the female have the most marked effect. Large doses of progesterone are also effective in the female, while in the presence of smaller doses of progesterone, the dose of estrogen necessary to produce sexual activity is lowered. Large doses of testosterone and other androgens in castrate females initiate female behavior, and large doses of estrogens in castrate males trigger male mating responses. It is unsettled why responses appropriate to the sex of the animal occur when the hormones of the opposite sex are injected.

Effects of Hormones in Humans

In adult women, ovariectomy does not necessarily reduce libido (defined in this context as sexual interest and drive) or sexual ability. Postmenopausal women continue to have sexual relations, often without much change in frequency from their premenopausal pattern. This persistence may be due to continued secretion of estrogens and androgens from the adrenal cortex but may also be due to the greater degree of encephalization of sexual functions in humans and their relative emancipation from instinctual and hormonal control. Treatment with sex hormones increases sexual interest and drive in humans. Testosterone, for example, increases libido in males, and so does estrogen used to treat diseases such as carcinoma of the prostate. The behavioral pattern present before treatment is stimulated but not redirected. Thus, administration of testosterone to homosexuals intensifies their homosexual drive but does not convert it to a heterosexual drive.

Neural Control in the Male

In male animals, removal of the neocortex generally inhibits sexual behavior. Partial cortical ablations also produce some inhibition, the degree of the inhibition being independent of the coexisting motor deficit and most marked when the lesions are in the frontal lobes. On the other hand, cats and monkeys with bilateral limbic lesions localized to the piriform cortex overlying the amygdala (Fig 15–3) develop a marked intensification of sexual activity. These animals not only mount adult females; they also mount immature females and other males, and attempt to copulate with animals of other species and with inanimate objects. Despite some claims to the contrary, such behavior is clearly abnormal in the species studied. The behavior is dependent upon the presence of testosterone but is not due to any increase in its secretion.

The hypothalamus is also involved in the control of sexual activity in males. Stimulation along the medial forebrain bundle and in neighboring hypothalamic areas causes penile erection with considerable emotional display in monkeys. In castrated rats, intrahypothalamic implants of testosterone restore the complete pattern of sex behavior; and in intact rats, appropriately placed anterior hypothalamic lesions abolish interest in sex.

The extent to which the findings in male animals with periamygdaloid lesions are applicable to men is, of course, difficult to determine, but there are reports of hypersexuality in men with bilateral lesions in or near the amygdaloid nuclei.

Sexual Behavior in the Female

In mammals, the sexual activity of the male is more or less continuous, but in most species, the sexual activity of the female is cyclic. Most of the time, the female avoids the male and repulses his sexual advances. Periodically, however, there is an abrupt change in behavior and the female seeks out the male, attempting to mate. These short episodes of **heat** or

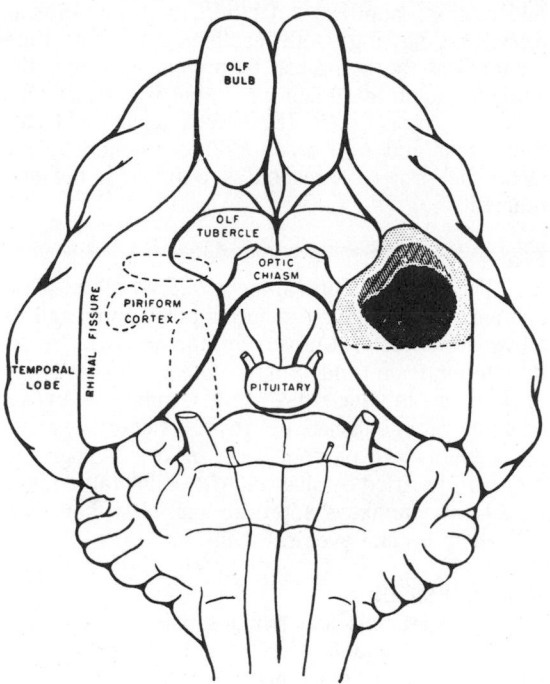

Figure 15–3. Site of lesions producing hypersexuality in male cats. When the black area was destroyed, hypersexuality was always present. The incidence of hypersexuality in animals with lesions in the surrounding lighter zones was not so high. Olf, olfactory. (Reproduced, with permission, from Green J & others: Rhinencephalic lesions and behavior in cats. J Comp Neurol 108:505, 1957.)

estrus are so characteristic that the sexual cycle in mammalian species that do not menstruate is named the **estrous cycle.**

This change in female sexual behavior is brought on by a rise in the circulating blood estrogen level. Some animals, notably the rabbit and the ferret, come into heat and remain estrous until pregnancy or pseudopregnancy results. In these species, ovulation is due to a neuroendocrine reflex. Stimulation of the genitalia and other sensory stimuli at the time of copulation provoke release from the pituitary of the LH that makes the ovarian follicles rupture. In many other species, spontaneous ovulation occurs at regular intervals, and the periods of heat coincide with its occurrence. This is true in monkeys and apes. In captivity, these species mate at any time; but in the wild state, the females accept the male more frequently at the time of ovulation.

In women, sexual activity is generally not confined to any period of heat, although some studies indicate an increase at about the time of ovulation. Others show some increase near the menses. There are reports of transient hypersexuality in women after surgical procedures involving manipulation of the anterior hypothalamus and neighboring structures. Because these reported effects were short-lived, they

were probably due to inadvertent stimulation of diencephalic structures.

In monkeys, the sex drive of the male is greater when he is exposed to a female at the time of ovulation than when he is exposed to a female at another time of her cycle. The "message" sent by the female to the male in this situation is olfactory, and the substances responsible are certain fatty acids in the vaginal secretions. These fatty acids are also found in increased amounts in human vaginal secretions at about midcycle. Substances produced by an animal that act at a distance to produce behavioral or other physiologic changes in another animal of the same species have been called **pheromones.** The sex attractants of certain insects are particularly well known examples, but it appears from the evidence cited above that pheromones also operate in the regulation of sexual behavior in primates.

Neural Control in the Female

In female animals, removal of the neocortex and the limbic cortex abolishes active seeking out of the male ("enticement reactions") during estrus, but other aspects of heat are unaffected. Amygdaloid and periamygdaloid lesions do not produce hypersexuality as they do in the male. However, discrete anterior hypothalamic lesions abolish behavioral heat (Fig 15–4) without affecting the regular pituitary-ovarian cycle (see Chapter 23).

Implantation of minute amounts of estrogen in the anterior hypothalamus causes heat in ovariectomized rats (Fig 23–29). Implantation into other parts of the brain and outside the brain does not have this effect. Apparently, therefore, some element in the hypothalamus is sensitive to circulating estrogen, and is stimulated by the hormone to initiate estrous behavior.

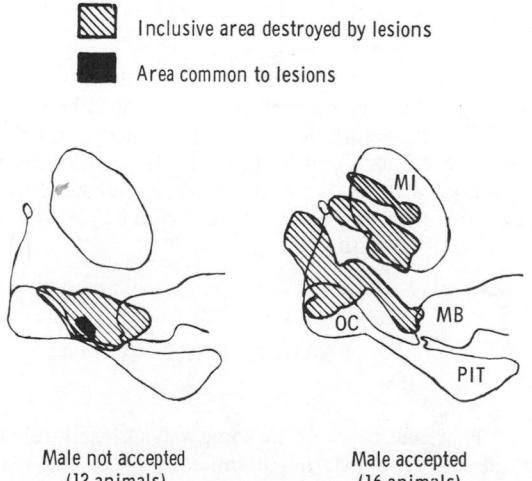

Inclusive area destroyed by lesions

Area common to lesions

Male not accepted (12 animals)

Male accepted (16 animals)

Figure 15–4. Sites of hypothalamic lesions that blocked behavioral heat without affecting ovarian cycles in ewes. MI, massa intermedia; MB, mammillary body; OC, optic chiasm; PIT, pituitary. (From data of MT Clegg and WF Ganong.)

Effects of Sex Hormones in Infancy on Adult Behavior

In female experimental animals, exposure to sex steroids in utero or during early postnatal development causes marked abnormalities of sexual behavior when the animals reach adulthood. Female rats treated with a single relatively small dose of androgen before the fifth day of life do not have normal heat periods when they mature; they generally will not mate, even though they have cystic ovaries that secrete enough estrogen to cause the animals to have a persistently estrous type of vaginal smear (Chapter 23). These rats do not show the cyclic release of pituitary gonadotropins characteristic of the adult female, but rather the tonic, steady secretion characteristic of the adult male; their brains have been "masculinized" by the single brief exposure to androgens. Conversely, male rats castrated at birth develop the female pattern of cyclic gonadotropin secretion and show considerable female sexual behavior when given doses of ovarian hormones that do not have this effect in intact males. Thus, the development of a "female hypothalamus" depends simply on the absence of androgens in early life rather than on exposure to female hormones.

Rats are particularly immature at birth, and animals of other species in which the young are more fully developed at birth do not show these changes when exposed to androgens during the postnatal period. However, these animals develop genital abnormalities when exposed to androgens in utero (Chapter 23). Monkeys exposed to androgens in utero do not lose the female pattern of gonadotropin secretion but do develop abnormalities of sexual behavior in adulthood.

Early exposure to androgens in human females does not change the cyclic pattern of gonadotropin secretion in adulthood (see Chapter 23). However, there is evidence that masculinizing effects on behavior do occur.

Maternal Behavior

Maternal behavior is depressed by lesions of the cingulate and retrosplenial portions of the limbic cortex in animals. Hormones do not appear to be necessary for its occurrence, but certain hormones may facilitate its appearance. Prolactin from the anterior pituitary, which is secreted in large amounts during lactation, may exert a facilitatory effect by acting directly on the brain.

FEAR & RAGE

Fear and rage are in some ways closely related emotions. The external manifestations of the **fear, fleeing,** or **avoidance reaction** in animals are autonomic responses such as sweating and pupillary dilatation, cowering, and turning the head from side to side to seek escape. The **rage, fighting,** or **attack reaction** is associated in the cat with hissing, spitting, growling, piloerection, pupillary dilatation, and well-directed biting and clawing. Both reactions—and sometimes mixtures of the two—can be produced by hypothalamic stimulation. When an animal is threatened, it usually attempts to flee. If cornered, an animal fights. Thus, fear and rage reactions are probably related instinctual protective responses to threats in the environment.

Fear

The fear reaction can be produced in conscious animals by stimulation of the hypothalamus and the amygdaloid nuclei. Conversely, the fear reaction and its autonomic and endocrine manifestations are absent in situations in which they would normally be evoked when the amygdalae are destroyed. A dramatic example is the reaction of monkeys to snakes. Monkeys are normally terrified by snakes. After bilateral temporal lobectomy, monkeys approach snakes without fear, pick them up and even eat them.

Rage & Placidity

Most animals and humans maintain a balance between rage and its opposite, the emotional state which for lack of a better name is called here placidity. Major irritations make normal individuals "lose their temper," but minor stimuli are ignored. In animals with certain brain lesions, this balance is altered. Some lesions produce a state in which the most minor stimuli evoke violent episodes of rage; others produce a state in which the most traumatic and anger-provoking stimuli fail to ruffle the animal's abnormal calm.

Rage responses to minor stimuli are observed after removal of the neocortex and after lesions of the ventromedial hypothalamic nuclei and septal nuclei in animals with intact cerebral cortices. On the other hand, bilateral destruction of the amygdaloid nuclei causes in monkeys a state of abnormal placidity. Similar responses are usually seen in cats and dogs. Wild rats which are vicious in captivity are transformed by this operation into animals that are as tractable and calm as ordinary laboratory white rats. Stimulation of some parts of the amygdala in cats produces rage. The placidity produced by amygdaloid lesions in animals is converted into rage by subsequent destruction of the ventromedial nuclei of the hypothalamus.

Rage can also be produced by stimulation of an area extending back through the lateral hypothalamus to the central gray area of the midbrain, and the rage response usually produced by amygdaloid stimulation is abolished by ipsilateral lesions in the lateral hypothalamus or rostral midbrain.

Gonadal hormones appear to affect aggressive behavior. In animals, aggression is decreased by castration and increased by androgens. It is also conditioned by social factors; it is more prominent in males that live with females, and increases when a stranger is introduced into an animal's territory.

"Sham Rage"

It was originally thought that rage attacks in animals with diencephalic and forebrain lesions represented only the physical, motor manifestations of anger, and the reaction was therefore called "sham rage." This now appears to be incorrect. Although rage attacks in animals with diencephalic lesions are induced by minor stimuli, they are usually directed with great accuracy at the source of the irritation. Furthermore, hypothalamic stimulation that produces the fear-rage reaction is apparently unpleasant to animals because they become conditioned against the place where the experiments are conducted and try to avoid the experimental sessions. They can easily be taught to press a lever or perform some other act to avoid a hypothalamic stimulus that produces the manifestations of fear or rage. It is difficult if not impossible to form conditioned reflex responses (see Chapter 16) by stimulation of purely motor systems, and it is also difficult if the unconditioned stimulus does not evoke either a pleasant or unpleasant feeling. The fact that hypothalamic stimulation is a potent unconditioned stimulus for the formation of conditioned avoidance responses and the fact that the avoidance responses are extremely persistent indicates that the stimulus is unpleasant. There is therefore little doubt that rage attacks include the mental as well as the physical manifestations of rage, and the term "sham rage" should be dropped.

Significance & Clinical Correlates

It is tempting on the basis of the evidence cited above to speculate that there are 2 intimately related mechanisms in the hypothalamus and limbic system, one promoting placidity and the other rage. If this is true, the emotional state is probably determined by afferent impulses that adjust the balance between them. An arrangement of this sort would be analogous to the systems controlling feeding and body temperature.

Although emotional responses are much more complex and subtle in humans than in animals, the neural substrates are probably the same. It is doubtful if placidity would be recognized as a clinical syndrome in our culture, but rage attacks in response to trivial stimuli have been observed many times in patients with brain damage. They are a complication of pituitary surgery when there is inadvertent damage to the base of the brain. They also follow a number of diseases of the nervous system, especially epidemic influenza and encephalitis, which destroy neurons in the limbic system and hypothalamus. Stimulation of the amygdaloid nuclei and parts of the hypothalamus in conscious humans produces sensations of anger and fear. In Japan, bilateral amygdaloid lesions have been produced in agitated, aggressive mental patients. The patients are said to have become placid and manageable, and it is of some interest that they were reported not to have developed hypersexuality or memory loss.

MOTIVATION

If an animal is placed in a box with a pedal or bar that can be pressed, the animal sooner or later accidentally presses it. Olds and his associates have shown that if the bar is connected in such a way that each press delivers a stimulus to an electrode implanted in certain parts of the brain (Fig 15–5), the animal returns to the bar and presses it again and again. Pressing the bar soon comes to occupy most of the animal's time. Some animals go without food and water to press the bar for brain stimulation, and some will continue until they fall over exhausted. Rats press the bar 5000–12,000 times per hour, and monkeys have been clocked at 17,000 bar presses per hour. On the other hand, when the electrode is in certain other areas, the animals avoid pressing the bar, and stimulation of these areas is a potent unconditioned stimulus for the development of conditioned avoidance responses.

The points where stimulation leads to repeated bar pressing are located in a medial band of tissue passing from the amygdaloid nuclei through the hypothalamus to the midbrain tegmentum (Fig 15–6). The highest rates are generally obtained from points in the tegmentum, posterior hypothalamus, and septal nuclei. The points where stimulation is avoided are in the lateral portion of the posterior hypothalamus and dorsal midbrain and in the entorhinal cortex. The latter points are sometimes close to points where bar pressing is repeated, but they are part of a separate system. The areas where bar pressing is repeated are much more extensive than those where it is avoided. It has

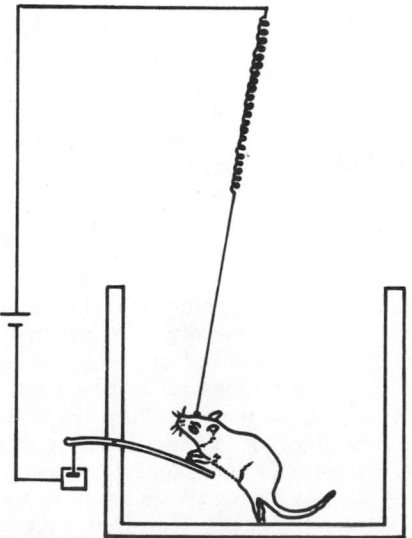

Figure 15–5. Diagram of the apparatus in self-stimulation experiments. Each time the animal steps on the pedal, the electrical circuit is closed and a single current pulse is delivered to its brain through implanted electrodes. (Modified from Olds J in: *Electrical Stimulation of the Unanesthetized Brain.* Ramey E, O'Doherty J [editors]. Hoeber, 1960.)

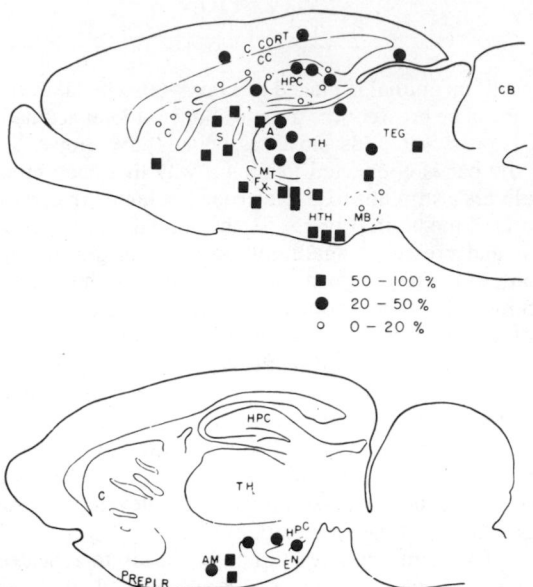

Figure 15–6. Location of electrodes in self-stimulation studies, projected on parasagittal sections of the rat brain. The figures in the legend are percentages of time spent pressing the bar in a 6-hour test period. C, caudate; HPC, hippocampus; AM, amygdala; TH, thalamus; HTH, hypothalamus; MB, mammillary bodies; FX, fornix; TEG, tegmentum; S, septum; CB, cerebellum; EN, entorhinal cortex; CC, corpus callosum; C CORT, cerebral cortex; A, anterior commissure; MT, mammillothalamic tract; PREPIR, prepiriform cortex. (Reproduced, with permission, from Olds J: A preliminary mapping of electrical reinforcing effects in the rat brain. J Comp Physiol Psychol 49:281, 1956.)

other tasks. Hungry rats will cross an electrified grid to obtain food only when the current in the grid is less than 70 microamperes, but when self-stimulation is the reward, they will brave currents of 300 microamperes or more. A rat may even take a shock so strong that it will be stunned, but when it recovers consciousness will roll over and again struggle toward the bar.

To a certain extent, the reward system can be broken down into subsystems. In rats with certain lateral hypothalamic electrode placements, for example, self-stimulation rates are higher when the animals are hungry than when they are sated. In other hypothalamic locations, especially in the medial forebrain bundle, castration decreases and androgen treatment increases the self-stimulation rate. However, feeding and androgen treatment do not modify the responses in other locations.

Studies of the kind described above provide physiologic evidence that behavior is motivated not only by reduction or prevention of an unpleasant affect but also by primary rewards such as those produced by stimulation of the approach system of the brain. The implications of this fact are great in terms of the classical drive-reduction theory of motivation, in terms of the disruption and facilitation of ongoing behavior, and in terms of normal and abnormal emotional responses.

BRAIN CHEMISTRY, BEHAVIOR, & SYNAPTIC TRANSMISSION IN THE CNS

been calculated that in rats repeated pressing is obtained from 35% of the brain, avoidance from 5%, and indifferent responses (neither repetition nor avoidance) from 60%.

It is obvious that some effect of the stimulation causes the animals to stimulate themselves again and again, but what the animals feel is, of course, unknown. There are a number of reports of bar-pressing experiments in humans with chronically implanted electrodes. Most of the subjects were schizophrenics or epileptics, but a few were patients with visceral malignancies and intractable pain. Like animals, humans press the bar repeatedly. They generally report that the sensations evoked are pleasurable, using phrases like "relief of tension" and "a quiet, relaxed feeling" to describe the experience. However, they rarely report "joy" or "ecstasy," and some persons with the highest self-stimulation rates cannot tell why they keep pushing the bar. When the electrodes are in the areas where stimulation is avoided, patients report sensations ranging from vague fear to terror. It is probably wise, therefore, to avoid vivid terms and call the brain systems involved the **reward** or **approach system** and the **punishment** or **avoidance system.**

Stimulation of the approach system provides a potent motivation for learning mazes or performing

Drugs that modify human behavior include **psychotomimetic agents,** drugs that produce hallucinations and other manifestations of the psychoses; **tranquilizers,** drugs that allay anxiety and various psychiatric symptoms; and **psychic energizers,** antidepressant drugs that elevate mood and increase interest and drive. These and many other drugs appear to act by modifying transmission at synaptic junctions in the brain, and their discovery has stimulated great interest in the nature and properties of the transmitter agents involved.

Various agents have been suspected of being transmitters. Uneven distribution of a given substance in the various parts of the CNS and a parallel distribution of the enzymes responsible for the substance's synthesis and catabolism suggest that it may play a transmitter role. A change in behavior or some other CNS function coincident with a drug-induced change in the concentration of a substance is also indirect evidence that the substance is a transmitter. More direct evidence is provided by differential centrifugation of brain tissue, which has demonstrated the presence of a number of suspected mediators in fractions known to contain nerve endings. Agents found in nerve ending fractions in the CNS include acetylcholine, norepinephrine, dopamine, and serotonin.

Table 15–1. Known and suspected synaptic transmitter agents and "neural hormones" in mammals.

Substance	Locations Where Substance is Secreted	
	Known	**Suspected**
Acetylcholine	Myoneural junction Preganglionic autonomic endings, postganglionic parasympathetic endings, postganglionic sympathetic sweat gland and muscle vasodilator endings Many parts of the brain Retina	Primary visual afferents Primary auditory afferents
Norepinephrine	Most postganglionic sympathetic endings Cerebral cortex, hypothalamus, brain stem, cerebellum, spinal cord	
Dopamine	SIF cells in sympathetic ganglia Striatum, median eminence and other parts of hypothalamus, limbic system, parts of neocortex Retina	
Epinephrine	Hypothalamus, thalamus, periaqueductal gray matter, spinal cord	
Serotonin	Hypothalamus, limbic system, cerebellum, spinal cord	Retina Gastrointestinal tract
Substance P	Endings of primary afferent neurons, many other parts of brain	Retina Gastrointestinal tract
Histamine		Hypothalamus
Vasopressin	Posterior pituitary	Other parts of brain
Oxytocin	Posterior pituitary	Other parts of brain
Hypothalamic stimulating and inhibiting hormones (see Chapter 14)		
CRH	Median eminence of hypothalamus	
TRH	Median eminence of hypothalamus	Other parts of brain Retina
GRH	Median eminence of hypothalamus	
Somatostatin	Median eminence of hypothalamus	Substantia gelatinosa, other parts of brain
LRH	Median eminence of hypothalamus	Circumventricular organs Preganglionic autonomic endings
PRH	Median eminence of hypothalamus	
Glycine	Neurons mediating direct inhibition in spinal cord Retina	
Gamma-aminobutyric acid (GABA)	Cerebellum, cerebral cortex Neurons mediating presynaptic inhibition in spinal cord Retina	
Enkephalins, endorphins	Substantia gelatinosa, many other parts of CNS Gastrointestinal tract	
Cholecystokinin (CCK)		Cerebral cortex
Vasoactive intestinal peptide (VIP)		Hypothalamus Gastrointestinal tract Vasomotor nerves in female reproductive tract
Neurotensin		Hypothalamus Gastrointestinal tract
Bombesin		Hypothalamus Gastrointestinal tract

Additional evidence is provided by histochemical localization, which is now available for norepinephrine, epinephrine, serotonin, dopamine and a variety of different peptides. It has also been shown that certain of the suspected mediators are liberated from the brain in vitro, and that acetylcholine, glutamic acid, and some other suspected CNS mediators excite single neurons when applied to their membranes by means of a micropipette (**microiontophoresis**). The list of substances that have been proposed as synaptic mediators at central or peripheral synapses is now very long, and the strength of the evidence for a transmitter role for each varies. A somewhat arbitrary compilation of the agents for which there is appreciable evidence is presented in Table 15–1.

Serotonin

Serotonin (5-hydroxytryptamine, 5-HT) is present in highest concentration in blood platelets and in the gastrointestinal tract, where it is found in the enterochromaffin cells and the myenteric plexus (see Chapter 26). Lesser amounts are found in the brain, particularly in the hypothalamus (Table 15–2), and in the retina (see Chapter 8).

The monoamines in tissues can be demonstrated histochemically. The method makes serotonin, norepinephrine, epinephrine, and dopamine all fluoresce, but comparing the histologic pictures in animals treated with drugs that selectively deplete the various amines makes it possible to identify each amine. With this technic, it has been demonstrated that serotonin, norepinephrine, and dopamine are all localized in nerve endings. Serotonin is found in relatively high concentrations in the lateral gray horns of the spinal cord and in a number of areas in the brain. Histochemically, it can be shown that there is a system of serotonin-containing neurons that have their cell bodies in the raphe nuclei of the brain stem and project to portions of the hypothalamus, the limbic system, the neocortex, and the spinal cord (Fig 15–7).

Serotonin is formed in the body by hydroxylation and decarboxylation of the essential amino acid tryptophan (Fig 15–8). After release from serotonergic neurons, much of the released amine is recaptured by an active reuptake mechanism. It is also inactivated by monoamine oxidase (Fig 15–9) to form 5-hydroxyindoleacetic acid (5-HIAA). This substance is the principal urinary metabolite of serotonin, and the urinary output of 5-HIAA is used as an index of the rate of serotonin metabolism in the body. In the pineal gland, serotonin is converted to melatonin (see Chapter 24).

The psychotomimetic agent lysergic acid diethylamide (LSD) is a serotonin antagonist. The transient hallucinations and other mental aberrations produced by this drug were discovered when the chemist who synthesized it inhaled some by accident. Although the relation of LSD to brain serotonin remains unsettled, its discovery called attention to the correlation between behavior and variations in brain serotonin content. Several substances that, like serotonin, are derivatives

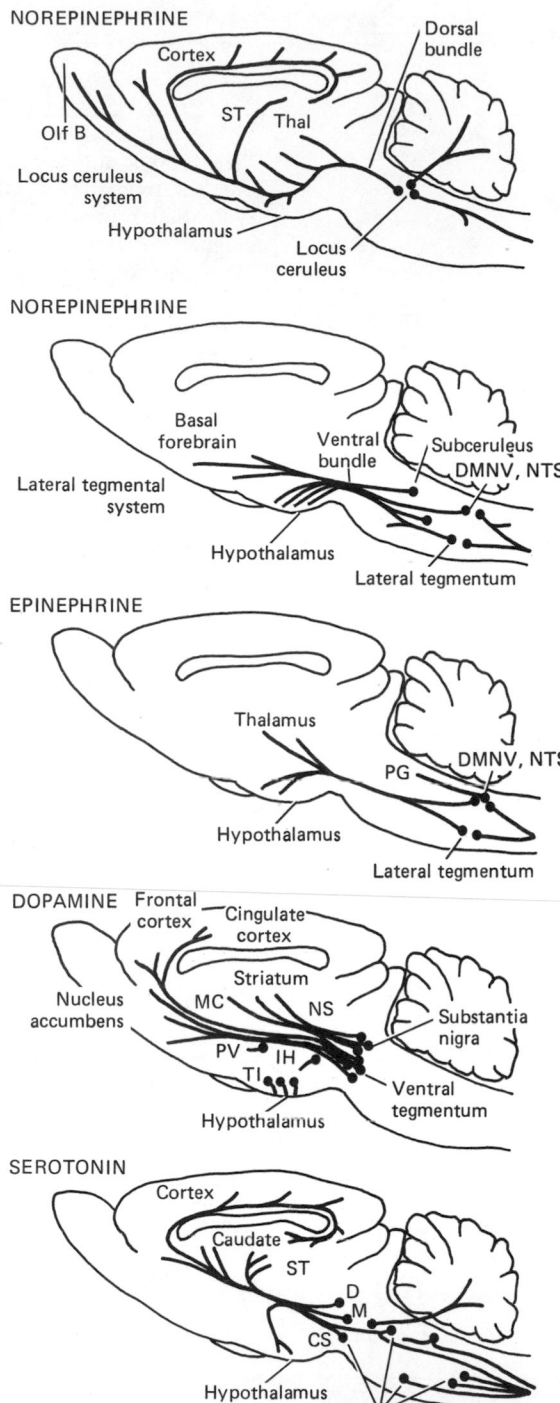

Figure 15–7. Aminergic pathways in rat brain. The pathways in humans are similar. The 2 principal noradrenergic systems (locus ceruleus and lateral tegmental) are shown separately. Olf B, olfactory bulb; Thal, thalamus; ST, stria terminalis; DMNV, dorsal motor nucleus of vagus; NTS, nucleus of tractus solitarius; PG, periaqueductal gray; NS, nigrostriatal system; MC, mesocortical system; PV, periventricular system; IH, incertohypothalamic system; TI, tuberoinfundibular system; D, M, and CS; dorsal, medial, and central superior raphe nuclei.

Table 15–2. Brain content of GABA and a number of known or suspected transmitter agents at synapses in the CNS.

	DOG					RAT
	Acetyl-choline ($\mu g/g^*$)	Substance P (units/g*)	Sero-tonin ($\mu g/g^*$)	Norepi-nephrine ($\mu g/g^*$)	Hista-mine ($\mu g/g^*$)	GABA ($\mu g/g^\dagger$)
Cerebral cortex—somesthetic	2.8	‡	‡	0	0	} 210
Cerebral cortex—motor	4.5	19	0.02	0.18	0	
Caudate nucleus	2.7	46	0.10	0.06	0	‡
Thalamus	3.0	13	0.02	0.16	0	‡
Hypothalamus	1.8	70	0.25	1.03	30	380
Hippocampus	‡	15	0.05	‡	‡	‡
Medulla	1.6	25	0.03	‡	‡	200
Cerebellum	0.2	2	0.01	0.07	0	160
Spinal cord	1.6	29	0	‡	0	‡
Sympathetic ganglia	30.0	7	0	6.00	5	‡
Area postrema	‡	460	0.24	1.04	‡	‡

*Data on dog from various authors, compiled by Paton WDM: Annu Rev Physiol 20:431, 1958.
†Data on rat GABA (gamma-aminobutyric acid) from Berl S, Waelsch H: J Neurochem 3:161, 1958.
‡No data.

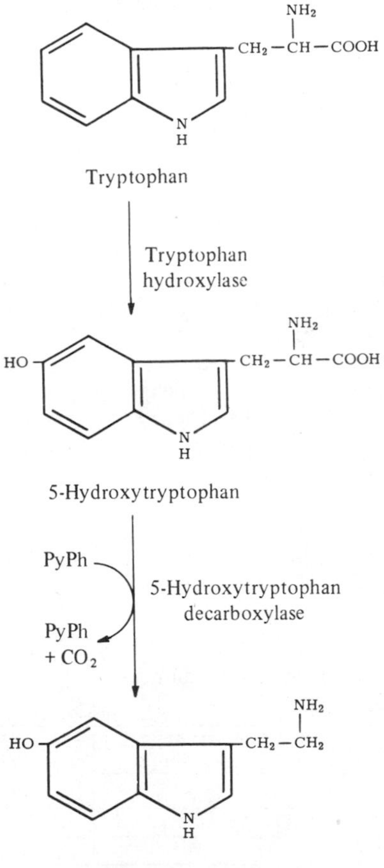

Figure 15–8. Biosynthesis of serotonin (5-hydroxytryptamine). PyPh, pyridoxal phosphate. The enzyme that catalyzes the decarboxylation of 5-hydroxytryptophan is very similar but probably not identical to the enzyme that catalyzes the decarboxylation of dopa.

of tryptamine have psychotomimetic actions; psilocybin, a hallucinogenic agent found in certain mushrooms, is the best known of these compounds. Selective depletion of brain serotonin can be produced by administering *p*-chlorophenylalanine, a compound that blocks conversion of tryptophan to 5-hydroxytryptophan (Fig 15–8). This is the rate-limiting step in serotonin biosynthesis. In animals, *p*-chlorophenylalanine produces prolonged wakefulness, suggesting (along with other evidence) that serotonin plays a role in sleep. However, wakefulness is not produced in humans, and no clear-cut psychic changes are produced even by large doses. Thus, the relation of serotonin to mental function remains uncertain. Serotonin probably plays an excitatory role in the regulation of the secretion of prolactin (see Chapter 23). There is some evidence that serotonin is a mediator in descending fiber systems that inhibit the initiation of autonomic impulses in the lateral gray columns of the spinal cord. In addition, there is a prominent serotonergic innervation of the suprachiasmatic nuclei of the hypothalamus, and serotonin may play some role in the regulation of circadian rhythms (see Chapter 14).

Norepinephrine

The distribution of norepinephrine in the brain parallels that of serotonin (Tables 15–2 and 15–3). The cell bodies of most if not all of the norepinephrine-containing neurons are located in the locus ceruleus and other nuclei in the pons and medulla. From the locus ceruleus, the axons of the noradrenergic neurons form a **locus ceruleus system** that descends into the spinal cord, enters the cerebellum, and ascends to innervate the paraventricular, supraoptic, and periventricular nuclei of the hypothalamus, the thalamus, the basal telencephalon, and the entire

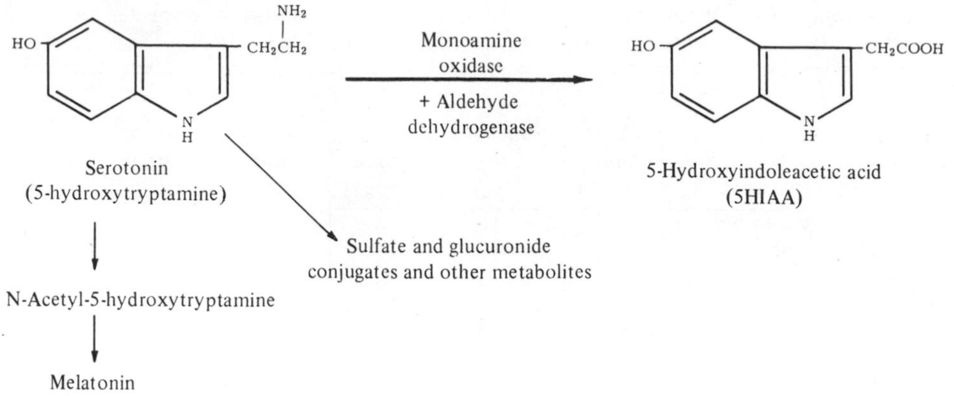

Figure 15-9. Catabolism of serotonin. In oxidative deaminations catalyzed by monoamine oxidase, an aldehyde is formed first and then in the presence of aldehyde dehydrogenase oxidized to the corresponding acid. Some of the aldehyde is also reduced to the corresponding alcohol (5-hydroxytryptophol). The heavy arrow indicates the major metabolic pathway. The details of the formation of melatonin are shown in Fig 24-7.

neocortex (Fig 15-7). From cell bodies in the dorsal motor nucleus of the vagus, nucleus tractus solitarius, and areas in the dorsal and lateral tegmentum, the axons of the noradrenergic neurons form a **lateral tegmental system** that projects to the spinal cord, the brain stem, all of the hypothalamus, and the basal telencephalon.

Evidence has now accumulated that the norepinephrine in the brain is related to mental function. Studies with drugs that affect norepinephrine indicate that mood is related to the amount of free norepinephrine available at synapses in the brain. When too little norepinephrine is available, depression results. Conversely, drugs such as monoamine oxidase inhibitors and amphetamine, which increase free norepinephrine, elevate mood. The tricyclic antidepressants such as desipramine appear to act in the same way; they decrease the reuptake of liberated norepinephrine (see Chapter 13), thus leaving more available to act on the postsynaptic structures.

In the cerebellum, adrenergic neurons inhibit Purkinje cells, and there is evidence that these inhibitory effects are mediated via β receptors and cyclic AMP.

The norepinephrine-containing neurons in the hypothalamus are involved in regulation of the secretion of anterior pituitary hormones (see Chapter 14), and they appear to inhibit the secretion of vasopressin and oxytocin. There is some evidence that norepinephrine is involved in the control of food intake and self-stimulation. Along with serotonin, it appears to be involved in the regulation of body temperature. An inhibitory effect on autonomic discharge from the spinal cord has also been suggested.

Epinephrine

There is a system of PNMT-containing neurons with cell bodies in the medulla that project to the hypothalamus. Those neurons secrete epinephrine, but their function is uncertain. Epinephrine-secreting neurons also appear to project to the thalamus, periaqueductal gray, and spinal cord. The biosynthesis and metabolism of norepinephrine and epinephrine are discussed in Chapter 13. There are appreciable quantities of tyramine in the CNS, but no function has been assigned to this agent.

Dopamine

Dopamine is the immediate precursor of norepinephrine (Fig 13-3). In certain parts of the brain,

Table 15-3. Amine and substance P content of selected portions of the human brain. Data compiled from various authors.

	Norepinephrine	Dopamine	Serotonin	Histamine	Substance P (units/g)
	(μg/g fresh tissue)				
Amygdala	0.21	0.6	0.26	*	*
Caudate nucleus	0.09	3.5	0.33	0.5	85
Putamen	0.12	3.7	0.32	0.7	*
Globus pallidus	0.15	0.5	0.23	0.6	*
Thalamus	0.13	0.3	0.26	0.4	12
Hypothalamus	1.25	0.8	0.29	2.5	102
Substantia nigra	0.21	0.9	0.55	*	699

*No data.

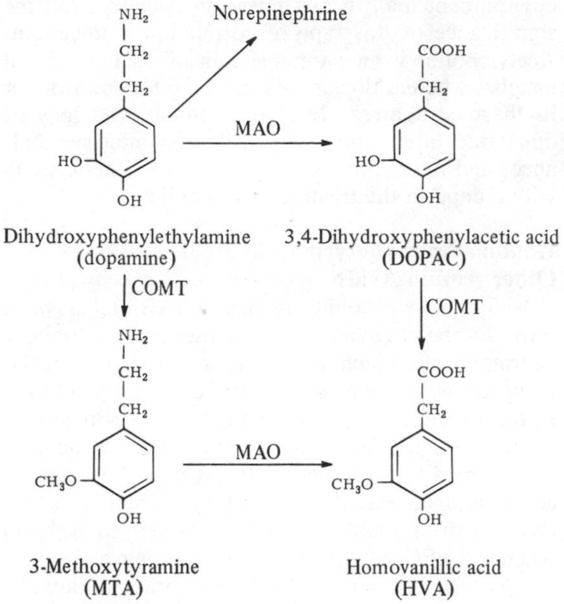

Norepinephrine

MAO

Dihydroxyphenylethylamine
(dopamine)

COMT

MAO

3-Methoxytyramine
(MTA)

3,4-Dihydroxyphenylacetic acid
(DOPAC)

COMT

Homovanillic acid
(HVA)

Figure 15–10. Catabolism of dopamine. MAO, monoamine oxidase; COMT, catechol-O-methyltransferase. As in other oxidative deaminations catalyzed by monoamine oxidase, aldehydes are formed first and then oxidized in the presence of aldehyde dehydrogenase to the corresponding acids (DOPAC and HVA). The aldehydes are also reduced to 3,4-dihydroxyphenylethanol (DOPET) and 3-methoxy-4-hydroxyphenylethanol.

catecholamine synthesis stops at dopamine and this amine is secreted as a synaptic transmitter.

Released dopamine is recaptured by an active reuptake mechanism. It is inactivated by monoamine oxidase and by catechol-O-methyltransferase (Fig 15–10) in a manner analogous to the inactivation of norepinephrine (Fig 13–5).

Many dopaminergic neurons have their cell bodies in the midbrain (Fig 15–7). They project from the substantia nigra to the striatum (**nigrostriatal system**) and from other portions of the midbrain to the olfactory tubercle, nucleus accumbens, related limbic areas, and the frontal, cingulate, entorhinal, and perirhinal cortex (**mesocortical system**). A separate intrahypothalamic system of dopaminergic neurons (**tuberoinfundibular system**) projects from cell bodies in the arcuate nucleus to the external layer of the median eminence of the hypothalamus (Fig 15–11). There is in addition an **incertohypothalamic system,** with cell bodies in the zona incerta and endings in the septum and dorsal hypothalamus and a **periventricular system** made up of short dopaminergic neurons around the third and fourth ventricle. There are dopaminergic neurons in the **olfactory bulb** and in the **retina,** where some of the amacrine cells have been shown to contain dopamine (see Chapter 8).

The nigrostriatal system is related in some way to motor function. In Parkinson's disease (see Chapter 12), the dopamine content of the caudate nucleus and

putamen is about 50% of normal. Hypothalamic norepinephrine is also reduced, but not to so great a degree. Several drugs that produce parkinsonism-like states as undesirable side-effects have been shown to alter the metabolism of dopamine or block dopamine receptors in the brain. On the other hand, L-dopa (levodopa) has been found to be very effective in the treatment of Parkinson's disease when administered in large doses. This compound, unlike dopamine, crosses the blood-brain barrier (see Chapter 32) and produces an increase in brain dopamine content.

Dopamine is also involved in the control of prolactin secretion. L-Dopa and drugs such as bromocriptine, which are dopamine receptor agonists, inhibit prolactin secretion in experimental animals and humans and have been used in the treatment of conditions in which there is abnormal milk secretion (galactorrhea). On the other hand, drugs that deplete brain catecholamines or block dopamine receptors increase prolactin secretion and can cause galactorrhea. Dopamine can act directly on the anterior pituitary to inhibit prolactin secretion and has been found in portal hypophyseal blood. Thus, it seems clear that dopamine is the hypothalamic prolactin-inhibiting hormone.

There is increasing evidence that dopamine is involved in the pathogenesis of schizophrenia. Am-

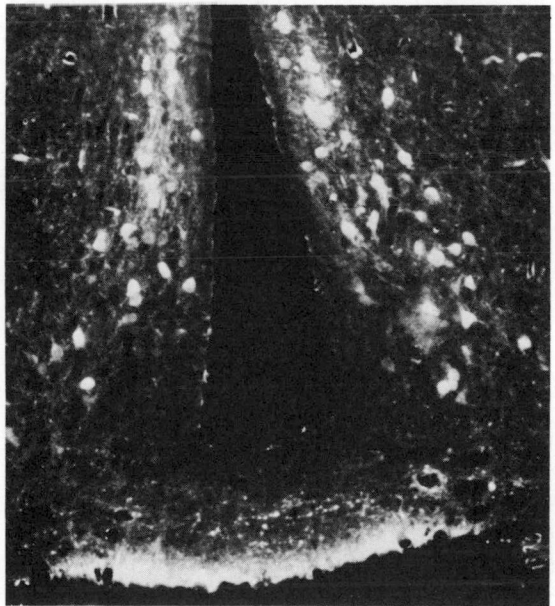

Figure 15–11. Dopaminergic neurons in the hypothalamus of the rat. α-Methylnorepinephrine injected before sacrifice to intensify fluorescence. Transverse section. Cell bodies can be seen above in the arcuate nucleus on either side of the third ventricle, and the dense nerve terminals can be seen below in the external layer of the median eminence. (Reproduced, with permission, from Hökfelt T, Fuxe K: On the morphology and the neuroendocrine role of the hypothalamic catecholamine neurons. In: *Brain-Endocrine Interaction.* Knigge K, Scott D, Weindl A [editors]. Karger, 1972.)

phetamine, which stimulates dopamine secretion, produces a psychosis that resembles schizophrenia when administered in large doses, and several dopamine derivatives are hallucinogens. On the other hand, the phenothiazine tranquilizers are effective in the relief of many of the symptoms of schizophrenia, and their antipsychotic activity parallels their ability to block dopamine receptors.

Acetylcholine

Acetylcholine is distributed throughout the CNS with the highest concentrations in the motor cortex and the thalamus (Tables 15–1 and 15–2). The distribution of choline acetyltransferase and acetylcholinesterase parallels that of acetylcholine. Most of the acetylcholinesterase is in neurons, but some is found in glia. Pseudocholinesterase is found in many parts of the CNS.

Acetylcholine has been linked directly or indirectly to a variety of brain functions. Many cholinergic neurons in the CNS form a large ascending system. The cell bodies of these neurons are in the reticular formation and their axons radiate to all parts of the forebrain, including the hypothalamus, thalamus, visual pathways, basal ganglia, hippocampus, and neocortex. This system appears to be the ascending reticular activating system, which produces EEG arousal and maintains consciousness (see Chapter 11).

A number of hallucinogenic agents are derivatives of atropine, a drug that blocks muscarinic cholinergic receptors. Injections of acetylcholine into the hypothalamus and parts of the limbic system cause drinking. Application of acetylcholine to the supraoptic nucleus in dogs causes increased secretion of vasopressin. In blinded rats, acetylcholinesterase activity is decreased in the superior colliculi and elevated in the occipital cortex. Cortical levels of acetylcholinesterase are greater in rats raised in a complex

environment than in rats raised in isolation, but the significance of this type of correlation is uncertain. Acetylcholine is an excitatory transmitter in the basal ganglia, whereas dopamine is an inhibitory transmitter in these structures. In parkinsonism, the loss of dopamine alters the cholinergic-dopaminergic balance, and anticholinergic drugs are of benefit along with L-dopa in the treatment of the disease.

Gamma-Aminobutyric Acid & Other Amino Acids

Gamma-aminobutyric acid (GABA) has been proved to be the synaptic transmitter at the inhibitory neuromuscular junctions in crustaceans. In mammals, it appears to be the mediator for presynaptic inhibition in the spinal cord (see Chapter 4) and an inhibitory mediator in the brain and in the retina. It acts by increasing Cl^- conductance (see Chapter 4), and its action is antagonized by picrotoxin. There is an increase in the amount of GABA released from the brain when the EEG pattern is that of slow wave sleep.

GABA is formed by decarboxylation of glutamic acid (Fig 15–12). The enzyme that catalyzes this reaction is glutamic decarboxylase (GAD), which has been demonstrated by immunocytochemical technics to be present in nerve endings in many parts of the brain. GABA is metabolized primarily by transamination to succinic semialdehyde and thence to succinic acid in the citric acid cycle (see Chapter 17). GABA transaminase (GABA-T) is the enzyme that catalyzes the transamination. Pyridoxal phosphate, a derivative of the B complex vitamin pyridoxine, is a cofactor for GAD and GADA-T. However, the decarboxylation, unlike the transamination, is essentially irreversible. Consequently, the GABA content of the brain is reduced in pyridoxine deficiency. Pyridoxine deficiency is associated with signs of neural hyperexcitability and convulsions, although pyridoxine treatment is unfor-

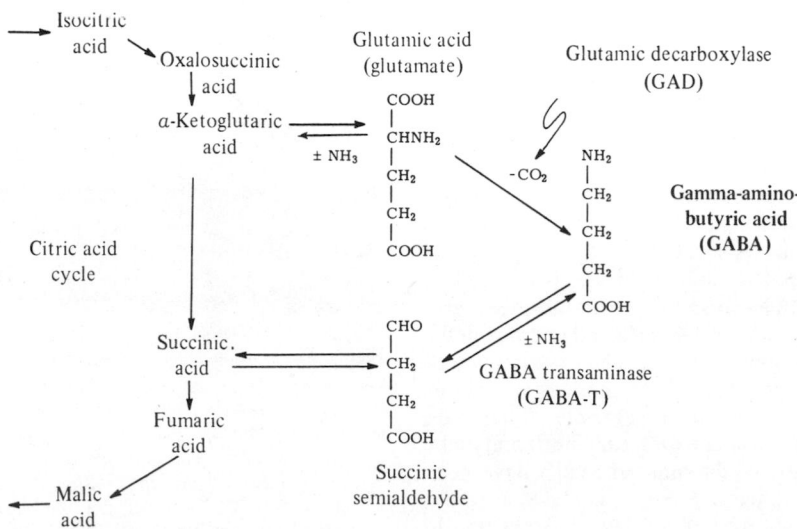

Figure 15–12. Formation and metabolism of gamma-aminobutyric acid.

tunately of no value in most clinical cases of idiopathic epilepsy.

Glutamic acid (glutamate) has been shown to be the excitatory mediator at myoneural junctions in certain insects. Glutamic acid and aspartic acid (aspartate) depolarize mammalian neurons when placed directly on their membranes by microelectrophoresis, but they have not been proved to be transmitters at any specific location in mammals.

Evidence is now accumulating that the ubiquitous amino acid **glycine** is the mediator responsible for direct inhibition in the spinal cord. When applied directly to the membranes of neurons, it produces hyperpolarization, and its action is antagonized by strychnine.

One conceptual objection to glycine and other amino acids as transmitters is the fact that these amino acids probably occur not only in neurons but in most if not all living cells. However, the necessary specificity for chemical transmission is provided not by unique chemicals but by specialized neuronal mechanisms for the storage, release, and postsynaptic action of a particular substance. Thus, almost any small diffusible substance could be a transmitter.

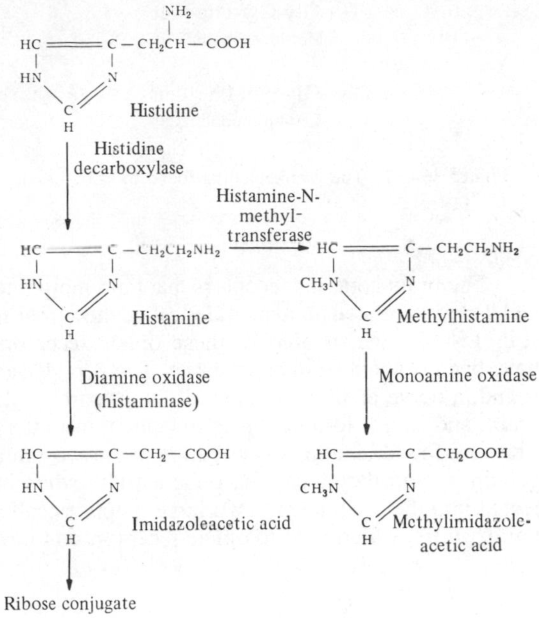

Figure 15–13. Synthesis and catabolism of histamine.

Histamine

There are large amounts of histamine in the anterior and posterior lobes of the pituitary and in the adjacent median eminence of the hypothalamus. The heparin-containing tissue cells called **mast cells** have a high histamine content, and most of the histamine in the posterior pituitary is in mast cells although the histamine in the anterior pituitary and the hypothalamus is not. In other parts of the brain, the histamine content is low, but various parts of the brain have been shown to contain histamine-activated adenylate cyclase. Histamine is formed by decarboxylation of the amino acid histidine (Fig 15–13). The enzyme that catalyzes this step differs from the L-aromatic amino acid decarboxylases that decarboxylate 5-hydroxytryptophan and dopa. Histamine is converted to methylhistamine, or alternately, to imidazoleacetic acid. The latter reaction is quantitatively less important in humans. It requires the enzyme **diamine oxidase (histaminase)** rather than monoamine oxidase, even though monoamine oxidase catalyzes the oxidation of methylhistamine to methylimidazoleacetic acid.

So far, there is relatively little evidence other than uneven distribution to suggest that histamine is a synaptic mediator in the brain. However, there are 2 known types of histamine receptors (H_1 and H_2 receptors; see Chapter 26), and both are found in the brain. The histamine content of the brain is increased by the tremor-producing drug tremorine; by the psychotomimetic agent mescaline; and by the tranquilizer chlorpromazine. The content is decreased by reserpine.

Substance P

Substance P is a peptide that is found in appreciable quantities in the intestine, where it may be a chemical mediator in the myenteric reflex (Chapter 26). Its structure is shown in Table 26–1. In the nervous system, it is found in nerve endings in many different locations. Little is known about its synthesis and catabolism. However, it is produced by primary afferent neurons in tissue culture, and is almost certainly the transmitter released by the neurons in the substantia gelatinosa. It is also found in the trigeminal ganglia. Upon subcutaneous injection, substance P produces vasodilatation, and its release from the peripheral ends of the primary afferent neurons is presumably responsible for the axon reflex (see Chapter 32).

Other Peptides

The hypothalamic hormones somatostatin and TRH (see Chapter 14) are found in other parts of the brain in addition to the hypothalamus, and somatostatin-containing granules have been reported to be present in primary afferent neurons that are different from those containing substance P. LRH is found in neurons not only in the median eminence but also in other circumventricular organs (see Chapter 32). Its function in the latter locations is unknown. There is evidence that vasopressin- and oxytocin-secreting neurons project to the choroid plexus, brain stem, and spinal cord. The gastrointestinal hormones VIP and CCK are also found in the brain, the former in highest concentration in the hypothalamus and the latter in highest concentration in the cerebral cortex. The peptides neurotensin and bombesin are also found in the gastrointestinal tract and the brain. VIP produces vasodilatation and is found in nerve fibers in the female reproductive tract. However, the function of VIP, CCK, neurotensin, and bombesin in the brain is unknown.

Tyr-Gly-Gly-Phe-Met
Met-enkephalin

Tyr-Gly-Gly-Phe-Leu
Leu-enkephalin

Figure 15–14. The 2 enkephalins found in brain tissue.

The brain contains receptors that bind morphine, and 2 closely related pentapeptides called **enkephalins** (Fig 15–14), which bind to these opiate receptors, have been isolated from brain tissue. The peptides are found in nerve endings in many different parts of the brain, and appear to function as synaptic transmitters. They are found in high concentration in the substantia gelatinosa and they have analgesic activity when injected into the brain stem. Two larger peptides called **endorphins,** which bind to opiate receptors and have analgesic activity, are also found in the body. One contains 17 amino acid residues (α-endorphin) and the other contains these 17 plus 16 additional amino acid residues (β-endorphin). Both contain the amino acid sequence of Met-enkephalin. The amino acid sequence found in β-endorphin is in turn found in a polypeptide called β-lipotropin that is secreted by the anterior pituitary gland (see Chapter 22). The significance of this fact is as yet unknown.

Prostaglandins

Prostaglandins—fatty acid derivatives found in high concentration in semen (see Chapter 17)—are also found in the brain. They have been shown to be present in nerve ending fractions of brain homogenates and to be released from the cortex, the cerebellum, and the spinal cord. However, it seems likely that they exert their effects by modulating reactions mediated by cyclic AMP rather than by functioning as synaptic transmitters.

"Higher Functions of the Nervous System": Conditioned Reflexes, Learning, & Related Phenomena | 16

In previous chapters, somatic and visceral input to the brain and output from it have been discussed. The functions of the reticular core in maintaining an alert, awake state have been described, and the functions of the limbic-midbrain circuit in the maintenance of homeostatic equilibriums and the regulation of instinctual and emotional behavior have been catalogued (Fig 16–1). There remain the phenomena called, for lack of a better or more precise term, the "higher functions of the nervous system": learning, memory, judgment, language, and the other functions of the mind. As Penfield has said, those who study the neurophysiology of the mind are "like men at the foot of a mountain. They stand in the clearings they have made on the foothills, looking up at the mountain they hope to scale. But the pinnacle is hidden in eternal clouds."* These "clearings on the foothills" are the subject of this chapter.

*From *Handbook of Physiology*. Field J, Magoun HW (editors). Washington: The American Physiological Society, 1960. Section 1, page 1441.

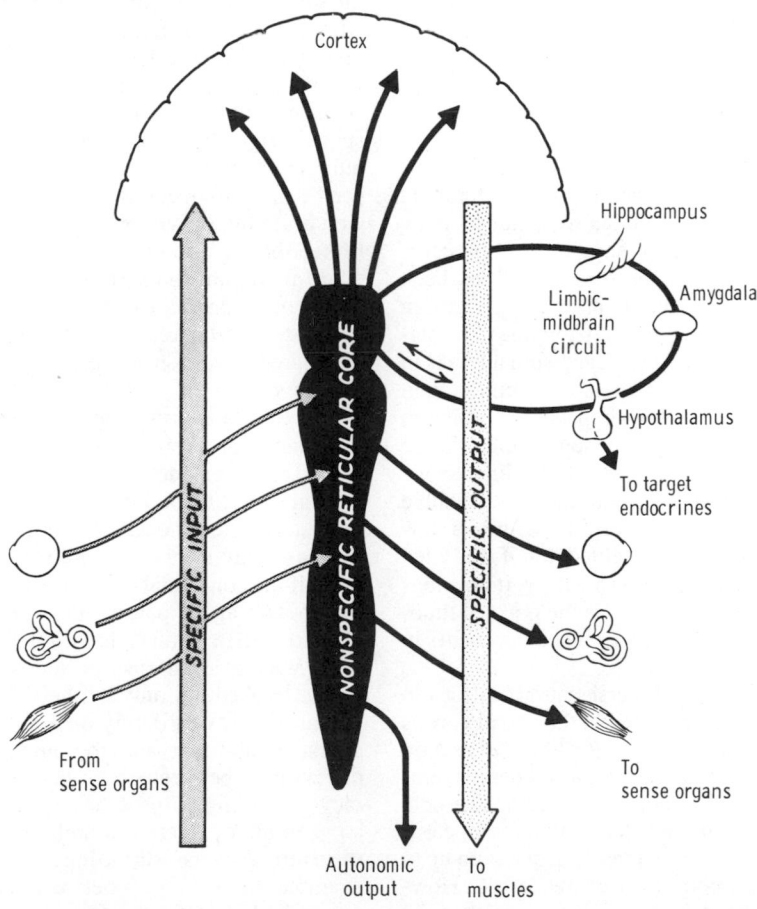

Figure 16–1. Organization of the nervous system. (Modified from Galambos R, Morgan CT, in: *Handbook of Physiology*. Field J, Magoun HW [editors]. Washington: The American Physiological Society, 1960. Section 1, pages 1471–1500.)

Methods

Some of the phenomena of the mind, such as learning and possibly memory, occur in many animal species, whereas others probably only occur to a significant degree in humans. All are hard to study because it is difficult to communicate with animals and because moral and legal considerations rightly limit experimental studies in humans. In general, the available data have been obtained by 6 methods. The oldest method consists of correlating clinical observations in humans with the site and extent of brain pathology discovered at autopsy. Information obtained in this way has been supplemented by studying the effects of stimulation of the exposed cerebral cortex during neurosurgical procedures under local anesthesia. Another method is study of the effects of stimulating subcortical structures with chronically implanted electrodes in patients with parkinsonism, schizophrenia, epilepsy, and incurable malignancies. There has been a good deal of work on changes in brain morphology and chemistry coincident with learning in animals. These studies have been supplemented in animals and in humans by measurements of regional variations in cortical blood flow during mental activities (see Chapter 32). The sixth approach has been the study of conditioned reflexes.

LEARNING

Learning is sometimes assumed to be a function of the cerebral hemispheres, but it also occurs in many animal species that have no cerebral cortex. It occurs readily in animals such as the octopus; it has been demonstrated in worms; and it may even occur in unicellular organisms. In addition, phenomena resembling learning occur at subcortical and spinal levels in mammals. Post-tetanic potentiation, the facilitation in a synaptic pathway that follows repeated stimulation (see Chapter 4), is such a phenomenon. Another is the long-term response to the injection of formalin into one paw in kittens. The inflammation and other visible effects of such an injection subside within a few weeks. However, it has been reported that if the kitten is decerebrated months or even years later, it develops flexor rather than extensor rigidity in the injected limb, even though the expected extensor response occurs in the other 3 extremities.

The rapidity with which persistent alterations in neural pathways can be produced in the spinal cord is illustrated by experiments on the effect of cord section in rats with unilateral cerebellar lesions. These lesions cause the rats to assume abnormal postures. The postural abnormalities in the limbs and trunk disappear if the spinal cord is transected in the cervical region up to 45 minutes after the production of the lesion. However, if the spinal cord is transected more than 45 minutes after the lesion has been produced, the abnormalities persist.

More advanced types of learning are largely cortical phenomena, but the brain stem is also involved in these processes. Some types of learning have been shown to produce structural changes in the cerebral cortex. For example, rats exposed to visually complex environments and trained to perform various tasks have thicker, heavier cerebral cortices than control rats exposed to monotonously uniform environments. Mice raised in darkness and then exposed to light develop additional spines on the dendrites of their pyramidal cortical cells.

Conditioned Reflexes

Conditioned reflexes are an important type of learning. A conditioned reflex is a reflex response to a stimulus which did not previously elicit the response, acquired by repeatedly pairing the stimulus with another stimulus that normally does produce the response. In Pavlov's classical experiments, the salivation normally induced by placing meat in the mouth of a dog was studied. A bell was rung just before the meat was placed in the dog's mouth, and this was repeated a number of times until the animal would salivate when the bell was rung even though no meat was placed in its mouth. In this experiment, the meat placed in the mouth was the **unconditioned stimulus** (US), the stimulus that normally produces a particular innate response. The **conditioned stimulus** (CS) was the bell-ringing. After the CS and US had been paired a sufficient number of times, the CS produced the response originally evoked only by the US. An immense number of somatic, visceral, and other neural changes can be made to occur as conditioned reflex responses. Conditioning of visceral responses is often called **biofeedback.** The changes that can be produced include alterations in heart rate and blood pressure, and conditioned decreases in blood pressure have been advocated for the treatment of hypertension. However, the depressor responses that are produced in this fashion are small.

If the CS is presented repeatedly without the US, the conditioned reflex eventually dies out. This process is called **extinction** or **internal inhibition.** If the animal is disturbed by an external stimulus immediately after the CS is applied, the conditioned response may not occur **(external inhibition).** However, if the conditioned reflex is **reinforced** from time to time by again pairing the CS and US, the conditioned reflex persists indefinitely.

When a conditioned reflex is first established, it can be evoked not only by the CS but also by similar stimuli. However, if only the CS is reinforced and the similar stimuli are not, the animal can be taught to discriminate between different signals with great accuracy. The elimination of the response to other stimuli is an example of internal inhibition. By means of such **discriminative conditioning,** dogs can be taught, for example, to distinguish between a tone of 800 Hz and one of 812 Hz. Most of the data on pitch discrimination, color vision, and other sensory discriminations in animals have been obtained in this way.

For conditioning to occur, the CS must precede the US. If the CS follows the US, no conditioned response develops. The conditioned response follows the CS by the time interval that separated the CS and US during training. The delay between stimulus and response may be as long as 90 s. When the time interval is appreciable, the response is called a **delayed conditioned reflex.**

As noted in Chapter 15, conditioned reflexes are difficult to form if the US provokes a purely motor response. They are relatively easily formed if the US is associated with a pleasant or unpleasant affect. Stimulation of the brain reward system is a powerful US (pleasant, or **positive reinforcement**), and so is stimulation of the avoidance system or a painful shock to the skin (unpleasant, or **negative reinforcement**).

Operant conditioning has been the subject of considerable research, especially in the United States. This is a form of conditioning in which the animal is taught to perform some task ("operate on the environment") in order to obtain a reward or avoid punishment. The US is the pleasant or unpleasant event, and the CS is a light or some other signal that alerts the animal to perform the task. Conditioned motor responses that permit an animal to avoid an unpleasant event are called **conditioned avoidance reflexes.** For example, an animal is taught that by pressing a bar it can prevent an electric shock to the feet. Reflexes of this type are extensively used in testing tranquilizers and other drugs that affect behavior.

Physiologic Basis of Conditioned Reflexes

The essential feature of the conditioned reflex is the formation of a new functional connection in the nervous system. In Pavlov's experiment, for example, salivation in response to bell-ringing indicates that a functional connection has developed between the auditory pathways and the autonomic centers controlling salivation. Because decortication interferes with the formation of many conditioned reflexes, it was originally thought that these new connections were intracortical. However, the effects of cortical ablation on conditioned reflexes are complex. When the CS is a com-

plex sensory stimulus, the cortical sensory area for the sensory modality involved must be present. The rest of the cortex is not necessary, however, and nondiscriminative conditioned responses to simple sensory stimuli can be formed in the absence of the whole cortex. These and other experiments indicate that the new connections are formed in subcortical structures.

Electroencephalographic & Evoked Potential Changes During Conditioning

When a new sensory stimulus is first presented to an animal, it produces diffuse EEG arousal and prominent evoked secondary responses in many parts of the brain. Behaviorally, the human or animal becomes alert and attentive, a response that Pavlov called the **orienting reflex** (the "What is it?" response). If the stimulus is neither pleasurable nor noxious, it evokes less electrical response when repeated, and the EEG and other changes eventually cease; the animal "becomes accustomed to" the stimulus and ignores it. These electrical and behavioral phenomena are thus examples of habituation. Changes in sensory stimuli also provoke arousal. For example, when an animal becomes habituated to a stimulus such as a regularly repeated tone, stopping the tone produces arousal. Habituation is a very general phenomenon in the nervous system. In the sea snail *Aplysia,* it has been shown to be associated with a decreased release of synaptic transmitter in response to a constant recurring stimulus.

If a signal to which an animal has become habituated is paired with another stimulus that evokes EEG arousal, conditioning occurs; after relatively few pairings, the previously neutral stimulus alone evokes desynchronization. This conditioned response to the neutral stimulus is an example of **electrocortical conditioning,** and is sometimes called the **alpha block conditioned reflex.** An example in the human of the alpha block conditioned reflex is shown in Fig 16–2. Electrocortical conditioning is unaffected by cutting the lateral connections of the cortical sensory areas but is prevented by lesions in the nonspecific projection nuclei of the thalamus, which indicates that the new

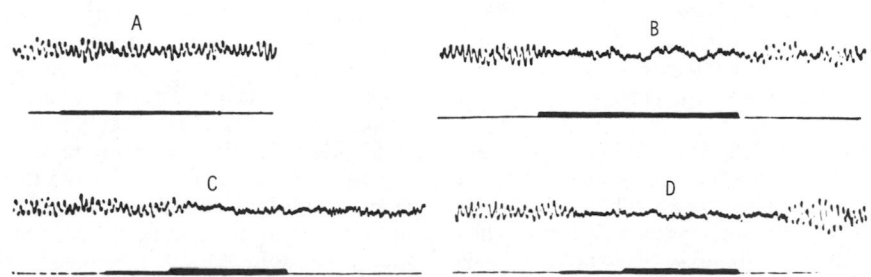

Figure 16–2. Conditioned blocking of the alpha rhythm in the occipital region in a normal human. *A:* Lack of response to a tone to which the subject was habituated (thin black signal). *B:* Unconditioned alpha block (desynchronization) in response to a bright light (heavy black signal). *C:* Failure of the tone to produce desynchronization when first paired with the light. *D:* After ninth pairing of tone and light, the tone produces conditioned alpha block before the light is turned on. (Reproduced, with permission, from Morrell F, Ross M: Central inhibition in cortical reflexes. Arch Neurol Psychiatry 70:611, 1953.)

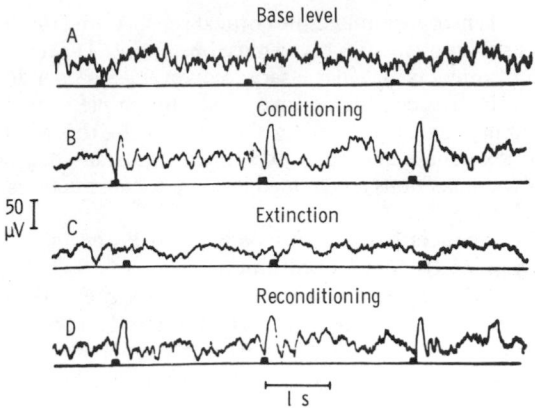

Figure 16–3. Records of the electrical activity of the hippocampus in a monkey exposed repeatedly to a tone stimulus (black signal marks). *A:* Control. *B:* After the tone was paired with a reward of food. *C:* After extinction of this response. *D:* After reconditioning by again pairing the tone with food. (Reproduced, with permission, from Hearst E & others: Some electrophysiological correlates of conditioning in the monkey. Electroencephalogr Clin Neurophysiol 12:137, 1960.)

connections involved are formed at or below the thalamic level. If an alpha block conditioned reflex is not reinforced, extinction occurs. Extinction is associated with the development of EEG hypersynchrony (extremely regular, large amplitude waves) in the cortical area concerned with the US that generated the reflex. This observation and various psychologic data suggest that extinction, or "unlearning," is not passive but, like learning, involves an active process in the nervous system.

A stimulus produces EEG and behavioral arousal and widespread evoked potentials not only if it is new but also if it has been paired with a pleasant or unpleasant experience. For example, if a tone to which the animal has become habituated is paired a few times with an electric shock to the feet, the tone will produce large evoked responses in the brain stem reticular formation and throughout much of the cortex. A similar response is observed if the tone is positively reinforced. An example of these changes in a record of the electrical activity of the hippocampus is shown in Fig 16–3. The hippocampus is not in the direct sensory pathways, but evoked potentials are regularly produced in it by sensory stimuli, presumably via the RAS.

It is common knowledge that, at least at a behavioral level, similar conditioning of the arousal value of stimuli occurs in humans. The mother who sleeps through many kinds of noise but wakes promptly when her baby cries is one example. The intern who is unaware of the calls on the loudspeaker unless his or her own name is called is another example of a conditioned arousal response to a particular stimulus.

Attention

The generalized arousal response to a stimulus can progress to focused attention. When such focusing occurs, other sensory inputs are inhibited. This inhibition is common knowledge; we have all had the experience of having to say, "I'm sorry, but I didn't hear you. I was reading the newspaper." In animals, this inhibition can occur at many levels, from the sense organs themselves to the cortex (see Chapter 11).

Intercortical Transfer of Learning

If a cat or monkey is conditioned to respond to a visual stimulus with one eye covered and then tested with the blindfold transferred to the other eye, it performs the conditioned response. This is true even if the optic chiasm has been cut, making the visual input from each eye go only to the ipsilateral cortex. If, in addition to the optic chiasm, the anterior and posterior commissures and the corpus callosum are sectioned ("split brain animal"), no transfer of learning occurs. Similar results have been obtained in humans in whom the corpus callosum is congenitally absent or in whom it has been sectioned surgically in an effort to control epileptic seizures. This demonstrates that the neural coding necessary for "remembering with one eye what has been learned with the other" has been transferred somehow to the opposite cortex via the commissures. There is evidence for similar transfer of information acquired through other sensory pathways. "Split brain animals" can even be trained to respond to different and conflicting stimuli, one with one eye and another with the other—literally an example of not letting the right side know what the left side is doing. Attempts at such training in normal animals and humans lead to confusion, but they do not faze the animals with split brains.

MEMORY

In discussions of the memory process, it is important to distinguish between remote and recent memories. It now appears that 3 mechanisms interact in the production of memories, one mediating immediate recall of the events of the moment, another mediating memories of events that occurred minutes to hours before, and a third mediating memories of the remote past. Memory for recent events is impaired or lost in individuals with certain neurologic diseases, but remote memories are remarkably resistant and persist in the presence of severe brain damage.

Stimulation of portions of the temporal lobe in patients with temporal lobe epilepsy evokes detailed memories of events that occurred in the remote past, often beyond the power of voluntary recall. This response has not been definitely proved to occur in individuals with normal temporal lobe function, but exposure of the temporal lobe or implantation of electrodes in it has been carried out in relatively few individuals who were not suffering from brain disease. The memories produced by temporal lobe stimulation are "flashed back" complete, as if they were replays of a segment of experience. A particular memory is generally evoked by stimulation of a given point; it unfolds as long as the stimulus is applied and stops when the stimulus is discontinued. For a number of reasons, it seems unlikely that the memories themselves are localized in the temporal lobes. Instead, the temporal lobe points are probably "keys" that unlock memory traces stored elsewhere in the brain and the brain stem. Normally, a key is turned by some sort of comparing, associating circuit when there is a similarity between the memory and the current sensory input or stream of thought.

Stimulation of other parts of the temporal lobes sometimes causes a change in interpretation of one's surroundings. For example, when the stimulus is applied, the subject may feel strange in a familiar place or may feel that what is happening now has happened before. The occurrence of a sense of familiarity or a sense of strangeness in appropriate situations probably helps the normal individual adjust to the environment. In strange surroundings, one is alert and on guard, whereas in familiar surroundings, vigilance is relaxed. An inappropriate feeling of familiarity with new events or in new surroundings is known clinically as the *déjà vu* **phenomenon,** from the French words meaning "already seen." The phenomenon occurs from time to time in normal individuals, but it also may occur as an aura (a sensation immediately preceding a seizure) in patients with temporal lobe epilepsy.

Other data pertinent to the physiology of memory are the clinical and experimental observations showing that there is frequently a loss of memory for the events immediately preceding brain concussion or electroshock therapy **(retrograde amnesia).** In humans, this amnesia encompasses longer periods than it does in animals—sometimes days, weeks, and even years—but remote memory is not affected. In animals, acquisition of learned responses—or at least their retrieval—is prevented if, within 5 minutes after each training session, the animals are anesthetized, given electroshock treatment, or subjected to hypothermia. Such treatment 4 hours after the training sessions has no effect on acquisition. It thus appears that there is a period of "encoding" or "consolidation" of memory during which the memory trace is vulnerable. However, following this period, a stable and remarkably resistant memory engram exists.

There is considerable evidence that the encoding process involves the hippocampus and its connections. Bilateral destruction of the ventral hippocampus in humans and bilateral lesions of the same area in experimental animals cause striking defects in recent memory. Humans with such destruction have intact remote memory, and they perform adequately as long as they concentrate on what they are doing. However, if they are distracted for even a very short period, all memory of what they were doing and proposed to do is lost. They are thus capable of new learning and retain old memories, but they are deficient in forming new memories.

Additional evidence for the involvement of the hippocampus is the observation that in humans with chronically implanted electrodes, stimuli producing seizures in the hippocampus cause loss of recent memory. The hippocampal neurons are particularly prone to iterative discharge, and hippocampal seizures presumably disrupt the normal function of this structure. Several drugs that impair or alter recent memory produce abnormal electrical discharges in the hippocampus. Some alcoholics with brain damage develop considerable impairment of recent memory, and it has been claimed that the occurrence of this defect correlates well with the presence of pathologic changes in the mammillary bodies.

Ribonucleic Acid (RNA), Protein Synthesis, & Memory

The nature of the stable memory trace is largely unknown, but its resistance to electroshock and concussion suggests that memory might be stored as an actual biochemical change in the neurons. The ability of regenerated planarians to retain learned habits indicates that such changes occur in some animal species. Planarians are flatworms with rudimentary nervous systems and a remarkable ability to regenerate when cut in pieces. They can be taught to avoid certain visual stimuli. If a trained worm is divided in two, not only does the worm regenerated from the head piece retain the response but so does the worm regenerated from the tail.

One possible explanation of this phenomenon is the hypothesis that the acquisition of the learned response is associated with an increase in the synthesis of new ribonucleic acid (RNA) in the cells. RNA provides a template for protein synthesis (see Chapters 1 and 17). If learning causes a stable alteration in the RNA, the learning response could conceivably be passed on to the new parts of the regenerated planarians. In support of this idea is the observation that treatment of the cut pieces of conditioned planarians with ribonuclease, the enzyme that destroys RNA, prevents the tail segments from regenerating into fully conditioned worms. Indeed, it has been claimed that if trained planarians are ground up and fed to untrained planarians, the untrained worms acquire with much greater facility than controls the responses the trained worms had learned. It has also been reported that in goldfish and rats, injection of brain extracts of trained animals improves learning in untrained animals.

There is additional evidence that protein synthesis is involved in some way in the processes responsible for memory. In rats, increased RNA turnover occurs in nerve cells subjected to intense stimulation. In goldfish, the antibiotics puromycin and acetoxycycloheximide prevent the retention of conditioned avoidance responses when given up to 1 hour after the training session, although they have no effect on their acquisition. Puromycin also disrupts recent memory in mice. These antibiotics inhibit protein synthesis (see Chapter 17). Theoretically, the discharge of neurons during learning sessions could lead to changes in the phosphorylation of nuclear proteins, the methylation of DNA bases, or both. This could in turn enhance synthesis of mRNA and hence the synthesis of particular proteins. These proteins could modify synaptic transmission by affecting transmitter synthesis, membrane permeability, or some other neural process. However, it is a long way from these speculations to an understanding of the relationship of RNA and protein synthesis to the formation of the stable memory trace.

Drugs That Facilitate Learning

A variety of CNS stimulants have been shown to improve learning in animals when administered immediately before or after the learning sessions. These include caffeine, physostigmine, amphetamine, nicotine, and the convulsants picrotoxin, strychnine, and pentylenetetrazol (Metrazol). They seem to act by facilitating consolidation of the memory trace. In senile humans, small doses of pentylenetetrazol appear to improve memory and general awareness. The β-adrenergic blocking drug propranolol has been reported to improve learning in the elderly, and a theory has been advanced that decreased learning in these individuals is related to increased autonomic activity. Another drug that appears to facilitate learning in animals is pemoline (Cylert). This compound is a mild CNS stimulant, but it has attracted attention because it has also been shown to stimulate RNA synthesis.

FUNCTIONS OF THE NEOCORTEX

Memory and learning are functions of large parts of the brain, but the centers controlling some of the other ''higher functions of the nervous system,'' particularly the mechanisms related to language, are more or less localized to the neocortex. It is interesting that speech and other intellectual functions are especially well developed in humans—the animal species in which the neocortical mantle is most highly evolved.

Anatomic Considerations

There are 3 living species with brains larger than a human's (the porpoise, the elephant, and the whale), but in humans, the ratio between brain weight and body weight far exceeds that of any of their animal relatives. From the comparative point of view, the most prominent gross feature of the human brain is the immense growth of the 3 major **association areas:** the **frontal,** in front of the motor cortex; the **temporal,** between the superior temporal gyrus and the limbic cortex; and the **parieto-occipital,** between the somesthetic and visual cortices.

The association areas are part of the 6-layered neocortical mantle of gray matter that spreads over the lateral surfaces of the cerebral hemispheres from the concentric allocortical and juxtallocortical rings around the hilus (see Chapter 15). The minor histologic differences in various portions of the cortex

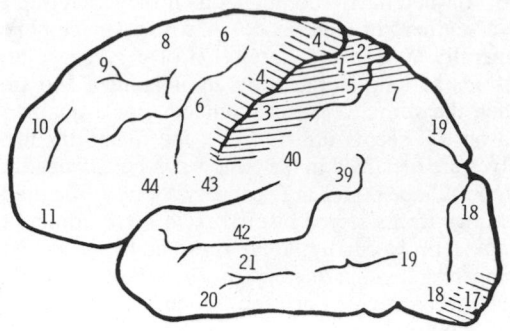

Figure 16–4. Lateral view of the human cerebral cortex, showing various numbered areas of Brodmann. The shaded areas represent the primary sensory and motor areas. The remaining white areas are the association areas. (Reproduced, with permission, from Cobb S: *Foundations of Neuropsychiatry,* 6th ed. Williams & Wilkins, 1958.)

that are the basis for numbering cortical areas (Fig 16–4) are generally but not always correlated with differences in function.

The neuronal connections within the neocortex form a complicated network (Fig 11–2). The descending axons of the larger cells in the pyramidal cell layer give off collaterals that feed back via association neurons to the dendrites of the cells from which they originate, laying the foundation for complex reverberation. The recurrent collaterals also connect to neighboring cells and some end on inhibitory neurons which in turn end on the original cell, forming loops that mediate negative feedback inhibition (Chapter 4). The large, complex dendrites of the deep cells receive ascending fibers, nonspecific thalamic and reticular afferents and association fibers ending in all layers, and specific thalamic afferents ending in layer 4 of the cortex. The function of the intracortical association fibers is uncertain, but they can be cut with little evident effect. Thus, the term association areas is somewhat misleading; these areas must have a much more complex function than simple interconnection of cortical regions.

Aphasia & Allied Disorders

One group of functions that are more or less localized to the neocortex in humans are those related to language, ie, to understanding the spoken and printed word and to expressing ideas in speech and writing. Abnormalities of these functions that are not due to defects of vision or hearing or to motor paralysis are called **aphasias.** Many different classifications of the aphasias have been published, and the nomenclature in this area is chaotic. In a general way, the aphasias can be divided into **sensory** (or **receptive**) aphasias and **motor** (or **expressive**) aphasias. They can be further subdivided into **word deafness,** inability to understand spoken words; **word blindness,** inability to understand written words; **agraphia,** inability to express ideas in writing; and the defect com-

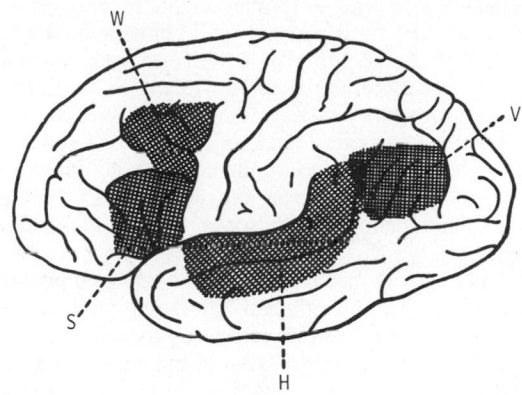

Figure 16–5. One theory of the localization of the language functions. In the hemisphere concerned with language functions, lesions at W are said to cause difficulty in expressing ideas in writing; at S, difficulty in oral expression; at H, difficulty in understanding spoken words; and at V, difficulty in understanding written words. (Reproduced, with permission, from *Physiology and Biophysics,* 19th ed. Ruch TC, Patton HD [editors]. Saunders, 1965.)

monly signified by the term **motor aphasia,** inability to express ideas in speech. Inability to carry out learned motor acts is called **apraxia.** Motor aphasia is divided into **nonfluent aphasia,** in which speech is slow and words hard to come by; and **fluent aphasia,** in which speech is normal or even rapid but key words are missing. Patients with severe degrees of nonfluent aphasia are limited to 2 or 3 words with which they must attempt to express the whole range of meaning and emotion. Sometimes the words retained are those which were being spoken at the time of injury or vascular accident that caused the aphasia. More commonly they are frequently used **automatic words** such as the days of the week, or, for some reason, ''dirty'' words and swear words.

Only one of the cerebral hemispheres is primarily concerned with the language function (see below). In this hemisphere, the locations said to be associated with the various forms of aphasia are shown in Fig 16–5. These localizations have been supported by recent studies in conscious humans demonstrating an increase in blood flow in Broca's area during talking, and increased blood flow in the superior temporal gyrus during reading (see Chapter 32). In clinical cases, however, more than one form of aphasia is usually present. Frequently, the aphasia is general, or **global,** involving both receptive and expressive functions. Lesions of area 44 in the inferior frontal gyrus (**Broca's area,** area S in Fig 16–5) cause nonfluent aphasia; in patients with fluent aphasia, Broca's area is intact and the lesions are generally in the temporal or parietal lobe.

Complementary Specialization of the Hemispheres Versus ''Cerebral Dominance''

It is a well-established fact that human language functions depend more on one cerebral hemisphere

than on the other. This hemisphere is concerned with categorization and symbolization and has often been called the **dominant hemisphere.** However, it is now clear that the other hemisphere is not simply less developed or ''nondominant''; instead, it is specialized in the area of spatiotemporal relations. It is this hemisphere which is concerned, for example, with the recognition of faces, the identification of objects by their form, and the recognition of musical themes. Consequently, the concept of ''cerebral dominance'' and a dominant and nondominant hemisphere has been replaced by a concept of complementary specialization of the hemispheres, one for language functions and sequential-analytic processes (the **categorical hemisphere**) and one for visuospatial relations (the **representational hemisphere**).

Lesions in the categorical hemisphere produce aphasia whereas extensive lesions of the representational hemisphere do not. Instead, lesions in the representational hemisphere produce **astereognosis**—inability to identify objects by feeling them—and other agnosias. **Agnosia** is the general term used for the inability to recognize objects by a particular sensory modality even though the sensory modality itself is intact. Lesions producing these defects are generally in the parietal lobe.

Hemispheric specialization is related to handedness. Handedness appears to be genetically determined. In right-handed individuals, it is the left hemisphere that is the dominant or categorical hemisphere; in approximately 30% of left-handed individuals, the right hemisphere is the categorical hemisphere. However, in the remaining 70% of left-handers, the left hemisphere is the categorical hemisphere. In adults, the characteristic defects produced by lesions in either the categorical or the representational hemisphere are long-lasting. However, in young children subjected to hemispherectomy for brain tumors or other diseases, the functions of the missing hemisphere may be largely taken over by the remaining hemisphere no matter which hemisphere is removed.

There are anatomic differences between the 2 hemispheres which may correlate with the functional differences. For example, it can be shown by computerized axial tomography that the right frontal lobe is normally thicker than the left and that the left occipital lobe is wider and protrudes across the midline. Portions of the upper surface of the left temporal lobe are regularly larger in right-handed individuals.

The Frontal Lobes

Some insight into the other functions of the various parts of the cerebral cortex is gained by ablation studies. Bilateral removal of the neocortical portions of the frontal lobes in primates produces, after a period of apathy, hyperactivity and constant pacing back and forth. General intelligence is little affected, and tests involving immediate responses to environmental stimuli are normal. However, responses requiring the use of previously acquired information are abnormal. In humans, frontal lobectomy leads to deficiencies in the temporal ordering of events. For example, humans who have been lobectomized have difficulty remembering how long ago they saw a particular stimulus card. Interestingly, left frontal lobectomy causes the biggest deficit in tests involving word stimuli, while right frontal lobectomy causes the biggest deficit in tests involving picture stimuli. Frontal lobectomy also abolishes the experimental neurosis.

Experimental Neurosis

As noted above, animals can be conditioned to respond to one stimulus and not to another even when the 2 stimuli are very much alike. However, when the stimuli are so nearly identical that they cannot be distinguished, the animal becomes upset, whines, fails to cooperate, and tries to escape. Pavlov called these symptoms the **experimental neurosis.** One may quarrel about whether this reaction is a true neurosis in the psychiatric sense, but the term is convenient. In some species, the experimental neurosis affects behavior in conditioning tests as well as general behavior.

Frontal lobectomized animals are still capable of discriminating between like stimuli up to a point; but when they can no longer discriminate, their failure does not upset them. As a result of these experiments in animals, **prefrontal lobotomy** and various other procedures aimed at cutting the connections between the frontal lobes and the deeper portions of the brain were used to treat various mental diseases in humans.

In some mental patients, tensions resulting from real or imagined failures of performance and the tensions caused by delusions, compulsions, and phobias are so great as to be incapacitating. Successful lobotomy reduces the tension. The delusions and other symptoms are still there, but they no longer bother the patient. A similar lack of concern over severe pain has led to the use of lobotomy in treating patients with intractable pain (see Chapter 7). Unfortunately, this lack of concern often extends to other aspects of the environment, including relations with associates, social amenities, and even toilet habits. Furthermore, the relief from the suffering associated with pain usually lasts less than a year.

The effects that lobotomy can have on the personality were well described over 110 years ago by the physician who cared for a man named Phineas P. Gage. Gage was a construction foreman who was packing blasting powder into a hole with a tamping iron. The powder exploded, driving the tamping iron through his face and out the top of his skull, transecting his frontal lobes. After the accident, he became, in the words of his physician, ". . . fitful, irreverent, indulging at times in the grossest profanity (which was not previously his custom), manifesting but little deference to his fellows, impatient of restraint or advice when it conflicts with his desires, at times pertinaciously obstinate yet capricious and vacillating, devising many plans for future operation which are no sooner arranged than they are abandoned in turn for others appearing more feasible. . . . His mind was radically changed, so that his friends and acquain-

tances said he was no longer Gage.''*

This description is classical, but it cannot be said to be typical. The effects of lobotomy in humans are highly variable from patient to patient. This variability has been attributed to variations in the milieu in which different patients are observed, and to differences in the extent and site of brain destruction. However, studies in which these variables were controlled make it clear that identical operations produce widely differing results which depend upon each patient's preoperative personality and past experiences. Attempts have been made to reduce the variability and the incidence of undesirable effects by selective procedures such as lesions in the anterior portion of the cingulate gyrus. Nevertheless, the complications are frequent, and because the desirable effects of lobotomy can generally be achieved with tranquilizers and other drugs, lobotomies are now performed rarely, if ever, for the treatment of mental disease.

Temporal Lobes

The effects of bilateral temporal lobectomy were first described by Klüver and Bucy. Because of removal of limbic structures, temporal lobectomized monkeys ("Klüver-Bucy animals") are docile and hyperphagic and the males are hypersexual. The animals also demonstrate visual agnosia, and a remarkable increase in oral activity. The monkeys repeatedly pick up all movable objects in their environment. They manipulate each object in a compulsive way, mouth, lick, and bite it, and then, unless it is edible, discard it. However, discarded objects are picked up again in a few minutes as if the animal had never seen them before and subjected to the same manipulation and oral exploration. It has been suggested that the cause of this pattern of behavior may be an inability to identify objects. It could well be a manifestation of a memory loss due to hippocampal ablation. In addition, the animals are easily distracted. They heed every stimulus, whether it is novel or not, and usually approach, explore, manipulate, and, if possible, bite its source. This failure to ignore peripheral stimuli is called **hypermetamorphosis.**

Clinical Implications & Significance

Various parts of the syndrome described by Klüver and Bucy in monkeys are seen in humans with temporal lobe disease. Impaired recent memory follows bilateral damage to the hippocampus. Hypersexuality may develop in some individuals with bilateral damage in the amygdaloid nuclei and piriform cortex. It is obvious, however, that in the present state of our knowledge the abnormalities seen with temporal lobe lesions and, more generally, those produced by other neocortical lesions cannot be fitted into any general hypothesis of intellectual function. Future research may provide such a synthesis and a better understanding of the neural basis of mental phenomena.

*From Harlow JM: Recovery from the passage of an iron bar through the head. Mass Med Soc Publications 2:329, 1868.

References: Section III.
Functions of the Nervous System

Beaven MA: Histamine. N Engl J Med 294:30, 1976.

Bonica JJ: *The Management of Pain,* 2nd ed. Lea & Febiger, 1974.

Bradshaw J, Geffen G, Nettleton N: Our two brains. New Scientist 54:62, 1972.

Bronisch FW: *The Clinically Important Reflexes.* Grunc & Stratton, 1952.

Burnstock G, Costa M: *Adrenergic Neurons.* Wiley, 1975.

Chusid JG: *Correlative Neuroanatomy & Functional Neurology,* 17th ed. Lange, 1979.

Davson H: *The Physiology of the Eye,* 3rd ed. Academic Press, 1972.

Desmedt JE: Physiological studies of the efferent recurrent auditory system. In: *Handbook of Sensory Physiology.* Vol 5, part 2: Keidel WD, Neff WD (editors). Springer, 1975.

Dinarello CA, Wolff SM: Pathogenesis of fever in man. N Engl J Med 298:607, 1978.

Eccles JC: *The Understanding of the Brain.* McGraw-Hill, 1973.

Elul R: The genesis of the EEG. Int Rev Neurobiol 15:1227, 1972.

Evans EF, Wilson JP (editors): *Psychophysics and Physiology of Hearing.* Academic Press, 1977.

Fields HL, Basbaum AI: Brainstem control of spinal pain-transmission neurons. Annu Rev Physiol 40:217, 1978.

Fitzsimons JT: The physiological basis of thirst. Kidney Int 10:3, 1976.

Galaburda AM & others: Right-left asymmetries in the brain. Science 199:852, 1978.

Ganong WF, Martini L (editors): *Frontiers in Neuroendocrinology.* Vol 5. Raven, 1978.

Gaze RM, Kenting MJ: Development and regeneration of the nervous system. Br Med Bull 30:105, 1974.

Geschwind N: The apraxias: Neural mechanisms of disorders of learned movement. Am Sci 63:188, 1975.

Gillin JC & others: The neuropharmacology of sleep and wakefulness. Annu Rev Pharmacol Toxicol 18:324, 1978.

Goldberg AM, Hanin I (editors): *Biology of Cholinergic Function.* Raven, 1975.

Granit R: *Mechanisms Regulating the Discharge of Motoneurons.* Thomas, 1972.

Greengard P, Kebabian JW: Role of cyclic AMP in synaptic transmission in the mammalian peripheral nervous system. Fed Proc 33:1059, 1974.

Haigler HJ, Aghajanian GJ: Serotonin receptors in the brain. Fed Proc 36:2159, 1977.

Hensel H: Neural processes in thermoregulation. Physiol Rev 53:948, 1973.

Hughes J (editor): *Centrally Acting Peptides.* University Park Press, 1978.

Ingvar DH, Lassen NA (editors): *Brain Work.* Munksgaard, 1976.

Iverson LL: Dopamine receptors in the brain. Science 188:1084, 1975.

Kales A, Kales JD: Sleep disorders. N Engl J Med 290:487, 1974.

Kornhuber HH: Motor functions of the cerebellum and basal ganglia: The cerebellocortical saccadic (ballistic) clock, the cerebellonuclear hold regulator, and the basal ganglia ramp (voluntary speed smooth movement) generator. Kybernetik 8:157, 1971.

Kuffler SW, Nicholls JG: *From Neuron to Brain.* Sinauer Associates, 1976.

Landsberg L, Young JB: Fasting, feeding and regulation of the sympathetic nervous system. N Engl J Med 298:1295, 1978.

Lefkowitz RJ: Biochemical properties of alpha- and beta-adrenergic receptors and their relevance to the clinician. Cardiovasc Med 2:573, 1977.

Lipton MA, DiMascio A, Killam KF (editors): *Psychopharmacology: A Generation of Progress.* Raven, 1978.

Llinás RR: The cortex of the cerebellum. Sci Am 232:56, Jan 1975.

Lowenstein OE (editor): *Mechanisms of Taste and Smell in Vertebrates.* Churchill-Livingstone, 1970.

Michael R: Determinants of primate reproductive behavior. In: *The Use of Nonhuman Primates in Research on Human Reproduction.* Diczfalusy E, Standley CG (editors). WHO Research and Training Centre on Human Reproduction, 1972.

Moore RY, Bloom F: Central catecholamine neuronal systems: Anatomy and physiology of dopaminergic systems. Annu Rev Neurosci 1:129, 1978.

Moulton DG: Spatial patterning of response to odors in the peripheral olfactory system. Physiol Rev 56:578, 1976.

Mountcastle VB: The world around us: Neural command functions for selective attention. Neurosci Res Program Bull 14 (Suppl):1, 1976.

Naunton RF (editor): *The Vestibular System.* Academic Press, 1975.

Novin D, Wyrwicka W, Bray GA (editors): *Hunger: Clinical Implications and Basic Mechanisms.* Raven, 1975.

Pavlov IP: *Conditioned Reflexes.* Oxford Univ Press, 1928.

Penfield W: Engrams in the human brain. Proc R Soc Med 61:831, 1968.

Purves D, Lichtman JW: Formation and maintenance of synaptic connections in autonomic ganglia. Physiol Rev 58:821, 1978.

Rakic P: *Local Circuit Neurons.* MIT Press, 1976.

Rodieck RW: *The Vertebrate Retina.* Freeman, 1973.

Rushton WAH: Visual pigments and color blindness. Sci Am 232:64, March 1975.

Schally AV, Coy DH, Meyers CA: Hypothalamic regulatory hormones. Annu Rev Biochem 47:104, 1978.

Schneider DJ (editor): *Proteins of the Nervous System.* Raven, 1973.

Schwartz GE: Biofeedback, self-regulation, and the patterning of physiological processes. Am Sci 63:314, 1975.

Seif SM, Robinson AG: Localization and release of neurophysins. Annu Rev Physiol 40:345, 1978.

Sherrington CS: *The Integrative Action of the Nervous System.* Cambridge Univ Press, 1947.

Snyder SH: Opiate receptors in the brain. N Engl J Med 296:266, 1977.

Snyder SH, Bennett JP Jr: Neurotransmitter receptors in the brain: Biochemical identification. Annu Rev Physiol 38:153, 1976.

Snyder SH & others: Drugs, neurotransmitters, and schizophrenia. Science 184:1243, 1974.

Van de Wiele RL: Anorexia nervosa and the hypothalamus. Hosp Pract 12:45, Dec 1977.

Van Harreveld A: *Brain Tissue Electrolytes*. Butterworth, 1965.

Von Euler US, Pernow B (editors): *Substance P*. Raven, 1977.

Weiner RW, Ganong WF: Role of brain monoamines and histamine in regulation of anterior pituitary secretion. Physiol Rev 58:905, 1978.

Wightman FL, Green DM: The perception of pitch. Am Sci 62:208, 1974.

Williams LT, Lefkowitz RJ: *Receptor Binding Studies in Adrenergic Pharmacology*. Raven, 1978.

Wilson VJ: The labyrinth, the brain and posture. Am Sci 63:325, 1975.

Symposium: Alcoholism and the central nervous system. Ann NY Acad Sci 215:1, 1973.

Symposium: Structure and function of the visual system. Fed Proc 35:36, 1976.

Section IV. Endocrinology & Metabolism

Energy Balance, Metabolism, & Nutrition | 17

The endocrine system, like the nervous system, adjusts and correlates the activities of the various body systems, making them appropriate to the changing demands of the external and internal environment. This integration is brought about by the secretion of **hormones,** chemical agents produced by ductless glands and passed into the circulation to regulate the metabolic processes of various cells. The term **metabolism,** meaning literally ''change,'' is used to refer to all the chemical and energy transformations that occur in the body.

The animal organism oxidizes carbohydrates, proteins, and fats, producing principally CO_2, H_2O, and the energy necessary for life processes. CO_2, H_2O, and energy are also produced when food is burned outside the body. However, in the body, oxidation is not a one-step, semiexplosive reaction but a complex, slow, stepwise process called **catabolism,** which liberates energy in small, usable amounts. Energy can be stored in the body in the form of special energy-rich phosphate compounds and in the form of proteins, fats, and complex carbohydrates synthesized from simpler molecules. Formation of these substances by processes that take up rather than liberate energy is called **anabolism.**

ENERGY METABOLISM

METABOLIC RATE

The amount of energy liberated by the catabolism of food in the body is the same as the amount liberated when food is burned outside the body. The energy liberated by catabolic processes in the body appears as external work, heat, and energy storage:

$$\text{Energy output} = \text{External work} + \text{Energy storage} + \text{Heat}$$

The amount of energy liberated per unit of time is the **metabolic rate.** Isotonic muscle contractions perform work at a peak efficiency approximating 50%:

$$\text{Efficiency} = \frac{\text{Work done}}{\text{Total energy expended}}$$

Essentially all of the energy of isometric contractions appears as heat because little or no external work (the product of force times the distance the force moves a mass) is done (see Chapter 3). Energy is stored by forming energy-rich compounds. The amount of energy storage varies, but in fasting individuals it is zero or negative. Therefore, in an individual who is not moving and who has not eaten recently, essentially all of the energy output appears as heat. When food is burned outside the body, all of the energy liberated also appears as heat.

Calories

The standard unit of heat energy is the **calorie** (cal), defined as the amount of heat energy necessary to raise the temperature of 1 g of water 1 degree from 15 to 16 C. This unit is also called the gram calorie, small calorie, or standard calorie. The unit commonly used in physiology and medicine is the **Calorie,** or **kilocalorie** (kcal), which equals 1000 cal.

Calorimetry

The energy released by combustion of foodstuffs outside the body can be measured directly (**direct calorimetry**) by oxidizing the compounds in an apparatus such as a **bomb calorimeter,** a metal vessel surrounded by water inside an insulated container. The food is ignited by an electric spark. The change in the temperature of the surrounding water is a measure of the calories produced. Similar measurements of the energy released by combustion of compounds in living animals and humans are much more complex, but large calorimeters have been constructed that can physically accommodate human beings. The heat produced by their bodies is measured by the change in temperature of the water circulating through the calorimeter (Fig 17–1).

The caloric values of the common foodstuffs, as measured in a bomb calorimeter, are found to be 4.1 kcal/g of carbohydrate, 9.3 kcal/g of fat, and 5.3 kcal/g of protein. In the body, similar values are obtained for carbohydrate and fat, but the oxidation of protein is incomplete, the end products of protein catabolism being urea and related nitrogenous compounds in addi-

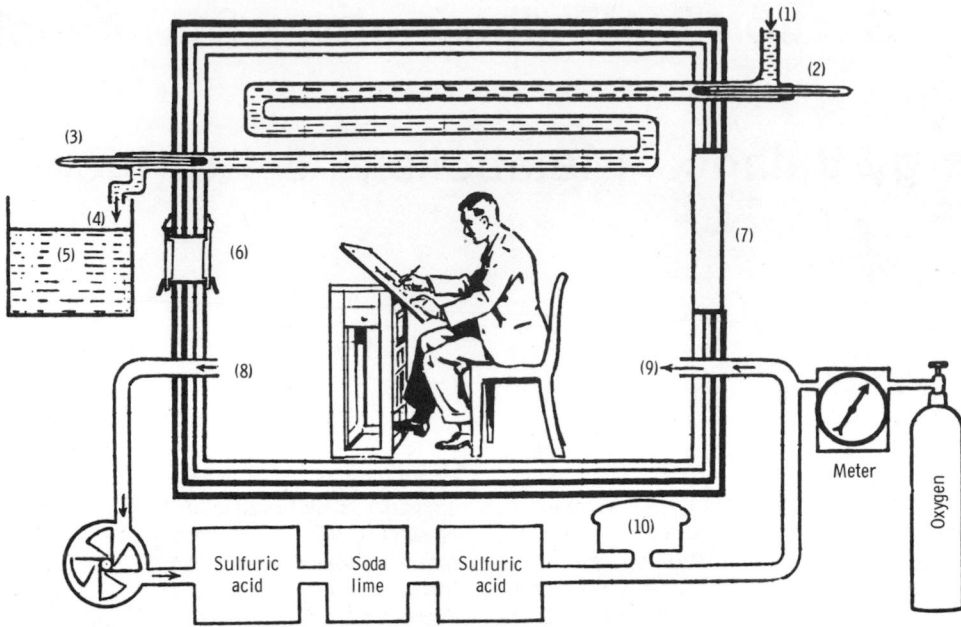

Figure 17–1. Diagram of Atwater-Benedict respiration calorimeter. Water flows from (1) to (4), and its temperature is measured at the inlet and the outlet. Air leaves at (8); water is removed from it by sulfuric acid, CO_2 is removed by soda lime, and O_2 is added at a measured rate; and the gas mixture reenters the chamber at (9). (2), inlet thermometer; (3), outlet thermometer; (6), porthole; (7), window; (9), air inlet; (10), air cushion. (Reproduced, with permission, from Bell GH, Davidson JN, Scarborough G: *Textbook of Physiology and Biochemistry,* 7th ed. Livingstone, 1969.)

tion to CO_2 and H_2O (see below). Therefore, the caloric value of protein in the body is only 4.1 kcal/g.

Indirect Calorimetry

Energy production can also be calculated, at least in theory, by measuring the products of the energy-producing biologic oxidations—ie, the CO_2, H_2O, and the end products of protein catabolism produced—or by measuring the O_2 consumed. This is **indirect calorimetry.** It is difficult to measure all of the end products, but measurement of O_2 consumption is relatively easy. Since O_2 is not stored and since its consumption, except when an O_2 debt is being incurred or repaid, always keeps pace with immediate needs, the amount of O_2 consumed per unit of time is proportionate to the energy liberated.

One problem with using O_2 consumption as a measure of energy output is that the amount of energy released per mole of O_2 consumed varies slightly with the type of compound being oxidized. The approximate energy liberation per liter of O_2 consumed is 4.82 kcal, and for many purposes this value is accurate enough. More accurate measurements require data on the foods being oxidized. Such data can be obtained from an analysis of the respiratory quotient and the nitrogen excretion.

Respiratory Quotient (RQ)

The respiratory quotient (RQ) is the ratio of the volume of CO_2 produced to the volume of O_2 con-

sumed per unit of time. It can be calculated for reactions outside the body, for individual organs and tissues, and for the whole body. The RQ of carbohydrate is 1.00 and that of fat is about 0.70. This is because O_2 and H are present in carbohydrate in the same proportions as in water, whereas in the various fats extra O_2 is necessary for the formation of H_2O.

Carbohydrate:

$$C_6H_{12}O_6 + 6O_2 \longrightarrow 6CO_2 + 6H_2O$$
$$\text{(glucose)}$$

$$RQ = 6/6 = 1.00$$

Fat:

$$2C_{51}H_{98}O_6 + 145O_2 \longrightarrow 102CO_2 + 98H_2O$$
$$\text{(tripalmitin)}$$

$$RQ = 102/145 = 0.703$$

Determining the RQ of protein in the body is a complex process, but an average value of 0.82 has been calculated.

RQs of some other important substances are:

Glycerol	0.86
β-Hydroxybutyric acid	0.89
Acetoacetic acid	1.00
Pyruvic acid	1.20
Ethyl alcohol	0.67

The approximate amounts of carbohydrate, protein, and fat being oxidized in the body at any given time can be calculated from the CO_2 expired, the O_2 inspired, and the urinary nitrogen excretion. However, the values calculated in this fashion are only approximations. Furthermore, the volume of CO_2 expired and the volume of O_2 inspired may vary with factors other than metabolism. For example, if the individual hyperventilates, the RQ rises because CO_2 is being blown off. During exercise, the RQ may reach 2.00 because of hyperventilation and blowing off of CO_2 while contracting an O_2 debt. After exercise, it falls for a while to 0.50 or less. In metabolic acidosis, the RQ rises because respiratory compensation for the acidosis causes the amount of CO_2 expired to rise (see Chapter 40). In severe acidosis, the RQ may be greater than 1.00. In metabolic alkalosis, the RQ falls. Because the RQ of the whole body is affected by respiratory factors as well as metabolism, many authors now refer to it as the **respiratory exchange ratio,** which they abbreviate R rather than RQ.

The O_2 consumption and CO_2 production of an organ can be calculated by multiplying its blood flow per unit of time by the arteriovenous differences for O_2 and CO_2 across the organ, and the RQ can then be calculated. Data on the RQ of individual organs are of considerable interest in drawing inferences about the metabolic processes occurring in them. For example, the RQ of the brain is regularly 0.97 to 0.99, indicating that its principal but not its only fuel is carbohydrate. During secretion of gastric juice, the stomach has a negative RQ because it takes up more CO_2 from the arterial blood than it puts into the venous blood (see Chapter 26).

Measuring the Metabolic Rate

In determining the metabolic rate, O_2 consumption is usually measured with some form of oxygen-filled spirometer and a CO_2 absorbing system. Such a

Table 17–1. Factors affecting the metabolic rate. The first group of factors is eliminated by measuring the rate in the basal state or is accounted for in calculating the rate. The second group must be considered in interpreting the calculated value.

Muscular exertion during or just before measurement
Recent ingestion of food
High or low environmental temperature
Height, weight, and surface area

Sex
Age
Emotional state
Climate
Body temperature
Pregnancy or menstruation
Circulating levels of thyroid hormones
Circulating epinephrine and norepinephrine levels

device is illustrated in Fig 17–2. The spirometer bell is connected to a pen that writes on a rotating drum as the bell moves up and down. The slope of a line joining the ends of each of the spirometer excursions is proportionate to the O_2 consumption. The amount of O_2 (in ml) consumed per unit of time is corrected to standard temperature and pressure and then converted to energy production by multiplying by 4.82 kcal/L of O_2 consumed.

The metabolic rate is affected by many factors (Table 17–1). The most important is muscular exertion. O_2 consumption is elevated not only during exertion but for as long afterward as is necessary to repay the O_2 debt (see Chapter 3). Recently ingested foods also increase the metabolic rate because of their **specific dynamic action (SDA).** The SDA of a food is the obligatory energy expenditure that occurs during its assimilation into the body. An amount of protein suffi-

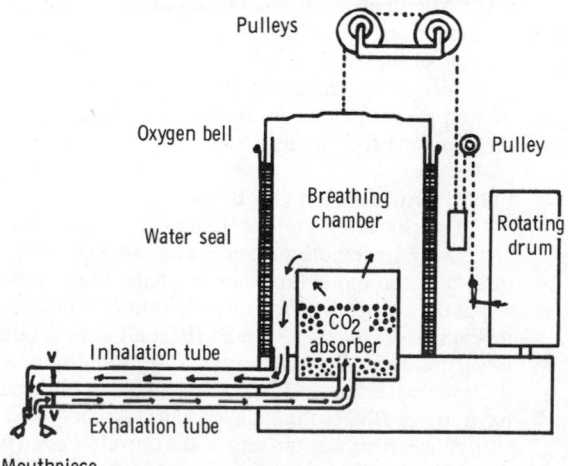

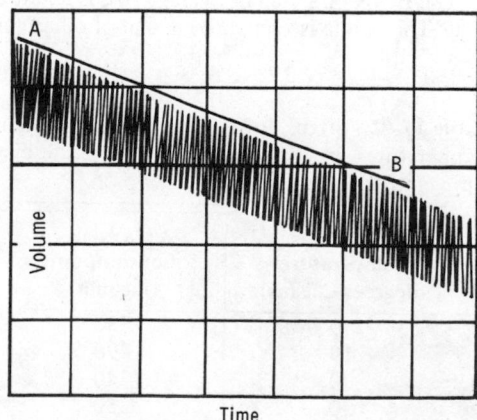

Figure 17–2. Diagram of modified Benedict apparatus, a recording spirometer used for measuring human O_2 consumption, and record obtained with it. The slope of the line AB is proportionate to the O_2 consumption. V, V: one-way check valves.

cient to provide 100 kcal increases the metabolic rate a total of 30 kcal; a similar amount of carbohydrate increases it 6 kcal; and a similar amount of fat, 4 kcal. This means, of course, that the amount of calories available from the 3 foods is in effect reduced by this amount; the energy used in their assimilation must come from the food itself or the body energy stores. The cause of the SDA is uncertain. It may be due in part to increased sympathetic discharge after feeding, with increased release of epinephrine and norepinephrine and a consequent increase in metabolic rate (see below). The SDA of proteins may also be related to the process of deamination of the constituent amino acids in the liver after their absorption. The SDA of fats may be due to a direct stimulation of metabolism by liberated fatty acids. That of carbohydrate may be a manifestation of the extra energy required to form glycogen. The stimulating effects of food on metabolism may last 6 hours or more.

Another factor that stimulates metabolism is the environmental temperature. When the environmental temperature is lower than body temperature, heat-conserving mechanisms such as shivering are activated, and the metabolic rate rises. When the temperature is high enough to raise the body temperature, there is a general acceleration of metabolic processes, and the metabolic rate also rises (Table 17–2).

Basal Metabolic Rate (BMR)

In order to make possible a comparison of the metabolic rates of different individuals and different species, metabolic rates are usually determined at as complete mental and physical rest as possible, in a room at a comfortable temperature, 12–14 hours after the last meal. The metabolic rate determined under these conditions is called the **basal metabolic rate (BMR).** Actually, the rate is not truly "basal"; the metabolic rate during sleep is lower than the "basal" rate. What the term basal actually denotes is a set of widely known and accepted standard conditions.

The BMR of a man of average size is about 2000 kcal/d. This value is compared to that of other animal

Table 17–2. Effect of different environmental temperatures on O_2 consumption at rest. Subjects were clothed in "their usual attire."*

Room Temperature (degrees Celsius)	Oxygen Consumption (ml/min)
0	330
10	290
20	240
30	250
40	255
45	260

*Data from Grollman A: Physiologic variations of the cardiac output in man. Am J Physiol 95:263, 1930.

Table 17–3. "Basal" metabolic rate in various animal species in relation to body weight.*

Animal	Metabolic Rate (kcal/d)	Weight (kg)
Mouse	3.82	0.018
Dog	773.	15
Human	2054	64
Pig	2444	128
Horse	4983	441

*Data largely from Rubner M: Z Biol 19:535, 1883; 30:73, 1894.

species in Table 17–3. Large animals have higher absolute BMRs, but the ratio of BMR to body weight in small animals is much greater. One variable that correlates well with the metabolic rate in different species is the body surface area. However, there is a better correlation to body weight raised to the 0.75 power (Fig 17–3). This correlation may be due to the fact that the metabolic rate correlates with the body proportions of the animal and that these proportions are dictated by its size in a systematic way. Nevertheless, BMRs in humans are regularly related to body surface area.

The relationship between weight and height and body surface area in humans can be expressed by the following formula:

$$S = 0.007184 \times W^{0.425} \times H^{0.725}$$

Where S = Surface area in m^2
  W = Body weight in kg
  H = Height in cm

Nomograms constructed from this formula are often used for easy estimation of body surface area. A normal BMR in an adult male is about 40 kcal/m^2/h. For convenience, the BMR is usually expressed as a percentage of increase or decrease above or below a set of generally used standard normal values. Thus, a value of +65 means that the individual's BMR is 65% above the standard for that age and sex.

Factors Influencing the BMR

Factors affecting the BMR in humans include age, sex, race, emotional state, climate, body temperature, and the circulating levels of the hormones epinephrine, norepinephrine, triiodothyronine, and thyroxine. In females, the BMR at all ages is slightly lower than in males. The rate is high in children and declines with age. It is said that Chinese and Indians have lower BMRs than Caucasians. Anxiety and tension cause increased tensing of the muscles, even when the individual is quiet, and increased secretion of epinephrine. Both effects raise the BMR. On the other hand, apathetic, depressed patients may have low BMRs. In the tropics, BMRs are lower than in temper-

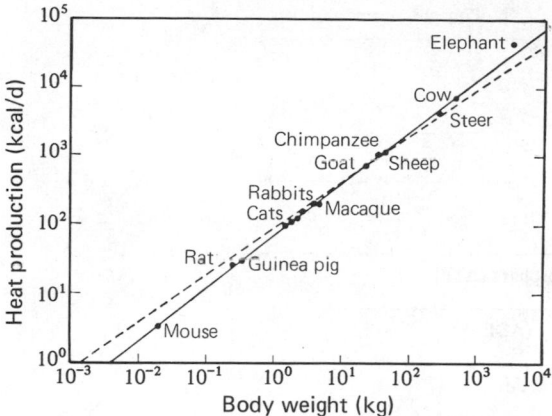

Figure 17–3. Correlation between metabolic rate and body weight, plotted on logarithmic scales. The slope of the solid line is 0.75. The dashed line represents the way surface area increases with weight for geometrically similar shapes and has a slope of 0.67. (Modified from Kleiber M and reproduced, with permission, from McMahon TA: Size and shape in biology. Science 179:1201, 1973. Copyright 1973 by the American Association for the Advancement of Science.)

ate climates and are more closely related to body weight than to surface area. An increase in body temperature speeds up chemical reactions, and the BMR rises approximately 14% for each Celsius degree of fever (7% per Fahrenheit degree). The stimulatory effects of catecholamines and thyroid hormones on the BMR are discussed in the chapters on those hormones. During prolonged starvation, the BMR falls. Sympathetic function is also depressed, and the decrease in circulating catecholamines may be responsible for the decrease in BMR. Conversely, sympathetic function and BMR increase after feeding. The decrease in metabolic rate during starvation is the explanation of why, when an individual reduces, weight loss is initially rapid and then slows down.

ENERGY BALANCE

The first law of thermodynamics, the principle which states that energy is neither created nor destroyed when it is converted from one form to another, applies to living organisms as well as inanimate systems. One may therefore speak of an **energy balance** between caloric intake and energy output. If the caloric content of the food ingested is less than the energy output—ie, if the balance is negative—endogenous stores are utilized, glycogen, body protein, and fat are catabolized, and the individual loses weight. If the caloric value of the food intake exceeds energy loss due to heat and work and the food is properly digested and absorbed—ie, if the balance is positive—energy is stored, and the individual gains weight. It is remarkable how often, in the wishful thinking of the obese,

this law is forgotten. There are only 2 ways to lose weight: by increasing energy expenditure or by decreasing food intake.

Except in humans and some hibernating and domesticated animals, the appetite mechanism regulates food intake with such precision that obesity is rare. Appetite is regulated as if it were determined by caloric needs. However, there is no evidence for a direct link between caloric consumption and appetite. As described in Chapter 14, food intake is regulated primarily by a mechanism that responds to changes in the level of glucose utilization in the cells of the hypothalamus.

To balance basal output so that the energy-consuming tasks essential for life can be performed, the average adult must take in about 2000 kcal/d. Caloric requirements above the basal level depend upon the individual's activity. The average sedentary student (or professor) needs another 500 kcal, whereas a lumberjack needs up to 3000 additional kcal/d. Children require a lower absolute intake because of their smaller size, but a larger relative intake is essential to promote growth. Recommended dietary caloric allowances in various conditions are included in Table 17–10.

INTERMEDIARY METABOLISM

GENERAL CONSIDERATIONS

The end products of the digestive processes discussed in Chapters 25 and 26 are for the most part amino acids, fat derivatives, and hexoses such as fructose and glucose. These compounds are absorbed and metabolized in the body by various routes. The details of their metabolism are the concern of biochemistry and are not considered here. However, an outline of carbohydrate, protein, and fat metabolism is included for completeness and because some knowledge of the pathways involved is essential to an understanding of the action of thyroid, pancreatic, and adrenal hormones.

General Plan of Metabolism

The short-chain fragments produced by hexose, amino acid, and fat catabolism are very similar. From this **common metabolic pool** of intermediates, carbohydrates, proteins, and fats can be synthesized or the fragments can enter the citric acid cycle, a sort of final common pathway for catabolism, in which they are broken down to hydrogen atoms and CO_2. The hydrogen atoms are oxidized to form water by a chain of flavoprotein and cytochrome enzymes.

Energy Transfer

The energy liberated by catabolism is not used

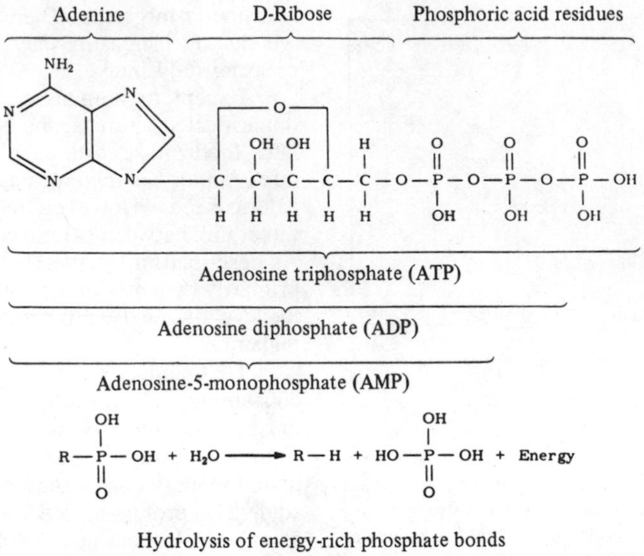

Adenine   D-Ribose   Phosphoric acid residues

Adenosine triphosphate (ATP)

Adenosine diphosphate (ADP)

Adenosine-5-monophosphate (AMP)

$$R - \overset{\overset{\displaystyle OH}{|}}{\underset{\underset{\displaystyle O}{||}}{P}} - OH + H_2O \longrightarrow R - H + HO - \overset{\overset{\displaystyle OH}{|}}{\underset{\underset{\displaystyle O}{||}}{P}} - OH + \text{Energy}$$

Hydrolysis of energy-rich phosphate bonds

Figure 17–4. Energy-rich phosphate compounds.

directly by cells but is applied instead to the formation of ester bonds between phosphoric acid residues and certain organic compounds. Because the energy of bond formation in these phosphates is particularly high, relatively large amounts of energy (10–12 kcal/mol) are released when the bond is hydrolyzed. Compounds containing such bonds are called **high-energy phosphate compounds.** Not all organic phosphates are of the high-energy type. Many, like glucose-6-phosphate, are low-energy phosphates that on hydrolysis liberate 2–3 kcal/mol. Some of the intermediates formed in carbohydrate metabolism are high-energy phosphates, but the most important high-energy phosphate compound is **adenosine triphosphate (ATP).** This ubiquitous molecule (Fig 17–4) is the energy storehouse of the body. Upon hydrolysis to adenosine diphosphate (ADP), it liberates energy directly to such processes as muscle contraction, active transport, and the synthesis of many chemical compounds. Loss of another phosphate to form adenosine monophosphate (AMP) liberates more energy. Another energy-rich phosphate compound found in muscle is creatine phosphate (phosphocreatine, CrP; Fig 17–24). Other important phosphorylated compounds, at least some of which can serve as energy donors, include the triphosphate derivatives of pyrimidine or purine bases other than adenine (Fig 17–25). These include the guanine derivative, guanosine triphosphate (GTP); the cytosine derivative, cytidine triphosphate (CTP); the uracil derivative, uridine triphosphate (UTP); and the hypoxanthine derivative, inosine triphosphate (ITP). Many catabolic reactions are associated with the formation of energy-rich phosphates.

Another group of high-energy compounds are the thioesters, the acyl derivatives of mercaptans. **Coenzyme A (CoA)** is a widely distributed mercaptan con-

taining adenine, ribose, pantothenic acid, and thioethanolamine (Fig 17–5). Reduced CoA (usually abbreviated HS-CoA) reacts with acyl groups (R–CO–) to form R–CO–S–CoA derivatives. A prime example is the reaction of HS-CoA with acetic acid to form acetylcoenzyme A (acetyl-CoA), a compound of pivotal importance in intermediary metabolism. Because acetyl-CoA has a much higher energy content than acetic acid, it combines readily with substances in reactions that would otherwise require outside energy. Acetyl-CoA is therefore often called "ac-

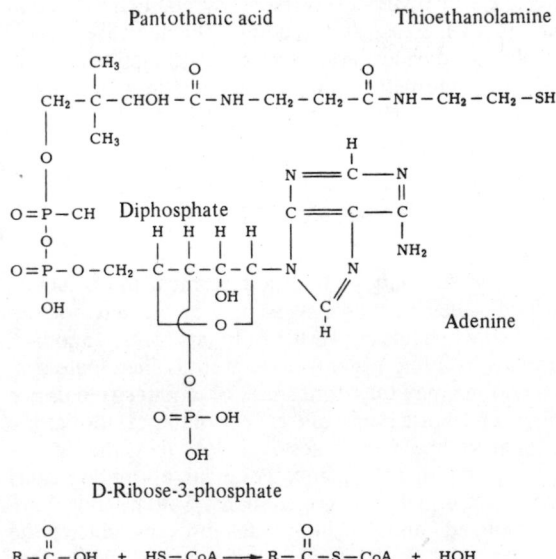

Figure 17–5. *Above:* Formula of reduced CoA (HS-CoA). *Below:* Type formula for reaction of CoA with biologically important compounds to form thioesters.

tive acetate." From the point of view of energetics, formation of 1 mol of any acyl-CoA compound is equivalent to the formation of 1 mol of ATP.

Biologic Oxidations

Oxidation is the combination of a substance with O_2, or loss of hydrogen, or loss of electrons. The corresponding reverse processes are called reduction. Biologic oxidations are catalyzed by enzymes, a particular protein enzyme being responsible in most cases for one particular reaction. Cofactors (simple ions) or coenzymes (organic, nonprotein substances) are accessory substances that usually act as carriers for products of the reaction. Unlike the enzymes, the coenzymes may catalyze a variety of reactions.

A number of coenzymes serve as hydrogen acceptors. One common form of biologic oxidation is removal of hydrogen from an R–OH group, forming R=O. In such dehydrogenation reactions, nicotinamide adenine dinucleotide (**NAD⁺**) and nicotinamide adenine dinucleotide phosphate (**NADP⁺**) pick up hydrogen, forming dihydronicotinamide adenine dinucleotide (**NADH**) and dihydronicotinamide adenine dinucleotide phosphate (**NADPH**) (Fig 17–6). The hydrogen is then transferred to the flavoprotein-cytochrome system, reoxidizing the NAD⁺ and NADP⁺. NAD⁺ is also known as diphosphopyridine nucleotide (**DPN** or coenzyme I), NADH as reduced DPN or **DPNH**, NADP⁺ as triphosphopyridine nucleotide (**TPN** or coenzyme II), and NADPH as reduced TPN or **TPNH.** The terms DPN, DPNH, TPN, and TPNH are still used, but the newer terminology

has gained such general acceptance that it seems appropriate to use NAD⁺, NADH, NADP⁺, and NADPH in this book.

The flavoprotein-cytochrome system is a chain of enzymes that transfers hydrogen to oxygen, forming water. This process occurs in the mitochondria. Each enzyme in the chain is reduced and then reoxidized as the hydrogen is passed down the line (Fig 17–7). Each of the enzymes is a protein with an attached nonprotein prosthetic group. The flavoprotein prosthetic group is a derivative of the B complex vitamin riboflavin. The prosthetic groups of the cytochromes contain iron in a porphyrin configuration that resembles hemoglobin (see Chapter 27).

Oxidative Phosphorylation

The transfer of hydrogen from NADH to flavoprotein is associated with the formation of ATP from ADP, and the further transfer along the flavoprotein-cytochrome system generates 2 more molecules of ATP per pair of protons transferred (Fig 17–7). Production of ATP coupled to oxidation in this situation is called **oxidative phosphorylation.** The detailed mechanism by which energy from oxidation of substrate is captured in ATP is still unknown, although changes in the conformation of proteins in the mitochondrial membranes may play a role. The process depends on an adequate supply of ADP and consequently is under a form of feedback control; the more rapid the utilization of ATP in the tissues, the greater the accumulation of ADP and, consequently, the more rapid the rate of oxidative phosphorylation.

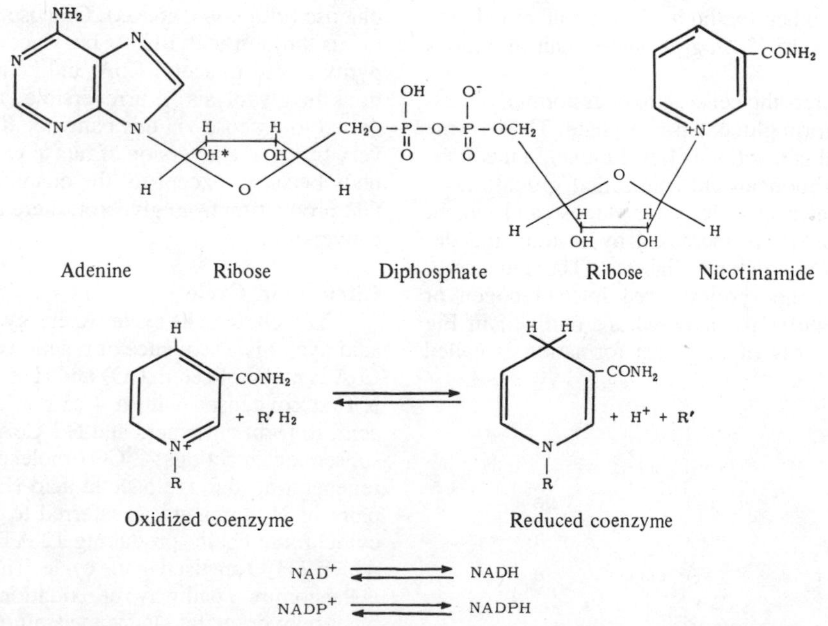

Figure 17–6. *Above:* Formula of oxidized form of nicotinamide adenine dinucleotide (NAD⁺, DPN, coenzyme I). Nicotinamide adenine dinucleotide phosphate (NADP⁺, TPN, coenzyme II) has an additional phosphate group at the location marked by the asterisk. ***Below:*** Reaction by which NAD⁺ and NADP⁺ become reduced to form NADH and NADPH. R, remainder of molecule; R', hydrogen donor.

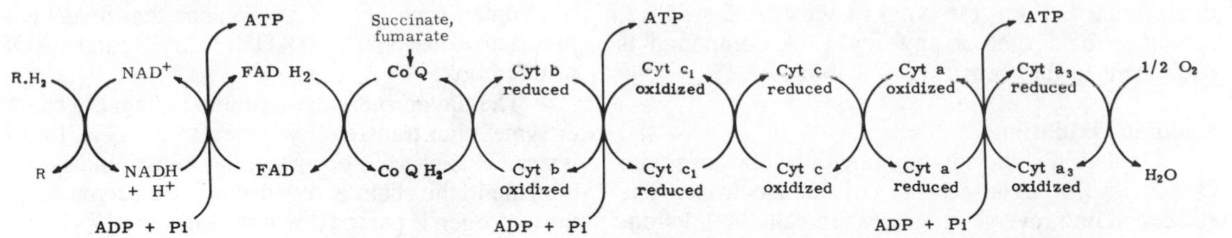

Figure 17–7. Outline of respiratory chain oxidation. Pi, inorganic phosphate; FAD, flavoprotein; CO Q, coenzyme Q; R, proton donor; Cyt, cytochrome.

In addition to its function in energy transfer, ATP is the precursor of cyclic adenosine-3',5'-monophosphate. The function of this compound is discussed in Chapter 1.

CARBOHYDRATE METABOLISM

Dietary carbohydrates are for the most part polymers of hexoses, of which the most important are galactose, fructose, and glucose (Fig 17–8). Most of the monosaccharides occurring in the body are the D-isomers. The principal product of carbohydrate digestion and the principal circulating sugar is glucose. The normal fasting level of glucose in peripheral venous blood, determined by the highly specific glucose oxidase method, is 60–80 mg/dl (3.4–4.5 mmol/L); substances other than glucose that cause similar reducing reactions are responsible for the higher values obtained with other methods. In arterial blood, the glucose level is 15–30 mg/dl higher than in venous blood.

Once it enters the cells, glucose is normally phosphorylated to form glucose-6-phosphate. The enzyme that catalyzes this reaction is **hexokinase.** In the liver, there is in addition an enzyme called **glucokinase,** which has greater specificity for glucose and which, unlike hexokinase, is increased by insulin and decreased in starvation and diabetes. The glucose-6-phosphate is either polymerized into glycogen or catabolized. The steps involved are outlined in Fig 17–9. The process of glycogen formation is called **glycogenesis,** and glycogen breakdown is called **glycogenolysis.** Glycogen, the storage form of glucose, is present in most body tissues, but the major supplies are in the liver and in skeletal muscle. The breakdown of glucose to pyruvic acid or lactic acid (or both) is called **glycolysis.** Glucose catabolism proceeds in 2 ways: via cleavage to trioses, or via oxidation and decarboxylation to pentoses. The pathway to pyruvic acid through the trioses is the **Embden-Meyerhof pathway,** and the pathway through gluconic acid and the pentoses is the **direct oxidative pathway,** or **hexosemonophosphate shunt** (Fig 17–9). Pyruvic acid is converted to acetyl-CoA. Interconversions between carbohydrate, protein, and fat (see below) include the conversion of the glycerol from fats to dihydroxyacetone phosphate and the conversion of a number of amino acids with carbon skeletons resembling intermediates in the Embden-Meyerhof pathway and citric acid cycle to these intermediates by deamination. In this way, and by conversion of lactate to glucose, nonglucose molecules can be converted to glucose (**gluconeogenesis**). Glucose can be converted to fats through acetyl-CoA, but since the conversion of pyruvic acid to acetyl-CoA, unlike most of the reactions in glycolysis, is irreversible, fats are not converted to glucose via this pathway. There is therefore very little net conversion of fats to carbohydrate in the body because, except for the quantitatively unimportant production from glycerol, there is no pathway for conversion.

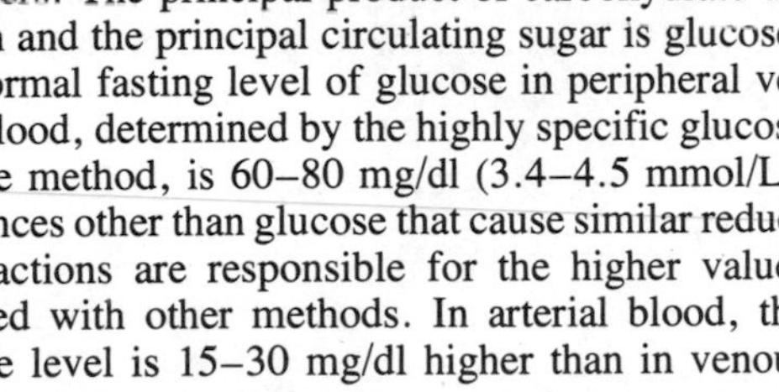

Citric Acid Cycle

The **citric acid cycle** (Krebs cycle, tricarboxylic acid cycle) is a sequence of reactions in which acetyl-CoA is metabolized to CO_2 and H atoms. Acetyl-CoA is first condensed with a 4-carbon acid, oxaloacetic acid, to form citric acid and HS-CoA. In a series of 7 subsequent reactions, 2 CO_2 molecules are split off, regenerating the oxaloacetic acid (Fig 17–10). Four pairs of H atoms are transferred to the flavoprotein-cytochrome chain, producing 12 ATP and 4 H_2O, of which 2 H_2O are used in the cycle. The citric acid cycle is the common pathway for oxidation to CO_2 and H_2O of carbohydrate, fat, and some amino acids. The major entry into it is through acetyl-CoA, but pyruvic acid also enters by taking up CO_2 to form oxaloacetic acid, and a number of amino acids can be converted to citric acid cycle intermediates by deamination (Fig 17–9).

Figure 17–8. Structure of principal dietary hexoses. The naturally occurring D isomers are shown.

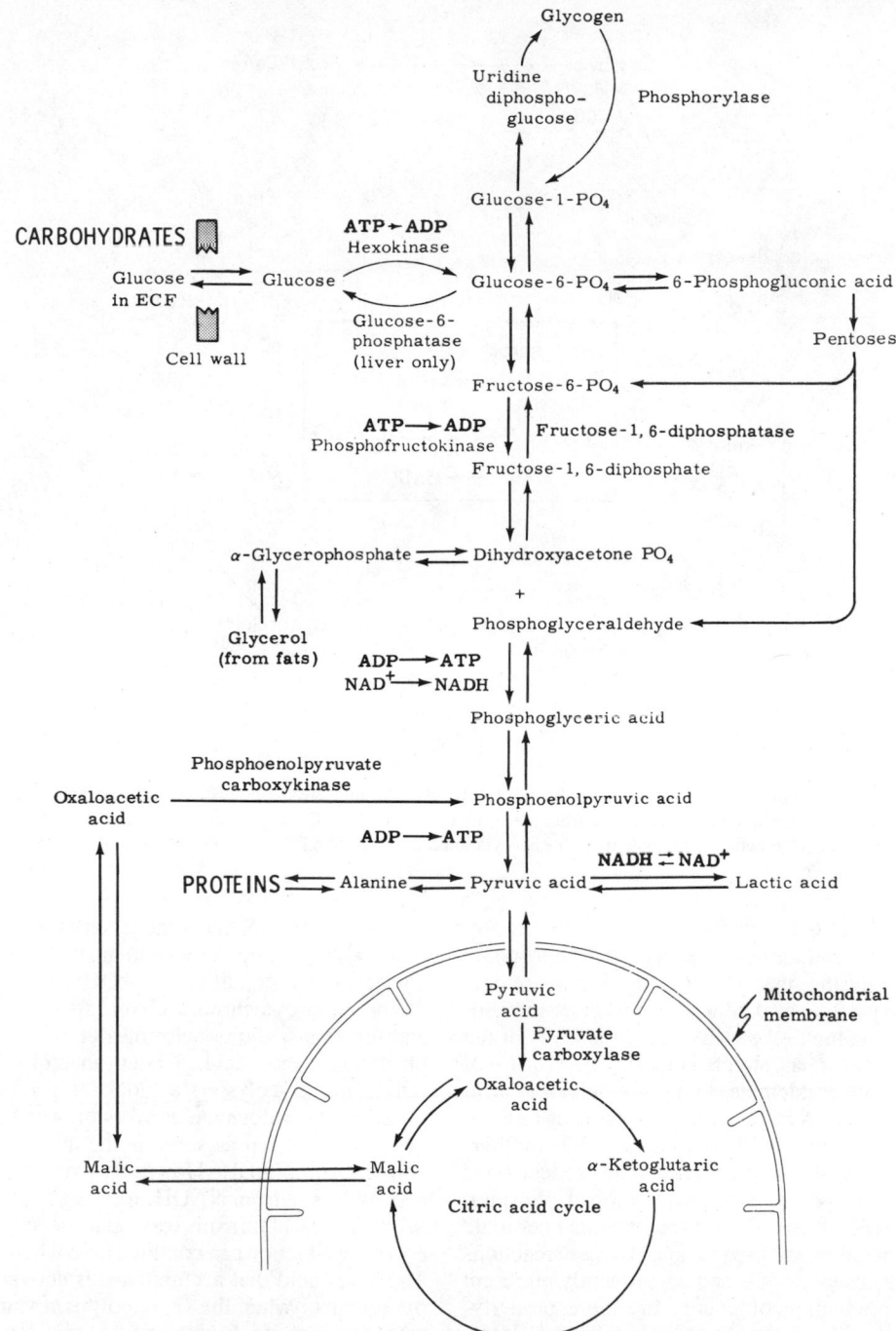

Figure 17-9. Outline of the metabolism of carbohydrate in cells, showing some of the principal enzymes involved.

The combination of pyruvic acid with CO_2 to form oxaloacetic acid is but one of a considerable number of metabolic reactions in which CO_2 is a building block rather than a waste substance. The citric acid cycle requires O_2 and does not function under anaerobic conditions.

Glycolysis to pyruvate occurs outside the mitochondria. Pyruvic acid then enters the mitochondria and is metabolized. Oxidative phosphorylation occurs only in the mitochondria. Within the mitochondria, the enzymes involved in this process are arranged in orderly sequences along the shelves and inner walls.

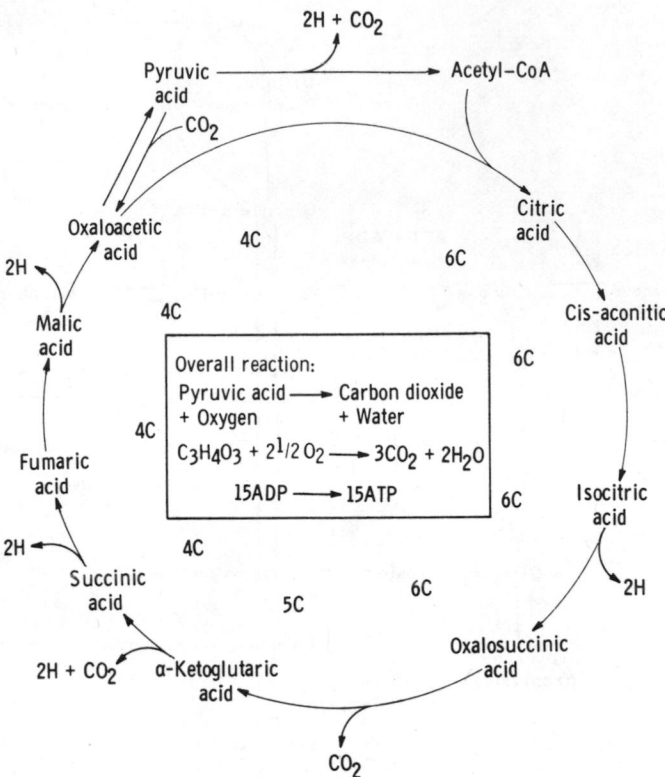

Figure 17–10. Citric acid cycle. The numbers in the circle (6C, 5C, 4C) indicate the number of carbon atoms in each of the acid intermediates. Note that 2 H atoms are transferred from the pyruvic acid → acetyl-CoA reaction and 8 H atoms are transferred for each turn of the cycle proper, generating by oxidative phosphorylation a total of 15 ATP.

Energy Production

The net production of energy-rich phosphate compounds during the metabolism of glucose and glycogen to pyruvic acid depends on whether metabolism occurs via the Embden-Meyerhof pathway or the hexosemonophosphate shunt. The conversion of 1 mol of phosphoglyceraldehyde to phosphoglyceric acid generates 1 mol of ATP, and the conversion of 1 mol of phosphoenolpyruvic acid to pyruvic acid another. Since each mole of glucose-6-phosphate produces, via the Embden-Meyerhof pathway, 2 mol of phosphoglyceraldehyde, 4 mol of ATP are generated per mole of glucose metabolized to pyruvate. All these reactions occur in the absence of O_2 and consequently represent anaerobic production of energy or, more properly, "anaerobic oxidation at the substrate level." However, 1 mol of ATP is used in forming fructose-1,6-diphosphate from fructose-6-phosphate and 1 mol in phosphorylating glucose when it enters the cell. Consequently, when pyruvic acid is formed anaerobically from glycogen, there is a **net** production of 3 mol of ATP per mole of glucose-6-phosphate; but when pyruvic acid is formed from 1 mol of blood glucose, the net gain is only 2 mol of ATP. Another high-energy bond formed anaerobically is the thioester linkage of acetyl-CoA. Its energy is used in the further conversion of acetate in the citric acid cycle.

A supply of NAD^+ is necessary for the conversion of phosphoglyceraldehyde to phosphoglyceric acid. Under aerobic conditions, NADH is oxidized via the flavoprotein-cytochrome chain, regenerating NAD^+ and forming 6 additional moles of ATP per 2 mol of phosphoglyceric acid. Under anaerobic conditions (anaerobic glycolysis), a block of glycolysis at the phosphoglyceraldehyde conversion step might be expected to develop as soon as the available NAD^+ is converted to NADH. However, pyruvic acid can accept hydrogen from NADH, forming NAD^+ and lactic acid (Fig 17–11). In this way, glucose metabolism and energy production can continue for a while without O_2. The lactic acid that accumulates is converted back to pyruvic acid when the O_2 supply is restored, NADH transferring its hydrogen to the flavoprotein-cytochrome chain.

$$
\begin{array}{ccc}
CH_3 & & CH_3 \\
| & & | \\
C{=}O + 2NADH \rightleftharpoons 2NAD^+ + & HCOH \\
| & & | \\
COOH & & COOH
\end{array}
$$

Pyruvic acid   Lactic acid

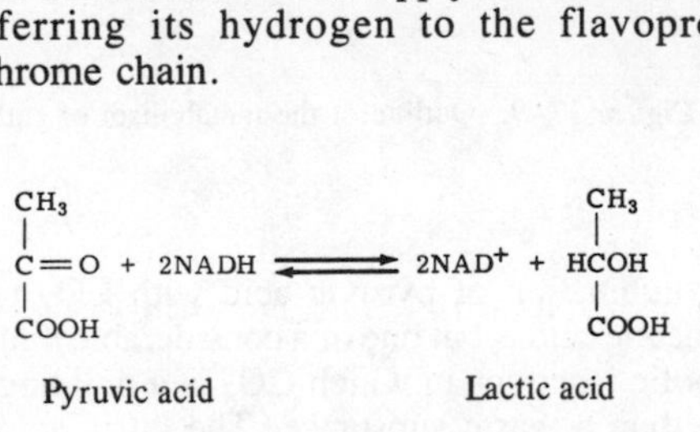

Figure 17–11. Oxidation of NADH by reduction of pyruvic acid to lactic acid.

During aerobic glycolysis, the production of ATP is 19 times as great as it is under anaerobic conditions. Not only are 6 additional moles of ATP formed by NADH oxidation via the flavoprotein-cytochrome chain, but similar oxidation of the 2 mol of NADH formed by the conversion of 2 mol of pyruvic acid to acetyl-CoA produces 6 mol of ATP, and each turn of the strictly aerobic citric acid cycle generates 12 mol of ATP. Therefore, the net production per mole of blood glucose metabolized aerobically via the Embden-Meyerhof pathway and citric acid cycle is 38 mol (2 + [2 × 3] + [2 × 3] + [2 × 12]) of ATP.

Glucose oxidation via the hexosemonophosphate shunt generates large amounts of NADPH. A supply of this reduced coenzyme is essential for many metabolic processes. The pentoses formed in the process are building blocks for nucleotides (see below). The amount of ATP generated depends upon the amount of NADPH converted to NADH and then oxidized.

"Directional Flow Valves"

Metabolism is regulated by a variety of hormones and other factors. To bring about any net change in a particular metabolic process, regulatory factors obviously must drive a chemical reaction in one direction. Most of the reactions in intermediary metabolism are freely reversible, but there are a number of "directional flow valves," reactions that proceed in one direction under the influence of one enzyme or transport mechanism and in the opposite direction under the influence of another. Five examples in the intermediary metabolism of carbohydrate are shown in Fig 17–12. The different pathways for fatty acid synthesis and catabolism (see below) are another example. Regulatory factors exert their influence on metabolism by acting directly or indirectly at these "directional flow valves."

Phosphorylase

Glycogen breakdown is regulated by several hormones. Glycogen is synthesized from glucose-1-phosphate via uridine diphosphoglucose (UDPG; Fig 17–13), with the enzyme **glycogen synthetase** catalyzing the final step. Glycogen is a branched glucose polymer with 2 types of glucoside linkage. Cleavage of the 1:4α linkage in the polymer chain is catalyzed by **phosphorylase,** while cleavage of the 1:6α linkages at branching points is catalyzed by another enzyme.

Phosphorylase is activated by epinephrine in a sequence of reactions that provides a classic example of hormonal action via cyclic AMP. These reactions are summarized in Fig 17–14. Protein kinase is activated by cyclic AMP (see Fig 1–13) and catalyzes the transfer of a phosphate group to phosphorylase kinase, converting it to its active form (Fig 17–14). The phosphorylase kinase in turn catalyzes the phosphorylation and consequent activation of phosphorylase. Inactive phosphorylase is known as phosphorylase b, or dephosphophosphorylase, and activated phosphorylase as phosphorylase a, or phosphophosphorylase.

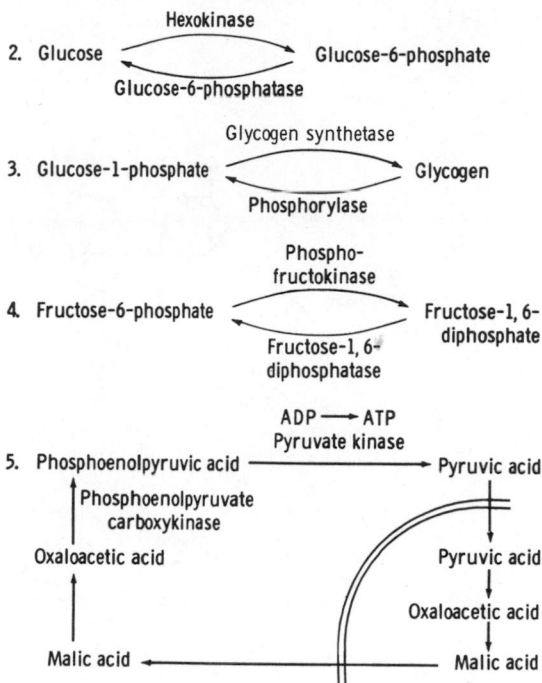

Figure 17–12. Five examples of "directional flow valves" in carbohydrate metabolism: reactions that proceed in one direction by one mechanism and in the other direction by a different mechanism. The double line in 5 represents the mitochondrial membrane. Pyruvic acid is converted to malic acid in mitochondria, and the malic acid diffuses out of the mitochondria to the cytosol, where it is converted to phosphoenolpyruvic acid.

Activation of protein kinase by cyclic AMP not only increases glycogen breakdown but also inhibits glycogen synthesis. Glycogen synthetase (Fig 17–13) is active in its dephosphorylated form and inactive when phosphorylated, and it is phosphorylated along with phosphorylase kinase when protein kinase is activated.

Because the liver contains the enzyme **glucose-6-phosphatase,** much of the glucose-6-phosphate that is formed in this organ can be converted to glucose and enter the bloodstream, raising the blood glucose level. The kidneys can also contribute to the elevation. Other tissues do not contain this enzyme, so in them a large proportion of the glucose-6-phosphate is catabolized via the Embden-Meyerhof pathway and hexosemonophosphate shunt pathway. Increased glucose catabolism in skeletal muscle causes a rise in the blood lactic acid level (Chapter 3).

By stimulating adenylate cyclase, epinephrine causes activation of the phosphorylase in liver and skeletal muscle. The consequences of this activation are a rise in the blood glucose and lactic acid levels. Glucagon has a similar action, but it exerts its effect only on the phosphorylase in the liver. Consequently, glucagon causes a rise in blood glucose without any change in blood lactic acid.

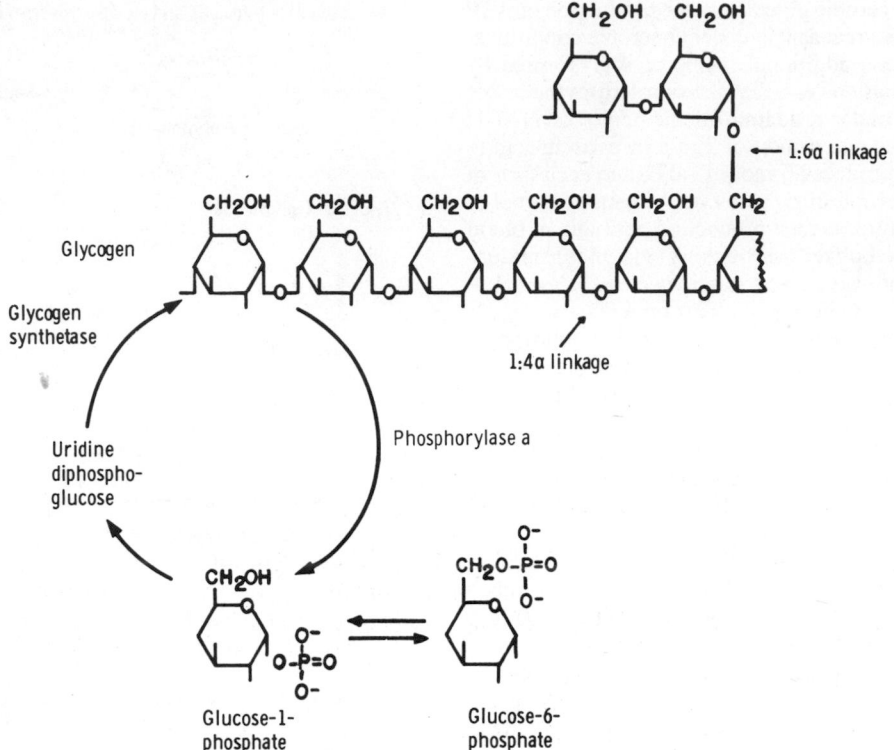

Figure 17–13. Glycogen formation and breakdown. The activation of phosphorylase a is summarized in Fig 17–14.

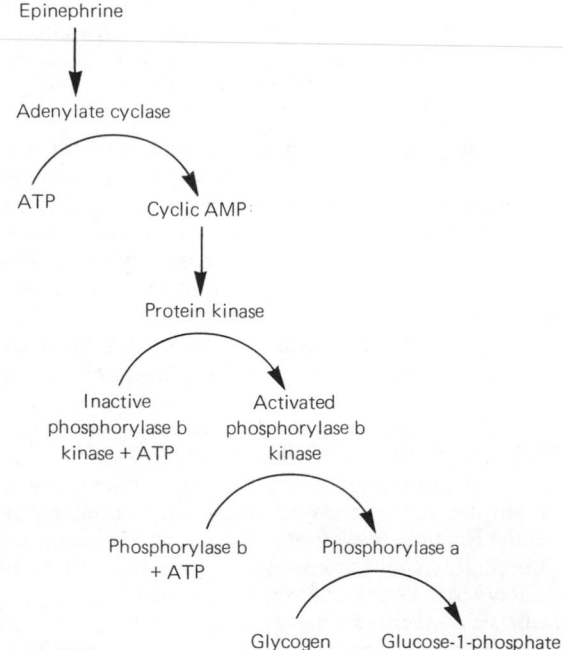

Figure 17–14. Cascade sequence of reactions by which epinephrine activates phosphorylase. Glucagon has a similar action in liver but not in skeletal muscle. (Reproduced, with permission, from Peake GT: The role of cyclic nucleotides in the secretion of pituitary growth hormone. In: *Frontiers of Neuroendocrinology, 1973.* Ganong WF, Martini L [editors]. Oxford Univ Press, 1973.)

McArdle's Syndrome

In the clinical condition known as **McArdle's syndrome,** or **myophosphorylase deficiency glycogenosis,** glycogen accumulates in skeletal muscles because of a deficiency of muscle phosphorylase. As would be predicted, patients with this disease have a greatly reduced exercise tolerance; they cannot break down their muscle glycogen to provide the energy for muscle contraction (Chapter 3), and the glucose reaching their muscles from the bloodstream is sufficient only for the demands of very mild exercise. Patients with McArdle's syndrome respond with a normal rise in blood glucose when given glucagon or epinephrine, indicating that their hepatic phosphorylase is normal.

The "Hepatic Glucostat"

There is a net uptake of glucose by the liver when the blood glucose is high and a net discharge when it is low. The liver thus functions as a sort of "glucostat," maintaining a constant circulating glucose level. This function is not automatic; glucose uptake and glucose discharge are affected by the actions of numerous hormones. Endocrine regulation of the blood glucose level and of carbohydrate metabolism in general is discussed in Chapter 19.

Effects of Glycogen on Hepatic Function

When the hepatic glycogen level is high, the rate of deamination of amino acids is depressed, and the amino acids are thus preserved for other uses. Protein catabolism is decreased by the administration of glucose (**protein-sparing** effect of glucose; see below), and part of this sparing may be mediated via the effect of glycogen on deamination. Ketone body formation is also depressed when the liver glycogen content is high (see below). Acetylation and glucuronide conjugation of various substances in the liver progress at a faster rate when the glycogen content is high, and the glycogen-rich liver is more resistant to toxic agents and pathologic processes. This is why it is important in the treatment of infectious hepatitis to maintain a high carbohydrate intake.

Renal Handling of Glucose

In the kidney, glucose is freely filtered; but at normal blood glucose levels, all but a very small amount is reabsorbed in the proximal tubules (see Chapter 38). When the amount filtered increases, reabsorption increases, but there is a limit to the amount of glucose the proximal tubules can reabsorb. When the tubular maximum for glucose (TmG) is exceeded, appreciable amounts of glucose appear in the urine (**glycosuria**). The **renal threshold** for glucose, the arterial blood level at which glycosuria appears, is reached when the venous blood glucose concentration is usually about 180 mg/dl, but it may be higher if the glomerular filtration rate is low.

Glycosuria

Glycosuria occurs when the blood glucose is elevated because of relative insulin deficiency (diabetes mellitus) or because of excessive glycogenolysis after physical or emotional trauma. In some individuals, the glucose transport mechanism in the renal tubules is congenitally defective, so that glycosuria is present at normal blood glucose levels. This condition is called **renal glycosuria**. **Alimentary glycosuria,** glycosuria after ingestion of a high-carbohydrate meal, has been claimed to occur in normal individuals, but many of these people actually have mild diabetes mellitus. The maximal rate of glucose absorption from the intestine is about 120 g/h.

Factors Determining the Blood Glucose Level

The blood glucose level at any given time is determined by the balance between the amount of glucose entering the bloodstream and the amount leaving it. The principal determinants are therefore the dietary intake; the rate of entry into the cells of muscle, adipose tissue, and other organs; and the glucostatic activity of the liver (Fig 17–15). Five percent of ingested glucose is promptly converted into glycogen in the liver and 30–40% is converted into fat. The remainder is metabolized in muscle and other tissues. During fasting, liver glycogen is broken down and the liver adds glucose to the bloodstream. With more prolonged fasting, glycogen is depleted and there is increased gluconeogenesis from amino acids and glycerol in the liver. There is a modest decline in blood glucose to about 65 mg/dl in men and about 40 mg/dl in

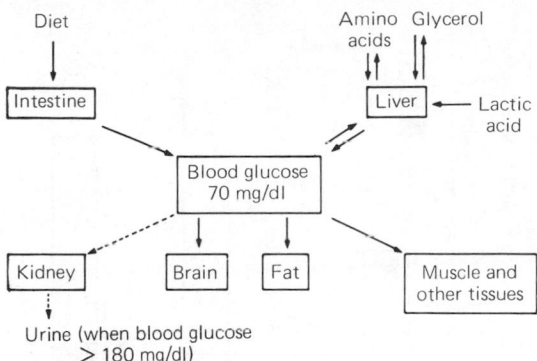

Figure 17–15. Blood glucose homeostasis, illustrating the glucostatic function of the liver.

premenopausal women, but gluconeogenesis prevents the occurrence of more severe hypoglycemia, even during prolonged starvation. The cause of the lower fasting blood glucose concentrations in women is unknown, but it is interesting that values similar to those seen in women are seen in fasting prepuberal boys.

Carbohydrate Homeostasis in Exercise

In a 70 kg man, stored carbohydrate totals about 1900 kcal: 350 g of muscle glycogen, 85 g of liver glycogen, and 20 g of glucose in extracellular fluid. In contrast, 140,000 kcal, or 80–85% of body fuel supplies, are stored in fat and the remainder in protein. Resting muscle utilizes fatty acids for its metabolism.

During exercise, the caloric needs of muscle are initially met by glycogenolysis in muscle and increased uptake of muscle glucose. Blood glucose initially rises with increased hepatic glycogenolysis but may fall with strenuous, prolonged exercise. There is an increase in gluconeogenesis (Fig 17–16). Plasma insulin falls, and plasma glucagon rises.

After exercise, liver glycogen is replenished by additional gluconeogenesis and a decrease in hepatic glucose output. Insulin levels rise sharply, especially in hepatic portal blood. The insulin entering the liver presumably promotes glycogen storage (see Chapter 19).

Metabolism of Hexoses Other Than Glucose

Other hexoses that are absorbed from the intestine include galactose, which is liberated by the digestion of lactose and converted to glucose in the body; and fructose, part of which is ingested and part liberated by hydrolysis of sucrose. After phosphorylation, galactose is converted to uridine diphosphogalactose. The uridine diphosphogalactose is converted to uridine diphosphoglucose, which functions in glycogen synthesis (Fig 17–13). The latter reaction is reversible, and this is the way the galactose necessary for formation of glycolipids and mucoproteins is formed when dietary galactose intake is inadequate. The utilization of galactose, like that of glucose, is dependent upon insulin (see Chapter 19). In the inborn error of metabo-

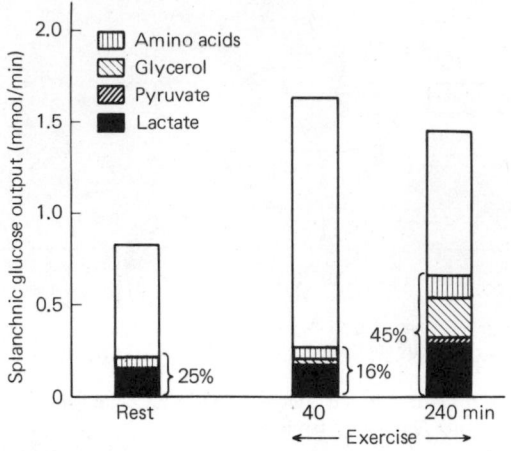

Figure 17–16. Splanchnic (hepatic) glucose output, showing output due to glycogenolysis (open bars) and output presumably due to gluconeogenesis (in brackets). The values for gluconeogenesis are measured values for splanchnic uptake of the various gluconeogenetic precursors. (Reproduced, with permission, from Felig P, Wahren J: Fuel homeostasis in exercise. N Engl J Med 293:1078, 1975.)

lism known as **galactosemia,** there is a congenital deficiency of phosphogalactose uridyl transferase, the enzyme responsible for the reaction between galactose-1-phosphate and uridine diphosphoglucose, so that ingested galactose accumulates in the circulation. Serious disturbances of growth and development result. Treatment with galactose-free diets improves this condition without leading to galactose deficiency because the enzymes necessary for the formation of uridine diphosphogalactose from uridine diphosphoglucose are present.

Fructose may be phosphorylated on the sixth carbon atom, competing with glucose for the hexokinase involved; or it may be phosphorylated on the first carbon atom, a reaction catalyzed by a specific fructokinase. Fructose-1-phosphate is then split into dihydroxyacetone phosphate and glyceraldehyde. The glyceraldehyde is phosphorylated, and it and the dihydroxyacetone phosphate enter the pathways for glu-

cose metabolism. Fructose-1-phosphate may also be phosphorylated to form fructose-1,6-diphosphate (Fig 17–17). Since the reactions proceeding through phosphorylation of fructose in the 1- position can occur at a normal rate in the absence of insulin, it has been recommended that fructose be given to diabetics to replete their carbohydrate stores. However, because appreciable quantities of fructose are metabolized only in the intestines and the liver, fructose treatment is of limited value.

PROTEIN METABOLISM

Proteins

Proteins are made up of amino acids (Fig 17–18) linked into chains by **peptide bonds** joining the amino group of one amino acid to the carboxyl group of the next. In addition, some proteins contain carbohydrates (glycoproteins) and lipids (lipoproteins). The order of the amino acids in the chains is called the **primary structure** of a protein. The chains are twisted and folded in complex ways, and the term **secondary structure** of a protein refers to the spatial arrangement produced by the twisting and folding. The most common secondary structure is a regular coil with 3.7 amino acid residues per turn (α-helix). The **tertiary structure** of a protein is the arrangement of the twisted chains into layers, crystals, or fibers. Some protein molecules are made of subunits (eg, hemoglobin; see Chapter 27), and the term **quaternary structure** is used to refer to the arrangement of the subunits.

Amino Acids

The amino acids that are found in proteins are shown in Table 17–4. Various other important amino acids such as ornithine, 5-hydroxytryptophan, L-dopa, and thyroxine occur in the body but are not found in proteins to any appreciable degree. In higher animals, the L-isomers of the amino acids are the only naturally occurring forms. The L-isomers of thyroxine and hormones such as epinephrine that are formed from amino acids are much more active than the D-isomers. The

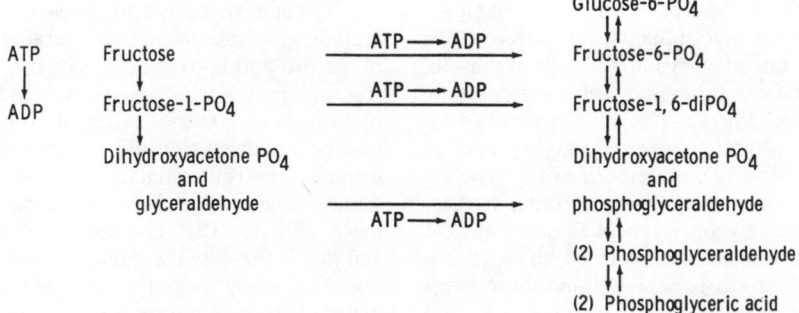

Figure 17–17. Metabolism of fructose, showing how fructose enters the Embden-Meyerhof pathway for glucose catabolism.

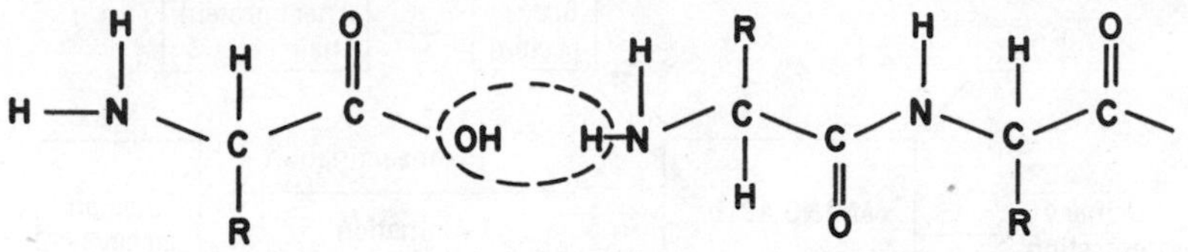

Amino acid   Polypeptide chain

Figure 17–18. Amino acid structure and formation of peptide bonds. The dotted lines show how the peptide bonds are formed, with the production of H_2O. R, remainder of amino acid. For example, in glycine, R = H; in glutamic acid, R = $-(CH_2)_2-COOH$.

amino acids are acidic, neutral, or basic in reaction, depending upon the relative proportions of free acidic ($-COOH$) or basic ($-NH_2$) groups in the molecule.

The Amino Acid Pool

Proteins are absorbed from the gastrointestinal tract in infants, but only amino acids are absorbed in normal adults. The body's own proteins are being continuously hydrolyzed to amino acids and resynthesized. The turnover rate of endogenous proteins averages 80–100 g/d, being highest in the intestinal mucosa and practically nil in collagen. The amino acids formed by endogenous protein breakdown are in no way different from those derived from ingested protein. With the latter, they form a common **amino acid pool** that supplies the needs of the body (Fig 17–19). In the kidney, most of the filtered amino acids are reabsorbed; but in diseases such as the Fanconi syndrome, **aminoaciduria** is present, apparently as a result of congenital defects in the renal tubules. During growth, the equilibrium between amino acids and body proteins shifts toward the latter, so that synthesis exceeds breakdown. At all ages, a small amount of protein is lost as hair. Some small proteins are lost in the urine, and there are unreabsorbed protein digestive secretions in the stools. These losses are made up by synthesis from the amino acid pool.

Specific Metabolic Functions of Amino Acids

Thyroxine, catecholamines, histamine, serotonin, melatonin, and intermediates in the urea cycle are formed from specific amino acids. Methionine, cystine, and cysteine provide the sulfur contained in proteins, coenzyme A, taurine, and other biologically important compounds. Methionine is converted into S-adenosylmethionine, which is the active methylating agent in the synthesis of compounds such as epinephrine, acetylcholine, and creatine. It is a major donor of biologically labile methyl groups, but methyl groups can also be synthesized from a derivative of formic acid bound to folic acid derivatives if the diet contains adequate amounts of folic acid and cyanocobalamin.

Urinary Sulfates

Sulfur-containing amino acids are the source of the sulfates in the urine. A few unoxidized sulfur-containing compounds are excreted (urinary **neutral sulfur**), but most of the urinary excretion is in the form of **sulfate** (SO_4^{2-}) accompanied by corresponding amounts of cation (Na^+, K^+, NH_4^+, or H^+). The **ethereal sulfates** in the urine are organic sulfate esters ($R-O-SO_3H$) formed in the liver from endogenous and exogenous phenols, including estrogens and other steroids, indoles, and drugs.

Table 17–4. Amino acids found in proteins. Those in bold type are essential amino acids.

Neutral Amino Acids	Acidic Amino Acids (Monoamino acids containing 2 or
Amino acids with unsubstituted chains	more carboxyl groups)
Glycine	Aspartic acid
Alanine	Asparagine
Valine	Glutamic acid
Leucine	Glutamine
Isoleucine	γ-Carboxyglutamic acid
Hydroxyl-substituted amino acids	Basic Amino Acids (Diaminomonocarboxylic acids)
Serine	**Arginine***
Threonine	**Lysine**
Sulfur-containing amino acids	Hydroxylysine
Cysteine	**Histidine***
Methionine	Imino Acids (contain imino group but no amino group)
Aromatic amino acids	Proline
Phenylalanine	4-Hydroxyproline
Tyrosine	
Tryptophan	

*Arginine and histidine are sometimes called "semi-essential"; they are not necessary for maintenance of nitrogen balance, but are needed for normal growth

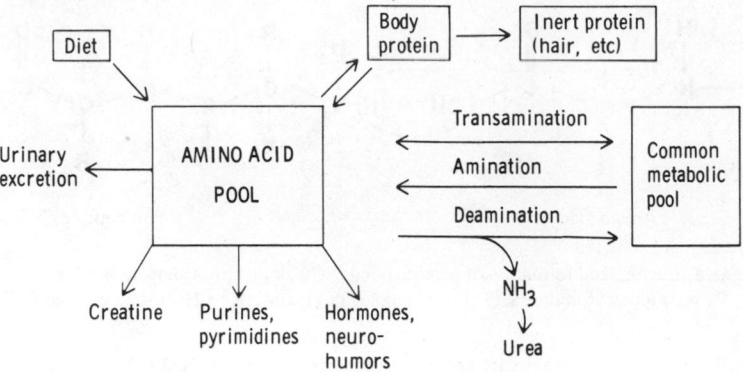

Figure 17–19. Amino acid metabolism.

Deamination, Amination, & Transamination

Interconversions between amino acids and the products of carbohydrate and fat catabolism at the level of the common metabolic pool and the citric acid cycle involve transfer, removal, or formation of amino groups. **Transamination** reactions, conversion of one amino acid to the corresponding keto acid, with simultaneous conversion of another keto acid to an amino acid (Fig 17–20), occur in many tissues. The **transaminase** enzymes involved are also present in the circulation. When damage to many active cells occurs as a result of a pathologic process, serum transaminase levels rise. An example is the rise in **serum glutamic-oxaloacetic transaminase (SGOT)** following myocardial infarction.

Oxidative deamination of amino acids occurs in the liver. An imino acid is formed by dehydrogenation, and this compound is hydrolyzed to the corresponding keto acid, with the liberation of ammonia (Fig 17–21). Amino acids can also take up NH_3, forming the corre-

sponding amide. An example is the binding of NH_3 in the brain by glutamic acid (Fig 17–22). The reverse reaction occurs in the kidney, with the liberation of NH_3 into the urine. The NH_3 reacts with H^+ to form NH_4^+, thus permitting more H^+ to be secreted into the urine (see Chapter 38).

Interconversions between the amino acid pool and the common metabolic pool are summarized in Fig 17–23. Leucine, isoleucine, phenylalanine, and tyrosine are said to be **ketogenic** because they are converted to the ketone body acetoacetic acid (see below). Alanine and many other amino acids are **glucogenic** or **gluconeogenic,** ie, they give rise to compounds that can readily be converted to glucose.

Urea Formation

Most of the NH_3 formed by deamination of amino acids in the liver is converted to urea, and the urea is excreted in the urine. Except for the brain, the liver is probably the only site of urea formation, and in severe

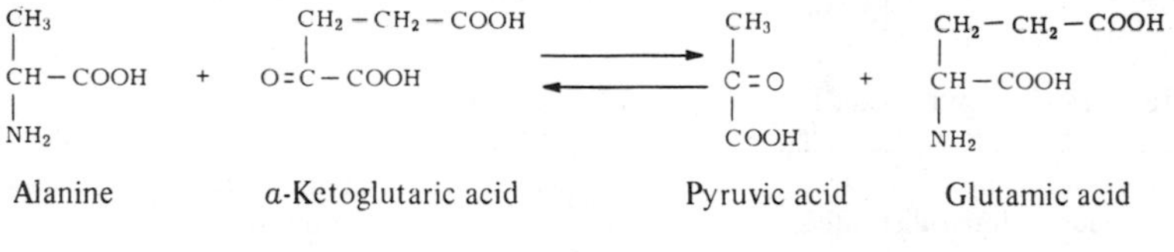

Figure 17–20. Transamination.

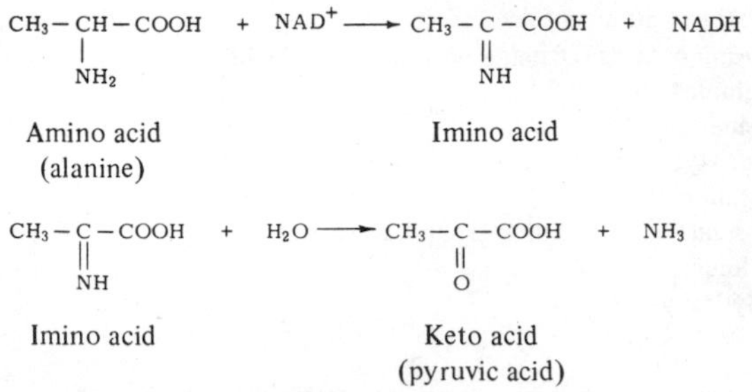

Alanine   a-Ketoglutaric acid   Pyruvic acid   Glutamic acid

Figure 17–21. Oxidative deamination.

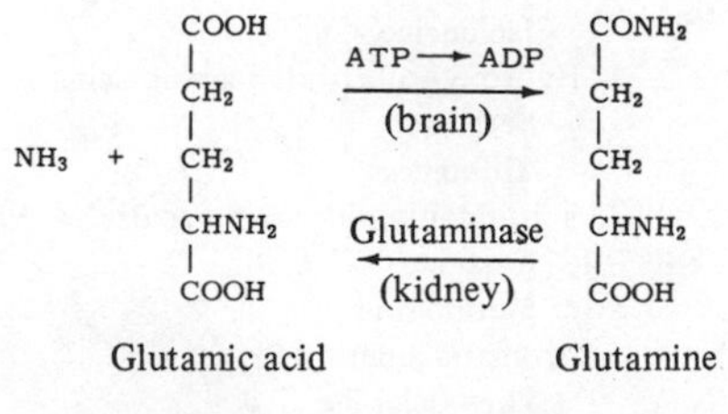

Figure 17–22. Uptake and release of NH_3 by interconversion of glutamic acid and glutamine. The reaction goes predominantly to the right in the brain, binding NH_3; and predominantly to the left in the kidney tubules, liberating NH_3 into the urine.

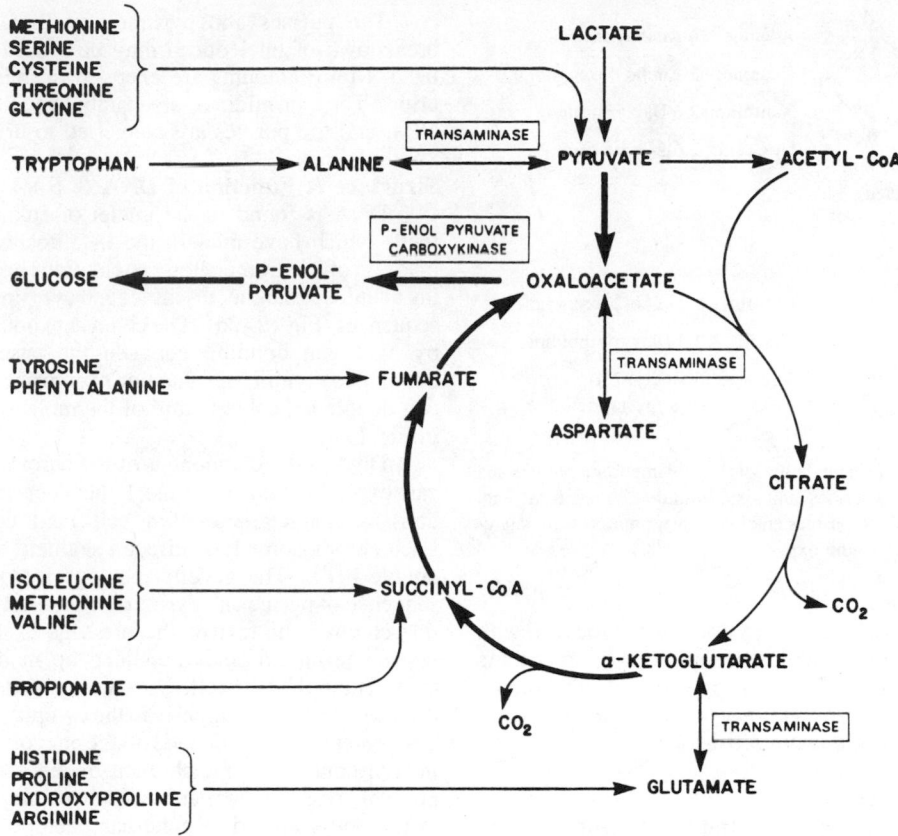

Figure 17–23. Involvement of the citric acid cycle in transamination and gluconeogenesis. (Reproduced, with permission, from Harper HA, Rodwell VW, Mayes PA: *Review of Physiological Chemistry,* 17th ed. Lange, 1979.)

hepatic disease, the blood urea nitrogen level falls. The raw materials are 2 mol of NH_3 and 1 mol of CO_2 from the plasma HCO_3^-. The synthesis via the **urea cycle** (Krebs-Henseleit cycle) involves conversion of the amino acid ornithine to citrulline and then to arginine, following which urea is split off and ornithine is regenerated. CO_2 and NH_3 are introduced into the cycle by "carrier" molecules, the formation of which requires ATP.

Creatine & Creatinine

Creatine is synthesized in the liver from methionine, glycine, and arginine. In skeletal muscle, it is phosphorylated to form phosphocreatine (Fig 17–24). Phosphocreatine is the "back-up" energy store for ATP synthesis (see Chapter 3). The ATP formed by glycolysis and oxidative phosphorylation reacts with creatine to form ADP and large amounts of phosphocreatine. During exercise, the reaction is reversed, maintaining the supply of ATP, which is the immediate source of the energy for muscle contraction.

The creatinine in the urine is formed from phosphocreatine. Creatine is not converted directly to creatinine. The rate of creatinine excretion is relatively constant from day to day. Indeed, creatinine output is

sometimes measured as a check on the accuracy of the urine collections in metabolic studies; an average daily creatinine output is calculated, and the values for the daily output of other substances are corrected to what they would have been at this creatinine output.

Creatinuria occurs normally in children, in women during and after pregnancy, and occasionally in nonpregnant women. There is very little, if any, creatine in the urine of normal men, but appreciable

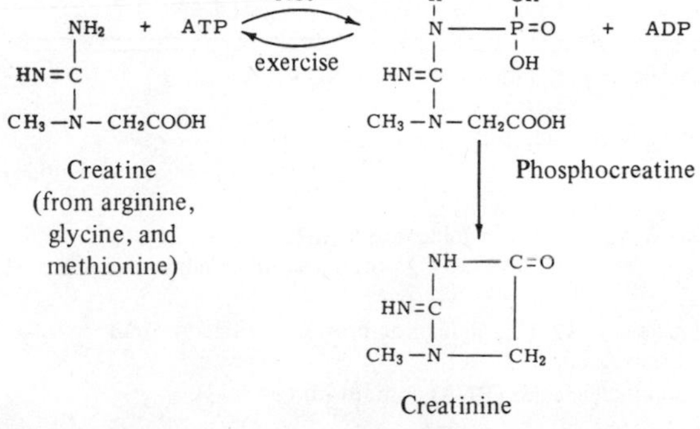

Figure 17–24. Creatine, phosphocreatine, and creatinine.

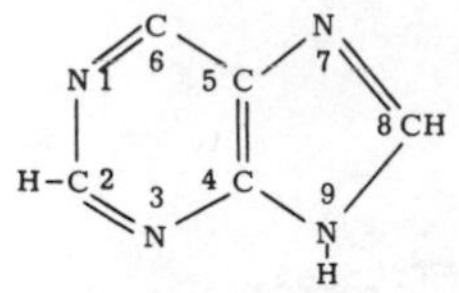

Adenine: 6-Aminopurine

Guanine: 2-Amino-6-oxypurine

Xanthine: 2,6-Dioxypurine

Uric acid: 2,6,8-Trioxypurine

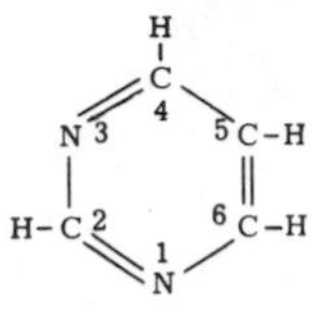

Purine nucleus

Cytosine: 4-Amino-2-oxypyrimidine

Uracil: 2,4-Dioxypyrimidine

Thymine: 5-Methyl-2,4-dioxypyrimidine

Pyrimidine nucleus

Figure 17–25. Principal physiologically important purines and pyrimidines. Oxypurines and oxypyrimidines may form enol derivatives (hydroxypurines and hydroxypyrimidines) by migration of hydrogen to the oxygen substituents.

quantities are excreted in any condition associated with extensive muscle breakdown. Thus, creatinuria occurs in starvation, thyrotoxicosis, poorly controlled diabetes mellitus, and the various primary and secondary diseases of muscle (**myopathies**).

Purines & Pyrimidines

The physiologically important **purines** and **pyrimidines** are shown in Fig 17–25. **Nucleosides**—purines or pyrimidines combined with ribose—are components not only of a variety of coenzymes and related substances (NAD$^+$, NADP$^+$, ATP, UDPG, etc) but of ribonucleic acid (RNA) and deoxyribonucleic acid (DNA) as well (Table 17–5).

Nucleic acids in the diet are digested and their constituent purines and pyrimidines absorbed, but most of the purines and pyrimidines are synthesized from amino acids, principally in the liver. The nucleotides and RNA and DNA are then synthesized. RNA is in dynamic equilibrium with the amino acid pool, but DNA, once formed, is metabolically stable throughout life.

Table 17–5. Purine- and pyrimidine-containing compounds.

Purine or pyrimidine + Ribose = Nucleoside

Nucleoside + Phosphoric acid residue = Nucleotide (mononucleotide)

Many nucleotides forming double helical structure of 2 polynucleotide chains = Nucleic acid

Nucleic acid + 1$^+$ Simple basic protein = Nucleoprotein

Ribonucleic acids (RNA) contain ribose

Deoxyribonucleic acids (DNA) contain 2-deoxyribose

The purines and pyrimidines liberated by the breakdown of nucleotides may be reused or catabolized. Minor amounts are excreted unchanged in the urine. The pyrimidines are catabolized to CO_2 and NH_3, and the purines are converted to uric acid.

Structure & Function of DNA & RNA

DNA is found in the nuclei of eukaryotic cells (cells which have nuclei) and in mitochondria. It is made up of 2 extremely long nucleotide chains containing adenine, guanine, thymine, and cytosine in various sequences (Fig 17–26). The chains are bound together by hydrogen bonding between the bases, adenine bonding to thymine and guanine to cytosine. The resultant double helical structure of the molecule is shown in Fig 17–27.

DNA is the component of the chromosomes that carries the "genetic message," the blueprint for all the heritable characteristics of the cell and its descendants. Each chromosome is in effect a segment of the DNA double helix. The genetic message is coded by the sequence of purine and pyrimidine bases in the nucleotide chains. The text of the message is the order in which the amino acids are lined up in the proteins manufactured by the cell. The message is transferred to the sites of protein synthesis in the cytoplasm by RNA. The proteins formed include all the enzymes, and these in turn control the metabolism of the cell. There is probably one gene for each enzyme or enzyme subunit in the body; indeed, a gene has been defined as the amount of information necessary to specify a single peptide molecule. Mutations occur when the base sequence in the DNA is altered by x-rays, cosmic rays, or other mutagenic agents.

At the time of each somatic cell division (**mitosis**), the 2 DNA chains separate, each serving as a template for the synthesis of a new complementary chain. **DNA polymerase** catalyzes this reaction. One of the double helices thus formed goes to one daughter cell and one to the other, so the amount of DNA in each daughter cell is the same as the amount in the parent cell. In the case of germ cells, reduction division (**meiosis**) takes place during maturation. The net result is that 1 DNA chain goes to each mature germ cell; consequently, each mature germ cell contains half the amount of chromosomal material found in somatic cells. Therefore, when a sperm unites with an ovum, the resulting zygote has the full complement of DNA, half of which came from the father and half from the mother. The chromosomal events that occur at the time of fertilization are discussed in more detail in Chapter 23.

The strands of the DNA double helix not only replicate themselves, but they serve as templates by lining up complementary bases for the formation in the nucleus of **messenger RNA (mRNA)** and **soluble,** or **transfer, RNA (tRNA).** Once mRNA is formed, it moves out of the nucleus and becomes associated with the ribosomes in the cytoplasm (Chapter 1). In the ribosomes, it serves as a template for the formation of a particular protein by the cell. tRNA attaches the amino

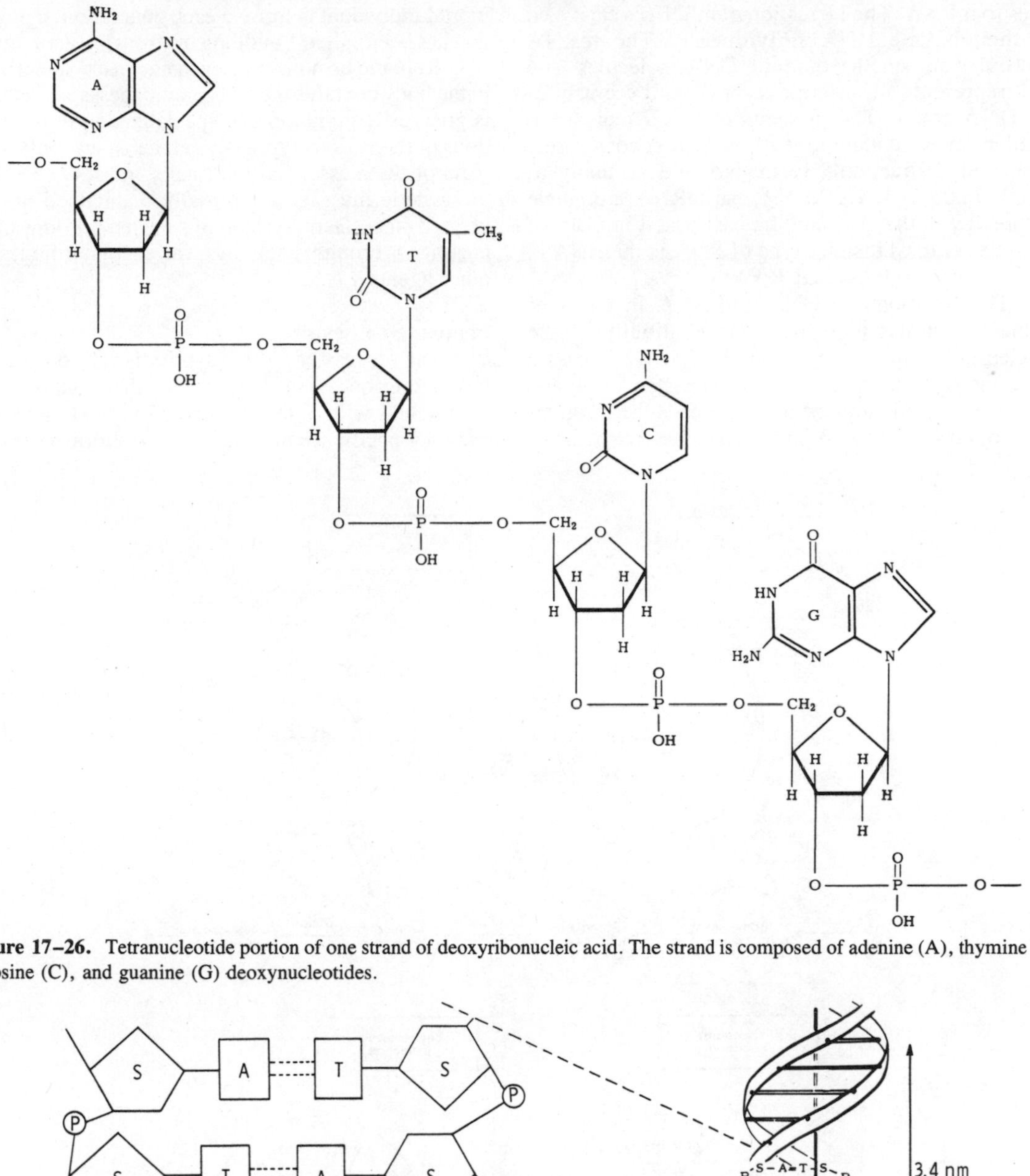

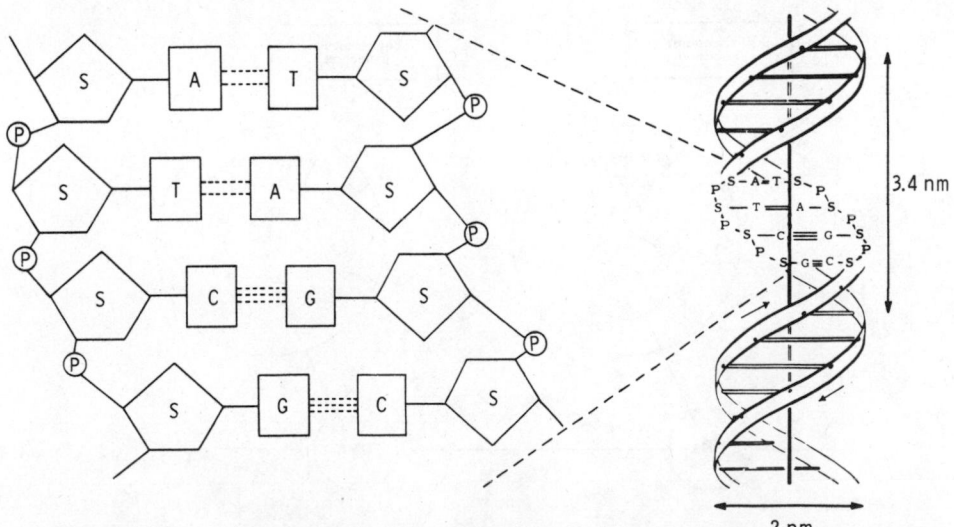

Figure 17–26. Tetranucleotide portion of one strand of deoxyribonucleic acid. The strand is composed of adenine (A), thymine (T), cytosine (C), and guanine (G) deoxynucleotides.

Figure 17–27. Diagram of the Watson and Crick model, slightly modified, of the double helical structure of DNA. On the left, the hydrogen bonding between the bases of the 2 nucleotide chains is shown. A, adenine; T, thymine; C, cytosine; G, guanine; S, deoxyribose; P, phosphate. (Reproduced, with permission, from Harper HA: *Review of Physiological Chemistry,* 15th ed. Lange, 1975.)

acids to mRNA. The formation of mRNA is catalyzed by the enzyme **RNA polymerase.** The mRNA molecules are smaller than the DNA molecules, and each represents a transcription of a small segment of the DNA chain. The molecules of tRNA are even smaller. They contain only 70–80 nitrogenous bases, compared to hundreds in mRNA and as many as 500,000,000 in DNA. tRNA and mRNA are single stranded, and they contain the base uracil in place of thymine. A third distinct type of RNA is the RNA in the ribosomes **(ribosomal RNA).**

The functions of DNA and RNA in terms of formation of the individual and continuity of the species are summarized in Fig 17–28. DNA passes from one generation to the next in the germ cells, and in this sense, it is immortal. RNA reads the information coded in the DNA and transcribes it so that a mortal individual is formed each generation, a process that has been called "budding off from the germ line."

It should be noted that each nucleated somatic cell in the body contains the full genetic message, yet there is great differentiation and specialization in the functions of the various types of adult cells, and only small parts of the message are normally transcribed. Thus, the genetic message is normally maintained in a repressed state. Derepression of selected portions of the message is brought about by a variety of hormones and other agents.

Protein Synthesis

The process of protein synthesis is a complex but fascinating one. The first step is the reaction of an amino acid with ATP and an amino acid–activating enzyme specific for that amino acid to form a complex

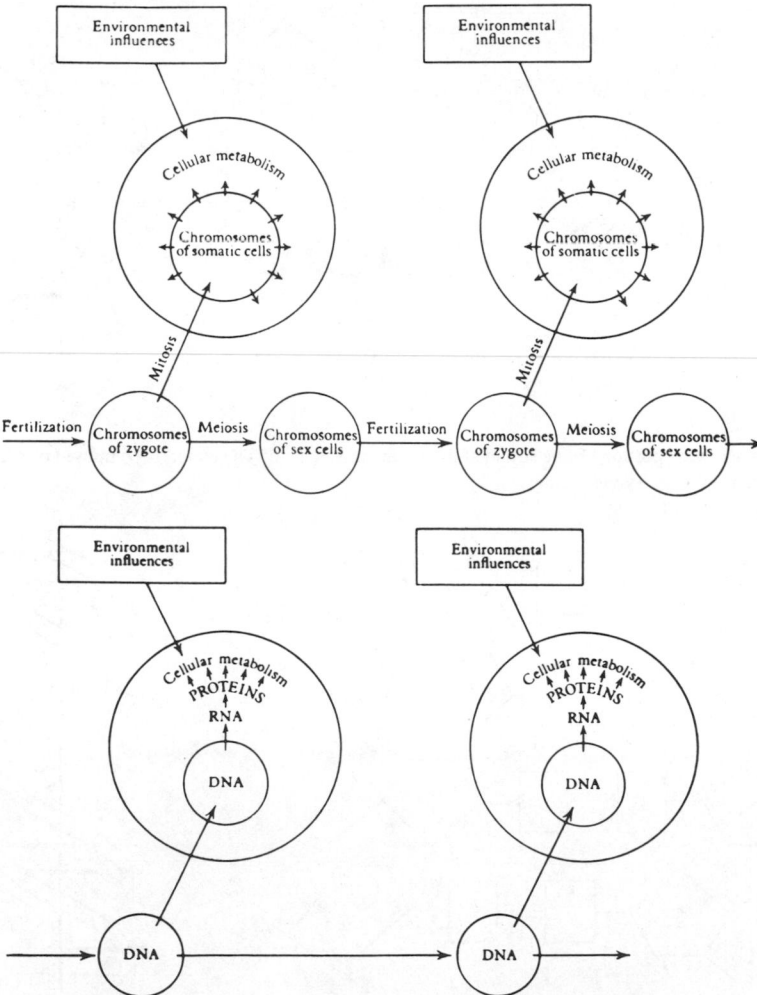

Figure 17–28. The functions of DNA and RNA in terms of the formation of the individual and the continuity of species. Germ plasm (DNA) passes from generation to generation via the germ cells. From this "germ line" the mortal soma, or body, buds off each generation. Formation of the individual depends upon transcription of the genetic message by RNA, thus determining the enzymes formed and consequently controlling the metabolism of the cell. (Reproduced, with permission, from Haggis GH & others: *Introduction to Molecular Biology.* Wiley, 1964.)

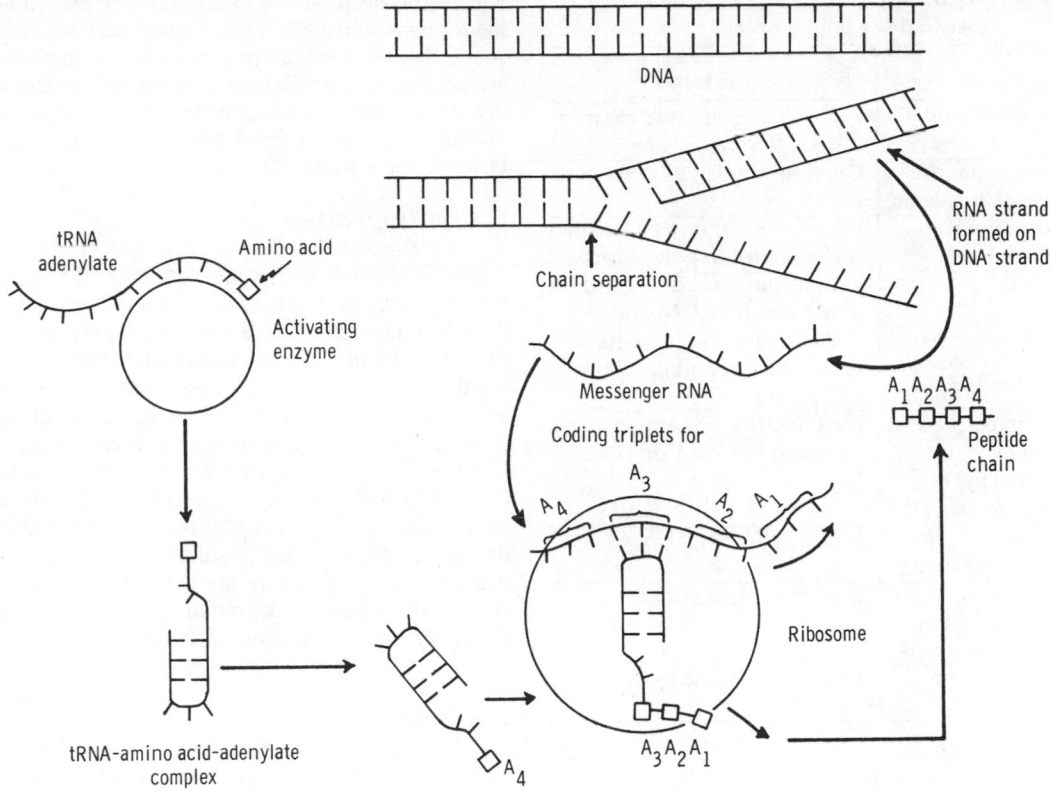

Figure 17–29. Diagrammatic outline of protein synthesis. The nucleic acids are represented as lines with multiple short projections representing the individual bases. (Reproduced, with permission, from Haggis GH & others: *Introduction to Molecular Biology*. Wiley, 1964.)

made up of the amino acid, the enzyme, and adenosine monophosphate (adenylate). This **activated amino acid** then combines with a specific molecule of tRNA. There are 20 different kinds of tRNA molecules, one for each of the 20 amino acids found in large quantities in the body proteins of animals. The tRNA–amino acid–adenylate complex is next attached to the mRNA template, a process that occurs in the ribosomes. This process is shown diagrammatically in Fig 17–29. The tRNA ''recognizes'' the proper spot to attach on the mRNA template because it has on its active end a set of 3 bases that are complementary to a set of 3 in a particular spot on the mRNA chain. The genetic code is made up of such **triplets,** sequences of 3 purine or pyrimidine bases or both; each triplet stands for a particular amino acid.

Proteins are formed in the ribosomes (see Chapter 1), beginning with the N-terminal amino acid, and the chain is lengthened one amino acid at a time. The messenger RNA attaches to the 30S subunit of the ribosome during protein synthesis; the polypeptide chain being formed attaches to the 50S subunit; and the tRNA attaches to both. As the amino acids are added in the order dictated by the triplet code, the ribosome moves along the mRNA molecule like a bead on a string. Typically, there is more than 1 ribosome on the mRNA chain at one time. The mRNA chain plus its collection of ribosomes is visible under the electron microscope as an aggregation of ribosomes called a **polyribosome,** or **polysome.** When the ribosome reaches the end of the mRNA chain, it liberates the protein. The tRNA molecules are used again. The mRNA chains are also reused approximately 10 times before they are replaced by newly synthesized chains.

Effects of Antibiotics on Protein Synthesis

Many antibiotics inhibit protein synthesis. Some of them have this effect primarily in bacteria, but others inhibit protein synthesis in the cells of other animals, including mammals. This fact makes them of great value as research tools. Antibiotics have now been shown to disrupt a variety of different steps in the synthetic process (Table 17–6).

The details of protein synthesis vary somewhat between bacteria and multicellular organisms. From a therapeutic point of view, the best antibiotic is one that kills bacteria while affecting the human host of the bacteria to the slightest possible degree. Some antibiotics are capable of such selective action. Others, such as puromycin, act on the cells of both to such a degree that their therapeutic usefulness is limited. The opposite extreme is represented by diphtheria toxin, an

Table 17–6. Mechanisms by which antibiotics and related drugs inhibit protein synthesis.

Agent	Effect
Chloramphenicol	Prevents normal association of mRNA with ribosomes
Streptomycin, neomycin, kanamycin	Cause misreading of genetic code
Cycloheximide, tetracycline	Inhibit transfer of tRNA-amino acid complex to polypeptide
Puromycin	Puromycin-amino acid complex substitutes for tRNA-amino acid complex and prevents addition of further amino acids to polypeptide
Mithramycin, mitomycin C, dactinomycin (actinomycin D)	Bind to DNA, preventing polymerization of RNA on DNA
Chloroquine, colchicine, novobiocin	Inhibit DNA polymerase
Nitrogen mustards, eg, mechlorethamine (Mustargen)	Bind to guanine in base pairs
Diphtheria toxin	Prevents ribosome from moving on mRNA

"antibiotic in reverse" which is tolerated by the bacteria that produce it but is lethal to the cells of the human infected with diphtheria bacteria. Antibiotics are also useful in the treatment of cancer, since rapidly dividing tumor cells are more susceptible to their action than resting normal cells.

Enzyme Induction

The velocity of enzyme-controlled reactions in the body can be increased by increasing the availability of substrate, by removing an inhibitor of the enzyme, by increasing the availability of a necessary coenzyme or energy source, by conversion of an inactive enzyme precursor into an active enzyme, or by the synthesis of more enzyme molecules. Increased enzyme activity can be induced by supplying cells with various organic substances (**inducers**). Addition of the substrate for the enzyme often brings on increased activity (**substrate induction**). This induction may be due in part to activation of preformed inactive enzyme molecules, but it may also be due to the formation of more enzyme molecules. Synthesis of more enzyme can be triggered by various substances, including some hormones. These substances bring out in the cell its latent ability to synthesize the particular enzyme by activating the appropriate gene to produce the appropriate mRNA.

Hormones That Act by Stimulating Enzyme Synthesis

The first concrete evidence that a hormone could act by stimulating the synthesis of certain enzymes came from studies of the insect hormone **ecdysone**, which controls moulting. This hormone was shown to induce increased mRNA synthesis in part of a chromosome. It is clear that all mammalian steroid hormones act at least in part by stimulating DNA-dependent mRNA synthesis, leading to the increased synthesis of certain enzymes. Thyroid hormones also act in this fashion (see Chapter 1).

Protein Degradation

Like protein synthesis, protein degradation is a carefully regulated, complex process. The rates at which individual proteins are metabolized vary, and the body appears to have mechanisms by which abnormal proteins are recognized and degraded more rapidly than normal body constituents. For example, abnormal hemoglobins are metabolized rapidly in individuals with congenital hemoglobinopathies (see Chapter 27). The rate of protein degradation is decreased during hypertrophy in exercised skeletal muscle, and increased during atrophy in denervated or unused skeletal muscle. In addition, the rate of protein degradation is a factor in the determination of organ size (eg, the rate of degradation of liver protein is markedly reduced during the compensatory hypertrophy that follows partial hepatectomy).

Uric Acid

Uric acid is formed by the breakdown of purines and by direct synthesis from 5-phosphoribosyl pyrophosphate (5-PRPP) and glutamic acid (Fig 17–30). In humans, uric acid is excreted in the urine; but in other mammals—except, curiously, the Dalmatian coach dog—uric acid is further oxidized to allantoin before excretion. The normal blood uric acid level in humans

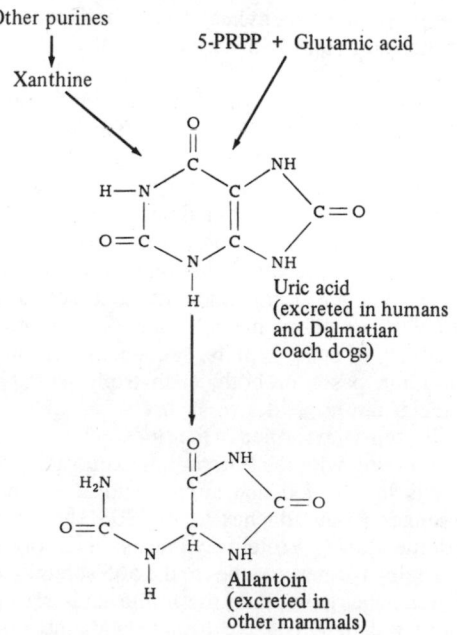

Figure 17–30. Uric acid metabolism.

is approximately 4 mg/dl (0.24 mmol/L). In the kidney, uric acid is filtered, reabsorbed, and secreted. Normally, 98% of the filtered uric acid is reabsorbed, and the remaining 2% makes up approximately 20% of the amount excreted. The remaining 80% comes from tubular secretion. The uric acid excretion on a purine-free diet is about 0.5 g/24 h and on a regular diet about 1 g/24 h.

"Primary" & "Secondary" Gout

Gout is a disease characterized by recurrent attacks of arthritis, urate deposits in the joints, kidneys, and other tissues, and elevated blood and urine uric acid levels. The joint most commonly affected initially is the metatarsophalangeal joint of the great toe. There are 2 forms of "primary" gout: one in which, for unknown reasons, uric acid production is increased and another in which there is a selective deficit in renal tubular transport of uric acid. In "secondary" gout, the uric acid levels in the body fluids are elevated as a result of decreased excretion or increased production secondary to some other disease process. For example, excretion is decreased in renal disease, and production is increased in leukemia and pneumonia because of increased breakdown of uric acid–rich white blood cells. Starvation also causes a rise in the blood uric acid level and may precipitate symptoms of gout, presumably because of increased nucleic acid breakdown. The treatment of gout is aimed at relieving the acute arthritis with drugs such as colchicine and decreasing the uric acid level in the blood. Colchicine does not affect uric acid metabolism, and it apparently relieves gouty attacks by inhibiting the phagocytosis of uric acid crystals by leukocytes, a process that in some way produces the joint symptoms. Adrenal glucocorticoid hormones and their synthetic derivatives increase uric acid excretion. So do salicylates and probenecid, which decrease tubular uric acid reabsorption. Allopurinol, which inhibits xanthine oxidase, is used to decrease uric acid production. Xanthine oxidase is the enzyme responsible for the conversion of xanthine to uric acid (Fig 17–30).

Nitrogen Balance

A moderate daily protein intake is necessary to replace protein and amino acid losses. This requirement is not for protein itself but for the constituent amino acids, and the need can be met by feeding pure amino acids. Loss of protein and its derivatives in the stools is normally very small. Consequently, the amount of nitrogen in the urine is a reliable indicator of the amount of irreversible protein and amino acid breakdown. When the amount of nitrogen in the urine is equal to the nitrogen content of the protein in the diet, the individual is said to be in **nitrogen balance.** If protein intake is increased in a normal individual, the extra amino acids are deaminated and urea excretion increases, maintaining nitrogen balance. However, in conditions in which secretion of the catabolic hormones of the adrenal cortex is elevated or that of insulin is decreased, and during starvation and forced immobilization, nitrogen losses exceed intake and the nitrogen balance is **negative.** During growth or recovery from severe illnesses, or following administration of anabolic steroids such as testosterone, nitrogen intake exceeds excretion and nitrogen balance is **positive.**

Essential Amino Acids

Animals fed a protein-free but otherwise adequate diet become sick and eventually die. In humans, nitrogen balance is not maintained unless 8 amino acids—phenylalanine, valine, tryptophan, threonine, lysine, leucine, isoleucine, and methionine—are added to the diet. These amino acids are called the **essential amino acids** (Table 17–4). Histidine and arginine are not essential in this sense but are required for normal growth. All other amino acids in the body can be synthesized in vivo at rates sufficient to meet needs by amination of carbohydrate and fat residues.

When any one of the amino acids necessary for synthesis of a particular protein is unavailable, the protein is not synthesized. The other amino acids that would have gone into the protein are deaminated, like other excess amino acids, and their nitrogen is excreted as urea. This is probably why nitrogen balance becomes negative whenever a single essential amino acid is omitted from the diet.

Response to Starvation

A syndrome called **kwashiorkor** is common in the tropics among those living on a diet adequate in calories but grossly deficient in animal protein. It is characterized by anemia, a fatty, enlarged liver, edema, and many other disturbances and is especially severe in children.

When an individual eats a diet that is low in protein but calorically adequate, excretion of urea and inorganic and ethereal sulfates declines. Uric acid excretion falls by 50%. Creatinine excretion is not affected (Table 17–7). The creatinine and about half of

Table 17–7. Effect of variations in protein intake on daily excretion of various protein and amino acid derivatives while consuming a calorically adequate diet.*

	Protein-Rich Diet	Protein-Poor Diet
Volume of urine (ml)	1170	385
Total nitrogen (g)	16.8	3.6
Urea nitrogen (g)	14.7	2.2
Uric acid nitrogen (g)	0.18	0.09
Ammonia nitrogen (g)	0.49	0.42
Creatinine nitrogen (g)	0.58	0.6
Inorganic SO_4 (g)	3.27	0.46
Ethereal SO_4 (g)	0.19	0.10
Neutral sulfur (g)	0.18	0.20

*Data from Folin O: Laws governing the chemical composition of urine. Am J Physiol 13:66, 1905.

Table 17–8. Lipids.

Typical fatty acids:

Palmitic acid:
$$CH_3(CH_2)_{14}-\overset{\overset{\displaystyle O}{\|}}{C}-OH$$

Stearic acid:
$$CH_3(CH_2)_{16}-\overset{\overset{\displaystyle O}{\|}}{C}-OH$$

Oleic acid:
$$CH_3(CH_2)_7CH=CH(CH_2)_7-\overset{\overset{\displaystyle O}{\|}}{C}-OH$$
(Unsaturated)

Triglycerides: Esters of glycerol and 3 fatty acids.

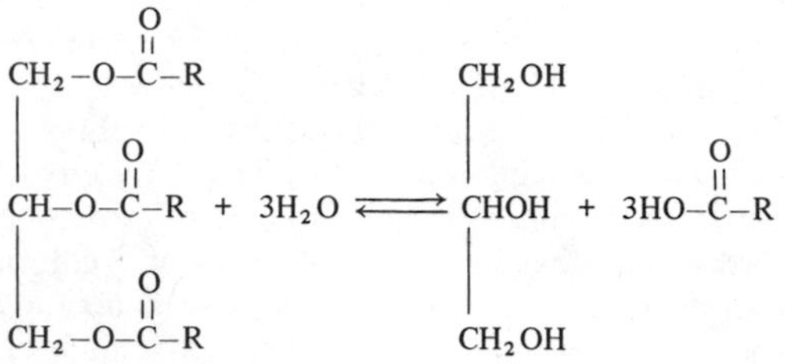

$$
\begin{array}{l}
CH_2-O-\overset{\overset{\displaystyle O}{\|}}{C}-R \\
CH-O-\overset{\overset{\displaystyle O}{\|}}{C}-R \quad + \quad 3H_2O \; \rightleftharpoons \\
CH_2-O-\overset{\overset{\displaystyle O}{\|}}{C}-R
\end{array}
\qquad
\begin{array}{l}
CH_2OH \\
CHOH \quad + \quad 3HO-\overset{\overset{\displaystyle O}{\|}}{C}-R \\
CH_2OH
\end{array}
$$

Triglyceride   Glycerol

R = Aliphatic chain of various lengths and degrees of saturation.

Phospholipids: Esters of glycerol, 2 fatty acids, and:
1. Phosphate = phosphatidic acid
2. Phosphate plus inositol = phosphatidyl inositol
3. Phosphate plus choline = lecithin
4. Phosphate plus ethanolamine = cephalin
5. Phosphate plus serine = phosphatidyl serine

Sphingomyelins: Esters of fatty acid, phosphate, choline, and the amino alcohol, sphingosine.

Cerebrosides: Compounds containing galactose, fatty acid, and sphingosine.

Sterols: Cholesterol and its derivatives, including steroid hormones, bile acids, and various vitamins.

Table 17–9. The principal lipoproteins.

	Size (nm)	Composition (%)				Origin
		Protein	Cholesterol	Triglyceride	Phospholipid	
Chylomicrons	75–100	2	5	90	3	Intestine
Very low density lipoprotein (VLDL)	30–80	10	12	60	18	Liver and small intestine
Intermediate-density lipoprotein (IDL)	25–40	10	30	40	20	VLDL
Low-density lipoprotein (LDL)	20	25	50	10	15	VLDL
High-density lipoprotein (HDL)	7.5–10	50	20	5	25	Liver

the uric acid in the urine must therefore be the result of "wear and tear" processes that are unaffected by the protein intake. Total nitrogen excretion fails to fall below 3.6 g/d during protein starvation when the diet is calorically adequate because of the negative nitrogen balance produced by essential amino acid deficiencies.

On a diet that is inadequate in calories as well, urea nitrogen excretion averages about 10 g/d as proteins are catabolized for energy. Small amounts of glucose counteract this catabolism to a marked degree (**protein-sparing** effect of glucose). This protein-sparing effect is probably due for the most part to the increased insulin secretion produced by the glucose. The insulin in turn inhibits the breakdown of protein in muscle. Intravenous injection of relatively small amounts of amino acids also exerts a considerable protein-sparing effect.

Fats also spare nitrogen. During prolonged starvation, keto acids derived from fats (see below) are used by the brain and other tissues. These substances share cofactors for metabolism in muscle with 3 branched-chain amino acids, leucine, isoleucine, and valine, and, to the extent that the fat-derived keto acids are utilized, these amino acids are apparently spared. Infusion of the non–nitrogen-containing analogs of these amino acids produces protein sparing and decreases urea and ammonia formation in patients with renal and hepatic failure.

Most of the protein burned during total starvation comes from the liver, spleen, and muscles and relatively little from the heart and brain. The blood glucose falls somewhat after liver glycogen is depleted (see above) but is maintained above levels that produce hypoglycemic symptoms by gluconeogenesis. Ketosis is present, and neutral fat is rapidly catabolized. When fat stores are used up, protein catabolism increases even further, and death soon follows. In hospitalized obese patients given nothing except water and vitamins, weight loss was observed to be about 1 kg/d for the first 10 days. It then declined and stabilized at about 0.3 kg/d. Some of these patients were starved for as long as 36 weeks. They did quite well on the whole, although postural hypotension and attacks of acute gouty arthritis were troublesome complications in some instances.

There has recently been considerable interest in reducing diets in which the sole source of calories is liquid protein or amino acid mixtures. Such diets have been hypothesized to promote ketosis, which in turn decreases appetite while sparing body protein. However, it is as yet uncertain whether these diets are more successful than others in reducing body weight, and there have been a relatively large number of unexplained sudden deaths in patients on these diets. Until the cause of these deaths is elucidated, it seems unwise to use them.

FAT METABOLISM

Lipids

The biologically important lipids are the neutral fats (triglycerides), the phospholipids and related compounds, and the sterols. The triglycerides are made up of 3 fatty acids bound to glycerol (Table 17–8). Naturally occurring fatty acids contain an even number of carbon atoms. They may be saturated (no double bonds) or unsaturated (dehydrogenated, with various numbers of double bonds). The phospholipids are constituents of cells, especially in the nervous system. The sterols include the various steroid hormones and cholesterol.

Plasma Lipids

The major lipids in plasma do not circulate in the free form. **Free fatty acids** (variously called FFA, UFA, or NEFA) are bound to albumin, whereas cholesterol, triglycerides, and phospholipids are transported in the form of lipoprotein complexes. There are 5 families of lipoproteins (Table 17–9), which are graded in size and lipid content. The density of these lipoproteins (and consequently the speed at which they sediment in the ultracentrifuge) is inversely proportionate to their lipid content.

Chylomicrons are formed in the intestinal mucosa during the absorption of long-chain fatty acids into the lymphatic ducts (see Chapter 25). After meals, there are so many of these large particles in the blood that the plasma may have a milky appearance (**lipemia**). The chylomicrons are cleared from the circulation by the action of **lipoprotein lipase**, which is located in the endothelium of the capillaries. This enzyme catalyzes the breakdown of the triglyceride in the chylomicrons to FFA and glycerol, which then enter the adipose cells and are reesterified. The remnants of the chylomicrons are metabolized in the liver. Lipoprotein lipase is also known as **clearing factor** and requires heparin as a cofactor.

Very low density lipoproteins (VLDL) are principally formed in the liver, and they in turn are converted to **intermediate-density lipoproteins (IDL)** and **low-density lipoproteins (LDL)** by loss of some of the triglyceride and protein in the complexes. LDL attach to receptors on the surface of many cells in the body and are ingested into the cell by endocytosis. Lysosomal enzymes then break down the protein, leaving the lipid free in the cell for incorporation into membranes or other uses. LDL are the principal carriers of cholesterol in the circulation and play an important role in cholesterol metabolism. The high-density lipoproteins (HDL) are formed in the liver, and they pick up cholesterol from parenchymal cells (see below).

Cellular Lipids

The lipids in cells are of 2 main types: **structural lipids,** which are an inherent part of the membranes and other parts of cells; and **neutral fat,** stored in the adipose cells of the fat depots. A third special type of fat is **brown fat,** which is found in infants but not in adult humans. It has a high metabolic rate and produces heat that aids in thermoregulation (see Chapter 14). Depot fat is mobilized during starvation, but structural lipid is preserved. The size of the fat depots obviously varies, but in nonobese individuals, they make up about 10% of the body weight. They are not the inert lumps they were once thought to be but active, dynamic tissues undergoing continuous breakdown and resynthesis. In the depots, glucose is metabolized to fatty acids, and neutral fats are synthesized. Neutral fat is also broken down, and free fatty acids are liberated into the circulation.

Fat Oxidation

The glycerol liberated when triglycerides are hydrolyzed can be converted to phosphoglyceraldehyde and thence to glucose or to CO_2 and H_2O. The fatty acids are broken down to acetyl-CoA, which enters the citric acid cycle. Fatty acid oxidation begins with activation of the fatty acid (Fig 17–31), and this reaction occurs both inside and outside the mitochondria. Active fatty acids formed outside the mitochondria cross the mitochondrial membrane by a process that is facilitated by **carnitine,** a butyric acid derivative which greatly stimulates fat oxidation. The rest of the steps occur in the mitochondria, where 2 carbon fragments are serially split off the fatty acid **(beta-oxidation).** The energy yield of this process is large. For example, catabolism of 1 mol of a 6-carbon fatty acid through the citric acid cycle to CO_2 and H_2O generates 44 mol of ATP, compared to the 38 mol generated by catabolism of 1 mol of the 6-carbon carbohydrate glucose.

Fat Synthesis

Many tissues can synthesize fatty acids from acetyl-CoA. Some synthesis of long-chain fatty acids

from short-chain fatty acids occurs in the mitochondria by simple reversal of the reactions shown in Fig 17–31. There is in addition a similar chain elongation system outside the mitochondria. However, most of the synthesis of fatty acids occurs de novo from acetyl-CoA via a different pathway located principally outside the mitochondria, in the microsomes. The steps in this pathway are summarized in Fig 17–32.

For unknown reasons, fatty acid synthesis stops in practically all cells when the chain is 16 carbon atoms long. Only small amounts of 12- and 14-carbon fatty acids are formed, and none with more than 16 carbons. Particularly in fat depots, the fatty acids are combined with glycerol to form neutral fats. This combination takes place in the mitochondria.

Ketone Bodies

In many tissues, acetyl-CoA units condense to form acetoacetyl-CoA (Fig 17–33). In the liver, which (unlike other tissues) contains a deacylase, free acetoacetic acid is liberated. This β-keto acid is converted to β-hydroxybutyric acid and acetone, and because these compounds are metabolized with difficulty in the liver, they diffuse into the circulation. Acetoacetic acid is also formed in the liver via the formation of β-hydroxy-β-methylglutaryl-CoA (Fig 17–33), and this pathway is quantitatively more important than deacylation. Acetoacetic acid, β-hydroxybutyric acid, and acetone are called **ketone bodies.** Tissues other than liver transfer CoA from succinyl-CoA to acetoacetic acid and metabolize the "active" acetoacetic acid to CO_2 and H_2O via the citric acid cycle. There are also other pathways whereby ketone bodies are metabolized. The ketones are an important source of energy in some conditions. Acetone is discharged in the urine and expired air.

The normal blood ketone level in humans is low (about 1 mg/dl), and less than 1 mg is excreted per 24

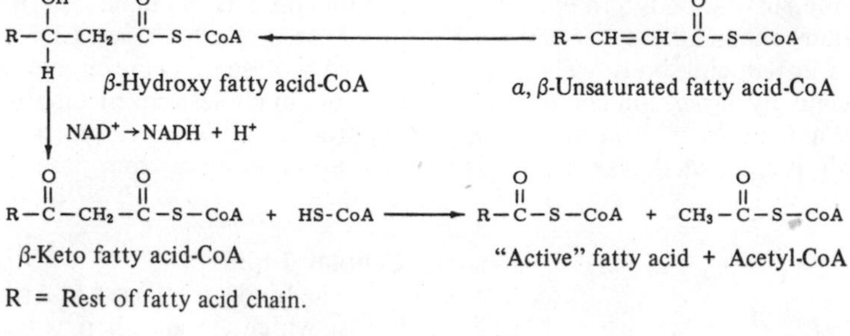

Figure 17–31. Fatty acid oxidation. This process, splitting off 2 carbon fragments at a time, is repeated to the end of the chain.

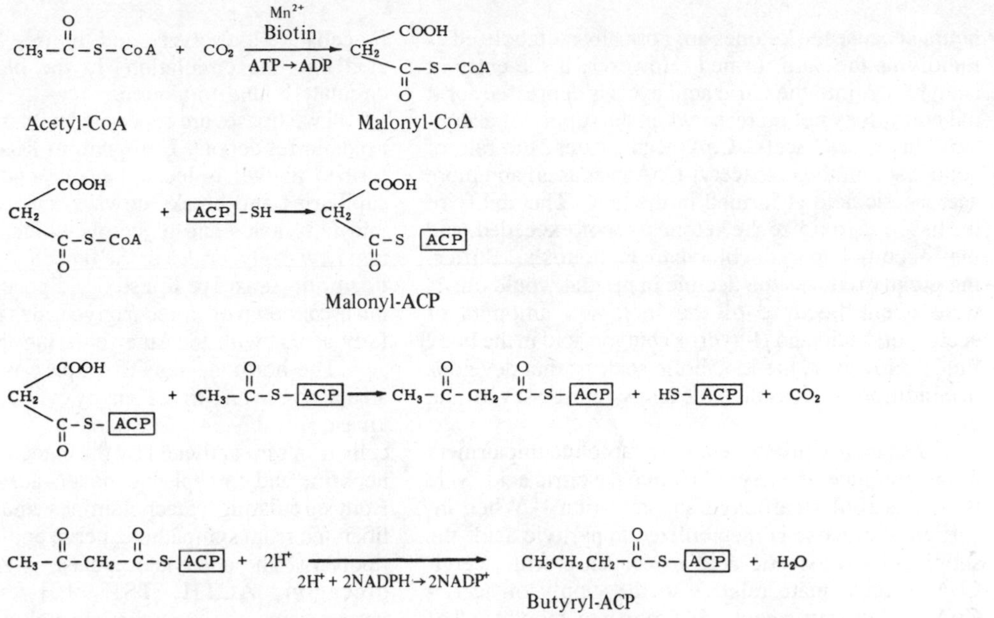

$$CH_3-\overset{\overset{O}{\|}}{C}-S-CoA + CO_2 \xrightarrow[\text{ATP} \rightarrow \text{ADP}]{\overset{Mn^{2+}}{\text{Biotin}}} \overset{COOH}{\underset{\overset{\|}{O}}{\underset{C-S-CoA}{CH_2}}}$$

Acetyl-CoA   Malonyl-CoA

$$\overset{COOH}{\underset{\overset{\|}{O}}{\underset{C-S-CoA}{CH_2}}} + \boxed{ACP}-SH \longrightarrow \overset{COOH}{\underset{\overset{\|}{O}}{\underset{C-S\ \boxed{ACP}}{CH_2}}}$$

Malonyl-ACP

$$\overset{COOH}{\underset{\overset{\|}{O}}{\underset{C-S-\boxed{ACP}}{CH_2}}} + CH_3-\overset{\overset{O}{\|}}{C}-S-\boxed{ACP} \longrightarrow CH_3-\overset{\overset{O}{\|}}{C}-CH_2-\overset{\overset{O}{\|}}{C}-S-\boxed{ACP} + HS-\boxed{ACP} + CO_2$$

$$CH_3-\overset{\overset{O}{\|}}{C}-CH_2-\overset{\overset{O}{\|}}{C}-S-\boxed{ACP} + 2H^+ \xrightarrow[2H^+ + 2NADPH \rightarrow 2NADP^+]{} CH_3CH_2CH_2-\overset{\overset{O}{\|}}{C}-S-\boxed{ACP} + H_2O$$

Butyryl-ACP

Figure 17–32. Fatty acid synthesis via pathway found in microsomes. ACP = acyl carrier protein, a protein that is part of an enzyme complex, to which the acyl residues are attached as fatty acid synthesis proceeds. The process shown here repeats itself, adding 1 acetyl-ACP unit to the butyryl-ACP to form a 6-carbon fatty acid–ACP derivative, then another acetyl-ACP to form an 8-carbon unit, etc.

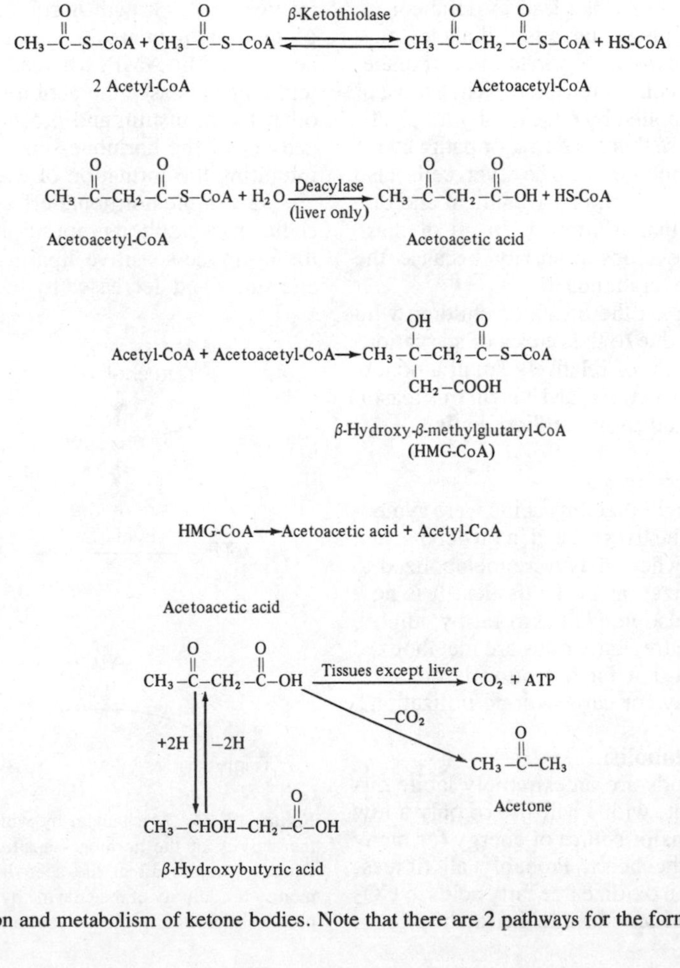

$$CH_3-\overset{\overset{O}{\|}}{C}-S-CoA + CH_3-\overset{\overset{O}{\|}}{C}-S-CoA \underset{}{\overset{\beta\text{-Ketothiolase}}{\rightleftharpoons}} CH_3-\overset{\overset{O}{\|}}{C}-CH_2-\overset{\overset{O}{\|}}{C}-S-CoA + HS-CoA$$

2 Acetyl-CoA   Acetoacetyl-CoA

$$CH_3-\overset{\overset{O}{\|}}{C}-CH_2-\overset{\overset{O}{\|}}{C}-S-CoA + H_2O \xrightarrow[\text{(liver only)}]{\text{Deacylase}} CH_3-\overset{\overset{O}{\|}}{C}-CH_2-\overset{\overset{O}{\|}}{C}-OH + HS-CoA$$

Acetoacetyl-CoA   Acetoacetic acid

$$\text{Acetyl-CoA} + \text{Acetoacetyl-CoA} \longrightarrow \underset{\underset{CH_2-COOH}{|}}{\overset{\overset{OH}{|}}{CH_3-C-CH_2-\overset{\overset{O}{\|}}{C}-S-CoA}}$$

β-Hydroxy-β-methylglutaryl-CoA
(HMG-CoA)

$$\text{HMG-CoA} \longrightarrow \text{Acetoacetic acid} + \text{Acetyl-CoA}$$

Acetoacetic acid

$$CH_3-\overset{\overset{O}{\|}}{C}-CH_2-\overset{\overset{O}{\|}}{C}-OH \xrightarrow{\text{Tissues except liver}} CO_2 + ATP$$

$$\xrightarrow{-CO_2} CH_3-\overset{\overset{O}{\|}}{C}-CH_3$$

Acetone

$$+2H \Big\updownarrow -2H$$

$$CH_3-CHOH-CH_2-\overset{\overset{O}{\|}}{C}-OH$$

β-Hydroxybutyric acid

Figure 17–33. Formation and metabolism of ketone bodies. Note that there are 2 pathways for the formation of acetoacetic acid.

hours because the ketones are normally metabolized as rapidly as they are formed. However, if the entry of acetyl-CoA into the citric acid cycle is depressed, or if the entry does not increase when the supply of acetyl-CoA increases, acetyl-CoA accumulates, the rate of condensation to acetoacetyl-CoA increases, and more acetoacetic acid is formed in the liver. The ability of the tissues to oxidize the ketones is soon exceeded, and they accumulate in the bloodstream (**ketosis**). Buffering greatly reduces the decline in pH that would otherwise occur because of the increased amounts of acetoacetic acid and β-hydroxybutyric acid in the body fluids. However, the metabolic acidosis that develops in conditions such as diabetic ketosis can be severe and even fatal.

The main cause of relative or absolute impairment of the entrance of acetyl-CoA into the citric acid cycle is "intracellular carbohydrate starvation." When insufficient glucose is metabolized to pyruvic acid, the supply of oxaloacetic acid to condense with acetyl-CoA is inadequate relative to the supply of acetyl-CoA, and the citric acid cycle cannot metabolize all of it. Furthermore, when glucose catabolism is deficient, less fat is synthesized from acetyl-CoA, adding to the accumulation of acetyl-CoA. In addition, the rate of fat oxidation is increased. Consequently, more acetoacetyl-CoA and more ketone bodies are formed.

There are 3 conditions that lead to deficient intracellular glucose supplies: starvation, diabetes mellitus, and a high-fat, low-carbohydrate diet. In diabetes, glucose entry into cells is impaired. When most of the caloric intake is supplied by fat, carbohydrate deficiency develops because there is no major pathway for converting fat to carbohydrate. The liver cells also become filled with fat, which damages them and displaces any glycogen that is formed. In all of these conditions, ketosis develops primarily because the supply of ketones is overabundant.

The acetone odor on the breath of children who have been vomiting is due to the ketosis of starvation. Parenteral administration of relatively small amounts of glucose abolishes the ketosis, and it is for this reason that carbohydrate is said to be **antiketogenic.**

Conversion of Glucose to Fat

It used to be thought that fatty acids were synthesized from glucose in the liver, stored in fat depots, and returned to the liver, where they were metabolized to ketone bodies for utilization by the tissues. It is now clear that glucose is also converted to fat by adipose tissue, that circulating free fatty acids are metabolized by many organs, and that fat formation is quantitatively a major pathway for carbohydrate utilization.

Free Fatty Acid Metabolism

The free fatty acids are an extremely labile circulating fat component, with a half-life of only a few minutes. They are a major source of energy for many organs, particularly the heart. Probably all tissues, including the brain, can oxidize free fatty acids to CO_2 and H_2O. The triglycerides stored in the fat droplets of fat cells are hydrolyzed and the free fatty acids liberated into the circulation. In the bloodstream, they circulate bound to albumin.

Two lipases are concerned with the metabolism of lipids in fat depots. **Lipoprotein lipase,** which is described above, is located in the endothelium of the capillaries and breaks down circulating triglycerides into fatty acids and glycerol, which are reassembled into new triglycerides in the fat cells. The intracellular **hormone-sensitive lipase** of adipose tissue catalyzes the breakdown of stored triglycerides into glycerol and fatty acids, with the latter entering the circulation.

The hormone-sensitive lipase is converted from an inactive to an active form by cyclic AMP via protein kinase (Fig 17–34). The adenylate cyclase in adipose cells is in turn activated by the catecholamines norepinephrine and epinephrine via a β-adrenergic receptor. Both circulating catecholamines and norepinephrine liberated from sympathetic nerve endings can increase lipolysis. The adenylate cyclase is also activated by glucagon, ACTH, TSH, LH, serotonin, and vasopressin, although the physiologic role of these substances in the regulation of lipolysis is uncertain. Growth hormone, glucocorticoids, and thyroid hormone also increase the activity of the hormone-sensitive lipase, but they do it by a slower process that requires synthesis of new protein and is independent of cyclic AMP. Growth hormone appears to produce a protein that increases the ability of catecholamines to activate cyclic AMP, whereas cortisol produces a protein that increases the action of cyclic AMP. On the other hand, insulin and prostaglandin E decrease the activity of the hormone-sensitive lipase, possibly by inhibiting the formation of cyclic AMP.

Given the hormonal effects described in the preceding paragraph, it is not surprising that the activity of the hormone-sensitive lipase is increased by fasting and stress and decreased by feeding and insulin. Con-

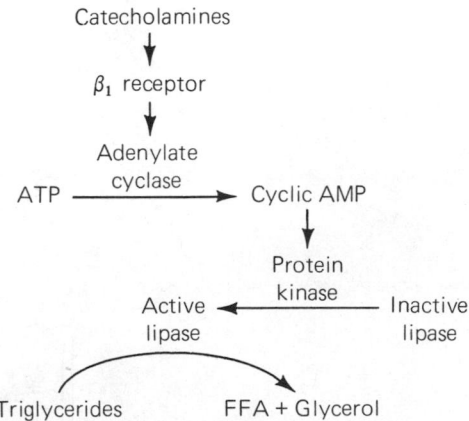

Figure 17–34. Mechanism by which catecholamines increase the activity of the hormone-sensitive lipase in adipose tissue. Other hormones affect the adenylate cyclase and still others modify the activity of the enzyme by stimulating the synthesis of proteins that modify the activation process.

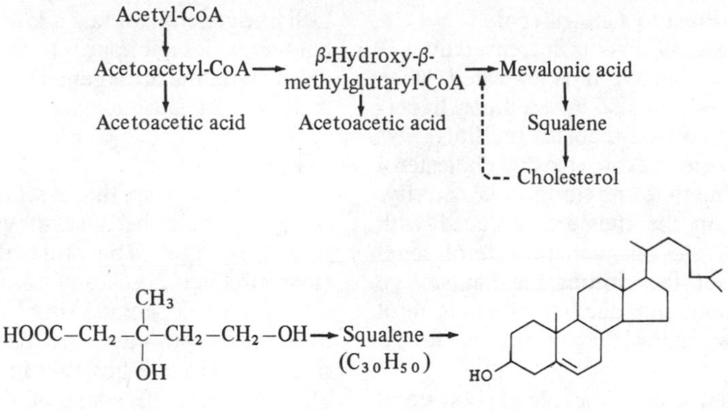

Acetyl-CoA
↓
Acetoacetyl-CoA ⟶ β-Hydroxy-β- ⟶ Mevalonic acid
            methylglutaryl-CoA ↑
↓   ↓   Squalene
Acetoacetic acid   Acetoacetic acid   ↓
                                           ┗-- Cholesterol

$$HOOC-CH_2-\overset{\displaystyle CH_3}{\underset{\displaystyle OH}{C}}-CH_2-CH_2-OH \longrightarrow \underset{(C_{30}H_{50})}{Squalene} \longrightarrow$$

Mevalonic acid   Cholesterol $(C_{27}H_{46}O)$

Figure 17–35. Biosynthesis of cholesterol. Six mevalonic acid molecules condense to form squalene, which is then hydroxylated and converted to cholesterol. The dashed arrow indicates feedback inhibition of mevalonic acid formation by cholesterol.

versely, feeding increases and fasting and stress decrease the activity of lipoprotein lipase.

There are 3 tissues that can liberate fats into the circulation: adipose tissue, the intestinal mucosa, and the liver. The function of the intestinal mucosa in fat absorption is discussed in Chapter 26. The liver takes up free fatty acids and forms triglycerides or ketone bodies. Normally, the triglycerides leave the liver as part of VLDL complexes.

Cholesterol Metabolism

Cholesterol is the precursor of the steroid hormones and bile acids. It is found only in animals. Related sterols occur in plants, but plant sterols are not absorbed from the gastrointestinal tract. Most of the dietary cholesterol is contained in egg yolks and animal fat.

Cholesterol is absorbed from the intestine and incorporated into the chylomicrons formed in the mucosa. After the chylomicrons discharge their triglyceride in adipose tissue, the chylomicron remnants bring cholesterol to the liver. The liver also synthesizes cholesterol. Some of the cholesterol in the liver is excreted in the bile, both in the free form and as bile acids. The rest of the cholesterol is incorporated into VLDL. The biosynthesis of cholesterol from acetate is summarized in Fig 17–35. Cholesterol feeds back to inhibit its own synthesis by inhibiting the enzyme that converts β-hydroxy-β-methylglutaryl-CoA to mevalonic acid.Thus, when dietary cholesterol intake is high, hepatic cholesterol synthesis is decreased, and vice versa. However, the feedback compensation is incomplete, and a low-cholesterol diet does lead to a modest decline in circulating blood cholesterol.

Most cells in the body can synthesize cholesterol, although much of it is synthesized in the liver. The cholesterol-containing VLDL formed in the liver are metabolized to IDL and LDL. The LDL then enter the cells in the extrahepatic tissues by endocytosis. The processes involved in the uptake and the subsequent intracellular metabolism of cholesterol are sum-

marized in Fig 17–36. LDL molecules bind to receptors on the cell membrane, and this interaction triggers endocytosis of the LDL. The LDL-containing vesicle fuses with a lysosome, and lysosomal enzymes hydrolyze the cholesterol esters in the core of the LDL. The free cholesterol formed enters the cytoplasm, where it inhibits cholesterol synthesis (Fig 17–36), inhibits the formation of LDL receptors, is partly converted back to cholesterol esters in the Golgi apparatus, and diffuses into the cell membrane. From the cell membrane, cholesterol is taken up by HDL. It is converted to cholesterol esters and moves to the core of the HDL, leaving the surface of the lipoprotein free to accept more cholesterol. The regulatory aspects of the metabolic pathways in Fig 17–36 are obvious. In addition, any rise in intracellular cholesterol inhibits cholesterol synthesis in the cell and decreases the supply of new LDL receptors, so cellular intake is reduced.

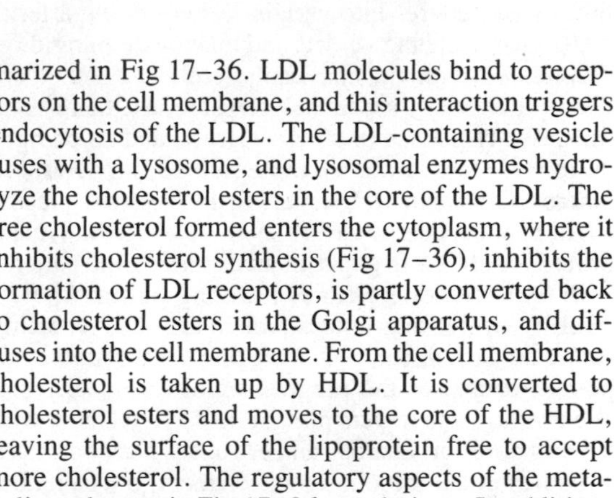

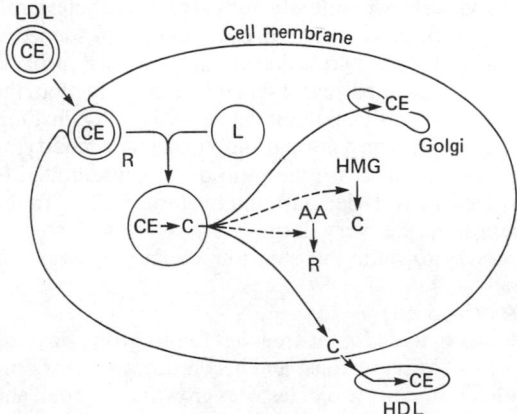

Figure 17–36. Cellular uptake, metabolism, and removal of cholesterol. R, LDL receptor; L, lysosome; CE, cholesterol ester; C, free cholesterol; HMG, β-hydroxy-β-methylglutaryl-CoA; AA, amino acids. (Modified from Small DM: Cellular mechanisms for lipid deposition in atherosclerosis. N Engl J Med 297:873, 1977.)

Factors Influencing Plasma Cholesterol

The plasma cholesterol level is decreased by thyroid hormones and estrogens. It is elevated when biliary flow is obstructed and also in hereditary hypercholesterolemia and untreated diabetes mellitus.

A high neutral fat diet elevates plasma cholesterol and also reduces clotting time and fibrinolytic activity. If the saturated fats in the diet are replaced with polyunsaturated fats, the plasma cholesterol level falls, and the effects on the clotting mechanism are reversed. As noted above, reduction of cholesterol intake also produces some lowering of plasma cholesterol in humans.

A subject of great interest is the role of cholesterol in the etiology and course of **atherosclerosis.** This extremely widespread disease of aging, which predisposes to myocardial infarction, cerebral thrombosis, and other serious illnesses, is characterized by infiltration of cholesterol into certain lesions of the arterial walls, distorting the vessels and making them rigid. In individuals with plasma cholesterol levels that are clearly elevated (**hypercholesterolemia),** there is an increased incidence of atherosclerosis and its complications. There is also evidence for accelerated atherosclerosis in individuals with elevated plasma LDL, and it appears that an elevated plasma HDL has a protective effect. In experimental animals and patients with hypercholesterolemia, lowering plasma cholesterol by decreasing cholesterol intake and replacing saturated fats in the diet with polyunsaturated compounds decreases the progression of atherosclerosis. Weight loss also lowers plasma lipids. Treatment with thyroid hormone analogs and estrogens has not proved to be beneficial for long-term treatment, but a number of other drugs lower plasma cholesterol. These include clofibrate and nicotinic acid, which decrease lipoprotein production, and cholestyramine, which increases lipoprotein catabolism.

On the other hand, it has not yet been proved that in individuals with initially normal plasma cholesterol, lowering plasma cholesterol decreases the incidence of atherosclerosis, myocardial infarctions, and strokes. After more than 10 years of intensive investigation, the data are suggestive but not yet definitive. Against this background, many normal individuals are modifying their diets to increase the ratio of polyunsaturated to saturated fat and decrease total caloric intake. In the meantime, the very large scale statistical studies necessary to settle the question are under way.

Essential Fatty Acids

Animals fed a fat-free diet fail to grow, develop skin and kidney lesions, and become infertile. Adding linolenic acid to the diet restores growth to normal, and linoleic and arachidonic acids cure all the deficiency symptoms. These 3 acids are polyunsaturated fatty acids and because of their action are called **essential fatty acids.** Similar deficiency symptoms have not been unequivocally demonstrated in humans, but there is reason to believe that some unsaturated fats are essential dietary constituents, especially in children.

Dehydrogenation of fats is known to occur in the body, but there does not appear to be any synthesis of carbon chains with the arrangement of double bonds found in the essential fatty acids.

Prostaglandins

It now appears that essential fatty acids are necessary for health because they are the precursors of **prostaglandins.** The prostaglandins are a series of closely related 20-carbon unsaturated fatty acids containing a cyclopentane ring. They were first isolated from semen but have now been shown to be synthesized in most and possibly in all organs in the body. The structures of some of them are shown in Fig 17–37. The prostaglandins are divided into 3 main groups—PGA, PGE, and PGF—on the basis of the configuration of the cyclopentane ring. The number of double bonds in the side chains is indicated by subscript numbers; for example, the E series prostaglandin shown in Fig 17–37 is PGE_2. The commonly occurring biologically active prostaglandins are PGA_1, PGA_2, PGE_1, PGE_2, $PGF_{1\alpha}$, and $PGF_{2\alpha}$.

Prostaglandins are synthesized from arachidonic acid and other essential fatty acids via endoperoxides (Fig 17–37). In addition to PGE_2, the biologically important products synthesized include thromboxanes and prostacyclin, a compound that is now called PGI_2.

The term **prostaglandin synthetase** was once used to refer to the enzymes that catalyze prostaglandin formation. The first enzyme involved, the cyclooxygenase that catalyzes the conversion of arachidonic acid to a cyclic endoperoxide, is inhibited by aspirin, indomethacin, and various other drugs. Some prostaglandins may enter the circulation, but the technics used to measure them in plasma have been criticized. It seems more likely that prostaglandins act mainly in the tissues in which they are formed. They have short half-lives and are metabolized to biologically inactive compounds by oxidation and isomerization. They are inactivated in many different tissues, but the greatest prostaglandin inactivating activity is found in renal cortex, lungs, and liver.

The prostaglandins have attracted great attention because they have profound effects when administered in very small doses. However, closely related prostaglandins often have opposite actions. For example, PGE_1 inhibits platelet aggregation (see Chapter 27), whereas PGE_2 augments aggregation. In addition, the prostaglandins have a bewildering array of actions. Prostaglandins of the E series lower blood pressure by dilating blood vessels in the splanchnic vascular bed. Prostaglandins of the A series also lower blood pressure but by a different mechanism (see Chapter 33). Prostaglandins may play a role in regulating the capacity of red blood cells to undergo deformation in passing through capillaries (see Chapter 30). Their actions on platelet aggregation and hence on hemostasis are mentioned above. Some of them decrease gastric acid secretion (see Chapter 26) and inhibit the formation of peptic ulcers in experimental animals. They cause luteolysis and may play a role in the regulation of the female reproductive cycle (see Chapter 23). They also have the capacity to modify pituitary responses to hypothalamic hormones. They induce abortion when injected intra-amniotically in midtrimester pregnancy, and they induce labor when injected near term. They can mimic the effects of TSH, ACTH, and other hormones. They stimulate renin secretion. Some of them are antilipolytic and may play a role along with glucagon, catecholamines, and other hormones in the regulation of FFA release (see above). They appear to be released from inflamed tissue and cause fever when injected into the third ventricle (see Chapter 14). Some of them relax bronchial smooth muscle, and they may play a role in asthma and other allergic diseases. They are found in the eye and produce miosis (see Chapter 8). They exist in the brain and may modulate the release or effects of neurotransmitters.

It is difficult to find a common theme in these multifarious actions, but it may be significant that cyclic AMP is involved in most if not all of them. Prostaglandins generally increase the cyclic AMP content of tissues, although in certain tissues, some pros-

taglandins decrease cyclic AMP content. It may be that the various prostaglandins act as modulators of the generation of cyclic AMP in response to various stimuli. However, the exact physiologic role of these ubiquitous fatty acids is still unknown.

In some tissues, the effects of prostaglandin endoperoxides are greater than the effects of the prostaglandins. This observation led to investigation of the effects of the thromboxanes, which are also formed from endoperoxides (Fig 17–37), and in platelets and vascular smooth muscle, thromboxane A_2 was found to be much more active than prostaglandins. However, endoperoxides are less active than prostaglandins in the corpus luteum, and it appears that some tissues do not make thromboxanes. Thus it appears likely that in some but not all tissues, the most active cell regulators formed from prostaglandin precursors are thromboxanes rather than prostaglandins. PGI_2 inhibits blood clotting and stimulates renin secretion. Thromboxane A_2 promotes clotting, and clot formation apparently depends on the balance between it and PGI_2.

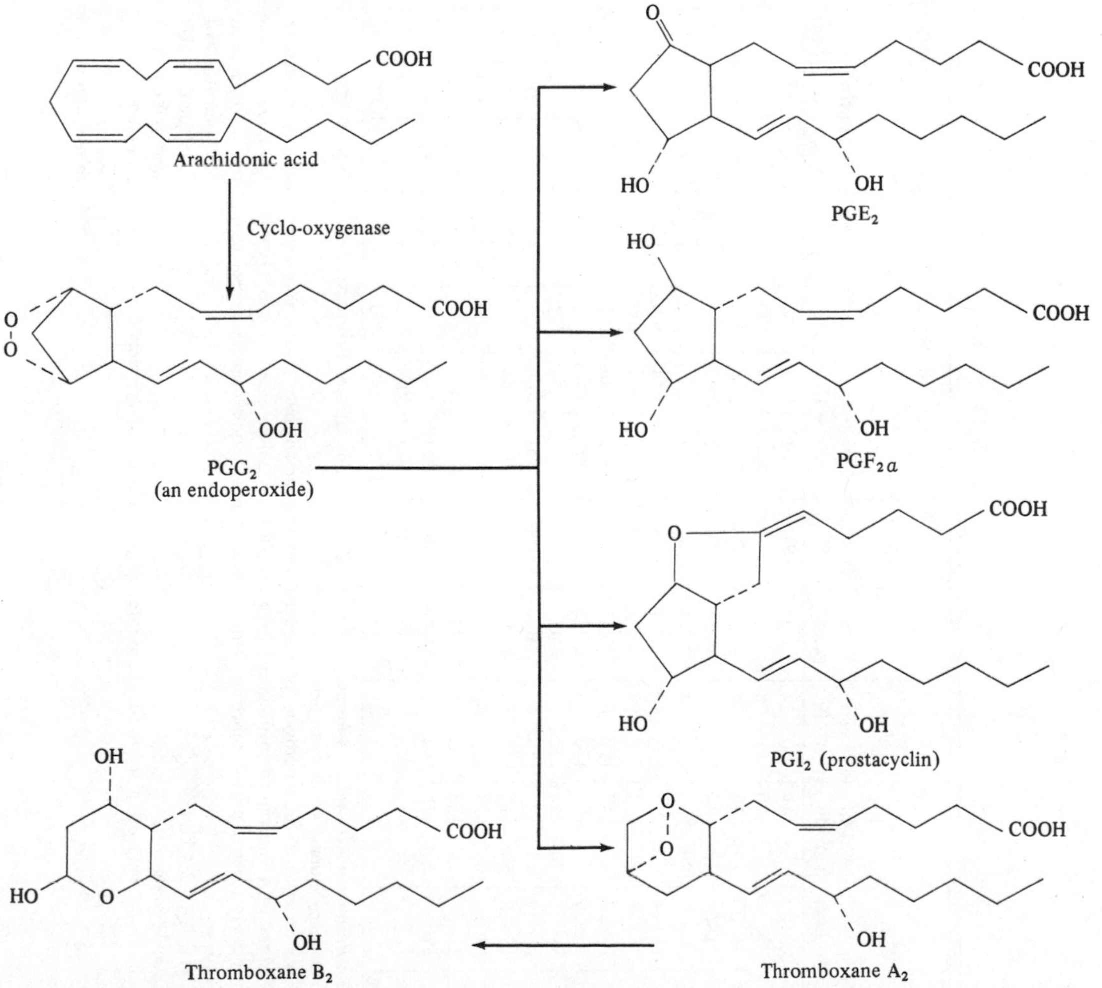

Figure 17–37. Synthesis of prostaglandins and thromboxanes from arachidonic acid.

Table 17–10. Recommended daily dietary allowances.[1] (Revised 1974.)

	Age (years)	Weight (kg)	Weight (lbs)	Height (cm)	Height (in)	Energy (kcal)[2]	Protein (g)	Vitamin A Activity (RE)[3]	Vitamin A Activity (IU)	Vitamin D (IU)	Vitamin E Activity[4] (IU)	Ascorbic Acid (mg)	Folacin[5] (µg)	Niacin[6] (mg)	Riboflavin (mg)	Thiamine (mg)	Vitamin B6 (mg)	Vitamin B12 (µg)	Calcium (mg)	Phosphorus (mg)	Iodine (µg)	Iron (mg)	Magnesium (mg)	Zinc (mg)
Infants	0.0–0.5	6	14	60	24	kg × 117	kg × 2.2	420[7]	1400	400	4	35	50	5	0.4	0.3	0.3	0.3	360	240	35	10	60	3
	0.5–1.0	9	20	71	28	kg × 108	kg × 2.0	400	2000	400	5	35	50	8	0.6	0.5	0.4	0.3	540	400	45	15	70	5
Children	1–3	13	28	86	34	1300	23	400	2000	400	7	40	100	9	0.8	0.7	0.6	1.0	800	800	60	15	150	10
	4–6	20	44	110	44	1800	30	500	2500	400	9	40	200	12	1.1	0.9	0.9	1.5	800	800	80	10	200	10
	7–10	30	66	135	54	2400	36	700	3300	400	10	40	300	16	1.2	1.2	1.2	2.0	800	800	110	10	250	10
Males	11–14	44	97	158	63	2800	44	1000	5000	400	12	45	400	18	1.5	1.4	1.6	3.0	1200	1200	130	18	350	15
	15–18	61	134	172	69	3000	54	1000	5000	400	15	45	400	20	1.8	1.5	2.0	3.0	1200	1200	150	18	400	15
	19–22	67	147	172	69	3000	54	1000	5000	400	15	45	400	20	1.8	1.5	2.0	3.0	800	800	140	10	350	15
	23–50	70	154	172	69	2700	56	1000	5000		15	45	400	18	1.6	1.4	2.0	3.0	800	800	130	10	350	15
	51+	70	154	172	69	2400	56	1000	5000		15	45	400	16	1.5	1.2	2.0	3.0	800	800	110	10	350	15
Females	11–14	44	97	155	62	2400	44	800	4000	400	12	45	400	16	1.3	1.2	1.6	3.0	1200	1200	115	18	300	15
	15–18	54	119	162	65	2100	48	800	4000	400	12	45	400	14	1.4	1.1	2.0	3.0	1200	1200	115	18	300	15
	19–22	58	128	162	65	2100	46	800	4000	400	12	45	400	14	1.4	1.1	2.0	3.0	800	800	100	18	300	15
	23–50	58	128	162	65	2000	46	800	4000		12	45	400	13	1.2	1.0	2.0	3.0	800	800	100	18	300	15
	51+	58	128	162	65	1800	46	800	4000		12	45	400	12	1.1	1.0	2.0	3.0	800	800	80	10	300	15
Pregnant						+300	+30	1000	5000	400	15	60	800	+2	+0.3	+0.3	2.5	4.0	1200	1200	125	18+[8]	450	20
Lactating						+500	+20	1200	6000	400	15	80	600	+4	+0.5	+0.3	2.5	4.0	1200	1200	150	18	450	25

Reference: *Recommended Dietary Allowances*, 8th rev ed. Food and Nutrition Board, National Research Council–National Academy of Sciences, 1974.

[1] The allowances are intended to provide for individual variations among most normal persons as they live in the USA under usual environmental stresses. Diets should be based on a variety of common foods in order to provide other nutrients for which human requirements have been less well defined.

[2] Kilojoules (kJ) = 4.2 × kcal.

[3] RE = Retinol equivalents.

[4] Total vitamin E activity, estimated to be 80% as α-tocopherol and 20% other tocopherols.

[5] The folacin allowances refer to dietary sources as determined by *Lactobacillus casei* assay. Pure forms of folacin may be effective in doses less than one-fourth of the recommended dietary allowance.

[6] Although allowances are expressed as niacin, it is recognized that on the average 1 mg of niacin is derived from each 60 mg of dietary tryptophan.

[7] Vitamin A activity is assumed to be all as retinol in milk during the first 6 months of life. All subsequent intakes are assumed to be half as retinol and half as β-carotene when calculated from international units. As retinol equivalents, three-fourths are as retinol and one-fourth as β-carotene.

[8] This increased requirement cannot be met by ordinary diets; therefore, the use of supplemental iron is recommended.

NUTRITION

The aim of the science of nutrition is the determination of the kinds and amounts of foods that promote health and well-being. This includes not only the problems of undernutrition but those of overnutrition, taste, and availability. However, certain substances are essential constituents of any human diet. Many of these compounds have been mentioned in previous sections of this chapter, and a brief summary of the essential and desirable dietary components is presented below.

ESSENTIAL DIETARY COMPONENTS

An optimal diet includes, in addition to sufficient water (see Chapter 38), adequate calories, protein, fat, minerals, and vitamins.

Caloric Intake & Distribution

As noted above, the caloric value of the dietary intake must equal the energy expended as heat and work if body weight is to be maintained. When the caloric intake is insufficient, body stores of protein and fat are catabolized, and when the intake is excessive, obesity results. In addition to the 2000 kcal/d necessary to meet basal needs, 500–2500 or more kcal/d are required to meet the energy demands of daily activities (Table 17–10).

The distribution of the calories among carbohydrate, protein, and fat foodstuffs is determined partly by physiologic factors and partly by taste and economic considerations. A daily protein intake of at least 1 g/kg body weight to supply the 8 essential amino acids and other amino acids is now regarded as desirable. The source of the protein is also important. **Grade I proteins,** the animal proteins of meat, fish, and eggs, are those which contain amino acids in approximately the proportions required for protein synthesis and other uses in the body. Some of the plant proteins are also grade I, but most are **grade II** because they supply different proportions of amino acids, and some lack one or more of the essential amino acids. Protein needs can be met with a mixture of grade II proteins, but the intake must be large because of the amino acid wastage.

Fat is the most compact form of food, since it supplies 9.3 kcal/g. However, it is also the most expensive. Indeed, there is a reasonably good positive correlation between fat intake and standard of living, and in the past, western diets have contained moderately large amounts (100 g/d or more). The evidence suggesting that a high unsaturated/saturated fat ratio in the diet is of value in the prevention of arteriosclerosis and the current interest in preventing obesity may change this. In Central and South American Indian communities where corn (carbohydrate) is the dietary

staple, adults live without ill effects for years on a very small fat intake. Therefore, provided the needs for essential fatty acids are met, a low fat intake does not seem to be harmful, and a diet low in saturated fats may be desirable.

Carbohydrate is the cheapest source of calories and provides 50% or more of the calories in most diets. In the average middle class American diet, approximately 50% of the calories come from carbohydrate, 15% from protein, and 35% from fat. When calculating dietary needs, it is usual to meet the protein requirement first and then split the remaining calories between fat and carbohydrate, depending upon taste, income, and other factors. For example, a 70 kg man who is moderately active needs about 2800 kcal/d. He should eat at least 65 g of protein/d, supplying 267 (65 × 4.1) kcal. Some of this should be grade I protein. Fat intake depends upon taste, but a reasonable figure is 60–70 g. The rest of the caloric requirement can be met by supplying carbohydrate.

Mineral Requirements

A number of minerals must be ingested daily for the maintenance of health. Besides those for which recommended daily dietary allowances have been set (Table 17–10), a variety of different trace elements should be included. Trace elements are defined as elements found in tissues in minute amounts. Those believed to be essential for life, at least in experimental animals, are listed in Table 17–11. Cobalt is part of the vitamin B_{12} molecule, and its deficiency leads to megaloblastic anemia (see Chapter 26). Iodine deficiency causes thyroid disorders (see Chapter 18). Zinc deficiency in humans causes skin ulcers, loss of hair, and hypogonadal dwarfism. Copper deficiency causes anemia and neutropenia and may cause CNS abnormalities. Trace element deficiencies are rare because any diet that is adequate in other respects easily supplies the needed minerals.

Sodium and potassium are also essential minerals, but listing them is academic because it is very difficult to prepare a sodium-free or a potassium-free diet. A low-salt diet is well tolerated for prolonged periods because of the compensatory mechanisms that conserve sodium, and salt depletion is a problem only when sodium is lost in excessive amounts in the stools, sweat, or urine.

Table 17–11. Trace elements believed to be essential for life.*

Chromium	Nickel
Cobalt	Selenium
Copper	Silicon
Fluorine	Tin
Iodine	Vanadium
Manganese	Zinc
Molybdenum	

*Data from Ulmer DD: Trace elements. N Engl J Med 297:318, 1977.

Table 17–12. Vitamins essential or probably essential to human nutrition. Choline is not listed because it is synthesized in the body in adequate amounts except in special circumstances.

Vitamin	Action	Deficiency Symptoms	Sources	Chemistry
A (A_1, A_2)	Constituents of visual pigments (Chapter 8); maintain epithelia.	Night blindness, dry skin	Yellow vegetables and fruit	Vitamin A_1 (alcohol)
B complex Thiamine (vitamin B_1)	Cofactor in decarboxylations.	Beriberi, neuritis	Liver, unrefined cereal grains	
Riboflavin (vitamin B_2)	Constituent of flavoproteins.	Glossitis, cheilosis	Liver, milk	
Niacin	Constituent of NAD^+, $NADP^+$.	Pellagra	Yeast, lean meat, liver	Can be synthesized in body from tryptophan.
Pyridoxine (vitamin B_6)	Forms prosthetic group of certain decarboxylases and transaminases. Converted in body into pyridoxal phosphate and pyridoxamine phosphate.	Convulsions, hyperirritability	Yeast, wheat, corn, liver	
Pantothenic acid	Constituent of CoA.	Dermatitis, enteritis, alopecia, adrenal insufficiency	Eggs, liver, yeast	
Biotin	Catalyzes CO_2 "fixation" (in fatty acid synthesis, etc).	Dermatitis, enteritis	Egg yolk, liver, tomatoes	
Folates (folic acid) and related compounds	Coenzymes for "one-carbon" transfer; involved in methylating reactions.	Sprue, anemia	Leafy green vegetables	Folic acid

Table 17–12 (cont'd). Vitamins essential or probably essential to human nutrition.

Vitamin	Action	Deficiency Symptoms	Sources	Chemistry
Cyanocobalamin (vitamin B_{12})	Coenzyme in amino acid metabolism. Stimulates erythropoiesis.	Pernicious anemia (Chapter 26)	Liver, meat, eggs, milk	Complex of 4 substituted pyrrole rings around a cobalt atom (Chapter 26).
C	Necessary for hydroxylation of lysine in collagen synthesis.	Scurvy	Citrus fruits, leafy green vegetables	Ascorbic acid (synthesized in all mammals except guinea pigs and humans).
D group	Increase intestinal absorption of calcium and phosphate (Chapter 21).	Rickets	Fish liver	Family of sterols (see Chapter 21).
E group	Antioxidants; cofactors in electron transport in cytochrome chain?	Muscular dystrophy and fetal death in animals; ? contributory factor in rentrolental fibroplasia in premature infants	Milk, eggs, meat, leafy vegetables	a-Tocopherol; β- and γ-tocopherol also active.
K group	Catalyze synthesis of prothrombin and several other clotting factors in the liver.	Hemorrhagic phenomena	Leafy green vegetables	Vitamin K_3; a large number of similar compounds have biologic activity.

Vitamins

Vitamins were discovered when it was observed that diets adequate in calories, essential amino acids, fats, and minerals failed to maintain health. The term **vitamin** has now come to refer to any organic dietary constituent necessary for life, health, and growth that does not function by supplying energy.

Because there are minor differences in metabolism between mammalian species, some substances are vitamins in one species and not in another. The sources and functions of the major vitamins in humans are listed in Table 17–12 and the recommended daily dietary allowances in Table 17–10. Most of them have important functions in intermediary metabolism or the special metabolism of the various organ systems. Those that are water-soluble (vitamin B complex, vitamin C) are easily absorbed, but the fat-soluble vitamins (vitamins A, D, E, and K) are poorly absorbed in the absence of bile or pancreatic lipase. Some dietary fat intake is necessary for their absorption, and in obstructive jaundice or in pancreatic disease, deficiencies of the fat-soluble vitamins can develop even if their intake is adequate (see Chapter 26).

The diseases caused by deficiency of each of these vitamins are listed in Table 17–12. It is worth remembering, however, particularly now that the well-advertised bottle of vitamin pills is frequently a fixture on the dinner table in the United States, that very large doses of vitamins A, D, and K are definitely toxic. **Hypervitaminosis A** is characterized by anorexia, headache, hepatosplenomegaly, irritability, scaly dermatitis, patchy loss of hair, and bone pain. Acute vitamin A intoxication was first described by Arctic explorers, who found that men developed headache, diarrhea, and dizziness after eating polar bear liver. The liver of this animal is particularly rich in vitamin A. **Hypervitaminosis D** is associated with weight loss and calcification of many soft tissues, and excessive vitamin D intake eventually causes renal failure. **Hypervitaminosis K** is characterized by gastrointestinal disturbances and anemia.

18 | The Thyroid Gland

The thyroid gland maintains the level of metabolism in the tissues that is optimal for their normal function. Thyroid hormone stimulates the O_2 consumption of most of the cells in the body, helps regulate lipid and carbohydrate metabolism, and is necessary for normal growth and maturation. The thyroid gland is not essential for life, but in its absence, there is poor resistance to cold, mental and physical slowing, and in children, mental retardation and dwarfism. Conversely, excess thyroid secretion leads to body wasting, nervousness, tachycardia, tremor, and excess heat production. Thyroid function is controlled by the thyroid-stimulating hormone (TSH) of the anterior pituitary. The secretion of this tropic hormone is in turn regulated in part by a direct inhibitory feedback of high circulating thyroid hormone levels on the pituitary and in part via neural mechanisms operating through the hypothalamus. In this way, changes in the internal and external environment bring about appropriate adjustments in the rate of thyroid secretion.

The thyroid gland also secretes calcitonin, a calcium-lowering hormone. This hormone is discussed in Chapter 21.

ANATOMIC CONSIDERATIONS

Thyroid tissue is present in all vertebrates. In mammals, the thyroid originates from an evagination of the floor of the pharynx, and a **thyroglossal duct** marking the path of the thyroid from the tongue to the neck sometimes persists in the adult. The 2 lobes of the human thyroid are connected by a bridge of tissue, the **thyroid isthmus,** and there is sometimes a **pyramidal lobe** arising from the isthmus in front of the larynx (Fig 18–1). The gland is well vascularized, and the thyroid has one of the highest rates of blood flow per gram of tissue of any organ in the body.

The thyroid is made up of multiple **acini,** or **follicles.** Each spherical follicle is surrounded by a single layer of cells and filled with pink-staining proteinaceous material called **colloid.** When the gland is inactive, the colloid is abundant, the follicles are large, and the cells lining them are flat. When the gland is active, the follicles are small, the cells are cuboid or columnar, and the edge of the colloid is scalloped, forming many small "reabsorption lacunae" (Fig 18–2).

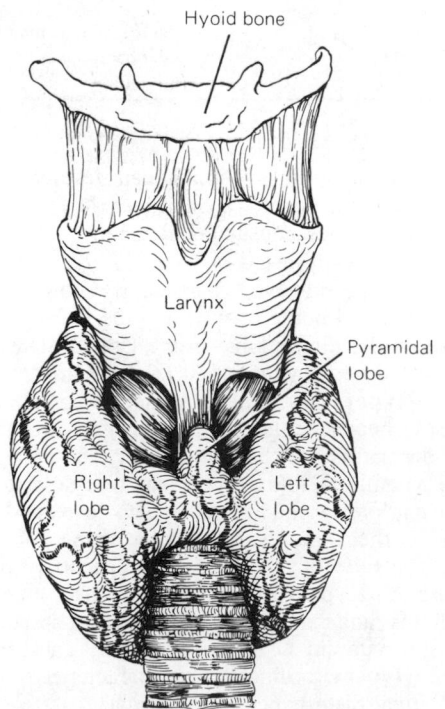

Figure 18–1. The human thyroid.

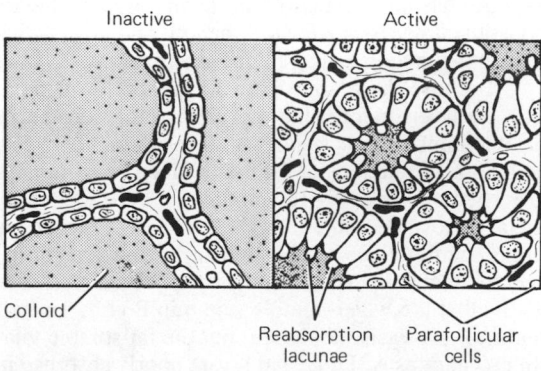

Figure 18–2. Thyroid histology. Notice the small, punched-out "reabsorption lacunae" in the colloid next to the cells in the active gland.

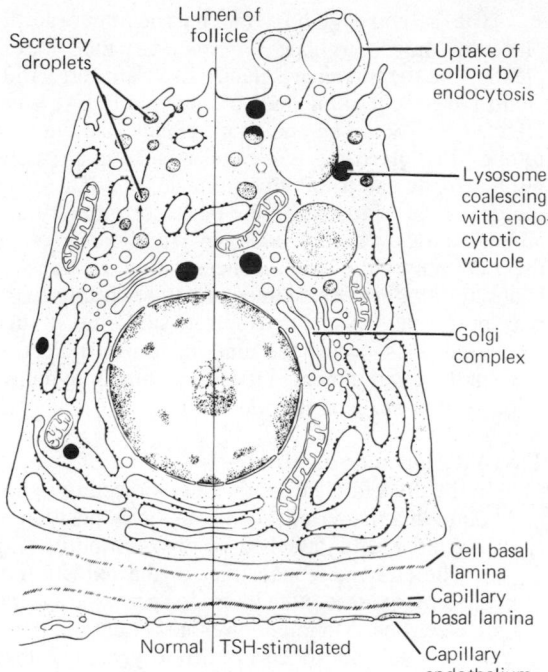

Figure 18–3. Thyroid cell. *Left:* Normal pattern. *Right:* After marked TSH stimulation. The arrows on the left show the secretion of thyroglobulin into colloid. On the right, endocytosis of the colloid and merging of a colloid-containing vacuole with a lysosome are shown. The cell rests on a capillary with gaps (fenestrations) in the endothelial wall. (Modified and reproduced, with permission, from Fawcett DW, Long JA, Jones AL: The ultrastructure of endocrine glands. Recent Prog Horm Res 25:315, 1969.)

Microvilli project into the colloid from the apexes of the thyroid cells, and canaliculi extend into them. There is a prominent endoplasmic reticulum, a feature common to most glandular cells, and secretory droplets of thyroglobulin are seen (Fig 18–3). The individual thyroid cells rest on a basal lamina that separates them from the adjacent capillaries. The endothelial cells are attenuated at places, forming gaps, or fenestrations, in the walls of the capillaries (Fig 18–3). This fenestration of the capillary walls also occurs in most other endocrine organs.

FORMATION & SECRETION OF THYROID HORMONES

Chemistry

The principal hormones secreted by the thyroid are **thyroxine (T_4)** and **triiodothyronine (T_3).** Triiodothyronine is also formed in the peripheral tissues by deiodination of thyroxine (see below). Both hormones are iodine-containing amino acids (Fig 18–4). Small amounts of reverse triiodothyronine,

monoiodotyrosine, and other compounds are also found in thyroid venous blood. The naturally occurring forms of thyroxine and its congeners with an asymmetrical carbon atom are the L-isomers. D-Thyroxine has only a small fraction of the activity of the L-form.

Thyroglobulin

Thyroxine and triiodothyronine are synthesized in the colloid by iodination and condensation of tyrosine molecules bound in peptide linkage in **thyroglobulin.** This glycoprotein has 4 peptide chains and a molecular weight of approximately 670,000. It is synthesized in the thyroid cells and secreted into the colloid. The hormones remain bound to thyroglobulin until secreted. When they are secreted, colloid is ingested by the thyroid cells, the peptide bonds are hydrolyzed, and free thyroxine and triiodothyronine are discharged into the capillaries. The thyroid cells thus have a dual function: They collect and transport the iodine and synthesize the thyroglobulin, then secrete it into the colloid; and they remove the thyroid hormones from thyroglobulin and secrete them into the circulation. Other iodinated proteins of uncertain function are also found in the thyroid.

Iodine Metabolism

Iodine is a raw material essential for thyroid hormone synthesis. Ingested iodine is converted to iodide and absorbed. The fate of the absorbed I^- is summarized in Fig 18–5. The minimum daily iodine intake that will maintain normal thyroid function is 100–150 μg in adults (Table 17–10), but in the USA, the average dietary intake is approximately 500 μg/d. The normal plasma I^- level is about 0.3 μg/dl, and I^- is distributed in a "space" of approximately 25 liters (35% of body weight). The principal organs that take up the I^- are the thyroid, which uses it to make thyroid hormones, and the kidneys, which excrete it in the urine. About 120 μg/d enter the thyroid at normal rates of thyroid hormone synthesis and secretion. The thyroid secretes 80 μg/d as iodine in triiodothyronine and thyroxine. It also releases 40 μg of I^- into the ECF,

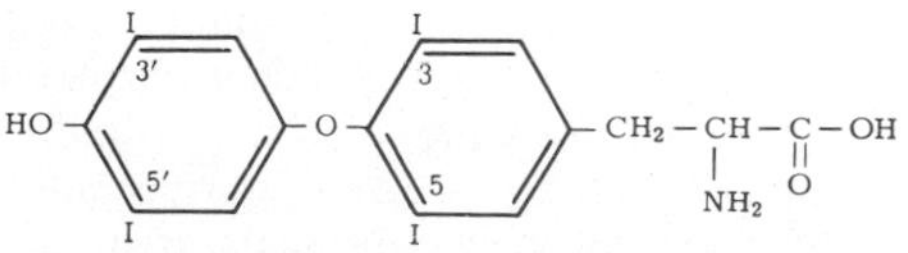

3,5,3′,5′-Tetraiodothyronine (thyroxine, T_4)

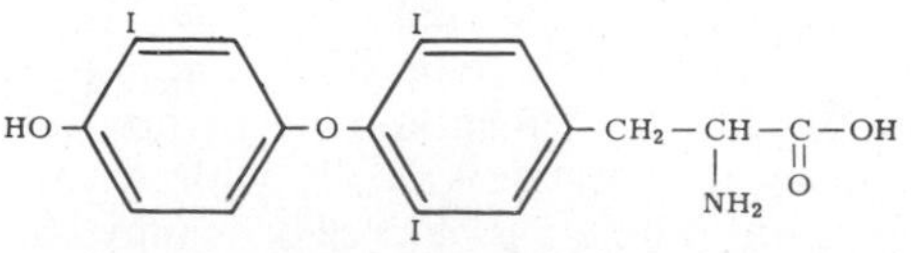

3,5,3′-Triiodothyronine (T_3)

Figure 18–4. Thyroid hormones. The numbers in the rings in the thyroxine formula indicate the numbering of positions in the molecule.

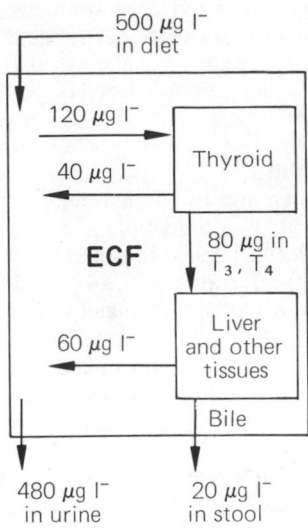

Figure 18–5. Iodine metabolism.

most of the released I⁻ coming from the deiodination of mono- and diiodotyrosine (see below). The secreted triiodothyronine and thyroxine are metabolized in the liver and other tissues, with the release of 60 μg of I⁻ into the ECF. Some thyroid hormone derivatives are excreted in the bile, and some of the iodine in them is reabsorbed (enterohepatic circulation), but there is a net loss of I⁻ in the stool of approximately 20 μg/d. The total amount of I⁻ entering the ECF is thus 500 + 40 + 60, or 600 μg/d; 20% of this I⁻ enters the thyroid, whereas 80% is excreted in the urine.

Iodide Trapping

The thyroid concentrates iodide by actively transporting it from the circulation to the colloid. The transport mechanism is frequently called the "iodide trapping mechanism" or "iodide pump." The thyroid cell is about 50 mV negative to the interstitial area and the colloid, ie, it has a resting membrane potential of −50 mV. Iodide is presumably pumped into the cell at its base against this electrical gradient, then diffuses down the electrical gradient into the colloid. Iodine uptake can be studied by administering radioactive iodine in **tracer doses,** amounts that are so small they do not significantly increase the amount of iodide in the body. The iodine isotope usually used is ¹³¹I, which has a half-life of 8 days, although ¹³²I and ¹²⁵I are also available. The ratio of thyroid to plasma or serum free iodide (**T/S ratio**) ranges from 10 to over 100. In the gland, iodide is rapidly oxidized and bound to tyrosine. If binding is blocked by antithyroid drugs such as thiouracil (see below), the T/S ratio may rise to 250. Perchlorate and a number of other anions decrease iodide transport by competitive inhibition. The active transport mechanism is stimulated by TSH and inhibited by ouabain.

The salivary glands, the gastric mucosa, the placenta, the ciliary body of the eye, the choroid plexus, and the mammary glands also transport iodide against a concentration gradient, but their uptake is not affected by TSH. The mammary glands also bind the iodine; diiodotyrosine is formed in mammary tissue but thyroxine and triiodothyronine are not. There is a minor uptake of iodide by the posterior pituitary and adrenal cortex. The physiologic significance of all these extrathyroidal iodide-concentrating mechanisms is obscure. It has been claimed that traces of thyroxine may be formed by nonthyroidal tissues, but if such formation does occur, the amount is insufficient to prevent the development of the full picture of hypothyroidism after surgical thyroidectomy.

Thyroid Hormone Synthesis

In the thyroid gland, iodide is oxidized to iodine and bound in a matter of seconds to the 3- position of tyrosine molecules attached to thyroglobulin (Fig 18–6). The enzyme responsible for the oxidation of iodide is a peroxidase, with hydrogen peroxide accepting the electrons. Monoiodotyrosine is next iodinated in the 5- position to form diiodotyrosine. Two diiodotyrosine molecules then undergo an oxidative condensation, with the liberation of an alanine residue and the formation of thyroxine, still in peptide linkage to thyroglobulin. Proof that the reactions occur in this sequence is the demonstration that injected radioactive iodine appears first in monoiodotyrosine, then in diiodotyrosine, and lastly in thyroxine. Triiodothyronine is probably formed by condensation of monoiodotyrosine with diiodotyrosine. A small amount of "reverse triiodothyronine" (3,3′,5′-triiodothyronine) is also formed, probably by condensation of diiodotyrosine and monoiodotyrosine. The condensation reaction is an aerobic, energy-requiring reaction. In the normal human thyroid, the average distribution of iodinated compounds is 23% monoiodotyrosine, 33% diiodotyrosine, 35% thyroxine, and 7% triiodothyronine. Only traces of reverse triiodothyronine and other components are present.

Secretion

The human thyroid secretes about 80 μg (103 nmol) of free thyroxine and up to 40 μg (63 nmol) of triiodothyronine per day. The thyroid cells ingest colloid by endocytosis (see Chapter 1). This chewing away at the edge of the colloid produces the reabsorption lacunae seen in active glands (Fig 18–2). In the cells, the globules of colloid merge with lysosomes (Fig 18–3). The peptide bonds between the iodinated residues and the thyroglobulin are broken by the proteases in the lysosomes, and thyroxine, triiodothyronine, diiodotyrosine, and monoiodotyrosine are liberated into the cytoplasm. The iodinated tyrosines are deiodinated by a microsomal **iodotyrosine dehalogenase,** but this enzyme does not attack iodinated thyronines, and thyroxine and triiodothyronine pass on into the circulation. The iodide liberated by deiodination of the tyrosines is reutilized.

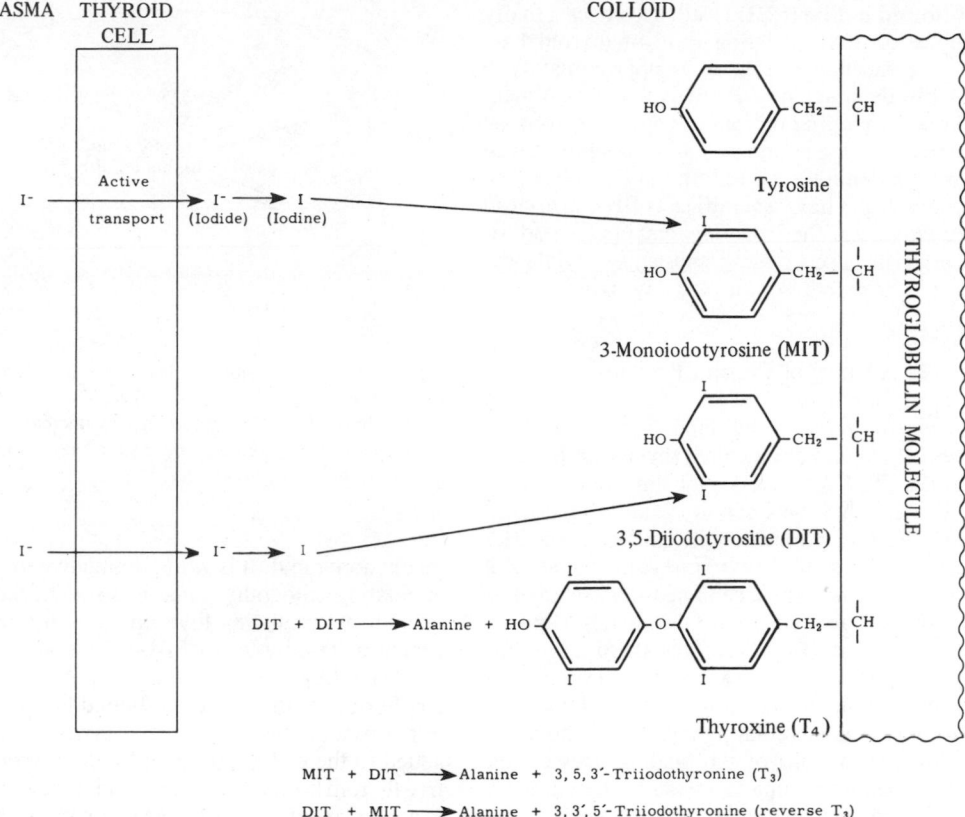

Figure 18–6. Outline of thyroxine biosynthesis. Iodination of tyrosine and the condensation reaction take place while molecules are bound in peptide linkage in thyroglobulin.

Effects of TSH on the Thyroid

When the pituitary is removed, thyroid function is depressed (Table 18–1); when TSH is administered, thyroid function is stimulated. Within a few hours after the injection of TSH, iodide uptake is increased; monoiodotyrosine, diiodotyrosine, and thyroxine synthesis are enhanced; endocytosis of colloid is increased; and more thyroxine and triiodothyronine are secreted. Later on, blood flow increases, and with chronic TSH treatment, the cells hypertrophy and the weight of the gland rises. TSH binds to receptors in thyroid cell membranes and activates adenylate cyclase in thyroid cell membranes. The resultant increase in intracellular cyclic AMP (see Chapter 17) produces a rapid increase in the endocytosis of colloid and a rapid increase in glucose oxidation in the gland,

primarily via the hexosemonophosphate shunt. The other changes produced by TSH follow these. The increase in glucose oxidation presumably increases the formation of NADPH and other coenzymes necessary for a variety of reactions in hormone synthesis and secretion. TSH also increases thyroglobulin synthesis, and this action is blocked by actinomycin D (see Chapter 17). However, there is little evidence that the other effects of TSH on thyroid function are due to stimulation of protein synthesis per se.

Whenever TSH stimulation is prolonged, the thyroid becomes detectably enlarged. Enlargement of the thyroid is called **goiter.**

TRANSPORT & METABOLISM OF THYROID HORMONES

Protein-Binding

The normal total plasma thyroxine is approximately 8 μg/dl, (103 nmol/L), and normal total plasma triiodothyronine is approximately 0.15 μg/dl (2.3 nmol/L). Both are bound to plasma proteins. Both are now measured by radioimmunoassay, but the

Table 18–1. Effect of hypophysectomy on thyroid weight and radioactive iodine uptake in dogs.*

	Normal	Hypophysectomized
Thyroid weight (mg/kg)	84.4 ± 22.8	70.0 ± 31.4
Uptake of ^{131}I (%†)	31.5 ± 13.4	3.4 ± 2.4

*Values are means ± one standard deviation.

†Percentage of dose in thyroid 72 hours after injection.

protein-bound iodine (PBI) is still used occasionally as an index of the circulating level of thyroid hormones. The normal PBI level is approximately 6 μg/dl. A disadvantage of the PBI is that it also measures iodine-containing radiopaque dyes and contrast media which become bound to plasma albumin. Since the iodine-containing dyes do not bind to TBG (see below), they do not have a significant effect on thyroid function. However, the PBI may remain elevated for months after the use of these substances, while the plasma total triiodothyronine and thyroxine remain normal.

Capacity & Affinity of Plasma Proteins for Thyroid Hormones

The plasma proteins that bind thyroid hormones are **albumin,** a prealbumin called **thyroxine-binding prealbumin (TBPA),** and a globulin with an electrophoretic mobility between α_1- and α_2-globulin, **thyroxine-binding globulin (TBG). The capacities** of these 3 proteins to bind thyroxine—the amounts of thyroxine they bind when saturated—are shown in Table 18–2. Albumin has by far the greatest capacity and TBG the least. However, the **affinities** of the proteins for thyroxine—ie, the avidity with which they bind thyroxine under physiologic conditions—are such that most of the circulating thyroxine is bound to TBG, with over a third of the binding sites on the protein occupied. Only small amounts of thyroxine are bound to TBPA and practically none to albumin.

Normally, 99.98% of the thyroxine in plasma is bound; the free thyroxine level is only about 2 ng/dl. There is very little thyroxine in the urine. Its biologic half-life is long (about 6–7 days), and its volume of distribution is less than that of ECF (10 liters, or about 15% of body weight). All of these properties are characteristic of a substance that is strongly bound to protein.

Triiodothyronine is not bound to as great an extent; of the 0.15 μg/dl normally found in plasma, 0.5%, or 0.8 ng/dl, is free. The remaining 99.5% is protein-bound, 75% to TBG and the remainder to albumin. Triiodothyronine does not bind to TBPA. The lesser binding to TBG and albumin correlates with the facts that triiodothyronine has a much shorter half-life than thyroxine and that its action on the tissues is

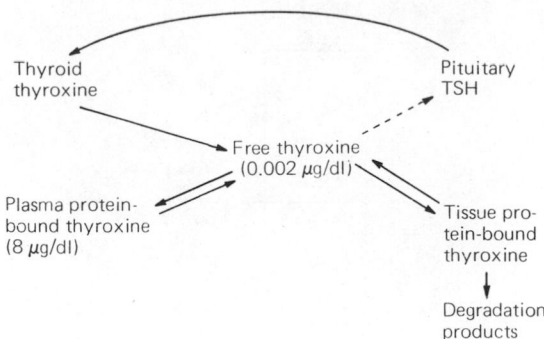

Figure 18–7. Distribution of thyroxine in the body. The distribution of triiodothyronine is similar. The dashed arrow indicates inhibition of TSH secretion by increases in the free thyroxine level of ECF. Approximate concentrations in human blood are shown in parentheses.

much more rapid. It is worth noting that the amount of circulating triiodothyronine is so low relative to the amount of circulating thyroxine that it does not contribute materially to the PBI.

The free thyroid hormones in plasma are in equilibrium with the protein-bound thyroid hormones in the tissues (Fig 18–7). Free thyroid hormones are added to the circulating pool by the thyroid. It is the free thyroid hormones in plasma that are physiologically active, and it is this fraction that inhibits the pituitary secretion of TSH (see below).

Because of the equilibriums shown in Fig 18–7, the entry of thyroid hormones into the tissues is increased whenever the concentration of free thyroid hormones in the plasma is elevated. The hormones are metabolized in the tissues, and consequently their rate of metabolism is increased. Conversely, when the free thyroid hormone level in the plasma is decreased, the tissue uptake and rate of hormone metabolism are reduced (Table 18–3). Red blood cells bind thyroid hormones, and these effects can easily be demonstrated in vitro in suspensions of red cells in plasma. For example, red blood cell uptake of thyroxine can be used in the diagnosis of various thyroid disorders. The plasma of hyperthyroid patients contains excess free thyroxine, and if this plasma is added to normal red

Table 18–2. Thyroxine-binding capacity and affinity of plasma protein constituents.

Protein	Plasma Level (mg/dl)	Thyroxine-Binding Capacity (μg/dl)	Affinity for Thyroxine	Approximate Amount of Thyroxine Bound in Normal Plasma (μg/dl)
Thyroxine-binding globulin (TBG)	1.0	20	High	7
Thyroxine-binding prealbumin (TBPA)	30.0	250	Moderate	1
Albumin	. . .	1000	Low	None
Total protein-bound thyroxine in plasma	. . .	. . .	. . .	8

Table 18–3. Effect of variations in the concentrations of thyroid hormone–binding proteins in the plasma on various parameters of thyroid function.

	Concentrations of Binding Proteins	Total Plasma T_3 and T_4	Free Plasma T_3 and T_4	Clinical State
Hyperthyroidism	Normal	High	High	Hyperthyroid
Hypothyroidism	Normal	Low	Low	Hypothyroid
Pregnancy, estrogen treatment, congenital elevation of TBG	High	High	Normal*	Euthyroid
Nephrosis, methyltestosterone, phenytoin, congenital depression of TBG	Low	Low	Normal*	Euthyroid

*After equilibrium is reached.

blood cells, thyroxine uptake is greater than normal. Conversely, when the plasma of patients with hypothyroidism is added to red cells, uptake is decreased. Similar results are obtained using a resin to take up triiodothyronine.

Fluctuations in Binding

When there is a sudden, sustained increase in the concentration of thyroid-binding proteins in the plasma, the concentration of free thyroid hormones falls. There is a consequent increase in TSH secretion, which in turn increases thyroid secretion. These changes are temporary, however, because as the level rises, a new equilibrium is reached at which the total concentration of thyroid hormones is elevated but the free thyroid hormone concentration and rate of TSH secretion are normal. Corresponding changes in the opposite direction occur when the concentration of thyroid-binding proteins is reduced.

TBG levels are elevated in estrogen-treated patients and during pregnancy (Table 18–3). They are depressed by methyltestosterone administration and are low in nephrosis. A few cases of congenital elevation or depression of TBG levels have been reported. Patients with abnormal TBG levels do not show signs of hyper- or hypothyroidism, ie, they are **euthyroid.** TBPA levels are nonspecifically depressed in severely ill patients, but rarely if ever to the point where measurable PBI changes are observed. However, depressed PBI values in patients treated with salicylates are apparently due to a decrease in thyroid hormone binding to TBPA.

Metabolism of Thyroid Hormones

Thyroxine and triiodothyronine are deiodinated and deaminated in many tissues. Most of the circulating thyroxine is deiodinated to triiodothyronine and reverse triiodothyronine, and most of the circulating triiodothyronine is formed in this fashion. Only small amounts of reverse triiodothyronine are found in adults. However, this compound is formed in large quantities in early fetal life, and the plasma level gradually falls during gestation. Because triiodothyronine acts more rapidly and is more potent than thyroxine, it has been suggested that thyroxine is metabolically inert until it is deiodinated to triiodothyronine, ie, that it is a prohormone. The find-

ing that the thyroxine-deiodinating activity of skeletal muscles parallels the metabolic rate supports this hypothesis. In addition, there is much more nuclear binding of triiodothyronine than thyroxine (see below). However, the more rapid action of triiodothyronine could also be due to the fact that it is less avidly bound in the circulation and consequently is more available.

Deamination in the tissues produces pyruvic acid analogs of thyroxine and triiodothyronine, and subsequent decarboxylation produces the acetic acid analogs TETRAC and TRIAC (Table 18–4). TETRAC lowers the plasma cholesterol level to a greater degree than it affects the BMR, and a dose of this compound that stimulates cardiac O_2 consumption to the same degree as a given dose of thyroxine has a far less stimulating effect on kidney metabolism than the thyroxine. It is tempting to speculate that various tissues produce degradation products tailored to their special metabolic needs. However, there is no direct evidence for this hypothesis.

In the liver, thyroxine and triiodothyronine are conjugated to form sulfates and glucuronides. These conjugates enter the bile and pass into the intestine. The thyroid conjugates are hydrolyzed, and some are reabsorbed (enterohepatic circulation), but some are excreted in the stool. The iodide lost in this way amounts to about 5% of the daily iodide loss.

EFFECTS OF THYROID HORMONES

Most of the widespread effects of thyroid hormones in the body are secondary to stimulation of O_2 consumption (**calorigenic action**), although they also affect growth and maturation in mammals, help regulate lipid metabolism, and increase the absorption of carbohydrates from the intestine. They also increase the dissociation of oxygen from hemoglobin by increasing red cell 2,3-DPG (see Chapter 35). In these actions, triiodothyronine is more potent than thyroxine (Fig 18–8), while the fatty acid analogs have selective effects (Table 18–4). Reverse triiodothyronine has an inhibitory effect on radioactive iodine uptake but is otherwise relatively inert. It is of interest that the

Table 18–4. Relative potencies of thyroxine derivatives.* Note that in each column the potency of the derivatives is stated relative to an arbitrary value of 100 for thyroxine.

Chemical Structure	Name	Synonyms	Relative Potency			
			^{131}I†	Goiter Prev ‡	BMR §	Cholesterol Lowering
HO⟨⟩–O–⟨⟩–CH$_2$CHCOOH / NH$_2$ (I,I,I,I)	L-3,5,3′,5′-Tetra-iodothyronine	L-Thyroxine; T$_4$	100	100	100	100
HO⟨⟩–O–⟨⟩–CH$_2$CHCOOH / NH$_2$ (I,I,I,I)	D-3,5,3′,5′-Tetra-iodothyronine	D-Thyroxine; D-T$_4$	30	...	...	500
HO⟨⟩–O–⟨⟩–CH$_2$CHCOOH / NH$_2$ (I,I,I)	L-3,5,3′-Triiodo-thyronine	Triiodothy-ronine; TIT; T$_3$	300	800	800	...
HO⟨⟩–O–⟨⟩–CH$_2$CHCOOH / NH$_2$ (I,I,I)	3,3′,5′-Triiodo-thyronine (D, L tested)	Reverse T$_3$	75	< 1	< 1	...
HO⟨⟩–O–⟨⟩–CH$_2$CH$_2$COOH (I,I,I,I)	3,5,3′,5′-Tetra-iodothyroprop-ionic acid	T$_4$ PROP	60	14	6	...
HO⟨⟩–O–⟨⟩–CH$_2$CH$_2$COOH (I,I,I)	3,5,3′-Triiodo-thyropropionic acid	T$_3$ PROP	60	28	10	...
HO⟨⟩–O–⟨⟩–CH$_2$COOH (I,I,I,I)	3,5,3′,5′-Tetra-iodothyroacetic acid	TETRAC	75	63	9	250
HO⟨⟩–O–⟨⟩–CH$_2$COOH (I,I,I)	3,5,3′-Triiodo-thyroacetic acid	TRIAC	75	51	21	...

*Data mostly from Money WL & others: Comparative effects of thyroxine analogues in experimental animals. Ann NY Acad Sci 86:512, 1960.

†Inhibition of radioactive iodine uptake.

‡Prevention of goiter in propylthiouracil-treated animals (pituitary-inhibiting effect).

§Calorigenic effect.

iodine atoms in thyroid hormone are not necessary for biologic activity; several active thyroxine analogs that do not contain iodine have recently been synthesized.

Calorigenic Action

Thyroxine and triiodothyronine increase the O$_2$ consumption of almost all metabolically active tissues (Fig 18–9). The exceptions are the adult brain, testes, uterus, lymph nodes, spleen, and anterior pituitary. Thyroxine actually depresses the O$_2$ consumption of the anterior pituitary, presumably because it inhibits TSH secretion. The increase in metabolic rate produced by a single dose of thyroxine becomes measurable after a latent period of several hours and lasts 6 or more days (Fig 18–9). The magnitude of the calorigenic effect depends upon the level of catecholamine secretion and on the metabolic rate before injection. If the initial rate is low, the rise is great; but if it is high, the rise is small. This is true not only in euthyroid subjects but in athyreotic thyroxine-treated patients as well. The cause of the decreased effect at higher metabolic rates is obscure. The amounts of various thyroid

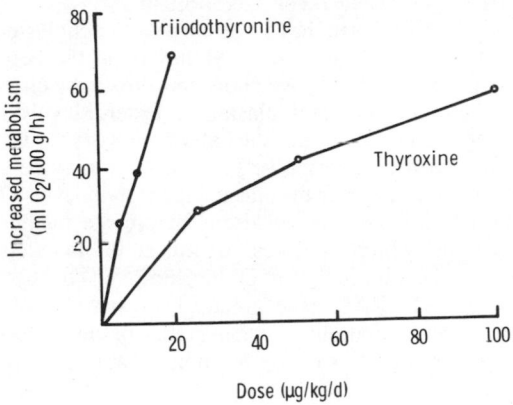

Figure 18–8. Calorigenic responses of thyroidectomized rats to subcutaneous injections of thyroxine and 3,5,3'-triiodothyronine. (Redrawn and reproduced, with permission, from Barker SB: Peripheral actions of thyroid hormones. Fed Proc 21:635, 1962.)

Table 18–5. Maintenance and suppressive doses of various thyroid preparations.* Sixty mg thyroid, USP, are approximately equal to 100 μg levothyroxine, but a rigid conversion cannot be made.

	Dose (mg/d) Required To:	
	Maintain Normal BMR in Athyreotic Humans	Suppress Thyroid ^{131}I Uptake in Euthyroid Humans
L-Triiodo-thyronine	0.05–0.1	0.07–0.1
Sodium levo-thyroxine	0.2–0.4	0.2–0.5
Desiccated thyroid	60–240	60–240

*Modified from Van Middlesworth L in: *Clinical Endocrinology I.* Astwood EB, Cassidy CE (editors). Grune & Stratton, 1960.

preparations required to maintain a normal BMR in thyroidectomized humans are shown in Table 18–5.

Effects Secondary to Calorigenesis

When the metabolic rate is increased by thyroxine or triiodothyronine in adults, nitrogen excretion is increased; if food intake is not increased, endogenous protein and fat stores are catabolized, and weight is lost. In hypothyroid children, small doses of thyroid hormones cause a positive nitrogen balance because they stimulate growth, but large doses cause protein catabolism similar to that produced in the adult. The catabolic response in skeletal muscle is sometimes so severe that muscle weakness is a prominent symptom and creatinuria is marked (thyrotoxic myopathy). The potassium liberated during protein catabolism appears in the urine, and there is an increase in urinary hexosamine and uric acid excretion. The mobilization of bone protein leads to hypercalcemia and hypercal-

ciuria, with some degree of osteoporosis (see Chapter 21).

The skin normally contains a variety of proteins combined with polysaccharides, hyaluronic acid, and chondroitin sulfuric acid. In hypothyroidism, these complexes accumulate, promoting water retention and the characteristic puffiness of the skin (myxedema). When thyroid hormones are administered, the proteins are mobilized, and diuresis continues until the myxedema is cleared.

Large doses of thyroid hormones cause enough extra heat production to cause a slight rise in body temperature (see Chapter 14), which in turn activates heat-dissipating mechanisms. Peripheral resistance decreases because of cutaneous vasodilatation, but cardiac output is increased by the combined action of thyroid hormones and catecholamines on the heart, so that pulse pressure and cardiac rate are increased and circulation time is shortened.

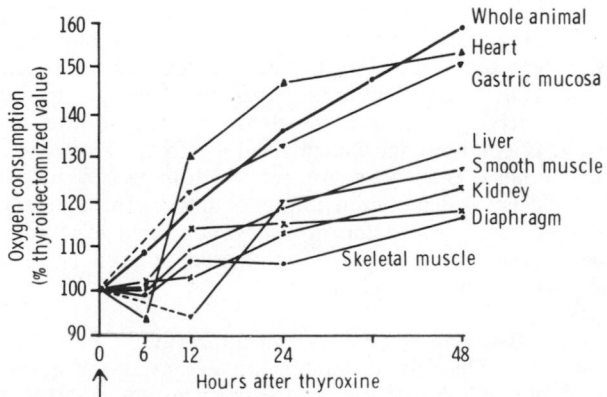

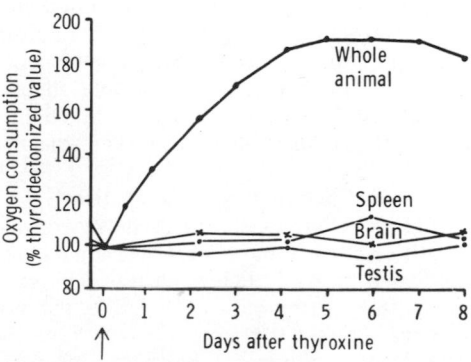

Figure 18–9. Change in metabolism of various tissues of thyroidectomized rats after the injection of a single dose of thyroxine. (Redrawn and reproduced, with permission, from Barker SB, Klitgaard HM: Metabolism of tissues excised from thyroxine-injected rats. Am J Physiol 170:81, 1952.)

In the absence of thyroid hormones, a moderate anemia occurs as a result of decreased bone marrow metabolism and poor absorption of cyanocobalamin (vitamin B_{12}) from the intestine. Thyroxine and triiodothyronine correct these defects.

When the metabolic rate is increased, the need for all vitamins is increased, and vitamin deficiency syndromes may be precipitated. Thyroid hormones are necessary for hepatic conversion of carotene to vitamin A, and the accumulation of carotene in the bloodstream (**carotenemia**) in hypothyroidism is responsible for the yellowish tint of the skin. Carotenemia can be distinguished from jaundice because in the former condition the scleras are not yellow.

Milk secretion is decreased in hypothyroidism and stimulated by thyroid hormones, a fact that is sometimes put to practical use in the dairy industry. Thyroid hormones do not stimulate the metabolism of the uterus but are essential for normal menstrual cycles and fertility.

Effects on the Nervous System

In adult hypothyroidism, mentation is slow and the CSF protein level elevated. Thyroid hormones reverse these changes, and large doses cause rapid mentation, irritability, and restlessness. This is somewhat surprising because it is generally agreed that cerebral blood flow and the glucose and O_2 consumption of the brain are normal in hypo- and hyperthyroidism, and only traces of thyroid hormones pass the blood-brain barrier (see Chapter 32). Some of the effects of thyroid hormones on the brain are probably secondary to increased responsiveness to catecholamines, with consequent increased activation of the reticular activating system (see Chapter 11). In infants, thyroid hormones may stimulate the O_2 consumption of the brain, and they appear to exert other actions on the nervous system, possibly because the blood-brain barrier is not developed. In hypothyroid infants, myelination is defective and mental development is seriously retarded. The mental changes are irreversible if replacement therapy is not begun soon after birth.

Thyroid hormones also exert effects on the peripheral nervous system. The reaction time of stretch reflexes (see Chapter 6) is shortened in hyperthyroidism and prolonged in hypothyroidism. Measurement of the reaction time of the ankle jerk (Achilles reflex) has attracted considerable attention as a clinical test for evaluating thyroid function, but the reaction time is also affected by certain other diseases.

Effects on Carbohydrate Metabolism

Thyroid hormones increase the rate of absorption of carbohydrate from the gastrointestinal tract, an action that is probably independent of their calorigenic action. In hyperthyroidism, therefore, the blood glucose rises rapidly after a carbohydrate meal, sometimes exceeding the renal threshold. However, it falls again at a rapid rate, and the increased catabolism and the increased action of epinephrine keep liver glycogen depleted.

Effects on Cholesterol Metabolism

Thyroid hormones lower circulating cholesterol. They stimulate cholesterol synthesis and the hepatic mechanisms that remove cholesterol from the circulation, and the decline in plasma cholesterol levels may occur because the rate of the latter process exceeds that of the former. Alternatively, the decline may be secondary to changes in the plasma lipoprotein levels. The plasma cholesterol level drops before the metabolic rate rises, which indicates that this action is independent of the stimulation of O_2 consumption. D-Thyroxine and TETRAC have greater cholesterol-lowering activity than naturally occurring L-thyroxine but less of the other activities of the hormone (Table 18–4).

Relation to Catecholamines

The actions of thyroid hormones and the catecholamines norepinephrine and epinephrine are intimately interrelated. Epinephrine increases the metabolic rate, stimulates the nervous system, and produces cardiovascular effects similar to those of thyroid hormones, although the duration of these actions is brief. Norepinephrine has generally similar actions. The effects of thyroid hormones on the heart resemble those of β-adrenergic stimulation, and there is evidence for 2 distinct adenylate cyclases in the heart, one stimulated by norepinephrine and the other by thyroxine. However, catecholamines have no calorigenic effect in the absence of the thyroid, and the toxicity of the catecholamines is markedly increased in rats treated with thyroxine. Although catecholamine secretion is usually normal in hyperthyroidism, the cardiovascular effects, tremulousness, and sweating produced by thyroid hormones can be reduced or abolished by sympathectomy. They can also be reduced by drugs such as reserpine and guanethidine that deplete tissue stores of catecholamines and drugs such as propranolol that block β-adrenergic receptors. Indeed, propranolol is used extensively in the treatment of thyrotoxicosis and in the treatment of the severe exacerbations of hyperthyroidism called **thyroid storms.** There is also some inhibition of the calorigenic effect of thyroxine when sympathetic outflow is blocked. However, plasma thyroxine does not change. Obviously, many of the effects of thyroid hormones, especially those on the nervous and cardiovascular systems, are due in large part to adrenergic nervous activity. It is also clear that thyroxine and triiodothyronine potentiate the effects of catecholamines. One hypothesis for which there is some evidence is that thyroid hormones increase the number of adrenergic receptors in tissues such as the heart. However, the basis of the catecholamine–thyroid hormone interaction is still unsettled.

Effects on Growth & Development

Thyroid hormones are essential for normal growth and skeletal maturation (see Chapter 22). In hypothyroid children, bone growth is slowed and epiphyseal closure delayed. In the absence of thyroid hormones, growth hormone secretion may also be depressed, and thyroid hormones potentiate the effect of growth hormone on the tissues.

Another example of the role of thyroid hormones in growth and maturation is their effect on amphibian metamorphosis. Tadpoles treated with thyroxine or triiodothyronine metamorphose early into dwarf frogs, whereas hypothyroid tadpoles never become frogs. The effects of thyroxine on metamorphosis are probably independent of its effects on O_2 consumption, even though it raises the O_2 consumption of metamorphosing tadpole skin in vitro. The hormone also exerts a calorigenic effect on tadpoles in vivo.

MECHANISM OF ACTION OF THYROID HORMONES

Thyroid hormones enter cells and bind to receptors in the nuclei. They appear to exert most if not all of their effects by acting on DNA to increase the synthesis of mRNA and ribosomal RNA. Triiodothyronine binds to a much greater extent than thyroxine, and the binding sites are in the nonhistone protein portion of the chromatin. The mRNA that is formed dictates the formation of proteins in the ribosomes, and these thyroid-induced proteins presumably act as enzymes that modify cell function. There must be a variety of different proteins involved, since it seems unlikely that any single group of enzymes could bring about the multiple and varied effects of thyroid hormones.

The calorigenic action of thyroid hormones appears to be mediated via an induced protein, since it is blocked by inhibitors of protein synthesis. The hormones increase the activity of the membrane-bound Na^+-K^+ ATPase in many tissues, and it has been argued that it is the increase in energy consumption associated with the increase in Na^+ transport which is responsible for the increase in metabolic rate. However, inhibition of the increase in Na^+-K^+ ATPase activity with ouabain does not completely abolish the calorigenic effect of thyroid hormones. Mitochondrial protein synthesis is increased, but the role of the mitochondria in the response is obscure. The old theory that thyroid hormones increased energy consumption by uncoupling oxidation of substrate from phosphorylation in the mitochondria has now been largely abandoned because such uncoupling could not be demonstrated in mitochondria from hyperthyroid rats. In addition, drugs such as 2,4-dinitrophenol uncouple oxidative phosphorylation without reproducing the full metabolic or other effects of thyroid hormones.

Studies on isolated tadpole tails provide another example of an effect on protein synthesis. The tail of a tadpole will live as an isolated organ for some time if it is placed in a suitable medium as soon as it is cut off. If the tail is treated with thyroxine, it regresses in the same way that it does when attached to a thyroxine-treated tadpole. This regression-producing effect of thyroxine on the isolated tail is blocked by actinomycin

D, and other studies indicate that thyroxine brings about regression of the tail by inducing the formation of tissue-destroying enzymes in the cells.

REGULATION OF THYROID SECRETION

Stimuli That Alter Thyroid Secretion

Although a number of vasoactive hormones such as vasopressin and epinephrine can affect thyroid secretion by a direct action on the gland, the primary control is effected by variations in the circulating level of pituitary TSH. TSH secretion is inhibited by a rise in the circulating free thyroxine and triiodothyronine levels and stimulated when the free thyroid hormone levels drop (Fig 18–10). TSH secretion is also increased by exposure to cold, at least in experimental animals and infants, and depressed by heat and stressful stimuli.

Chemistry & Metabolism of TSH

Human TSH is a glycoprotein that contains 211 amino acid residues, plus hexoses, hexosamines, and sialic acid. It is made up of 2 subunits, designated α and β. TSH-α is identical in structure to the α subunit of LH and FSH and differs only slightly from HCG-α

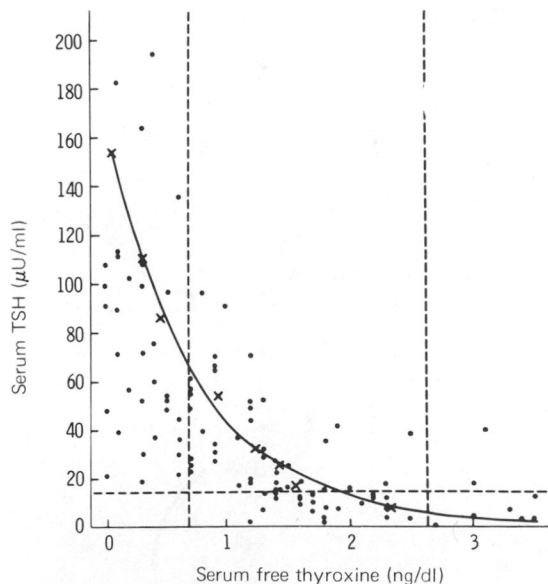

Figure 18–10. Relation between serum TSH and serum free thyroxine in patients with myxedema given various doses of L-thyroxine. The horizontal dashed line indicates the normal upper range for TSH; the vertical dashed lines enclose the normal range for free thyroxine. The solid curved line is the regression line based on the mean values at each dose of L-thyroxine. (Reproduced, with permission, from Cotton GE, Gorman CA, Mayberry WE: Suppression of thyrotropin [h-TSH] in serum of patients with myxedema of varying etiology treated with thyroid hormones. N Engl J Med 285:529, 1971.)

(see Chapters 22 and 23). The functional specificity of TSH is apparently conferred by the β unit. The structure of TSH varies from species to species, but other mammalian TSHs are biologically active in humans. The biologic half-life of human TSH is about 60 minutes. TSH is degraded for the most part in the kidney, and to a lesser extent in the liver. Secretion is pulsatile and greater at night than during the day. The normal secretion rate is about 110 μg/d. The average plasma level is about 10 pmol/L.

One substance (and possibly 2) with TSH activity is secreted by the placenta. However, it apparently has little effect on maternal thyroid functions, since secretion of pituitary TSH appears to remain normal during pregnancy.

Control Mechanisms

Hypothalamic lesions prevent the increased TSH secretion usually provoked by exposure to cold in rats. Electrical stimulation of the hypothalamus causes increased TSH secretion. A tripeptide that stimulates TSH secretion (thyrotropin-releasing hormone, TRH; see Fig 14–14), is normally secreted into the portal vessels in the median eminence (see Chapter 14). The part of the hypothalamus concerned with the regulation of TSH secretion is the region in and above the rostral end of the median eminence.

The negative feedback effect of thyroid hormones on TSH secretion may be exerted in part at the hypothalamic level, but it must be mainly on the pituitary, since thyroxine and triiodothyronine block the increase in TSH secretion produced by TRH. It seems likely that the day-to-day maintenance of thyroid secretion depends on the feedback interplay between thyroid hormones and TSH (Fig 18–11), whereas the hypothalamus adjusts TSH secretion in certain special situations. The principal adjustments that appear to be neurally mediated are the increased secretion produced by cold and, presumably, the decrease produced by heat. It is worth noting that although cold produces clear-cut increases in circulating TSH in experimental animals and human infants, the rise produced by cold in adult humans is negligible. Consequently, in adults, increased heat production due to increased thyroid hormone secretion (**thyroid hormone thermogenesis**) plays little if any role in the response to cold. The inhibiting effect of stress on TSH secretion is probably due to an inhibiting effect of glucocorticoids on TRH secretion, but the effect of stress is a minor one.

CLINICAL CORRELATES

Hypothyroidism & Hyperthyroidism

The signs, symptoms, and complications of hypothyroidism and hyperthyroidism in humans are predictable consequences of the physiologic effects of thyroid hormones discussed above. The syndrome of adult hypothyroidism is generally called **myxedema,** although the term myxedema is also used to refer specifically to the skin changes in this syndrome. Hypothyroidism may be the end result of a number of diseases of the thyroid gland, or it may be secondary to pituitary failure ("pituitary hypothyroidism") or hypothalamic failure ("hypothalamic hypothyroidism"). In the latter 2 conditions, unlike the first, the thyroid responds to a test dose of TSH, and hypothalamic hypothyroidism can be distinguished from pituitary hypothyroidism by the presence in the former of a rise in plasma TSH following a test dose of TRH. The TSH response to TRH is usually normal in hypothalamic hypothyroidism, while it is increased in hypothyroidism due to thyroid disease and decreased in hyperthyroidism due to the feedback of thyroid hormones on the pituitary gland.

In completely athyreotic humans, the BMR falls to about −40. The hair is coarse and sparse, the skin dry and yellowish (carotenemia), and cold is poorly tolerated. The voice is husky and slow, the basis of the aphorism that "myxedema is the one disease that can be diagnosed over the telephone." Mentation is slow and memory is poor, and in some patients severe mental symptoms develop ("myxedema madness").

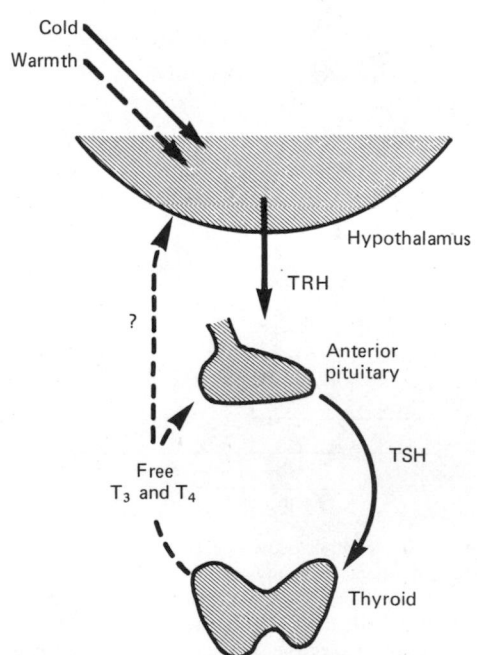

Figure 18–11. Diagram of the paths through which various physiologic stimuli presumably alter thyroid secretion. Solid arrows signify stimulation; dashed arrows, inhibition; T_3, triiodothyronine; T_4, thyroxine.

Cretinism

Children who are hypothyroid from birth are called cretins. They are dwarfed, mentally retarded, and have enlarged, protruding tongues and pot bellies (Fig 18–12). Before the use of iodized salt became widespread, the most common cause of cretinism was

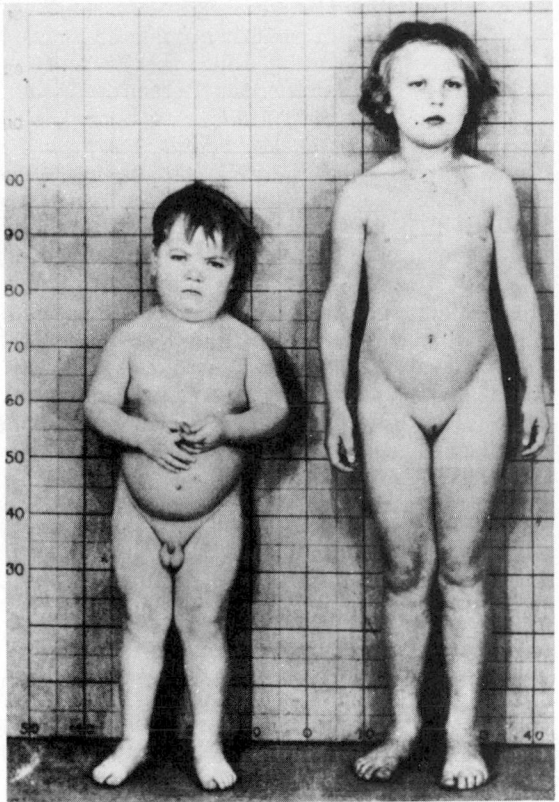

Figure 18–12. Fraternal twins, age 8 years. The boy has congenital hypothyroidism. (Reproduced, with permission, from Wilkins L, in: *Clinical Endocrinology I*. Astwood EB, Cassidy CE [editors]. Grune & Stratton, 1960.)

the negative feedback effect of the high circulating thyroxine and triiodothyronine levels. The cause of the thyroid stimulation is a group of antibodies against the TSH receptors in the thyroid that also have the capacity to stimulate the receptors and activate adenylate cyclase in the thyroid cells (Fig 18–14). The antibodies are produced by lymphocytes, are mostly in the IgG class of immunoglobulins (see Chapter 27), and are known collectively as **thyroid-stimulating immunoglobulins (TSI).** They include a substance with a prolonged action on the thyroid glands of mice **(long-acting thyroid stimulator, LATS)** as well as substances that stimulate human thyroid tissues and, by binding to the TSH receptors, prevent the inactivation of LATS by this tissue **(LATS protectors).** TSI are present in the plasma of almost all patients with Graves' disease. The cause of their formation is unsettled. Thyroid hormones are not responsible for the exophthalmos; in fact, the exophthalmos not infrequently becomes worse if the thyroid is removed. A factor that produces exophthalmos in experimental animals **(exophthalmos-producing factor)** has been extracted from the plasma of patients with the disease, and evidence is accumulating that it is a partly degraded TSH made up of the β subunit and a portion of the N-terminal end of the α subunit of this molecule.

maternal iodine deficiency. Increasing attention is now being paid to various congenital abnormalities of thyroid function that cause goiter and, in some instances, congenital hypothyroidism with cretinism. Unless the mother was severely hypothyroid, the stigmas of cretinism are preventable if treatment is started soon after birth; however, once the typical clinical picture has developed, it is usually too late to prevent permanent mental retardation.

Hyperthyroidism

Hyperthyroidism, or **thyrotoxicosis,** is characterized by nervousness; weight loss; hyperphagia; heat intolerance; increased pulse pressure; a fine tremor of the outstretched fingers; a warm, soft skin; and a basal metabolic rate from +10 to as high as +100. It may be caused by a variety of thyroid disorders, including, in rare instances, benign and malignant tumors, and cases due to TSH-secreting pituitary tumors have been reported. However, the most common form is **Graves' disease,** or **exophthalmic goiter.** In Graves' disease, the thyroid is diffusely enlarged and hyperplastic, and there is a protrusion of the eyeballs called **exophthalmos** (Fig 18–13). The secretion of TSH from the pituitary gland is depressed in this disease because of

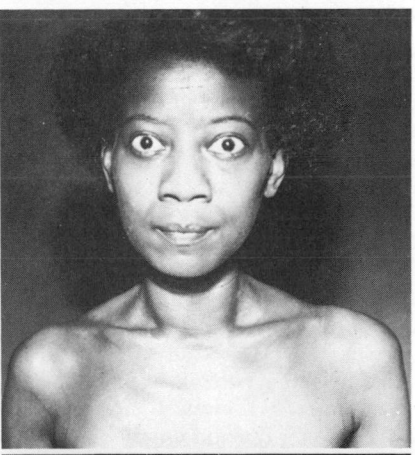

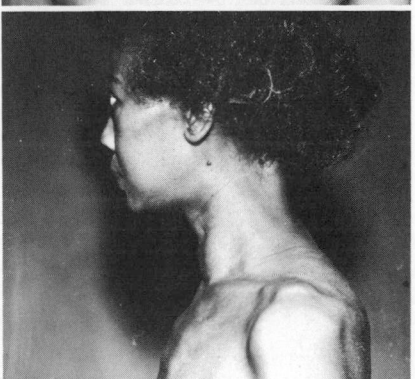

Figure 18–13. Graves' disease. Note the goiter and the exophthalmos. (Courtesy of PH Forsham.)

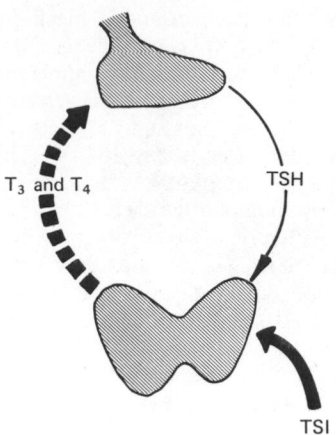

Figure 18–14. Thyroid and pituitary function in Graves' disease. Thyroid-stimulating immunoglobulins (TSI) act on the thyroid to produce a marked increase in the secretion of thyroxine and triiodothyronine, and secretion of TSH from the pituitary is markedly inhibited.

Thyrotoxicosis places a considerable load on the cardiovascular system, and in some patients with hyperthyroidism, most or even all of the symptoms are cardiovascular. Thyrotoxic heart disease is a curable form of heart disease, but the diagnosis is often missed. It is important to remember that heart failure develops whenever the cardiac output, even though it is elevated, is inadequate to maintain tissue perfusion. The drop in peripheral resistance due to cutaneous vasodilatation in thyrotoxicosis is equivalent to opening a large arteriovenous fistula; if the compensatory increase in cardiac output is not great enough, "high-output failure" results.

Another complication of severe, long-term thyrotoxicosis is liver failure. The chronic liver glycogen depletion in hyperthyroid patients makes the liver abnormally susceptible to injury. If the increased demands for calories and vitamins are not met, malnutrition adds to the hepatic damage. Hepatic failure makes the thyrotoxicosis worse because the thyroid hormones are less rapidly removed from the circulation.

In some instances, Graves' disease is due to increased secretion of triiodothyronine with normal levels of plasma thyroxine. This syndrome has been called T_3 **thyrotoxicosis.**

Iodine Deficiency

When the dietary iodine intake falls below 10 μg/d, thyroid hormone synthesis is inadequate, and secretion declines. As a result of increased TSH secretion, the thyroid hypertrophies, producing an **iodine deficiency goiter** that may become very large. Such "endemic goiters" have been known since ancient times. Before the practice of adding iodide to table salt became widespread, they were very common in Central Europe and the area around the Great Lakes in the USA, the inland "goiter belts" where iodine has been leached out of the soil by rain water so that food grown in the soil is iodine-deficient.

Radioactive Iodine Uptake

Iodine uptake is a parameter of thyroid function that can be easily measured, using tracer doses of ^{131}I which have no known deleterious effect on the thyroid. For routine clinical tests, the tracer is administered orally and the thyroid uptake determined by placing a gamma ray counter over the neck. An area such as the thigh is also counted, and counts in this region are subtracted from the neck counts to correct for nonthyroidal radioactivity in the neck. The uptake in a normal subject is plotted in Fig 18–15. In hyperthyroidism, iodide is rapidly incorporated into thyroxine and triiodothyronine, and these hormones are released at an accelerated rate. Therefore, the amount of radioactivity in the thyroid rises sharply, but it then levels off and may start to decline within 24 hours, at a time when the uptake in normal subjects is still rising. The uptake at 3 hours is consequently more likely to be abnormal than the 24-hour uptake in patients with hyperthyroidism. In hypothyroidism, the uptake is low. Uptake values must, of course, be interpreted with the physiology of iodine metabolism in mind. For example, on a diet high in iodine content, the ^{131}I uptake is low even though thyroid function may be normal because the iodide pool is so large that the tracer is excessively diluted. Conversely, ^{131}I uptake is high without hyperthyroidism in individuals whose daily iodine intake is adequate to prevent iodine deficiency goiter but chronically lower than the average intake. Variations in renal function also affect uptake, because of differences in the amount of tracer excreted in the urine.

Large amounts of radioactive iodine destroy thyroid tissue because the radiation kills the cells. Radioiodine therapy is useful in some cases of thyroid cancer and can be used to treat benign thyroid diseases, although, especially in young patients, the dangers of possible radiation carcinogenesis and germ cell mutations must be kept in mind.

Antithyroid Drugs

Most of the drugs that inhibit thyroid function act either by interfering with the iodide trapping mechanism or by blocking the organic binding of iodine. In either case, TSH secretion is stimulated by the decline in circulating thyroid hormones, and goiter is produced. A number of monovalent anions compete with iodide for active transport into the thyroid and therefore inhibit uptake to the point where the T/S ratio approaches unity; this inhibition of iodide transport can be overcome by administration of extra iodide. The anions include chlorate, pertechnetate, periodate, biiodate, nitrate, and perchlorate. Thiocyanate, another monovalent anion, inhibits iodide transport but is not itself concentrated within the gland. Thiocyanate and perchlorate are sometimes used clinically in the treatment of thyrotoxicosis. The activity of perchlorate is about 10 times that of thiocyanate.

The **thiocarbamides,** a group of compounds related to thiourea, inhibit the iodination of monoiodotyrosine and block the coupling reaction.

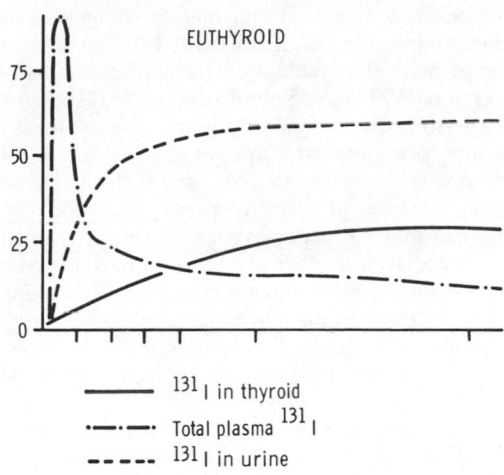

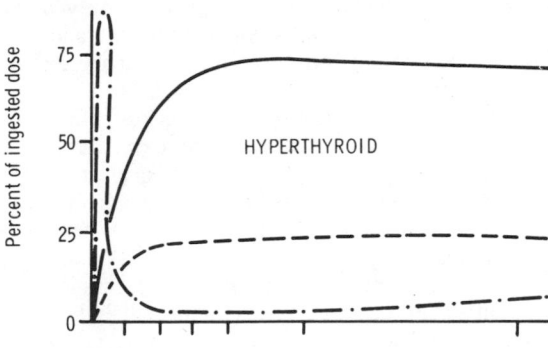

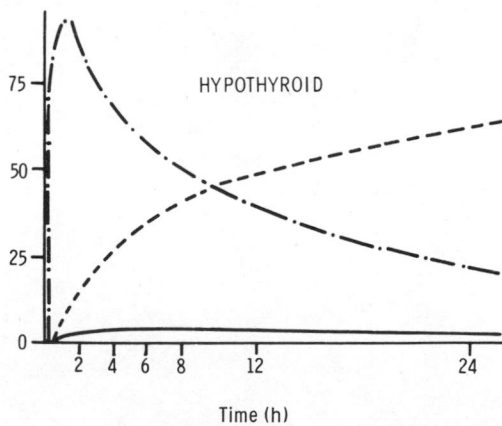

Time (h)

Figure 18–15. Radioactive iodine uptake in normal euthyroid, hyperthyroid, and hypothyroid subjects. Percentages of administered ^{131}I in thyroid, plasma, and urine are plotted against time after an oral dose of ^{131}I. In the hyperthyroid subject, plasma ^{131}I falls rapidly, then rises again as a result of release of ^{131}I-labeled thyroxine and triiodothyronine from the thyroid. (Reproduced, with permission, from Ingbar SH, Woeber KA, in: *Textbook of Endocrinology,* 4th ed. Williams RH [editor]. Saunders, 1968.)

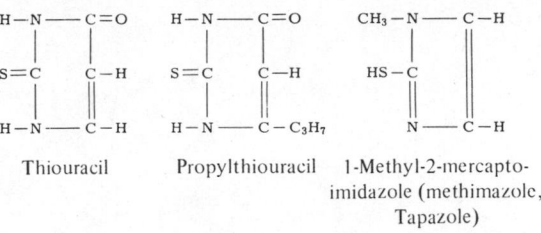

Thiouracil   Propylthiouracil   1-Methyl-2-mercapto-imidazole (methimazole, Tapazole)

Figure 18–16. Antithyroid thiocarbamides.

They do not block iodide trapping. Because of the increase in TSH secretion, the initial ^{131}I uptake is actually increased during thiocarbamide therapy, and the T/S ratio may reach 250. However, since binding is inhibited, the ^{131}I is not retained, and 24 hours after administration of the isotope, uptake is subnormal. It now appears that some of the thiocarbamides also prevent the conversion of thyroxine to triiodothyronine in extrathyroidal tissues.

Most of the thiocarbamides used in clinical practice are derivatives of thiouracil (Fig 18–16). Propylthiouracil and methimazole are used most often.

Another substance that inhibits thyroid function under certain conditions is iodide itself. In hyperthyroidism, large doses of iodides regularly inhibit thyroid hormone secretion. The position of iodide in thyroid physiology is thus unique in that a minimal amount is necessary for normal thyroid function, whereas a large amount is inhibitory when the gland is hyperplastic. The inhibitory effect lasts for 1–4 weeks and then wears off in spite of continuing therapy. Colloid accumulates and the vascularity of the hyperplastic gland is decreased, making iodide treatment of considerable value in preparing thyrotoxic patients for surgery. By contrast, iodide has little or no effect on thyroid function in normal individuals. This is why, in doubtful cases of thyrotoxicosis, the clinical response to iodide therapy can be used as a diagnostic test. However, goiters sometimes develop in euthyroid patients taking large amounts of iodine in cough medicines. There are apparently several different mechanisms by which excess I$^-$ inhibits thyroid function. It decreases the organic binding of iodine; it reduces the effect of TSH on the gland; and it inhibits proteolysis of thyroglobulin. There is no direct effect on the I$^-$ trapping mechanism, but the total I$^-$ uptake is low because of the inhibition of organic binding and, to a lesser extent, because the amount of circulating iodide is so great that added tracer is immensely diluted.

Naturally Occurring Goitrogens

Thiocyanates are sometimes ingested with food, and there are relatively large amounts of naturally occurring goitrogens in some foods. Vegetables of the Brassicaceae family, particularly rutabagas, cabbage, and turnips, contain **progoitrin** and a substance that converts this compound into **goitrin,** an active antithyroid agent (Fig 18–17). The progoitrin activator in

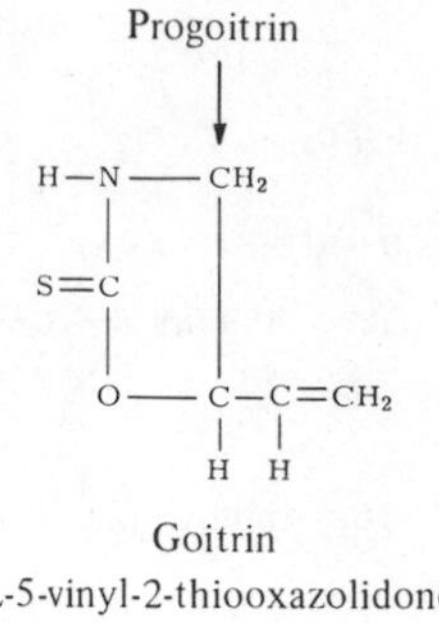

Progoitrin

↓

H—N——CH₂
|
S=C
|
O——C—C=CH₂
| |
H H

Goitrin
(L-5-vinyl-2-thiooxazolidone)

Figure 18–17. The naturally occurring goitrogen in vegetables of the family Brassicaceae.

vegetables is heat-labile; but because there are activators in the intestine (presumably of bacterial origin), goitrin is formed even if the vegetables are cooked. The goitrin intake on a normal mixed diet is usually not great enough to be harmful, but in vegetarians and food faddists, "cabbage goiters" do occur. Other as yet unidentified plant goitrogens probably exist and may be responsible for the occasional small "goiter epidemics" reported from various parts of the world.

Use of Thyroid Hormones in Nonthyroidal Diseases

When the pituitary-thyroid axis is normal, doses of exogenous thyroid hormone that provide less than the amount secreted endogenously have no significant effect on metabolism because there is a compensatory decline in endogenous secretion resulting from inhibition of TSH secretion. In euthyroid humans, the dose of desiccated thyroid that merely suppresses thyroid function (Table 18–5) is usually 60–240 mg/d, but in an occasional individual, no metabolic stimulation will occur on 600 mg/d. Suppression of TSH secretion due to thyroxine treatment or pituitary disease leads eventually to thyroid atrophy. An atrophic gland initially responds sluggishly to TSH, and if the TSH suppression has been prolonged, it may take some time for normal thyroid responsiveness to return. The adrenal cortex and some other endocrine glands respond in an analogous fashion; when they are deprived of the support of their tropic hormones for some time, they become atrophic and only sluggishly responsive to their tropic hormone until the hormone has had some time to act on the gland.

In patients with so-called metabolic insufficiency—fatigued individuals who feel weak and have a slightly low BMR with a normal plasma thyroxine and ^{131}I uptake—thyroid therapy has been proved to be of no more value than placebo medication. Use of thyroid to promote weight loss can be of value only if the patient pays the price of some nervousness and heat intolerance and curbs the appetite so that there is no compensatory increase in caloric intake.

Thyroxine and, more recently, its less calorigenic analogs such as TETRAC and D-thyroxine have been used to lower plasma cholesterol levels in an attempt to slow down or prevent arteriosclerotic vascular disease. However, the benefit of such treatments has been limited because, in practice, it has not been possible to produce adequate lowering of plasma cholesterol without an appreciable increase in the metabolic rate.

Endocrine Functions of the Pancreas & the Regulation of Carbohydrate Metabolism | 19

At least 4 peptides with hormonal activity are secreted by the islets of Langerhans in the pancreas. Two of these hormones, **insulin** and **glucagon,** have important functions in the regulation of the intermediary metabolism of carbohydrates, proteins, and fats. The third hormone, **somatostatin,** may play a role in the regulation of islet cell secretion, and the physiologic function of the fourth, **pancreatic polypeptide,** is unknown. Glucagon and somatostatin are also secreted by cells in the mucosa of the gastrointestinal tract.

Insulin is anabolic, increasing the storage of glucose, fatty acids, and amino acids. Glucagon is catabolic, mobilizing glucose, fatty acids, and amino acids from stores into the bloodstream. The 2 hormones are thus reciprocal in their overall action and are reciprocally secreted in most circumstances. Insulin excess causes hypoglycemia, which leads to convulsions and coma. Insulin deficiency, either absolute or relative, causes diabetes mellitus, a complex and debilitating disease that if untreated is eventually fatal. Glucagon deficiency can cause hypoglycemia, and glucagon excess makes diabetes worse. Excess pancreatic production of somatostatin produces hyperglycemia and other manifestations of diabetes.

A variety of other hormones also have important roles in the regulation of carbohydrate metabolism.

ISLET CELL STRUCTURE

The islets of Langerhans (Fig 19–1) are ovoid, 76 × 175 μm collections of cells scattered throughout the pancreas, although they are more plentiful in the tail than in the body and head. They make up 1–2% of the weight of the pancreas. In humans, there are 1–2 million islets. Each has a copious blood supply; and blood from the islets, like that from the gastrointestinal tract but unlike that from any other endocrine organs, drains into the portal vein.

The cells in the islets can be divided into types on the basis of their staining properties and morphology. There are at least 5 distinct cell types in humans. Three types, the A, B, and D cells, are designated by letters. These cells are also called α, β, and δcells. However, this leads to confusion in view of the use of Greek

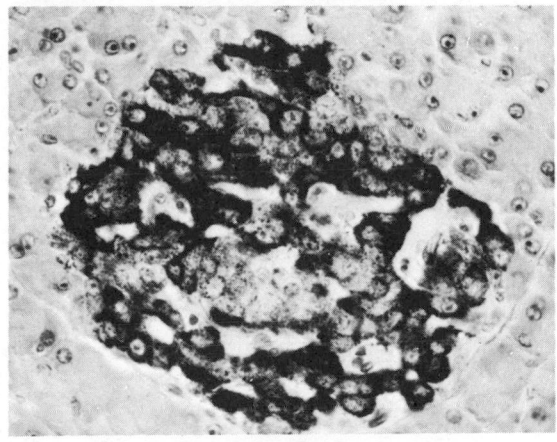

Figure 19–1. Islet of Langerhans, rat pancreas. Darkly stained cells are B cells. Surrounding pancreatic acinar tissue is light-colored. (× 400; courtesy of LL Bennett.)

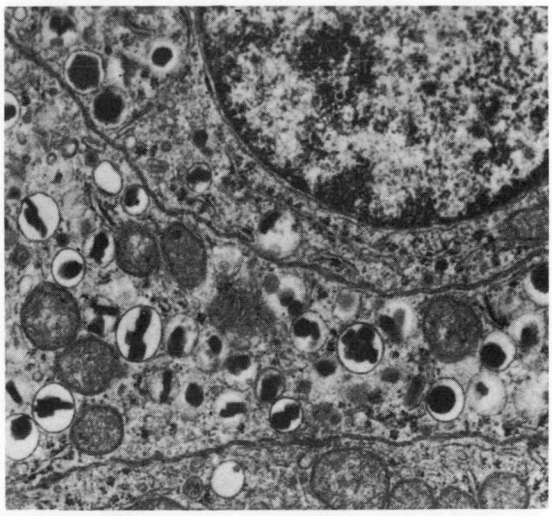

Figure 19–2. Electron micrograph of 2 adjoining B cells in human pancreas. The B granules are the membrane-lined vesicles containing crystals that vary in shape from rhombic to round. (× 26,000; courtesy of A Like. Reproduced, with permission, from Bloom W, Fawcett DW: *A Textbook of Histology,* 10th ed. Saunders, 1975.)

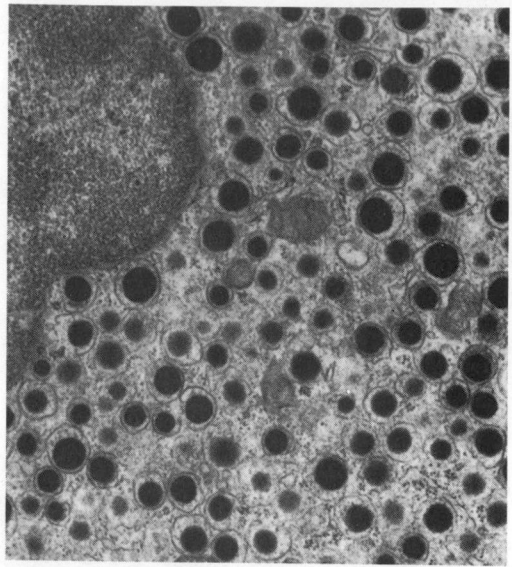

Figure 19–3. Electron micrograph of A cell in human pancreas. The granules are the dense round structures surrounded by membranes. (Reduced from × 24,000; courtesy of A Like. Reproduced, with permission, from Bloom W, Fawcett DW: *A Textbook of Histology,* 10th ed. Saunders, 1975.)

letters to refer to other structures in the body, particularly adrenergic receptors (see Chapter 13). Consequently, they are called A, B, and D cells in this book. The A cells, which make up approximately 20% of the granulated cells, secrete glucagon and stain red with the modified Mallory aniline blue stain. Over half

of the granulated cells are insulin-secreting B cells, which stain bluish-purple with Mallory stain. One to eight percent of the cells are D cells, which secrete somatostatin. The fourth morphologically distinct cell type, which does not have a letter designation, secretes pancreatic polypeptide. These cells are few in number, and they are also found in the exocrine portion of the pancreas. The fifth cell type has small granules and an as yet unidentified secretory product.

The B cell granules are packets of insulin in the cell cytoplasm. Each packet is contained in a membrane-lined vesicle (Fig 19–2). The shape of the packets varies from species to species; in humans, some are round while others are rectangular. In the B cells, the insulin molecule forms polymers and also complexes with zinc. The differences in shape of the packets are probably due to differences in the size of polymers or zinc aggregates of insulin. The A granules, which contain glucagon, are relatively uniform from species to species (Fig 19–3).

The number of granules in the B cells parallels the insulin content of the pancreas. Stimuli that increase insulin secretion cause B cell degranulation. The regulation of insulin secretion is discussed below.

STRUCTURE, BIOSYNTHESIS, & SECRETION OF INSULIN

Structure & Species Specificity

Insulin is a polypeptide containing 2 chains of amino acids linked by disulfide bridges (Table 19–1).

Table 19–1. Structure of human insulin (molecular weight 5734) and (below) variations in this structure in other mammalian species. In the rat, the islet cells secrete 2 slightly different insulins, and in certain fish 4 different chains are found.

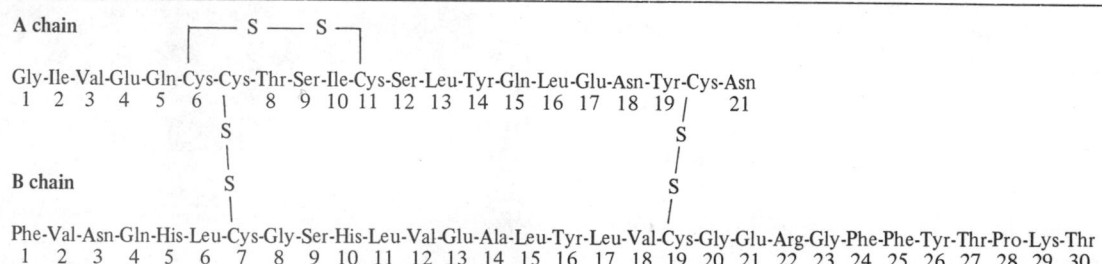

Species	Variations From Human Amino Acid Sequence			
	A Chain Position			B Chain Position
	8	9	10	30
Pig, dog, sperm whale	Thr	Ser	Ile	Ala
Rabbit	Thr	Ser	Ile	Ser
Cattle, goat	Ala	Ser	Val	Ala
Sheep	Ala	Gly	Val	Ala
Horse	Thr	Gly	Ile	Ala
Sei whale	Ala	Ser	Thr	Ala

There are minor differences in the amino acid composition of the molecule from species to species. The differences are generally not sufficient to affect the biologic activity of a particular insulin in heterologous species but are sufficient to make the insulin antigenic. If the insulin of one species is injected for a prolonged period into another species, the anti-insulin antibodies formed inhibit endogenously secreted insulin when injected into an animal of the species from which the injected insulin was prepared (see below). Almost all humans who have received commercial beef insulin for more than 2 months have antibodies against beef insulin, but the titer is usually low and presents no clinical problem. Patients who develop high titers and become resistant to beef insulin on this basis are usually responsive to insulins from other species.

Biosynthesis & Secretion

Insulin is synthesized in the endoplasmic reticulum of the B cells (Fig 19–4). It is then transported to the Golgi complex, where it is packaged in membrane-bound granules. These granules move to the cell wall, and their membranes fuse with the membrane of the cell, expelling the insulin to the exterior by exocytosis (see Chapter 1). The insulin must then cross the basal laminas of the B cell and a neighboring capillary and the fenestrated endothelium of the capillary (Fig 19–4) to reach the bloodstream.

The insulin molecule is synthesized as a single chain called **preproinsulin.** After a 23-amino-acid

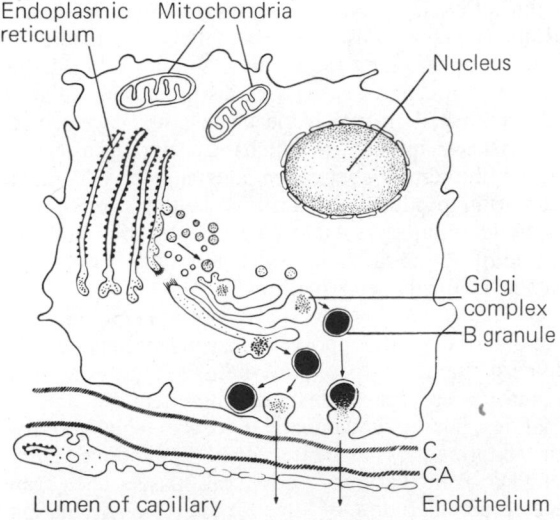

Figure 19–4. Schematic representation of insulin biosynthesis and secretion. Insulin is synthesized in the rough endoplasmic reticulum and translocated to the Golgi apparatus, where the B granules are formed. The granules fuse to the cell membranes, and their contents pass through the basal lamina of the B cell (C), the basal lamina of the capillaries (CA), and the fenestrated capillary endothelium to enter the bloodstream. (Modified from Orci L & others: The ultrastructural events associated with the action of tolbutamide and glybenclamide on pancreatic B cells. Acta Diabetol Lat 6 [Suppl 1]:271, 1969.)

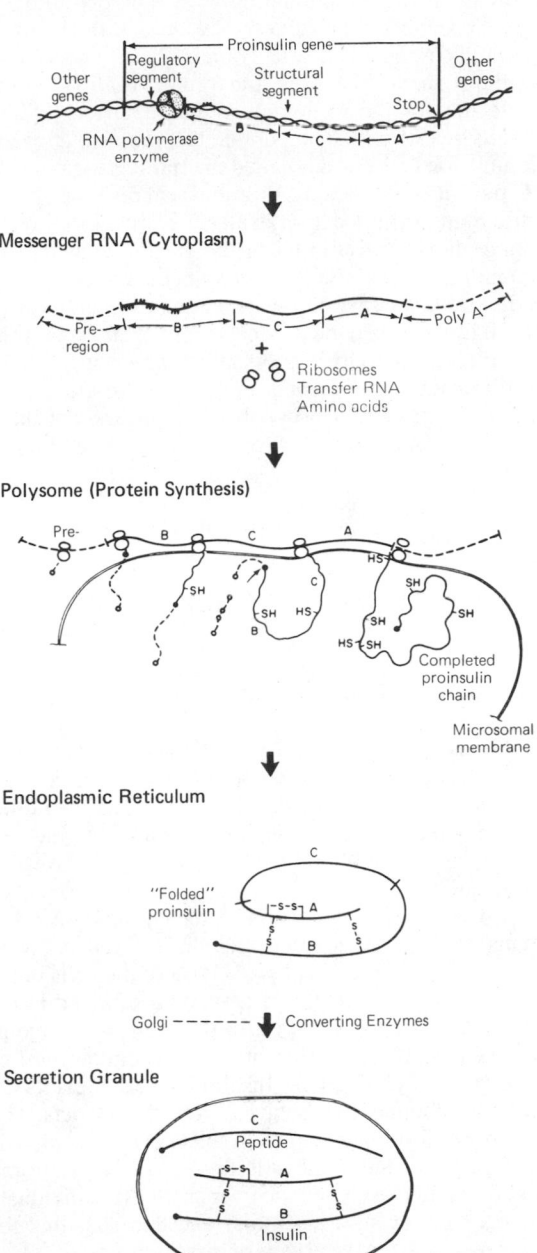

Figure 19–5. Biosynthesis of insulin via a short-lived preproinsulin. The letters A, B, and C identify the A and B chains of insulin and the connecting (C) peptide. A 23-amino-acid fragment transcribed by a segment of mRNA next to the portion that transcribes the B chain (dashed lines) is formed and then split off, possibly before the formation of the rest of the proinsulin molecule is completed. (Reproduced, with permission, from Steiner DW: Errors in insulin biosynthesis. N Engl J Med 294:952, 1976.)

fragment is removed from the C terminal of this peptide, it is folded in the B cell, and the disulfide links are formed (Fig 19–5). The resultant large molecule, which has been named **proinsulin,** is secreted after prolonged stimulation and by some islet cell tumors, but the connection between the A and B chains is normally removed in the granules before secretion. Without the connection, the proper folding of the molecule for the formation of the disulfide bridges would be difficult. The peptide that remains after the connection is severed is called the **connecting peptide (C peptide).** It contains 31 amino acid residues. It has little if any insulin activity and enters the bloodstream along with the insulin when the granule contents are extruded by exocytosis. It can be measured by radioimmunoassay, and its level provides an index of B cell function in patients receiving exogenous insulin. The biologic activity of proinsulin is about 10% that of insulin, but it cross-reacts with insulin in the insulin immunoassay (see below). It now appears that there are "pro" and "prepro" forms of many peptide hormones.

FATE OF SECRETED INSULIN

Transport & Binding

From time to time, there have been claims that insulin is bound to plasma proteins, but recent research casts considerable doubt on this possibility. A circulating protein with anti-insulin activity called **synalbumin** has received considerable attention, but the significance and even the existence of this factor have also been questioned.

The half-life of insulin in the circulation in humans is about 5 minutes. Insulin is fixed to many tissues, but red blood cells and most of the cells in the brain do not bind it. Large amounts are bound in the liver and kidneys. The insulin receptor on cell membranes is a glycoprotein with a molecular weight of approximately 300,000. Insulin probably exerts its effects without entering the cells on which it acts. The number of insulin receptors on cells varies, and there is evidence that the number is decreased when plasma insulin is increased and vice versa. Obese individuals have relatively few receptors, and this accounts for their resistance to the effects of insulin. Insulin binding is also reduced in maturity-onset diabetes (see below).

Metabolism

Almost all tissues have the ability to metabolize insulin, but over 80% of secreted insulin is normally degraded in the liver and kidneys. Three insulin-inactivating systems have been described. Two break the disulfide linkages in the molecule—one enzymatically and one nonenzymatically—and one cleaves the peptide chains. The enzyme involved in the enzymatic disruption of the disulfide linkages is **hepatic**

glutathione insulin transhydrogenase,** which breaks the insulin molecule into A and B chains. Glutathione is a sulfur-containing tripeptide that in this case is acting as a coenzyme for the transhydrogenase. The enzymes responsible for the inactivation of insulin used to be grouped together under the term "insulinase." Variations in the rate of insulin inactivation in various tissues have been reported, but their significance is uncertain.

CONSEQUENCES OF INSULIN DEFICIENCY & ACTIONS OF INSULIN

The biologic effects of insulin are so far-reaching and complex that they are best illustrated by a consideration of the consequences of insulin deficiency.

Diabetes Mellitus

In humans, insulin deficiency is a common and serious pathologic condition. In animals it can be produced by pancreatectomy or by the administration of alloxan (Fig 19–6), a compound relatively toxic to the liver and kidney that in appropriate doses causes selective destruction of the B cells of the pancreatic islets. Insulin deficiency can also be produced by drugs that inhibit insulin secretion or by administration of anti-insulin antibodies (Fig 19–7).

The constellation of abnormalities caused by insulin deficiency is called **diabetes mellitus.** Greek and Roman physicians used the term "diabetes" to refer to conditions in which the cardinal finding was a large urine volume, and 2 types were distinguished: "diabetes mellitus," in which the urine tasted sweet; and "diabetes insipidus," in which the urine was tasteless. Today the term diabetes insipidus is reserved for the condition produced by lesions of the supraoptic–posterior pituitary system (see Chapter 14), and the unmodified word diabetes is generally used as a synonym for diabetes mellitus.

Diabetes is characterized by polyuria, polydipsia, weight loss in spite of polyphagia (increased appetite), hyperglycemia, glycosuria, ketosis, acidosis, and coma. There are widespread biochemical abnormalities, but the fundamental defects to which most of the abnormalities can be traced are (1) a reduced entry of glucose into various "peripheral" tissues and (2) an increased liberation of glucose into the circulation from the liver (increased **hepatic glucogenesis**). There is therefore an extracellular glucose excess and an

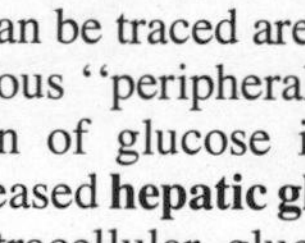

$$HN \text{---} C{=}O$$
$$O{=}C \quad\quad C{=}O$$
$$HN \text{---} C{=}O$$

Figure 19–6. Alloxan.

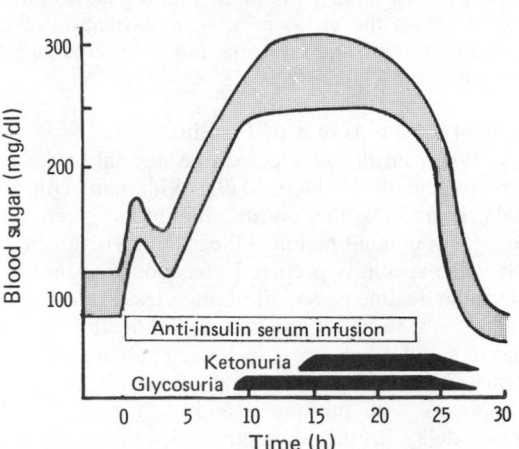

Figure 19–7. Hyperglycemia, glycosuria, and ketosis produced in rats by the injection of serum containing anti-insulin antibodies. The shaded area includes all blood glucose values found in 3 rats. (Redrawn and reproduced, with permission, from Armin J, Grant RT, Wright PH: Experimental diabetes in rats produced by parenteral administration of anti-insulin serum. J Physiol 153:146, 1960.)

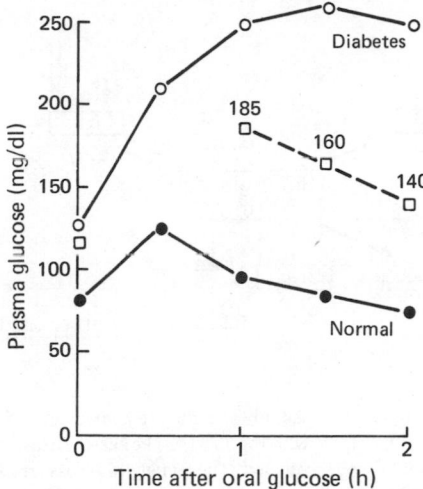

Figure 19–8. Glucose tolerance curves following oral administration of glucose, 40 g/m^2 body surface. According to American Diabetes Association's standards (Diabetes 18:299, 1969), chemical diabetes is present if the fasting glucose is greater than 115 mg/dl or if the 1-, 1.5- and 2-hour post-glucose values are greater than 185, 165, and 140 mg/dl, respectively, with all 3 values abnormal.

intracellular glucose deficiency, a situation that has been called "starvation in the midst of plenty." There is also a decrease in the entry of amino acids into muscle and an increase in lipolysis.

Recent research has made it clear that there is an absolute or relative hypersecretion of glucagon in diabetes. This is true even when the pancreas is removed, because glucagon is secreted by the gastrointestinal tract as well as the pancreas. Somatostatin inhibits the secretion of insulin and glucagon (see Chapter 14), and when it is infused in pancreatectomized animals, the blood glucose falls toward normal. Consequently, it appears that the extracellular glucose excess in diabetes is due in part to hyperglucagonemia.

Glucose Tolerance

In diabetes, glucose piles up in the bloodstream, especially after meals. If a glucose load is given to a diabetic, the blood glucose rises higher and returns to the baseline more slowly than it normally does. The response to a standard oral test dose of glucose, the **oral glucose tolerance test,** is used in the clinical diagnosis of diabetes (Fig 19–8).

Impaired glucose tolerance in diabetes is due in part to reduced entry of glucose into cells (**decreased peripheral utilization**). In the absence of insulin, the entry of glucose into skeletal muscle, cardiac and smooth muscle, and other tissues is decreased (Table 19–2). Glucose uptake by the liver is also reduced, but the effect is indirect (see below). Intestinal absorption of glucose is unaffected, as is its reabsorption from the urine by the cells of the proximal tubules of the kidney. Glucose uptake by most of the brain and the red blood cells is also normal.

The second (and probably the major) cause of hyperglycemia in diabetes is derangement of the glucostatic function of the liver (see Chapter 17). The liver takes up glucose from the bloodstream and stores it as glycogen, but because the liver contains glucose-6-phosphatase it also discharges glucose into the bloodstream. Indeed, Claude Bernard spoke of the liver as an endocrine gland that secreted glucose. Insulin facilitates glycogen synthesis and inhibits hepatic glucose output. When the blood glucose is high, insulin secretion is normally increased and hepatic

Table 19–2. Effect of insulin on glucose uptake in tissues in which it has been investigated.

Tissues in which insulin facilitates glucose uptake
Skeletal muscle
Cardiac muscle
Smooth muscle
Adipose tissue
Leukocytes
Crystalline lens of the eye
Pituitary
Fibroblasts
Mammary gland
Aorta
A cells of pancreatic islets
Tissues in which insulin does not facilitate glucose uptake
Brain (except probably part of hypothalamus)
Kidney tubules
Intestinal mucosa
Red blood cells

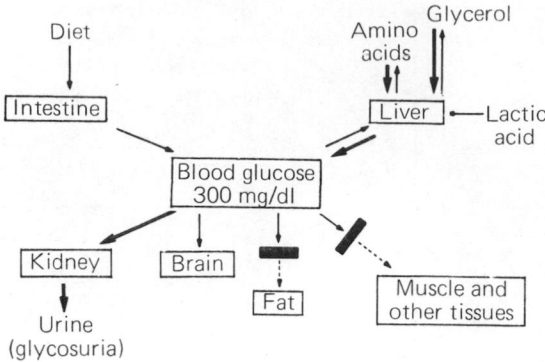

Figure 19–9. Disordered blood glucose homeostasis in insulin deficiency. Compare with Fig 17–15. The heavy arrows indicate reactions that are accentuated. The rectangles across arrows indicate reactions that are blocked.

glucogenesis is decreased. In diabetes, the glucose output remains elevated (Fig 19–9), in part because of the hyperglucagonemia. The degree to which the liver contributes to the abnormal glucose tolerance is shown by experiments on hepatectomized animals. In fasted hepatectomized dogs, the blood glucose falls steadily; but if hepatectomized dogs are given glucose, the glucose tolerance curves are of the diabetic type. This is true even if the pancreas is intact. However, pancreatectomized animals with intact livers given a constant infusion of insulin have essentially normal glucose tolerances.

Distribution of Endogenous & Exogenous Insulin

The action of insulin on the liver assumes added significance in view of the fact that endogenously secreted insulin enters the portal vein, so that the liver is normally exposed to concentrations of insulin which are 3–10 times greater than those in peripheral tissues. The liver binds about half of a dose of insulin injected into the portal vein but only 25% of a peripherally injected dose. It is worth noting that the exogenous insulin injected in the treatment of diabetes enters the peripheral rather than the portal circulation, although it does not appear that the resultant unphysiologic distribution of insulin has any important consequences in terms of the control of the disease or prevention of its complications.

Effects of Hyperglycemia

Hyperglycemia by itself can cause symptoms resulting from the hyperosmolality of the blood. In addition, there is glycosuria because the renal capacity for glucose reabsorption is exceeded. Excretion of the osmotically active glucose molecules entails the loss of large amounts of water (osmotic diuresis; see Chapter 38). The resultant dehydration activates the mechanisms regulating water intake, leading to polydipsia. There is an appreciable urinary loss of Na^+ and K^+ as well. For every gram of glucose excreted, 4.1 kcal are lost from the body. Increasing oral caloric intake to

cover this loss simply raises the blood glucose further and increases the glycosuria, so mobilization of endogenous protein and fat stores and weight loss are not prevented.

Hypoglycemic Action of Insulin

When insulin is injected into normal or diabetic persons, the blood glucose falls. With many commercial preparations, there is an initial blood glucose rise because of contamination of the insulin with glucagon, but when specially prepared glucagon-free insulin is used, the decline starts within minutes. Following intravenous insulin administration, the decline is maximal in about 30 minutes; following subcutaneous administration, it is maximal in 2–3 hours. Insulin forms complexes with protamine and with zinc, both of which delay insulin absorption. A number of long-acting zinc and protamine complexes are commercially available (Table 19–3).

Relation to Potassium

Insulin causes K^+ to enter cells, with a resultant lowering of the extracellular K^+ concentration. Infusions of insulin and glucose significantly lower the plasma K^+ level in normal individuals and are very effective for the temporary relief of hyperkalemia in patients with renal failure. Hypokalemia may develop when patients with diabetic acidosis are treated with insulin. The reason for the intracellular migration of K^+ is still obscure. However, insulin has been shown to increase the resting membrane potential (see Chapter 1) of skeletal muscle and fat cells, and it has been argued that this increased electrical gradient into the cells is the cause of the increase in intracellular K^+. It is possible under certain experimental conditions to dissociate the movement of K^+ from the movement of glucose into cells. K^+ depletion decreases insulin secretion, and K^+-depleted patients, eg, patients with primary hyperaldosteronism (see Chapter 20),develop diabetic glucose tolerance curves. These curves are restored to normal by K^+ repletion. The thiazide di-

Table 19–3. Characteristics of the blood glucose-lowering effects of crystalline zinc insulin and several modified insulins.

Type of Insulin	Hours After Subcutaneous Administration	
	Peak Action	Duration of Action
Crystalline zinc insulin (CZI)	2–3	5–7
Globin zinc insulin	6–10	18–24
NPH insulin (neutral protamine-Hagedorn insulin)	10–20	24–28
Lente insulin	10–20	24–28
Protamine zinc insulin (PZI)	16–24	36+

uretics, which cause loss of K^+ as well as Na^+ in the urine (Table 38–9), decrease glucose tolerance and make diabetes worse. They apparently exert this effect principally because of their K^+-depleting effects, although some of them also cause pancreatic islet cell damage.

Exercise

The entry of glucose into skeletal muscle is increased during exercise in the absence of insulin. The cause of the increased muscle uptake is not definitely known. Relative O_2 deficiency may be a factor because glucose entry into cells is increased under anaerobic conditions. On the other hand, increased circulating ketones and free fatty acids tend to inhibit glucose entry into muscle and other insulin-sensitive tissues. Exercise can precipitate hypoglycemia in diabetics taking insulin not only because of the effect of relative O_2 deficiency but also because absorption of injected insulin is more rapid during exercise. Patients with diabetes should take in extra calories or reduce their insulin dosage when they exercise.

Effects of Intracellular Glucose Deficiency

The plethora of glucose outside the cells in diabetes contrasts with the intracellular deficit. Glucose catabolism is normally a major source of energy for cellular processes (Fig 19–10), and in diabetes, energy requirements can be met only by drawing on protein and fat reserves. Mechanisms are activated that greatly increase the catabolism of protein and fat, and one of the consequences of increased fat catabolism is ketosis.

Deficient glucose utilization in the cells of the hypothalamic ventromedial nuclei is probably the cause of the hyperphagia in diabetes. When the activity of the satiety center is decreased in response to decreased glucose utilization in its cells, the lateral appetite center operates unopposed, and food intake is increased (see Chapter 14).

Glycogen depletion is a common consequence of intracellular glucose deficit, and the glycogen content of liver and skeletal muscle in diabetic animals is usually reduced. Insulin regularly increases the glycogen content of skeletal muscle, and it increases liver glycogen unless it produces sufficient hypoglycemia to also activate glycogenolytic mechanisms.

Changes in Protein Metabolism

In diabetes, the rate at which amino acids are catabolized to CO_2 and H_2O is increased. In addition, more amino acids are converted to glucose in the liver. This shift is indicated in Fig 19–11, which also shows the other principal abnormalities of intermediary metabolism in the liver.

Some idea of the rate of gluconeogenesis in fasting diabetic animals is obtained by measuring the ratio of glucose (dextrose) to nitrogen in the urine (**D/N ratio**). In fasting animals, liver glycogen is depleted and glycerol is converted to glucose at a very limited rate, so that the only important source of plasma glucose is protein (see Chapter 17). It can be calculated that the amount of carbon in the protein represented by 1 g of urinary nitrogen is sufficient to form 8.3 g of glucose. Consequently, the D/N ratio of approximately 3 seen in diabetes indicates the conversion to glucose of about 33% of the carbon of the protein metabolized.

The causes of the increased gluconeogenesis are multiple. There is an increased supply of amino acids

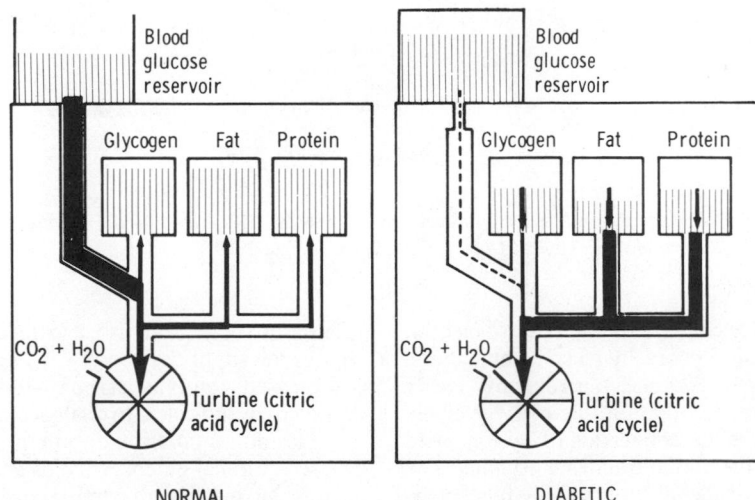

Figure 19–10. Effect of insulin on the cells of muscle and other "peripheral" tissues. The cell is represented as a mill that obtains fuel (glucose) from a reservoir (blood glucose). Normally (left), insulin is present and fuel enters through the pipeline in sufficient amounts to operate the turbine (citric acid cycle) and maintain a reserve supply in the storage tanks. When insulin is absent, the opening of the pipe is narrowed (right), and little fuel gets into the cell. The turbine can now turn at a nearly normal rate only by depleting the reserves, the major source of energy being fats and proteins. (Modified, redrawn, and reproduced, with permission, from MacLeod AG: *Diabetes*. Upjohn Co., 1969.)

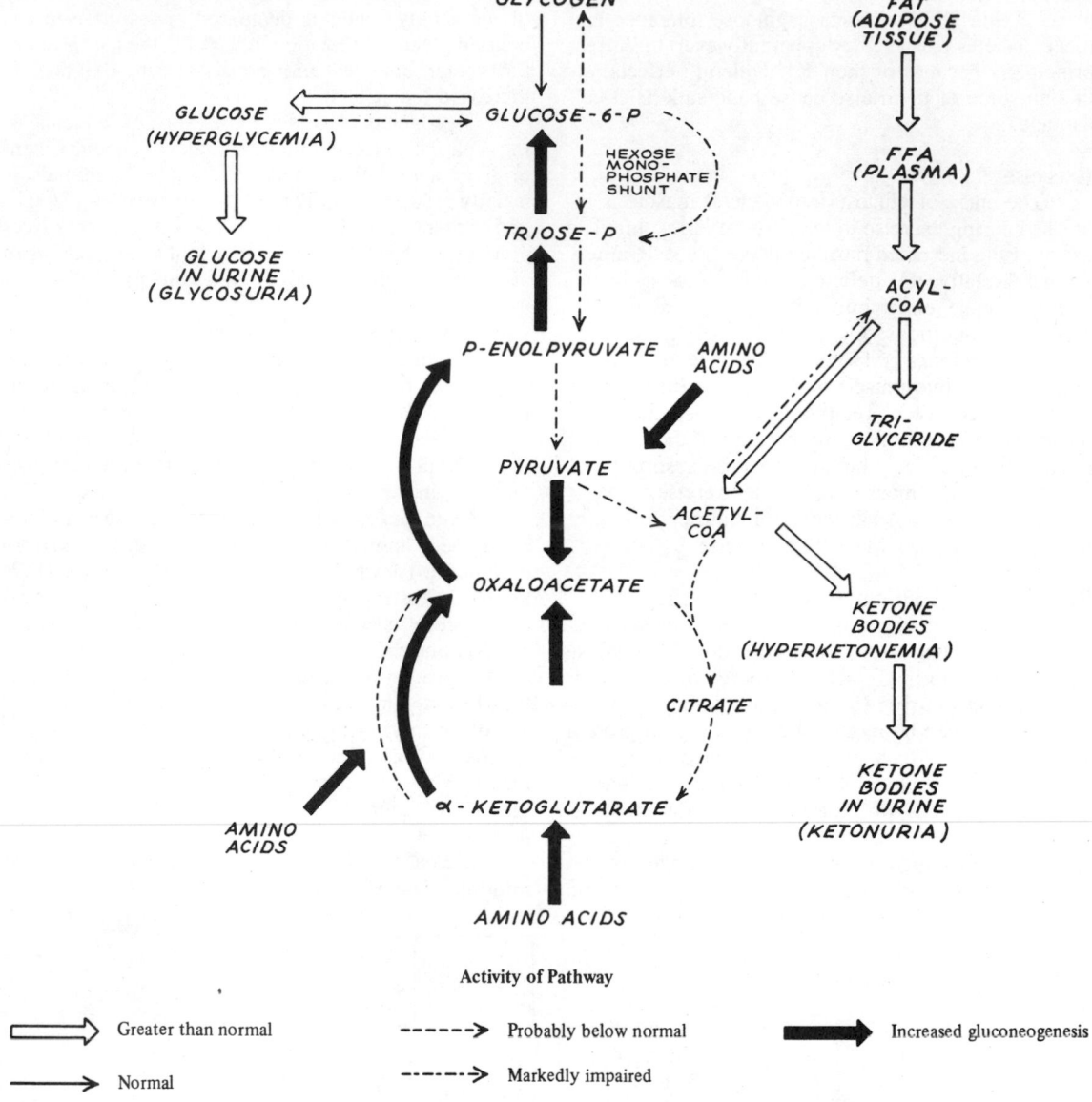

Figure 19–11. Metabolic abnormalities in the liver in uncontrolled diabetes. (Reproduced, with permission, from Harper HA, Rodwell VW, Mayes PA: *Review of Physiological Chemistry,* 17th ed. Lange, 1979.)

for gluconeogenesis because, in the absence of insulin, less protein synthesis occurs in muscle, and blood amino acid levels rise. Alanine is particularly easily converted to glucose. In addition, the activity of the enzymes that catalyze the conversion of pyruvic acid and other 2-carbon metabolic fragments to glucose is increased. These include phosphoenolpyruvate carboxykinase, which facilitates conversion of oxaloacetic acid to phosphoenolpyruvic acid (see Chapter 17). They also include fructose-1,6-diphosphatase, which catalyzes the conversion of fructose diphosphate to fructose-6-phosphate, and glucose-6-phosphatase, which controls the entry of glucose into the circulation from the liver. Increased acetyl-CoA increases pyru-

vate carboxylase activity, and insulin deficiency increases the supply of acetyl-CoA because lipogenesis is decreased. Pyruvate carboxylase catalyzes the conversion of pyruvic acid to oxaloacetic acid (Fig 17–9).

Hormones contribute to the increased gluconeogenesis. Adrenal glucocorticoids accelerate gluconeogenesis, but the level of adrenal cortical secretion is not elevated except in severely ill diabetics or in acidosis. Glucagon also stimulates gluconeogenesis, and, as noted above, hyperglucagonemia is present in most if not all diabetics.

Insulin & Growth

Not only is protein catabolism accelerated in the

absence of insulin, but protein synthesis is depressed and insulin stimulates protein formation. This anabolic effect of insulin is explained in part by the protein-sparing action of adequate intracellular glucose supplies. Insulin also increases the incorporation of amino acids into proteins by an action that is independent of its effects on glucose metabolism. This action may be due to an activation of the ribosomes (see Chapter 17) by insulin, but insulin also increases the transport of amino acids into cells in which protein synthesis has been blocked by puromycin. Failure to grow is a symptom of diabetes in children, and insulin stimulates the growth of immature hypophysectomized rats to almost the same degree as growth hormone. Maximum insulin-induced growth is present, however, only when the protein-sparing action of glucose is fostered by feeding a high-carbohydrate diet.

Negative Nitrogen Balance

In diabetes, the net effect of accelerated protein catabolism to CO_2 and H_2O and to glucose, plus diminished protein synthesis, is a markedly negative nitrogen balance, protein depletion, and wasting. Protein depletion from any cause is associated with poor "resistance" to infections, and the sugar-rich body fluids are undoubtedly good culture media for microorganisms. This is probably why diabetics are particularly prone to bacterial infections.

Fat Metabolism in Diabetes

The principal abnormalities of fat metabolism in diabetes are acceleration of lipid catabolism, with increased formation of ketone bodies, and decreased synthesis of fatty acids and triglycerides. The manifestations of the disordered lipid metabolism are so prominent that diabetes has been called "more a disease of lipid than of carbohydrate metabolism."

Fifty percent of an ingested glucose load is normally burned to CO_2 and H_2O; 5% is converted to glycogen; and 30–40% is converted to fat in the fat depots. In diabetes, less than 5% is converted to fat even though the amount burned to CO_2 and H_2O is also decreased and the amount converted to glycogen is not increased. Therefore, glucose accumulates in the bloodstream and spills over into the urine.

The role of lipoprotein lipase and hormone-sensitive lipase in the regulation of the metabolism of fat depots is discussed in Chapter 17. In diabetes, there is decreased conversion of glucose to fatty acids in the depots because of the intracellular glucose deficiency. Insulin inhibits the hormone-sensitive lipase in adipose tissue, and, in the absence of this hormone, the plasma level of **free fatty acids** (NEFA, UFA, FFA) is more than doubled. The increased glucagon also contributes to the mobilization of FFA. Thus, the FFA level parallels the blood glucose level in diabetes and in some ways is a better indicator of the severity of the diabetic state. In the liver and other tissues, the fatty acids are catabolized to acetyl-CoA. Some of the acetyl-CoA is burned along with amino acid residues to yield CO_2

and H_2O in the citric acid cycle. However, the supply exceeds the capacity of the tissues to catabolize the acetyl-CoA.

The events occurring in the liver in diabetes are summarized in Fig 19–11. In addition to the previously mentioned increase in gluconeogenesis and marked outpouring of glucose into the circulation, there is a marked impairment of the conversion of acetyl-CoA to malonyl-CoA and thence to fatty acids. This is due to a deficiency of acetyl carboxylase, the enzyme that catalyzes the conversion. The excess acetyl-CoA is converted to ketone bodies (see below).

In uncontrolled diabetes, there is an increase in the plasma concentration of triglycerides, lipoproteins, and chylomicrons as well as FFA, and the plasma is often lipemic. The rise in these constituents is due mainly to decreased removal of triglycerides into the fat depots. The decreased activity of lipoprotein lipase contributes to this decreased removal.

Ketosis

When there is excess acetyl-CoA in the body, some of it is converted to acetoacetyl-CoA and then, in the liver, to acetoacetic acid. Acetoacetic acid and its derivatives, acetone and β-hydroxybutyric acid, enter the circulation in large quantities (see Chapter 17).

These circulating ketone bodies are an important source of energy in fasting. Half of the metabolic rate in fasted normal dogs is said to be due to metabolism of ketones. The rate of ketone utilization in diabetics is also appreciable. It has been calculated that the maximal rate at which fat can be catabolized without significant ketosis is 2.5 g/kg body weight/d in diabetic humans. In untreated diabetes, production is much greater than this, and ketone bodies pile up in the bloodstream. There is some evidence that in severe diabetes the rate of ketone utilization may also decline, making the ketosis worse, and insulin is said to increase ketone uptake in muscle.

Acidosis

Most of the hydrogen ions liberated from acetoacetic acid and β-hydroxybutyric acid are buffered, but severe metabolic acidosis still develops. The low plasma pH stimulates the respiratory center, producing the rapid, deep respiration described by Kussmaul as "air hunger" and named, for him, **Kussmaul breathing.** The urine becomes acid; but when the ability of the kidney to replace the plasma cations accompanying the organic anions with H^+ and NH_4^+ is exceeded, Na^+ and K^+ are lost in the urine. The electrolyte and water losses lead to dehydration, hypovolemia, and hypotension. Finally, the acidosis and dehydration depress consciousness to the point of coma. Diabetic acidosis is a medical emergency. Now that the infections which used to complicate the disease can be controlled with antibiotics, acidosis is the commonest cause of early death in clinical diabetes.

In severe acidosis, total body sodium is markedly depleted, and when sodium loss exceeds water loss, plasma Na^+ is not infrequently low. Total body potassium is also low, but the plasma K^+ is usually normal, partly because ECF volume is reduced and partly because K^+ moves from cells to ECF when the ECF H^+ concentration is high. Another factor tending to maintain the plasma K^+ is the lack of insulin-induced entry of K^+ into cells. This must be kept in mind in treating acidosis; total body stores of this ion are low, and severe and even fatal hypokalemia may develop when insulin is given (see above).

The degree to which ketoacidosis complicates experimental diabetes varies in different species. The size of the body fat stores is also a factor conditioning the response to diabetes. Thin, wasted pancreatectomized dogs rarely develop ketoacidosis, whereas well-fed, plump animals do so readily. It is pertinent that before the isolation of insulin by Banting and Best in 1921 the principal treatment of human diabetes was a starvation diet (**Allen regimen**). This not only lowered the blood glucose level but also reduced depot fat stores to the point where there was little fat to mobilize.

Coma

Coma in diabetes can be due to acidosis and dehydration. However, the blood glucose can be elevated to such a degree that independent of plasma pH, the hyperosmolarity of the plasma causes unconsciousness (**hyperosmolar coma**). Accumulation of lactic acid in the blood (**lactic acidosis**) may also complicate diabetic ketoacidosis if the tissues become hypoxic (see Chapter 33), and lactic acidosis may itself cause coma.

Cholesterol Metabolism

In diabetes, the plasma cholesterol level is usually elevated, and this may play a role in the accelerated development of the arteriosclerotic vascular disease that is a major long-term complication of diabetes in humans. Although there has been some controversy on the point, it seems clear that, at least in severe diabetes, cholesterol synthesis is decreased. Part of the rise in plasma cholesterol level is due to an increase in the cholesterol containing very low density and low-density β-lipoproteins secondary to the great increase in circulating triglycerides. Another factor may be a decline in hepatic degradation of cholesterol, which, when it exceeds the decline in cholesterol synthesis, contributes to the rise.

Summary

Because of the complexities of the metabolic abnormalities in diabetes, a summary is in order. One of the key features of insulin deficiency (Fig 19–12) is decreased entry of glucose into many tissues (decreased peripheral utilization). There is also increased net release of glucose from the liver (increased production), due in part to glucagon excess. The resultant hyperglycemia leads to glycosuria and a dehydrating osmotic diuresis. Dehydration leads to polydipsia. In the face of intracellular glucose deficiency, appetite is stimulated, glucose is formed from protein (gluconeogenesis), and energy supplies are maintained by the

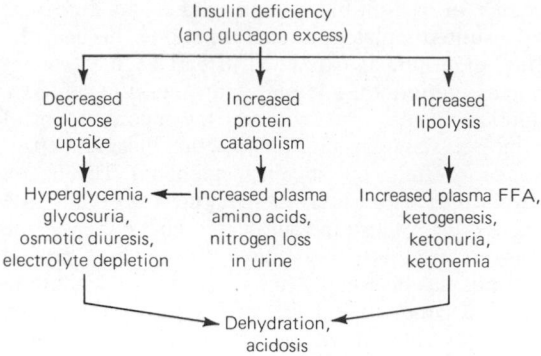

Figure 19–12. Effects of insulin deficiency. (Courtesy of RJ Havel.)

metabolism of proteins and fats. Weight loss, debilitating protein deficiency, and inanition are the result.

Fat catabolism is increased, and the system is flooded with triglycerides and free fatty acids. Fat synthesis is inhibited, and the overloaded catabolic pathways cannot handle the excess acetyl-CoA formed. In the liver, the acetyl-CoA is converted to ketone bodies. The ketones are for the most part organic acids, which accumulate in the circulation (ketosis) because their production rate exceeds the ability of the body to utilize them. Therefore, metabolic acidosis develops as the ketones accumulate.

Table 19–4. Principal actions of insulin.

Adipose tissue
1. Increased glucose entry
2. Increased fatty acid synthesis
3. Increased glycerol phosphate synthesis
4. Increased triglyceride deposition
5. Activation of lipoprotein lipase
6. Inhibition of hormone-sensitive lipase
7. Increased K^+ uptake

Muscle
1. Increased glucose entry
2. Increased glycogen synthesis
3. Increased amino acid uptake
4. Increased protein synthesis in ribosomes
5. Decreased protein catabolism
6. Decreased release of gluconeogenic amino acids
7. Increased ketone uptake
8. Increased K^+ uptake

Liver
1. Decreased cyclic AMP
2. Decreased ketogenesis
3. Increased protein synthesis
4. Increased lipid synthesis
5. Decreased glucose output due to decreased gluconeogenesis and increased glycogen synthesis

Na^+ and K^+ depletion are added to the dehydration because these plasma cations are excreted with the organic anions not covered by the H^+ and NH_4^+ secreted by the kidney. Finally, the acidotic, hypovolemic, hypotensive, depleted animal or patient becomes comatose because of the toxic effects of acidosis, dehydration, and hyperosmolarity on the nervous system and dies if treatment is not instituted.

All of these abnormalities are corrected by administration of insulin. Although emergency treatment of acidosis also includes administration of alkali to combat the acidosis and parenteral water, Na^+, and K^+ to replenish body stores, only insulin repairs the fundamental defects in a way that permits a return to normal.

The principal actions of insulin are summarized in Table 19–4. It is secreted after meals (see below), and its net effect is to promote the storage of carbohydrate, protein, and fat. It is therefore appropriately called the "hormone of abundance."

INSULIN EXCESS

Symptoms

All the known consequences of insulin excess are manifestations, directly or indirectly, of the effects of hypoglycemia on the nervous system. Except in individuals who have been fasting for some time, glucose is the only fuel used in appreciable quantities by the brain. The carbohydrate reserves in neural tissue are very limited, and normal function depends upon a continuous glucose supply. As the blood glucose level falls, the cortex and the other brain areas with high metabolic rates are affected first, followed by the more slowly respiring vegetative centers in the diencephalon and hindbrain (see Chapter 32). Thus, early cortical symptoms of confusion, weakness, dizziness, and hunger are followed by convulsions and coma. If the hypoglycemia is prolonged, irreversible changes develop in the same cortical-diencephalic-medullary sequence, and death results from depression of the respiratory center. Therefore, prompt treatment with glucose is in order. Although a dramatic disappearance of symptoms is the usual response, abnormalities ranging from some intellectual dulling to permanent coma may persist if hypoglycemia was severe or prolonged. Hypoglycemia is a potent stimulus to sympathetic discharge and increased secretion of catecholamines, particularly epinephrine. The tremors, palpitations, and nervousness in hypoglycemia are probably due to sympathetic overactivity.

The blood glucose concentration at which symptoms of hypoglycemia appear is variable. Some normal humans have no definite symptoms with values as low as 35 mg/dl. Some patients with insulin-secreting tumors adapt to blood glucose levels as low as 20 mg/dl, whereas diabetics adapted to chronic hyperglycemia may have definite symptoms of hypoglycemia with values of 100 mg/dl. The mechanisms responsible for this adaptation are unknown.

Compensatory Mechanisms

The increase in adrenal medullary secretion produced by hypoglycemia is accomplished by increased adrenocortical secretion, and both tend to compensate for the hypoglycemia, the epinephrine by causing glycogenolysis with consequent liberation of glucose from the liver, and the glucocorticoids by increasing gluconeogenesis and by their anti-insulin action. Insulin tolerance is significantly reduced in animals depleted of catecholamines by drug treatment. A decline in blood glucose also stimulates glucagon secretion, increasing gluconeogenesis and glycogenolysis. The blood glucose fall produced by insulin is more pronounced in fasting animals than in fed animals with abundant liver glycogen reserves. Finally, growth hormone secretion is also increased, and by decreasing glucose utilization in peripheral tissues, the growth hormone helps to make more glucose available to the brain.

MECHANISM OF ACTION
OF INSULIN

There is an appealing parsimony to the concept that insulin has a single action that underlies all of its diverse effects on metabolism. It seems clear that the hormone binds to receptors that are located for the most part on cell membranes (see above) and that this binding triggers its actions. However, at least 5 of the different actions mentioned above cannot be causally related to one another at this time: (1) The increase in the entry of glucose into muscle and certain other tissues (Table 19–2). (2) The inhibition of the hormone-sensitive lipase. (3) The stimulation of protein synthesis, an effect that can occur in the absence of extracellular glucose. (4) The increase in the transport of amino acids into cells. (5) The increase in the membrane potential of the cells in skeletal muscle and adipose tissue. Insulin may also have additional effects on the liver. However, much of what happens in diabetes can be explained by decreased entry of glucose into muscle.

An effect of insulin on the entry of sugars into cells is indicated by the observation that in hepatectomized nephrectomized animals the volume of distribution of galactose and several other sugars with similar structure is increased by insulin (Fig 19–13). In the absence of the liver and the kidneys, these sugars are not metabolized or excreted. Since their volume of distribution after insulin administration is greater than the ECF space, the sugars must have entered cells. Similar effects on the distribution of glucose can be demonstrated (Fig 19–14).

In muscle, adipose tissue, and connective tissue, insulin facilitates the entry of glucose into the cells by an action on the cell membranes. The rate of phosphorylation of the glucose, once it has entered the cells, is apparently controlled by other hormones. Growth

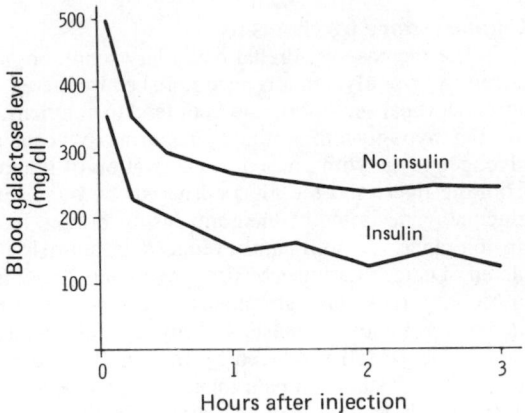

Figure 19–13. The capacity of insulin to increase the volume of distribution of galactose. The sugar was infused in hepatectomized nephrectomized dogs, and the changes in its blood level followed. (Redrawn and reproduced, with permission, from Goldstein MS & others: Action of insulin on transfer of sugars across cell barriers. Am J Physiol 173:207, 1953.)

the most part to glucose and a few other sugars with the same configuration in the first 3 carbon atoms; furthermore, these sugars compete with one another for transport. Even though glucose transport does not involve movement against a concentration gradient, it is more sensitive to temperature changes than passive diffusion.

Insulin does not affect the movement of glucose across the membranes of hepatic cells directly, but it brings about a facilitation of glycogen synthesis and a decrease in glucose output. Consequently, there is a net increase in glucose uptake. Insulin suppresses the synthesis of key gluconeogenic enzymes and induces the synthesis of key glycolytic enzymes such as glucokinase. Glycogen synthetase activity is also increased. However, it has not been proved that these increases are directly due to insulin.

hormone and cortisol both have been reported to inhibit phosphorylation in certain tissues. However, the process is normally so rapid that it is a rate-limiting step in glucose metabolism only when the rate of glucose entry is high.

Because of the rapid phosphorylation, the intracellular free glucose concentration is normally low, and the concentration gradient for glucose is directed inward. Some glucose moves down this gradient into cells in the absence of insulin, but insulin greatly increases the rate of movement in a selective fashion. A carrier of some sort is probably involved because the process shows the saturation kinetics characteristic of a system in which there is limited availability of a specific carrier. It is thus an example of **facilitated diffusion.** The process is highly specific, being limited for

REGULATION OF INSULIN SECRETION

Insulin secretion is now known to be influenced by a variety of stimulatory and inhibitory factors (Table 19–5). However, many of these factors are either substances related to glucose metabolism or agents that affect cyclic AMP. Normal secretion requires the presence of adequate quantities of calcium and potassium ions.

Measurement of Insulin in Body Fluids

Insulinlike activity (ILA) in plasma has been bioassayed by comparing the effects of plasma samples with those of known amounts of insulin on a variety of physiologic parameters. These bioassays have now been replaced by a radioimmunoassay for insulin. **Radioimmunoassays** have come into extremely widespread use in the measurement of protein

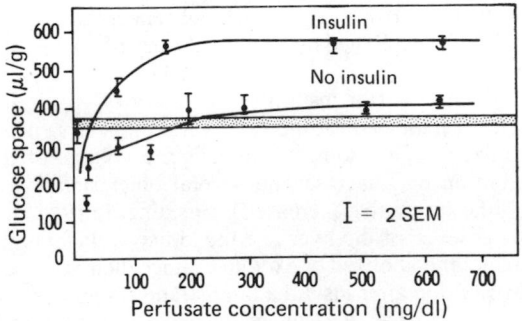

Figure 19–14. Volume of distribution of glucose in the perfused normal rat heart as a function of the glucose concentration in the perfusing medium. The horizontal bar indicates the size of the extracellular space. SEM, standard error of the mean. (Redrawn and reproduced, with permission, from Morgan HE & others: Regulation of glucose uptake in heart muscle from normal and alloxan-diabetic rats. Ann NY Acad Sci 82:387, 1959.)

Table 19–5. Factors affecting insulin secretion.

Stimulators	Inhibitors
Glucose	Somatostatin
Mannose	2-Deoxyglucose
Amino acids (leucine, arginine, others)	Mannoheptulose
	α-Adrenergic stimulating agents (norepinephrine, epinephrine)
Intestinal hormones (GIP, gastrin, secretin, CCK, glucagon, others?)	
β-Keto acids	β-Adrenergic blocking agents (propranolol)
Acetylcholine	Diazoxide
Glucagon	Thiazide diuretics
Cyclic AMP and various cyclic AMP-generating substances	Phenytoin
	Alloxan
	Microtubule inhibitors
β-Adrenergic stimulating agents	
Theophylline	
Sulfonylureas	

and polypeptide hormones. They depend on interference by unlabeled hormones with the binding of radioactivity-labeled hormones to antibodies. Immunoassays of nonprotein substances such as steroids have also been developed, using antibodies produced by injecting the substances bound to proteins.

The ILA values in plasma are generally higher than the values determined by immunoassay, and a significant ILA titer persists after pancreatectomy, so that factors other than insulin definitely contribute to the observed values. The normal concentration of insulin measured by radioimmunoassay in the peripheral venous plasma of fasting normal humans is 0–70 μU/ml (0–502 pmol/L). The amount of insulin secreted per day in a normal human has been calculated to be about 40 units (287 nmol).

Effect of the Blood Glucose Level

The major control of insulin secretion is exerted by a feedback effect of the blood glucose level directly on the pancreas. Glucose penetrates the islets readily, and its rate of entrance is unaffected by insulin. When the level of glucose in the blood perfusing the pancreas is elevated (above 110 mg/dl in rats), insulin secretion in the pancreatic venous blood is increased; when the level is normal or low, the rate of insulin secretion is low (Fig 19–15). Mannose also stimulates insulin secretion. Fructose has a moderate stimulatory effect, but it is converted intracellularly into glucose. Although the entry of galactose, D-xylose, and L-arabinose into cells is facilitated by insulin, these sugars do not stimulate insulin secretion. Neither do a variety of citric acid cycle intermediates and nonmetabolizable sugars. However, the stimulatory effect of glucose depends on its metabolism, since 2-deoxyglucose and mannoheptulose, agents that prevent glucose from being metabolized, also inhibit insulin secretion.

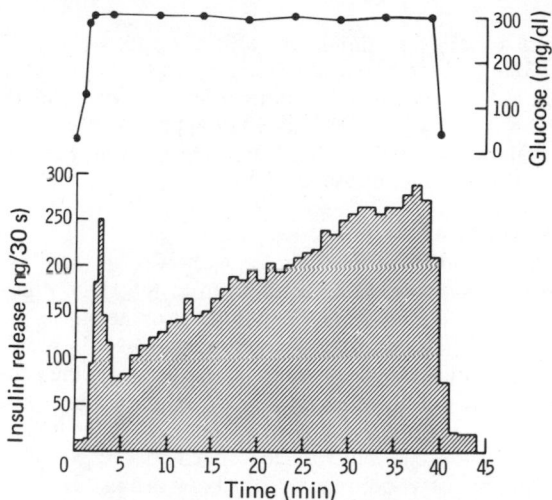

Figure 19–16. Insulin secretion from perfused rat pancreas in response to sustained glucose infusion. Values are means of 3 preparations. The top record shows the glucose concentration in the effluent perfusion mixture. (Reproduced, with permission, from Curry DL, Bennett LL, Grodsky GM: Dynamics of insulin secretion by the perfused rat pancreas. Endocrinology 83:572, 1968.)

In experimental animals (Fig 19–16) and humans, the action of glucose on insulin secretion is biphasic; there is a rapid increase in secretion followed by a more slowly developing prolonged response. The latter response is inhibited by inhibitors of protein synthesis. If glucose perfusion is resumed after a rest period, the response to glucose is increased.

The feedback control of blood glucose on insulin secretion normally operates with great precision, so that blood glucose and blood insulin levels parallel each other with remarkable consistency.

Protein & Fat Derivatives

Arginine, leucine, and certain other amino acids stimulate insulin secretion, and so do β-keto acids such as acetoacetic acid. The mechanisms by which these acids bring about the stimulation are unknown. However, it is worth noting in this regard that insulin stimulates the incorporation of amino acids into proteins and combats the fat catabolism that produces the β-keto acids.

Insulin Secretion & Cyclic AMP

Epinephrine and norepinephrine inhibit insulin secretion by a direct action on the pancreas. The inhibitory effect of epinephrine is blocked by drugs that block α-adrenergic receptors but not by drugs that block β-adrenergic receptors. There is some evidence that α-adrenergic stimulating agents such as epinephrine and norepinephrine decrease intracellular cyclic AMP. On the other hand, β-stimulating drugs stimulate insulin secretion. So does theophylline, which inhibits the phosphodiesterase that catalyzes the breakdown of cyclic AMP (see Chapter 17). Propran-

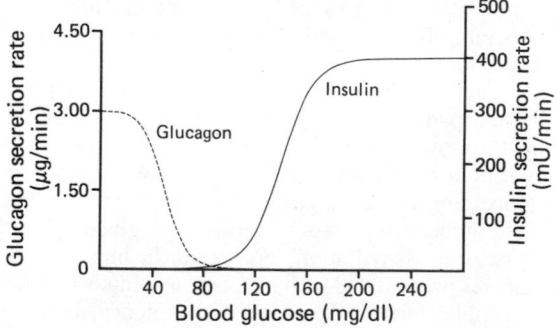

Figure 19–15. Mean rates of insulin and glucagon delivery from an artificial pancreas at various blood glucose levels. The device was programmed to establish and maintain normal blood glucose in insulin-requiring diabetic humans, and the values for hormone output approximate the output of the normal human pancreas. (Reproduced, with permission, from Marliss EB & others: Normalization of glycemia in diabetics during meals with insulin and glucagon delivery by the artificial pancreas. Diabetes 26:663, 1977.)

olol blocks the stimulatory effect of catecholamines without affecting the response to glucose. Some other stimuli to insulin secretion may act via cyclic AMP. However, cyclic AMP does not appear to be an obligatory intermediate in the mechanism by which glucose stimulates insulin secretion.

Effect of Autonomic Nerves

Branches of the right vagus nerve innervate the pancreatic islets, and stimulation of the right vagus causes increased insulin secretion. Atropine blocks the response, and acetylcholine stimulates insulin secretion. Stimulation of the sympathetic nerves to the pancreas inhibits insulin secretion. The inhibition is produced via the release of norepinephrine, and the inhibitory response is converted to an excitatory response by infusion of α-adrenergic blocking drugs. The autonomic innervation of the pancreas apparently modulates insulin secretion. The effects of glucose do not require an intact innervation, since they occur in the transplanted pancreas, but there is some evidence that the nerve fibers maintain normal islet sensitivity to glucose.

Intestinal Hormones

It has been clearly demonstrated that orally administered glucose exerts a greater insulin-stimulating effect than intravenously administered glucose, and orally administered amino acids also produce a greater insulin response than intravenous amino acids. These observations led to exploration of the possibility that a substance secreted by the gastrointestinal mucosa stimulated insulin secretion. Glucagon, secretin, cholecystokinin-pancreozymin (CCK), gastrin, and gastric inhibitory peptide (GIP) all have such an action (see Chapter 26). However, it appears that GIP is the physiologic "gut factor" that normally stimulates insulin secretion, since this factor produces stimulation when administered in doses that produce blood GIP levels comparable to those produced by oral glucose. The possible role of somatostatin in the regulation of insulin secretion is discussed below.

Oral Hypoglycemic Agents

Tolbutamide and other sulfonylurea derivatives such as chlorpropamide lower the blood glucose level, but only when a functioning pancreas is present. They act by stimulating the secretion of insulin, and there is some evidence that they do this by inhibiting phosphodiesterase, thus increasing the amount of cyclic AMP in B cells. It has also been claimed that they reduce glucagon secretion. However, their ability to produce consistent, clinically significant lowering of blood glucose has been questioned, and there is some evidence that these agents cause premature deaths from cardiovascular disease.

Phenformin and other biguanides that have been used as oral hypoglycemic agents do not affect insulin secretion but increase glucose utilization, apparently because they inhibit oxidative metabolism of glucose and consequently increase anaerobic glycolysis within the cells. They also decrease glucose absorption from the gastrointestinal tract. However, they cause lactic acidosis in a significant number of patients, and because of the seriousness of this complication, they have been removed from the market in the USA.

Drugs That Inhibit Insulin Secretion

The drug diazoxide, which was originally developed for the treatment of hypertension, has been found to be diabetogenic, and it exerts this effect by inhibiting insulin secretion. It is sometimes used in the treatment of hyperinsulinism due to diffuse islet cell hyperplasia. A number of other drugs that inhibit insulin secretion have been reported, and in some individuals the commonly used thiazide diuretics may exert an inhibitory effect.

Long-Term Changes in B Cell Responses

The magnitude of the insulin response to a given stimulus is determined in part by the past secretory history of the B cells. Individuals fed a high-carbohydrate diet for several weeks not only have higher fasting plasma insulin levels but also show a greater secretory response to a glucose load than individuals fed an isocaloric low-carbohydrate diet.

Although the B cells respond to stimulation with hypertrophy like other endocrine cells, they become exhausted and stop secreting (**B cell exhaustion**) when the stimulation is marked or prolonged. With such stimulation, they become vacuolated and hyalinized (hydropic and hyaline degeneration). If the stimulation stops soon after the cells stop secreting, they can recover; but if it is continued, the cells eventually die and disappear. In spite of some claims to the contrary, there is no convincing evidence that such "exhaustion atrophy" occurs in any other endocrine gland.

The pancreatic reserve is large, and it is difficult to produce B cell exhaustion in normal animals; but if the pancreatic reserve is reduced by partial pancreatectomy or small doses of alloxan, exhaustion of the remaining B cells can be produced by any procedure that chronically raises the blood glucose level. This is the cause of the diabetes produced in animals with limited pancreatic reserves by anterior pituitary extracts, growth hormone, thyroxine, or the prolonged continuous infusion of glucose alone. In rare instances, prolonged ingestion of a high-carbohydrate diet has been reported to cause hyperglycemia with glycosuria, dehydration, and coma in humans. The diabetes precipitated by hormones in animals is at first reversible, but with prolonged treatment it becomes permanent. The diabetes is usually named for the agent producing it, eg, "hypophyseal diabetes," "thyroid diabetes." Permanent diabetes persisting after treatment has been discontinued is indicated by the prefix meta-, eg, "metahypophyseal diabetes" or "metathyroid diabetes." When insulin is administered along with the diabetogenic hormones, the B cells are protected, probably because the blood glucose is lowered, and diabetes does not develop. Adrenal glucocorticoids raise blood glucose, but it has proved difficult to produce permanent diabetes in animals with adrenal steroid treatment alone. Exhaustion atrophy of the remaining B cells in diabetics treated with sulfonylureas has not been a problem; indeed, it has been claimed that these drugs induce islet cell hypergranulation and hypertrophy when administered for prolonged periods.

Effect of Exogenous Insulin

When insulin is administered to normal individuals, the rate at which they secrete their own insulin drops; this rate can be measured by following the circulating level of C peptide or the endogenous insulin level by radioimmunoassay with an antibody that does not cross-react with the administered insulin. When insulin treatment is stopped, the B cells are hyperresponsive, as if they had been "rested." This is probably the explanation of why, when many juvenile diabetics are first treated with insulin, their insulin requirement decreases as their condition improves. Sometimes it falls to zero and the diabetes "disappears" for some time, although it always reappears later on.

GLUCAGON

Chemistry

Human glucagon is a linear polypeptide with a molecular weight of 3485. It contains 29 amino acids and has the same structure as porcine glucagon (Table 26–1). However, bovine and porcine glucagon provoke the formation of antiglucagon antibodies in rabbits. These antibodies have been used to measure glucagon in dogs and humans. There is evidence for the formation of glucagon from a larger polypeptide precursor (proglucagon) in the A cells.

Action

Glucagon is glycogenolytic, gluconeogenic, and lipolytic (Fig 19–17). It raises the blood sugar because it stimulates adenylate cyclase in liver cells. This leads to the activation of phosphorylase and therefore to increased breakdown of glycogen. The steps involved in this classic example of mediation of a hormone effect via cyclic AMP are discussed in Chapter 17. Glucagon does not cause glycogenolysis in muscle. It increases gluconeogenesis from available amino acids in the liver and elevates the metabolic rate. Its lipolytic activity, which leads in turn to increased ketogenesis, is discussed in Chapter 17. The calorigenic action of glucagon is not due to the hyperglycemia per se but probably to the increased hepatic deamination of amino acids.

Large doses of exogenous glucagon exert a positively inotropic effect on the heart (see Chapter 29) without producing increased myocardial excitability, presumably because they increase myocardial cyclic AMP. Use of the hormone in the treatment of heart disease has been advocated, but there is no evidence

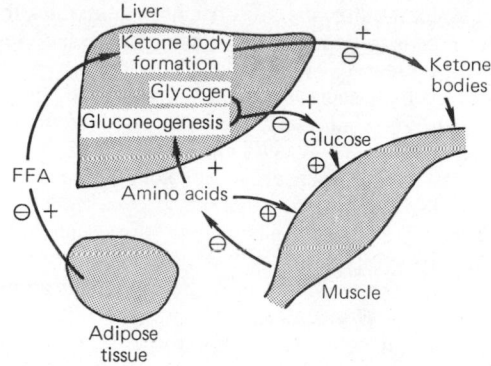

Figure 19–17. Bihormonal control of human substrate metabolism. $\oplus$, increased by insulin; $\ominus$, decreased by insulin; +, increased by glucagon. (Modified from Gerich J & others: Prevention of human diabetic ketoacidosis by somatostatin. N Engl J Med 292:985, 1975.)

for a physiologic role of glucagon in the regulation of cardiac function.

Glucagon also stimulates the secretion of growth hormone, insulin, and pancreatic somatostatin.

Glucagon receptors have been identified in a variety of tissues and partially purified. The molecular weight of the receptor protein is approximately 190,000.

Metabolism

Glucagon has a half-life in the circulation of 5–10 minutes. It is degraded by many tissues but particularly by the liver. Since glucagon is secreted into the portal vein and reaches the liver before it reaches the peripheral circulation, peripheral blood levels are relatively low. The rise in peripheral blood glucagon levels produced by excitatory stimuli (see below) is exaggerated in patients with cirrhosis, presumably because of decreased hepatic degradation of the hormone.

Regulation of Secretion

The principal factors known to affect glucagon secretion are summarized in Table 19–6. Secretion is decreased by a rise in plasma glucose, and this inhibi-

Table 19–6. Factors affecting glucagon secretion.

Stimulators	Inhibitors
Amino acids (particularly the glucogenic amino acids: alanine, serine, glycine, cysteine, and threonine)	Glucose
	Somatostatin
	Secretin
	FFA
CCK, gastrin	Ketones
Cortisol	Insulin
Exercise	Phenytoin
Infections	α-Adrenergic stimulators
Other stresses	
β-Adrenergic stimulators	
Theophylline	

tory effect requires the presence of insulin; thus, the A cells appear to be an insulin-dependent tissue. Secretion is increased by stimulation of the sympathetic nerves to the pancreas, and this sympathetic effect is mediated via β-adrenergic receptors and cyclic AMP. It appears that the A cells are like the B cells in that stimulation of β-adrenergic receptors increases secretion and stimulation of α-adrenergic receptors inhibits secretion (see above). However, the pancreatic response to sympathetic stimulation in the absence of blocking drugs is increased secretion of glucagon, so the effect of β-receptors predominates in the glucagon-secreting cells. The stimulatory effects of various stresses and possibly of exercise and infection are mediated at least in part via the sympathetic nervous system.

A protein meal and infusion of various amino acids increase glucagon secretion. It seems appropriate that the glucogenic amino acids are particularly potent in this regard, since these are the amino acids that are converted to glucose in the liver under the influence of glucagon. The increase in glucagon secretion following a protein meal is also valuable, since the amino acids stimulate insulin secretion, and the secreted glucagon prevents the development of hypoglycemia while the insulin promotes storage of the absorbed carbohydrates, fat, and lipids. Glucagon secretion increases during starvation. It reaches a peak on the third day of a fast, at the time of maximum gluconeogenesis. Thereafter, the plasma glucagon level declines as fatty acids and ketones become the major sources of energy.

The glucagon response to oral administration of amino acids is greater than the response to intravenous infusion of amino acids, suggesting that a glucagon-stimulating factor is secreted from the gastrointestinal mucosa. Cholecystokinin-pancreozymin (CCK) and gastrin increase glucagon secretion, whereas secretin inhibits it. Since CCK and gastrin secretion are both increased by a protein meal, either hormone could be the gastrointestinal mediator of the glucagon response. The inhibition produced by somatostatin is discussed below.

Glucagon secretion is also inhibited by free fatty acids and ketones. However, this inhibition can apparently be overridden, since plasma glucagon levels are high in diabetic ketoacidosis.

Insulin-Glucagon Molar Ratios

As noted above, insulin is glycogenic, antigluconeogenetic, and antilipolytic in its actions. It thus favors storage of absorbed nutrients and is a "hormone of energy storage." Glucagon, on the other hand, is glycogenolytic, gluconeogenetic, and lipolytic. It mobilizes energy stores and is a "hormone of energy release." Because of their opposite effects, the blood levels of both hormones must be considered in any given situation. It is convenient to think in terms of their molar ratios. The insulin-glucagon molar ratio in any given blood specimen can readily be calculated from the blood levels of the hormones, as determined by immunoassays, and their molecular weights.

Table 19–7. Insulin/glucagon molar ratios (I/G) in blood in various conditions. 1+ to 4+ indicate relative magnitude. (Courtesy of RH Unger.)

Condition	Hepatic Glucose Storage (S) or Production (P)	I/G
Glucose availability		
Large carbohydrate meal	4+ (S)	70
IV glucose	2+ (S)	25
Small meal	1+ (S)	7
Glucose need		
Overnight fast	1+ (P)	2.3
Low carbohydrate diet	2+ (P)	1.8
Starvation	4+ (P)	0.4

It has been shown that the insulin-glucagon molar ratios fluctuate markedly because the secretion of glucagon and insulin are both modified by the conditions that preceded the application of any given stimulus. Thus, for example, the insulin-glucagon molar ratio on a balanced diet is approximately 2.3. An infusion of arginine increases the secretion of both hormones and raises the ratio to 3.0. After 3 days of starvation, the ratio falls to 0.4, and an infusion of arginine in this state lowers the ratio to 0.3. Conversely, the ratio is 25 in individuals receiving a constant infusion of glucose, and ingestion of a protein meal during the infusion causes the ratio to rise to 170. The rise is due to the fact that insulin secretion rises sharply, while the usual glucagon response to a protein meal is abolished. Thus, when energy is needed during starvation, the insulin-glucagon molar ratio is low, favoring glycogen breakdown and gluconeogenesis; conversely, when the need for energy mobilization is low, the ratio is high, favoring the deposition of glycogen, protein, and fat. These relations are summarized in Table 19–7.

Extrapancreatic Glucagon & GLI

Glucagon is secreted not only by A cells of the pancreatic islets but by similar cells in the wall of the stomach and duodenum. Consequently, the plasma glucagon level does not fall to zero after pancreatectomy; indeed, it may even be elevated.

A substance that resembles glucagon is also found in the walls of the small intestine. This material cross-reacts with many but not all antiglucagon antibodies, and it has therefore been called **glucagonlike immunoreactive factor (GLI).** It is secreted in response to glucose in the intestinal lumen in rats, but its structure and physiologic role are unsettled.

OTHER ISLET CELL HORMONES

In addition to insulin and glucagon, the pancreatic islets secrete somatostatin and pancreatic polypeptide.

These substances are released from the pancreas. Pancreatic polypeptide is found in peripheral blood, and somatostatin may be involved in regulatory processes within the islets that adjust the pattern of hormones secreted in response to various stimuli.

Somatostatin

Somatostatin is a tetradecapeptide that contains a disulfide bridge (Table 26–1). It was first isolated from the hypothalamus, where it functions as the growth hormone–inhibiting hypophyseotropic hormone (see Chapter 14). It plays a role, probably as a synaptic transmitter, in the spinal cord and other parts of the nervous system (see Chapters 7 and 15), and it may be involved in the regulation of gastrointestinal function. It also inhibits the secretion of insulin, glucagon, and pancreatic polypeptide, so its function in the pancreatic islets is of considerable interest. Furthermore, patients with somatostatin-secreting pancreatic tumors develop hyperglycemia and other manifestations of diabetes that disappear when the tumor is removed. The secretion of pancreatic somatostatin is increased by several of the same stimuli that increase insulin secretion, ie, glucose and amino acids, particularly arginine and leucine. Its secretion is also increased by CCK. Somatostatin is released from the pancreas, but it has not been possible to obtain reliable measurements of the hormone in peripheral blood.

Pancreatic Polypeptide

Human pancreatic polypeptide is a linear peptide containing 36 amino acid residues. In chickens, from which the peptide was first isolated, it produces a decrease in hepatic glycogen without a change in plasma glucose and a fall in plasma glycerol and FFA. It may affect gastrointestinal secretion in mammals, but no definite function has been established. However, it can be measured by radioimmunoassay in peripheral blood, and in humans its secretion is increased by ingestion of protein, fasting, exercise, and acute hypoglycemia. Its secretion is decreased by somatostatin and intravenous glucose. Infusions of leucine, arginine, and alanine do not affect it, so the stimulatory effect of a protein meal may be mediated indirectly, possibly via a gastrointestinal hormone.

Organization of the Pancreatic Islets

The presence in the pancreatic islets of hormones that affect the secretion of other islet hormones raises the possibility that the islets function as secretory units in the regulation of nutrient homeostasis. Somatostatin inhibits the secretion of insulin, glucagon, and pancreatic polypeptide (Fig 19–18), whereas insulin inhibits the secretion of glucagon, and glucagon stimulates the secretion of insulin and somatostatin. A and D cells and pancreatic polypeptide–secreting cells are generally located around the periphery of the islets with the B cells in the center. It is possible that the islet cell hormones released into the ECF diffuse to other islet cells and influence their function, but this is difficult to prove. It has been demonstrated that there are gap

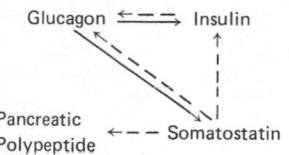

Figure 19–18. Effects of islet cell hormones on the secretion of other islet cell hormones. Solid arrows indicate stimulation; dashed arrows indicate inhibition.

junctions between secretory cells, and these could permit the passage of ions and other molecules from one cell to another, coordinating their secretory functions.

It should be noted that the postulated spread of islet cell hormones via the ECF to exert effects on other islet cells represents a form of intercellular communication via chemical messengers that is different from neural or endocrine regulation. Neurotransmitters act across a very narrow synaptic cleft, whereas hormones reach their target cells via the bloodstream. The postulated intermediate form in which chemical messengers diffuse some distance to their target cells via the ECF has been called **paracrine regulation.** It has been postulated to occur not only in the islets but also in the nervous system and various other parts of the body.

ENDOCRINE REGULATION OF CARBOHYDRATE METABOLISM

Many hormones in addition to insulin, glucagon, and somatostatin have important roles in the regulation of carbohydrate metabolism. The other functions of these hormones are considered elsewhere, but it seems wise to summarize their effects on carbohydrate metabolism in the context of the present chapter. They include epinephrine, thyroid hormones, glucocorticoids, and growth hormone. The "directional flow valves" in metabolism at which these hormones act are discussed in Chapter 17.

Epinephrine

The activation of phosphorylase in liver and muscle by epinephrine is discussed in Chapter 17. Norepinephrine has less effect. Hepatic glucose output is increased, producing hyperglycemia. In muscle, the glucose-6-phosphate formed can only be catabolized to pyruvate because of the absence of glucose-6-phosphatase. For reasons that are not entirely clear, large amounts of pyruvate are converted to lactic acid, which diffuses from the muscle into the circulation (Fig 19–19). The lactic acid is oxidized in the liver to pyruvic acid and converted to glycogen, so the response to epinephrine is an initial glycogenolysis followed by a rise in hepatic glycogen content. Lactic acid oxidation may be responsible for the calorigenic

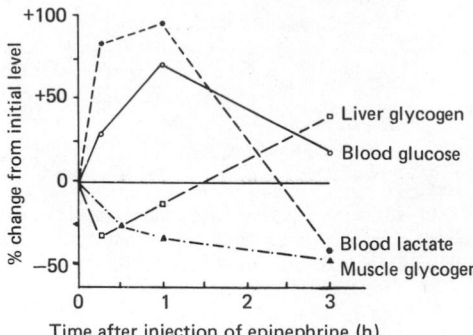

Figure 19–19. Effect of epinephrine on tissue glycogen, blood glucose, and blood lactate levels in fed rats. (After Cori GT, Russell JA in: *Physiology and Biophysics,* 20th ed. Vol 3. Ruch TC, Patton HD [editors]. Saunders, 1973.)

effect of epinephrine (see Chapter 20). Epinephrine also liberates FFA into the circulation.

Adrenal medullary tumors (pheochromocytomas) that secrete epinephrine cause hyperglycemia, glycosuria, and an elevated metabolic rate. However, the hyperglycemic effect of epinephrine is generally too transient to produce permanent diabetes, and the metabolic abnormalities disappear as soon as the tumors are removed.

Thyroid Hormones

Thyroxine and triiodothyronine make experimental diabetes worse; thyrotoxicosis aggravates clinical diabetes; and metathyroid diabetes can be produced in animals with decreased pancreatic reserve. The principal diabetogenic effect of thyroid hormones is to increase absorption of glucose from the intestine, but the hormones also cause (probably through liberation of epinephrine) some degree of hepatic glycogen depletion. Glycogen-depleted liver cells are easily damaged. When the liver is damaged, the glucose tolerance curve is diabetic because the liver takes up less of the absorbed glucose. Thyroid hormones may also accelerate the degradation of insulin. All these actions have a hyperglycemic effect and, if the pancreatic reserve is low, may lead to B cell exhaustion.

Adrenal Glucocorticoids

The 17-hydroxycorticoids secreted by the adrenal cortex (see Chapter 20) elevate the blood glucose and produce a diabetic type of glucose tolerance curve. In humans, this effect may occur only in individuals with a genetic predisposition to diabetes. Glucose tolerance is reduced in 80% of patients with Cushing's syndrome (see Chapter 20), and 20% of these patients have frank diabetes. The glucocorticoids are necessary for glucagon to exert its gluconeogenetic action during fasting. They are gluconeogenetic themselves, but their role is mainly permissive, since glucocorticoid secretion increases only after very prolonged starvation. In adrenal insufficiency, the blood glucose is normal as long as food intake is maintained, but fasting precipitates

hypoglycemia and collapse. The blood glucose–lowering effect of insulin is greatly enhanced in patients with adrenal insufficiency. In animals with experimental diabetes, adrenalectomy markedly ameliorates the diabetes.

The complex actions of the glucocorticoids on intermediary metabolism are incompletely understood. Known or suspected actions that affect carbohydrate metabolism are summarized in Table 19–8. The major diabetogenic effects are an increase in protein catabolism with increased gluconeogenesis in the liver; increased hepatic glycogenesis and ketogenesis; and a decrease in peripheral glucose utilization that may be due to inhibition of glucose phosphorylation (see below).

Growth Hormone

The diabetogenic effect of anterior pituitary extracts is due in part to the ACTH and TSH they contain, but it is also due to growth hormone. There is some species variation in the diabetogenicity of growth hormone; but human growth hormone makes clinical diabetes worse, and 25% of patients with growth hormone–secreting tumors of the anterior pituitary have diabetes. Hypophysectomy ameliorates diabetes and increases sensitivity to insulin even more than adrenalectomy, whereas growth hormone treatment decreases insulin responsiveness.

Growth hormone mobilizes free fatty acids from adipose tissue, thus favoring ketogenesis. It decreases glucose uptake into some tissues ("anti-insulin action"), increases hepatic glucose output, and may decrease tissue binding of insulin. Indeed, it has been suggested that the ketosis and decreased glucose tolerance produced by starvation are due to hypersecretion of growth hormone. Growth hormone does not stimulate insulin secretion directly, but the hyperglycemia it produces secondarily stimulates the pancreas and may eventually exhaust the B cells.

Table 19–8. Actions of glucocorticoids that affect carbohydrate metabolism. Items 1–6 represent reactions leading to an elevated blood glucose due to increased gluconeogenesis.

1. Increased protein catabolism in periphery, resulting in increased concentration of amino acids in plasma
2. Increased hepatic uptake ("trapping") of amino acids
3. Increased deamination and transamination of amino acids
4. Increased hepatic conversion of oxaloacetic acid to phosphopyruvic acid
5. Increased hepatic fructose diphosphatase activity, facilitating dephosphorylation of fructose-1,6-diphosphate
6. Increased hepatic glucose-6-phosphatase activity, releasing more glucose into the circulation
7. Decrease in glucose utilization peripherally and in the liver, possibly due to inhibition of phosphorylation
8. Increased blood lactate and pyruvate
9. Decreased hepatic lipogenesis
10. Increased plasma free fatty acid levels and increased ketone formation (when pancreatic reserve is low)
11. Increased formation of the active form of glycogen synthetase

There is evidence that growth hormone and glucocorticoids inhibit the phosphorylation of glucose rather than its entry into cells. Entry into cells is usually the rate-limiting step in glucose metabolism, but when adequate insulin is present, a decline in phosphorylation could produce decreased utilization of glucose.

HYPOGLYCEMIA & DIABETES MELLITUS IN HUMANS

Hypoglycemia

"Insulin reactions" are common in juvenile diabetics, and in many diabetics, occasional hypoglycemic episodes are the price of good diabetic control. The increase in glucose uptake of skeletal muscle independent of insulin and the increased absorption of injected insulin during exercise have been mentioned above. Diabetics taking insulin should be taught to anticipate this effect by adjusting their diet or insulin dose when they exercise.

Symptomatic hypoglycemia also occurs in nondiabetics, and a review of some of the more important causes serves to emphasize the variables affecting blood glucose homeostasis. Chronic mild hypoglycemia can cause incoordination and slurred speech, and the condition can be mistaken for drunkenness. Mental aberrations and convulsions in the absence of frank coma also occur. When the level of insulin secretion is chronically elevated by an insulin-secreting tumor (**insulinoma**) or as a result of hyperplasia of the B cells, symptoms are most common in the morning. This is because a night of fasting has depleted hepatic glycogen reserves. However, symptoms can develop at any time, and in such patients, the diagnosis may be missed. Some cases of insulinoma have been erroneously diagnosed as epilepsy or psychosis. Hypoglycemia also occurs in some patients with large malignant tumors, and some of these tumors apparently secrete an insulinlike substance. In liver disease, the glucose tolerance curve is diabetic but the fasting blood glucose level is low (Fig 19–20). In **functional hypoglycemia,** the blood glucose rise is normal after a test dose of glucose, but the subsequent fall overshoots to hypoglycemic levels, producing symptoms 3–4 hours after meals. This pattern is sometimes seen in individuals who later develop diabetes. Most patients with this syndrome are tense, conscientious people with symptoms of autonomic overactivity. It has been postulated that the overshoot of the blood glucose is due to insulin secretion stimulated by impulses in the right vagus, but cholinergic blocking agents do not routinely correct the abnormality. In some thyrotoxic patients and in patients who have had gastrectomies or other operations that speed the passage of food into the intestine, glucose absorption is abnormally rapid. The blood glucose rises to a high, early peak, but it then falls rapidly to hypoglycemic levels because the wave

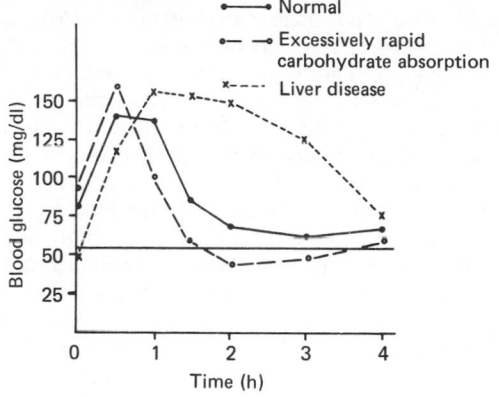

Figure 19–20. Typical glucose tolerance curves after an oral glucose load in liver disease and in conditions causing excessively rapid absorption of glucose from the intestine. Horizontal line is approximate blood glucose level at which hypoglycemic symptoms appear.

of hyperglycemia evokes a greater than normal rise in insulin secretion. Symptoms characteristically occur about 2 hours after meals.

Diabetes Mellitus

Spontaneously occurring diabetes is much more common in humans than in other species. The evidence is clear that a predisposition to diabetes is inherited, although the inheritance is complex and not, as is sometimes claimed, that of a simple autosomal recessive trait. Part of the complexity arises from the fact that there are at least 2 types of diabetes (see below), and diabetes also develops as a complication of various endocrine diseases. In any case, over 20% of the relatives of diabetic patients have abnormal glucose tolerance curves, compared to less than 1% of those without a family history of the disease. For unknown reasons, women who have the genetic predisposition to diabetes but no clinical evidence of the disease often have large babies. Many of these women subsequently develop overt diabetes.

There are 2 types of human diabetes. The type that has its onset in childhood or adolescence (**juvenile diabetes**) is often severe and is frequently complicated by ketoacidosis. The diabetes that develops late in life (**maturity-onset diabetes**) is mild, and ketoacidosis is rare. Maturity-onset diabetes occurs much more frequently in obese people, and weight reduction improves glucose tolerance. In juvenile diabetes, B cell disorders are common and the pancreatic insulin content is low, whereas in maturity-onset diabetes, the insulin content and B cell morphology are usually normal.

The cause of clinical diabetes is always insulin deficiency, but this deficiency may be relative rather than absolute. There is also a relative or absolute hyperglucagonemia (see below). Insulin levels are elevated in patients who develop diabetes as a complication of acromegaly resulting from hypersecretion of growth hormone or Cushing's syndrome due to hypersecretion of adrenal glucocorticoids. However, the circulating growth hormone and glucocorticoid levels are normal in most diabetics. In many patients with early maturity-onset diabetes, fasting insulin levels are elevated, and there is an exaggerated, prolonged increase in insulin levels following the administration of glucose. However, most patients with maturity-onset diabetes are obese, and obese nondiabetic individuals also have elevated insulin levels and an exaggerated response to glucose. Obese subjects are resistant to the action of insulin, apparently because when adipose cells are filled with fat, there is a decrease in the number of available insulin receptors on their surfaces. When obese diabetics are compared to obese subjects without diabetes and nonobese diabetics to nonobese normal subjects, the insulin levels in the diabetics are subnormal. Consequently, the presence of a circulating insulin antagonist seems unlikely, at least as a primary pathogenic abnormality. The insulin levels in juvenile diabetes are usually low. The cause of diabetes in most patients who do not have other complicating endocrine diseases would therefore appear to be a defect in the insulin-secreting mechanism. There is some evidence that especially in juvenile diabetes, the defect is caused by a virus in genetically predisposed individuals. The insulin response to isoproterenol, secretin, and glucagon is normal in early maturity-onset diabetes; only the glucose response is abnormal. This indicates that the receptor for glucose is separate from the receptors for the other agents.

The dose of insulin required to control the diabetes varies from patient to patient and from time to time in the same patient. As discussed in previous sections of this chapter, the factors affecting insulin requirements are those which influence glucose tolerance. Thus, insulin requirements rise when patients gain weight, when they secrete or receive increased amounts of glucocorticoids and other hormones that are diabetogenic, during pregnancy, and in the presence of infection and fever. They fall when patients lose weight and during exercise.

Relation of Glucagon to Diabetes

The relation of glucagon to diabetes in experimental animals and the evidence for secretion of glucagon in pancreatectomized as well as alloxan-treated animals have been discussed above. Somatostatin also lowers plasma glucose in diabetic humans, but the glucose does not stay down. In addition, there is an increase in blood amino acids and ketones. Thus, insulin deficiency in the absence of hyperglucagonemia still causes hyperglycemia and ketosis. However, at any given blood glucose level, glucagon levels are higher in diabetics than they are in nondiabetics. Furthermore, glucose fails to suppress glucagon secretion in diabetics, whereas protein has its normal stimulating effect. This is true even in the presence of large amounts of insulin, so it cannot be explained as being due to insulin deficiency. Thus, there is a relative hyperglucagonemia in diabetes that contributes to the hyperglycemia, and it appears that at least in some diabetics, there is a defect of both the insulin- and the glucagon-secreting mechanisms.

The Adrenal Medulla & Adrenal Cortex | 20

There are 2 endocrine organs in the adrenal gland, one surrounding the other. The inner **adrenal medulla** (Fig 20–1) secretes the catecholamines **epinephrine** and **norepinephrine;** the outer **adrenal cortex** secretes steroid hormones.

The adrenal medulla is in effect a sympathetic ganglion in which the postganglionic neurons have lost their axons and become secretory cells. The cells secrete when stimulated by the preganglionic nerve fibers that reach the gland via the splanchnic nerves. Adrenal medullary hormones are not essential for life, but they help to prepare the individual to deal with emergencies.

The adrenal cortex secretes **glucocorticoids,** steroids with widespread effects on the metabolism of carbohydrate and protein; a **mineralocorticoid** essential to the maintenance of sodium balance and ECF volume; and **sex hormones** that exert minor effects on reproductive function. Unless mineralocorticoid and glucocorticoid replacement therapy is administered postoperatively, adrenalectomy is followed by collapse and death. Adrenocortical secretion is controlled primarily by ACTH from the anterior pituitary, but mineralocorticoid secretion is also subject to independent control by circulating factors, of which the most important is angiotensin II, a polypeptide formed in the bloodstream. The formation of angiotensin is in turn dependent on renin, which is secreted by the kidney.

ADRENAL MORPHOLOGY

The adrenal medulla is made up of interlacing cords of densely innervated granule-containing cells that abut on venous sinuses. Two cell types can be distinguished morphologically: an epinephrine-secreting type that has larger, less dense granules; and a norepinephrine-secreting type in which the smaller, very dense granules fail to fill the vesicles in which they are contained (Fig 20–2). **Paraganglia,** small groups of cells resembling those in the adrenal medulla, are found near the thoracic and abdominal sympathetic ganglia (Fig 20–1).

In adult mammals, the adrenal cortex is divided into 3 zones of variable distinctness (Fig 20–3). The outer **zona glomerulosa** is made up of whorls of cells that are continuous with the columns of cells which form the **zona fasciculata.** These columns are separated by venous sinuses. The inner portion of the zona fasciculata merges into the **zona reticularis,** where the cell columns become interlaced in a network. The cells contain abundant lipid, especially in the outer portion of the zona fasciculata. All 3 cortical zones secrete corticosterone (see below), but the enzymatic mechanism for aldosterone biosynthesis is limited to the zona glomerulosa, while the enzymatic mechanism for forming cortisol and sex hormones is found in the 2 inner zones.

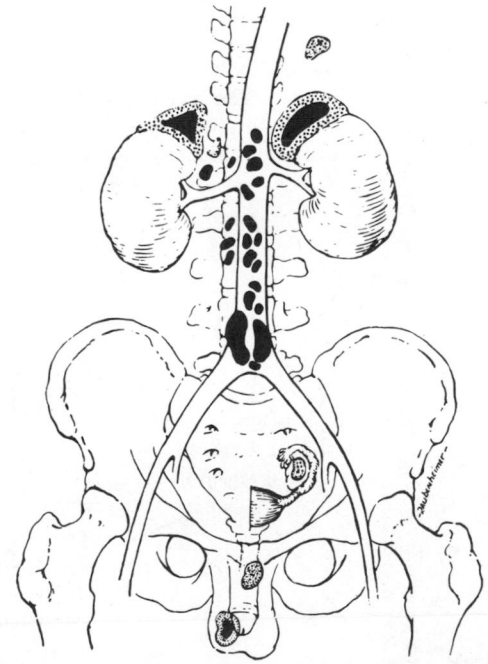

Figure 20–1. Human adrenal glands. Adrenocortical tissue is stippled; adrenal medullary tissue is black. Note location of adrenals at superior pole of each kidney. Also shown are extra-adrenal sites at which cortical and medullary tissue is sometimes found. (Reproduced, with permission, from Forsham PH: *Textbook of Endocrinology,* 4th ed. Williams RH [editor]. Saunders, 1968.)

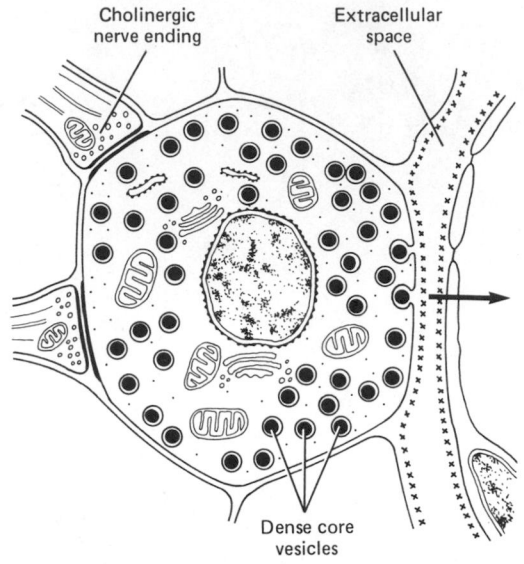

Figure 20–2. Norepinephrine-secreting adrenal medullary cell. The granules are released by exocytosis and the granule contents enter the bloodstream (arrow). (Modified from Poirier J, Dumas JLR: *Review of Medical Histology*. Saunders, 1977.)

Arterial blood reaches the adrenal from many small branches of the phrenic and renal arteries and the aorta. From a plexus in the capsule, blood flows to the sinusoids of the medulla. The medulla is also supplied by a few arterioles that pass directly to it from the capsule. In most species, including humans, there is a single large adrenal vein. The blood flow through the adrenal is large, as it is in most endocrine glands.

During fetal life, the human adrenal is large and under pituitary control, but the 3 zones of the permanent cortex represent only 20% of the gland. The remaining 80% is the large **fetal adrenal cortex,** which undergoes rapid degeneration at the time of birth. A major function of this fetal adrenal is secretion of sulfate conjugates of androgens that are converted in the placenta to androgens and estrogens which enter the maternal circulation. There is no structure comparable to the fetal adrenal in laboratory animals. In the mouse, cat, rabbit, and female hamster, there is a layer of cortical cells called the **X zone** between the zona reticularis and the medulla. This zone is maintained by pituitary gonadotropins, and it degenerates when androgen secretion increases during puberty in the male and during the first pregnancy in the female.

An important function of the zona glomerulosa, in addition to aldosterone biosynthesis, is the formation of new cortical cells. Like other tissues of neural origin, the adrenal medulla does not regenerate; but when the inner 2 zones of the cortex are removed, a new zona fasciculata and zona reticularis regenerate from glomerular cells attached to the capsule. Small capsular remnants will regrow large pieces of adrenocortical tissue. Immediately after hypophysectomy, the zona fasciculata and zona reticularis begin to atrophy, whereas the zona glomerulosa is unchanged (Fig 20–3), because of the action of the renin-angiotensin system on this zone. However, in long-standing hypopituitarism, degenerative changes appear in the zona glomerulosa. In hypopituitarism, the

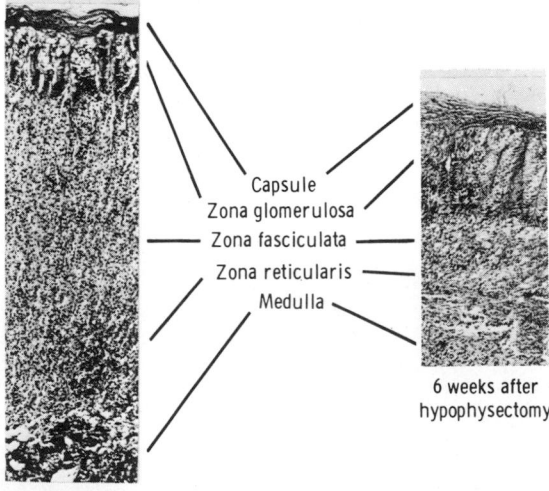

Figure 20–3. Effect of hypophysectomy on the morphology of the adrenal cortex of the dog. Note that the atrophy does not involve the zona glomerulosa. The morphology of the human adrenal is similar.

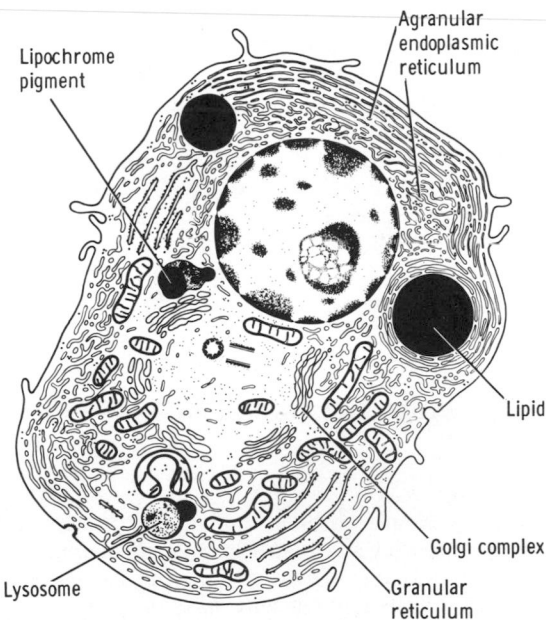

Figure 20–4. Diagrammatic representation of the cytologic features of steroid-secreting cells. Note the abundant agranular endoplasmic reticulum, the pleomorphic mitochondria, and the lipid droplets. (Reproduced, with permission, from Fawcett DW, Long JA, Jones AL: The ultrastructure of endocrine glands. Recent Prog Horm Res 25:315, 1969.)

ability to conserve Na^+ is usually normal; but in patients who have had the disease for a long time, aldosterone deficiency may develop. Injections of ACTH and stimuli that cause endogenous ACTH secretion produce hypertrophy of the zona fasciculata and zona reticularis but do not increase the size of the zona glomerulosa.

The cells of the adrenal cortex contain large amounts of smooth endoplasmic reticulum, which seems to be involved in the steroid-forming process. Other steps in steroid biosynthesis occur in the mitochondria. The structure of steroid-secreting cells is very similar throughout the body. The typical features of such cells are shown in Fig 20–4.

ADRENAL MEDULLA

STRUCTURE & FUNCTION OF MEDULLARY HORMONES

Biosynthesis, Metabolism, & Excretion

Norepinephrine and epinephrine are both secreted by the adrenal medulla. Cats and some other species secrete mainly norepinephrine, but in dogs and humans 80% of the catecholamine output in the adrenal vein is epinephrine. Norepinephrine also enters the circulation from adrenergic nerve endings.

The details of the biosynthesis and catabolism of norepinephrine and epinephrine are described in Chapter 13 and summarized in Figs 13–3 and 13–5. Norepinephrine is formed by hydroxylation and decarboxylation of tyrosine, and epinephrine by the methylation of norepinephrine. Phenylethanolamine-N-methyltransferase (PNMT), the enzyme that catalyzes the formation of epinephrine from norepinephrine, is found in appreciable quantities only in the brain and the adrenal medulla. In the medulla, it is induced by glucocorticoids in the large amounts found in the blood draining from the cortex to the medulla. After hypophysectomy, epinephrine synthesis is decreased.

In recumbent humans, the normal plasma norepinephrine level is about 300 pg/ml (1.8 nmol/L). There is a 50–100% increase upon standing. Plasma norepinephrine is generally unchanged after adrenalectomy, but the epinephrine level, which is normally about 30 pg/ml (0.16 nmol/L), falls to essentially zero. The epinephrine found in tissues other than the adrenal medulla and the brain is for the most part absorbed from the bloodstream rather than synthesized in situ. The plasma dopamine level is about 200 pg/ml (1.3 nmol/L), and there are appreciable quantities of dopamine in the urine. There is evidence that about half the plasma dopamine comes from the adrenal medulla, whereas the remaining half presumably comes from the sympathetic ganglia or other components of the autonomic nervous system.

In the medulla, the amines are stored in granules bound to ATP and protein. Their secretion is initiated by acetylcholine released from the preganglionic neurons that innervate the secretory cells. The acetylcholine increases the permeability of the cells, and the Ca^{2+} that enters the cells from the ECF triggers exocytosis (see Chapter 1). In this fashion, the catecholamines, ATP, and proteins in the granules are all extruded from the cell.

The catecholamines have a very short half-life in the circulation. For the most part, they are methoxylated, then oxidized to 3-methoxy-4-hydroxymandelic acid (vanillylmandelic acid, VMA). About 50% of the secreted catecholamines appear in the urine as free or conjugated metanephrine and normetanephrine, and 35% as VMA. Only small amounts of free norepinephrine and epinephrine are excreted. In normal humans, about 30 μg of norepinephrine, 6 μg of epinephrine, and 700 μg of VMA are excreted per day.

Effects of Epinephrine & Norepinephrine

In addition to mimicking the effects of adrenergic nervous discharge (Table 13–1), norepinephrine and epinephrine stimulate the nervous system and exert metabolic effects that include glycogenolysis in liver and skeletal muscle, mobilization of free fatty acids, and stimulation of the metabolic rate (Table 20–1).

Norepinephrine and epinephrine both increase the force and rate of contraction of the isolated heart. They also increase myocardial excitability, causing extrasystoles and, occasionally, more serious cardiac

Table 20–1. Comparison of the effects of epinephrine and norepinephrine on some physiologic parameters. Where pertinent, the activity of the more active compound has been indicated as ++++ and the activity of the other is compared to it on a scale of + to ++++.

Norepinephrine	Parameter	Epinephrine
Decreased (due to reflex bradycardia)	Cardiac output	Increased
Increased	Peripheral resistance	Decreased
++++	Blood pressure elevation	++
++++	Free fatty acid release	+++
++++	Stimulation of CNS	++++
+++	Increased heat production	++++
+	Glycogenolysis	++++

arrhythmias. Norepinephrine produces vasoconstriction in most if not all organs, but epinephrine dilates the blood vessels in skeletal muscle and the liver. This overbalances the vasoconstriction it produces elsewhere, and the total peripheral resistance drops. When norepinephrine is infused slowly in normal animals or humans, the systolic and diastolic blood pressures rise. The hypertension stimulates the carotid and aortic baroreceptors, producing reflex bradycardia that overrides the direct cardioacceleratory effect of norepinephrine. Consequently, cardiac output per minute falls. Epinephrine causes a widening of the pulse pressure; but, because baroreceptor stimulation is insufficient to obscure the direct effect of the hormone on the heart, cardiac rate and output increase. These changes are summarized in Fig 20–5.

The increased alertness that is produced by catecholamines is described in Chapter 11. Epinephrine and norepinephrine are equally potent in this regard, although in humans epinephrine usually evokes more anxiety and fear.

The one effect of epinephrine that is shared to only a small extent by norepinephrine, at least in some species, is its glycogenolytic action. Epinephrine activates phosphorylase in liver and skeletal muscle (see Chapter 17), and the blood glucose rises. The blood lactic acid also rises. The liver glycogen first falls and then rises as the lactic acid is oxidized (Fig 19–19). Plasma K^+ rises coincident with the glycogenolysis.

Norepinephrine and epinephrine are almost equally potent in their free fatty acid–mobilizing activity (see Chapter 17) and their calorigenic action. They produce a prompt rise in the metabolic rate which is independent of the liver and a smaller, delayed rise which is abolished by hepatectomy and coincides with the rise in blood lactic acid. The calorigenic action does not occur in the absence of the thyroid and the adrenal cortex. The cause of the initial rise in metabolic rate is not clearly understood. It may be due to cutaneous vasoconstriction, which decreases heat loss and leads to a rise in body temperature, or to increased muscular activity, or to both. The second rise is probably due to oxidation of lactic acid in the liver.

On the basis of their differential sensitivity to drugs, the effects of epinephrine and norepinephrine have been divided into 2 groups. Those in one group are brought about by catecholamines interacting with α receptors in the effector organs, whereas those in the other group are brought about by catecholamines interacting with β receptors (see Chapter 13 and Table 13–1). Drugs that are α blockers inhibit actions such as the pressor effects of the catecholamines. Drugs that are β blockers generally inhibit actions such as the chronotropic and inotropic effects of catecholamines on the heart and their glycogenolytic and free fatty acid–mobilizing effects. β-Mediated effects are due to stimulation of adenylate cyclase, with resultant increased formation of cyclic AMP (see Chapter 17).

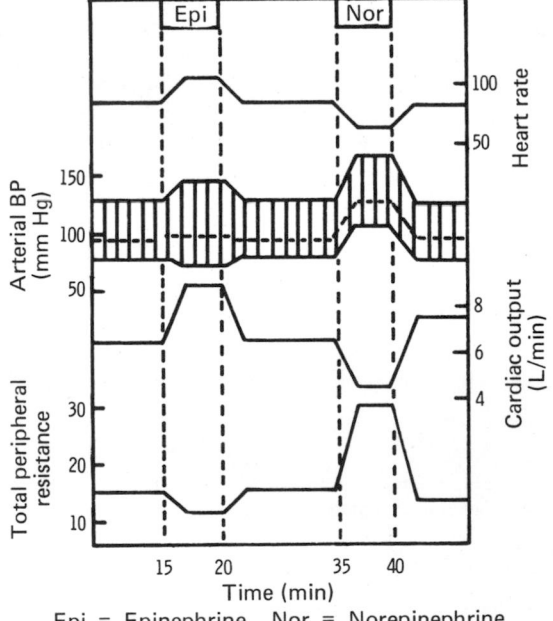

Epi = Epinephrine Nor = Norepinephrine

Figure 20–5. Circulatory changes produced in humans by the slow intravenous infusion of epinephrine and norepinephrine. (Modified and reproduced, with permission, from Barcroft H, Swan HJC: *Sympathetic Control of Human Blood Vessels.* Arnold, 1953.)

REGULATION OF ADRENAL MEDULLARY SECRETION

Neural Control

Certain drugs act directly on the adrenal medulla, but physiologic stimuli affect medullary secretion through the nervous system. Catecholamine secretion is low in basal states, but the secretion of epinephrine and, to a lesser extent, that of norepinephrine is reduced even further during sleep.

There is evidence that adrenal medullary secretion is increased when the "cholinergic sympathetic vasodilator" system discharges at the start of exercise, the increased epinephrine secretion reinforcing the vasodilatation produced by sympathetic vasodilator fibers to skeletal muscle (see Chapter 31).

Increased adrenal medullary secretion is part of the diffuse adrenergic discharge provoked in emergency situations, which Cannon called the "emergency function of the sympathoadrenal system." The ways in which this discharge prepares the individual for flight or fight are described in Chapter 13. It is worth mentioning, however, that when adrenal medullary hormones are injected into control animals in the amounts secreted in response to splanchnic nerve stimulation, they exert effects on the musculature of the skin, kidneys, and spleen that are only 10–20% as great as the effects produced by comparable stimulation of the sympathetic innervation of these structures. Thus, the action of secreted catecholamines in augmenting the effects of adrenergic nerve discharges on the vascular system is relatively slight.

The metabolic effects of circulating catecholamines are probably more important, especially in certain situations. The calorigenic action of catecholamines in animals exposed to cold is an example. Animals with denervated adrenal glands shiver sooner and more vigorously than normal controls when exposed to cold. The glycogenolysis produced by epinephrine in hypoglycemic animals is another example. Hypoglycemia is a potent stimulus to catecholamine secretion, and insulin tolerance appears to be reduced when adrenal medullary secretion is blocked.

Selective Secretion

When adrenal medullary secretion is increased, the ratio of epinephrine to norepinephrine in the adrenal effluent is generally unchanged or elevated. However, asphyxia and hypoxia increase the ratio of norepinephrine to epinephrine. The fact that the output of norepinephrine can be increased selectively has unfortunately led to the teleologic speculation that the adrenal medulla secretes epinephrine or norepinephrine depending upon which hormone best equips the animal to meet the emergency it faces. The fallacy of such speculation is illustrated by the response to hemorrhage, in which the predominant catecholamine secreted is not norepinephrine but epinephrine, which lowers the peripheral resistance. Norepinephrine secretion is increased by emotional stresses with which the individual is familiar, whereas epinephrine secretion rises in situations in which the individual does not know what to expect.

ADRENAL CORTEX

STRUCTURE & BIOSYNTHESIS OF ADRENOCORTICAL HORMONES

Classification & Structure

The hormones of the adrenal cortex are derivatives of cholesterol. Like cholesterol, bile acids, vitamin D, and ovarian and testicular steroids, they contain the **cyclopentanoperhydrophenanthrene nucleus** (Fig 20–6). The adrenocortical steroids are of 2 structural types (Fig 20–7): those that have a 2-carbon side chain attached at position 17 of the D ring and contain 21 carbon atoms ("C 21 steroids"), and those that have a keto or hydroxyl group at position 17 and contain 19 carbon atoms ("C 19 steroids"). Most of the C 19 steroids have a keto group at position 17 and are therefore called **17-ketosteroids.** The C 21 steroids that have a hydroxyl group at the 17 position in addi-

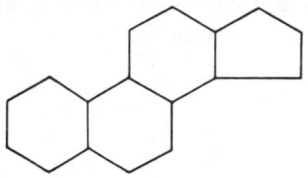

Figure 20–6. The cyclopentanoperhydrophenanthrene nucleus.

tion to the side chain are often called 17-hydroxycorticoids or 17-hydroxycorticosteroids.

The C 19 steroids have androgenic activity. The C 21 steroids are classified, using Selye's terminology, as mineralocorticoids or glucocorticoids. All secreted C 21 steroids have both mineralocorticoid and glucocorticoid activity; **mineralocorticoids** are those in which effects on Na^+ and K^+ excretion predominate, and **glucocorticoids** those in which effects on glucose and protein metabolism predominate.

Steroid Nomenclature & Isomerism

For the sake of simplicity, the steroid names used here and in Chapter 23 are the most commonly used trivial names. A few common synonyms are shown in Table 20–2. The details of steroid nomenclature and

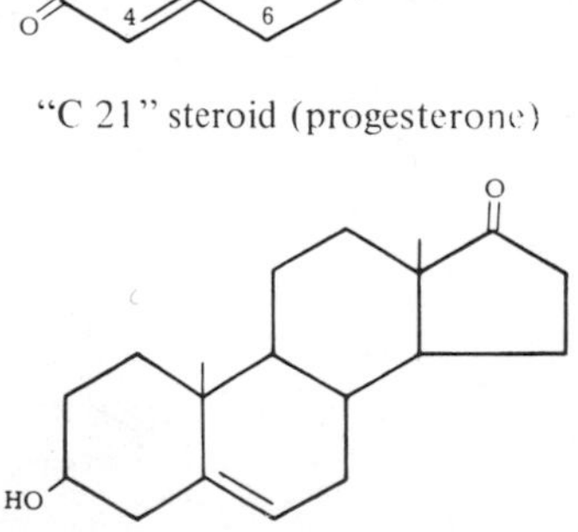

"C 21" steroid (progesterone)

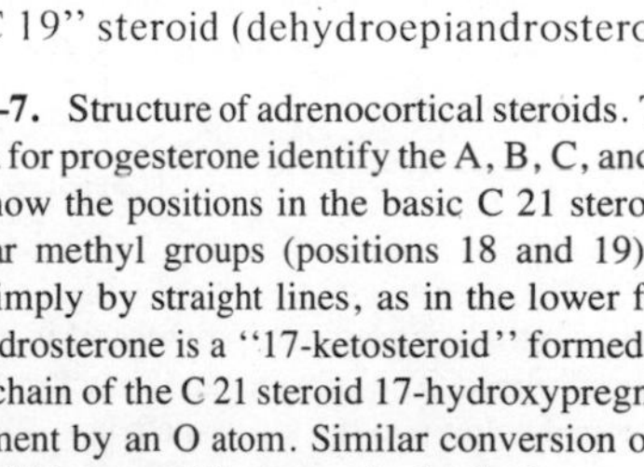

"C 19" steroid (dehydroepiandrosterone)

Figure 20–7. Structure of adrenocortical steroids. The letters in the formula for progesterone identify the A, B, C, and D rings; the numbers show the positions in the basic C 21 steroid structure. The angular methyl groups (positions 18 and 19) are usually indicated simply by straight lines, as in the lower formula. Dehydroepiandrosterone is a "17-ketosteroid" formed by cleavage of the side chain of the C 21 steroid 17-hydroxypregnenolone and its replacement by an O atom. Similar conversion of other C 21 steroids to 17-ketosteroids occurs in the body.

Table 20–2. Principal adrenocortical hormones in adult humans.

Name	Synonyms	Average Plasma Concentration (Free and Bound) (μg/dl)	Average Amount Secreted (mg/24 h)
Cortisol	Compound F, hydrocortisone	13.9	20
Corticosterone	Compound B	0.4	3
Aldosterone		0.006	0.15
Deoxycorticosterone	DOC	0.006	0.20
Dehydroepiandrosterone	DEA, DHEA	45.0	15 (males) 10 (females)

*All plasma concentration values except DEA are morning values after overnight recumbency. (Data partly from Oddie CJ, Coghlan JP, Scoggins BA: Plasma desoxycorticosterone levels in man with simultaneous measurement of aldosterone, corticosterone, cortisol, and 11-deoxycortisol. J Clin Endocrinol Metab 34:1039, 1972.)

isomerism can be found in the texts listed in the references, but it is pertinent to mention that the Greek letter Δ indicates a double bond and that the groups which lie above the plane of each of the steroid rings are indicated by the Greek letter β and a solid line (–OH), whereas those which lie below are indicated by α and a dotted line (---OH). Thus, the C 21 steroids secreted by the adrenal have a Δ^4-3-keto configuration in the A ring. In most naturally occurring adrenal steroids, 17-hydroxy groups are in the α configuration, while 3-, 11-, and 21-hydroxy groups are in the β configuration. The 18-aldehyde configuration on naturally occurring aldosterone is the D-form. L-Aldosterone is physiologically inactive.

Secreted Steroids

Innumerable steroids have been isolated from adrenal tissue, but the only steroids normally secreted in physiologically significant amounts are the mineralocorticoid **aldosterone,** the glucocorticoids **cortisol** and **corticosterone,** and the androgen **dehydroepiandrosterone.** The structures of these steroids are shown in Figs 20–8 and 20–9. **Deoxycorticosterone** is a mineralocorticoid that is normally secreted in about the same amount as aldosterone (Table 20–2) but has only 3% of the mineralocorticoid activity of aldosterone. Its effect on mineral metabolism is usually negligible, but in diseases in which its secretion is increased, its ef-

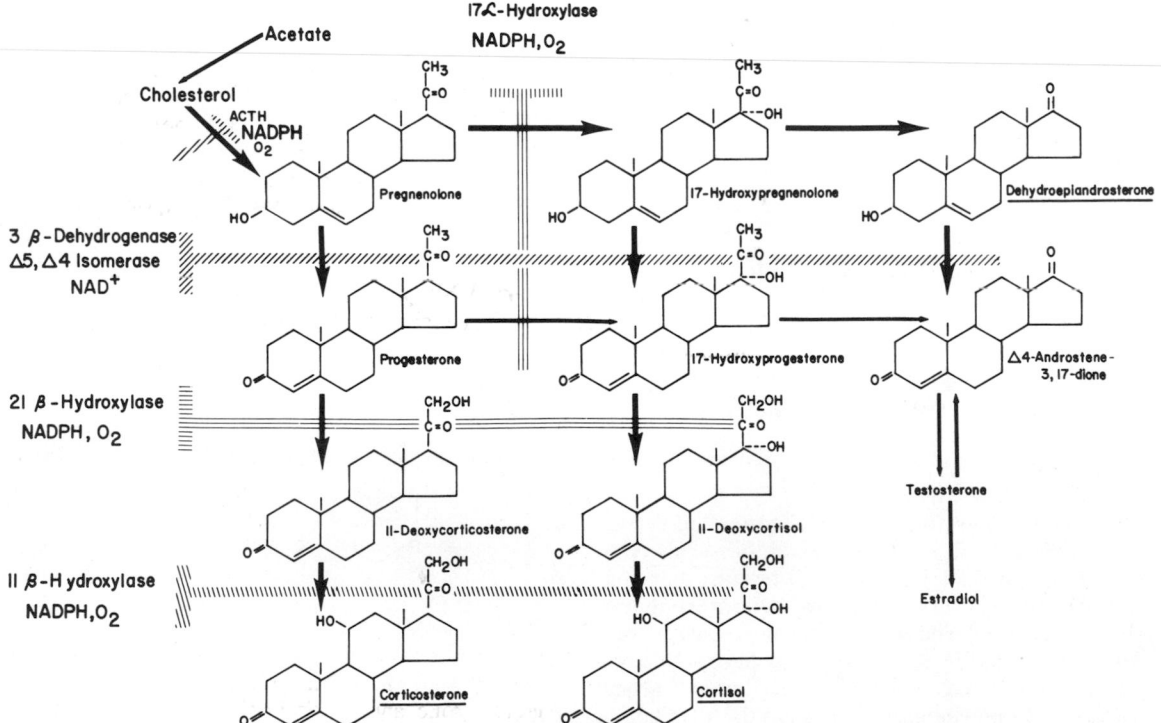

Figure 20–8. Outline of hormone biosynthesis in the zona fasciculata and zona reticularis of the adrenal cortex. The major secretory products are underlined. The enzymes and cofactors for the reactions progressing down each column are shown on the left and from the first to the second column at the top of the chart. When a particular enzyme is deficient, hormone production is blocked at the points indicated by the shaded bars.

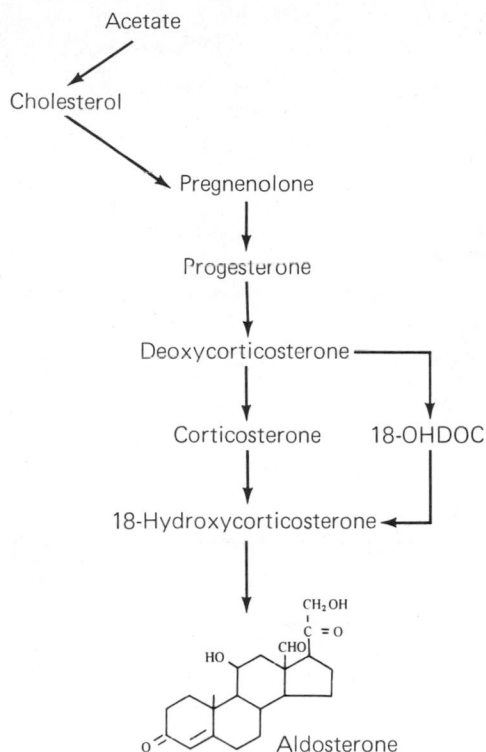

Figure 20–9. Outline of hormone synthesis in the zona glomerulosa. The steps from acetate to corticosterone are the same as in the zona fasciculata and reticularis. However, the zona glomerulosa contains the enzymes for converting corticosterone to aldosterone, whereas it lacks 17α-hydroxylase activity. 18-OHDOC, 18-hydroxydeoxycorticosterone.

Table 20–3. Relative potencies of corticosteroids compared to cortisol. Values are approximations based on liver glycogen deposition or anti-inflammatory assays for glucocorticoid activity, and effect on urinary Na$^+$/K$^+$ or maintenance of adrenalectomized animals for mineralocorticoid activity. The last 3 steroids listed are synthetic compounds that do not occur naturally. (Data from various sources.)

	Glucocorticoid Activity	Mineralocorticoid Activity
Cortisol	1.0	1.0
Corticosterone	0.3	15
Aldosterone	0.3	3000
Deoxycorticosterone	0.2	100
Cortisone	0.7	1.0
Prednisolone	4	0.8
9α-Fluorocortisol	10	125
Dexamethasone	25	~0

almost exclusively; dogs secrete approximately equal amounts of the 2 glucocorticoids; and cats, sheep, monkeys, and humans secrete predominantly cortisol. In humans, the ratio of secreted cortisol/corticosterone is approximately 7.

Synthetic Steroids

The glucocorticoids are among the increasing number of naturally occurring substances that chemists have been able to improve upon. A number of synthetic steroids are now available that have many times the activity of cortisol. The relative glucocorticoid and mineralocorticoid potencies of the natural steroids are compared to those of the synthetic steroids 9α-fluorocortisol, prednisolone, and dexamethasone in Table 20–3. The potency of dexamethasone is due to its high affinity for glucocorticoid receptors and its long half-life (see below). Prednisolone also has a long half-life.

Steroid Biosynthesis

The major paths by which the naturally occurring adrenocortical hormones are synthesized in the body are summarized in Figs 20–8 and 20–9. The major precursor of cortisol is 17α-hydroxypregnenolone, and the major precursor of corticosterone and aldosterone is pregnenolone. The secreted steroids are synthesized by formation of the Δ^4-3-keto configuration in the A ring and then hydroxylation in the 21 and, finally, the 11 position. Some of these reactions occur in the smooth endoplasmic reticulum and others in mitochondria (Fig 20–10). Aldosterone is formed by replacement of the angular methyl group in position 18 of corticosterone with an aldehyde group. Androgens are formed by side chain cleavage to form dehydroepiandrosterone and its derivatives, and estrogens are formed from androgens.

Action of ACTH

ACTH acts via adenylate cyclase and a protein kinase to increase the amount of free cholesterol that

fects can be appreciable. Other steroids that are secreted in small amounts include 18-hydroxycorticosterone, pregnenolone, progesterone, some of the derivatives of dehydroepiandrosterone, and testosterone. The adrenals may also secrete small amounts of estrogen, although most of the estrogens that are not formed in the ovaries are produced in the circulation from adrenal androstenedione. Dehydroepiandrosterone is secreted conjugated with sulfate, although most if not all of the other steroids are secreted in the free, unconjugated form.

The secretion rate for individual steroids can be determined by injecting a very small dose of isotopically labeled steroid and determining the degree to which the radioactive steroid excreted in the urine is diluted by unlabeled secreted hormone. This technic is used to measure the output of many different hormones.

Species Differences

In all species from amphibia to humans, the major C 21 steroid hormones secreted by adrenocortical tissue appear to be aldosterone, cortisol, and corticosterone, although the ratio of cortisol to corticosterone varies. Birds, mice, and rats secrete corticosterone

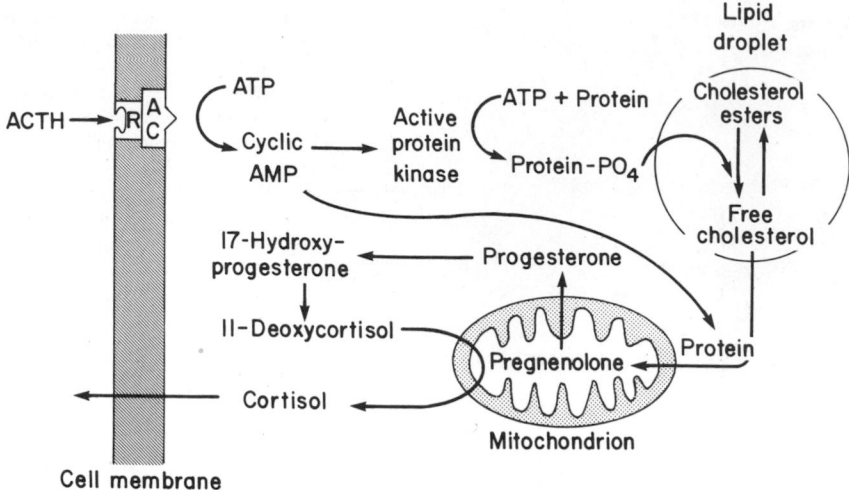

Figure 20–10. Mechanism of action of ACTH on cortisol-secreting cells of the adrenal cortex. AC, adenylate cyclase; R, receptor.

enters mitochondria and is converted to pregnenolone. The reactions involved are summarized in Fig 20–10. The cyclic AMP also acts in some way to increase the synthesis of, or possibly to phosphorylate, a protein that increases the conversion of cholesterol to pregnenolone. ACTH acts in a similar fashion on the cells in the zona glomerulosa that secrete aldosterone, but angiotensin II and K^+ stimulate aldosterone secretion without affecting cyclic AMP.

Enzyme Deficiencies

The consequences of inhibiting any of the enzyme systems involved in steroid biosynthesis can be predicted from Figs 20–8 and 20–9. Single enzyme defects can occur as congenital "inborn errors of metabolism" or can be produced by drugs. Congenital blockade of the formation of pregnenolone causes the syndrome of **congenital adrenal hyperplasia.** The hyperplasia is due to increased ACTH secretion. The disease is severe, with diffuse adrenal insufficiency and death soon after birth. Androgen formation is blocked, and female genitalia develop regardless of genetic sex (see Chapter 23). Congenital 3β-dehydrogenase, 21β-hydroxylase, and 11β-hydroxylase deficiency all cause congenital adrenal hyperplasia associated with **virilization.** In this condition, glucocorticoid secretion is deficient, and ACTH secretion is consequently stimulated. The steroid intermediates that pile up behind the block are converted via the remaining unblocked pathways to androgens. In 3β-dehydrogenase deficiency, the glucocorticoid and mineralocorticoid deficiency is usually fatal. 21β-Hydroxylase deficiency is usually incomplete, so that enough glucocorticoids and mineralocorticoids are formed to sustain life; but 30% of the patients with this syndrome show abnormal sodium loss (**salt-losing form** of congenital virilizing adrenal hyperplasia). The sodium loss is due both to the mineralocorticoid deficiency and to the aldosterone-antagonizing effect of

some of the steroids being secreted in excess amounts. In 11β-hydroxylase deficiency, there is excess secretion of 11-deoxycortisol and deoxycorticosterone; since the latter is an active mineralocorticoid, salt and water retention and hypertension result (**hypertensive form** of congenital virilizing adrenal hyperplasia). Glucocorticoid treatment is indicated in all of these forms of the syndrome because it repairs the glucocorticoid deficit and inhibits ACTH secretion (see below), thus preventing the abnormal secretion of androgens and other steroids.

17α-Hydroxylase deficiency is a rare condition that is apparently congenital in origin. Patients with this disorder secrete large amounts of corticosterone but no cortisol and no androgens or estrogens, since 17α-hydroxylation is a necessary step in the biosynthesis of these sex hormones (see Chapter 23).

Enzyme Inhibition With Drugs

Metyrapone (methopyrapone, SU-4885, Metopirone) inhibits adrenal 11β-hydroxylase when administered in proper doses. It is used clinically to test pituitary reserve by producing a transient cortisol deficiency. The deficiency stimulates ACTH secretion, and the resultant increase in 11-deoxycortisol secretion is proportionate to the ability of the pituitary to respond. **Amphenone** and the *o,p'* isomer of DDD (mitotane, Lysodren) block the secretion of all steroids. The latter compound is a derivative of DDT. Amphenone causes adrenocortical hypertrophy, but **o,p'DDD** produces necrosis of cortical cells and is of value in the treatment of adrenocortical cancer. Other drugs that inhibit 17α-hydroxylase and other specific adrenocortical enzyme systems have been developed.

Adrenal Cholesterol & Ascorbic Acid

The adrenal cortex contains large amounts of cholesterol and ascorbic acid, and the content of both substances falls transiently when ACTH is injected.

Adrenal ascorbic acid and cholesterol depletion have both been used as indicators of increased ACTH secretion in animals. The cholesterol in the adrenal is the store from which steroids are synthesized, but the function of the ascorbic acid in the adrenal is not known.

TRANSPORT, METABOLISM, & EXCRETION OF ADRENOCORTICAL HORMONES

Glucocorticoid Binding

Cortisol is bound in the circulation to an α globulin called **transcortin** or **corticosteroid-binding globulin (CBG)**. There is also a minor degree of binding to albumin. Corticosterone is similarly bound, but to a lesser degree. The half-life of cortisol in the circulation is therefore longer (about 60–90 minutes) than that of corticosterone (50 minutes). Bound steroids appear to be physiologically inactive. Because of protein binding, there is relatively little free cortisol and corticosterone in the urine.

The equilibrium between cortisol and its binding protein and the implications of binding in terms of tissue supplies and ACTH secretion are summarized in Fig 20–11. The bound cortisol probably functions as a circulating reservoir of hormone that keeps a supply of free cortisol available to the tissues. The relationship is similar to that of thyroxine and its binding protein (Fig 18–7). The usual methods for determining unconjugated "free 17-hydroxycorticoids" in the plasma measure both unbound and bound cortisol. At normal levels of total plasma cortisol (14 μg/dl, or 386 nmol/L), there is very little free cortisol in the plasma, but the binding sites on CBG become saturated when the total plasma cortisol exceeds 20 μg/dl. At higher

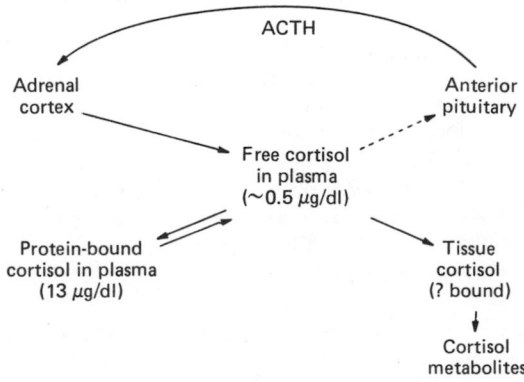

Figure 20–11. The interrelationships of free and bound cortisol. The dashed arrow indicates that cortisol inhibits ACTH secretion. The value for free cortisol is an approximation; in most studies, it is calculated by subtracting the protein-bound cortisol from the total plasma cortisol. Some authors report lower or higher free cortisol values.

plasma levels, there is some increased binding to albumin, but the main increase is in the unbound fraction.

CBG is synthesized in the liver, and its production is increased by estrogen. CBG levels are elevated during pregnancy and depressed in cirrhosis, nephrosis, and multiple myeloma. When the CBG level rises, more cortisol is bound, and initially, there is a drop in the free cortisol level. This stimulates ACTH secretion, and more cortisol is secreted until a new equilibrium is reached at which the free cortisol level returns to normal. The bound cortisol level remains elevated, but ACTH secretion returns to normal. Changes in the opposite direction occur when the CBG level falls. This explains why pregnant women have high total plasma 17-hydroxycorticoid levels without symptoms of glucocorticoid excess; conversely, it also explains why some patients with nephrosis have low plasma 17-hydroxycorticoids without adrenal insufficiency.

Metabolism & Excretion of Glucocorticoids

Cortisol is metabolized in the liver, which is the principal site of glucocorticoid catabolism. Most of the cortisol is reduced to dihydrocortisol and then to tetrahydrocortisol, which is conjugated to glucuronic acid (Fig 20–12). The glucuronyl transferase system responsible for this conversion also catalyzes the formation of the glucuronides of bilirubin (see Chapter 26) and a number of hormones and drugs. There is competitive inhibition between these substrates for the enzyme system.

Some of the cortisol in the liver is converted to cortisone. It should be emphasized that cortisone and other steroids with an 11-keto group are metabolites of the secreted glucocorticoids. Cortisone is an active glucocorticoid and is well known because of its extensive use in medicine, but it is not secreted in appreciable quantities by the adrenal glands. Little if any of the cortisone formed in the liver enters the circulation because it is promptly reduced and conjugated to form tetrahydrocortisone glucuronide. The tetrahydroglucuronide derivatives ("conjugates") of cortisol and corticosterone are freely soluble. They enter the circulation, where they do not become bound to protein. They are rapidly excreted in the urine, in part by tubular secretion.

About 10% of the secreted cortisol is converted in the liver to the 17-ketosteroid derivatives of cortisol and cortisone. The ketosteroids are conjugated for the most part to sulfate and then excreted in the urine. Other metabolites, including 20-hydroxy derivatives, are formed. There is an enterohepatic circulation of glucocorticoids, and about 15% of the secreted cortisol is excreted in the stool. The distribution of cortisol and its derivatives in the plasma and urine is summarized in Table 20–4. The metabolism of corticosterone is similar to that of cortisol except that it does not form a 17-ketosteroid derivative.

Variations in the Rate of Hepatic Metabolism

The rate of hepatic inactivation of glucocorticoids

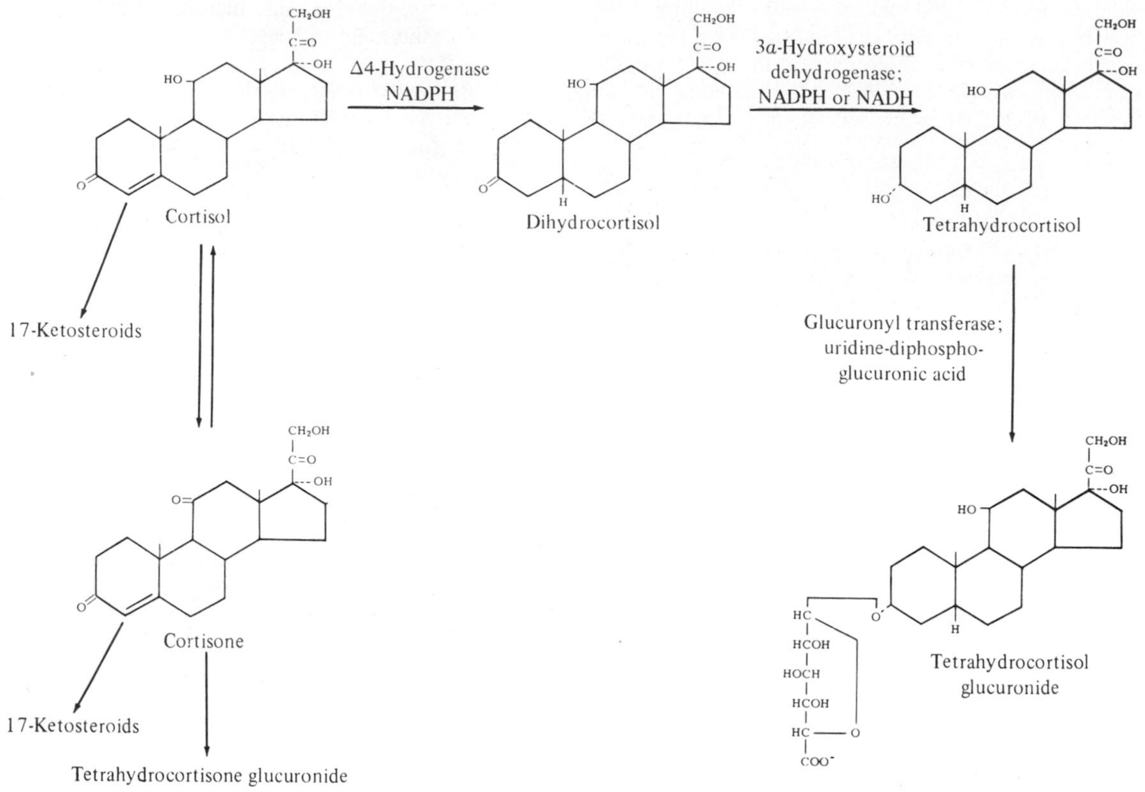

Figure 20–12. Outline of hepatic metabolism of cortisol.

is depressed in liver disease and, interestingly, during surgery and other stresses. Thus, in stressed humans, the plasma free cortisol level rises higher than it does with maximal ACTH stimulation in the absence of stress. Glucocorticoids are not degraded in the process of exerting their physiologic effects.

Aldosterone

Aldosterone is bound to protein to only a slight extent, and its half-life is short (about 20 minutes). The amount secreted is small (Table 20–2), and the normal plasma aldosterone level in humans is about 0.006 μg/dl (0.17 nmol/L), compared to a cortisol level (bound and free) of about 14 μg/dl (386 nmol/L). Much of the aldosterone is converted in the liver to the tetrahydroglucuronide derivative, but some is changed in the liver and in the kidneys to an 18-glucuronide. This glucuronide, which is unlike the breakdown products of other steroids, is converted to free aldosterone by hydrolysis at pH 1.0, and it is therefore often referred to as the "acid-labile conjugate." Less than 1% of the secreted aldosterone appears in the urine in the free form. Another 5% is in the form of the acid-labile conjugate, and up to 40% is in the form of the tetrahydroglucuronide.

17-Ketosteroids

The major adrenal androgen is the 17-ketosteroid

dehydroepiandrosterone, although its Δ^4-3-keto and 11-hydroxy-Δ^4-3-keto derivatives are also secreted. This last compound and the 17-ketosteroids formed from cortisol and cortisone by side chain cleavage in the liver are the only 17-ketosteroids that have an $=O$ or an $-OH$ group in the 11 position ("11-oxy-17-ketosteroids"). Testosterone is also converted to a 17-ketosteroid. Since the daily 17-ketosteroid excretion in normal adults is 15 mg in men and 10 mg in women, about two-thirds of the urinary ketosteroids in men are secreted by the adrenal or formed from cortisol in the liver, and about one-third is of testicular origin.

Etiocholanolone, one of the metabolites of the adrenal androgens and testosterone (Fig 23–17), is capable of causing fever when it is unconjugated (see Chapter 14). Certain individuals have episodic bouts of fever due to periodic accumulation in the blood of unconjugated etiocholanolone ("etiocholanolone fever").

EFFECTS OF ADRENAL ANDROGENS & ESTROGENS

Androgens

Androgens are the hormones that exert masculinizing effects, and they promote protein anabolism and growth (see Chapter 23). Testosterone from the testes is the most active androgen, and the adrenal androgens have less than 20% of its activity. Secretion of the adrenal androgens is controlled by ACTH, not by gonadotropins. The amount of adrenal androgens secreted is almost as great in castrated males and females as in normal males, so it is clear that they exert very little masculinizing effect when secreted in normal amounts. When secreted in abnormal amounts, as they are in patients with congenital enzyme deficiencies in the adrenal (see above) or adrenal tumors, their effects depend on the age and sex of the individual.

In adult males, excess adrenal androgen secretion merely accentuates existing characteristics; but in prepuberal boys, it causes precocious development of the secondary sex characteristics without testicular growth (**precocious pseudopuberty**). In prepuberal and adult females, it causes masculinization, which, when marked, produces the striking clinical picture of the **adrenogenital syndrome** (Fig 20–13). When excess

Table 20–4. Distribution of cortisol and its principal derivatives in human plasma and urine. Note that the derivatives of corticosterone and the 17-ketosteroids from other sources are not included. The "plasma 17-hydroxycorticoids" include, in addition to cortisol and its derivatives, small amounts of other 17a-hydroxylated steroids.

Plasma: Average concentration at 8:00 a.m.		
	μg/dl	
Free cortisol	0.5	
Protein-bound cortisol	13	90% of "plasma 17-hydroxy-corticoids"
Unconjugated dihydro- and tetrahydro-cortisol and -cortisone	Traces	
Tetrahydrocortisol glucuronide	10	"Conjugates"
Tetrahydrocortisone glucuronide	6	
17-Ketosteroids derived from cortisol and cortisone (mostly sulfate conjugates)	Actual plasma concentrations have not been measured	

Urine: Average amount excreted per 24 hours	
	(mg)
Free cortisol	0.03
Tetrahydrocortisol glucuronide	5
Tetrahydrocortisone glucuronide	3
20-Hydroxy derivatives of tetrahydro glucuronides	6
17-Ketosteroids derived from cortisol and cortisone (mostly sulfate conjugates)	1
Unidentified metabolites	7

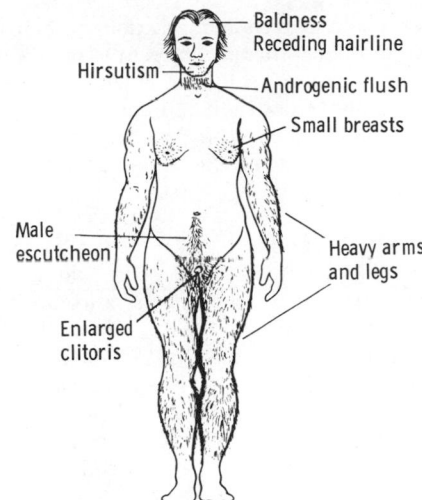

ADRENOGENITAL SYNDROME

Figure 20–13. Typical findings in the adrenogenital syndrome in a woman. (Reproduced, with permission, from Forsham PH, Di Raimondo VC: *Traumatic Medicine and Surgery for the Attorney.* Butterworth, 1960.)

androgen secretion occurs in genetically female fetuses before the 12th week of gestation, the development of male type external genitalia is stimulated, and various degrees of female **pseudohermaphroditism** result. The role of hormones in the in utero development of the genitalia is discussed in Chapter 23.

Estrogens

The adrenal androgen androstenedione is converted to estrogens in the circulation, and the adrenal may also secrete some estrogens. In ovariectomized women, urinary estrogen levels rise when ACTH is injected and fall when the adrenals are removed. The amount of estrogen formed is normally too small to have any apparent physiologic effect. However, feminizing estrogen-secreting tumors of the adrenal cortex have been described, and ovariectomized patients with estrogen-dependent breast cancer improve when their adrenals are removed or when they are treated with glucocorticoids in doses sufficient to inhibit ACTH secretion.

PHYSIOLOGIC EFFECTS OF GLUCOCORTICOIDS

Adrenal Insufficiency

In untreated adrenalectomized animals and humans, there is Na^+ loss with circulatory insufficiency, hypotension, and, eventually, fatal shock due to the mineralocorticoid deficiency. Because glucocorticoids are absent, water, carbohydrate, protein, and fat metabolism are abnormal, and collapse and death follow exposure to even minor noxious stimuli. Small amounts of glucocorticoids correct the metabolic abnormalities, in part directly and in part by permitting other reactions to occur. It is important to separate these physiologic actions of glucocorticoids from the quite different effects produced by large amounts of the hormones.

Mechanism of Action

The multiple effects of glucocorticoids are due to an action on the genetic mechanism controlling protein synthesis; the hormones act by stimulating DNA-dependent synthesis of certain mRNAs in the nuclei of their target cells (Fig 1–15). This in turn leads to the formation of enzymes that alter cell function. Aldosterone acts similarly (see below), and androgens, estrogens, and progesterone—indeed, all steroid hormones—appear to exert their effects in a similar way.

Effects on Intermediary Metabolism

The actions of glucocorticoids on the intermediary metabolism of carbohydrate, protein, and fat are discussed in Chapter 19. They include increased protein catabolism and increased hepatic glycogenesis and gluconeogenesis (Fig 20–14). Glucose-6-phosphatase activity is increased, and the blood glucose rises. Glucocorticoids exert an anti-insulin action in peripheral tissues and make diabetes worse. However, the brain and the heart are spared, and the extra glucose assures a supply of glucose to these vital organs. In diabetics, glucocorticoids raise plasma lipid levels and increase ketone body formation, but in normal individuals, the increase in insulin secretion provoked by the rise in blood glucose obscures these actions. In adrenal insufficiency, the blood glucose is normal as long as an adequate caloric intake is maintained, but fasting causes hypoglycemia that can be fatal. The adrenal cortex is not essential for the ketogenic response to fasting.

Permissive Action

Small amounts of glucocorticoids must be present for a number of metabolic reactions to occur, although the glucocorticoids do not produce the reactions by themselves. This effect is called their **permissive action.** Permissive effects include the requirement for glucocorticoid to be present for glucagon and catecholamines to exert their calorigenic effects (see above and Chapter 19), for catecholamines to exert their lipolytic effects, and for catecholamines to produce pressor responses and bronchodilatation.

Effects on ACTH Secretion

Glucocorticoids inhibit ACTH secretion, and ACTH secretion is increased in adrenalectomized animals. The consequences of the feedback action of cortisol on ACTH secretion are discussed below in the section on regulation of glucocorticoid secretion.

Vascular Reactivity

In adrenally insufficient animals, vascular smooth muscle becomes unresponsive to norepinephrine and epinephrine. The capillaries dilate and, terminally, become permeable to colloidal dyes. Failure to respond to the norepinephrine liberated at adrenergic nerve endings probably impairs vascular compensation for the hypovolemia of adrenal insufficiency and promotes vascular collapse. Glucocorticoids restore vascular reactivity.

Effects on Cardiac & Skeletal Muscle

In adrenalectomized animals, skeletal muscle becomes fatigued more rapidly than in normal animals, and glucocorticoid treatment is necessary to restore the muscles to normal. Glucocorticoids and mineralocorticoids have a positively inotropic effect on cardiac muscle in vitro, but there is no evidence that this digitalis-like action is of any significance in vivo. Heart failure is certainly not part of the clinical picture of adrenal insufficiency. The PR interval of the ECG is prolonged in adrenal insufficiency and shortened in patients who have excess circulating glucocorticoids.

Effects on the Nervous System

There are changes in the nervous system in adrenal insufficiency that are reversed only by glucocorticoids. These include the appearance of EEG waves slower than the normal alpha rhythm, personality changes, and increased sensitivity to olfactory and gustatory stimuli. The mild but definite personality

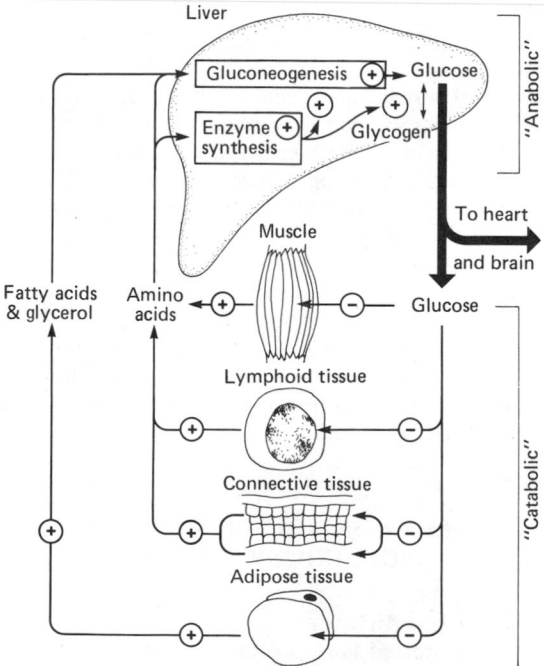

Figure 20–14. Actions of glucocorticoids in promoting gluconeogenesis. −, inhibition; +, stimulation. (Modified and reproduced, with permission, from Baxter JD, Forsham PH: Tissue effects of glucocorticoids. Am J Med 53:573, 1972.)

Table 20–5. Taste thresholds in adrenal insufficiency.*

| Substance | Lowest Concentration Detected (mmol/L), Median Value | |
	Normal Subjects	Patients With Adrenal Insufficiency
Urea	90	0.8
HCl	0.3	0.006
Sucrose	12	0.1
KCl	12	0.1
NaHCO$_3$	12	0.1
NaCl	12	0.3

*Data from Henkin RI, Gill JR Jr, Bartter FC: Studies on taste thresholds in normal man and in patients with adrenal insufficiency: The role of the adrenal cortical steroids and serum sodium concentration. J Clin Invest 42:727, 1963.

changes include irritability, apprehension, and inability to concentrate. The greater sensitivity of the olfactory apparatus and the taste mechanism, which includes all 4 taste modalities (Table 20–5), is unexplained.

Glucocorticoids decrease the amount of current necessary to produce convulsions in rats (lower the **convulsive threshold**), whereas mineralocorticoids have the opposite effect. Indeed, mineralocorticoids have been used in the treatment of epilepsy. However, it is difficult to say what the convulsive threshold means in terms of normal brain function.

Effects on the Gastrointestinal System

Glucocorticoids and ACTH increase gastric acid and pepsin secretion in some species (see Chapter 26). Absorption of water-insoluble fats from the intestine into the lymph is decreased in adrenal insufficiency and facilitated by glucocorticoids (see Chapter 25).

Effects on Water Metabolism

Adrenal insufficiency is characterized by inability to excrete a water load (Fig 20–15), and only

glucocorticoids repair this deficit. The load is eventually excreted, but the excretion is so slow that there is danger of water intoxication. In patients with adrenal insufficiency who have not received glucocorticoids, glucose infusions may cause high fever ("glucose fever") followed by collapse and death. Presumably, the glucose is metabolized, the water dilutes the plasma, and the resultant osmotic gradient between the plasma and the cells causes the cells of the thermoregulatory centers in the hypothalamus to swell to such an extent that their function is disrupted. It should be noted that water intoxication can occur in adrenal insufficiency even without an absolute excess of water in the body; the important factor is retention of water in excess of Na$^+$.

The cause of defective water excretion in adrenal insufficiency is still the subject of much debate. There may be decreased hepatic inactivation of vasopressin, but this would only promote hemodilution, which would in turn inhibit vasopressin secretion unless there were a coexisting defect in the osmoreceptor mechanism (see Chapter 14). Some investigators claim that in the absence of glucocorticoids there is an abnormally high rate of vasopressin secretion, but it has been reported that the plasma vasopressin level is lower in water-loaded adrenalectomized animals than in water-loaded controls. The glomerular filtration rate is low, and this probably contributes to the deficiency in water excretion. The selective effect of glucocorticoids on the abnormal water excretion is consistent with this possibility, because even though the mineralocorticoids improve filtration by restoring plasma volume, the glucocorticoids raise the glomerular filtration rate to a much greater degree. Another factor may be a direct effect of glucocorticoid deficiency on the distal tubules and collecting ducts, making them permeable to water in the absence of vasopressin (see Chapter 38).

Effects on the Blood Cells & Lymphatic Organs

Glucocorticoids decrease the number of circulat-

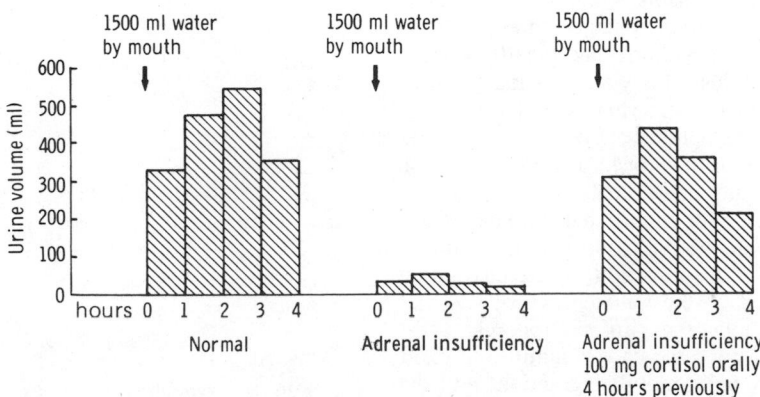

Figure 20–15. Response to a 1500 ml water load in a normal subject and a patient with adrenal insufficiency before and after cortisol treatment.

Table 20–6. Typical effects of cortisol on the white and red blood cell counts in humans (cells/μl).

	Normal	Cortisol-Treated
White blood cells		
Total	9000	10000
PMNs	5760	8330
Lymphocytes	2370	1080
Eosinophils	270	20
Basophils	60	30
Monocytes	450	540
Red blood cells	5 million	5.2 million

ing eosinophils by increasing their sequestration in the spleen and lungs. Changes in the eosinophil level have been used as an index of changes in ACTH secretion, but they are an unreliable indicator because some stresses cause eosinopenia in the absence of the adrenals. Glucocorticoids also lower the number of basophils in the circulation and increase the number of neutrophils, platelets, and red blood cells (Table 20–6). Moderate anemia is one of the findings in chronic adrenal insufficiency, but there is a brisk erythropoietic response to hypoxia (see Chapter 24) in the absence of the adrenals.

Glucocorticoids decrease the circulating lymphocyte count and the size of the lymph nodes and thymus by both inhibiting lymphocyte mitotic activity and increasing destruction of lymphocytes.

Resistance to "Stress"

When an animal or human is exposed to any of an immense variety of noxious or potentially noxious stimuli, there is an increased secretion of ACTH and, consequently, a rise in the circulating glucocorticoid level. This rise is essential for survival. Hypophysectomized animals, or adrenalectomized animals treated with maintenance doses of glucocorticoids, die when exposed to the same noxious stimuli.

Selye defined noxious stimuli that increase ACTH secretion as "stressors," and it is fashionable today to lump these stimuli together under the term "stress." This word is a short, emotionally charged word for something that otherwise takes many words to say, and it is a convenient term to use as long as it is understood that, in the context of this book, it denotes only those stimuli that have been proved to increase ACTH secretion in normal animals and humans.

Most of the stressful stimuli that increase ACTH secretion also activate the sympathoadrenal medullary system, and part of the function of the circulating glucocorticoids may be the maintenance of vascular reactivity to catecholamines. In addition, glucocorticoids are necessary for the catecholamines to exert their full free fatty acid–mobilizing action, and the FFAs are an important emergency energy supply. However, sympathectomized animals tolerate a variety of stresses with impunity. The reason why an elevated circulating glucocorticoid level is essential for resisting stress therefore remains for the most part unknown.

PHARMACOLOGIC & PATHOLOGIC EFFECTS OF GLUCOCORTICOIDS

Cushing's Syndrome

The clinical picture produced by glucocorticoid excess is called **Cushing's syndrome** (Fig 20–16). It may be caused not only by the administration of large amounts of exogenous hormones but also by glucocorticoid-producing adrenocortical tumors and by hypersecretion of ACTH. Many (perhaps all) patients with hypersecretion of ACTH from the pituitary have small pituitary tumors (**microadenomas**) that are often so small that the sella turcica is not enlarged. However, some cases of excess ACTH secretion may be due to hypersecretion of corticotropin-releasing hormone (CRH). Cushing's syndrome is also produced by tumors of nonendocrine tissues that secrete substances with CRH activity or substances very similar to and possibly identical with pituitary ACTH. Tumors of nonendocrine tissues have also been reported to secrete substances with actions like those of almost every known hormone.

Patients with Cushing's syndrome are protein-depleted as a result of excess protein catabolism. The skin and subcutaneous tissues are therefore thin, and the muscles are poorly developed. Wounds heal poorly, and minor injuries cause bruises and ec-

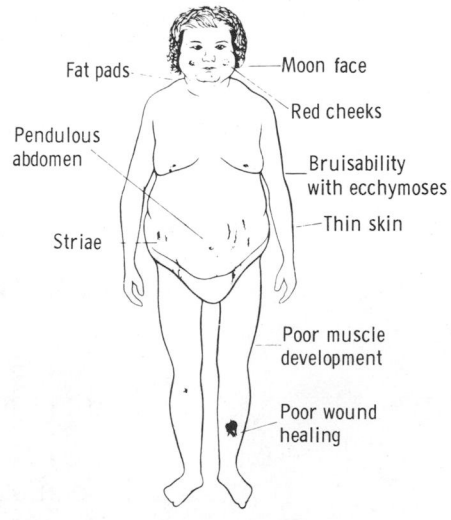

CUSHING'S SYNDROME

Figure 20–16. Typical findings in Cushing's syndrome. (Reproduced, with permission, from Forsham PH, Di Raimondo VC: *Traumatic Medicine and Surgery for the Attorney.* Butterworth, 1960.)

chymoses. The hair is thin and scraggly. Many patients with the disease have some increase in facial hair and acne, but this is caused by the increased secretion of adrenal androgens that often accompanies the increase in glucocorticoid secretion.

Body fat is redistributed in a characteristic way. The extremities are thin, but fat collects in the abdominal wall, face, and upper back, where it produces a "buffalo hump." As the thin skin of the abdomen is stretched by the increased subcutaneous fat depots, the subdermal tissues rupture to form prominent reddish-purple **striae**. These scars are seen normally whenever there is rapid stretching of the skin (eg, around the breasts of girls at puberty or in the abdominal skin during pregnancy), but in normal individuals, the striae are usually inconspicuous and lack the intense purplish color.

Many of the amino acids liberated from catabolized proteins are converted into glucose in the liver, and the resultant hyperglycemia and decreased peripheral utilization of glucose may be sufficient to precipitate insulin-resistant diabetes mellitus, especially in patients genetically predisposed to diabetes. Hyperlipemia and ketosis are associated with the diabetes, but acidosis is usually not severe.

The glucocorticoids are present in such large amounts in Cushing's syndrome that they exert a significant mineralocorticoid action. Deoxycorticosterone secretion is also elevated in cases due to ACTH hypersecretion. The salt and water retention plus the facial obesity cause the characteristic plethoric, rounded "moon-faced" appearance, and there may be significant K^+ depletion and weakness. About 85% of patients with Cushing's syndrome are hypertensive. The hypertension may be due to increased deoxycorticosterone secretion, increased secretion of angiotensinogen (see Chapter 24), or a direct glucocorticoid effect on blood vessels.

Excess glucocorticoids lead to bone dissolution for 3 reasons: excess protein catabolism inhibits new bone formation and breaks down existing bone matrix; glucocorticoids exert an anti–vitamin D action; and glucocorticoids elevate the glomerular filtration rate, increasing calcium excretion. The result is **osteoporosis** (see Chapter 21), a softening and demineralization of bone that leads eventually to collapse of vertebral bodies and skeletal deformity.

Glucocorticoids in excess accelerate the basic EEG rhythms and produce mental aberrations ranging from increased appetite, insomnia, and euphoria to frank toxic psychoses. As noted above, glucocorticoid deficiency is also associated with mental symptoms, but the symptoms produced by glucocorticoid excess are more severe.

Anti-inflammatory & Antiallergic Effects of Glucocorticoids

In large doses, glucocorticoids inhibit the inflammatory response to tissue injury. This reaction is discussed in Chapter 27. The glucocorticoids also suppress manifestations of allergic disease that are due to

the release of histamine from tissues. Neither of these pharmacologic effects is produced by glucocorticoids in physiologic doses, and the effects cannot be produced without producing the other manifestations of glucocorticoid excess. Furthermore, large doses of exogenous glucocorticoids inhibit ACTH secretion to the point that severe adrenal insufficiency can be a dangerous problem when therapy is stopped.

Glucocorticoids inhibit fibroblastic activity, decrease local swelling, and block the systemic effects of bacterial toxins. The decreased local reaction may be due to inhibition of kinin release by the steroids (see Chapter 33). There is evidence that by stabilizing the lysosomal membranes, glucocorticoids inhibit the breakdown of lysosomes that takes place in inflamed tissue. Despite their protein catabolic effects, they slow the degrading effect of collagenase on joint tissues in rheumatoid arthritis, and this is the basis of their effectiveness following intra-articular administration. The glucocorticoids also inhibit the release of endogenous pyrogen from granulocytes (see Chapter 14). Large doses of glucocorticoids in humans initially elevate and later depress antibody levels. The effects on inflammation can be demonstrated in experimental animals with granulomas produced by the subcutaneous injection of turpentine or croton oil or implantation of cotton pledgets. The inhibition of fibroblastic activity prevents the walling off of infections and also prevents such phenomena as keloid formation and the development of adhesions after abdominal surgery.

The actions of glucocorticoids in patients with bacterial infections are dramatic but dangerous. For example, in pneumococcal pneumonia or active tuberculosis, the febrile reaction, the toxicity, and the lung symptoms disappear; but unless antibiotics are given at the same time, the bacteria spread throughout the body. It is important to remember that the symptoms are the warning that disease is present; when these symptoms are masked by glucocorticoid treatment, there may be serious and even fatal delays in diagnosis and the institution of antibiotic treatment.

When certain types of antibodies combine with their antigens, they provoke the release of histamine from various tissues, and this in turn causes many of the symptoms of allergy. Glucocorticoids do not affect the combination of antigen with antibody and have no influence on the effects of histamine once it is released, but they prevent histamine release. Glucocorticoids therefore relieve the symptoms of asthma and delayed hypersensitivity reactions and may be of benefit in such immunoglobulin-mediated diseases as serum sickness. They are also of symptomatic benefit in rheumatoid arthritis, disseminated lupus erythematosus, dermatomyositis, Guillain-Barré syndrome, and related diseases in which allergic and autoimmune reactions probably play a role.

Other Effects

Large doses of glucocorticoids inhibit growth, decrease growth hormone secretion (see Chapter 22), induce PNMT, and decrease TSH secretion.

REGULATION OF GLUCOCORTICOID SECRETION

Role of ACTH

Both basal secretion of glucocorticoids and the increased secretion provoked by stress are dependent upon ACTH from the anterior pituitary. Angiotensin II also stimulates the adrenal cortex, but its effect is mainly on aldosterone secretion. Large doses of a number of other naturally occurring substances, including vasopressin and serotonin, are capable of stimulating the adrenal directly, but there is no evidence that these agents play any role in the physiologic regulation of glucocorticoid secretion.

Chemistry & Metabolism of ACTH

ACTH is a single-chain polypeptide containing 39 amino acids. Its origin in the pituitary is discussed in Chapter 22. The first 23 amino acids in the chain, which are the same in all species that have been examined, constitute the active "core" of the molecule, and a synthetic peptide containing these 23 amino acids has been shown to have the full activity of the 39–amino acid peptide. Amino acids 24–39 are therefore a "tail" that apparently stabilizes the molecule and varies slightly in amino acid composition from species to species (Fig 20–17). Each of the ACTHs that have been isolated is active in all species but probably antigenic in heterologous species.

ACTH is inactivated in blood in vitro, but at a much slower rate than it is in vivo; its half-life in the

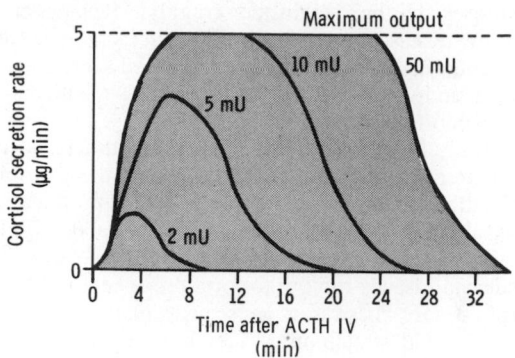

Figure 20–18. Changes in cortisol output in the hypophysectomized dog following the administration of various doses of ACTH. (Reproduced, with permission, from Ganong WF: The central nervous system and the synthesis and release of ACTH. In: *Advances in Neuroendocrinology.* Nalbandov A [editor]. Univ of Illinois Press, 1963.)

circulation in humans is about 10 minutes. A large part of an injected dose of ACTH is found in the kidneys, but neither nephrectomy nor evisceration appreciably enhances its in vivo activity, and the site of its inactivation is not known. ACTH is apparently not altered in the process of exerting its effects on adrenal tissue.

Effect of ACTH on the Adrenal

After hypophysectomy, glucocorticoid synthesis and output decline within 1 hour to very low levels, although some hormone is still secreted. Within a short time after an injection of ACTH (in dogs, less than 2 minutes), glucocorticoid output rises (Fig 20–18). With low doses of ACTH, there is a linear relationship between the log of the dose and the increase in glucocorticoid secretion. However, the maximal rate at which glucocorticoids can be secreted is rapidly reached; and in dogs, doses larger than 10 milliunits (mU) only prolong the period of maximal secretion. A similar "ceiling on output" exists in rats and humans. The effects of ACTH on adrenal morphology and the mechanism by which it increases steroid secretion are discussed above.

Adrenal Responsiveness

In chronically hypophysectomized animals and patients with hypopituitarism, single doses of ACTH do not increase glucocorticoid secretion, and repeated injections or prolonged infusions of ACTH are necessary to restore normal adrenal responses to ACTH. Decreased responsiveness is also produced by doses of glucocorticoids that inhibit ACTH secretion. The decreased adrenal responsiveness to ACTH is detectable within 24 hours after hypophysectomy and increases progressively with time (Fig 20–19). It is marked when the adrenal is atrophic but develops before there are visible changes in adrenal size or morphology.

Circadian Rhythm

ACTH is secreted in irregular bursts throughout

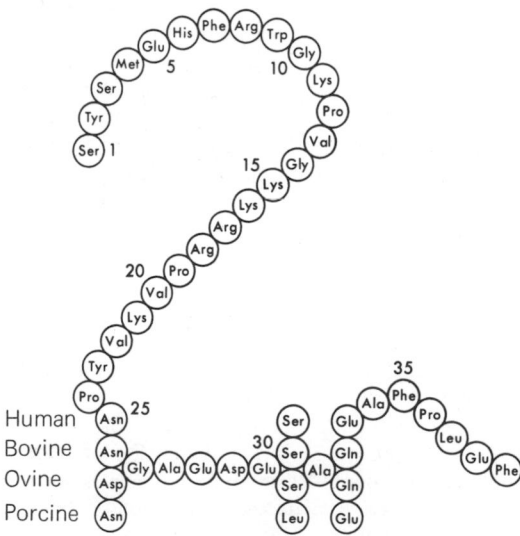

Figure 20–17. Structure of ACTH in various species. The amino acid composition varies only at positions 25, 31, and 33. Thus, human ACTH has Asn in position 25, Ser in position 31, and Glu in position 33; bovine ACTH has Asn in position 25, Ser in position 31, and Gln in position 33; etc. (Reproduced, with permission, from Li CH: Adrenocorticotropin 45: Revised amino acid sequences for sheep and bovine hormones. Biochem Biophys Res Commun 49:835, 1972.)

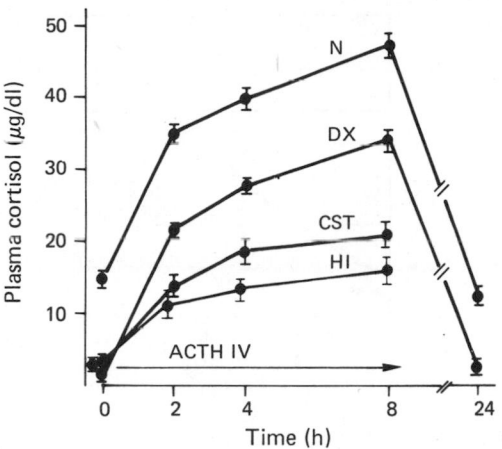

Figure 20–19. Loss of ACTH responsiveness when ACTH secretion is decreased in humans. The 1–24 amino acid sequence of ACTH was infused intravenously in a dose of 250 μg over 8 h. N, normal subjects; DX, dexamethasone 0.75 mg every 8 h for 3 days; CST, long-term corticosteroid therapy; HI, anterior pituitary insufficiency. (Reproduced, with permission, from Kolanowski J & others: Adrenocortical response upon repeated stimulation with corticotrophin in patients lacking endogenous corticotrophin secretion. Acta Endocrinol [Kbh] 85:595, 1977.)

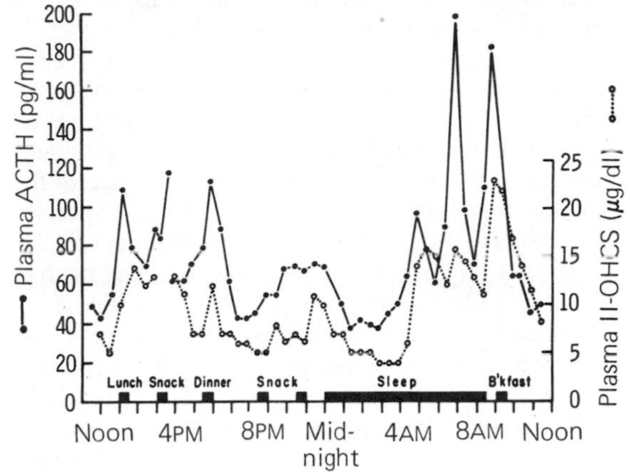

Figure 20–20. Fluctuations in plasma ACTH and glucocorticoids throughout the day in a normal girl (age 16). The ACTH was measured by immunoassay and the glucocorticoids as 11-oxysteroids (11-OHCS). Note the greater ACTH and glucocorticoid rises in the morning, before awakening from sleep. (Reproduced, with permission, from Krieger DT & others: Characterization of the normal temporal pattern of plasma corticosteroid levels. J Clin Endocrinol Metab 32:266, 1971.)

the day, and plasma cortisol tends to rise and fall in response to these bursts (Fig 20–20). However, in all mammalian species studied, most of the ACTH secretion occurs during one part of the day. In humans, the bursts are most frequent in the early morning and least frequent in the evening. This **diurnal,** or **circadian, rhythm** in ACTH secretion is present in patients with adrenal insufficiency receiving constant doses of glucocorticoids. It is not due to the stress of getting up in the morning, traumatic as that may be, because the increased ACTH secretion occurs before waking up. If the "day" is lengthened experimentally to more than 24 hours—ie, if the individual is isolated and the day's activities are spread over more than 24 hours—the adrenal cycle also lengthens, but the increase in ACTH

secretion still occurs during the period of sleep. The biologic clock responsible for the diurnal ACTH rhythm is apparently located in the suprachiasmatic nuclei of the hypothalamus (see Chapter 14). The circadian rhythm is absent in patients with hypothalamic disease.

The Response to Stress

The morning plasma ACTH concentration in a healthy resting human is about 0.5 mU/dl (25 pg/ml or 5.5 pmol/L). ACTH and cortisol values in various abnormal conditions are summarized in Fig 20–21. During severe stress, the amount of ACTH secreted exceeds the amount necessary to produce maximal glucocorticoid output. However, prolonged exposure

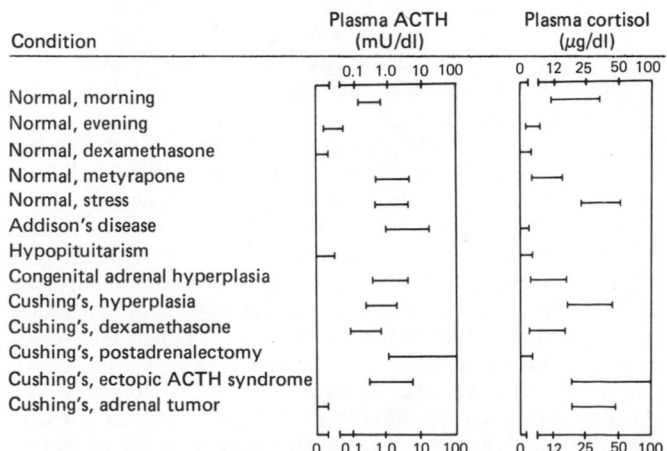

Figure 20–21. Plasma concentrations of ACTH and cortisol in various clinical states. (Reproduced, with permission, from Liddle G: *Textbook of Endocrinology,* 5th ed. Williams RH [editor], Saunders, 1974.)

to ACTH in conditions such as the ectopic ACTH syndrome increases the adrenal maximum.

Increases in ACTH secretion to meet emergency situations are mediated almost exclusively through the hypothalamus. The median eminence–portal vessel system is the final common pathway to the pituitary; the release of CRH from the median eminence of the hypothalamus and its transport via the portal-hypophyseal vessels to the anterior pituitary to stimulate ACTH secretion are discussed in Chapter 14. If the median eminence is destroyed, some basal glucocorticoid secretion continues and the adrenals do not atrophy, but increased secretion in response to many different stresses is blocked. Afferent nerve pathways from many parts of the brain converge on the median eminence. Fibers from the amygdaloid nuclei mediate responses to emotional stresses, and fear, anxiety, and apprehension cause marked increases in ACTH secretion. Input from the suprachiasmatic nuclei also provides the drive for the diurnal rhythm. Impulses ascending to the hypothalamus in the reticular formation trigger ACTH secretion in response to injury (Fig 20–22). There is also some evidence that the median eminence–anterior pituitary unit can be stimulated by humoral agents reaching it via the bloodstream. Contrary to previously proposed theories, circulating epinephrine and norepinephrine do not increase ACTH secretion in humans, and adrenocortical and adrenal medullary secretion are independently regulated from the hypothalamus.

Glucocorticoid Feedback

High circulating levels of free glucocorticoids inhibit ACTH secretion, and the degree of pituitary inhibition is apparently a linear function of the circulating glucocorticoid level. The inhibition appears to be rapid in onset but relatively prolonged. When a single

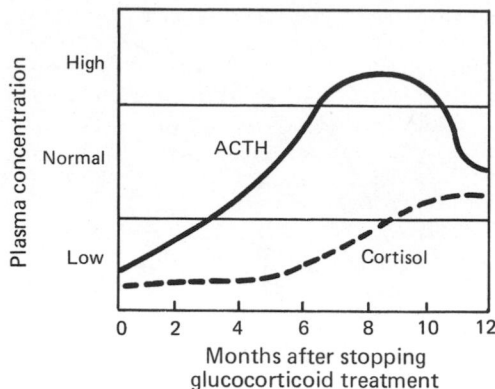

Figure 20–23. Pattern of plasma ACTH and cortisol values in patients recovering from prior long-term daily treatment with large doses of glucocorticoids. (Modified from Ney R: *Steroid Therapy: A Clinical Update for the 1970s.* Thorn GW [editor]. Medcom, 1974.)

dose of glucocorticoid is injected, peak inhibition occurs after the circulating steroid level has fallen to its preinjection level. This delay is probably due to the time required to synthesize new protein (see above). There is a similar delay in the time to the peak of eosinopenic and other actions of glucocorticoids.

The pituitary-inhibiting activity of the various steroids parallels their glucocorticoid potency. The site at which glucocorticoids act to inhibit ACTH secretion is still a matter of debate. It seems probable that they act on both the hypothalamus and the pituitary.

The dangers involved when prolonged treatment with anti-inflammatory doses of glucocorticoids is stopped deserve emphasis. Not only is the adrenal atrophic and unresponsive after such treatment; even if its responsiveness is restored by injecting ACTH, the pituitary may be unable to secrete normal amounts of ACTH for as long as a month. The cause of the deficiency is presumably diminished ACTH synthesis. Thereafter, there is a slow rise in ACTH to supranormal levels. These in turn stimulate the adrenal, and glucocorticoid output rises with feedback inhibition gradually reducing the elevated ACTH levels to normal (Fig 20–23). The complications of sudden cessation of steroid therapy can usually be avoided by slowly decreasing the steroid dose over a long period of time.

It should be noted that the level of unbound glucocorticoids in the plasma is normally very low, so that there is little pituitary inhibition in the absence of stress. A drop from this level does stimulate increased ACTH secretion, and in chronic adrenal insufficiency there is a marked increase in the rate of ACTH synthesis and secretion. However, an acute drop in circulating glucocorticoid levels is not a potent stimulus to ACTH secretion.

It was once thought that stress stimulated ACTH secretion by initially lowering the plasma corticoid level, but this has been shown to be incorrect. In fact,

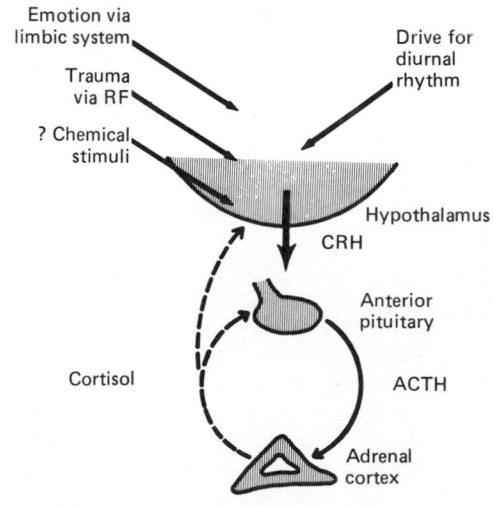

Figure 20–22. Diagram of current concepts of the control of ACTH secretion. The dashed arrows indicate inhibitory effects and the solid arrows stimulating effects. RF, reticular formation.

an untreated adrenalectomized animal whose circulating corticoid level is zero responds to stress with a much greater than normal rise in plasma ACTH. Thus, it seems clear that the rate of ACTH secretion is determined by 2 opposing forces: the sum of the neural and possibly other stimuli converging through the median eminence to increase ACTH secretion, and the magnitude of the braking action of glucocorticoids on ACTH secretion, which is proportionate to their level in the circulating blood (Fig 20–22).

EFFECTS OF MINERALOCORTICOIDS

Actions

Aldosterone and other steroids with mineralocorticoid activity increase the reabsorption of Na^+ from the urine, sweat, saliva, and gastric juice. Thus, they cause retention of Na^+ in the ECF. In the kidney, they act on the epithelium of the distal tubule and collecting duct. They may also increase the K^+ and decrease the Na^+ in muscle and brain cells. Under the influence of aldosterone, increased numbers of sodium ions are in effect exchanged for K^+ and H^+ in the renal tubules, producing a K^+ diuresis (Fig 20–24) and an increase in urine acidity.

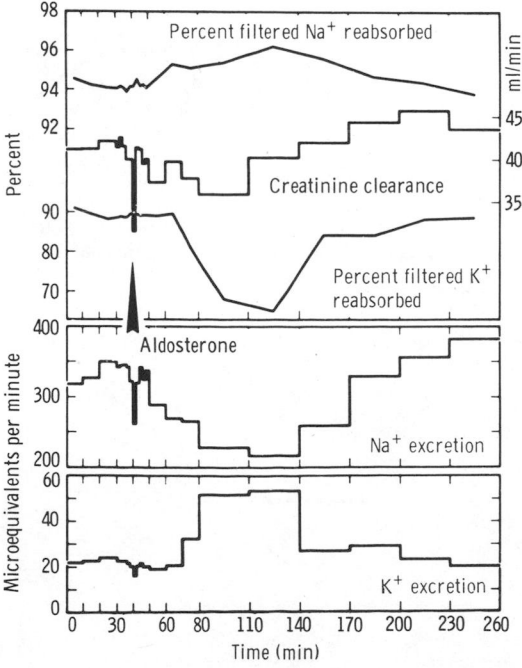

Figure 20–24. Effect of aldosterone (5 μg as a single dose injected into the aorta) on electrolyte excretion in an adrenalectomized dog. (Data from Ganong WF, Mulrow PJ: Rate of change in sodium and potassium excretion after injection of aldosterone into the aorta and renal artery of the dog. Am J Physiol 195:337, 1958.)

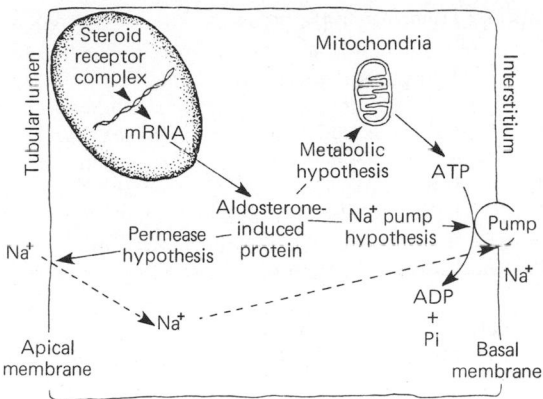

Figure 20–25. Mechanism of action of aldosterone. The steroid induces the formation of one or more proteins that in turn increase the permeability of the apical (luminal) membrane to Na^+, increase the active transport of Na^+ out of the cell across the basal (interstitial) membrane, or increase the energy available to the pump. (Modified from Edelman IS: Candidate mediators in the action of aldosterone on Na^+ transport. In: *Membrane Transport Processes.* Vol I. Hoffman JF [editor]. Raven, 1978.)

Mechanism of Action

Aldosterone, like other steroids, acts by stimulating DNA-dependent mRNA synthesis (see Chapter 17). Sodium ions diffuse out of the urine (or saliva, sweat, or gastric juice) into the surrounding epithelial cells and are actively transported from these cells into the interstitial fluid. The amount of Na^+ removed from these fluids is proportionate to the rate of active transport of Na^+. The energy for the active transport is supplied by ATP, and ATP synthesis depends for the most part on the oxidation of substrate to CO_2 and H_2O via the citric acid cycle. Aldosterone, like other steroids, binds to a cytoplasmic receptor, and the complex migrates to the nucleus, where it initiates an increase in mRNA synthesis at the level of transcription of DNA (Fig 20–25). The induced RNA stimulates protein synthesis at the ribosomal level. Aldosterone fails to exert any effect on Na^+ excretion for 10–30 minutes or more even when injected directly into the renal artery. This latent period represents the time needed to increase protein synthesis. The function of the aldosterone-induced protein or proteins is a topic of current debate. One hypothesis holds (Fig 20–25) that the protein increases the passive permeability of the cell to Na^+ from the tubular lumen (permease hypothesis); another holds that the protein increases the oxidation of substrate to provide ATP (metabolic hypothesis); and a third holds that the protein acts directly to increase the activity of the sodium pump (Na^+ pump hypothesis). In any case, the effect is increased active transport of Na^+ from the tubular lumen to the interstitium and thence to the bloodstream.

Aldosterone is the principal mineralocorticoid secreted by the adrenal, although corticosterone is secreted in sufficient amounts to exert a minor mineralocorticoid effect (Tables 20–2 and 20–3). Deoxycorticosterone, which is secreted in appreciable amounts only in abnormal situations, has about 3% of the activity of aldosterone. It is used clinically as a mineralocorticoid because its synthetic acetate (**desoxycorticosterone acetate, DOCA**) is cheaper and more readily available than aldosterone. Large amounts of progesterone and some other steroids cause natriuresis, but there is little evidence that they play any normal role in the control of Na^+ excretion.

Effect of Adrenalectomy

In adrenal insufficiency, Na^+ is lost in the urine. K^+ is retained, and the plasma K^+ rises. When adrenal insufficiency develops rapidly, the decline in ECF Na^+ exceeds the amount excreted in the urine, indicating that Na^+ also must be entering the cells. When the posterior pituitary is intact, salt loss exceeds water loss, and the plasma Na^+ falls (Table 20–7). However, plasma volume also is reduced, resulting in hypotension, circulatory insufficiency, and, eventually, fatal shock. These changes can be prevented to a degree by increasing the dietary salt intake. Rats survive indefinitely on extra salt alone, but in dogs and most humans, the amount of supplementary salt needed is so large that it is almost impossible to prevent eventual collapse and death unless mineralocorticoid treatment is also instituted.

Table 20–7. Typical plasma electrolyte levels in normal humans and patients with adrenocortical diseases.

	Plasma Electrolytes (mEq/L)			
	Na^+	K^+	Cl^-	HCO_3^-
Normal	142	4.5	105	25
Adrenal insufficiency	120	6.7	85	25
Primary hyperaldosteronism	148	2.4	96	41

Secondary Effects of Excess Mineralocorticoids

K^+ depletion due to prolonged K^+ diuresis is a prominent feature of prolonged mineralocorticoid treatment (Table 20–7). When the K^+ loss is marked, intracellular K^+ is replaced by Na^+. This shift can be prevented by the administration of supplemental K^+ along with the mineralocorticoid. There is no net increase in body sodium if salt intake is restricted to the level of output, but on a normal diet, total body sodium rises. However, the plasma Na^+ is elevated only slightly, if at all, because water is retained with the osmotically active sodium ions. Consequently, ECF volume is expanded and the blood pressure rises. It has also been claimed that aldosterone and deoxycorticosterone have a direct effect on blood vessels that con-

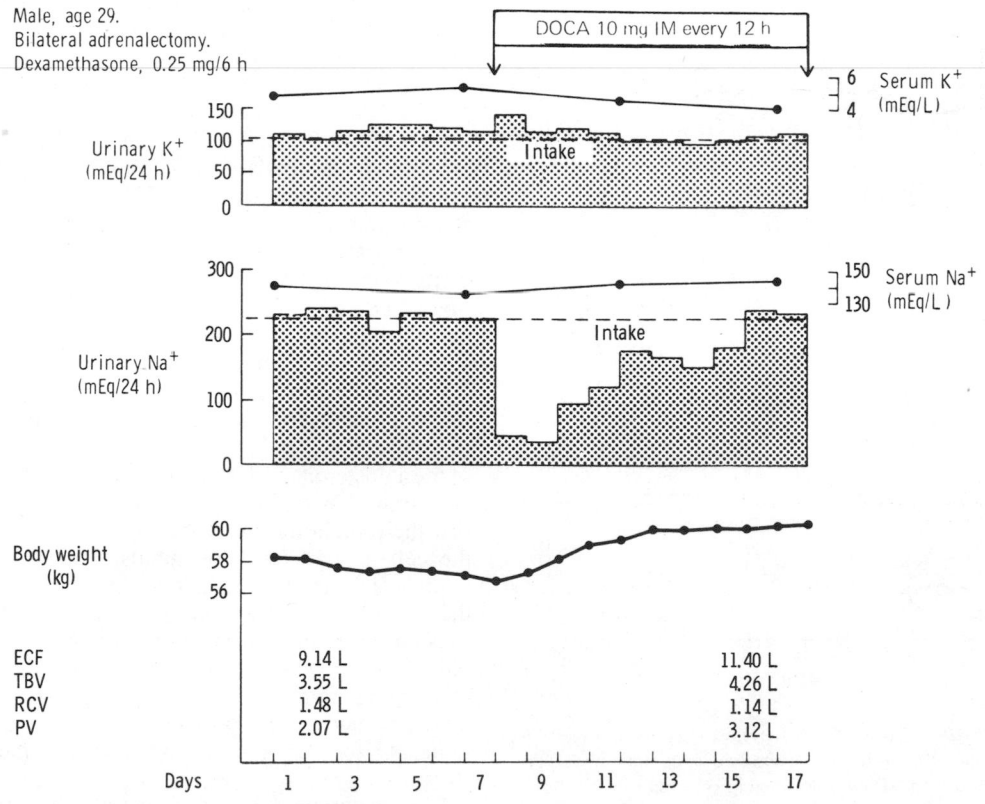

Figure 20–26. "Escape" from the sodium-retaining effect of desoxycorticosterone acetate (DOCA) in an adrenalectomized patient. ECF, extracellular fluid volume; TBV, total blood volume; RCV, red cell volume; PV, plasma volume. (Courtesy of EG Biglieri.)

tributes to the rise in blood pressure. When the ECF expansion passes a certain point, Na^+ excretion is usually increased in spite of the continued action of mineralocorticoids on the renal tubules. This "escape phenomenon" (Fig 20–26) is due mostly to decreased reabsorption of Na^+ in the proximal tubules, but how this decrease is brought about is not known. It is because of this increased excretion of Na^+ when the ECF volume is expanded that mineralocorticoids do not produce edema in normal individuals and patients with hyperaldosteronism. However, escape may not occur in certain disease states, and in these situations, continued expansion of ECF volume leads to edema (see Chapter 38).

Primary Hyperaldosteronism

The effects of chronic mineralocorticoid excess are seen in patients with aldosterone-secreting tumors of the adrenal cortex that produce the syndrome of **primary hyperaldosteronism** (Conn's syndrome). These patients are severely K^+-depleted. They are hypertensive, and their ECF volume is expanded, but they are not edematous or markedly hypernatremic because the escape phenomenon discussed in the preceding paragraph causes the excretion of extra ingested salt.

Prolonged K^+ depletion damages the kidney, resulting in a loss of concentrating ability and polyuria (**hypokalemic nephropathy**). The K^+ depletion also causes muscle weakness and metabolic alkalosis (see Chapter 38), and the alkalosis lowers the plasma Ca^{2+} level to the point where latent or even frank tetany is present (see Chapter 21). For unknown reasons, the muscle weakness and tetany are much more common in females. The K^+ depletion causes a minor but detectable decrease in glucose tolerance that is corrected by K^+ repletion (see Chapter 19).

REGULATION OF ALDOSTERONE SECRETION

Stimuli

The stimuli that increase aldosterone secretion are summarized in Table 20–8. Some of them also increase glucocorticoid secretion; others selectively affect the output of aldosterone. The regulatory factors involved appear to be ACTH from the pituitary, renin from the kidney, and a direct stimulatory effect of a rise in plasma K^+, or a drop in plasma Na^+, on the adrenal cortex. Except in a few unusual situations such as a high-potassium diet, it seems unlikely that changes in plasma electrolyte levels are a major regulatory mechanism because it appears that the changes must be relatively large before any stimulating effect is seen. In dogs, the plasma K^+ concentration must rise approximately 1 mEq/L or the plasma Na^+ fall by about 20 mEq/L to increase aldosterone secretion, and few of the stimuli that increase aldosterone secretion

Table 20–8. Stimuli that increase aldosterone secretion.

Glucocorticoid secretion also increased
Surgery
Anxiety
Physical trauma
Hemorrhage
Glucocorticoid secretion unaffected
High potassium intake
Low sodium intake
Constriction of inferior vena cava in thorax
Standing
Secondary hyperaldosteronism (in some cases of congestive heart failure, cirrhosis, and nephrosis)

produce electrolyte changes of this magnitude. In experimental animals, the aldosterone response to a low-Na^+ diet is decreased by a low-K^+ diet, but in clinical situations, K^+ depletion is usually produced by an aldosterone-producing tumor or is secondary to hyperaldosteronism from another cause.

Effect of ACTH on Aldosterone Secretion

When first administered, ACTH stimulates the output of aldosterone as well as that of glucocorticoids and sex hormones. Although the amount of ACTH required to increase aldosterone output is somewhat greater than the amount that stimulates maximal glucocorticoid secretion (Fig 20–27), it is well within the range of endogenous ACTH secretion. The effect is transient, and even if ACTH secretion remains elevated, aldosterone output begins to decline in 1 or 2 days. On the other hand, the output of the mineralocorticoid deoxycorticosterone remains elevated. After hypophysectomy, the basal rate of aldosterone secre-

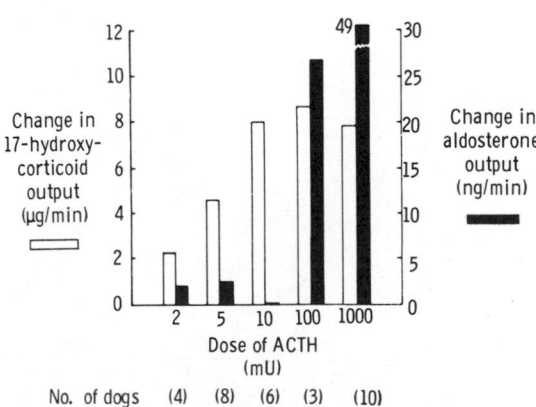

Figure 20–27. Changes in adrenal venous output of steroids produced by ACTH in nephrectomized hypophysectomized dogs. (Data from Ganong WF: The central nervous system and the synthesis and release of ACTH. In: *Advances in Neuroendocrinology.* Nalbandov A [editor]. Univ of Illinois Press, 1963.)

tion is normal, and the rise produced by dietary salt restriction is unaffected for some time; but the increases normally produced by surgical trauma and other stresses are absent. The atrophy of the zona glomerulosa that complicates the picture in long-standing hypopituitarism has been discussed above.

Effects of Angiotensin II & Renin

The octapeptide angiotensin II is formed in the body from angiotensin I, which is liberated by the action of renin on a circulating α_2 globulin (see Chapter 24). Injections of angiotensin II stimulate adrenocortical secretion and, in small doses, affect primarily the secretion of aldosterone (Fig 20–28). In humans, angiotensin II does not increase the secretion of deoxycorticosterone, which is controlled by ACTH.

Renin is secreted from the juxtaglomerular cells that surround the renal afferent arterioles as they enter the glomeruli (see Chapter 24). Aldosterone secretion is regulated via the renin-angiotensin system in a feedback fashion (Fig 20–29). A drop in ECF volume or intra-arterial vascular volume leads to a reflex increase in renal nerve discharges and decreases renal arterial pressure. Both changes increase renin secretion, and the angiotensin II formed by the action of the renin increases the rate of secretion of aldosterone. The aldosterone causes Na^+ and water retention, expanding ECF volume and shutting off the stimulus that initiated increased renin secretion.

Hemorrhage stimulates ACTH secretion, but it also increases aldosterone secretion in the absence of the pituitary. Like hemorrhage, standing and constriction of the thoracic inferior vena cava decrease intra-arterial vascular volume. Dietary sodium restriction also increases aldosterone secretion via the renin-angiotensin system (Fig 20–30). Such restriction reduces ECF volume, but aldosterone and renin secretion are increased before there is any measurable change in blood pressure. Consequently, dietary sodium restriction may initially increase renin secre-

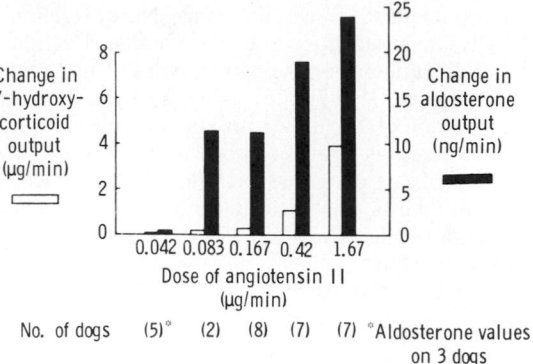

Figure 20–28. Changes in adrenal venous output of steroids produced by angiotensin II in nephrectomized hypophysectomized dogs. (Data from Mulrow PJ & others: The nature of the aldosterone-stimulating factor in dog kidneys. J Clin Invest 41:505, 1962.)

tion via reflex increases in the activity of the renal nerves.

In normal individuals, there is an increase in plasma aldosterone concentration during the portion of the day that the individual is carrying on activities in the upright position. This increase is due to a decrease in the rate of removal of aldosterone from the circulation by the liver and an increase in aldosterone secretion due to a postural increase in renin secretion. Aldosterone and renin secretion are low during the hours of sleep.

Clinical Correlates

It has been established that circulating renin and angiotensin II levels are elevated in many patients with congestive heart failure, nephrosis, or cirrhosis of the liver. It therefore seems likely that when elevated aldosterone secretion (**secondary hyperaldostero-**

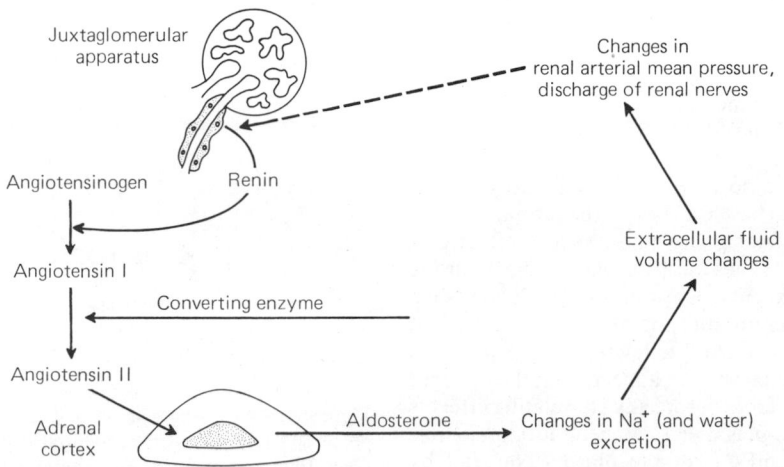

Figure 20–29. A postulated feedback mechanism regulating aldosterone secretion.

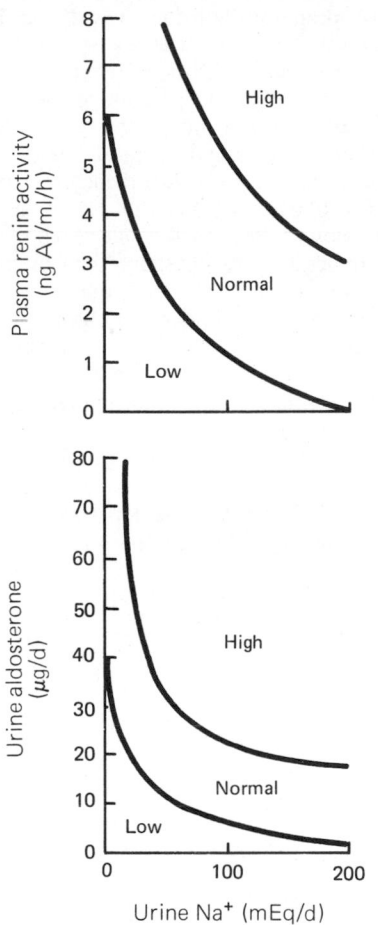

Figure 20–30. Correlation between urinary Na⁺ excretion and plasma renin and aldosterone secretion. Renin is measured by the amount of angiotensin I (AI) generated. In normal subjects, urinary Na⁺ excretion is a reflection of dietary intake. (Courtesy of JA Laragh.)

nism) is seen in these diseases, it is mediated via the renin-angiotensin system. Changes in plasma electrolyte levels in patients are rarely great enough to act directly on the adrenal. Increased renin secretion is also found in individuals with the salt-losing form of the adrenogenital syndrome (see above), presumably because their ECF volume is low. In patients with elevated renin secretion due to renal artery constriction, aldosterone secretion is increased; in those in whom renin secretion is not elevated, aldosterone secretion is normal. The relationship of aldosterone to hypertension is discussed in Chapter 24.

ROLE OF MINERALOCORTICOIDS IN THE REGULATION OF SALT BALANCE

Variation in aldosterone secretion is only one of many factors affecting Na⁺ excretion. Other major factors include the glomerular filtration rate, the presence or absence of osmotic diuresis, and changes in tubular reabsorption of Na⁺ independent of aldosterone. It should also be remembered that it takes some time for aldosterone to act. Thus, for example, when one rises from the supine to the standing position, aldosterone secretion is increased and there is Na⁺ retention; but the decrease in Na⁺ excretion develops too rapidly to be explained solely by increased aldosterone secretion. The primary function of the aldosterone-secreting mechanism is probably the defense of intravascular volume, but it is only one of the homeostatic mechanisms involved.

SUMMARY OF THE EFFECTS OF ADRENOCORTICAL HYPER– & HYPO– FUNCTION IN HUMANS

Recapitulating the manifestations of excess and deficiency of the adrenocortical hormones in humans is a convenient way to summarize the multiple and complex actions of these steroids. There is a characteristic clinical syndrome associated with excess secretion of each of the types of hormones. Excess androgen secretion causes masculinization (**adrenogenital syndrome),** precocious pseudopuberty, or female pseudohermaphroditism, depending upon the age at which androgen hypersecretion develops. Feminizing estrogen-secreting adrenal tumors are sometimes seen. Excess glucocorticoid secretion produces a moon-faced, plethoric appearance, with trunk obesity, purple abdominal striae, hypertension, osteoporosis, protein depletion, mental abnormalities, and, frequently, diabetes mellitus (**Cushing's syndrome).** Excess mineralocorticoid secretion leads to K⁺ depletion and Na⁺ retention, generally without edema but with weakness, hypertension, tetany, polyuria, and hypokalemic alkalosis (**Conn's syndrome).**

If hormone treatment is stopped in a surgically adrenalectomized patient, the plasma K⁺ rises and the plasma Na⁺ falls as Na⁺ excretion is increased and Na⁺ enters the cells. The plasma volume declines, the blood pressure falls, and fatal shock develops in a few days if treatment is not reinstituted.

These changes can be prevented by mineralocorticoids. Many adrenalectomized patients, provided they eat regularly, can be maintained for prolonged periods on mineralocorticoid replacement alone, but their existence is a precarious one. Fasting causes fatal hypoglycemia, and any stress causes collapse. Water is poorly excreted, and there is always the danger of water intoxication. Circulating ACTH levels are elevated. The diffuse tanning of the skin and the spotty pigmentation characteristic of chronic glucocorticoid deficiency (Fig 20–31) are due, at least in part, to the melanocyte-stimulating hormone (MSH) activity of the ACTH in the blood (see Chapter 22). Minor menstrual abnormalities occur in women, but the defi

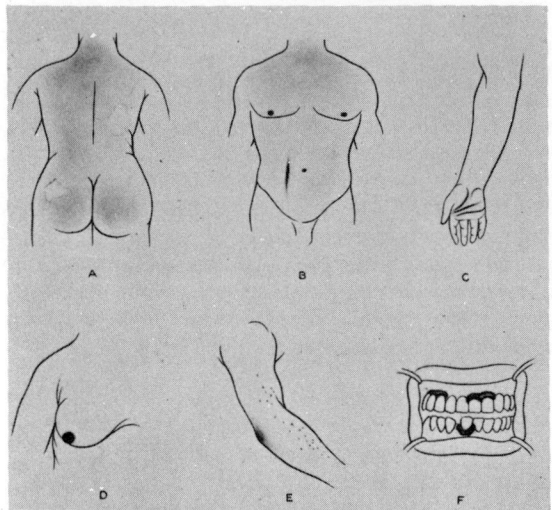

Figure 20–31. Pigmentation in Addison's disease. *A*, tan and vitiligo; *B*, pigmentation of scars from lesions that occurred after the development of the disease; *C*, pigmentation of skin creases; *D*, darkening of areolas; *E*, pigmentation of pressure points; *F*, pigmentation of the gums. (Reproduced, with permission, from Forsham PH, Di Raimondo VC: *Traumatic Medicine and Surgery for the Attorney*. Butterworth, 1960.)

ciency of adrenal sex hormones usually has little effect in the presence of normal testes or ovaries.

Adrenocortical insufficiency in cases of idiopathic adrenocortical atrophy due to autoimmune disease or destruction of the adrenal glands by diseases such as tuberculosis and cancer is called **Addison's disease.** Total adrenal insufficiency is rapidly fatal, but the loss of adrenocortical function in these patients develops slowly. Because their adrenal insufficiency is relative rather than absolute, they have time to develop marked pigmentation and a decrease in cardiac size that is apparently secondary to chronic hypotension and a decrease in cardiac work. They often get along fairly well until some minor stress precipitates a collapse **(addisonian crisis)** requiring emergency medical treatment.

Cases of isolated aldosterone deficiency have also been reported in patients with renal disease and a low circulating renin level. These patients have marked hyperkalemia and may develop metabolic acidosis.

Hormonal Control of Calcium Metabolism & the Physiology of Bone | 21

Three hormones are primarily concerned with the regulation of calcium metabolism. 1,25-Dihydroxycholecalciferol is a steroid hormone formed from vitamin D by successive hydroxylations in the liver and kidney. It increases calcium absorption from the intestine and bone. Parathyroid hormone, which is secreted by the parathyroid glands, mobilizes calcium from bone and increases urinary phosphate excretion. Calcitonin, a calcium-lowering hormone that in mammals is primarily secreted by cells in the thyroid gland, inhibits bone resorption. All 3 hormones operate in concert to maintain the constancy of the Ca^{2+} level in the body fluids. Glucocorticoids and growth hormone also affect calcium metabolism.

CALCIUM METABOLISM

The adult human body contains about 1100 g of calcium (1.5% of body weight). Most of the calcium is in the skeleton. The plasma calcium, normally about 10 mg/dl (5 mEq/L, 2.5 mmol/L), is partly bound to protein and partly diffusible (Table 21–1).

It is the free, ionized calcium in the body fluids that is necessary for blood coagulation, normal cardiac and skeletal muscle contraction, and nerve function. A decrease in extracellular Ca^{2+} at the myoneural junction inhibits transmission (see Chapter 4), but this effect is overbalanced by the excitatory effect of a low Ca^{2+} level on nerve and muscle cells (see Chapter 2).

Table 21–1. Distribution (mmol/L) of calcium in normal human plasma.

Diffusible		1.34
Ionized (Ca^{2+})	1.18	
Complexed to HCO_3^-, citrate, etc	0.16	
Nondiffusible (protein-bound)		1.16
Bound to albumin	0.92	
Bound to globulin	0.24	
Total plasma calcium		2.50

The result is **hypocalcemic tetany,** which is due to increased activity of the motor nerve fibers. This condition is characterized by extensive spasms of skeletal muscle, involving especially the muscles of the extremities and the larynx. Laryngospasm becomes so severe that the airway is obstructed, and fatal asphyxia is produced. Ca^{2+} plays an important role in clotting (see Chapter 27) and other systems; in vivo, however, the level of plasma Ca^{2+} at which fatal tetany occurs is still above the level at which clotting defects would occur.

Since the extent of Ca^{2+} binding by plasma proteins is proportionate to the plasma protein level, it is important to know the plasma protein level when evaluating the total plasma calcium. Plasma ionized calcium can be measured chemically or by use of a calcium-sensitive electrode. Other electrolytes and pH affect the Ca^{2+} level. The actions of the electrolytes in plasma are conveniently summarized in the following expression:

$$\text{Tendency to tetany} \cong \frac{[HCO_3^-]\,[HPO_4{}^{2-}]}{[Ca^{2+}]\,[Mg^{2+}]\,[H^+]}$$

Thus, for example, the symptoms of tetany appear at much higher Ca^{2+} levels if the patient hyperventilates (decreased plasma H^+). Plasma proteins are more ionized when the pH is high, providing more protein anion to bind with Ca^{2+}.

The calcium in bone is of 2 types: a readily exchangeable reservoir and a larger pool of stable calcium that is only slowly exchangeable. The plasma calcium is in equilibrium with the readily exchangeable bone calcium (Fig 21–1).

Calcium absorption from the gastrointestinal tract undergoes adaptation, ie, it is high when the calcium intake is low and decreased when the calcium intake is high. Calcium absorption is also decreased by substances which form insoluble salts with Ca^{2+} (eg, phosphates and oxalates) or by alkalies, which favor formation of insoluble calcium soaps. A high-protein diet increases absorption in adults.

Calcium is actively transported out of the intestine by a system in the brush border of the epithelial cells that involves a calcium-dependent ATPase. Phosphate is also transported by an active process.

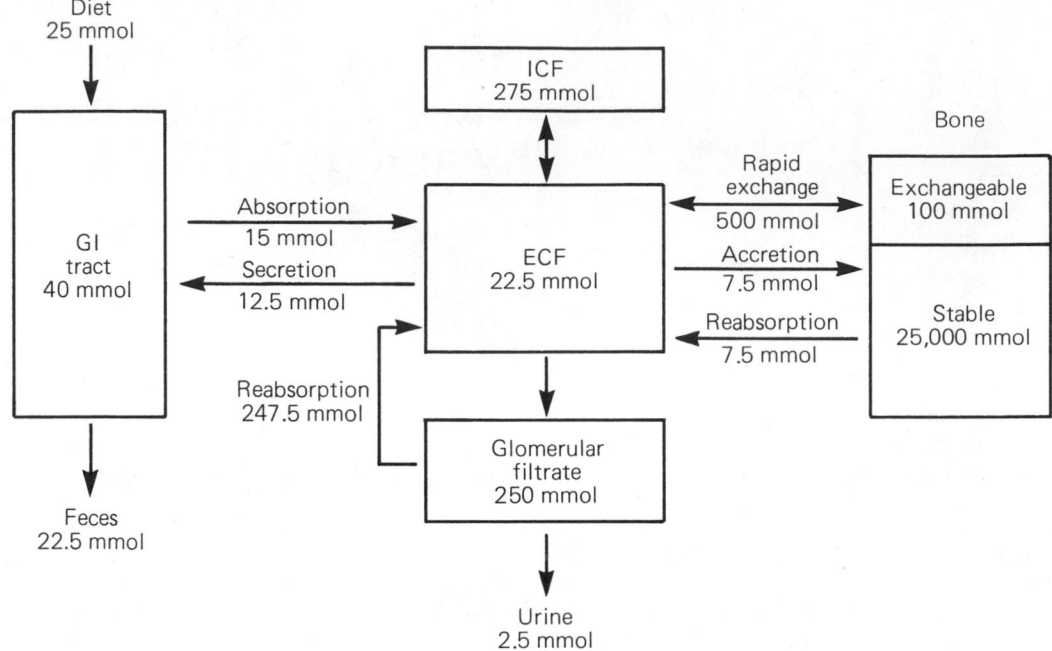

Figure 21–1. Calcium metabolism in an adult human ingesting 1000 mg (25 mmol) of calcium per day. (Modified from Rasmussen H: Parathyroid hormone, calcitonin and calciferols. In: *Textbook of Endocrinology,* 5th ed. Williams RH [editor]. Saunders, 1974.)

BONE PHYSIOLOGY

Structure of Bone

Bone is a living tissue with a collagenous protein matrix that has been impregnated with mineral salts, especially phosphates of calcium. The protein in the collagen fibers that form bone matrix is complex. Adequate amounts of both protein and minerals must be available for the maintenance of normal bone structure. Mineral in bone is mostly in the form of a complex salt that resembles and may be identical with **hydroxyapatite,** $Ca_{10}(PO_4)_6(OH)_2$. This salt forms crystals that measure 20 by 3–7 nm. Sodium and small amounts of magnesium and carbonate are also present in bone.

Bone is cellular and well vascularized; the total bone blood flow in humans has been estimated to be 200–400 ml/min. Throughout life, the mineral in the skeleton is being actively turned over, and bone is constantly being resorbed and reformed. The calcium in bone turns over at a rate of 100% per year in infants and 18% per year in adults.

It is generally stated that the cells in bone which are primarily concerned with bone formation and resorption are the osteoblasts, the osteocytes, and the osteoclasts. However, these 3 cell types are apparently interconvertible, and seem to be phases of a single cell type. **Osteoblasts** are the bone-forming cells that secrete collagen, forming a matrix around themselves which then calcifies. **Osteocytes** are bone cells surrounded by calcified matrix. They send processes into the canaliculi that ramify throughout the bone and are capable of considerable bone resorption. **Osteoclasts** are multinuclear cells that erode and resorb previously formed bone. Progenitor cells form osteoblasts when the concentration of parathyroid hormone is low, but when it is high, they form osteoclasts. Parathyroid hormone also causes osteoblasts to become osteoclasts. Calcitonin fosters the conversion of osteoclasts to osteoblasts.

Bone Formation

The bones of the skull are formed by ossification of membranes (**intramembranous** bone formation). The long bones are first modeled in cartilage and then transformed into bone by ossification that begins in the shaft and in the ends of the bone (**enchondral** bone formation). Osteoblasts form a network of collagen fibers. This matrix then calcifies. In the meantime, the cartilage in the center of the shaft is invaded by osteoclasts that erode it away.

During growth, specialized areas at the ends of each long bone (**epiphyses**) are separated from the shaft of the bone by a plate of actively proliferating cartilage, the **epiphyseal plate.** Growth in bone length occurs as this plate lays down new bone on the end of the shaft. The width of the epiphyseal plate is proportionate to the rate of growth. Its width is affected by a number of hormones but most markedly by the pituitary growth hormone via somatomedin (see Chapter 22). Changes in the width of the tibial epiphyseal plate are used as the end point in the "tibia test," a bioassay that has been used to measure growth hormone.

Linear bone growth can occur as long as the epiphyses are separated from the shaft of the bone, but such growth ceases after the epiphyses unite with the shaft (**epiphyseal closure**). The epiphyses of the various bones close in an orderly temporal sequence, the last epiphyses closing after puberty. The normal age at which each of the epiphyses closes is known, and the "bone age" of an individual can be determined by x-raying the skeleton and noting which epiphyses are open and which are closed.

Calcification

The details of the process responsible for the calcification of newly formed bone matrix are uncertain despite intensive investigation. Whether or not calcium phosphate precipitates out of a solution depends upon the product of the concentrations of Ca^{2+} and $PO_4{}^{3-}$. At a certain value for this product (the **solubility product**), the solution is saturated. Whenever $[Ca^{2+}] \times [PO_4{}^{3-}]$ exceeds the solubility product, calcium phosphate precipitates. Associated with the osteoblasts in new bone is an alkaline phosphatase that hydrolyzes phosphate esters. It has been postulated that phosphates liberated by such ester hydrolysis increase the concentration of phosphate in the vicinity of the osteoblasts to a point where the solubility product is exceeded and calcium phosphate precipitates. This mechanism may be involved in the calcification process, but it is almost certainly only part of the story. There is some evidence that mineralization is a consequence of the stereochemical configuration of the collagen molecule itself.

In the same way that alkaline phosphatase is associated with the osteoblasts, acid phosphatase is associated with the osteoclasts. The significance of this association is not known, and the mechanisms by which the osteoclasts cause bone resorption are incompletely understood. They may secrete an acid which demineralizes the bone in their vicinity or a chelating agent which ties up calcium, causing more bone calcium to go into solution. Other investigations suggest that osteoclasts phagocytose bone, digesting it in their cytoplasm.

Uptake of Other Minerals

Lead and some other toxic elements are taken up and released by bone in a manner similar to that in which calcium is turned over. The rapid bone uptake of these elements is sometimes called a "detoxifying mechanism" because it serves to remove them from the body fluids, thus ameliorating the toxic manifestations. The radioactive elements radium and plutonium (and the radioactive isotope of strontium that is a by-product of atomic bomb explosions) are also taken up by bone. In this situation, the uptake is definitely harmful, because radiation from these elements may cause malignant degeneration of bone cells and the formation of osteogenic sarcomas. Fluoride is taken up by bone and is incorporated into the enamel of the teeth. When the amount incorporated is large, a discoloration of the enamel (**mottled enamel**) results.

However, small amounts endow the teeth with a significantly increased resistance to dental caries.

Metabolic Bone Disease

There are a variety of diseases in which bone changes are secondary to generalized disturbances in metabolism. Terminology in this field has been changing and unsettled, but a number of names are in general use. **Osteosclerosis,** the presence of increased amounts of calcified bone, occurs in patients with metastatic tumors, lead poisoning, and hypoparathyroidism. **Osteoporosis,** a decrease in bone mass with preservation of the normal ratio of mineral to matrix, is a common abnormality that can be due to increased bone resorption or decreased bone formation. Bone formation is decreased in patients who are immobilized for any reason and in patients with excess glucocorticoid secretion (Cushing's syndrome). Osteoporosis is also common in postmenopausal women, possibly because the decrease in blood estrogen concentration increases the sensitivity of bone to parathyroid hormone. The term **osteomalacia** is usually used to refer to disorders such as rickets in which the amount of mineral accretion in bone per unit of bone matrix is deficient.

VITAMIN D & THE HYDROXYCHOLECALCIFEROLS

The active transport of Ca^{2+} and phosphate from the intestine is increased by a metabolite of vitamin D. The term vitamin D is used to refer to a group of closely related sterols produced by the action of ultraviolet light on certain provitamins (Fig 21–2). Vitamin D_3, which is also called cholecalciferol, is produced in the skin of mammals from 7-dehydrocholesterol by the action of sunlight. The reaction involves the rapid formation of a closely related compound, previtamin D_3, and slower conversion of the previtamin to vitamin D_3. Vitamin D_3 is also ingested in the diet. In the liver, vitamin D_3 is converted to a metabolite, 25-hydroxycholecalciferol. The 25-hydroxycholecalciferol is converted in turn in the kidney into the physiologically active metabolite 1,25-dihydroxycholecalciferol. All the hydroxycholecalciferols are transported in the plasma bound to a specific α globulin–binding protein. The normal plasma level of 25-hydroxycholecalciferol is about 50 ng/ml, and the normal plasma level of 1,25-dihydroxycholecalciferol is about 0.03 ng/ml (approximately 100 pmol/L).

Because 1,25-dihydroxycholecalciferol is produced in the body and transported in the bloodstream to act at a distance from its site of production, it can be called a hormone. It acts on the nuclei of the intestinal epithelial cells to initiate the formation of mRNA. The mRNA dictates the formation of a protein that binds Ca^{2+}, but the details of the mechanism by which 1,25-dihydroxycholecalciferol increases Ca^{2+} absorp-

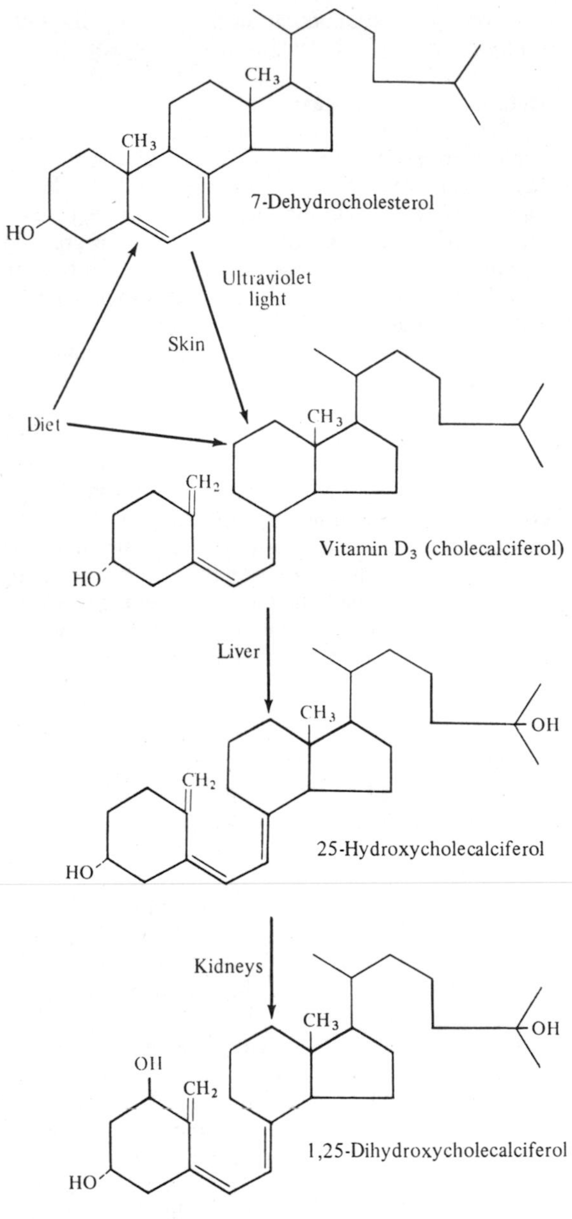

7-Dehydrocholesterol

Ultraviolet light

Skin

Diet

Vitamin D₃ (cholecalciferol)

Liver

25-Hydroxycholecalciferol

Kidneys

1,25-Dihydroxycholecalciferol

Figure 21–2. Vitamin D metabolism. The provitamin 7-dehydrocholesterol is converted to vitamin D_3 in the skin of mammals, and the active metabolite, 1,25-dihydroxycholecalciferol, is formed by hydroxylation in the liver and kidneys.

tion are still unsettled. 1,25-Dihydroxycholecalciferol also mobilizes Ca^{2+} from bone. However, the poor absorption of Ca^{2+} in vitamin D deficiency often leads to hypocalcemia, and because of the calcium deficiency, the protein of new bone fails to mineralize. The result in children and young animals is the disease called **rickets.** Rickets can be due to inadequate intake of the provitamins that are converted to vitamin D_3 by sunlight, to inadequate exposure to sun, or to failure of the kidneys to produce normal amounts of 1,25-dihydroxycholecalciferol.

Formation of 1,25-dihydroxycholecalciferol in the kidneys, which is catalyzed by renal 1α-hydroxylase, is regulated in a feedback fashion by plasma Ca^{2+} and PO_4^{3-} (Fig 21–3). The hormone acts on intestine and bone to increase plasma Ca^{2+} and PO_4^{3-}. Its formation is facilitated by parathyroid hormone, and when the plasma Ca^{2+} is low, parathyroid hormone secretion is increased. When the plasma Ca^{2+} is high, little 1,25-dihydroxycholecalciferol is produced, and the kidney produces the relatively inactive metabolite 24,25-dihydroxycholecalciferol instead. This effect of Ca^{2+} on production of 1,25-dihydroxycholecalciferol is the mechanism that brings about adaptation of Ca^{2+} absorption from the intestine (see above). The production of 1,25-dihydroxycholecalciferol is also increased by low and inhibited by high plasma PO_4^{3-}, apparently by a direct inhibitory effect of PO_4^{3-} on renal 1α-hydroxylase. Additional control of 1,25-dihydroxycholecalciferol formation is exerted by a negative feedback effect of the metabolite on renal 1α-hydroxylase. There is evidence that this effect is exerted directly on the kidney, but there has been speculation that it may also be mediated via inhibition of parathyroid hormone secretion, since there are 1,25-dihydroxycholecalciferol receptors in the parathyroid glands. Prolactin increases the activity of renal 1α-hydroxylase, and circulating 1,25-dihydroxycholecalciferol is increased during lactation. Estrogens also increase renal 1α-hydroxylase activity.

THE PARATHYROID GLANDS

Anatomy

In humans there are usually 4 parathyroid glands: 2 embedded in the superior poles of the thyroid and 2 in

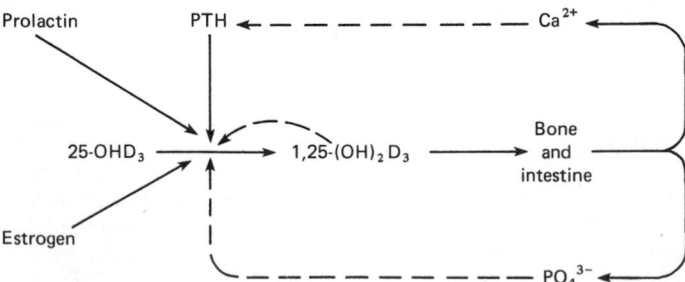

Figure 21–3. Feedback control of the formation of 1,25-dihydroxycholecalciferol (1,25-$[OH]_2D_3$) from 25-hydroxycholecalciferol (25-OHD_3) in the kidney. Solid arrows indicate stimulation, dashed arrows inhibition.

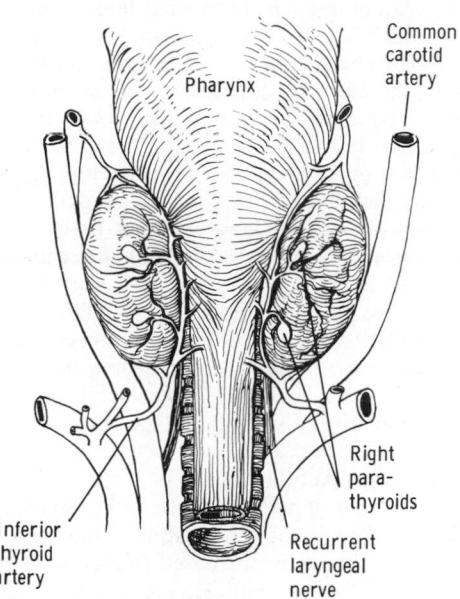

Figure 21–4. The human parathyroid glands, viewed from behind. (Redrawn and reproduced, with permission, from Goss CM [editor]: *Gray's Anatomy of the Human Body,* 29th ed. Lea & Febiger, 1973.)

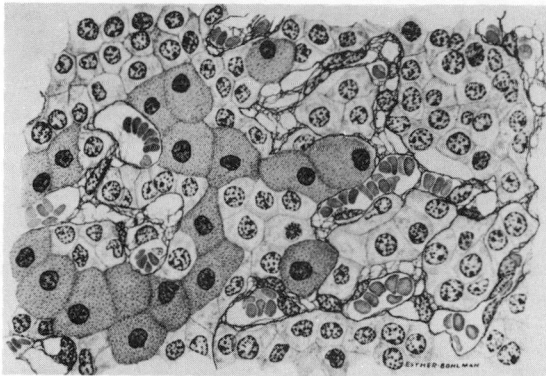

Figure 21–5. Section of human parathyroid. (Reduced 50% from × 960.) Small cells are chief cells; large cells with granules in cytoplasm (especially prominent in lower left of picture) are oxyphil cells. (Reproduced, with permission, from Bloom W, Fawcett DW: *A Textbook of Histology,* 10th ed. Saunders, 1975.)

its inferior poles (Fig 21–4). However, the location of the individual parathyroids and their number vary considerably. Parathyroid tissue is sometimes found in the mediastinum.

Each parathyroid gland is a richly vascularized disk, about 3 × 6 × 2 mm, containing 2 distinct types of cells. The abundant **chief cells,** which have a clear cytoplasm, secrete parathyroid hormone. The less abundant and larger **oxyphil cells,** which have oxyphil granules in their cytoplasm (Fig 21–5), contain large numbers of mitochondria. The function of the oxyphil cells is unknown.

Effects of Parathyroidectomy

Parathyroid hormone (parathormone, PTH) is essential for life. After parathyroidectomy, there is a steady decline in the plasma calcium level (Fig 21–6). Signs of neuromuscular hyperexcitability appear, followed by full-blown hypocalcemic tetany (see above). Plasma phosphate levels usually rise as the calcium falls after parathyroidectomy, but the rise does not always occur. In experimental animals, the rise is preceded by a fall.

In humans, tetany is most often due to inadvertent parathyroidectomy during thyroid surgery. Symptoms usually develop 2–3 days postoperatively but may not appear for several weeks or more. In rats on a low-calcium diet, tetany develops much more rapidly, and death occurs 6–10 hours after parathyroidectomy. Injections of parathyroid hormone correct the chemical abnormalities (Fig 21–6), and the symptoms disappear. Injections of calcium salts give temporary re-

lief, and 1-hydroxylated derivatives of vitamin D restore plasma Ca^{2+} to normal. 25-Hydroxycholecalciferol has a direct stimulatory effect on Ca^{2+} absorption from the intestine when administered in large doses, and it is sometimes used in the treatment of hypoparathyroidism even though there is little 1-hydroxylation of vitamin D metabolites in the absence of parathyroid hormone.

The signs of tetany in humans include **Chvostek's sign,** a quick contraction of the ipsilateral facial muscles elicited by tapping over the facial nerve at the angle of the jaw; and **Trousseau's sign,** a spasm of the muscles of the upper extremity that causes flexion of the wrist and thumb with extension of the fingers (Fig 21–7). In individuals with mild tetany in whom spasm is not evident, Trousseau's sign can sometimes be produced by occluding the circulation for a few minutes with a blood pressure cuff.

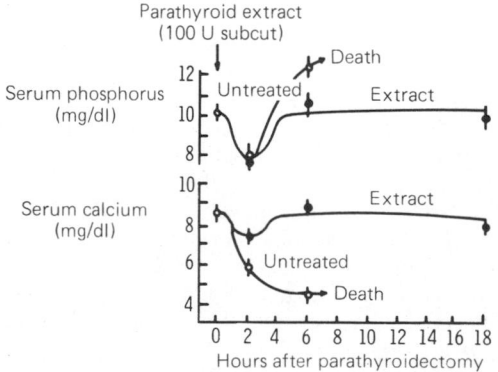

Figure 21–6. Effect of parathyroidectomy (open circles) and parathyroidectomy plus parathyroid extract (solid circles) in rats. Vertical bars are standard errors, each point being a mean of the values for 6 rats. (Redrawn and reproduced, with permission, from Munson PL: Recent advances in parathyroid hormone research. Fed Proc 19:593, 1960.)

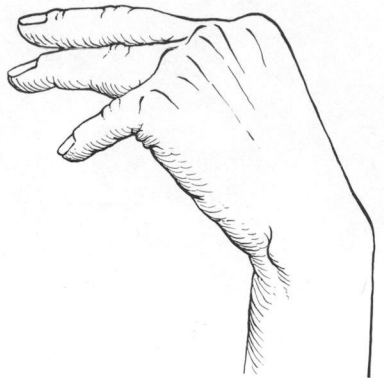

Figure 21–7. Position of the hand in hypocalcemic tetany (Trousseau's sign).

Parathyroid Hormone Excess

Hyperparathyroidism due to injections of large doses of parathyroid extract in animals, or hypersecretion of a functioning parathyroid tumor in humans, is characterized by hypercalcemia, hypophosphatemia, demineralization of the bones, hypercalciuria, and the formation of calcium-containing kidney stones. The bone disease caused by hyperparathyroidism (**osteitis fibrosa cystica**) is characterized by multiple bone cysts.

Synthesis & Metabolism of PTH

Human parathyroid hormone is a linear peptide with a molecular weight of 9500 that contains 84 amino acid residues (Fig 21–8). Its structure is very similar to that of bovine and porcine PTH. It is synthesized as part of a larger molecule containing 115 amino acid residues (**pre–pro-PTH**). During or immediately after synthesis, 25 amino acid residues are removed from the N terminal of this peptide to form the 90–amino acid peptide **pro-PTH.** Six additional amino acid residues are removed from the N terminal of pro-PTH in the Golgi apparatus, and the 84–amino acid peptide PTH is the main secretory product of the chief cells.

The half-life of PTH is short, and the secreted peptide is rapidly cleaved in the liver and kidneys into 2 peptides, a biologically inactive C-terminal fragment with a molecular weight of 7000 and a biologically active N-terminal fragment with a molecular weight of 2500. Further metabolism occurs at a slower rate. There is some evidence that the 2500– and 7000–molecular weight fragments are also formed in the chief cells, with secretion of small amounts of the 2 fragments.

Actions

In addition to increasing the plasma Ca^{2+} and depressing the plasma phosphate, parathyroid hormone increases phosphate excretion in the urine. This **phosphaturic action** is due to a decrease in tubular reabsorption of phosphate. It was once believed that the increase in the plasma calcium level produced by parathyroid hormone was secondary to the decrease in plasma phosphate level, and, therefore, that the entire effect of the hormone could be explained by its phosphaturic action on the kidney. The rough reciprocal relationship between the plasma calcium and the plasma phosphate levels has been mentioned above. However, parathyroid hormone has a direct calcium-mobilizing action on bone in addition to its action on the kidney. It also increases renal tubular reabsorption of calcium, although calcium excretion is usually increased in hyperparathyroidism because the increase in the amount filtered overwhelms the effect on reabsorption. Parathyroid hormone also increases the formation of 1,25-dihydroxycholecalciferol, the physiologically active metabolite of vitamin D (see above).

Mechanism of Action

The actions of parathyroid hormone on the bones and the kidneys involve activation of adenylate cyclase, with consequent increased formation of cyclic AMP in the affected cells. How cyclic AMP affects calcium in bone is unsettled. The hormone promotes a rapid release of calcium and phosphorus from bone mineral into ECF, probably by stimulating bone resorption by the osteocytes. It also promotes on a more long-term basis increased osteoclastic activity and

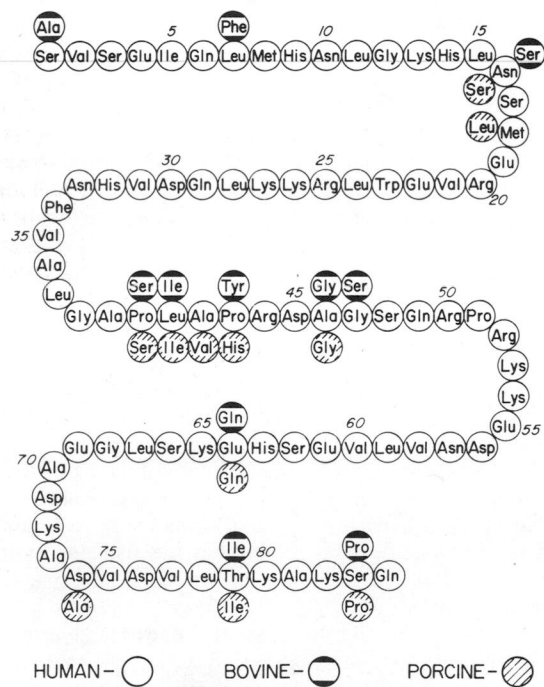

Figure 21–8. Parathyroid hormone. The structure of human PTH is shown with the positions indicated above and below the human structure where amino acid residues are different for bovine and porcine PTH. (Reproduced, with permission, from Keutmann H & others: Complete amino acid sequence of human parathyroid hormone. Biochemistry 17:5723, 1978.)

triggers the formation of more osteoclasts while inhibiting the formation of osteoblasts. There is some evidence that the cyclic AMP generated by parathyroid hormone increases the entry of calcium into the bone cells from bone matrix and that the calcium in turn activates—via the formation of mRNA—the synthesis of bone-resorbing enzymes. 1,25-Dihydroxycholecalciferol has an action on bone similar to parathyroid hormone and synergizes with it but does not affect cyclic AMP.

In pseudohypoparathyroidism, a rare disease in which the signs and symptoms of hypoparathyroidism develop but the circulating level of parathyroid hormone is elevated, parathyroid hormone fails to increase cyclic AMP in the kidney. This results in decreased formation of 1,25-dihydroxycholecalciferol, which in turn decreases the skeletal response to parathyroid hormone. The cause of the disease is apparently an abnormality of the receptors for parathyroid hormone.

Regulation of Secretion

It has been proved by perfusion experiments that the circulating level of ionized calcium acts directly on the parathyroid glands in a feedback fashion to regulate the secretion of parathyroid hormone. When the plasma Ca^{2+} level is high, secretion is inhibited, and the calcium is deposited in the bones. When it is low, secretion is increased, and calcium is mobilized from the bones. Magnesium appears to have a similar direct effect, with a decrease in plasma magnesium concentration stimulating parathyroid secretion. Another factor regulating the plasma Ca^{2+} is the readily exchangeable bone calcium pool. However, this pool can only maintain the total plasma calcium at about 7 mg/dl in the absence of parathyroid hormone, and maintenance of the normal level of 10 mg/dl is due to the activity of the parathyroid glands. Elevated plasma phosphate levels stimulate parathyroid secretion, but only because they lower the plasma Ca^{2+} level; they do not act directly on the gland.

In conditions such as chronic renal disease and rickets, in which the plasma Ca^{2+} is chronically low, feedback stimulation of the parathyroid glands causes compensatory parathyroid hypertrophy and **secondary hyperparathyroidism.** The plasma Ca^{2+} is low in chronic renal disease primarily because the diseased kidneys lose the ability to form 1,25-dihydroxycholecalciferol.

CALCITONIN

Origin

In dogs, perfusion of the thyroparathyroid region with solutions containing high concentrations of Ca^{2+} leads to a fall in peripheral plasma Ca^{2+}, and after damage to this region, Ca^{2+} infusions cause a greater increase in plasma Ca^{2+} than they do in control ani-

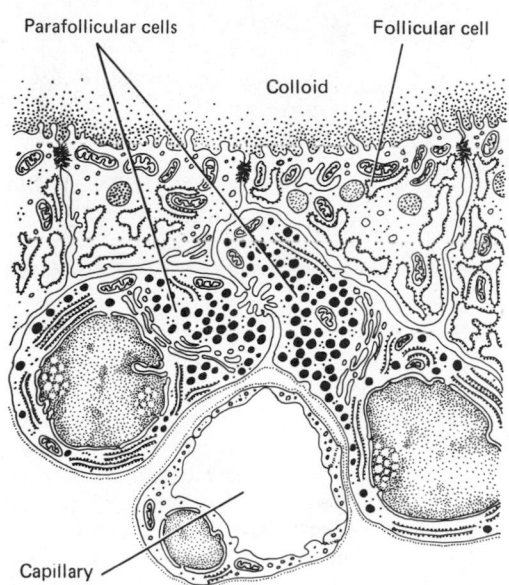

Figure 21–9. Parafollicular cells in thyroid. (Modified from Poirier J, Dumas JLR: *Review of Medical Histology*. Saunders, 1977.)

mals. These and other observations led to the discovery that a calcium-lowering as well as a calcium-elevating hormone was secreted by structures in the neck. The calcium-lowering hormone has been named **calcitonin.** In nonmammalian vertebrates, the source of calcitonin is the **ultimobranchial bodies,** a pair of glands derived embryologically from the fifth branchial arches. In mammals, these bodies have for the most part become incorporated into the thyroid gland, where the ultimobranchial tissue is distributed around the follicles as the **parafollicular cells** (Figs 18–2, 21–9). Since these cells, also known as clear cells or C cells, secrete the hormone, it is often referred to as **thyrocalcitonin.** However, total thyroidectomy does not always reduce the circulating level of the hormone to zero, and the hormone has been reported to be present in the thymus. Therefore, it seems more appropriate to refer to it by its original name, calcitonin.

Structure

The structure of human calcitonin (Fig 21–10) has been determined by analysis of extracts of medullary carcinomas of the thyroid. These are calcitonin-secreting tumors rich in parafollicular cells. The calcitonins of the other species that have been studied contain 32 amino acid residues, but the amino acid composition varies considerably. Salmon calcitonin is of interest because it is 20 or more times as active in humans as human calcitonin.

Secretion

Secretion of calcitonin is increased when the thyroid gland is perfused with solutions containing a high

$$S \text{——————} S$$

Cys-Gly-Asn-Leu-Ser-Thr-Cys-Met-Leu-Gly-Thr-Tyr-Thr-Gln-Asp-Phe-Asn-
1   2   3   4   5   6   7   8   9   10   11   12   13   14   15   16   17

Lys-Phe-His-Thr-Phe-Pro-Gln-Thr-Ala-Ile-Gly-Val-Gly-Ala-Pro-NH$_2$
18   19   20   21   22   23   24   25   26 27 28 29 30 31 32

Figure 21–10. Human calcitonin.

Ca^{2+} concentration. Measurement of circulating calcitonin by immunoassay indicates that it is not secreted until the plasma calcium reaches approximately 9.5 mg/dl and that, above this calcium level, plasma calcitonin is directly proportionate to plasma calcium (Fig 21–11). The normal rate of secretion appears to be about 0.5 mg/d. Cyclic AMP may be involved in the regulation of calcitonin secretion. There is some evidence that a "gut factor"—possibly gastrin (see Chapter 26)—stimulates calcitonin secretion, and it may be that calcium in the intestine initiates secretion of the calcium-lowering hormone before the calcium is absorbed.

Actions

Calcitonin lowers the circulating calcium and phosphate levels. An example of its action is shown in Fig 21–12, which also shows that porcine calcitonin fails to affect the plasma magnesium level in humans. It exerts its calcium-lowering effect by inhibiting bone resorption. This effect occurs in the absence of the parathyroid glands, gastrointestinal tract, and kidneys and is due to a direct action of the hormone on bone. There is evidence that it acts by inhibiting the active transport of calcium from bone cells into the ECF. It does not appear to affect cyclic AMP or the genetic mechanism regulating protein synthesis.

The exact physiologic role of calcitonin is uncertain. The calcitonin content of the human thyroid is very low, and in thyroidectomized animals, it is only after injecting calcium or parathyroid extract that any definite abnormality of calcium metabolism can be demonstrated. This may be explained in part by calcitonin from tissues other than the thyroid. However, there is general agreement that the hormone is relatively inactive in adult animals and humans. In addition, patients with medullary carcinoma of the thyroid and high circulating calcitonin levels have no symptoms directly attributable to the hormone. Similarly, a syndrome due to calcitonin deficiency has not been described. The hormone is more active in young individuals and may play a role in skeletal development.

Summary

In summary, there are 3 principal hormones that regulate the plasma concentration of Ca^{2+}. Parathyroid hormone increases plasma Ca^{2+}, primarily by mobiliz-

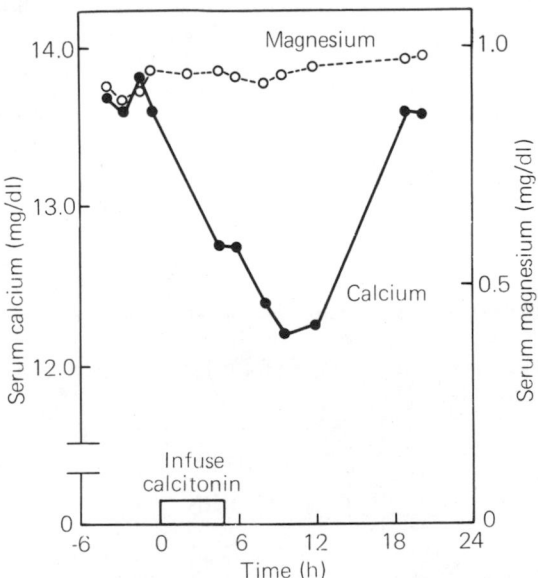

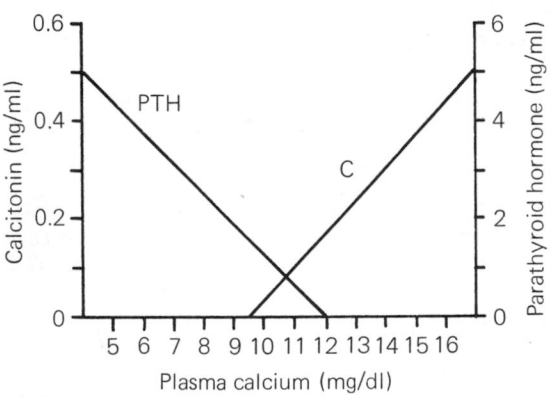

Figure 21–11. Concentration of calcitonin (C) and parathyroid hormone (PTH) as a function of plasma calcium level. (Modified and reproduced, with permission, from Aurbach GD & others: Polypeptide hormones and calcium metabolism. Ann Intern Med 70:1243, 1969.)

Figure 21–12. Effect of porcine calcitonin on serum calcium and magnesium in a patient with hypercalcemia. (Reproduced, with permission, from Foster GV & others: Effect of thyrocalcitonin in man. Lancet 1:107, 1966.)

ing this ion from bone and increasing its reabsorption in the renal tubules. 1,25-Dihydroxycholecalciferol increases plasma Ca^{2+} by increasing intestinal absorption of Ca^{2+} and mobilizing Ca^{2+} from bone. Calcitonin decreases plasma Ca^{2+} by inhibiting bone resorption.

EFFECTS OF OTHER HORMONES ON CALCIUM METABOLISM

In addition to 1,25-dihydroxycholecalciferol, parathyroid hormone, and calcitonin, the hormones affecting calcium metabolism include adrenal glucocorticoids and growth hormone. The glucocorticoids tend to lower plasma calcium levels. They tear down the protein matrix of bone, leading to osteoporosis (see Chapter 20), but they also inhibit the action of 1,25-dihydroxycholecalciferol on the intestine. This is why they depress the hypercalcemia of vitamin D intoxication. In addition, there is evidence that prostaglandins of the E series secreted by certain tumors increase plasma calcium, and glucocorticoids have been reported to inhibit prostaglandin synthesis. Growth hormone increases calcium excretion in the urine, but it also increases intestinal absorption of calcium, and this effect may be greater than the effect on excretion, with a resultant positive calcium balance.

22 | The Pituitary Gland

The anterior, intermediate, and posterior lobes of the pituitary gland are actually 3 more or less separate endocrine organs that secrete altogether at least 10 hormones. The 6 established hormones of the anterior pituitary are **thyroid-stimulating hormone (TSH), adrenocorticotropic hormone (ACTH), luteinizing hormone (LH), follicle-stimulating hormone (FSH), prolactin,** and **growth hormone** (Table 22–1). All of these except growth hormone and prolactin regulate the function of other endocrine organs, and growth hormone causes secretion of a peptide from the liver (see below). In addition, the anterior lobe of the pituitary secretes β-lipotropin (β-LPH). This peptide contains 91 amino acid residues, and although its physiologic role is uncertain, it may be the precursor in peripheral tissues of endorphins and enkephalins, peptides that bind to opiate receptors (see Chapter 15). The hormones that are tropic to a particular endocrine gland are discussed in the chapter on that gland: TSH in Chapter 18; ACTH in Chapter 20; and the gonadotropins FSH and LH in Chapter 23, along with prolactin. The hormones secreted by the posterior pituitary in mammals **(oxytocin** and **vasopressin)** and the neural regulation of anterior and posterior pituitary secretion

are discussed in Chapter 14. Growth hormone, β-lipotropin, and the melanocyte-stimulating hormones of the intermediate lobe of the pituitary, α-**MSH** and β-**MSH,** are the subject of this chapter, along with a number of general considerations about the pituitary.

MORPHOLOGY

Gross Anatomy

The anatomy of the pituitary gland is summarized in Fig 22–1 and discussed in detail in Chapter 14. The posterior pituitary is innervated by fibers from the supraoptic and paraventricular nuclei of the hypothalamus, whereas the anterior pituitary has a special vascular connection with the brain, the portal hypophyseal vessels. The intermediate lobe is formed from the dorsal half of **Rathke's pouch** in the embryo but is closely adherent to the posterior lobe in the adult. It is separated from the anterior lobe by the remains of Rathke's pouch, the **residual cleft.**

Table 22–1. Pituitary hormones.

Name and Source	Principal Actions
Anterior lobe	
Thyroid-stimulating hormone (TSH, thyrotropin)	Stimulates thyroid secretion and growth
Adrenocorticotropic hormone (ACTH, corticotropin)	Stimulates adrenocortical secretion and growth
Growth hormone (GH, somatotropin, STH)	Accelerates body growth
Follicle-stimulating hormone (FSH)	Stimulates ovarian follicle growth in female and spermatogenesis in male
Luteinizing hormone (LH, interstitial cell-stimulating hormone, ICSH)	Stimulates ovulation and luteinization of ovarian follicles in female and testosterone secretion in male
Prolactin (luteotropic hormone, LTH, luteotropin, lactogenic hormone, mammotropin)	Stimulates secretion of milk and maternal behavior. Maintains corpus luteum in female rodents but apparently not in other species
β-Lipotropin (β-LPH)	?
Intermediate lobe	
α- and β- Melanocyte-stimulating hormones (α- and β-MSH; referred to collectively as melanotropin or intermedin)	Expand melanophores
Posterior lobe	
Vasopressin (antidiuretic hormone, ADH)	Promotes water retention
Oxytocin	Causes milk ejection

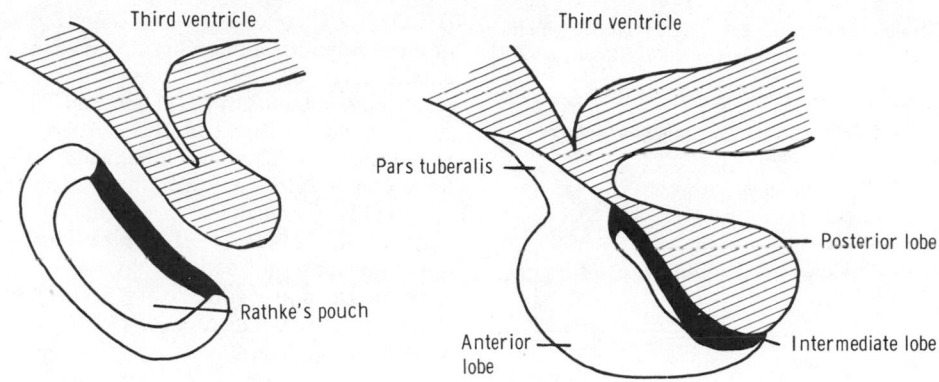

Figure 22–1. Diagrammatic outline of the formation of the pituitary and the various parts of the organ in the adult.

Histology

In the posterior lobe, the endings of the supraoptic and paraventricular axons can be observed in close relation to blood vessels. In some species, the endings are rodlike palisaded structures. There are also neuroglial cells and **pituicytes,** stellate cells containing fat globules that were once thought to secrete posterior lobe hormones but are now believed to be modified astroglia.

The intermediate lobe is rudimentary in humans. Most of its cells are agranular, although there are often a few basophilic elements that resemble anterior lobe cells. Along the residual cleft are small thyroidlike follicles, some containing a little colloid. The function of the colloid, if any, is unknown.

The anterior pituitary is made up of interlacing cell cords and an extensive network of sinusoids. The endothelium of the sinusoids is fenestrated, like that in other endocrine organs. The cells contain granules of stored hormone that are extruded from the cells by exocytosis (Fig 22–2). The granules have not been seen entering the capillaries, and they presumably dissolve in the perisinusoidal space.

Cell Types in the Anterior Pituitary

In rats, 6 types of secretory cells have been identified in the anterior pituitary, and it has been postulated that each cell type secretes one of the 6 established anterior pituitary hormones. However, it has recently been demonstrated that FSH and LH are present in the same cell.

Human anterior pituitary cells have traditionally been divided on the basis of their staining reactions into agranular chromophobes and granular chromophils. The chromophobes are probably secretory cells that are quiescent and not forming secretory granules, or are secreting so rapidly that their stores of granules are exhausted. The chromophilic cells are subdivided into acidophils, which contain large granules that stain readily with acidic dyes, and basophils, which contain small glycoprotein granules with an affinity for basic dyes. Three of the hormones secreted by the basophils are glycoproteins. There has been debate about the

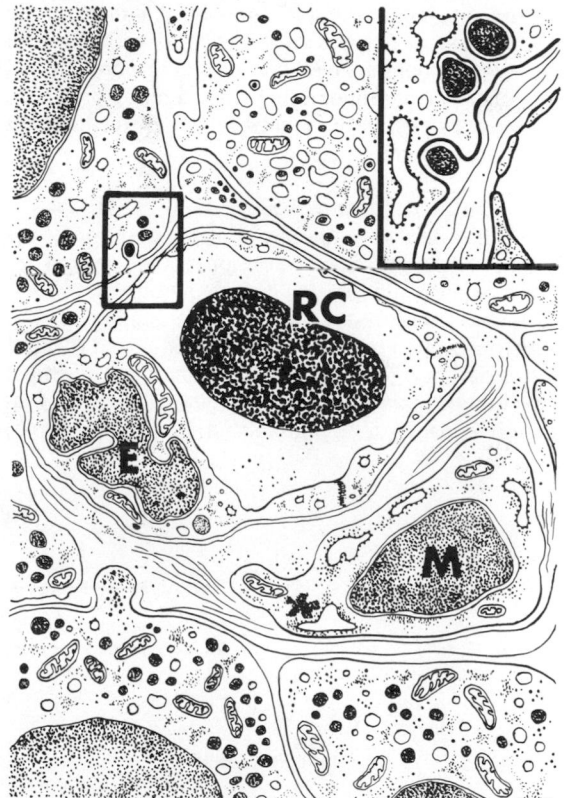

Figure 22–2. Sinusoid in anterior pituitary of rat, surrounded by granule-containing anterior pituitary cells. *RC,* red cell in lumen of sinusoid; *E,* endothelial cell; *M,* macrophage in perisinusoidal space. **Inset:** Higher magnification of area such as that enclosed in the small rectangle, showing release of granule by exocytosis. Structures are, from the left, pituitary cell containing granules, basal lamina of pituitary cell, perisinusoidal space, basal lamina of endothelial cell, endothelial cell, lumen of sinusoid. Note that at 2 locations in the inset the endothelial cell cytoplasm is attenuated (fenestrated). (Redrawn and reproduced, with permission, from Farquhar MG: Fine structure and function in capillaries of the anterior pituitary gland. Angiology 12:270, 1961.)

Table 22–2. Hormone-secreting cells in the human anterior pituitary. PAS, periodic acid–Schiff reaction. (Courtesy of C Ezrin.)

Cell Type	Hormone Secreted	Staining Reactions		
		General	Orange G	PAS
Somatotrop	Growth hormone	Acidophil	+	−
Mammotrop	Prolactin	Acidophil	+	−
Corticotrop	ACTH	Basophil	−	+
FSH gonadotrop	FSH	Basophil	−	+
LH gonadotrop	LH	Basophil	−	+
Thyrotrop	TSH	Basophil	−	+

ACTH-secreting cells. Tumors made up of what appear to be chromophobes secrete ACTH, but there is considerable evidence that the ACTH-secreting cells in normal humans are basophils (Table 22–2). The findings in rats mentioned above have not yet been extended to humans, but it is possible that there is only one instead of 2 types of gonadotrops. There are 2 types of acidophils, one secreting growth hormone and the other (the carminophilic cells) secreting prolactin. However, some chromophobe tumors of the pituitary may also secrete prolactin.

Two-Unit Structure of FSH, LH, & TSH

An observation that bears on the question of the cells of origin of pituitary hormones is the demonstration that the 3 pituitary glycoprotein hormones, FSH, LH, and TSH, are each made up of 2 subunits. The subunits, which have been designated α and β, have some activity but must be combined for maximal physiologic activity. In addition, the placental glycoprotein gonadotropin, human chorionic gonadotropin,

(HCG) (see Chapter 23) has an α and a β subunit. All of the α subunits of these hormones are similar to one another even though they are produced in different cells; the α subunits of LH, FSH, and TSH are identical, and the α subunit of HCG differs only slightly from the others. The β subunits, which differ in structure, confer hormonal specificity. The α units are remarkably interchangeable, and the hybrid molecule made up of TSH-α and LH-β, for example, has much more gonadotropic activity than LH-β alone. The physiologic and evolutionary significance of the unique 2-unit structure of these glycoprotein hormones remains to be determined.

INTERMEDIATE LOBE HORMONES

In the skins of fish, reptiles, and amphibians, there are cells called **melanophores.** These contain melanin granules. Other cells called **iridophores** contain reflecting platelets. When the granules aggregate around the nuclei of melanophores and the reflecting platelets disperse to the periphery of the iridophores, the color of the skin lightens; when the melanin granules disperse and the reflecting platelets aggregate, the skin darkens. Birds and mammals do not have pigment cells of this type, but their pituitaries contain 2 polypeptides called **melanotropins** or **melanocyte-stimulating hormones (MSHs),** which when injected into lower vertebrates disperse melanophore granules and aggregate iridophore platelets.

α-MSH is made up of amino acid residues 1–13 of the ACTH molecule (Fig 22–3). β-MSH is a some-

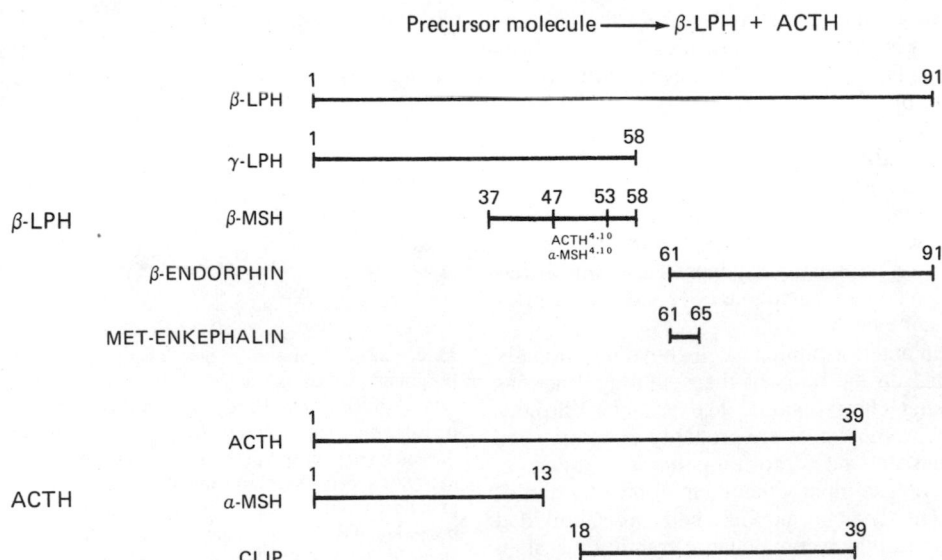

Figure 22–3. Diagrammatic representation of the relation of β-LPH and its fragments to ACTH and its fragments. Identical sequences are found in ACTH 4–10, α-MSH 4–10, and β-MSH 11–17 (β-MSH 47–53 in this diagram). The whole molecule of β-MSH is labeled 37–58 in this diagram to emphasize its relation to γ-LPH. (Courtesy of G Pelletier.)

what larger peptide with considerable variation in structure from species to species. However, it contains a 7-amino acid sequence that is identical to amino acid residues 4–10 in α-MSH and ACTH (Fig 22–3). Consequently, it is not surprising that ACTH has considerable MSH activity.

The origin of the intermediate lobe hormones and their relation to β-LPH and ACTH is currently a matter of debate. The problem is compounded by the fact that in humans and a few other mammalian species, the intermediate lobe is rudimentary or absent. One hypothesis that appears to fit the available data is that both the anterior and intermediate lobes contain cells which manufacture a large precursor molecule that splits intracellularly into β-LPH and ACTH (Fig 22–3). In the anterior lobe, these 2 products are secreted, whereas in the intermediate lobe, when it is present, β-LPH is cleaved intracellularly to γ-LPH and then to β-MSH, and ACTH is cleaved to α-MSH and corticotropinlike intermediate lobe peptide (CLIP). Presumably the α- and β-MSH are then secreted. According to this hypothesis, there should be no circulating MSHs and no α- or β-MSH in the pituitaries of species that lack an intermediate lobe. This appears to be the case in humans. Human blood contains MSH activity, but this is presumably due to ACTH and possibly to β-LPH. It is known that the amount of β-LPH in the blood parallels the amount of ACTH, but the function of circulating β-LPH is not known. The functions of the endorphins and the enkephalins in the CNS are discussed in Chapter 15.

Changes in skin coloration in fish, reptiles, and amphibians are probably mediated in part via neuroendocrine reflex mechanisms. The receptors for these reflexes are in the retina. The hypothalamus has been reported to contain an MSH-stimulating factor and an MSH-inhibiting factor, but the intermediate lobe is also believed to be innervated by fibers from the hypothalamus that inhibit MSH secretion. On a dark background, MSH secretion is not inhibited, and the animal is dark. On a white background, release of MSH is inhibited, and the animal's color lightens.

Melatonin, an indole derivative secreted by the pineal glands of mammals and other vertebrates (see Chapter 24), lightens the skin of embryonic fish and larval amphibians by causing aggregation of melanophore granules without any change in the iridophores. However, it does not exert a lightening effect in adult animals and apparently does not play any role in regulating their skin color.

In humans and other mammals there are melanin-containing cells called **melanocytes** but no melanophores containing pigment granules that move, and the functions of the MSHs and melatonin, if any, are uncertain. It has been claimed that the MSHs exert effects on the nervous system, but the physiologic significance of these effects is not known. Prolonged treatment with natural and synthetic MSH preparations darkens the skin of blacks, and such preparations have been reported to accelerate melanin synthesis. The pigmentary changes in several endocrine diseases are

probably due to changes in circulating ACTH, since ACTH has MSH activity. For example, abnormal pallor is a hallmark of hypopituitarism. Hyperpigmentation occurs in patients with ACTH-secreting tumors and in patients with adrenal insufficiency due to primary adrenal disease. Indeed, the presence of hyperpigmentation in association with adrenal insufficiency rules out the possibility that the insufficiency is secondary to pituitary disease because the pituitary must be intact for pigmentation to occur.

GROWTH HORMONE

Chemistry & Species Specificity

Growth hormone, like other protein hormones, varies considerably in structure from species to species. For example, the growth hormone of the rhesus monkey has a molecular weight of 25,400 and 4 disulfide bridges, while human growth hormone has a molecular weight of 21,500 and 2 disulfide bridges (Fig 22–4). Human growth hormone (HGH) has now been synthesized. It bears a marked structural resemblance to prolactin and a placental hormone, human chorionic somatomammotropin (HCS), that has growth-promoting activity (see Chapter 23). On the basis of the structural similarities, it has been suggested that growth hormone, prolactin, and HCS all evolved from a common single hormone. Porcine and simian growth hormones have only a transient effect in the guinea pig, probably because they stimulate the rapid formation of anti–growth hormone antibodies. In monkeys and humans, bovine and porcine growth hormones do not even have a significant transient effect on growth, although monkey and human growth hormones are fully active in both monkeys and humans (Table 22–3). Human growth hormone has intrinsic lactogenic activity.

Table 22–3. Activities of growth hormones in various species. (+), active; (−), inactive.

Growth Hormone From	Stimulates Growth In				
	Fish	Birds	Rats	Monkeys	Humans
Fish	+		−		
Reptiles			+		
Amphibia			+		
Birds		+	+		
Cows	+	−*	+	−	−†
Sheep	+		+		−
Pigs	+	−*	+	−	−†
Whales			+		−
Monkeys	+		+	+	+
Humans	+		+	+	+

*Probable diabetogenic effect.
†Slight diabetogenic effect.

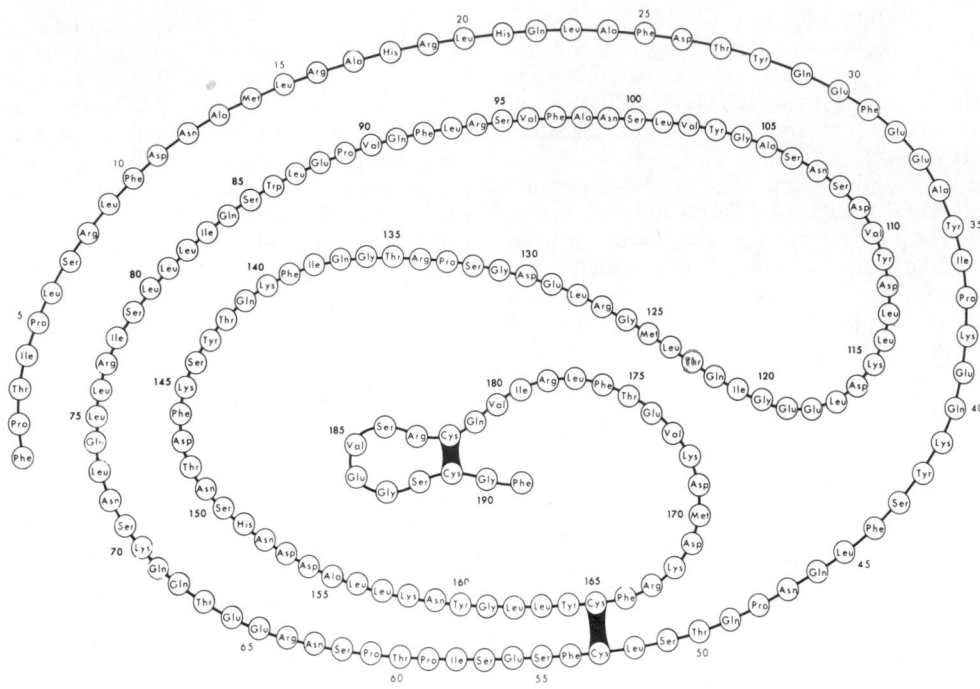

Figure 22–4. Structure of human growth hormone. The black bars indicate the disulfide bridges. (Courtesy of CH Li.)

Plasma Levels & Metabolism

Plasma growth hormone levels are routinely measured by radioimmunoassay. The basal growth hormone level in adult humans is normally less than 3 ng/ml. Growth hormone is metabolized rapidly, probably at least in part in the liver. The half-life of circulating growth hormone in humans is 20–30 minutes, and the daily growth hormone output has been calculated to be 0.2–1.0 mg/d in adults.

Effects on Growth

The place of growth hormone in the complex of factors that promote growth is discussed below. In young animals in which the epiphyses have not yet fused to the long bones (see Chapter 21), growth is inhibited by hypophysectomy (Fig 22–5) and stimulated by growth hormone. Chondrogenesis is accelerated, and as the cartilaginous epiphyseal plates widen, they lay down more matrix at the ends of long bones (Fig 22–6). In this way, stature is increased, and prolonged treatment leads to gigantism. The increase in width of the tibial epiphyseal plate in hypophysectomized rats has been used as a bioassay for growth hormone ("tibia test"). However, it is now known that the effects of growth hormone on cartilage are indirect and are actually mediated by somatomedin (see below).

When the epiphyses are closed, linear growth is no longer possible, and growth hormone produces the pattern of bone and soft tissue deformities (Fig 22–7) known in humans as **acromegaly.** The size of most of the viscera is increased. Endocrine organs may also be

Figure 22–5. Effect of hypophysectomy on growth of the immature rhesus monkey. Both monkeys were the same size and weight 2 years previously, when the one on the left was hypophysectomized. (Reproduced, with permission, from Knobil E: *Growth in Living Systems.* Zarrow MX [editor]. Basic Books, 1961.)

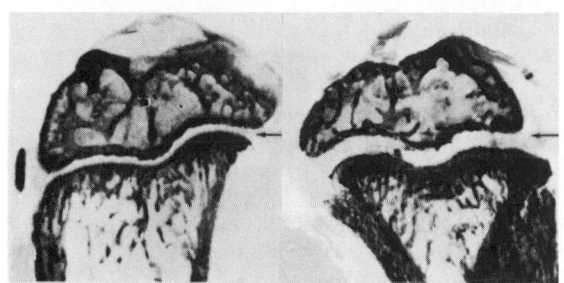

Figure 22–6. Effect of growth hormone treatment for 4 days on the proximal tibial epiphysis of the hypophysectomized rat. Note the increased width of the unstained cartilage plate in the tibia of the treated animal on the right, compared with the control on the left. (Reproduced, with permission, from Evans HM & others: Bioassay of pituitary growth hormone. Endocrinology 32:14, 1943.)

Figure 22–7. Effect of chronic treatment with anterior pituitary extract. The animal in the lower picture was treated from the sixth to the thirty-second week of life. The animal in the upper picture is a littermate control. (Reproduced, with permission, from Evans HM, Meyer K, Simpson ME: *Growth and Gonad-Stimulating Hormones of the Anterior Hypophysis.* Univ of California Press, 1933.)

affected by growth hormone, and the hormone is said to synergize with ACTH in increasing adrenal size and with androgens in increasing the size of accessory reproductive organs. The protein content of the body is increased and the fat content decreased.

Effects on Protein & Electrolyte Metabolism

Growth hormone is a protein anabolic hormone and produces a positive nitrogen and phosphorus balance (Fig 22–8), a rise in plasma phosphorus, and a fall in the blood urea nitrogen and amino acid levels. It also stimulates erythropoiesis. Gastrointestinal absorption of calcium is increased. Na^+ and K^+ excretion are reduced by an action independent of the adrenal glands, probably because these electrolytes are di-

verted from the kidney to the growing tissues. Excretion of the amino acid hydroxyproline is increased during growth and in acromegaly, but it is also increased in a number of other diseases. Hydroxyproline is believed to come from collagen, and growth hormone increases collagen synthesis.

Mechanism of Anabolic Action

The stimulatory effect of growth hormone on protein synthesis appears to be exerted at the ribosomal level, where it has been postulated to affect either ribosomal attachment or translation. It also increases the transport of neutral and basic amino acids into cells, and this action is said to occur even when protein synthesis is blocked by puromycin. Insulin stimulates

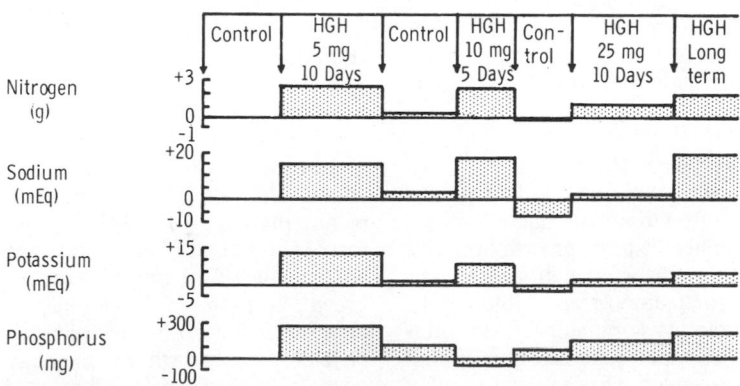

Figure 22–8. Effects of human growth hormone (HGH) on the daily balance (intake minus output) of nitrogen, sodium, potassium, and phosphorus in a female pituitary dwarf. A positive balance is plotted upward from the zero line; a negative balance is plotted downward. (Redrawn and reproduced, with permission, from Hutchings JJ & others: Metabolic growth changes produced by human growth hormone [Li] in pituitary dwarf. J Clin Endocrinol 19:759, 1959.)

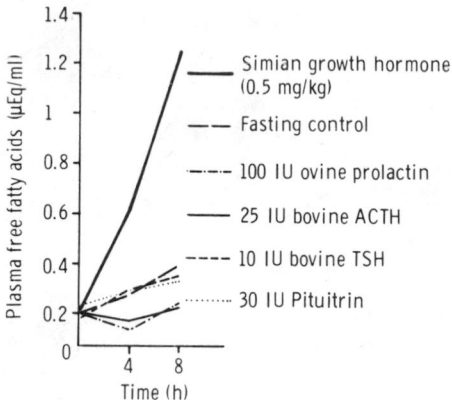

Figure 22–9. Effect of various hormones on plasma free fatty acid levels in fasting hypophysectomized rhesus monkeys. Pituitrin is an extract of posterior pituitary tissue. (Redrawn and reproduced, with permission, from Goodman HM, Knobil E: The effects of fasting and of growth hormone administration on plasma fatty acid concentration in normal and hypophysectomized rhesus monkeys. Endocrinology 65:451, 1959.)

the transport of amino acids into cells by a mechanism separate from that which is stimulated by growth hormone, and this action of insulin is also unaffected by puromycin.

Effects on Carbohydrate & Fat Metabolism

The actions of growth hormone on carbohydrate metabolism are discussed in Chapter 19. Growth hormone is diabetogenic because it increases hepatic glucose output and exerts an anti-insulin effect in muscle. It is ketogenic because it increases circulating free fatty acid levels (Fig 22–9). The increase in plasma free fatty acids, which takes several hours to develop, provides a ready source of energy for the tissues during hypoglycemia, fasting, and stressful stimuli. Growth hormone does not stimulate the B cells of the pancreas directly, but it increases the ability of the pancreas to respond to insulinogenic stimuli such as arginine and glucose. This is one way growth hormone promotes growth, since insulin has a protein anabolic effect (see Chapter 19). Quantitatively, however, the direct effect of growth hormone on protein formation is much more important.

Somatomedin & Other Growth Factors

The effects of growth hormone on cartilage and consequently on linear growth are not due to a direct action of growth hormone. Instead, growth hormone stimulates the liver and perhaps other tissues to produce a peptide factor (or factors) responsible for the skeletal effects. The factor was originally called **sulfation factor** because it stimulates the incorporation of sulfate into cartilage. However, it has a variety of other effects on cartilage including stimulation of DNA and RNA synthesis and collagen formation and is now more widely known as **somatomedin.** Somatomedin activity has been measured in the plasma in a variety of

disease states and has been found to be better correlated to growth than plasma growth hormone concentration.

It now appears that there are a variety of different growth factors in the circulation. Those that have been partly characterized include somatomedin A, somatomedin G, nonsuppressible insulinlike activity (NSILA), multiplication-stimulating activity (MSA), nerve growth factor (see Chapter 2), epidermal growth factor (EGF), ovarian growth factor (OGF), fibroblast growth factor (FGF), thymosin (see Chapter 27), and others. Some of these may be identical, and the exact identity of the somatomedins responsible for the growth-promoting effects of growth hormone has not been established.

The role of somatomedin in the mediation of other effects of growth hormone is also unsettled. However, it is clear that not all of the effects of growth hormone are mediated via somatomedin, since somatomedin has insulinlike properties, including inhibition of lipolysis, whereas growth hormone has anti-insulin activity and causes lipolysis. Other actions that appear to be direct rather than somatomedin-mediated include stimulation of erythropoiesis, increased insulin responses to insulinogenic stimuli, and increased cellular uptake of amino acids.

Hypothalamic Control of Growth Hormone Secretion

The secretion of growth hormone is controlled via the hypothalamus. A growth hormone–releasing hormone and a growth hormone–inhibiting hormone have been extracted from hypothalamic tissue (see Chapter 14), and hypothalamic lesions or section of the pituitary stalk have been shown to inhibit growth hormone secretion. Anterior median eminence lesions not only inhibit growth; they also block the increase in growth hormone levels normally produced by hypoglycemia (see below). If growth hormone were secreted in a constant and continuous fashion and only in children, the hypothalamic control of its secretion might be surprising; however, both in children and in adults, the rate of growth hormone secretion undergoes marked and rapid fluctuations in response to a variety of stimuli.

Stimuli Affecting Growth Hormone Secretion

As noted above, the basal plasma growth hormone concentration ranges from 0 to 3 ng/ml in normal adults. The values in newborn infants are higher, but resting plasma growth hormone levels throughout the rest of childhood are not significantly greater than they are in adults. Furthermore, there are large quantities of growth hormone in the pituitaries of adults. It is not clear what these observations mean in terms of the physiology of growth, but they have focused attention on the possible functions of growth hormone in adults.

The stimuli that increase growth hormone secretion are summarized in Table 22–4. Most of them fall into 3 general categories: (1) conditions such as hypoglycemia and fasting, in which there is an actual or

Table 22—4. Stimuli that affect growth hormone secretion in humans.

Stimuli that increase secretion
Deficiency of energy substrate
  IIypoglycemia
  2-Deoxyglucose
  Exercise
  Fasting
Increase in circulating levels of certain amino acids
  Protein meal
  Infusion of arginine and some other amino acids
Glucagon
Stressful stimuli
  Pyrogen
  Lysine vasopressin
  Various psychologic stresses
Going to sleep
L-Dopa and α-adrenergic agonists that penetrate the brain
Apomorphine and other dopamine receptor agonists

Stimuli that decrease secretion
REM sleep
Glucose
Cortisol
Free fatty acids
Medroxyprogesterone
Growth hormone

threatened decrease in the substrate for energy production in the cells; (2) conditions in which there are increased amounts of certain amino acids in the plasma; and (3) stressful stimuli. It has been claimed that the response to glucagon is useful as a test of the growth hormone–secreting mechanism in patients with endocrine diseases. Although the growth hormone responses to the other stimuli are relatively reproducible, they may vary from individual to individual and are generally smaller in children than in adults. There are also irregular "spikes" in the plasma growth hormone level during the day in the absence of any identifiable stimulus to growth hormone secretion. Such a spike occurs with considerable regularity upon going to sleep, but the significance of the association between growth hormone and sleep is an enigma. Growth hormone secretion is increased in subjects deprived of REM sleep (see Chapter 11) and inhibited during normal REM sleep.

Glucose infusions lower plasma growth hormone levels and inhibit the response to exercise. The increase produced by 2-deoxyglucose is presumably due to intracellular glucose deficiency, since this compound blocks the catabolism of glucose-6-phosphate. Although the basal growth hormone levels and the response to hypoglycemia are comparable in males and females, the responses to exercise and arginine are generally greater in women than in men, and the response to arginine in men is increased by estrogen treatment. Growth hormone feeds back to inhibit its

own secretion; high plasma growth hormone levels reduce pituitary secretion of the hormone. Growth hormone secretion is also inhibited by cortisol, free fatty acids, and medroxyprogesterone.

The growth hormone responses to hypoglycemia, fasting, and exercise are reduced in obese subjects. The explanation of this reduction and its possible relationship to the pathogenesis of the obesity are currently unsettled.

Growth hormone secretion is increased by increased discharge of norepinephrine-secreting neurons in the brain (see Chapter 15), and in humans it also appears that dopaminergic neurons stimulate secretion. L-Dopa increases brain dopamine and norepinephrine, and apomorphine stimulates dopamine receptors.

PHYSIOLOGY OF GROWTH

Growth is a complex phenomenon that is affected not only by growth hormone but also by thyroid hormones, androgens, glucocorticoids, and insulin. It is also affected by extrinsic and genetic factors. It is normally accompanied by an orderly sequence of maturational changes, and it involves accretion of protein and increase in length and size, not just an increase in weight, which may be due to the formation of fat or retention of salt and water.

Genetic & Extrinsic Factors

The food supply is the most important extrinsic factor affecting growth. The diet must be adequate not only in protein content but also in essential vitamins and minerals (see Chapter 17) and in calories, so that ingested protein is not burned for energy. Injury and disease stunt growth because they increase protein catabolism.

Following illnesses in children there is a period of "catch-up growth" during which the growth rate may be as much as 400% above normal. The acceleration continues until the previous growth curve is reached, at which point growth slows to normal. The mechanisms that bring about and control "catch-up growth" are not known.

Growth Periods

Patterns of growth vary somewhat from species to species. Rats continue to grow, although at a declining rate, throughout life. In humans, there are 2 periods of rapid growth (Fig 22–10), first in infancy and then in late puberty just before growth stops. The first period of accelerated growth is partly a continuation of the fetal growth period. The second growth spurt and subsequent cessation of growth are due mainly to the action of sex hormones.

Hormonal Effects

The contributions of hormones to growth after

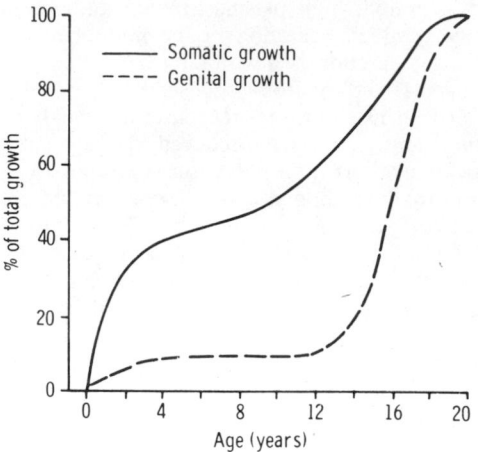

Figure 22–10. Normal somatic and genital growth in male humans. Growth of the whole body and of the testes is plotted as a percentage of total growth at ages up to 20 years. (Data from Harris JA & others: *The Measurement of Man.* Univ of Minnesota Press, 1930.)

birth are shown diagrammatically in Fig 22–11. In laboratory animals and in humans, growth in utero is independent of fetal growth hormone. Rats hypophysectomized at birth continue to grow for about 30 days before they stop. Interestingly, the brain continues to grow in these rats after growth of the skull stops, and the resulting compression of the brain may lead to death.

When growth hormone is administered to hypophysectomized animals, the animals do not grow as rapidly as they do when treated with growth hormone plus thyroid hormones. Thyroid hormones alone have no effect on growth in this situation. Their action is therefore permissive to that of growth hormone. Thyroid hormones also appear to be necessary for a completely normal rate of growth hormone secretion; basal growth hormone levels are normal in hypothyroidism, but the response to hypoglycemia is frequently subnormal in hypothyroid children. Thyroid hormones

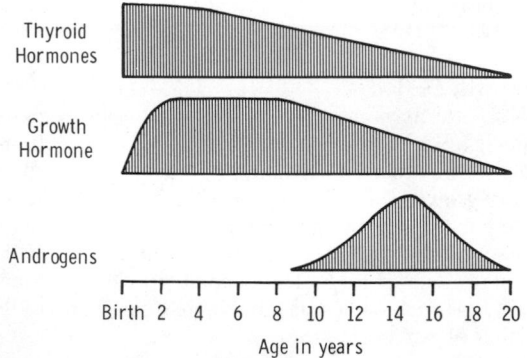

Figure 22–11. Relative importance of hormones in human growth at various ages. (Courtesy of DA Fisher.)

have widespread effects on the ossification of cartilage, the growth of teeth, the contours of the face, and the proportions of the body. Cretins are therefore dwarfed and have infantile features (Fig 22–12). Patients who are dwarfed because of panhypopituitarism have features consistent with their chronologic age until puberty, but since they do not mature sexually, they have juvenile features in adulthood.

The effect of insulin on growth is discussed in Chapter 19. Diabetic animals fail to grow; and insulin causes growth in hypophysectomized animals. However, the growth is appreciable only when large amounts of carbohydrate and protein are supplied with the insulin.

The growth spurt at the time of puberty is due largely to the protein anabolic effect of androgens (see Chapter 23). The ovaries secrete small amounts of androgens, but adolescent growth in girls must be due primarily to androgens secreted from the adrenal cortex. At the time of puberty, 17-ketosteroid excretion rises in girls as well as boys, although the rise in boys is greater because testosterone begins to be secreted from the testes. The increase in adrenal androgen secretion appears to be due to an increase in the activity of the enzymes catalyzing androgen formation in the gland. It is ACTH-dependent, but there is no apparent increase in ACTH secretion during puberty, since cortisol secretion does not change.

Other adrenocortical hormones exert a permissive action on growth in the sense that adrenalectomized animals fail to grow unless their blood pressures and circulations are maintained by replacement therapy. On the other hand, glucocorticoids are potent inhibitors of growth because of their direct action on cells, and treatment of children with pharmacologic doses of steroids slows or stops growth for as long as the treatment is continued.

Although androgens initally stimulate growth, they ultimately terminate growth by causing the epiphyses to fuse to the long bones (epiphyseal closure). Once the epiphyses have closed, linear growth ceases (see Chapter 21). This is why pituitary dwarfs treated with testosterone first grow a few inches and then stop. It is also why patients with sexual precocity are apt to be dwarfed. Estrogens have similar effects, but some investigators argue that the effects of estrogens are due to stimulation of androgen secretion by the adrenals.

Short stature can be due to growth hormone deficiency, to somatomedin deficiency, or to failure of the tissues to respond to somatomedin. Growth hormone deficiency can in turn be due to pituitary disease or to a defect at the hypothalamic level, with failure to stimulate the secretion of growth hormone. Individuals with congenital isolated growth hormone deficiency are called **sexual ateliotic dwarfs.** They remain short, but they mature sexually, and women with the disease can become pregnant, deliver, and lactate normally. In another group of dwarfed children, plasma growth hormone concentration is elevated but there is a deficiency of circulating somatomedin. This syndrome was described by Laron, and the condition is known as

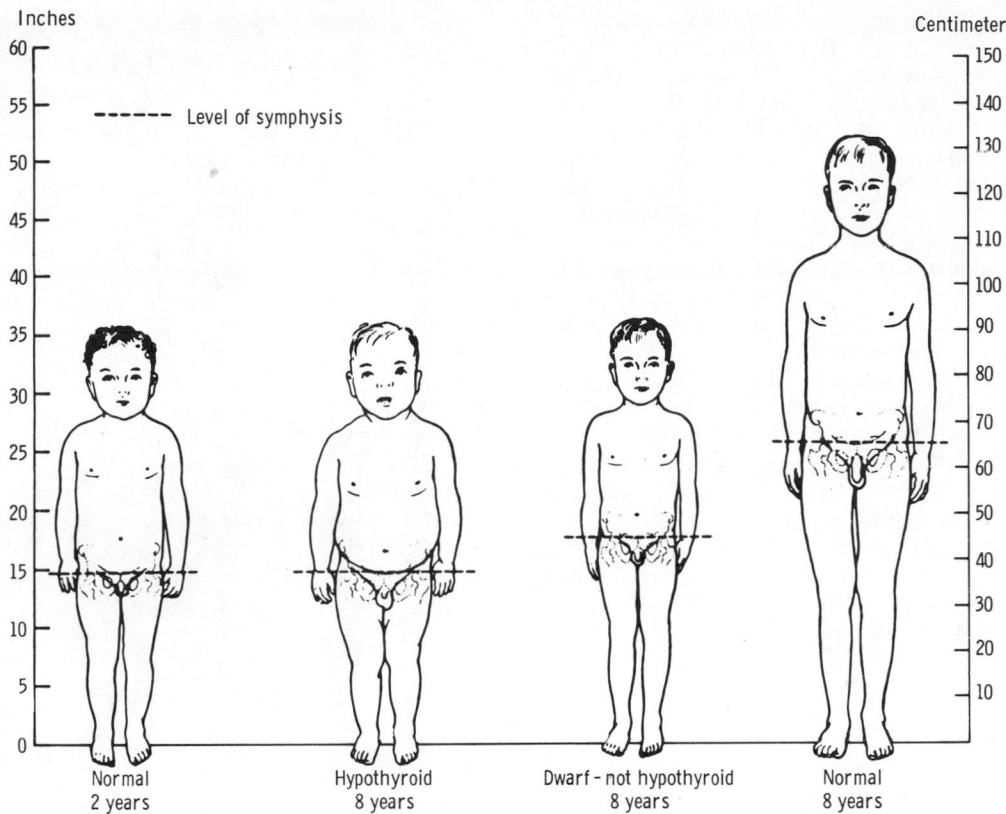

Figure 22–12. Normal and abnormal growth. Hypothyroid dwarfs retain their infantile proportions, whereas dwarfs of the constitutional type and, to a lesser extent, of the hypopituitary type have proportions characteristic of their chronologic age. (Reproduced, with permission, from Wilkins L: *The Diagnosis and Treatment of Endocrine Disorders in Childhood and Adolescence,* 3rd ed. Thomas, 1966.)

Laron dwarfism. African pygmies have normal plasma growth hormone levels and appear to secrete somatomedin, but their tissues fail to respond, so their stature remains short.

Short stature is also part of the syndrome of **gonadal dysgenesis** seen in patients who have an XO chromosomal pattern instead of an XX or XY pattern (see Chapter 23). Various bone and metabolic diseases also cause stunted growth, and in many cases there is no known cause ("constitutional delayed growth").

PITUITARY INSUFFICIENCY

Changes in Other Endocrines

The widespread changes that develop when the pituitary is removed surgically or destroyed by disease in humans or animals are predictable in terms of the known hormonal functions of the gland. The adrenal cortex atrophies, and the secretion of adrenal glucocorticoids and sex hormones falls to low levels, although some secretion persists. Stress-induced rises in aldosterone secretion are absent, but basal aldosterone secretion and increases induced by salt depletion are

normal, at least for some time. Since there is no mineralocorticoid deficiency, salt loss and hypovolemic shock do not develop, but the inability to increase glucocorticoid secretion makes patients with pituitary insufficiency sensitive to stress. Growth is inhibited (see above). Thyroid function is depressed to low levels, and cold is tolerated poorly. The gonads atrophy, sexual cycles stop, and some of the secondary sex characteristics disappear.

Insulin Sensitivity

Hypophysectomized animals have a tendency to become hypoglycemic, especially when fasted. In some species, but not in humans, fatal hypoglycemic reactions are fairly common. Hypophysectomy ameliorates diabetes mellitus (see Chapter 19) and markedly increases the hypoglycemic effect of insulin. This is due in part to the deficiency of adrenocortical hormones, but hypophysectomized animals are more sensitive to insulin than adrenalectomized animals because they also lack the anti-insulin effect of growth hormone.

Water Metabolism

Although selective destruction of the supraoptic–posterior pituitary mechanism causes diabetes insipidus (see Chapter 14), removal of both the anterior and posterior pituitary usually causes no more than a transient polyuria. In the past, there was speculation that the anterior pituitary secreted a "diuretic hormone," but the amelioration of the diabetes insipidus is probably explained on the basis of a decrease in the osmotic load presented for excretion. Osmotically active particles hold water in the renal tubules (see Chapter 38). Because of the ACTH deficiency, the rate of protein catabolism is decreased in hypophysectomized animals. Because of the TSH deficiency, the metabolic rate is low. Consequently, fewer osmotically active products of catabolism are filtered and urine volume declines, even in the absence of vasopressin. Growth hormone deficiency contributes to the depression of the glomerular filtration rate in hypophysectomized animals, and growth hormone increases the glomerular filtration rate and renal plasma flow in humans. Finally, because of the glucocorticoid deficiency, there is the same defective excretion of a water load that is seen in adrenalectomized animals. The "diuretic" activity of the anterior pituitary can thus be explained in terms of the actions of ACTH, TSH, and growth hormone.

Other Defects

The deficiency of ACTH and other pituitary hormones with MSH activity may be responsible for the pallor of the skin in patients with hypopituitarism. Growth hormone deficiency causes dwarfism in young individuals and may be responsible for some loss of protein in adults. However, it should be emphasized that wasting is not a feature of hypopituitarism in humans, and most patients with pituitary insufficiency are well nourished (Fig 22–13). It used to be thought that cachexia was part of the clinical picture, but it is now generally accepted that emaciated patients described in the older literature had anorexia nervosa rather than hypopituitarism.

Causes of Pituitary Insufficiency in Humans

Tumors of the anterior pituitary are generally classified on the basis of staining characteristics as chromophobe, acidophil, or basophil tumors. Most of the apparently nonfunctioning tumors are chromophobe tumors, and they produce hypopituitarism by destroying normal pituitary tissue. It has recently been demonstrated that up to 70% of patients with these chromophobe tumors have high circulating levels of prolactin. This suggests that some of the tumors secrete prolactin, but the increase could also be due to pressure on the hypothalamus or pituitary stalk interrupting the transport of PIH from the hypothalamus to the pituitary (see Chapter 23). Suprasellar cysts, remnants of Rathke's pouch that enlarge and compress the pituitary, are another cause of hypopituitarism. In women who have an episode of shock in the course of pregnancy, the pituitary may become infarcted, with the subsequent development of postpartum necrosis. The blood supply to the anterior lobe is vulnerable

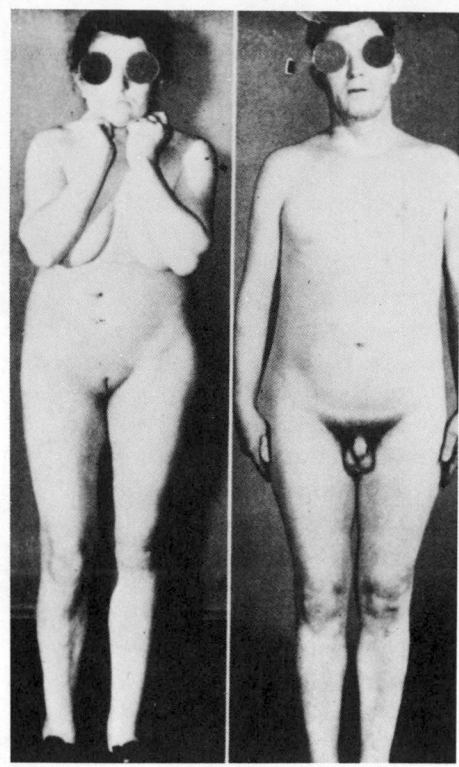

Figure 22–13. Typical picture of hypopituitarism in adults. Note well-nourished appearance and pallor. (From Daughaday WH: *Textbook of Endocrinology,* 5th ed. Williams RH [editor]. Saunders, 1974.)

because it descends on the pituitary stalk through the rigid diaphragma sellae, and during pregnancy, the pituitary is enlarged. Pituitary infarction is extremely rare in men, but it was fairly common in soldiers who contracted hemorrhagic fever in Korea. In hemorrhagic fever, there was a diffuse vasculitis that probably caused pituitary enlargement due to edema, and the patients who developed pituitary infarction were those who went into shock in the course of their disease.

Partial Pituitary Insufficiency

The anterior pituitary has a large reserve, and much of it can be destroyed without producing detectable endocrine abnormalities. It now appears that with progressive loss of pituitary tissue, growth hormone secretion is the first function to be impaired. In dogs and rats, there is a depression of gonadotropin secretion when 70–90% of the anterior pituitary is removed or destroyed. When 90–95% is destroyed, thyroid function is also impaired, but almost 100% of the anterior pituitary must be destroyed before a marked degree of adrenal insufficiency is seen (Table 22–5). The same relationships hold in humans. Isolated growth hormone deficiency occurs as a congenital abnormality (see above). Isolated corticotropin deficiency has also been described. However, in many

Table 22–5. Effects of removing various amounts of pituitary tissue on endocrine function in male dogs.* (+) indicates that the finding was present and (0) that it was absent.

Number of Dogs	Gonadal Atrophy	Thyroid Atrophy	Adrenal Atrophy	Mean % Anterior Pituitary Remaining
6	0	0	0	27
3	+	0	0	11
2	+	+	0	5
19	+	+	+	2

*Data from Ganong WF, Hume DM: The effect of graded hypophysectomy on thyroid, gonadal, and adrenocortical function in the dog. Endocrinology 59:293, 1956.

instances, isolated pituitary tropin deficiencies are due to hypothalamic rather than pituitary disorders. For example, it has recently been shown that an appreciable number of patients with isolated TSH deficiency show an increase in TSH secretion when thyrotropin-releasing hormone (TRH) is injected. Similarly, some patients with gonadotropin deficiency respond to luteinizing hormone–releasing hormone (LRH).

In rats and in some other species, there appears to be some localization within the pituitary of the cells secreting the various hormones. It is not known if similar localization occurs in humans.

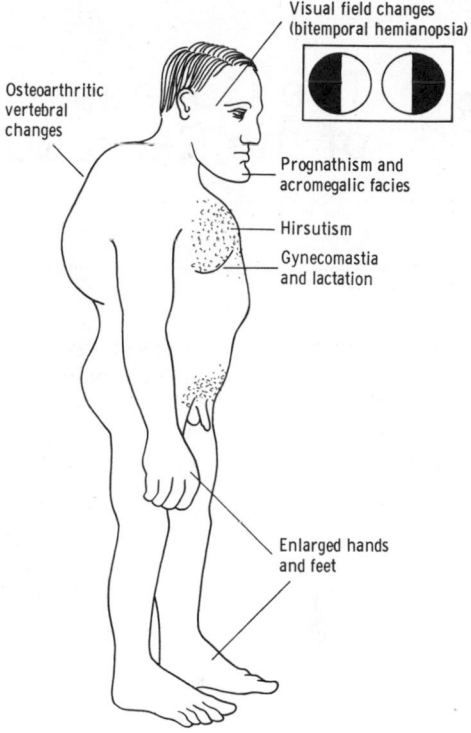

Figure 22–14. Typical findings in acromegaly.

PITUITARY HYPERFUNCTION IN HUMANS

Acromegaly

Acidophil cell tumors of the anterior pituitary secrete large amounts of growth hormone, leading in children to **gigantism** and in adults to **acromegaly.** The principal findings are those related to the local effects of the tumor (enlargement of the sella turcica, headache, visual disturbances) and those due to growth hormone secretion. In adults, there is enlargement of the hands and feet (**acral** parts; hence the term acromegaly) and a protrusion of the lower jaw called **prognathism** (Fig 22–14). Overgrowth of the malar, frontal, and basal bones combines with prognathism to produce the coarse facial features called **acromegalic facies.** Body hair is increased in amount. The skeletal changes predispose to osteoarthritis. About 25% of patients have abnormal glucose tolerance tests, and 4% develop lactation in the absence of pregnancy.

Cushing's Syndrome

The clinical picture of Cushing's syndrome is described in Chapter 20. Many patients with bilaterally hyperplastic adrenals have small ACTH-secreting pituitary tumors (microadenomas) that are difficult to detect. However, a significant percentage of the patients who have bilaterally hyperplastic adrenals removed develop rapidly growing ACTH-secreting pituitary tumors (**Nelson's syndrome).** These tumors cause hyperpigmentation of the skin and neurologic signs due to pressure on structures in the sellar region. Most of them are made up of chromophobic cells rather than basophils, and some are malignant. Blood ACTH levels are extremely high, and the intrinsic MSH activity of the ACTH probably accounts for the cutaneous pigmentation. It is difficult to say whether these patients had undetected tumors to start with or developed neoplastic changes in the pituitary when the feedback check on ACTH secretion was removed. Animals sometimes develop TSH-secreting tumors after thyroidectomy and gonadotropin-secreting tumors after gonadectomy, but such tumors are rare in humans.

23 | The Gonads: Development & Function of the Reproductive System

Modern genetics and experimental embryology make it clear that in higher animals the multiple differences between the male and the female depend primarily on a single chromosome (the Y chromosome) and a single pair of endocrine structures, the testes in the male and the ovaries in the female. The differentiation of the primitive gonads into testes or ovaries in utero is genetically determined in humans, but the formation of male genitalia depends upon the presence of a functional testis. There is evidence that male sexual behavior and, in some species, the male pattern of gonadotropin secretion are also due to the action of male hormones on the brain in early development. After birth, the gonads remain quiescent until adolescence, when they are activated by gonadotropins from the anterior pituitary. Hormones secreted by the gonads at this time cause the appearance of features typical of the adult male or female and the onset of the sexual cycle in the female. In males, the gonads remain more or less active from puberty onward. In human females, ovarian function regresses after a period of time, and sexual cycles cease (the menopause).

In both sexes, the gonads have a dual function: the production of germ cells (**gametogenesis**) and the secretion of **sex hormones.** The **androgens** are the steroid sex hormones that are masculinizing in their action; the **estrogens** are those that are feminizing. Both types of hormones are normally secreted in both sexes. The testes secrete large amounts of androgens, principally **testosterone,** but they also secrete small amounts of estrogens. The ovaries secrete large amounts of estrogens and small amounts of androgens. Androgens and, probably, small amounts of estrogens are secreted from the adrenal cortex in both sexes. The ovaries also secrete **progesterone,** a steroid that has special functions in preparing the uterus for pregnancy. During pregnancy, the ovaries secrete the peptide hormone **relaxin,** which loosens the ligaments of the pubic symphysis and softens the cervix, facilitating delivery of the fetus.

The secretory and gametogenic functions of the gonads are both dependent upon the secretion of the anterior pituitary gonadotropins, FSH and LH. The sex hormones feed back through the hypothalamus to inhibit gonadotropin secretion. In males, gonadotropin secretion is noncyclic; but in postpuberal females an orderly, sequential secretion of gonadotropins is necessary for the occurrence of menstruation, pregnancy, and lactation.

SEX DIFFERENTIATION & DEVELOPMENT

CHROMOSOMAL SEX

The Sex Chromosomes

Sex is determined genetically by 2 chromosomes called the **sex chromosomes** to distinguish them from the other **somatic chromosomes (autosomes).** In humans and many other animal species, the sex chromosomes are called the X and Y chromosomes. The Y chromosome contains a gene that codes for the production of testes, and it appears that the testis-determining gene product is a membrane protein known as the **H-Y antigen.** Male cells with the diploid number of chromosomes contain an X and a Y chromosome (XY pattern), whereas female cells contain two X chromosomes (XX pattern). As a consequence of meiosis during gametogenesis, each normal ovum contains a single X chromosome, but half the normal sperms contain an X chromosome and half contain a Y chromosome (Fig 23–1). When a sperm containing a Y chromosome fertilizes an ovum, an XY pattern results, and the zygote develops into a **genetic male.** When fertilization occurs with an X-containing sperm, an XX pattern and a **genetic female** result. Cell division and the chemical nature of chromosomes are discussed in Chapters 1 and 17.

Human Chromosomes

Human chromosomes can be studied in detail. Human cells are grown in tissue culture; treated with the drug colchicine, which arrests mitosis at the metaphase; exposed to a hypotonic solution that makes the chromosomes swell and disperse; and then "squashed" onto slides. Fluorescent and other staining technics make it possible to identify the individual chromosomes and study them in detail (Fig 23–2). There are 46 chromosomes: in males, 22 pairs of autosomes plus a large X chromosome and a small Y chromosome; in females, 22 pairs of autosomes plus two X chromosomes. The individual chromosomes are usually arranged in an arbitrary pattern, or **karyotype.** The individual autosome pairs are identified by the numbers 1–22 on the basis of their morphologic characteristics. Because the human Y chromosome is

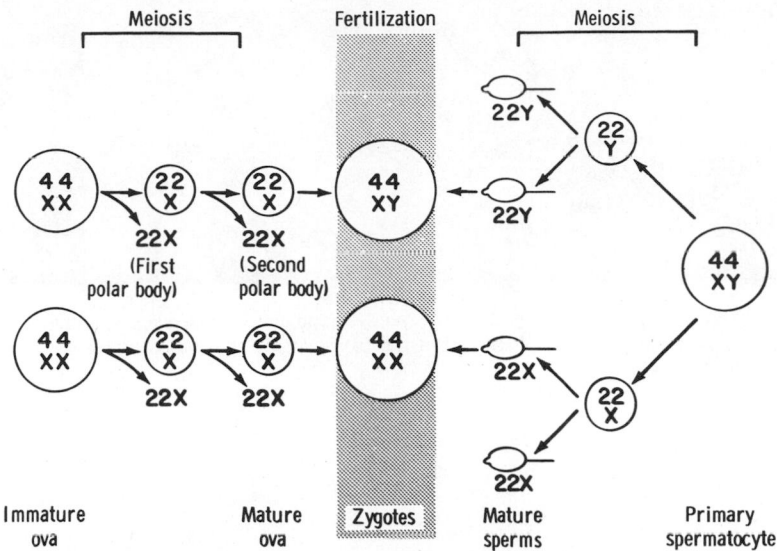

Figure 23-1. Basis of genetic sex determination. In the case of the 2-stage meiotic division in the female, 4 bodies form, but only one survives as the mature ovum. In the case of the male, the meiotic division results in the formation of 4 sperms, 2 containing the X and 2 the Y chromosome. Fertilization thus produces a 44XY (male) zygote or a 44XX (female) zygote.

smaller than the X chromosome, it has been hypothesized that sperms containing the Y chromosome are lighter and able to "swim" faster up the female genital tract, thus reaching the ovum more rapidly. This supposedly accounts for the fact that the number of males born is slightly greater than the number of females.

Sex Chromatin

Soon after cell division has started during em-

bryonic development, one or the other of the two X chromosomes of the somatic cells in normal females becomes functionally inactive. The choice of which X chromosome becomes inactive in any given cell is apparently random, so one X chromosome is inactivated in approximately half of the cells and the other X chromosome in the other half. The selection persists through subsequent divisions of these cells, and consequently some of the somatic cells in adult females contain an active X chromosome of paternal origin and

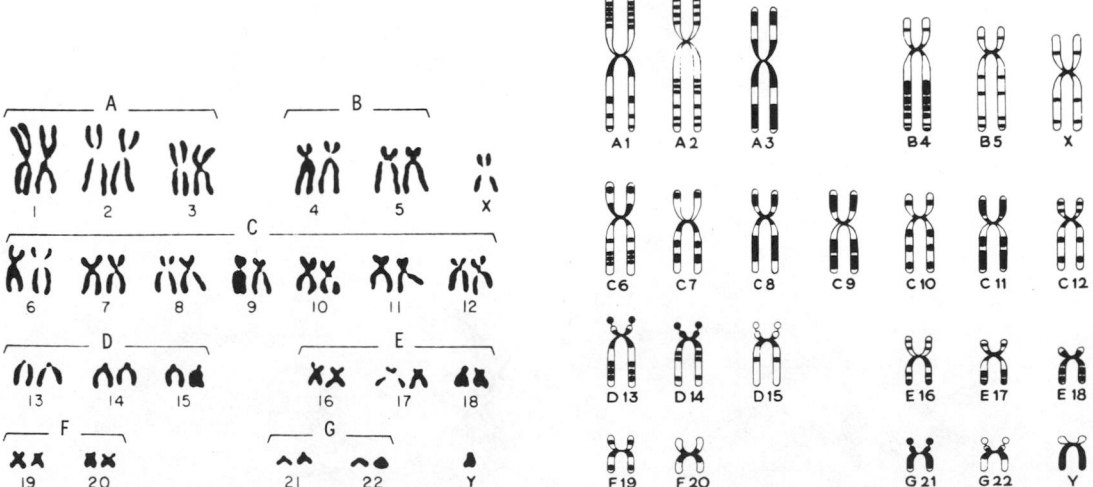

Figure 23-2. *Left:* Karyotype of chromosomes from normal male arranged in conventional groups (A-G). (Reproduced, with permission, from Barr ML: Some properties of the sex chromosomes and their bearing on normal and abnormal development. In: *Congenital Malformations.* International Medical Congress, 1964.) *Right:* Diagram of human chromosomes, idealized, showing one of each pair. Characteristic banding is produced by the Giemsa method of staining. This banding, and the patterns produced by other technics, make it possible to identify individual chromosomes with great accuracy. (Reproduced, with permission, from Drets ME, Shaw MW: Specific banding patterns of human chromosomes. Proc Natl Acad Sci USA 68:2073, 1971.)

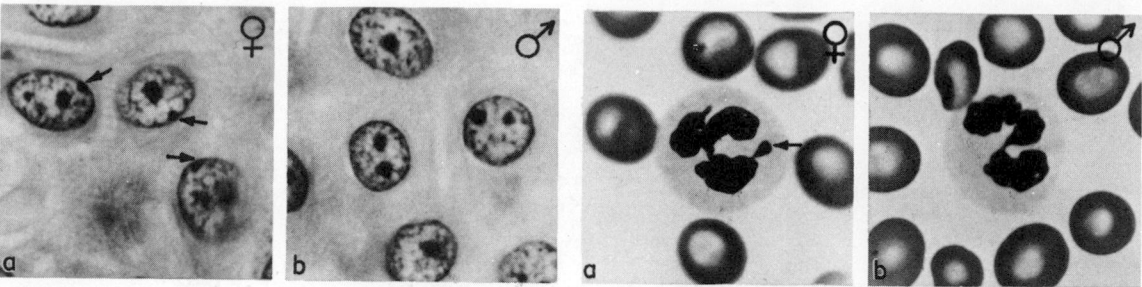

Figure 23–3. Barr body (arrows) in epidermal spinous cell layer *(left)* and nuclear appendage ("drumstick") in white blood cells *(right).* (Reproduced, with permission, from Grumbach MM, Barr ML: Cytologic tests of chromosomal sex in relation to sex anomalies in man. Recent Prog Horm Res 14:255, 1958.)

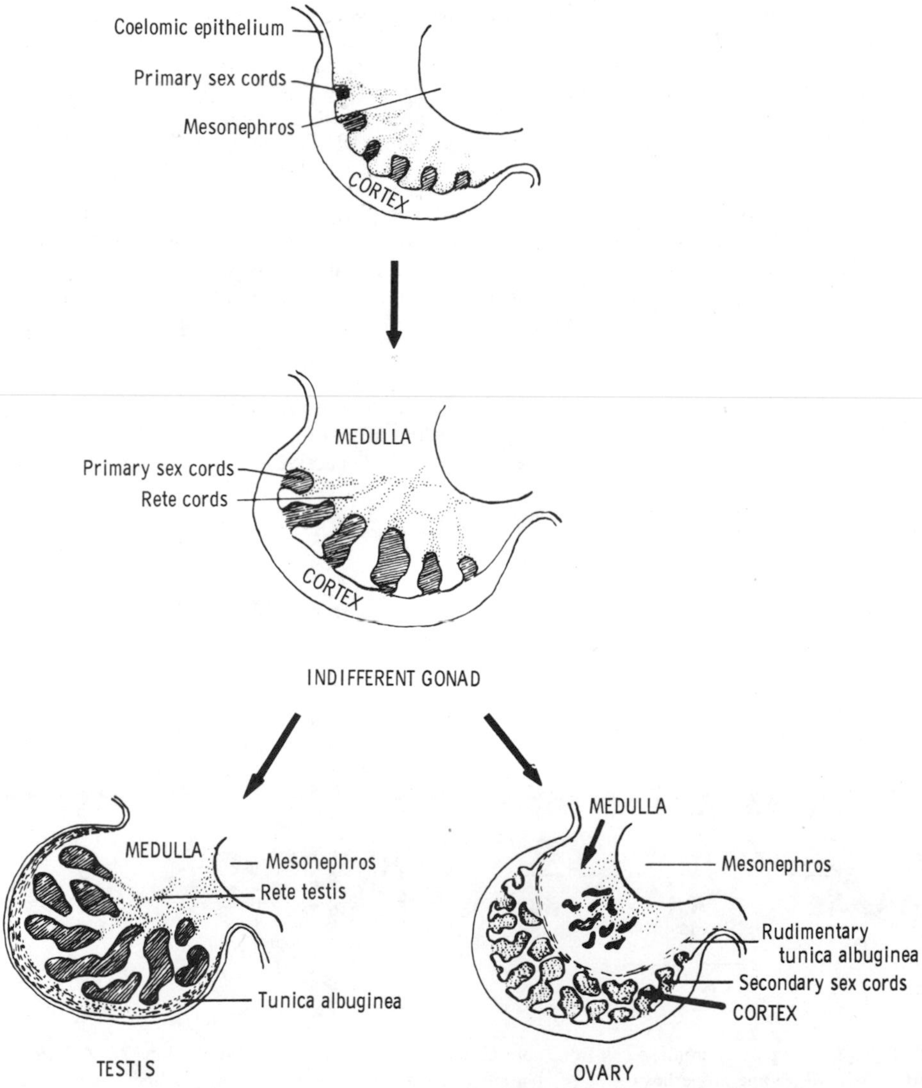

Coelomic epithelium
Primary sex cords
Mesonephros

CORTEX

MEDULLA

Primary sex cords
Rete cords

CORTEX

INDIFFERENT GONAD

MEDULLA
Mesonephros
Rete testis

Tunica albuginea

TESTIS

MEDULLA
Mesonephros
Rudimentary tunica albuginea
Secondary sex cords
CORTEX

OVARY

Figure 23–4. Diagrammatic representation of the development of an ovary from the cortex or a testis from the medulla of a bipotential primordial human gonad. (Reproduced, with permission, from Grumbach M in: *Clinical Endocrinology I.* Astwood EB [editor]. Grune & Stratton, 1960.)

some contain an active chromosome of maternal origin.

The inactive X chromosome condenses and can be seen in various types of cells, usually near the nuclear membrane, as the **Barr body** (Fig 23–3). Thus, there is a Barr body for each X chromosome in excess of one in the cell. The inactive X chromosome is also visible as a small "drumstick" of chromatin projecting from the nuclei of 1–15% of the polymorphonuclear leukocytes in females but not in males (Fig 23–3).

The Barr body has also been called sex chromatin. Another form of sex chromatin is the **F body,** a portion of the Y chromosome that can be stained with modern fluorescence technics. Thus, the number of Y chromosomes in a cell can be estimated by the number of F bodies it contains.

EMBRYOLOGY OF THE HUMAN REPRODUCTIVE SYSTEM

Development of the Gonads

On each side of the embryo, a primitive gonad arises from the genital ridge, a condensation of tissue near the adrenal gland. The gonad develops a **cortex** and a **medulla** (Figs 23–4 and 23–5). Until the sixth week of development, these structures are identical in both sexes. In genetic males, the medulla develops during the seventh and eighth weeks into a testis, and the cortex regresses. This development apparently depends on the presence of the H-Y antigen. Leydig cells appear, and testosterone and a peptide factor (see below) are secreted. In genetic females, the cortex develops into an ovary, and the medulla regresses. The embryonic ovary does not secrete hormones. Hormonal treatment of the mother has no effect on gonadal differentiation in humans, although it does have marked effects on genital development (see below).

Embryology of the Genitalia

In the seventh week of gestation, the embryo has both male and female primordial genital ducts (Fig 23–6). In a normal female fetus, the müllerian duct system then develops into oviducts and a uterus. In the normal male fetus, the wolffian duct system on each side develops into the epididymis and vas deferens. The external genitalia are similarly bipotential until the eighth week (Fig 23–7). Thereafter, the urogenital slit disappears and male genitalia form, or alternatively, it remains open and female genitalia form.

When there are functional testes in the embryo, male internal and external genitalia develop. The fetal testis secretes testosterone and a **müllerian regression factor (MRF),** which may be a polypeptide and acts unilaterally. The müllerian regression factor acts alone to inhibit the müllerian ducts; the müllerian regression factor and testosterone act together to develop the vas deferens and related structures on each side; and testosterone acts alone to induce the formation of male external genitalia (Fig 23–5).

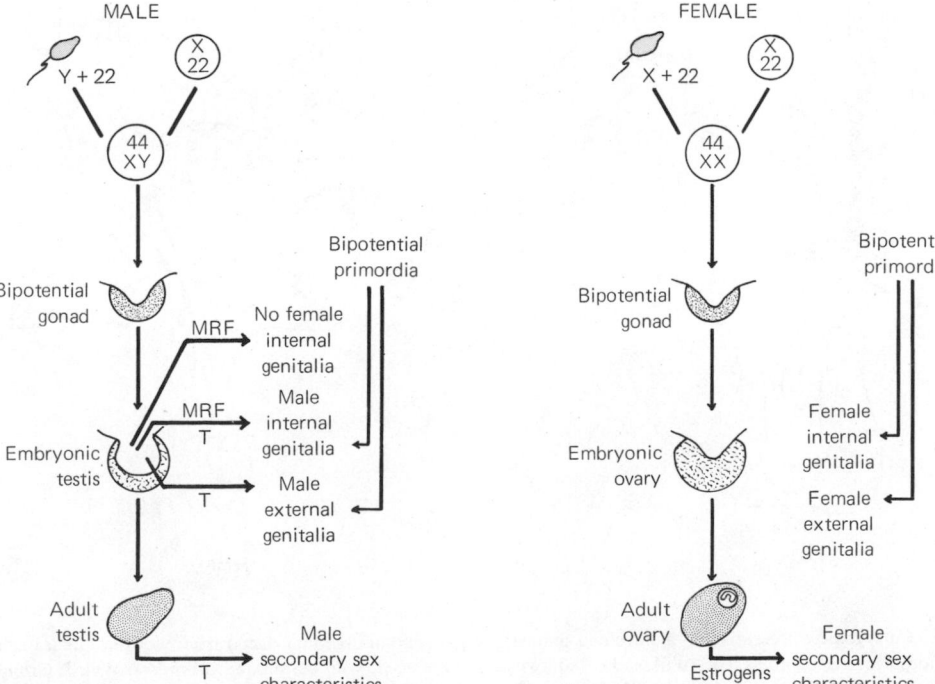

Figure 23–5. Diagrammatic summary of normal sex determination, differentiation, and development in humans. MRF, müllerian regression factor; T, testosterone or other androgen.

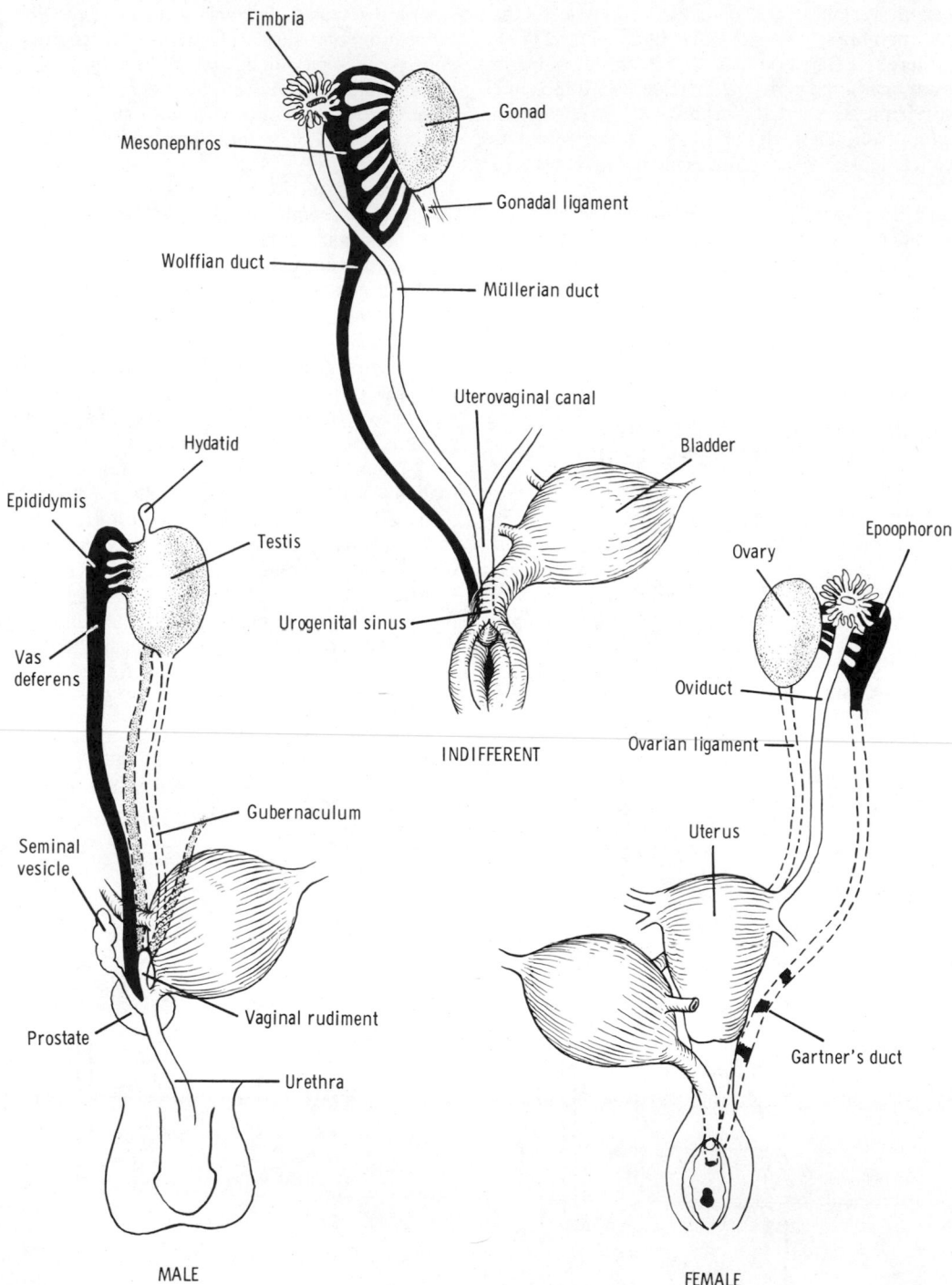

Figure 23–6. Embryonic differentiation of male and female internal genitalia (genital ducts) from wolffian (male) and müllerian (female) primordia. (After Corning HK, Wilkins L. Redrawn and reproduced, with permission, from Van Wyk J, Grumbach M in: *Textbook of Endocrinology,* 5th ed. Williams RH [editor]. Saunders, 1974.)

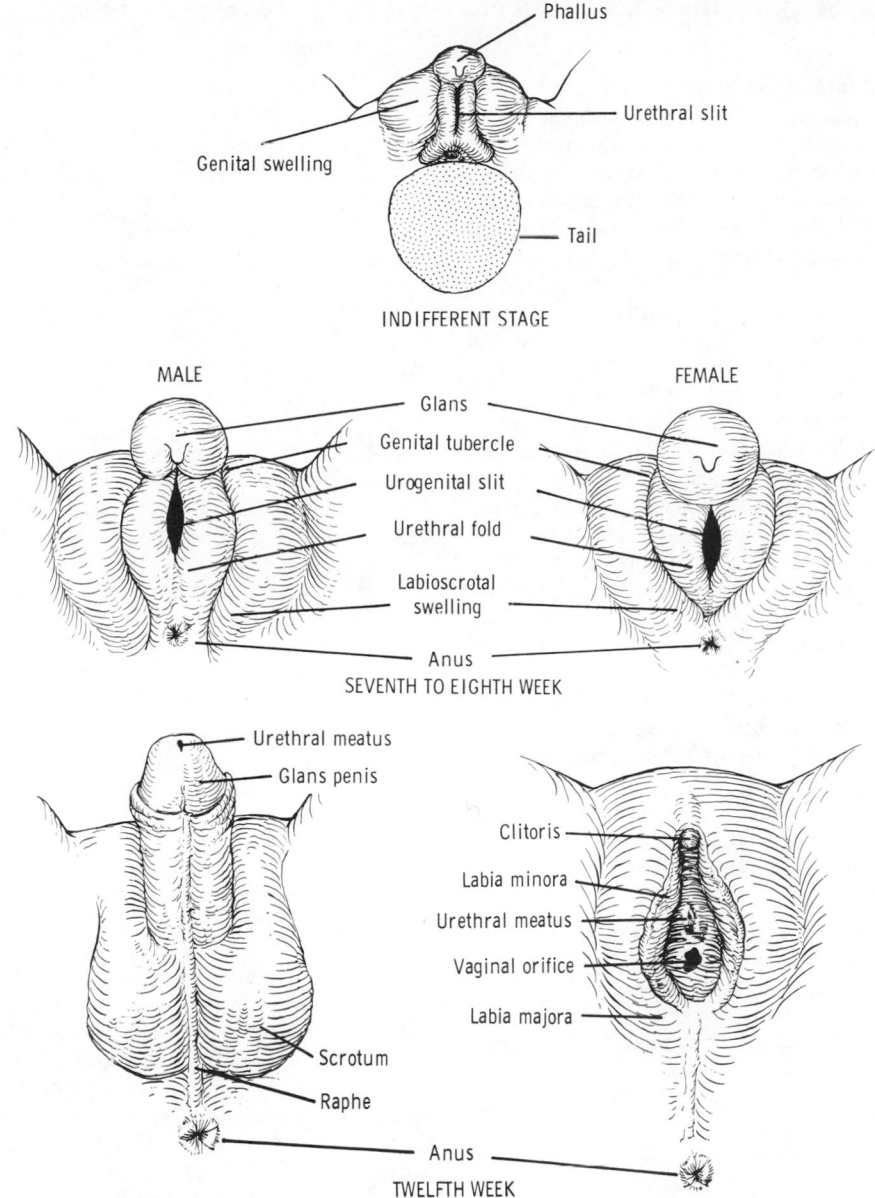

Figure 23–7. Differentiation of male and female external genitalia from indifferent primordial structures in the embryo. (Redrawn from Spaulding MH: The development of the external genitalia in the human embryo. Contributions to Embryology 13:69, 1921.)

Development of the Brain

At least in some species, the development of the brain as well as the external genitalia is affected by androgens early in life. In rats, a brief exposure to androgens during the first few days of life causes the male pattern of sexual behavior and the male pattern of hypothalamic control of gonadotropin secretion to develop after puberty. In the absence of androgens, female patterns develop (see Chapter 15). In monkeys, similar effects on sexual behavior are produced by exposure to androgens in utero, but the pattern of gonadotropin secretion remains cyclic. Early exposure of female human fetuses to androgens also appears to cause subtle but significant masculinizing effects on behavior. However, women with adrenogenital syndrome due to congenital adrenocortical enzyme deficiency (see Chapter 20) develop normal menstrual cycles when treated with cortisol. Thus, the human, like the monkey, appears to retain the cyclic pattern of gonadotropin secretion despite the exposure to androgens in utero.

ABERRANT SEXUAL DIFFERENTIATION

Chromosomal Abnormalities

From the preceding discussion, it might be expected that abnormalities of sexual development could be caused by genetic or hormonal abnormalities as well as by other nonspecific teratogenic influences, and this is indeed the case. The major classes of abnormalities are listed in Table 23–1.

An established defect in gametogenesis is **nondisjunction,** a phenomenon in which a pair of chromosomes fail to separate, so that both go to one of the daughter cells during meiosis. Four of the abnormal zygotes that can form as a result of nondisjunction of one of the X chromosomes during oogenesis are shown in Fig 23–8. In individuals with the XO chromosomal pattern, the gonads are rudimentary or absent, so that female external and internal genitalia develop. Stature is short, other congenital abnormalities are often present, and no maturation occurs at puberty. This syndrome is now called **gonadal dysgenesis** or, alternatively, **ovarian agenesis** or **Turner's syndrome.** Individuals with the XXY pattern, the most common sex chromosome disorder, have the genitalia of a normal male. Testosterone secretion at puberty is often great enough for the development of male characteristics. However, the seminiferous tubules are abnormal, and there is a higher than normal incidence of mental retardation. This syndrome is known as **seminiferous tubule dysgenesis,** or **Klinefelter's syndrome.** The XXX ("superfemale") pattern is second in frequency

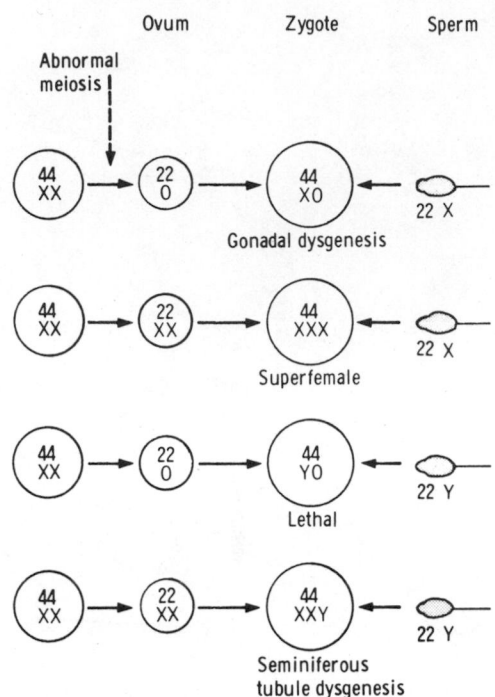

Figure 23–8. Summary of 4 possible defects produced by maternal nondisjunction of the sex chromosomes at the time of meiosis. The YO combination is believed to be lethal, and the fetus dies in utero.

Table 23–1. Classification of the major disorders of sex differentiation in humans. Many of these syndromes can have great variation in degree and, consequently, in manifestations.

Chromosomal disorders
    Gonadal dysgenesis (XO and variants)
    "Superfemales" (XXX)
    Seminiferous tubule dysgenesis (XXY and variants)
    True hermaphroditism
Developmental disorders
    Female pseudohermaphroditism
        Congenital virilizing adrenal hyperplasia of fetus
        Maternal androgen excess
            Virilizing ovarian tumor
            Iatrogenic: Treatment with androgens or certain synthetic progestational drugs
    Male pseudohermaphroditism
        Testicular feminization and variants
        Leydig cell agenesis
    Congenital 17α-hydroxylase deficiency
    Congenital adrenal hyperplasia due to blockade of pregnenolone formation
    Various nonhormonal anomalies

---

only to the XXY pattern and may be even more common in the general population, since it does not seem to be associated with any characteristic abnormalities. The YO combination is probably lethal.

Meiosis is a 2-stage process, and nondisjunction can occur in both meiotic divisions, with the production of more complex chromosomal abnormalities. In addition, nondisjunction or simple loss of a sex chromosome can occur during the early mitotic divisions after fertilization. Chromosome loss occurs when a chromosome fails to line up properly during mitosis and is extruded from the cell rather than moving to one daughter cell **(anaphase lag).** The result of faulty mitoses in the early zygote is the production of a mosaic, an individual with 2 or more populations of cells with different chromosome complements. Some of the karyotypes that have been reported in patients with Klinefelter's syndrome, in addition to XXY, are XXYY, XXXY, XXXYY, XXXXY, and XY/XXY mosaicism. The cause of the condition in the vast majority of cases is at least one extra X chromosome in testicular tissue, but there are cases in which an extra X chromosome cannot be found. Gonadal dysgenesis has been reported in patients with XO/XX and XO/XX/XXX mosaicism. It can also occur in individuals who have the XX pattern but in whom one of the X chromosomes is abnormal. **True hermaphroditism,** the condition in which the individual has both ovaries and testes, is probably due to XX/XY mosaicism and related mosaic patterns, although other genetic aberrations are possible.

A number of sex chromosome abnormalities are not associated with gonadal defects. The XXX pattern has been mentioned above. XXXX and XXXXX have also been reported in patients with mental retardation. Males with the XYY pattern tend to be tall and to have severe acne. The karyotype has attracted considerable attention because its incidence was initially reported to be high in prison populations. However, it is also relatively common in the general population, and there is little solid evidence that individuals with the XYY pattern are predisposed to aggressive behavior.

Sex chromosome abnormalities are of course not the only abnormalities associated with disease states; nondisjunction of several different autosomal chromosomes is known to occur. For example, nondisjunction of chromosome 21 (Fig 23–2) produces **trisomy 21,** the chromosomal abnormality associated with Down's syndrome (mongolism).

There are many other chromosomal abnormalities as well as numerous diseases due to defects in single genes. Over 2300 different inherited disorders in humans have been catalogued in the literature.

Hormonal Abnormalities

Development of male external genitalia occurs normally in genetic males in response to androgen secreted by the embryonic testes, but male genital development may also occur in genetic females exposed to androgens from some other source during the eighth to the thirteenth weeks of gestation. The syndrome that results is **female pseudohermaphroditism.** A pseudohermaphrodite is an individual with the genetic constitution and gonads of one sex and the genitalia of the other. After the 13th week, the genitalia are fully formed, but exposure to androgens can cause hypertrophy of the clitoris. Female pseudohermaphroditism may be due to congenital virilizing adrenal hyperplasia (see Chapter 20), or it may be caused by androgens administered to the mother. Conversely, female external genital development in genetic males (**male pseudohermaphroditism**) occurs when the embryonic testes are defective. Because the testes are also the source of müllerian regression factor, genetic males with defective testes have female internal genitalia. Another cause of male pseudohermaphroditism is the **testicular feminizing syndrome.** In this condition, testes are present and testosterone is secreted, but the hormone cannot act on its target cells (see below). Consequently, the tissues are resistant to testosterone, and female external genitalia develop. However, müllerian regression factor is present, so there are no female internal genitalia. In one form of this syndrome, there is a defect in an X-linked gene, and the androgen receptor protein is not synthesized. In others, there are less marked congenital abnormalities in the various steps by which testosterone exerts its action at the tissue level.

It is worth noting that genetic males with congenital adrenal hyperplasia due to blockade of the formation of pregnenolone are pseudohermaphrodites because testicular as well as adrenal androgens are normally formed from pregnenolone. Male pseudohermaphroditism also occurs when there is a congenital deficiency of 17α-hydroxylase (see Chapter 20).

PUBERTY

After birth, the androgen-secreting Leydig cells in the fetal testes become quiescent. There follows in all mammals a period in which the gonads of both sexes are quiescent until they are activated by gonadotropins from the pituitary to bring about the final maturation of the reproductive system. This period of growth and maturation is known as **adolescence.** It is often also called **puberty,** although puberty, strictly defined, is the period when the endocrine and gametogenic functions of the gonads have first developed to the point where reproduction is possible. **Menarche** is the first menstrual period at puberty. In humans as well as animals, castration increases gonadotropin secretion before there is any evident stimulation of the gonads, but the nature of the pituitary-inhibiting gonadal secretion is uncertain. In children between the ages of 7 and 10, a slow increase in estrogen and androgen secretion precedes the more rapid rise in the early teens (Fig 23–9). The age at the time of puberty is variable, but it averages 14 years in boys and 12 years in girls.

Control of the Onset of Puberty

A neural mechanism is responsible for the onset of puberty. The gonads of immature animals can be stimulated by gonadotropins; their pituitaries contain gonadotropins; and their hypothalami contain LRH (see Chapter 14). However, their gonadotropin are not secreted. When the pituitary of an immature animal is transplanted into an adult animal, it secretes gonadotropins like an adult pituitary. In experimental animals and in humans, lesions in the ventral hypothalamus near the infundibulum cause precocious puberty (Fig 23–10). This suggests that there is a hypothalamic mechanism which normally holds gonadotropin secretion in check until puberty. However, no substance that inhibits FSH and LH secretion has been extracted from the brain, and it is possible that the effect of lesions is due instead to chronic stimulation originating in irritative foci in tissue around the lesion. Another theory of the control of the onset of puberty is based on the observation that before puberty the brain is very sensitive to the inhibiting effects of gonadal steroids on gonadotropin secretion. According to this view, small amounts of steroids secreted by the gonads hold gonadotropin secretion in check, and puberty is due to a decrease in the sensitivity of the brain to this inhibition.

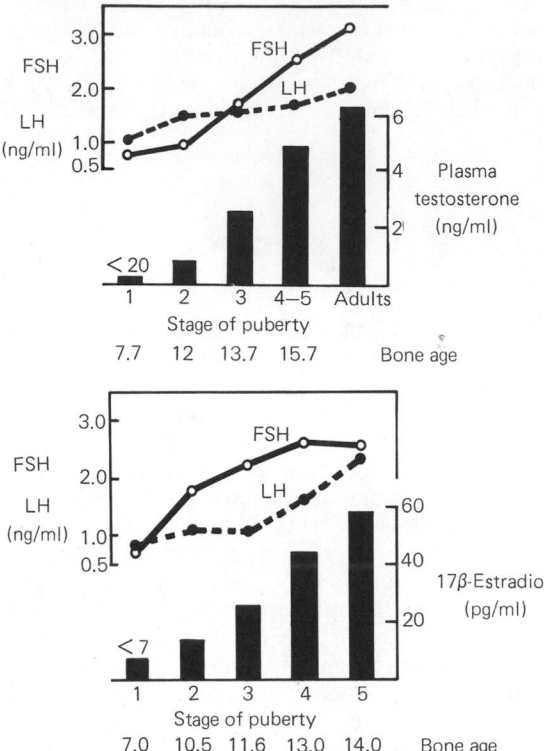

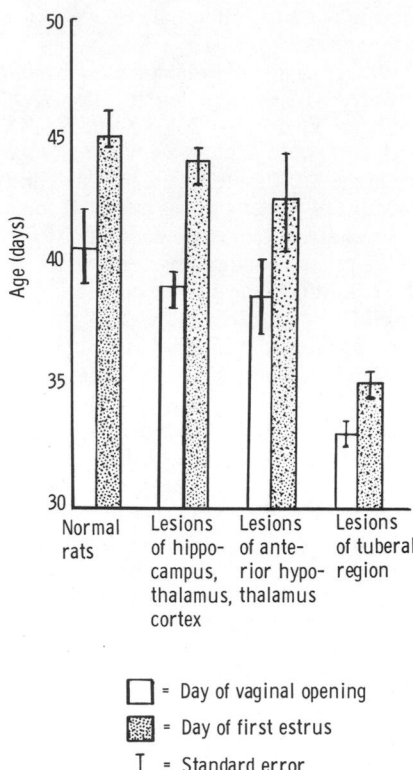

= Day of vaginal opening

= Day of first estrus

= Standard error

Figure 23–9. Changes in plasma hormone concentrations during puberty in boys *(top)* and girls *(bottom)*. Stage 1 of puberty is preadolescence in both sexes. In boys, stage 2 is characterized by beginning enlargement of the testes, stage 3 by penile enlargement, stage 4 by growth of the glans penis, and stage 5 by adult genitalia. In girls, stage 2 is characterized by breast buds, stage 3 by elevation and enlargement of the breasts, stage 4 by projection of the areolas, and stage 5 by adult breasts. (Courtesy of S Kaplan.)

Figure 23–10. Effect of brain lesions on the onset of puberty in female rats. In rats the vagina stays closed until just before the onset of the first estrus.

PRECOCIOUS & DELAYED PUBERTY

Sexual Precocity

The common causes of precocious sexual development in humans are listed in Table 23–2. Early development of secondary sexual characteristics without gametogenesis is caused by abnormal exposure of immature males to androgen or females to estrogen. This syndrome should be called **precocious pseudopuberty** to distinguish it from **true precocious puberty** due to an early but otherwise normal pubertal pattern of gonadotropin secretion from the pituitary (Fig 23–11). In one large series of cases, precocious puberty was the commonest endocrine symptom of hypothalamic disease (see Chapter 14). Pineal tumors are sometimes associated with precocious puberty, and it is possible that melatonin (see Chapter 24) or some other substance from the pineal normally inhibits the onset of puberty. However, there is evidence that pineal tumors are associated with precocious puberty only when there is secondary damage to the hypothal-

Table 23–2. Classification of the causes of precocious sexual development in humans.*

True precocious puberty
    Constitutional
    Cerebral: Disorders involving posterior hypothala-
           mus
        Tumors
        Infections
        Developmental abnormalities

Precocious pseudopuberty (no spermatogenesis or ovarian development)
    Adrenal
        Congenital virilizing adrenal hyperplasia
           (without treatment in males; following
           cortisone treatment in females)
        Androgen-secreting tumors (in males)
        Estrogen-secreting tumors (in females)
    Gonadal
        Interstitial cell tumors of testis
        Granulosa cell tumors of ovary
    Miscellaneous

*Modified from Jolly H: *Sexual Precocity*. Thomas, 1955.

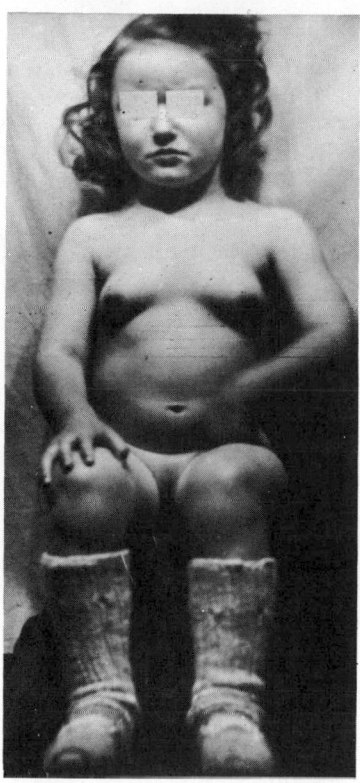

Figure 23–11. Constitutional precocious puberty in a 3½-year-old girl. The patient developed pubic hair and started to menstruate at the age of 17 months. (Reproduced, with permission, from Jolly H: *Sexual Precocity*. Thomas, 1955.)

amus. Precocity due to this and other forms of hypothalamic damage probably occurs with equal frequency in both sexes, although the constitutional form of precocious puberty is more common in girls.

Delayed or Absent Puberty

The normal variation in the age at which adolescent changes occur is so wide that puberty cannot be considered to be pathologically delayed until the menarche has failed to occur by the age of 17 or testicular development by the age of 20. Failure of maturation due to panhypopituitarism is associated with dwarfing and evidence of other endocrine abnormalities. Patients with the XO chromosomal pattern and gonadal dysgenesis are also dwarfed. In some individuals, puberty is delayed even though the gonads are present and other endocrine functions are normal. In males, this clinical picture is called **eunuchoidism.** In females, it is called **primary amenorrhea** (see below).

MENOPAUSE

The human ovary gradually becomes unresponsive to gonadotropins with advancing age, and its function declines, so that sexual cycles disappear **(menopause).** Old female mice and rats have long periods of diestrus and increased levels of gonadotropin secretion, but a clear-cut "menopause" has apparently not been described in animals.

In women, the menses usually become irregular and cease between the ages of 45 and 55. The average age at onset of the menopause has been increasing since the turn of the century and is currently 52 years. Sensations of warmth spreading from the trunk to the face ("hot flashes") and various psychic symptoms are common at this time. The hot flashes are prevented by estrogen treatment. They are not peculiar to females and sometimes occur in males castrated in adulthood.

Although the function of the testes does tend to decline slowly with advancing age, the evidence is clear that there is no "male menopause," or **climacteric,** similar to that occurring in women.

PITUITARY GONADOTROPINS & PROLACTIN

Actions

The testes and ovaries become atrophic when the pituitary is removed or destroyed. The actions of prolactin and the gonadotropins FSH and LH, as well as those of the gonadotropin secreted by the placenta, are described in detail in succeeding sections of this chapter. In brief, FSH helps maintain the spermatogenic epithelium in the male and is responsible for the early growth of ovarian follicles in the female. LH is tropic to the Leydig cells, and testosterone output in the spermatic vein is increased within minutes after its injection in dogs. In females, LH is responsible for the final maturation of the ovarian follicles and estrogen secretion from them. It is also responsible for ovulation and the initial formation of the corpus luteum and secretion of progesterone. Prolactin causes milk secretion from the breast after estrogen and progesterone priming. It also inhibits the effects of gonadotropins, possibly by an action at the level of the ovary. Its role in preventing ovulation in lactating women is discussed below. The function of prolactin in males (if any) is unknown. In rodents, prolactin maintains the corpus luteum, but it is not luteotropic in humans, and the corpus luteum appears to be maintained by LH. An action of prolactin that has been used as the basis for bioassay of this hormone is stimulation of the growth and "secretion" of the crop sacs in pigeons and other birds. The paired crop sacs are outpouchings of the esophagus which form, by desquamation of their inner

Table 23–3. Characteristics of human pituitary gonadotropins.*

	FSH	LH
Molecular weight	31,000	26,000
Hexose (%)	3.9	5.9
Hexosamine (%)	2.4	5.1
Fucose (%)	0.4	0.6
Sialic acid (%)	1.4	0.7
Amino acid residues	210	204

*Data courtesy of H Papkoff.

cell layers, a nutritious material ("milk") that the birds feed to their young. However, prolactin, FSH, and LH are now regularly measured by radioimmunoassay.

Chemistry

FSH and LH are glycoproteins that contain the hexoses mannose and a galactose; the hexosamines N-acetylgalactosamine and N-acetylglycosamine; and the methyl pentose fucose (Table 23–3). They also contain sialic acid. Both hormones are made up of an α and a β subunit (see Chapter 22). The α subunits of FSH and TSH are identical and differ only slightly from the α subunit of the placental gonadotropin HCG, whereas the β subunits confer hormonal specificity. The carbohydrate in the gonadotropin molecules increases their potency by markedly slowing their metabolism. The half-life of human FSH is about 170 minutes; the half-life of LH is about 60 minutes.

Ovine prolactin is a simple protein that resembles human growth hormone and the placental hormone HCS (see below). It has a disulfide bridge at the carboxy end and 2 additional disulfide bridges (Fig 23–12). It contains 199 amino acid residues.

It is difficult to separate human prolactin from growth hormone because human growth hormone has lactogenic activity, and except during pregnancy and lactation, there is very little prolactin in the human pituitary. Indeed, it was argued at one time that the 2 hormones were identical. However, it is now clear that there is a separate human prolactin. The amino acid sequence of human prolactin is now known. It contains 198 amino acid residues and 3 disulfide bridges.

Regulation of Prolactin Secretion

In laboratory animals and in humans, the secretion of prolactin is clearly independent of growth hormone. The normal plasma prolactin concentration is approximately 5 ng/ml in men and 8 ng/ml in women. Secretion is tonically inhibited by the hypothalamus, and section of the pituitary stalk leads to an increase in circulating prolactin. Thus, the effect of hypothalamic prolactin-inhibiting hormone (PIH) usually overbalances the effect of the putative prolactin-releasing hormone (see Chapter 14). It now seems clear that PIH is dopamine secreted by the tuberoinfundibular dopaminergic neurons into the portal hypophyseal vessels. In humans, prolactin secretion is increased by exercise, surgical and psychologic stresses, and stimulation of the nipple (Table 23–4). Plasma prolactin rises during sleep, the rise starting after the onset of sleep and persisting throughout the sleep period. Secretion is increased during pregnancy, reaching a peak at the time of parturition. After delivery, plasma concentration falls to nonpregnant levels in about 8 days.

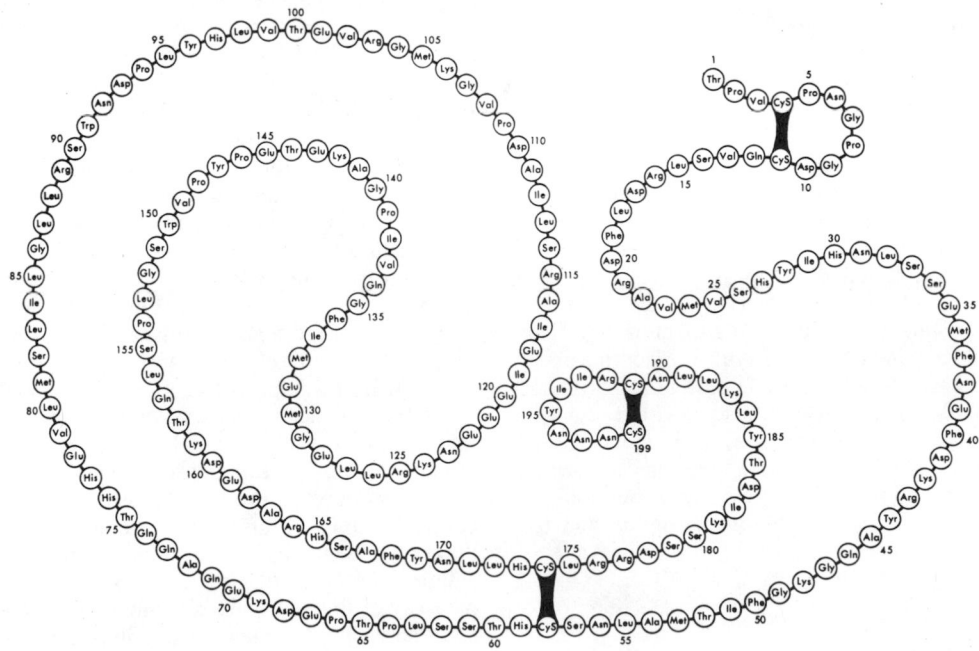

Figure 23–12. Ovine prolactin. The black bars indicate disulfide bridges. (Courtesy of CH Li.)

Table 23–4. Factors affecting the secretion of human prolactin and growth hormone. I, moderate increase; I+, marked increase; I++, very marked increase; N, no change; D, moderate decrease; D+, marked decrease.*

Factor	Prolactin	Growth Hormone
Sleep	I+	I+
Nursing	I++	N
Breast stimulation in nonlactating women	I	N
Stress	I+	I+
Hypoglycemia	I	I+
Strenuous exercise	I	I
Sexual intercourse in women	I	N
Pregnancy	I++	N
Estrogens	I	I
Hypothyroidism	I	N
TRH	I+	N
Phenothiazines, butyrophenones	I+	N
Opiates	I	I
Glucose	N	D
Somatostatin	N	D+
L-Dopa	D+	I+
Apomorphine	D+	I+
Bromocriptine and related ergot derivatives	D+	I

*Modified from Frantz A: Prolactin. N Engl J Med 298:201, 1978.

Suckling produces a prompt increase in secretion, but the magnitude of this rise gradually declines after a woman has been nursing for more than 3 months. With prolonged lactation, milk secretion occurs with prolactin levels that are in the normal range.

L-Dopa decreases prolactin secretion by increasing the formation of dopamine, and apomorphine and bromocriptine inhibit secretion because they stimulate dopamine receptors. Chlorpromazine and related drugs that block dopamine receptors increase prolactin secretion. TRH stimulates the secretion of prolactin as well as TSH, but it seems likely that there is an additional prolactin-releasing hormone (PRH) in hypothalamic tissue that is different from TRH. Estrogens also produce a slowly developing increase in prolactin.

It is now established that prolactin facilitates the secretion of dopamine in the median eminence. Thus, prolactin acts in the hypothalamus in a negative feedback fashion to inhibit its own secretion.

Hyperprolactinemia

An interesting recent discovery is that up to 70% of the patients with chromophobe adenomas of the anterior pituitary have elevated plasma prolactin levels. In some instances, the elevation may be due to damage to the pituitary stalks, but in most cases, the tumor cells are actually secreting the hormone. The hyperprolactinemia may cause galactorrhea, but in many individuals there are no demonstrable abnormalities. Indeed, most women with galactorrhea have normal prolactin levels; definite elevations are found in less than a third of patients with this condition.

Another interesting observation is that 15–20% of women with secondary amenorrhea have elevated prolactin levels and that when prolactin secretion is reduced, normal menstrual cycles and fertility return. It appears that the prolactin may produce amenorrhea by blocking the action of gonadotropins on the ovaries, but definitive proof of this hypothesis must await further research.

THE MALE REPRODUCTIVE SYSTEM

STRUCTURE

The testes are made up of loops of convoluted **seminiferous tubules,** along the walls of which the

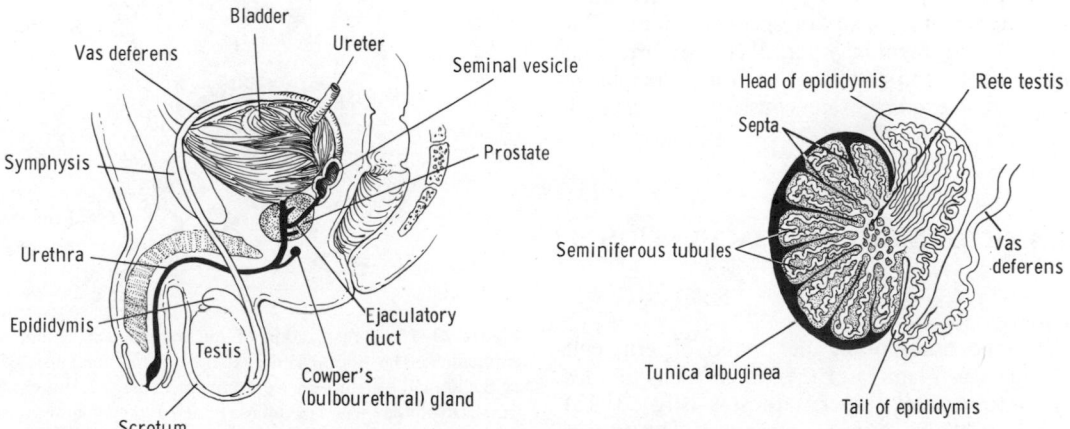

Figure 23–13. Male reproductive organs.

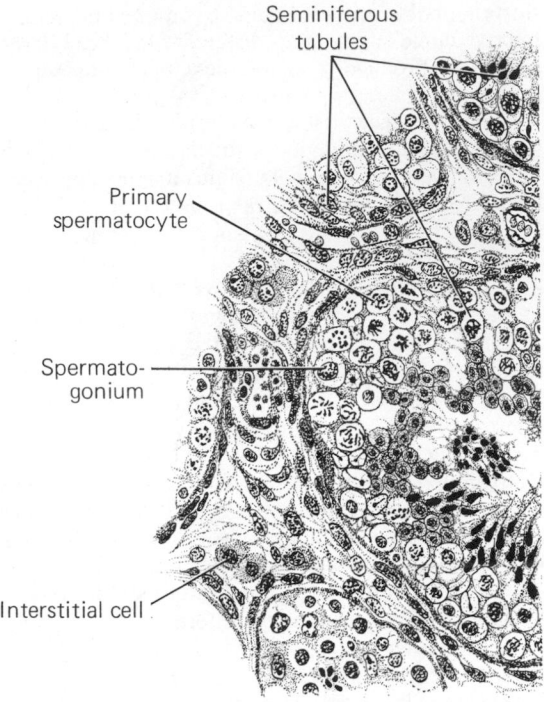

Figure 23–14. Section of human testis.

spermatozoa are formed from the primitive germ cells (**spermatogenesis**). Both ends of each loop drain into a network of ducts in the **epididymis.** From there, spermatozoa pass into the **vas deferens.** They enter through the **ejaculatory ducts** into the urethra in the body of the **prostate** at the time of ejaculation (Fig 23–13). Between the tubules in the testes are nests of cells containing lipid granules, the **interstitial cells of Leydig,** which secrete testosterone into the bloodstream (Figs 23–14 and 23–15). The capillaries of the testes are unusual in that, unlike those in most other endocrine organs, they are not fenestrated. The spermatic arteries to the testes are tortuous, and blood in them runs parallel but in the opposite direction to blood in the pampiniform plexus of spermatic veins. This anatomic arrangement may permit countercurrent exchange of heat and testosterone. The principles of countercurrent exchange are considered in detail in Chapter 38.

GAMETOGENESIS & EJACULATION

Spermatogenesis

The **spermatogonia,** the primitive germ cells next to the basal lamina of the seminiferous tubules, mature into **primary spermatocytes** (Fig 23–15). This process begins during adolescence. The primary spermatocytes undergo meiotic division, reducing the number of chromosomes. In this 2-stage process, they

divide into **secondary spermatocytes** and then into **spermatids,** which contain the haploid number of 23 chromosomes. The spermatids mature into **spermatozoa (sperms).** In humans, it takes an average of 74 days to form a mature sperm from a primitive germ cell by this orderly process of spermatogenesis. Each sperm is an intricate motile cell, rich in DNA, with a head that is made up mostly of chromosomal material (Fig 23–16).

The spermatids mature into spermatozoa in deep folds of the cytoplasm of the **Sertoli cells,** glycogen-containing cells in the tubules from which the sperms may obtain nourishment (Fig 23–15). Mature spermatozoa are released from the Sertoli cells and become free in the lumens of the tubules. The Sertoli cells may also secrete estrogens, and their development is stimulated by FSH.

Because of relatively tight connections between the Sertoli cells and other cells lining the tubular wall (''blood-testis barrier''), protein and some other substances penetrate poorly into the area near the wall of the tubule. However, testosterone and some other steroids penetrate readily, and the fact that the Leydig cells are close to the tubules probably ensures a high concentration of testosterone in the tubular wall.

FSH and androgens maintain the gametogenic function of the testis. After hypophysectomy, injection of LH produces a high local concentration of androgen in the testes, and this maintains spermatogenesis. There is some evidence that testosterone passes from the spermatic veins to the spermatic arteries as they parallel each other in the scrotum, thus helping to maintain a high androgen concentration in the testes. Less androgen is required if FSH is present. The role of FSH in spermatogenesis is uncertain. It appears to

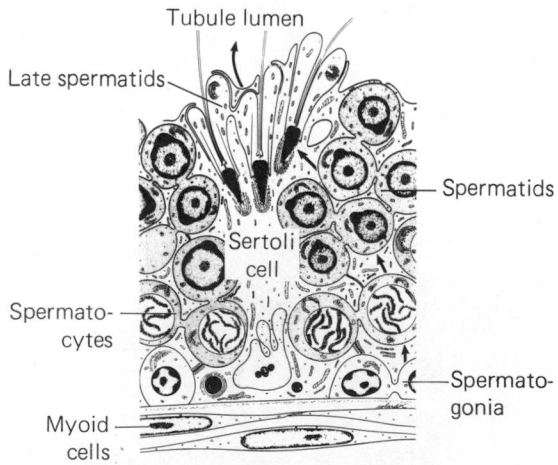

Figure 23–15. Organization of the mammalian seminiferous epithelium. The Sertoli cells extend the full thickness of the epithelium. The arrows trace the movement of the germ cells from the basal lamina toward the tubule lumen as they mature. (Reproduced, with permission, from Fawcett DW: Interactions between Sertoli cells and germ cells. In: *Male Fertility and Sterility.* Mancini RE, Martini L [editors]. Academic, 1974.)

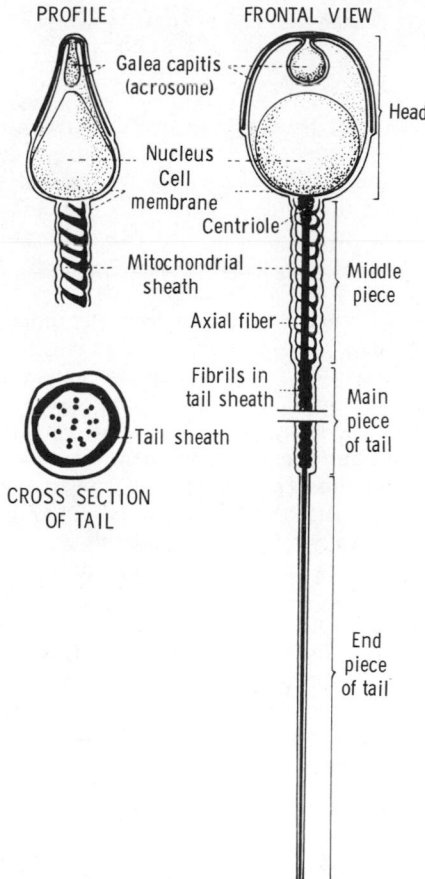

PROFILE   FRONTAL VIEW

Galea capitis (acrosome)

Head

Nucleus
Cell membrane

Centriole

Mitochondrial sheath

Middle piece

Axial fiber

Fibrils in tail sheath

Main piece of tail

Tail sheath

CROSS SECTION OF TAIL

End piece of tail

Figure 23–16. Human spermatozoon. (Redrawn and reproduced, with permission, from Schultz-Larsen J: The morphology of the human sperm. Acta Pathol Microbiol Scand, Suppl 128, 1958.)

facilitate the last stages of spermatid maturation, but it may exert this effect via its action on the Sertoli cells. There is some evidence that FSH promotes the production of an androgen-binding protein and that this protein stabilizes the supply of androgen to the developing germ cells.

Spermatozoa leaving the testes are incapable of sufficient motility to produce fertilization. They acquire the capacity to produce fertilization during their passage through the epididymis.

Effect of Temperature

Spermatogenesis requires a temperature considerably lower than that of the interior of the body. The testes are kept cool by air circulating around the scrotum and probably by heat exchange in a countercurrent fashion between the spermatic arteries and veins. When the testes are retained in the abdomen or when, in experimental animals, they are held close to the body by tight cloth binders, degeneration of the tubular walls and sterility result. Hot baths (43–45 C for 30 minutes per day) and insulated athletic sup-

porters reduce sperm counts in humans, but the reductions produced in this fashion have not been large enough or consistent enough to make the procedures reliable forms of male contraception.

Semen

The fluid that is ejaculated at the time of orgasm, the **semen,** contains sperms and the secretions of the seminal vesicles, prostate, Cowper's glands, and, probably, the urethral glands (Table 23–5). An average volume per ejaculate is 2.5–3.5 ml after several days of continence. Volume of semen and sperm count decrease rapidly with repeated ejaculation. Even though it takes only one sperm to fertilize the ovum, there are normally about 100 million sperms per milliliter of semen. Fifty percent of men with counts of 20–40 million/ml and essentially all of those with counts under 20 million/ml are sterile. The **prostaglandins** in semen, which actually come from the seminal vesicles, are in high concentration, but the function of these fatty acid derivatives in semen is not known. Their structure and actions are discussed in Chapter 17.

Human sperms move at a speed of about 3 mm/min through the female genital tract. Sperms reach the oviducts 30–60 minutes after copulation. In some species, contractions of the female organs facilitate the transport of the sperms to the uterine tubes, but it is not known if such contractions occur in humans.

Ejaculation

Ejaculation is a 2-part spinal reflex that involves **emission,** the movement of the semen into the urethra;

Table 23–5. Composition of human semen.

Color: White, opalescent
Specific gravity: 1.028
pH: 7.35–7.50
Sperm count: Average about 100 million/ml, with fewer than 20% abnormal forms
Other components:

Fructose (1.5–6.5 mg/ml) Phosphorylcholine Ergothioneine Ascorbic acid Flavins Prostaglandins	From seminal vesicles (contribute 60% of total volume)
Spermine Citric acid Cholesterol, phospholipids Fibrinolysin, fibrinogenase Zinc Acid phosphatase	From prostate (contributes 20% of total volume)
Phosphate Bicarbonate	Buffers
Hyaluronidase	

and **ejaculation** proper, the propulsion of the semen out of the urethra at the time of orgasm. The afferent pathways are mostly fibers from touch receptors in the glans penis that reach the spinal cord through the internal pudendal nerves. Emission is a sympathetic response, integrated in the upper lumbar segments of the spinal cord and effected by contraction of the smooth muscle of the vasa deferentia and seminal vesicles in response to stimuli in the hypogastric nerves. The semen is propelled out of the urethra by contraction of the bulbocavernosus muscle, a skeletal muscle. The spinal reflex centers for this part of the reflex are in the upper sacral and lowest lumbar segments of the spinal cord, and the motor pathways traverse the first to third sacral roots and the internal pudendal nerves.

Erection

Erection is initiated by dilatation of the arterioles of the penis. As the erectile tissue of the penis fills with blood, the veins are compressed, blocking outflow and adding to the turgor of the organ. The integrating centers in the lumbar segments of the spinal cord are activated by impulses in afferents from the genitalia and in men, descending tracts that mediate erection in response to erotic psychic stimuli. The efferent fibers are in the pelvic splanchnic nerves (**nervi erigentes**). Sympathetic vasoconstrictor impulses to the arterioles terminate the erection.

Vasectomy

Bilateral ligation of the vas deferens (vasectomy) has proved to be a relatively safe and convenient contraceptive procedure. However, it has proved difficult to restore the patency of the vas in those wishing to restore fertility, and the current success rate for such operations is less than 50%. Half of the men who have been vasectomized develop antibodies against spermatozoa, and in monkeys, the presence of such antibodies is associated with a higher incidence of infertility after restoration of the patency of the vas. However, there do not appear to be any other adverse effects of the antisperm antibodies.

ENDOCRINE FUNCTION OF THE TESTES

Chemistry & Biosynthesis of Testosterone

Testosterone, the principal hormone of the testes, is a C 19 steroid (see Chapter 20) with an –OH group in the 17 position (Fig 23–17). It is synthesized from cholesterol in the Leydig cells. According to current concepts, the biosynthetic pathways in all endocrine organs that form steroid hormones are similar, the organs differing from one another only in the enzyme systems they contain. In the Leydig cells, the 11- and 21-hydroxylases found in the adrenal cortex (Fig 20–8) are absent, but 17α-hydroxylase is present. Pregnenolone is therefore hydroxylated in the 17 position, then subjected to side chain cleavage to form 17-ketosteroids. These in turn are converted to testosterone. Testosterone is also formed via progesterone and 17-hydroxyprogesterone, but this pathway is less prominent in humans. The secretion of testosterone is under the control of LH, and the mechanism by which LH stimulates the Leydig cells involves increased formation of cyclic AMP (see Chapter 17). Cyclic AMP increases the formation of cholesterol from cholesterol esters and the conversion of cholesterol to pregnenolone via the activation of protein kinase. Testosterone is also formed in the adrenal cortex.

Secretion

The testosterone secretion rate is 4–9 mg/d (13.9–31.2 nmol/d) in the normal adult male. Small amounts of testosterone are also secreted in the female, probably from the ovary but possibly from the adrenal as well.

Transport & Metabolism

About two-thirds of the testosterone in plasma is bound to protein. Some is bound to albumin and some to a β globulin that also binds estradiol. The latter protein is therefore known as gonadal steroid–binding globulin (GBG). The plasma testosterone level (free and bound) is approximately 0.65 μg/dl (22.5 nmol/L) in adult men and 0.03 μg/dl (1.0 nmol/L) in adult women. It declines somewhat with age in males.

A small amount of circulating testosterone is con-

Table 23–6. Origin of principal plasma and urinary 17-ketosteroids. The boldface compounds and their derivatives are 17-ketosteroids with an –O or –OH group in position 11 ("11-oxy-17-ketosteroids").

	Adrenal Androgens and Their Metabolites	Hepatic Metabolite of Cortisol	Cortisone	Metabolite of Testosterone
Dehydroepiandrosterone	X			
Δ^4-Androstene-3,17-dione	X			
11β-Hydroxy-Δ^4-androstene-3,17-dione	X	X		X
Androsterone	X			X
Epiandrosterone	X			X
Etiocholanolone	X			X
Adrenosterone			X	

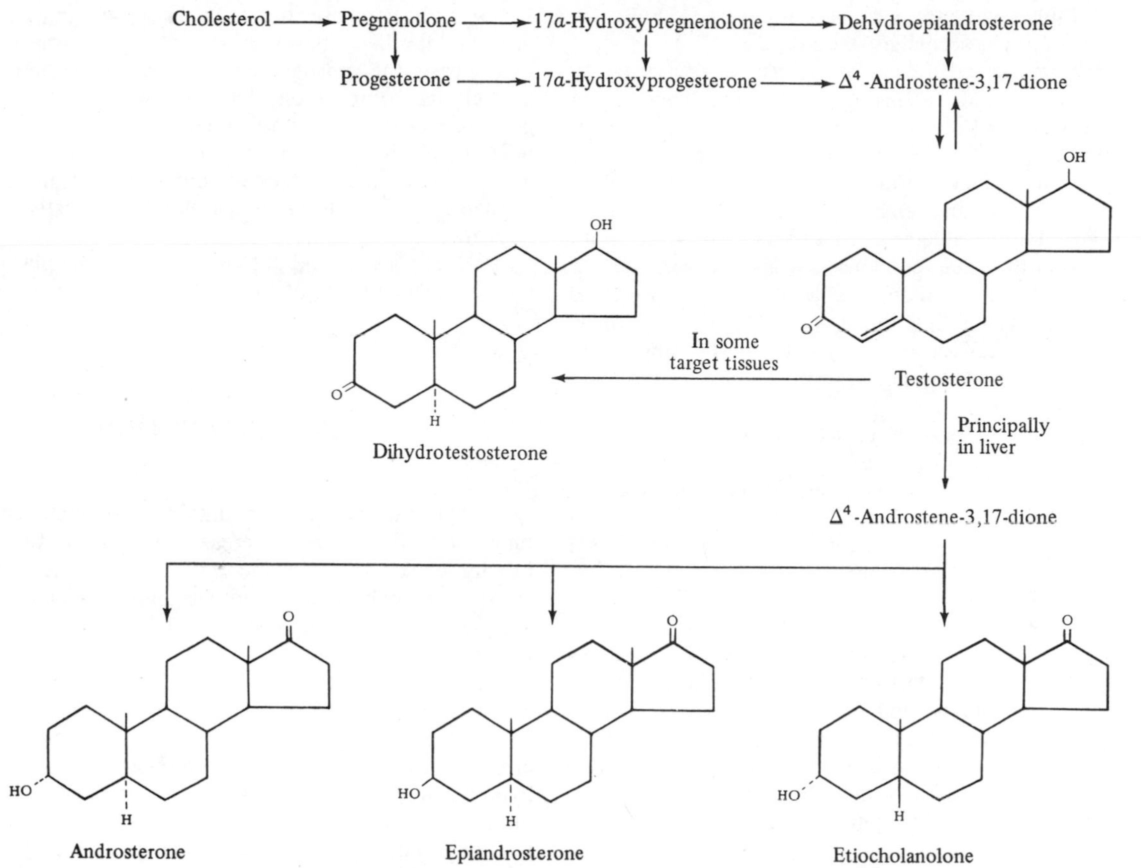

Figure 23-17. Biosynthesis and metabolism of testosterone. The formulas of the precursor steroids are shown in Fig 20–8. Although the main secretory product of the Leydig cells is testosterone, some of the precursors also enter the circulation. Note that dihydrotestosterone is formed in some target tissues and that the three 17-ketosteroids produced from testosterone in the liver are isomers of one another.

verted to estrogen somewhere in the body, but most of the testosterone is converted in the liver into 17-ketosteroids and excreted in the urine (Fig 23–17 and Table 23–6). About two-thirds of the urinary 17-ketosteroids are of adrenal origin, and one-third are of testicular origin. Although most of the 17-ketosteroids are weak androgens (they have 20% or less the potency of testosterone), it is worth emphasizing that not all 17-ketosteroids are androgens and not all androgens are 17-ketosteroids. Etiocholanolone, for example, has no androgenic activity, and testosterone itself is not a 17-ketosteroid.

Actions

Testosterone and other androgens exert an inhibitory feedback effect on pituitary LH secretion; develop and maintain the male secondary sex characteristics; and exert an important protein anabolic, growth-promoting effect. Along with FSH, testosterone is responsible for the maintenance of gametogenesis (see above).

Secondary Sex Characteristics

The widespread changes in hair distribution, body configuration, and genital size that develop in boys at puberty—the male **secondary sex characteristics**—are summarized in Table 23–7. Not only do the prostate and seminal vesicles enlarge, but the seminal vesicles begin to secrete fructose. This sugar appears to function as the main nutritional supply for the spermatozoa. The psychic effects of testosterone are difficult to define in humans, but in experimental animals, androgens provoke boisterous and aggressive play. The effects of androgens and estrogens on sexual behavior are considered in detail in Chapter 15. Although body hair is increased by androgens, scalp hair is decreased. Hereditary baldness often fails to develop unless androgens are present (Fig 23–18).

Anabolic Effects

Androgens increase the synthesis and decrease the breakdown of protein, leading to an increase in the rate of growth. They also cause the epiphyses to fuse to the long bones, thus eventually stopping growth. Their role in the adolescent growth spurt is discussed in Chapter 22. Secondary to their anabolic effect, they cause moderate sodium, potassium, water, calcium, sulfate, and phosphate retention, and they also in-

Table 23–7. Body changes at puberty in boys (male secondary sex characteristics).

External genitalia: Penis increases in length and width. Scrotum becomes pigmented and rugose.

Internal genitalia: Seminal vesicles enlarge and secrete and begin to form fructose. Prostate and bulbourethral glands enlarge and secrete.

Voice: Larynx enlarges, vocal cords increase in length and thickness, and voice becomes deeper.

Hair growth: Beard appears. Hairline on scalp recedes anterolaterally. Pubic hair grows with male (triangle with apex up) pattern. Hair appears in axillas, on chest, and around anus; general body hair increases.

Mental: More aggressive, active attitude. Interest in opposite sex develops.

Body conformation: Shoulders broaden, muscles enlarge.

Skin: Sebaceous gland secretion thickens and increases (predisposing to acne).

crease the size of the kidneys. Doses of exogenous testosterone that exert significant anabolic effects are also masculinizing and increase libido, which limits the usefulness of the hormone as an anabolic agent in patients with wasting diseases. Attempts to develop synthetic steroids in which the anabolic action is divorced from the androgenic action have not been particularly successful.

In the prostate and several other tissues that are primary targets for testosterone, testosterone is converted (Fig 23–17) to dihydrotestosterone (DHT), and it is the DHT rather than the testosterone that is physiologically active. The enzyme that catalyzes the conversion appears to be located in the nuclear membrane. Formation of the external genitalia and the prostate in the fetus is dependent on the formation of DHT, and so are the enlargement of the prostate, the facial hair, the temporal recession of the hairline, and the acne that occur at the time of puberty. On the other hand, the pubertal enlargement of the penis and

scrotum, the increase in muscle mass, and male sex drive and libido are mediated directly by testosterone. In any case, the androgen combines with a protein in the cell and brings about derepression of part of the genetic message, with resultant formation of new mRNA and stimulation of protein synthesis (see Chapter 17). In the testicular feminizing syndrome, there is an inability of the steroid to act on its target cells (see above).

DHT is also found in plasma, the normal plasma level being about 10% of the plasma testosterone level.

CONTROL OF TESTICULAR FUNCTION

FSH and androgens maintain the gametogenic function of the testes, whereas LH is tropic to the Leydig cells. Testosterone inhibits LH secretion. Hypothalamic lesions in animals and hypothalamic disease in humans lead to atrophy of the testes and loss of their function.

A current "working hypothesis" of the way the functions of the testes are regulated is shown in Fig 23–19. Castration is followed by a rise in the pituitary content and secretion of FSH and LH, and hypothalamic lesions prevent this rise. Implantation of minute amounts of testosterone in the hypothalamus but not in the pituitary causes testicular atrophy, indicating that the feedback effect of testosterone on gonadotropin secretion is at the level of the hypothalamus. Testosterone reduces plasma LH, but except in large doses it has no effect on plasma FSH. Plasma FSH is elevated in patients who have atrophy of the seminiferous tubules but normal levels of testosterone and LH secretion. These observations suggest that a factor other than testosterone regulates FSH secretion. Extracts of testicular tissue have been shown to contain an FSH-inhibiting nonsteroidal water-soluble substance that has been named **inhibin.** It appears to be a protein with a molecular weight of more than 10,000 and is

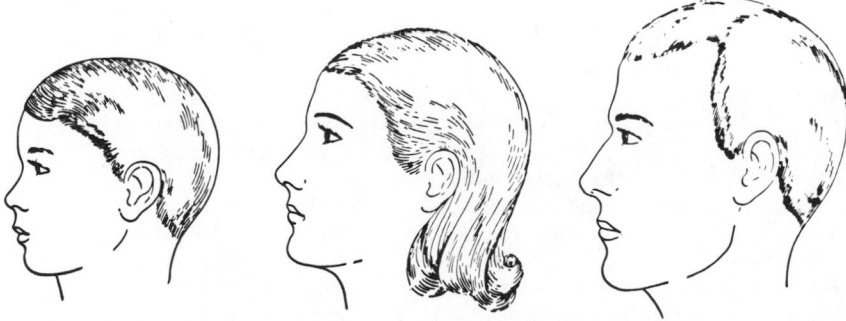

Figure 23–18. Hairline in children and adults. The hairline of the woman is like that of the child, whereas that of the man is indented in the lateral frontal region. (Reproduced, with permission, from Greulich WW & others: Somatic and endocrine studies of pubertal and adolescent boys. Monogr Soc Res Child Dev 7:1, 1942.)

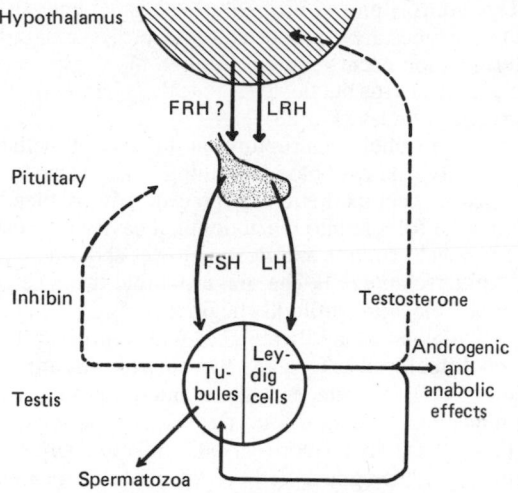

Figure 23-19. Postulated interrelationships between the hypothalamus, anterior pituitary, and testes. Solid arrows indicate excitatory effects; dashed arrows indicate inhibitory effects. The site of the inhibitory effect of inhibin on FSH secretion is unknown. Compare with Figs 18-11, 20-22, and 23-32.

presumably secreted by the Sertoli cells or some other component of the seminiferous tubules. Thus, it appears that testosterone feeds back to inhibit LH secretion, whereas the secretion of FSH is independently controlled by inhibin (Fig 23-19). Inhibin has also been found in the antral fluid of ovarian follicles (see below).

Estrogens lower plasma testosterone levels, presumably because they inhibit LH secretion. The estrogens from the testes might also play a role in the regulation of FSH secretion.

In response to LH, some of the testosterone secreted from the Leydig cells bathes the seminiferous epithelium and provides the high local concentration of androgen necessary for normal spermatogenesis. Systemically administered testosterone does not raise the androgen level in the testes to as great a degree, and it inhibits LH secretion. Consequently, the net effect of systemically administered testosterone is generally a decrease in sperm count. Testosterone therapy has been suggested as a means of male contraception. However, the dose of testosterone needed to suppress spermatogenesis causes sodium and water retention and may increase the risk of arteriosclerosis. The possible use of inhibin as a contraceptive awaits its isolation and detailed characterization.

ABNORMALITIES OF TESTICULAR FUNCTION

Cryptorchism

The testes develop in the abdominal cavity and normally migrate to the scrotum during fetal development. Testicular descent is incomplete on one or, less commonly, both sides in 10% of newborn males, the testes remaining in the abdominal cavity or inguinal canal. Spontaneous descent of these testes is the rule, however, and the proportion of boys with undescended testes (**cryptorchism**) falls to 2% at 1 year of age and 0.3% after puberty. Gonadotropic hormone treatment speeds descent in some cases, or the defect may be corrected surgically. Treatment should be instituted, probably before puberty, because there is a higher incidence of malignant tumors in undescended than in scrotal testes and because after puberty the higher temperature in the abdomen eventually causes irreversible damage to the spermatogenic epithelium.

Male Hypogonadism

The clinical picture of male hypogonadism depends upon whether testicular deficiency develops before or after puberty and whether the gametogenic or the endocrine function is compromised. The causes of testicular deficiency include hypothalamic and pituitary disease as well as a variety of primary testicular and chromosomal disorders. Loss or failure of maturation of the gametogenic function causes sterility. If the endocrine function is lost in adulthood, the secondary sex characteristics regress slowly because it takes very little androgen to maintain them once they are established. The growth of the larynx during adolescence is permanent, and the voice remains deep. Men castrated in adulthood suffer some loss of libido, although the ability to copulate persists for some time. They occasionally have hot flashes and are generally more irritable, passive, and depressed than men with intact testes. When the Leydig cell deficiency dates from childhood, the clinical picture is that of **eunuchoidism.** Eunuchoid individuals over the age of 20 are characteristically tall, although not so tall as hyperpituitary giants, because their epiphyses remain open and some growth continues past the normal age of puberty. They have narrow shoulders and small muscles, a body configuration resembling that of the adult female. The genitalia are small and the voice high-pitched. Pubic and axillary hair do appear, because of adrenocortical androgen secretion; but the hair is sparse, and the pubic hair has the female "triangle with the base up" distribution rather than the "triangle with the base down" pattern (male escutcheon) seen in normal males.

Androgen-Secreting Tumors

"Hyperfunction" of the testes in the absence of tumor formation is not a recognized entity. Androgen-secreting testicular tumors are rare and cause detectable endocrine symptoms only in prepuberal boys, who develop precocious pseudopuberty (Table 23-2).

THE FEMALE REPRODUCTIVE SYSTEM

THE MENSTRUAL CYCLE

The reproductive system of the female (Fig 23–20), unlike that of the male, shows regular cyclic changes that teleologically may be regarded as periodic preparations for fertilization and pregnancy. In primates, the cycle is a **menstrual** cycle, and its most conspicuous feature is the periodic vaginal bleeding that occurs with the shedding of the uterine mucosa **(menstruation).** The length of the cycle is notoriously variable in women, but an average figure is 28 days from the start of one menstrual period to the start of the next. By common usage, the days of the cycle are identified by number, starting with the first day of menstruation.

Ovarian Cycle

From the time of birth, there are many **primordial follicles** under the ovarian capsule. Each contains an immature ovum (Fig 23–21). At the start of each cycle, several of these follicles enlarge, and a cavity forms around the ovum **(antrum formation).** In humans, one of the follicles in one ovary starts to grow rapidly on about the sixth day, while the others regress. It is not known how one follicle is singled out for development. When women are given highly purified human pituitary gonadotropin preparations by injection, many follicles develop simultaneously. The structure of a maturing ovarian **(graafian)** follicle is shown in Fig 23–21. The cells of the **theca interna** of the follicle are the primary source of estrogens. However, the follicular fluid has a high estrogen content, and much of this estrogen appears to come from the granulosa cells.

At about the 14th day of the cycle, the distended follicle ruptures, and the ovum is extruded into the abdominal cavity. This is the process of **ovulation.** The ovum is picked up by the fimbriated ends of the uterine tubes and transported to the uterus and, unless fertilization occurs, on out through the vagina. Follicles that enlarge but fail to ovulate degenerate, forming **atretic follicles** (Fig 23–21).

The follicle that ruptures at the time of ovulation promptly fills with blood, forming what is sometimes called a **corpus hemorrhagicum.** Minor bleeding from the follicle into the abdominal cavity may cause peritoneal irritation and fleeting lower abdominal pain (''mittelschmerz''). The granulosa and theca cells of the follicle lining promptly begin to proliferate, and the clotted blood is rapidly replaced with yellowish, lipid-rich **luteal** cells, forming the **corpus luteum.** The luteal cells secrete estrogens and progesterone. If pregnancy occurs, the corpus luteum persists, and there are usually no more periods until after delivery. If there is no pregnancy, the corpus luteum begins to degenerate about 4 days before the next menses (24th day of the cycle) and is eventually replaced by scar tissue to form a **corpus albicans.**

The ovarian cycle in other mammals is similar, except that in many species more than one follicle ovulates, and multiple births are the rule. Corpora lutea form in some submammalian species but not in others.

In humans, no new ova are formed after birth. During fetal development, the ovaries contain over 7 million germ cells; however, many undergo atresia before birth, and others are lost after birth. At the time of birth, there are 2 million ova, but 50% of these are atretic. The million that are normal undergo the first part of the first meiotic division and enter a stage of arrest in which those that survive persist until adulthood. However, there is continuing atresia, and the number of ova in both of the ovaries at the time of puberty is less than 300,000. Only one of these ova per cycle (or about 500 in the course of a normal reproductive life) is stimulated to mature; the remainder degenerate. Just before ovulation, the first meiotic division is completed and the second begins, but the second is completed only after a sperm penetrates the ovum.

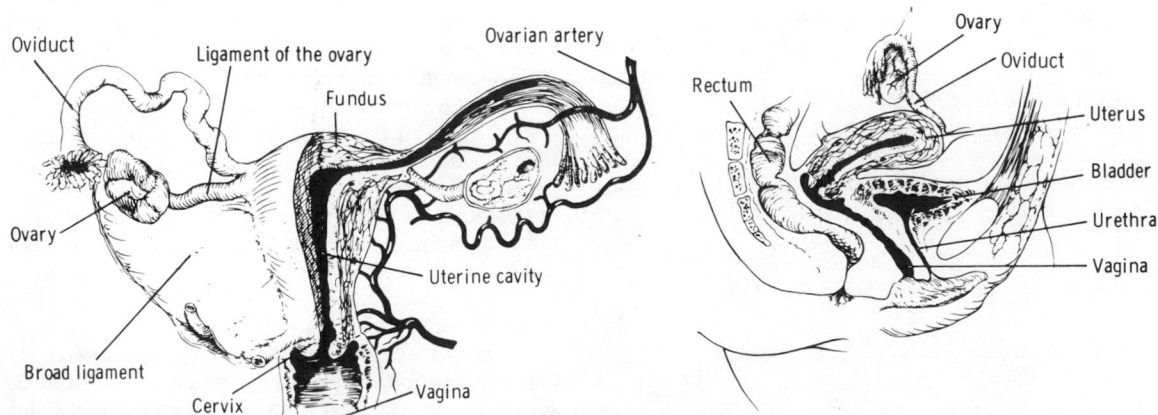

Figure 23–20. The female reproductive system.

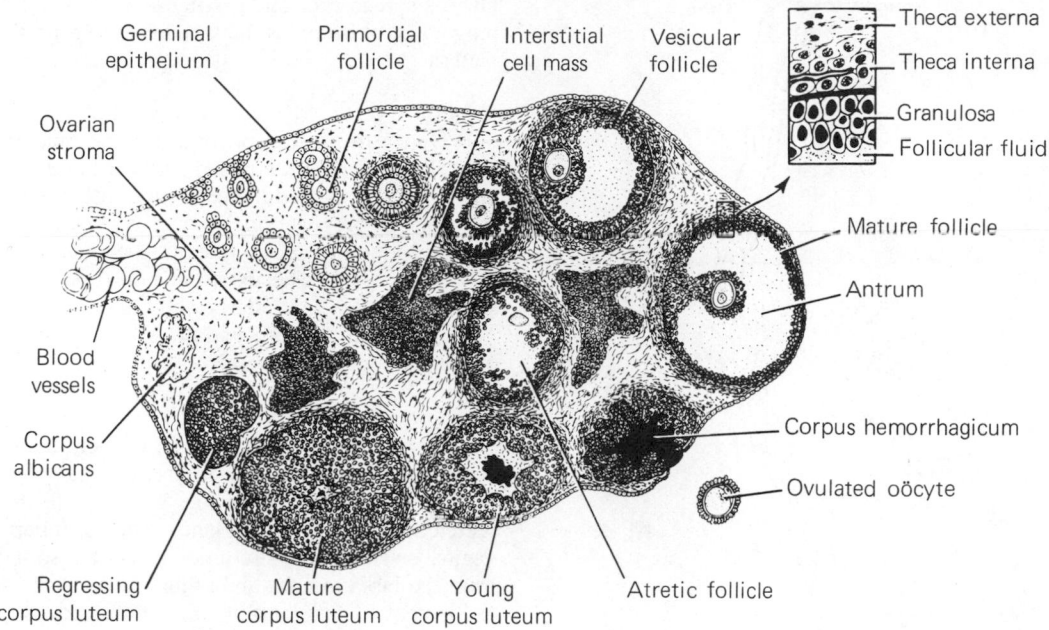

Figure 23–21. Diagram of a mammalian ovary, showing the sequential development of a follicle, formation of a corpus luteum, and, in the center, follicular atresia. A section of the wall of a mature follicle is enlarged at the upper right. The interstitial cell mass is not prominent in primates. (After Patten B, Eakin RM. Reproduced, with permission, from Gorbman A, Bern H: *Textbook of Comparative Endocrinology.* Wiley, 1962.)

Uterine Cycle

At the end of menstruation, all but the deep layers of the endometrium have sloughed. Under the influence of estrogens from the developing follicle, the endometrium increases rapidly in thickness during the period from the fifth to the fourteenth days of the menstrual cycle. The uterine glands increase in length but do not secrete to any degree (Fig 23–22). These endometrial changes are called **proliferative,** and this part of the menstrual cycle is sometimes called the **proliferative phase.** After ovulation, the endometrium becomes slightly edematous, and the actively secreting glands become tightly coiled and folded under the influence of estrogen and progesterone from the corpus luteum. These are **secretory,** or **progesta-**

tional, changes, and this period is sometimes called the **secretory phase** of the menstrual cycle. When the corpus luteum regresses, hormonal support of the endometrium is withdrawn. The **spiral arteries** (Fig 23–23) constrict, and the part of the endometrium they supply becomes ischemic. This part is sometimes called the **stratum functionale** of the endometrium to distinguish it from the deeper **stratum basale,** supplied by straight **basal arteries.** The damaged tissue probably liberates an anticoagulant. The spiral arteries then dilate one at a time, and their necrotic walls rupture, producing hemorrhage, sloughing, and menstrual flow. The sloughing is facilitated by prostaglandins liberated in the endometrium. Menstrual bleeding is predominantly arterial, only 25% of the

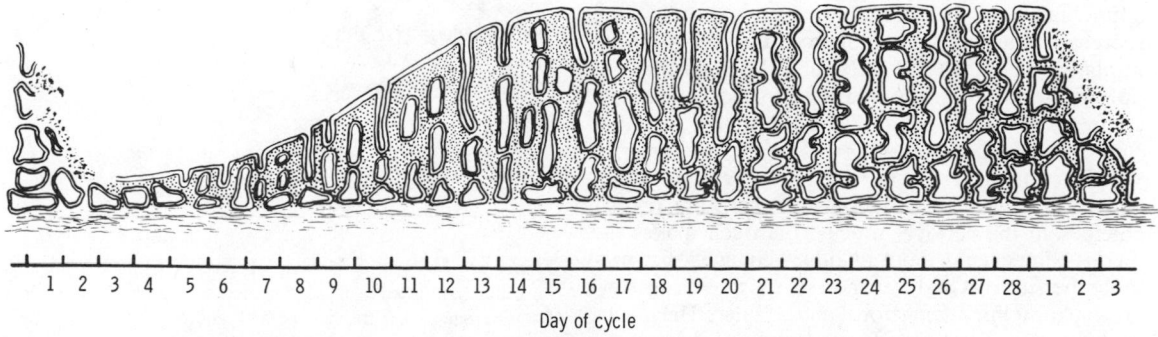

1 2 3 4 5 6 7 8 9 10 11 12 13 14 15 16 17 18 19 20 21 22 23 24 25 26 27 28 1 2 3

Day of cycle

Figure 23–22. Changes in the endometrium during the menstrual cycle.

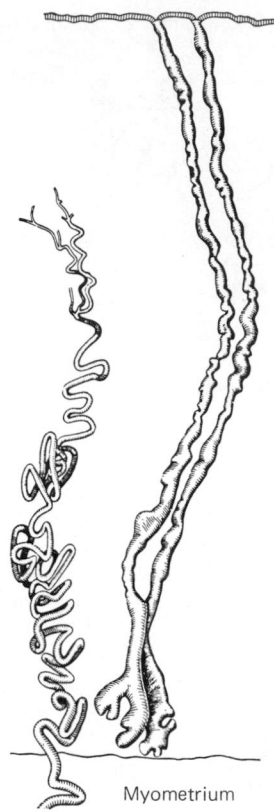

Myometrium

Figure 23–23. Spiral artery of endometrium. Drawing of a spiral artery *(left)* and 2 uterine glands *(right)* from the endometrium of a rhesus monkey; early progestational phase. The uterine cavity is at the top. (Reproduced, with permission, from Daron GH: The arterial pattern of the tunica mucosa of the uterus in the macacus rhesus. Am J Anat 58:349, 1936.)

blood in the flow being venous in origin. Unless the flow is excessive, it normally does not contain clots. The bleeding ends when the spiral arteries again constrict, and a new endometrium regenerates from the basal layers. The average duration of menstrual flow is 5 days. The average total blood loss is about 30 ml, although it varies considerably from woman to woman.

From the point of view of endometrial function, the proliferative phase represents the restoration of the epithelium from the preceding menstruation; and the secretory phase, the preparation of the uterus for the implantation of the fertilized ovum. When fertilization fails to occur, the endometrium is shed, and a new cycle starts. This is why it used to be said that "menstruation is the uterus crying for lack of a baby."

The mucosa of the uterine cervix does not undergo cyclic desquamation, but there are regular changes in the cervical mucus. Estrogen makes the mucus thinner and more alkaline, changes that promote the survival and transport of sperms. Progesterone makes it thick, tenacious, and cellular. The mucus is thinnest at the time of ovulation and dries in an arborizing, fernlike pattern (Fig 23–24) when a thin

layer is spread on a slide. After ovulation and during pregnancy, it becomes thick and fails to form the fern pattern.

Vaginal Cycle

Under the influence of estrogens, the vaginal epithelium becomes cornified, and cornified epithelial cells can be identified in the vaginal smear. Under the influence of progesterone, a thick mucus is secreted, and the epithelium proliferates and becomes infiltrated with leukocytes. The cyclic changes in the vaginal smear in rats are particularly well known (Fig 23–25). The changes in humans and other species are similar but unfortunately not so clear-cut.

Changes During Intercourse

During sexual excitement in women, the vaginal walls become moist as a result of transudation of fluid through the mucous membrane. A lubricating mucus is secreted by the vestibular glands. The upper part of the vagina is sensitive to stretch, while tactile stimulation from the labia minora and clitoris adds to the sexual excitement. These stimuli are reinforced by tactile stimuli from the breasts and, as in men, by visual, auditory, and olfactory stimuli, which may build to the crescendo known as orgasm. During orgasm, there are autonomically mediated rhythmic contractions of the vaginal walls. Impulses also travel via the pudendal nerves and produce rhythmic contraction of the bulbocavernosus and ischiocavernosus muscles. The va-

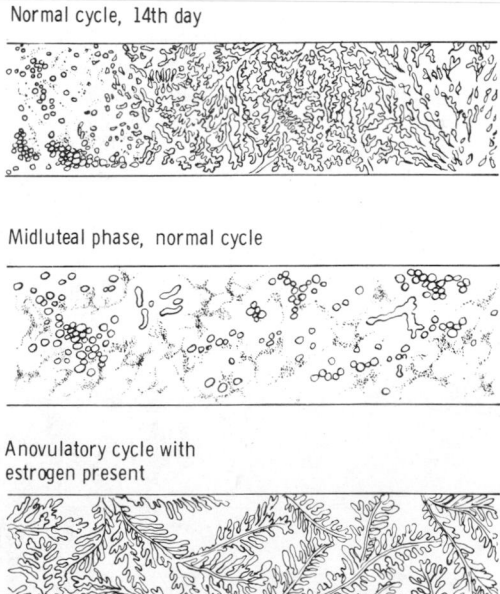

Normal cycle, 14th day

Midluteal phase, normal cycle

Anovulatory cycle with estrogen present

Figure 23–24. Patterns formed when cervical mucus is smeared on a slide, permitted to dry, and examined under the microscope. Progesterone makes the mucus thick and cellular. In the smear from a patient who failed to ovulate *(bottom)*, there is no progesterone to inhibit the estrogen-induced fern pattern.

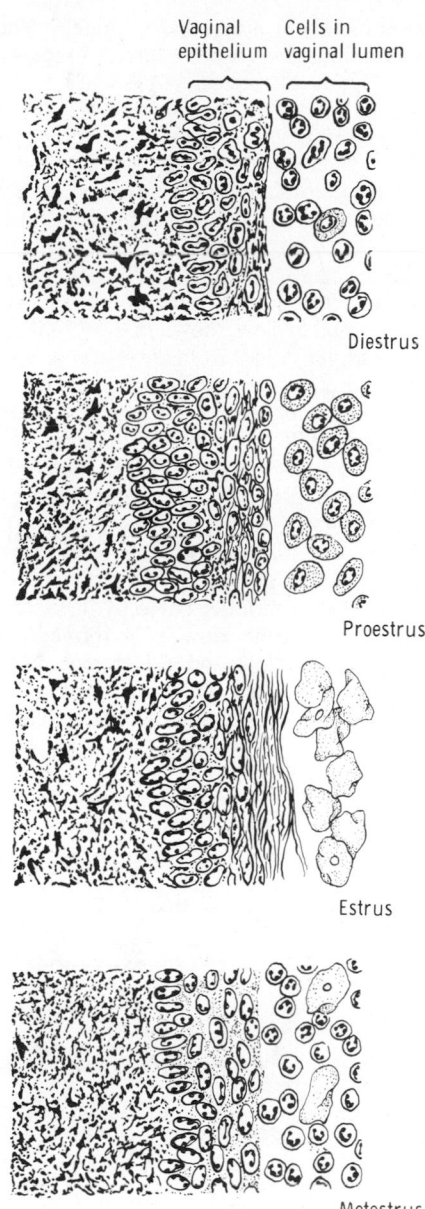

Vaginal epithelium   Cells in vaginal lumen

Diestrus

Proestrus

Estrus

Metestrus

Figure 23–25. Changes in the vaginal wall *(left)* and type of cells found in the vaginal smear *(right)* during the estrous cycle in rats. The vaginal smear pattern in women is similar but not so clear-cut. (Redrawn and reproduced, with permission, from Turner CD, Bagnara JT: *General Endocrinology,* 6th ed. Saunders, 1976.)

ginal contractions may aid sperm transport but are not essential for it, since fertilization of the ovum is not dependent on orgasm.

Indicators of Ovulation

It is often important in clinical practice to know that ovulation has occurred and to know when during the cycle it occurred. The finding of a secretory pattern in a biopsy of the endometrium (Fig 23–22) indicates that a functioning corpus luteum is present. Less reliably, finding thick, cellular cervical mucus that does not form a fern pattern in a woman who has regular menses is evidence of the same thing. A convenient and reasonably reliable indicator of the time of ovulation is a change—usually a rise—in the basal body temperature (Fig 23–28). Women interested in obtaining an accurate temperature chart should use a thermometer with wide gradations and take their temperatures (oral or rectal) in the morning before getting out of bed. The cause of the temperature change at the time of ovulation is unsettled, but it is probably due to the increase in progesterone secretion.

The ovum lives for approximately 72 hours after it is extruded from the follicle, and sperms apparently survive in the female genital tract for no more than 48 hours. Consequently, the "fertile period" during a 28-day cycle is no longer than 120 hours in length, and there is some evidence that it is shorter. Unfortunately for those interested in the "rhythm method" of contraception, the time of ovulation is rather variable even from one menstrual cycle to another in the same woman. Before the ninth and after the twentieth day, there is little chance of conception; but there are documented cases of pregnancy resulting from isolated coitus on every day of the cycle.

The Estrous Cycle

Mammals other than primates do not menstruate, and their sexual cycle is called an **estrous cycle.** It is named for the conspicuous period of "heat," or **estrus,** at the time of ovulation, normally the only time during which the sexual interest of the female is aroused (see Chapter 15). In spontaneously ovulating species such as the rat, the underlying endocrine events are essentially the same as those in the menstrual cycle, although the days of the cycle are numbered from the day of estrus (Fig 23–26). In other species, ovulation is produced by copulation (reflex ovulation).

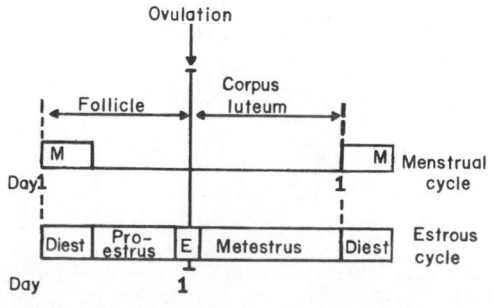

Figure 23–26. Timing of estrous cycle and menstrual cycle. M, menstruation; E, estrus, or "heat." Note that day 1 of a menstrual cycle is the first day of bleeding, while day 1 of an estrous cycle is the first day of heat.

OVARIAN HORMONES

Chemistry, Biosynthesis, & Metabolism of Estrogens

The naturally occurring estrogens are steroids that do not have an angular methyl group attached to the 10 position or a Δ^4-3-keto configuration in the A ring. They are secreted by the theca interna cells of the ovarian follicles, by the corpus luteum, by the placenta, and, in small amounts, by the adrenal cortex and the testis. The biosynthetic pathway (Fig 23–27) involves their formation from androgens. Granulosa cells also produce estrogens, and it appears that unlike the estrogens from the theca interna, the estrogens from the granulosa cells do not enter the circulation and remain in the follicular fluid. The stromal tissues of the ovary also have the potential to make androgens and estrogens. However, they probably do so in insignificant amounts in normal premenopausal women. **17β-Estradiol,** the major secreted estrogen, is in equilibrium in the circulation with **estrone.** Estrone is further metabolized to **estriol,** probably for the most part in the liver. Estradiol is the most potent estrogen of the three, and estriol the least. About 70% of the circulating estrogens are bound to protein. The main binding protein is the gonadal steroid–binding globulin that also binds testosterone (see above). In the liver, the estrogens are oxidized or converted to glucuronide and sulfate conjugates. Appreciable amounts are secreted in the bile and reabsorbed into the bloodstream (enterohepatic circulation). There are at least 10 different metabolites of estradiol in human urine.

Secretion

The concentration of estradiol in the plasma during the menstrual cycle is shown in Fig 23–28. Almost all of this estrogen comes from the ovary, and there are 2 peaks of secretion: one just before ovulation and one during the midluteal phase. The estradiol secretion rate is 0.07 mg/d (0.26 μmol/d) in the early follicular phase, 0.6 mg/d just before ovulation, and 0.25 mg/d during the midluteal phase. After menopause, estrogen secretion declines to low levels.

In men, the plasma estradiol level is approximately 2 ng/dl (70 pmol/L). The production rate is 0.05 mg/d (0.18 μmol/d), but only 15% of this is secreted; the rest of the estradiol is formed from circulating androstenedione and testosterone. In contrast to the situation in women, there is a moderate increase in estrogen production in men with advancing age.

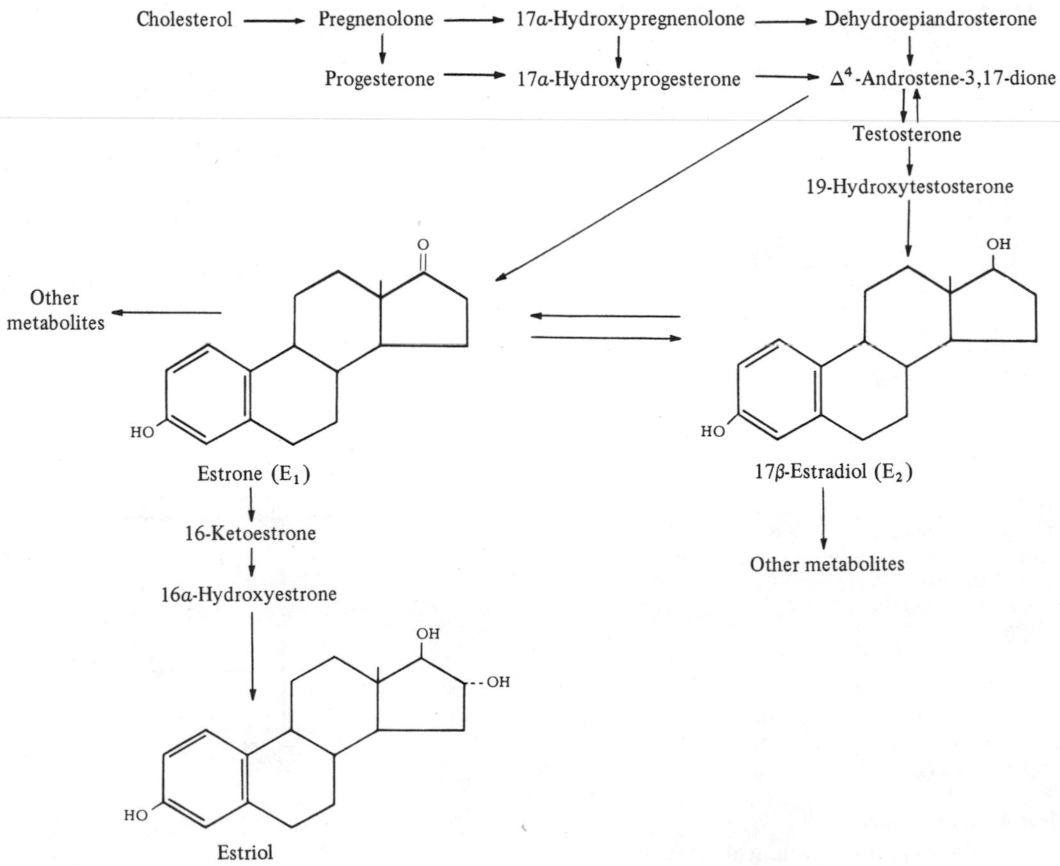

Figure 23–27. Biosynthesis and metabolism of estrogens. The formulas of the precursor steroids are shown in Fig 20–8.

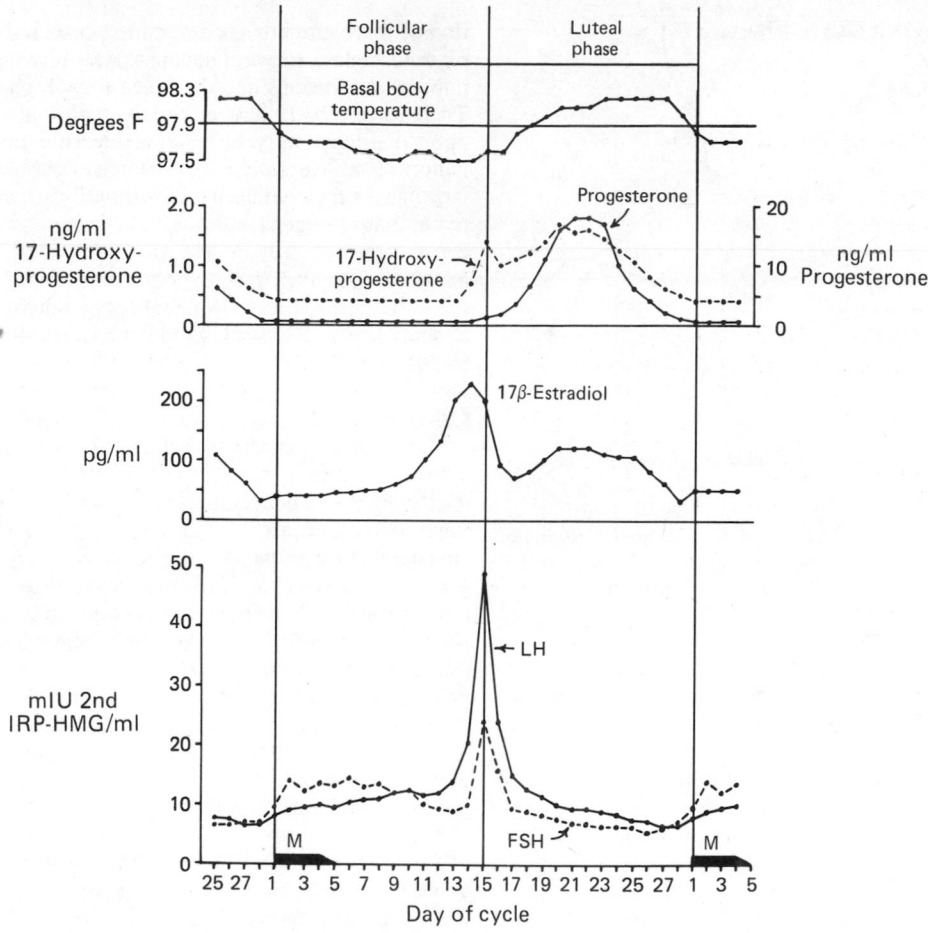

Figure 23–28. Typical basal body temperature and plasma hormone concentrations during a normal 28-day human menstrual cycle. M, menstruation; IRP-HMG, international reference standard for gonadotropins. (Reproduced, with permission, from Midgley AR in: *Human Reproduction.* Hafez ESE, Evans TN [editors]. Harper & Row, 1973.)

Effects on the Female Genitalia

Estrogens facilitate the growth of the ovarian follicles and increase the motility of the uterine tubes. Their role in the cyclic changes in the endometrium, cervix, and vagina is discussed above. They increase uterine blood flow and have important effects on the smooth muscle of the uterus. In immature and castrate females, the uterus is small and the myometrium atrophic and inactive. Estrogens increase the amount of muscle and its content of contractile proteins. Under the influence of estrogens, the uterine muscle becomes more active and excitable, and action potentials in the individual fibers become more frequent (see Chapter 3). The "estrogen-dominated" uterus is also more sensitive to oxytocin. There is evidence that estrogen influences the excitability of uterine muscle by changing the binding of Ca^{2+} in the muscle.

Chronic treatment with estrogens causes the endometrium to hypertrophy. When estrogen therapy is discontinued, there is sloughing with **withdrawal bleeding.** Some "breakthrough" bleeding may occur during treatment when estrogens are given for long periods of time.

Effects on Endocrine Organs

Estrogens decrease FSH secretion. Under some circumstances, they inhibit LH secretion (negative feedback); in other circumstances, they increase LH secretion (positive feedback; see below). Estrogens also increase the size of the pituitary. Women are sometimes given large doses of estrogens for 4–6 days to prevent conception after coitus during the fertile period (postcoital, or "morning after," contraception). However, in this instance, pregnancy is probably prevented by interference with implantation of the fertilized ovum rather than changes in gonadotropin secretion.

Estrogens cause increased secretion of angiotensinogen (see Chapter 24) and thyroid-binding globulin (see Chapter 18). They exert an important protein anabolic effect in chickens and cattle, possibly by stimulating the secretion of androgens from the adre-

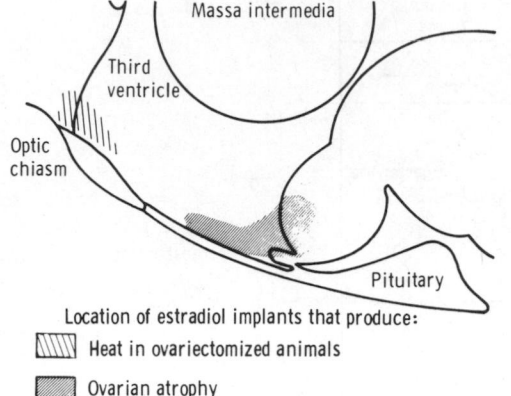

Location of estradiol implants that produce:

▨ Heat in ovariectomized animals

▨ Ovarian atrophy

Figure 23–29. Loci where implantations of estrogen in the hypothalamus affect ovarian weight and sexual behavior in rats, projected on a sagittal section of the hypothalamus of the rat. Note that the implants which stimulate sex behavior are located in the suprachiasmatic area, whereas ovarian atrophy is produced by implants in the arcuate nucleus and surrounding ventral hypothalamus.

nal, and estrogen treatment has been used commercially to increase the weight of domestic animals. Estrogens have been reported to exert anabolic effects and to cause epiphyseal closure in humans, but these effects may also be due to an increase in adrenal androgen secretion.

Behavioral Effects

The estrogens are responsible for estrous behavior in animals, and they increase libido in humans. They apparently exert this action by a direct effect on certain neurons in the hypothalamus (Fig 23–29). The relation of estrogens, progesterone, and androgens to sexual behavior is discussed in Chapter 15.

Effects on the Breast

Estrogens produce duct growth in the breasts and are largely responsible for breast enlargement at puberty in girls. Breast enlargement that occurs when estrogen-containing skin creams are applied locally is due primarily to systemic absorption of the estrogen, although a slight local effect is also produced. Estrogens are responsible for the pigmentation of the areolas, although pigmentation usually becomes more intense during the first pregnancy than it does at puberty. The role of the estrogens in the overall control of breast growth and lactation is discussed below.

Female Secondary Sex Characteristics

The body changes that develop in girls at puberty—in addition to enlargement of the breasts, uterus, and vagina—are due in part to estrogens, which are the "feminizing hormones," and in part simply to the absence of testicular androgens. Women have narrow shoulders and broad hips, thighs that converge, and arms that diverge (wide **carrying angle**). This body configuration, plus the female distribu-

tion of fat in the breasts and buttocks, is seen also in castrate males. In women, the larynx retains its prepuberal proportions and the voice stays high-pitched. There is less body hair and more scalp hair, and the pubic hair generally has a characteristic flat-topped pattern (female escutcheon). Growth of pubic and axillary hair in the female is due primarily to androgens rather than estrogens, although estrogen treatment may cause some hair growth. The androgens come from the adrenal cortex and, to a lesser extent, from the ovaries; the circulating level of dehydroepiandrosterone is about $0.17 \mu g/dl$ in adult women and about $0.12 \mu g/dl$ in adult men.

Other Actions

Estrogens cause some degree of salt and water retention. Normal women retain salt and water and gain weight just before menstruation. They are somewhat irritable, tense, and uncomfortable at this time (**premenstrual tension**), and the symptoms are prevented if the weight gain is prevented. However, the role of estrogens in premenstrual tension is uncertain because the tension develops late in the cycle, not at the time of ovulation, when estrogen secretion is at its peak. It is possible that increased vasopressin secretion contributes to the premenstrual fluid retention.

Estrogens are said to make sebaceous gland secretions more fluid and thus to counter the effect of testosterone and inhibit formation of **comedones** ("blackheads") and acne. The liver palms, spider angiomas, and slight breast enlargement seen in advanced liver disease are due to increased circulating estrogens. The increase is due not only to complex alterations in the hepatic metabolism of estrogens but also to increased conversion of androgens to estrogens.

Estrogens have a significant plasma cholesterol–lowering action, and they inhibit atherogenesis in chicks. The effect on cholesterol is probably due to an action of the hormone on the lipoproteins associated with cholesterol in the circulation. The higher estrogen level may be the reason for the low incidence of myocardial infarction and other complications of arteriosclerotic vascular disease in premenopausal women. However, pharmacologic doses of estrogen appear to promote thrombosis, and the value of estrogen treatment in the prevention of coronary artery disease is questionable.

Mechanism of Action

The actions of estrogens on the uterus, vagina, and several other target tissues involve interaction with a receptor protein in the cytoplasm of the cells. The steroid-receptor complex then moves to the nucleus, where it induces derepression of part of the genetic information coded in the nuclear DNA (see Chapter 20). New mRNA is formed, and protein synthesis is increased. It seems probable that all estrogen actions are produced in this fashion.

Synthetic Estrogens

The ethinyl derivative of estradiol (Fig 23–30) is

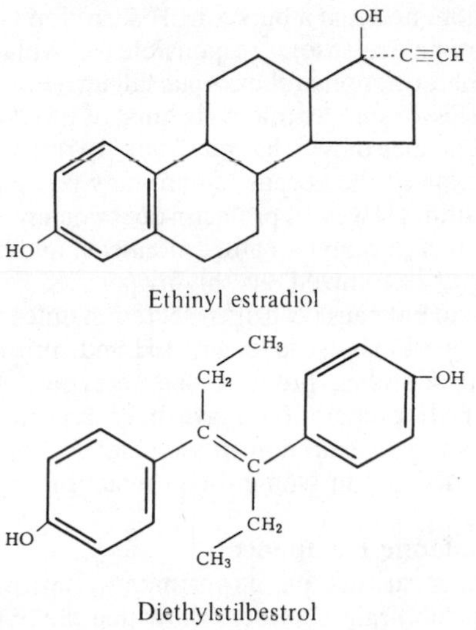

Ethinyl estradiol

Diethylstilbestrol

Figure 23-30. Synthetic estrogens.

a potent estrogen and—unlike the naturally occurring estrogens—is relatively active when given by mouth. The activity of the naturally occurring hormones is low when they are administered by mouth because the portal venous drainage of the intestine carries them to the liver, where they are inactivated before they can reach the general circulation. Many other nonsteroidal substances and compounds found in plants have estrogenic activity. The plant estrogens are rarely a problem in human nutrition, but they may cause undesirable effects in farm animals. Diethylstilbestrol (Fig 23-30) and a number of related compounds are estrogenic, possibly because they are converted to a steroidlike ring structure in the body.

Chemistry, Biosynthesis, & Metabolism of Progesterone

Progesterone is a C 21 steroid (Fig 23-31) secreted by the corpus luteum and the placenta. It is an important intermediate in steroid biosynthesis in all tissues that secrete steroid hormones, and small amounts apparently enter the circulation from the testes and adrenal cortex. 17α-Hydroxyprogesterone is apparently secreted along with estrogens from the ovarian follicle, and its secretion parallels that of 17β-estradiol. The 20α- and 20β-hydroxy derivatives of progesterone are formed in the corpus luteum. Secreted progesterone is probably bound to protein, although little is known about the details of the binding. It has a short half-life and is converted in the liver to pregnanediol, which is conjugated to glucuronic acid and excreted in the urine (Fig 23-31).

Secretion

In men, the plasma progesterone level is approximately 0.3 ng/ml (1 nmol/L). In women, the level is approximately 0.9 ng/ml (3 nmol/L) during the follicular phase of the menstrual cycle, the difference being

due to secretion of small amounts of progesterone by cells in the ovarian follicles. During the luteal phase, the corpus luteum produces large quantities of progesterone, and ovarian secretion increases more than 20-fold (Fig 23-28). The result is an increase in plasma progesterone to a peak value of approximately 15 ng/ml (50 nmol/L).

The stimulating effect of LH on progesterone secretion by the corpus luteum has been shown to be accompanied by an increased formation of cyclic AMP. The increase in progesterone secretion produced by LH or exogenous cyclic AMP is reduced by puromycin, which indicates that it depends upon the synthesis of new protein (see Chapter 17). However, the increase in the cyclic AMP content of the corpus luteum produced by LH is not blocked. The data suggest that LH activates adenylate cyclase in the corpus luteum and that in a series of events analogous to that triggered by ACTH in the adrenal, the increased cyclic AMP initiates a reaction which involves protein synthesis and facilitates steroid secretion.

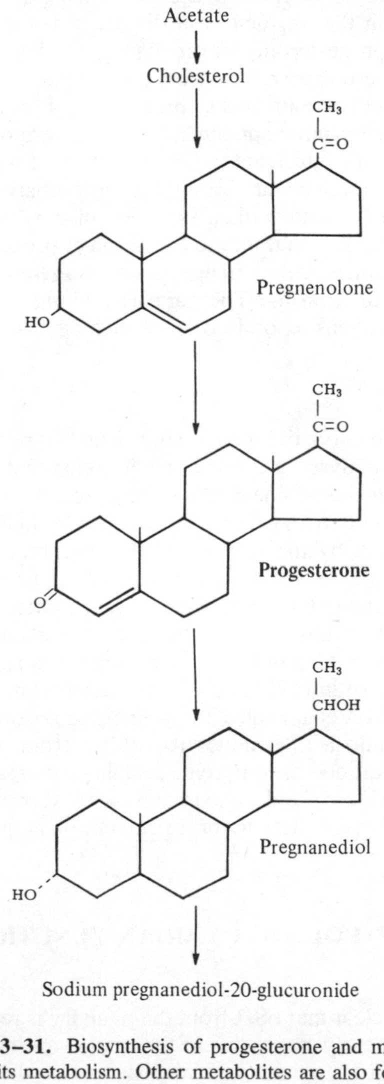

Figure 23-31. Biosynthesis of progesterone and major pathway for its metabolism. Other metabolites are also formed.

Actions

Progesterone is responsible for the progestational changes in the endometrium and the cyclic changes in the cervix and vagina described above. It has an antiestrogenic effect on the myometrial cells, decreasing their excitability, their sensitivity to oxytocin, and their spontaneous electrical activity while increasing their membrane potential. In the breast, it stimulates the development of lobules and alveoli.

Large doses of progesterone inhibit LH secretion and potentiate the inhibitory effect of estrogens. Progesterone injections can prevent ovulation in humans; but smaller doses actually cause ovulation in other species. Progesterone does not induce heat in castrate animals, except possibly in huge doses, but in some species it lowers the dose of estrogen necessary to produce estrous behavior.

Progesterone is thermogenic and is probably responsible for the rise in basal body temperature at the time of ovulation. It stimulates respiration, and the fact that the alveolar P_{CO_2} (PA_{CO_2}; see Chapter 34) in women during the luteal phase of the menstrual cycle is lower than that in men is attributed to the action of secreted progesterone. In pregnancy, the PA_{CO_2} falls as progesterone secretion rises. Large doses of progesterone produce natriuresis, probably by blocking the action of aldosterone on the kidney. The hormone does not have a significant anabolic effect. Like other steroids, its effects are brought about primarily by an action on DNA to initiate synthesis of new mRNA.

Substances that mimic the action of progesterone are sometimes called **progestational agents, gestagens,** or **progestins.** They are used along with synthetic estrogens as oral contraceptive agents (see below).

Relaxin

Relaxin is a polypeptide hormone that relaxes the pubic symphysis and other pelvic joints and softens and dilates the uterine cervix during pregnancy. Thus, it facilitates delivery. It has been suggested that relaxin is produced by the uterus and the placenta, but the primary source is the corpus luteum of pregnancy. Porcine relaxin has been isolated and characterized. It resembles insulin, with 2 peptide chains and 3 disulfide bridges located in the same relative positions as those in insulin (Table 19–1). However, it has a 22–amino acid A chain and a 26–amino acid B chain, with many amino acid residues that differ from those in insulin. Antibodies to porcine relaxin cross-react with human relaxin, and relaxin has been shown to be secreted by the human corpus luteum of pregnancy.

CONTROL OF OVARIAN FUNCTION

It is clear that FSH from the pituitary is responsible for the early maturation of the ovarian follicles, that FSH and LH together are responsible for their final maturation, and that a burst of LH secretion ("ovulating hormone" release) is responsible for ovulation and the initial formation of the corpus luteum (Fig 23–28). There is also a smaller midcycle burst of FSH secretion the significance of which is uncertain. In rats and mice, the function of the corpus luteum may be maintained by prolactin. However, prolactin does not have a luteotropic effect in rabbits, cattle, monkeys, and humans. In hypophysectomized rats, highly purified FSH preparations do not cause estrogen secretion unless a small amount of LH is also injected. LH and, presumably, prolactin stimulate progesterone secretion. Purified human FSH preparations have been reported to increase estrogen excretion in women, but the studies were carried out in women with intact pituitaries.

Hypothalamic Components

Observations on experimental animals and women with brain disorders show that the hypothalamus is involved in the control of gonadotropin secretion in the female. Lesions of the arcuate nucleus in the ventral hypothalamus cause ovarian atrophy in experimental animals. Hypothalamic control is exerted by LRH secreted into the portal hypophyseal vessels (see Chapter 14). LRH stimulates the secretion of FSH as well as LH, and it is uncertain whether there is an additional separate FRH. LRH is secreted in episodic bursts, and there is evidence that pulsatile rather than steady secretion is necessary to maintain normal LH secretion.

The presence of another hypothalamic center affecting gonadotropin secretion in rats is indicated by the observation that lesions below the paraventricular nuclei are associated with the development of multiple follicular ovarian cysts and constant vaginal cornification. Injections of exogenous LH cause the cystic follicles to ovulate and luteinize. There must be a considerable chronic secretion of FSH and LH in these rats to produce the follicles and the estrogen secretion responsible for the vaginal cornification, but the bursts of LH necessary to produce ovulation are apparently lacking.

Feedback Effects

Estrogens inhibit FSH and LH secretion during the early part of the follicular phase of the cycle (Fig 23–32). Inhibin has also been demonstrated in ovarian follicles, and it may play a role in the regulation of FSH secretion. The rise in circulating estrogens just before ovulation initiates the burst of LH secretion that produces ovulation. The secretion of FSH and LH is again inhibited by the high circulating estrogen and progesterone levels during the luteal phase of the menstrual cycle. Thus, a moderate, constant level of circulating estrogen exerts a negative feedback effect on LH secretion, whereas an elevated estrogen level exerts a positive feedback effect and stimulates LH secretion. In experiments on monkeys, it has been demonstrated that there is also a minimum time that estrogens must be elevated to produce positive feedback. When the circulating estrogen was increased about 300% for 24 hours, only negative feedback was seen; but when it

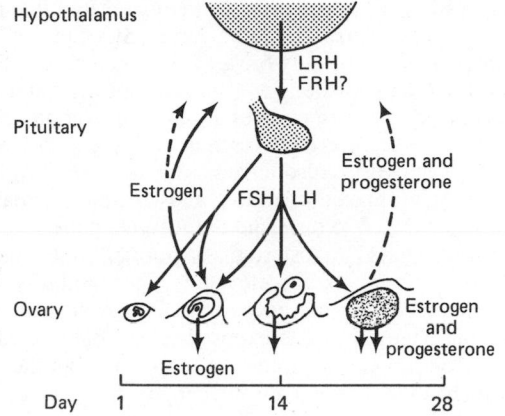

Figure 23–32. Summary of known and suspected endocrine changes during the menstrual cycle. The dashed arrows indicate inhibitory effects and the solid lines stimulatory effects. It is currently unsettled whether the positive and negative feedback effects of gonadal steroids in humans are exerted at the hypothalamic or pituitary level. The function of inhibin in women is also unsettled.

was increased about 300% for 36 hours or more, a brief decline in secretion was followed by a burst of LH secretion that resembled the midcycle surge. When circulating levels of progesterone were high, the positive feedback effect of estrogen was inhibited.

In rats, it is reasonable to postulate that the negative feedback effect of estrogen on FSH and LH secretion is exerted at the level of the ventral hypothalamus or the anterior pituitary, or both (Fig 23–29), whereas the positive feedback effect of estrogen is exerted in the anterior hypothalamic area. Lesions in this latter area abolish LH surges. However, there is evidence that the anterior area is not needed for positive feedback to occur in monkeys, and there is even some evidence that both the negative and the positive effects of estrogen are exerted on the anterior pituitary. In humans, the exact sites of estrogen feedback are unknown.

Control of the Cycle

It is not possible at present to arrange the known hormonal events of the menstrual cycle summarized in Fig 23–32 into an automatically cycling mechanism. One of the key problems is what causes regression of the corpus luteum (**luteolysis**). There is evidence that prostaglandins may play a role in this process, possibly by inhibiting the effect of LH on cyclic AMP, but their exact function is unknown. Once luteolysis begins, the estrogen and progesterone levels fall and the secretion of FSH and LH increases. A new follicle develops and matures as a result of the action of FSH and LH. Near midcycle, there is a rise in estrogen secretion from the follicle. This rise augments the responsiveness of the pituitary to LRH and triggers a burst of LH secretion. The resulting ovulation is followed by formation of a corpus luteum. There is a drop in estrogen secretion,

but progesterone and estrogen levels then rise together. The elevated estrogen and progesterone levels inhibit FSH and LH secretion for a while, but luteolysis again occurs and a new cycle starts.

Reflex Ovulation

Female cats, rabbits, mink, and some other animals have long periods of estrus, during which they ovulate only after copulation. Such **reflex ovulation** is brought about by afferent impulses from the genitalia and the eyes, ears, and nose that converge on the ventral hypothalamus and provoke an ovulation-inducing release of LH from the pituitary. In species such as rats, monkeys, and humans, ovulation is a spontaneous periodic phenomenon, but neural mechanisms are also involved. Ovulation can be prevented in rats by administering pentobarbital or various other neurally active drugs 12 hours before the expected time of ovulation. In women, menstrual cycles may be markedly influenced by emotional stimuli.

Effects of Intrauterine Foreign Bodies

Implantation of foreign bodies in the uterus causes changes in the duration of the sexual cycle in a number of mammalian species. In humans, such foreign bodies do not alter the menstrual cycle, but they act as effective contraceptive devices. Intrauterine implantation of plastic spirals is used in programs aimed at controlling population growth. The mechanism by which these devices exert their contraceptive effect is unsettled, but there is some evidence that they speed the passage of the fertilized ovum through the uterus, preventing its implantation in the endometrium. They also disturb the orderly sequential changes in the endometrium during the menstrual cycle, and this may be a factor.

Contraceptive Steroids

Women treated over a long period of time with relatively large doses of estrogen do not ovulate, probably because they have depressed FSH levels and multiple irregular bursts of LH secretion rather than a single midcycle peak. Women treated with similar doses of estrogen plus a progestational agent do not ovulate, because the secretion of both gonadotropins is suppressed. In addition, the progestin makes the cervical mucus thick and unfavorable to sperm migration, and it may also interfere with implantation. For contraception, an orally active estrogen such as ethinyl estradiol (Fig 23–30) is often combined with a synthetic progestin such as norethindrone (Fig 23–33). The pills are administered for 21 days, then withdrawn for 5–7 days to permit menstrual flow, and started again. Norethindrone has an ethinyl group on position 17 of the steroid nucleus, so it is resistant to hepatic metabolism and consequently effective by mouth. In addition to being a progestin, it is partly metabolized to ethinyl estradiol, and for this reason it also has estrogenic activity. In sequential therapy, which has been used as an alternative to combination therapy, an estrogen is administered and a progestin is added for

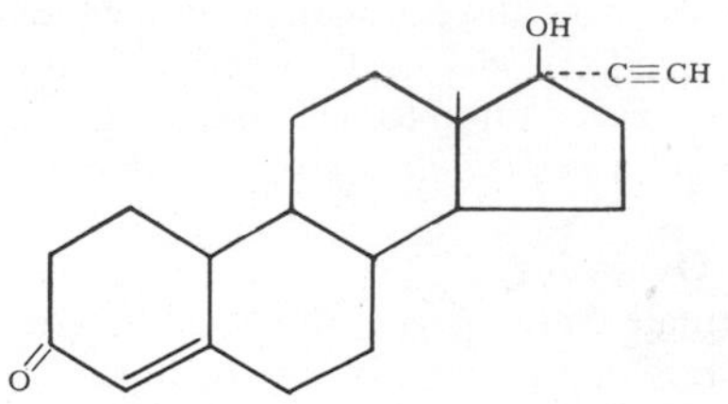

Figure 23–33. Norethindrone, a synthetic progestational agent.

the last 5 days of each cycle. Continuous therapy with progestins alone has also been used. The treatments are effective, but there are complications including thromboses in some women, and sequential therapy has been discontinued in the United States because of the possibility that it increases the incidence of carcinoma of the endometrium.

ABNORMALITIES OF OVARIAN FUNCTION

Menstrual Abnormalities

Some women who are infertile have **anovulatory cycles;** they fail to ovulate but have menstrual periods at fairly regular intervals. Such anovulatory cycles are the rule for the first 1–2 years after menarche and again before the menopause. **Amenorrhea** is the absence of menstrual periods. If menstrual bleeding has never occurred, the condition is called **primary amenorrhea.** Women with primary amenorrhea usually have small breasts and other signs of failure to mature sexually. Cessation of cycles in a woman with previously normal periods is called **secondary amenorrhea.** The commonest cause of secondary amenorrhea is pregnancy, and the old clinical maxim that "secondary amenorrhea should be considered to be due to pregnancy until proved otherwise" has considerable merit. Other causes of amenorrhea include emotional stimuli and changes in the environment, hypothalamic diseases, pituitary disorders, primary ovarian disorders, and various systemic diseases. Women whose ovaries are removed surgically or destroyed by disease in adulthood usually have uncomfortable hot flashes, but there is little change in body conformation or libido. The terms **oligomenorrhea** and **menorrhagia** refer to scanty and abnormally profuse flow, respectively, during regular periods. **Metrorrhagia** is bleeding from the uterus between periods. **Dysmenorrhea** is painful menstruation. The severe menstrual cramps that are common in young women quite often disappear after the first pregnancy.

The Polycystic Ovary Syndrome

An interesting cause of infertility and amenorrhea is the **polycystic ovary syndrome** (Stein-Leventhal syndrome), a condition characterized by thickening of the ovarian capsule and the formation of multiple follicular cysts, usually in both ovaries. Stripping off the ovarian capsule usually brings at least transient relief, but the thick capsule is not the cause of the failure to ovulate because resection of a wedge of ovarian tissue provides equally effective relief. Many patients with polycystic ovaries also have moderate degrees of hirsutism and masculinization and excrete increased amounts of 17-ketosteroids. In some patients, the excretion of 17-ketosteroids is normal, but plasma testosterone levels are elevated. The similarity between the cystic ovaries in this syndrome and the ovarian changes in rats exposed to androgen in early postnatal life (see Chapter 15) is obvious, but there is as yet no evidence that a similar exposure causes cystic ovaries in humans.

Ovarian Tumors

Androgen-secreting ovarian tumors can cause masculinization, and estrogen-secreting ovarian tumors in childhood can cause precocious sexual development (Table 23–2). Hormone-secreting ovarian tumors are rare, and there is no other syndrome related to "hyperfunction of the ovary."

PREGNANCY

Fertilization & Implantation

In humans, **fertilization** of the ovum by the sperm usually occurs in the mid portion of the uterine tube. One sperm penetrates the zona pellucida, possibly with the aid of lysosomal enzymes from the acrosome, and the membranes of the ovum and the sperm head fuse. Cell division begins at once. Only one sperm penetrates the ovum, because once the ovum has been fertilized a barrier forms around it that normally prevents other sperms from entering. The developing embryo, now called a **blastocyst,** moves down the tube into the uterus. Once in contact with the endometrium, the blastocyst becomes surrounded by an outer layer of **syncytiotrophoblast,** a multinucleate mass with no discernible cell boundaries, and an inner layer of **cytotrophoblast** made up of individual cells. The syncytiotrophoblast erodes the endometrium, and the blastocyst burrows into it **(implantation).** The implantation site is usually on the dorsal wall of the uterus. A placenta then develops, and the trophoblast remains associated with it.

Endocrine Changes

In all mammals, the corpus luteum in the ovary at the time of fertilization fails to regress and instead enlarges in response to stimulation by gonadotropic hormones secreted by the placenta. The placental gonadotropin in humans is called **human chorionic gonadotropin (HCG).** The enlarged **corpus luteum of**

pregnancy secretes estrogens, progesterone, and relaxin. In most species, removal of the ovaries at any time during pregnancy precipitates abortion. In humans, however, the placenta produces sufficient estrogen and progesterone from maternal and fetal precursors to take over the function of the corpus luteum after the sixth week of pregnancy. Ovariectomy before the sixth week leads to abortion but thereafter has no effect on the pregnancy. The function of the corpus luteum begins to decline after 8 weeks of pregnancy, but it persists throughout pregnancy. HCG secretion decreases after an initial marked rise, but estrogen and progesterone secretion increases until just before parturition (Fig 23–34).

HCG

HCG is a glycoprotein that contains galactose and hexosamine. Like the pituitary glycoprotein hormones, it is made up of α and β subunits. HCG-α is very similar to the α subunit of LH, FSH, and TSH, differing only in having 2 amino acid residues inverted and 3 amino acid residues deleted at the N terminal. The molecular weight of HCG-α is 18,000, and the molecular weight of HCG-β is 28,000. HCG is primarily luteinizing and luteotropic and has little FSH activity. It can be measured by radioimmunoassay and detected in the blood as early as 6 days after conception. Its presence in the urine in early pregnancy is the basis for the various laboratory tests for pregnancy, and it can sometimes be detected in the urine as early as 14 days after conception.

Pregnant Mare's Serum (PMS)

Another commercially available placental gonadotropin is that isolated from pregnant mare's serum (PMS). Unlike HCG, this substance has primarily follicle-stimulating activity and is a relatively weak luteinizing agent.

Other Placental Hormones

In addition to HCG, progesterone, and estrogens, the human placenta apparently secretes renin and relaxin. A factor extracted from the placenta has TSH activity, but it now appears that this may be HCG. Pure HCG has a small amount of TSH activity. The placenta also secretes a protein hormone that is lactogenic and has a small amount of growth-stimulating activity. This hormone has been called **chorionic growth hormone–prolactin** (CGP) and **human placental lactogen** (HPL), but it is now generally called **human chorionic somatomammotropin** (HCS). All of the placental protein hormones appear to be secreted by syncytiotrophoblast.

The structure of HCS is very similar to that of human growth hormone, and it appears that these 2 hormones and prolactin evolved from a common progenitor hormone. HCS has 2 disulfide bridges, both in the same position as the bridges in growth hormone. Both contain 191 amino acids, and 161 of these are identical in the 2 hormones. Large quantities of HCS are found in maternal blood, but very little reaches the

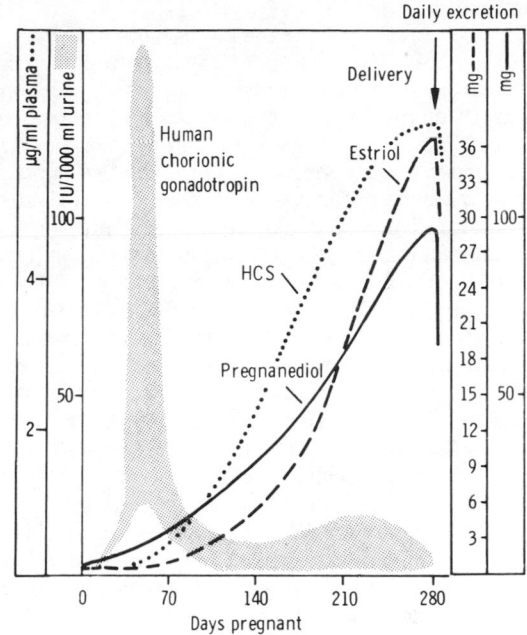

Figure 23–34. Hormone levels during normal pregnancy. (Data from various authors.)

fetus. Secretion of growth hormone from the maternal pituitary is not increased during pregnancy. Indeed, there is some evidence that HCS inhibits growth hormone secretion. However, HCS has most of the actions of growth hormone and apparently functions as a "maternal growth hormone of pregnancy" to bring about the nitrogen, potassium, and calcium retention and decreased glucose utilization seen in this state. The amount of HCS secreted is proportionate to the size of the placenta, and low levels are a sign of placental insufficiency.

Fetoplacental Unit

The fetus and the placenta interact in the formation of steroid hormones. The placenta synthesizes pregnenolone and progesterone from acetate. Some of the progesterone enters the fetal circulation and provides the substrate for the formation of cortisol and corticosterone in the fetal adrenal glands. Some of the pregnenolone enters the fetus, and, along with pregnenolone synthesized in the fetal liver, it is the substrate for formation of dehydroepiandrosterone (DHEA) and 16-hydroxydehydroepiandrosterone (16-OHDHEA) in the fetal adrenal. Some 16-hydroxylation also occurs in the fetal liver. The sulfate conjugate of 16-OHDHEA is then formed and carried back to the placenta, where it is converted to androstenedione and then to estrogens that enter the maternal circulation. The principal estrogen formed is estriol, and, since fetal 16-OHDHEA sulfate is the principal substrate for the estrogens, the urinary estriol excretion of the mother can be followed as an index of the state of the fetus.

Parturition

The duration of pregnancy in humans averages 270 days from fertilization, or 284 days from the first day of the menstrual period preceding conception. Irregular uterine contractions increase in frequency in the last month of pregnancy. The myometrium becomes increasingly sensitive to oxytocin late in pregnancy, possibly because of an increase in uterine prostaglandins. Once labor is initiated, stimuli from the genital tract cause reflex secretion of the hormone (see Chapter 14). This in turn augments uterine contractions (Fig 23–35). Women with diabetes insipidus have given birth without incident, and experimental animals whose posterior pituitary glands have been removed do not have abnormal deliveries. However, removal of the posterior pituitary alone leaves some oxytocin-secreting nerve endings in the pituitary stalk untouched; and hypothalamic lesions, which probably produce a more effective blockade of oxytocin secretion than posterior lobectomy, cause prolonged, desultory labor. Spinal reflexes and voluntary contractions of the abdominal muscles ("bearing down") also aid in expelling the uterine contents.

The mechanisms that initiate labor remain obscure. There is considerable evidence that in cows, sheep, and goats the signal that initiates parturition comes from the fetus. By an unknown mechanism, fetal glucocorticoid secretion is increased, and this increases maternal estrogen and decreases maternal progesterone, since the latter is the precursor for fetal glucocorticoids (see above). This in turn triggers an increase in the prostaglandin content of the uterus, and contractions ensue. However, the degree to which this mechanism operates in humans is uncertain.

Pseudopregnancy

In rats, mice, and various other species, sterile coitus, stimulation of the cervix with a glass rod, or suckling a foster litter initiates prolonged secretion of prolactin and retention of the corpus luteum, with a consequent delay in the return of normal cycles for some time. This state is called **pseudopregnancy.** The release of prolactin that maintains pseudopregnancy is clearly a neuroendocrine reflex response.

During pseudopregnancy in rodents and during the luteal phase of the menstrual cycle in monkeys, implantation of a glass bead, a piece of thread, or other foreign body in the uterus evokes a local endometrial response called a **deciduoma.** The maternal portion of the placenta forms as a result of a similar endometrial response when the implanted object is a developing embryo.

The type of pseudopregnancy seen in rodents does not occur in women, but women do sometimes imagine themselves pregnant. In false pregnancy, or **pseudocyesis,** there may be amenorrhea, abdominal enlargement, breast changes, and morning sickness. The fact that these changes can occur in the absence of pregnancy emphasizes the degree to which endocrine secretion can be affected by emotional states.

LACTATION

Development of the Breasts

Many hormones are necessary for full mammary development. In general, estrogens are primarily responsible for proliferation of the mammary ducts and progesterone for the development of the lobules. In rats, some prolactin is also needed for development of the glands at puberty, but it is not known if prolactin is necessary in humans. In hypophysectomized rats, glucocorticoids, insulin, and growth hormone are necessary for mammary development in response to other hormones, but they do not cause growth of the breasts by themselves (Fig 23–36). During pregnancy, prolactin levels increase steadily until term, and under the influence of this hormone plus the high levels of estrogens and progesterone, full lobulo-alveolar development of the breasts takes place.

Secretion & Ejection of Milk

The composition of human and cows' milk is shown in Table 23–8. In estrogen- and progesterone-primed rodents, injections of prolactin cause the formation of milk droplets and their secretion into the ducts. Oxytocin causes contraction of the myoepithelial cells lining the duct walls, with consequent ejection of the milk through the nipple (Fig 23–36). The

Onset of Labor

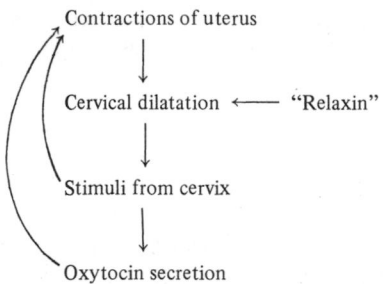

During Labor

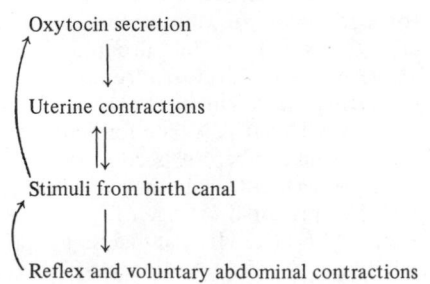

Figure 23–35. Role of oxytocin.

Table 23–8. Composition of colostrum and milk.*
(Units are weight per dl.)

	Human Colostrum	Human Milk	Cows' Milk
Water, g	...	88	88
Lactose, g	5.3	6.8	5.0
Protein, g	2.7	1.2	3.3
Casein: lactalbumin ratio	...	1:2	3:1
Fat, g	2.9	3.8	3.7
Linoleic acid	...	8.3% of fat	1.6% of fat
Sodium, mg	92	15	58
Potassium, mg	55	55	138
Chloride, mg	117	43	103
Calcium, mg	31	33	125
Magnesium, mg	4	4	12
Phosphorus, mg	14	15	100
Iron, mg	†0.09	†0.15	†0.10
Vit A, µg	89	53	34
Vit D, µg	...	†0.03	†0.06
Thiamine, µg	15	16	42
Riboflavin, µg	30	43	157
Nicotinic acid, µg	75	172	85
Ascorbic acid, mg	‡4.4	‡4.3	†1.6

*Reproduced, with permission from Findlay ALR: Lactation. Res Reproduction 6: No. 6, Nov 1974.
†Poor source.
‡Just adequate.

reflex release of oxytocin initiated by touching the nipples and areolas (milk ejection reflex) is discussed in Chapter 14. Oxytocin is not essential for milk ejection in some species, but it is in humans.

The other hormonal relations in humans are generally similar to those in rats, although normal breast growth and lactation can occur in dwarfs with congenital growth hormone deficiency.

Initiation of Lactation After Delivery

The breasts enlarge during pregnancy in response to high circulating levels of estrogens, progesterone, prolactin, and possibly HCG. Some milk is secreted into the ducts as early as the fifth month, but the amounts are small compared to the surge of milk secretion that follows delivery. A similar increase in milk secretion follows abortions after the fourth month, so expulsion of the uterine contents in some way stimulates milk secretion. In most animals, milk is secreted within an hour after delivery, but in women it takes 1–3 days for the milk to "come in."

After expulsion of the placenta at parturition, there is an abrupt decline in circulating estrogens and progesterone. The drop in circulating estrogen initiates lactation. Prolactin and estrogen synergize in producing breast growth, but estrogen antagonizes the secretory effect of prolactin on the breast. Indeed, in women who do not wish to nurse their babies, estrogens are administered to stop lactation.

Suckling not only evokes reflex oxytocin release and milk ejection, it also maintains and augments the secretion of milk because of the stimulation of prolactin secretion produced by suckling (see above).

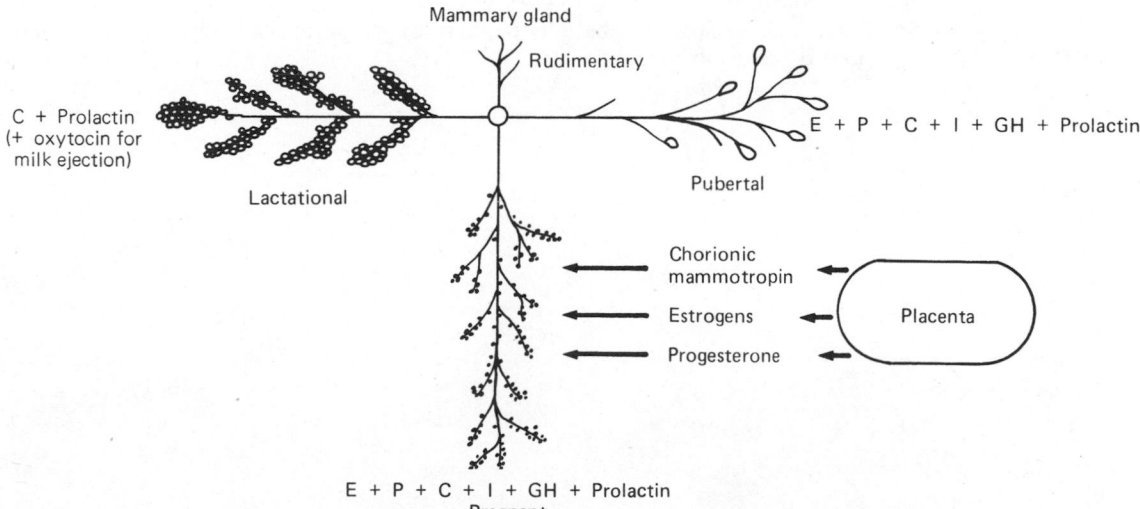

Figure 23–36. Hormonal control of breast development and lactation in rats. Estrogens (E) plus some progesterone (P) and some prolactin in the presence of glucocorticoids (C), insulin (I), and growth hormone (GH) cause duct proliferation and growth at puberty *(right)*. During pregnancy, all of these hormones bring about full alveolar development and some milk secretion *(below)*. After delivery, increased secretion of prolactin and a decline in estrogen and progesterone levels bring about copious secretion and, in the presence of oxytocin, ejection of milk *(left)*. Chorionic mammotropin is the lactogenic hormone presumably secreted by the placenta in rats and is analogous to human chorionic somatomammotropin. It supplements the action of prolactin.

Return of Menstrual Cycle After Delivery

Women who do not nurse their infants usually have their first menstrual period 6 weeks after delivery. Nursing stimulates prolactin secretion, and there is evidence that prolactin inhibits LRH secretion, inhibits the action of LRH on the pituitary, and antagonizes the action of gonadotropins on the ovaries. Ovulation is inhibited, and the ovaries are inactive, so estrogen and progesterone output fall to low levels. Fifty percent of nursing mothers do not ovulate until the child is weaned.

Chiari-Frommel Syndrome

An interesting although rare condition is persistence of lactation (**galactorrhea**) and amenorrhea in women who do not nurse after delivery. This condition, called the **Chiari-Frommel syndrome,** may be associated with some genital atrophy and is due to persistent prolactin secretion without the secretion of the FSH and LH necessary to produce maturation of new follicles and ovulation. A similar pattern of galactorrhea and amenorrhea with high circulating prolactin levels is sometimes seen in nonpregnant women with chromophobe tumors of the pituitary and in women in whom the pituitary stalk has been sectioned for treatment of cancer.

Gynecomastia

Breast development in the male is called **gynecomastia.** It may be unilateral but is more commonly bilateral. It is seen in mild, transient form in 70% of normal boys at the time of puberty. It is a complication of estrogen therapy and occurs in patients with estrogen-secreting tumors. It also occurs in a wide variety of seemingly unrelated conditions, including eunuchoidism due to primary testicular disease, hypothyroidism, hyperthyroidism, and cirrhosis of the liver. It occurs during initial digitalization in some patients with congestive heart failure and was seen in malnourished prisoners of war, but only after they were liberated and eating an adequate diet. There are many theories about the causes of gynecomastia, and the causes are probably multiple.

Hormones & Cancer

About 35% of carcinomas of the breast in women of childbearing age are **estrogen-dependent;** their continued growth depends upon the presence of estrogens in the circulation, and they are made worse by pregnancy and inhibited by castration. The tumors are not cured by decreasing estrogen secretion, but symptoms are dramatically relieved, and the tumor regresses for months or years before recurring. Women with estrogen-dependent tumors often have a remission when their ovaries are removed. When the disease recurs, another remission follows bilateral adrenalectomy or the administration of glucocorticoids in doses sufficient to inhibit ACTH secretion and thus reduce the secretion of estrogens or estrogen precursors from the adrenals. Since ovarian and adrenal estrogen secretion are both inhibited by hypophysectomy, this operation has been performed in cancer patients. The number of remissions produced by hypophysectomy is at least as great as the number produced by castration. There also is some evidence that growth hormone and prolactin stimulate the growth of breast carcinomas, and hypophysectomy removes these stimuli. Hypophysectomy induces a significant incidence of remissions in carcinoma of the male breast, an uncommon but serious disease. Some carcinomas of the prostate are **androgen-dependent** and regress temporarily after removal of the testes or hypophysectomy. The formation of pituitary tumors after removal of the target endocrine glands controlled by pituitary tropic hormones is discussed in Chapter 22.

The organs with endocrine functions include a number of structures in addition to the posterior, intermediate, and anterior lobes of the pituitary, the thyroid, the parathyroids, the pancreas, the adrenal cortex, the adrenal medulla, and the gonads. Hormones that stimulate or inhibit the secretion of anterior pituitary hormones are secreted by the hypothalamus (see Chapter 14), and a number of hormones are secreted by the mucosa of the gastrointestinal tract (see Chapter 26). The thymus also secretes one or more hormones that affect lymphocytes (see Chapter 27). Two hormones are produced by the kidney, and the pineal probably has an endocrine function.

THE ENDOCRINE
FUNCTIONS OF THE KIDNEYS:
RENIN & ERYTHROPOIETIN

Renin & Angiotensin

The rise in blood pressure produced by injection of kidney extracts is due to **renin,** a proteolytic enzyme secreted by the kidney into the bloodstream. This glycoprotein hormone has a molecular weight of approximately 42,000. The kidneys also contain a larger, relatively inactive renin with a molecular weight of approximately 60,000. This protein, called **prorenin,** or "big renin," is apparently the precursor of the active form. An even larger form ("big big renin") has also been identified in renal tissue.

Renin has a half-life in the circulation of 80 minutes or less. It acts on a glycoprotein in the α_2 globulin fraction of the proteins in the circulating plasma, releasing a decapeptide, **angiotensin I** (Fig 24–1). The α_2 globulin is synthesized in the liver and is called **angiotensinogen,** or **renin substrate.** Its circulating level is increased by glucocorticoid hormones and estrogens. There is some evidence that the estrogen-stimulated liver secretes more than one form of renin substrate. **Converting enzyme** is a dipeptidyl-carboxypeptidase that splits off histidyl-leucine from the physiologically inactive angiotensin I, forming the octapeptide **angiotensin II** (Fig 24–2). Most of this conversion occurs during the passage of the blood through the lungs, but converting enzyme is probably present in all endothelial cells, and conversion also occurs in many different parts of the body.

Angiotensin II is destroyed rapidly, its half-life in humans being 1–2 minutes. The enzymes that destroy angiotensin II are lumped together under the term **angiotensinase.** They include an aminopeptidase that removes the Asp residue from the N terminal of the peptide. The resulting heptapeptide, unlike the other peptide fragments, has physiologic activity and is sometimes called **angiotensin III** (see below). Angiotensinase activity is found in red blood cells and many tissues. In addition, angiotensin II appears to be removed from the circulation by some sort of trapping mechanism in the vascular beds of tissues other than the lungs.

Renin is usually measured by incubating the sample to be assayed with substrate and measuring by immunoassay the amount of angiotensin I generated. The normal plasma level in supine subjects eating a normal amount of sodium is approximately 1 ng angiotensin I generated per milliliter per hour. The plasma angiotensin II concentration in such subjects is about 25 pg/ml (approximately 25 pmol/L).

Actions of Angiotensins

Angiotensin I appears to function solely as the precursor of angiotensin II and does not have any other established action.

Angiotensin II—previously called hypertensin or angiotonin—produces arteriolar constriction and a

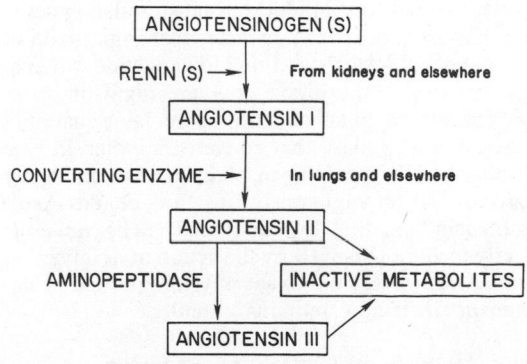

Figure 24–1. Formation and metabolism of angiotensins.

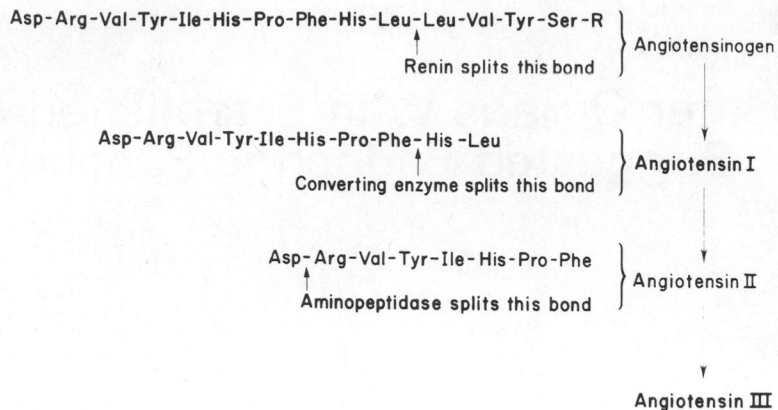

Figure 24–2. Structure of angiotensins I, II, and III. R, remainder of protein. The structure shown is that of angiotensin II of humans, dogs, rats, pigs, and horses. Bovine angiotensin II has valine in position 5.

rise in systolic and diastolic blood pressure. It is the most potent vasoconstrictor known, being 4–8 times as active as norepinephrine on a weight basis in normal individuals. However, its pressor activity is decreased in sodium-depleted individuals and in patients with cirrhosis and some other diseases. In salt depletion, ECF volume is reduced, and the arterioles are constricted owing to the high level of circulating endogenous angiotensin II (see below). Consequently, many of the angiotensin II receptors are occupied, and there are fewer to respond to injected angiotensin II.

Angiotensin II also acts directly on the adrenal cortex to increase the secretion of aldosterone, and the renin-angiotensin system is a major regulator of aldosterone secretion (see Chapter 20).

Angiotensin II acts on peripheral adrenergic neurons to facilitate catecholamine synthesis and release and in this way to modulate sympathetic function. It also acts on the area postrema and possibly on other circumventricular organs in the brain (see Chapter 32) to increase blood pressure. However, the physiologic significance of this action is uncertain. The action of angiotensin II on the brain to increase water intake and vasopressin secretion and its role in water metabolism are discussed in Chapter 14.

Angiotensin III ([des-Asp¹] angiotensin II) has about 40% of the pressor activity of angiotensin II and is at least equal to it in aldosterone-stimulating activity. It has therefore been suggested that angiotensin III is the natural aldosterone-stimulating peptide, whereas angiotensin II is the blood pressure–regulating peptide. The adrenal gland contains appreciable quantities of the aminopeptidase that converts angiotensin II to angiotensin III. It has been claimed that aminopeptidase can act on angiotensin I to produce (des-Asp¹) angiotensin I and that this compound can be converted directly to angiotensin III by the action of a converting enzyme. However, the exact physiologic role of angiotensin III, if any, remains unsettled.

Other Angiotensin-Generating Enzymes

There are other acid proteases in the body in addition to renal renin that are capable of splitting angiotensin I from angiotensinogen. Reninlike enzymes have been extracted from the uterus, placenta, fetal membranes, amniotic fluid, adrenal glands, pituitary gland, blood vessel walls, and brain. In mice, an angiotensin-generating enzyme is found in the submaxillary glands. It is probable that these enzymes differ from renin of renal origin, and it seems wise to call them isorenins or angiotensin-generating enzymes, rather than renins, until their structure and chemical properties are elucidated. Their physiologic roles are also uncertain; they contribute very little to the circulating renin pool, since plasma renin activity drops almost to zero when the kidneys are removed.

The Juxtaglomerular Apparatus

The source of the renin in kidney extracts is the **juxtaglomerular cells (JG cells).** These epithelioid cells are located in the media of the afferent arterioles as they enter the glomeruli. They contain membrane-lined secretory granules that have been shown to consist of renin.

At the point where the afferent arteriole enters the glomerulus and the efferent arteriole leaves it, the tubule of the nephron touches the arterioles and the glomerulus from which it arose. At this point, which marks the start of the distal convolution, there is a modified region of tubular epithelium called the macula densa (Fig 24–3). The macula densa is in close proximity to the JG cells, and a few granular cells are also found in the adjacent connective tissue. These cells, the JG cells, and the macula densa constitute the **juxtaglomerular apparatus.**

Regulation of Renin Secretion

Renin secretion is increased by stimuli that decrease ECF volume and blood pressure or increase sympathetic output (Table 24–1). At least 5 different regulating factors appear to be involved (Fig 24–4). One is an intrarenal baroreceptor mechanism that causes renin secretion to increase when the intra-arteriolar pressure at the level of the JG cells is decreased and to decrease when this pressure is in-

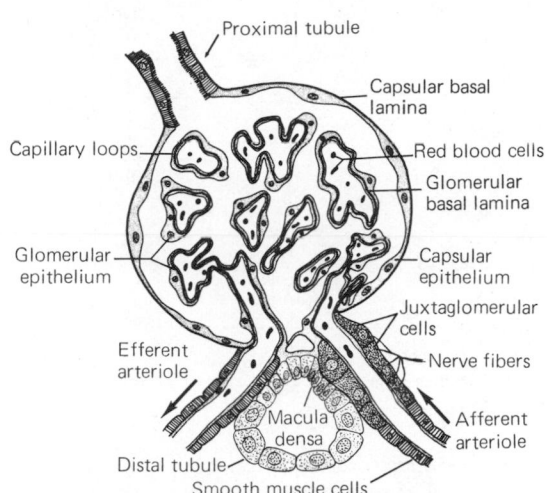

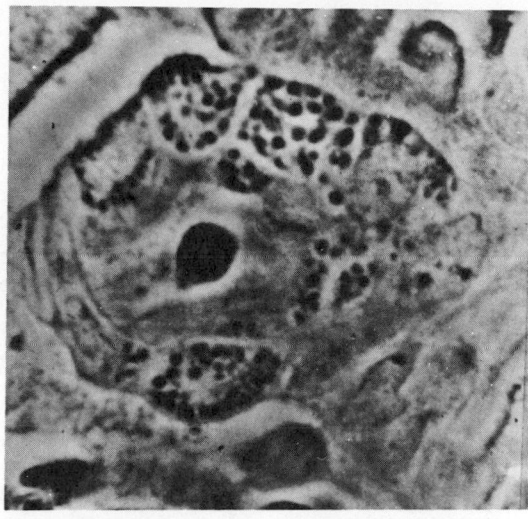

Figure 24–3. *Left:* Diagram of glomerulus, showing the juxtaglomerular apparatus. (Reproduced, with permission, from Ham AW: *Histology,* 6th ed. Lippincott, 1969.) *Right:* Phase contrast photomicrograph of afferent arteriole in unstained, freeze-dried preparation of the kidney of a mouse. Note the red blood cell in the lumen of the arteriole and the granulated juxtaglomerular cells in the wall. (Courtesy of C Peil.)

creased. Prostaglandins stimulate renin secretion, and there is evidence that the effects of pressure changes are mediated by a direct action on the JG cells of prostaglandins generated in the renal cortex. Another sensor involved in the regulation of renin secretion is the macula densa. There is some debate about what is being sensed, but the bulk of the evidence supports the view that renin secretion is inversely proportionate to the rate of transport of Cl^- or possibly Na^+ across this portion of the distal tubule. The rate of transport is dependent not only on the transport mechanisms in the macula densa cells but also on the amount of electrolyte reaching the macula densa. Therefore, decreased delivery of Na^+ and Cl^- to the distal tubules is associated with increased renin secretion. Renin secretion also varies inversely with the plasma K^+ level, but the effect of K^+ appears to be mediated by the changes it produces in Na^+ and Cl^- delivery to the macula densa. Angiotensin II feeds back to inhibit renin secretion by a direct action on the JG cells, and vasopressin also inhibits renin secretion. Finally, increased activity of the sympathetic nervous system increases renin secretion. The increase is mediated both by way of increased circulating catecholamines and by way of the

renal sympathetic nerves. The sympathetic effects on renin secretion are mostly mediated via β-adrenergic receptors. Evidence is accumulating that the effects are direct and are exerted via adenylate cyclase and cyclic AMP in the JG cells. Renin secretion at any given time is apparently due to the combined activity of these various regulators.

Role of Renin in Hypertension

Constriction of one renal artery causes the development of sustained hypertension (**renal,** or **Goldblatt, hypertension**). Since Goldblatt first demonstrated this effect of renal artery constriction, it has often been assumed that the hypertension is due to

Table 24–1. Stimuli that increase renin secretion.

Sodium depletion
Diuretics
Hypotension
Hemorrhage
Upright posture
Dehydration
Constriction of renal artery or aorta
Cardiac failure
Cirrhosis

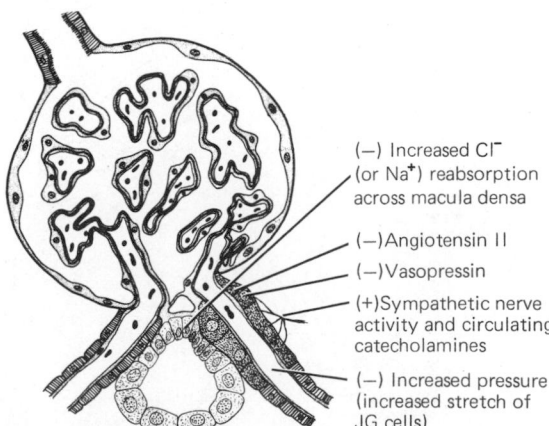

(−) Increased Cl^- (or Na^+) reabsorption across macula densa

(−) Angiotensin II

(−) Vasopressin

(+) Sympathetic nerve activity and circulating catecholamines

(−) Increased pressure (increased stretch of JG cells)

Figure 24–4. Factors that inhibit (−) and stimulate (+) renin secretion. (Reproduced, with permission, from Ganong WF: The renin-angiotensin system and the central nervous system. Fed Proc 36:1771, 1977.)

increased renin secretion. Removal of the ischemic kidney cures the hypertension if it has not persisted for too long. Some patients with unilateral renal artery stenosis have high circulating renin and angiotensin levels, hypokalemia, and high aldosterone secretion rates (see Chapter 20). However, most animals and humans with renal hypertension do not have high levels of aldosterone secretion. Furthermore, the circulating levels of renin and angiotensin are not elevated in chronic renal hypertension. These and other data indicate that after renal artery constriction, the increase in renin secretion is transient and that—1 day to several weeks later—renin secretion returns to normal while some other renal mechanism maintains the hypertension. The kidney contains a number of substances with vasodepressor activity, including prostaglandins, and decreased secretion of these substances might conceivably play a role. However, it is still uncertain whether renal prostaglandins enter the general circulation.

An interesting syndrome occurs in patients with idiopathic hypertrophy and hyperplasia of their juxtaglomerular apparatuses (**Bartter's syndrome**). These patients have persistent hypokalemia, elevated aldosterone secretion, and high circulating angiotensin II. However, their blood pressure is normal. The role of renin in a feedback mechanism that helps maintain the constancy of ECF volume through regulation of aldosterone secretion has been described in Chapter 20. A high level of renin secretion is apparently responsible for the elevated aldosterone secretion (**secondary hyperaldosteronism**) seen in some normotensive patients with cirrhosis and nephrosis.

Erythropoietin

When an animal is bled or made hypoxic, hemo-

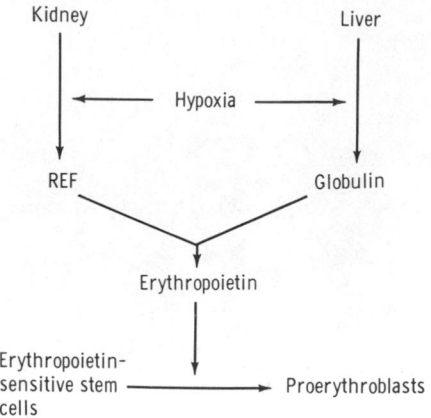

Figure 24–5. Proposed scheme for formation of erythropoietin. (Modified and reproduced, with permission, from Gordon AS, Cooper GW, Zanjani E: The kidney and erythropoiesis. Semin Hematol 4:337, 1967.)

globin synthesis is enhanced, and production and release of red blood cells from the bone marrow (**erythropoiesis**) is increased (see Chapter 27). Conversely, when the red cell volume is increased above normal by transfusion, the erythropoietic activity of the bone marrow decreases. These adjustments are brought about by changes in the circulating level of **erythropoietin,** a circulating glycoprotein with a molecular weight of about 23,000. The hormone causes certain stem cells in the bone marrow to be converted to proerythroblasts (Fig 27–2). Although they resemble other stem cells, they are somewhat more differentiated and are referred to as **erythropoietin-sensitive stem cells.** The action of erythropoietin is

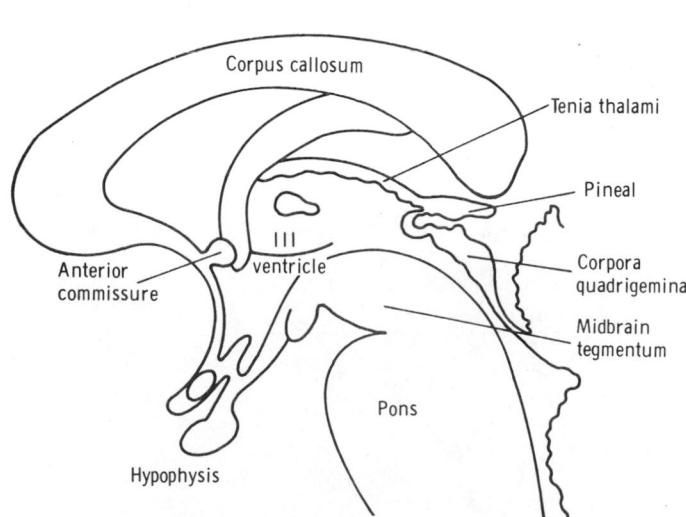

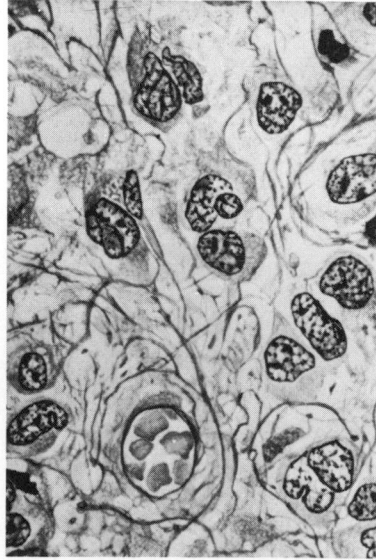

Figure 24–6. *Left:* Sagittal section of human brain stem showing relations of pineal. *Right:* Histology of pineal. Drawing of hematoxylin and eosin–stained section. (Reproduced, with permission, from Bloom W, Fawcett DW: *A Textbook of Histology,* 10th ed. Saunders, 1975.)

apparently mediated by stimulation of mRNA synthesis. The fact that antierythropoietin antibodies cause anemia indicates that the hormone is essential for the maintenance of normal erythropoiesis.

Current evidence indicates that erythropoietin is formed by the action of a substance secreted by the kidneys on a globulin in the plasma (Fig 24–5). This renal factor has been called **renal erythropoietic factor (REF)**, or **erythrogenin.** Its production is increased by hypoxia, cobalt salts, and androgens. Its secretion is facilitated by the alkalosis that develops at high altitude. Like renin, its secretion is increased by catecholamines via a β-adrenergic mechanism. In dogs, REF appears to be formed only in the kidneys, but in humans, some erythropoietin can be formed in the absence of the kidneys. The globulin on which REF acts is apparently formed in the liver, and there is some evidence that its production is also increased by hypoxia. The action of REF on the plasma globulin appears to be enzymatic, like that of renin on angiotensinogen. Erythropoietin is inactivated principally by the liver, and it has a half-life in the circulation of about 5 hours. However, the increase in circulating red cells that it triggers takes 2–3 days to appear, since red cell maturation is a relatively slow process.

The receptor that responds to changes in oxygen tension is unknown. It has been claimed that REF is secreted by the juxtaglomerular cells of the kidneys, but some evidence suggests that it is secreted by cells in the glomeruli. Androgens also increase the number of erythropoietin-sensitive cells in the bone marrow. It is clear that the REF-erythropoietin system and the renin-angiotensin system are separate; angiotensin II has no erythropoietic effect, and erythropoietin has no effect on blood pressure or aldosterone secretion.

Hypophysectomized animals become anemic, and pituitary extracts stimulate red blood cell production. However, hypophysectomy does not block the erythropoietic response to hemorrhage or hypoxia. Glucocorticoids and thyroxine stimulate erythropoiesis, and the erythropoietic activity of pituitary extracts has been shown to be due in part to their ACTH and TSH content. LH also contributes to the erythropoietic activity of pituitary extracts, since this hormone stimulates the secretion of testosterone and other androgens, and androgens increase REF secretion. On the other hand, estrogens inhibit erythropoiesis. This effect is not inhibited by nephrectomy, but it may be due in part to inhibition by estrogen of hepatic formation of the globulin substrate on which REF acts.

PINEAL

Anatomy

The **pineal**, or **epiphysis,** arises from the roof of the third ventricle under the posterior end of the corpus callosum and is connected by a stalk to the posterior commissure and habenular commissure. There are

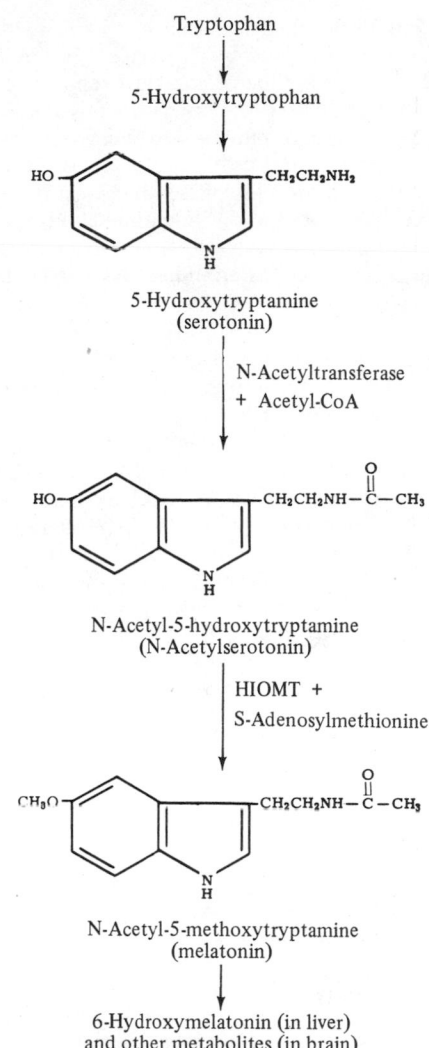

Figure 24–7. Formation and metabolism of melatonin. HIOMT, hydroxyindole-O-methyltransferase. For details of the synthesis of serotinin, see Fig 15–8.

nerve fibers in the stalk, but they apparently do not reach the gland. The pineal stroma contains neuroglia and parenchymal cells with features suggesting they have a secretory function (Fig 24–6). In young animals and infants, the pineal is large, and the cells tend to be arranged in alveoli. It begins to involute before puberty, and, in humans, small concretions of calcium phosphate and carbonate (**pineal sand**) appear in the tissue. Because the concretions are radiopaque, the normal pineal is often visible on x-ray films of the skull in adults. Displacement of a calcified pineal from its normal position indicates the presence of a space-occupying lesion such as a tumor in the brain. The pineal, like the other circumventricular organs (see Chapter 32), has highly permeable fenestrated capillaries and is "outside the blood-brain barrier."

Pineal Function

The pineal, believed by Descartes to be the seat of the soul, has at one time or another been regarded as having a wide variety of functions. Its possible role in inhibiting the onset of puberty is discussed in Chapter 23. There is some evidence that it contains gonadotropin-inhibiting peptides, but most recent research has been focused on indole metabolism in the gland.

The pineal contains an indole, N-acetyl-5-methoxytryptamine, named **melatonin** because it lightens the skin of tadpoles by an action on melanophores (see Chapter 22). Melatonin and the enzymes responsible for its synthesis from serotonin by N-acetylation and 5-methylation have been identified in mammalian pineal tissue (Fig 24–7), although some melatonin may be synthesized in other parts of the body as well. Melatonin synthesis occurs in pineal and parenchymal cells and is decreased in light and increased in darkness. The sympathetic nerves to the pineal (nervi conarii) regulate this circadian rhythm in melatonin synthesis by regulating the activity of the N-acetyltransferase that catalyzes the formation of N-acetyl-5-hydroxytryptamine in the gland. The discharge of the sympathetic nerves is entrained to the light-dark cycle via the retinohypothalamic nerve fibers and the suprachiasmatic nuclei (see Chapter 14). The norepinephrine released from the nerve endings acts via a β-adrenergic receptor and cyclic AMP to increase the activity of the enzyme and thus to increase melatonin synthesis and secretion. Melatonin is present in CSF and plasma, with a considerably higher concentration in CSF. It has been demonstrated that the plasma concentration of melatonin is high in the dark and dramatically decreased in the light. However, there is as yet no established function for melatonin in mammals. There has been speculation that it exerts an antigonadotropic effect, but it is difficult to see how the marked diurnal cyclicity in its secretion relates to the function of the gonads.

Circulating melatonin is rapidly metabolized in the liver by 6-hydroxylation followed by the conjugation. The pathway by which the brain metabolizes melatonin is unsettled but may involve cleavage of the indole nucleus.

References: Section IV.
Endocrinology & Metabolism

Axelrod J: The pineal gland: A neurochemical transducer. Science 183:1241, 1974.

Bennett JP: *Chemical Contraception*. Columbia Univ Press, 1974.

Bremmer WJ, deKrester DM: The prospects for new, reversible male contraceptives. N Engl J Med 295:1111, 1976.

Byyny RL: Withdrawal from glucocorticoid therapy. N Engl J Med 295:30, 1976.

Chan L, O'Malley BW: Mechanism of action of the sex steroid hormones. N Engl J Med 294:1322, 1976.

Cuatrecasas P: Membrane receptors. Annu Rev Biochem 43:169, 1974.

Davis JO, Freeman RH: Mechanisms regulating renin release. Physiol Rev 56:1, 1976.

Davis JO, Freeman RH: The other angiotensins. Biochem Pharmacol 26:93, 1977.

Dayhoff MO: *Atlas of Protein Sequence and Structure*. Vol 5. National Biomedical Research Foundation, 1972; Suppl 3, 1978.

Donovan BT, Van der Werff ten Bosch JJ: *Physiology of Puberty*. Williams & Wilkins, 1965.

Erbe RW: Principles of medical genetics. N Engl J Med 294:381, 1976.

Federman DD: Genetic control of sex difference. Prog Med Genet 9:215, 1973.

Felig P: Diabetic ketoacidosis. N Engl J Med 290:1360, 1974.

Felig P, Wahren J: Fuel homeostasis in exercise. N Engl J Med 293:1078, 1975.

Fieser LF, Fieser M: *Steroids*. Reinhold, 1959.

Floyd JC Jr, Fajans SS, Pek S: Regulation in healthy subjects of the secretion of human pancreatic polypeptide, a newly recognized pancreatic islet polypeptide. Trans Assoc Am Physicians 89:146, 1976.

Frantz AG: Prolactin. N Engl J Med 298:201, 1978.

Fredrickson DS: A physician's guide to hyperlipidemia. Mod Concepts Cardiovasc Dis 41:31, 1972.

Fuchs F, Klopper AI (editors): *Endocrinology of Pregnancy*. Harper, 1970.

Ganong WF, Martini L (editors): *Frontiers in Neuroendocrinology*. Vol 5. Raven Press, 1978.

Greengard P: Phosphorylated proteins as physiological effectors. Science 199:146, 1978.

Greer MA: The natural occurrence of goitrogenic agents. Recent Prog Horm Res 18:187, 1962.

Hancox NM: *Biology of Bone: Biological Structure and Function*. Vol 1. Cambridge Univ Press, 1972.

Haussler MR, McCain TA: Basic and clinical concepts related to vitamin D metabolism and action. N Engl J Med 297:974, 1977.

Havel RJ: Caloric homeostasis in health and disease. N Engl J Med 287:1186, 1972.

Hunt WB: Pregnancy tests—the current status. Population Reports 7:J–109, 1975.

Isselbacher KJ: Metabolic and hepatic effects of alcohol. N Engl J Med 296:612, 1977.

Jackson RL, Gotto AM Jr: Phospholipids in biology and medicine. N Engl J Med 290:24, 1974.

Kelley WN, Weiner IM (editors): Uric acid. In: *Handbook of Experimental Pharmacology*. Vol 51. Springer-Verlag, 1978.

Laragh JH & others: Blockade of renin or angiotensin for understanding human hypertension: A comparison of propranolol, saralasin and converting enzyme blockade. Fed Proc 36:1781,1977.

Levey GS: Catecholamine sensitivity, thyroid hormone and the heart. Am J Med 50:413, 1971.

Levy RI, Morganroth J, Rifkind BM: Treatment of hyperlipidemia. N Engl J Med 290:1295, 1974.

Martin JB, Reichlin S, Brown GM: *Clinical Neuroendocrinology.* Davis, 1977.

McKusick VA: *Mendelian Inheritance in Man: Catalogs of Autosomal Dominant, Autosomal Recessive, and X-linked Phenotypes,* 4th ed. Johns Hopkins Press, 1975.

Nakao K, Fisher JW, Takaku F (editors): *Erythropoiesis.* Univ Park Press, 1976.

Nathanielsz PW: Endocrine mechanisms of parturition. Annu Rev Physiol 40:411, 1978.

Page IH, McCubbin JW (editors): *Renal Hypertension.* Year Book, 1968.

Rees LH: The biosynthesis of hormones by nonendocrine tumors—A review. J Endocrinol 67:143, 1975.

Reid IA, Morris BJ, Ganong WF: The renin-angiotensin system. Annu Rev Physiol 40:377, 1978.

Rinehart W: Postcoital contraception—an appraisal. Population Reports 9:J–141, 1976.

Robertson JIS: Angiotensin, aldosterone, and hypertension. Hypertension, 1979. [In press.]

Samuelsson B & others: Prostaglandins and thromboxanes. Annu Rev Biochem 47:321, 1978.

Schally AV, Coy DH, Meyers CA: Hypothalamic regulatory hormones. Annu Rev Biochem 47:104, 1978.

Setchell BP, Davis RV, Main SJ: Inhibin. In: *The Testis.* Vol 4. Johnson AD, Gomes WR (editors). Academic Press, 1977.

Sönksen PH (editor): Radioimmunoassay and saturation analysis. Br Med Bull 30:1, 1974.

Spaziani E: Accessory reproductive organs in mammals: Control of cell and tissue transport by sex hormones. Pharmacol Rev 27:207, 1975.

Steinberger E: Hormonal control of mammalian spermatogenesis. Physiol Rev 51:1, 1971.

Sterling K: Thyroid hormone action at the cell level. N Engl J Med 300:117, 1979.

Stern C: *Principles of Human Genetics,* 3rd ed. Freeman, 1973.

Sutherland EW: Studies on the mechanism of hormone action. Science 177:401, 1972.

Unger RH, Dobbs RE, Orci L: Insulin, glucagon, and somatostatin secretion in the regulation of metabolism. Annu Rev Physiol 40:307, 1978.

Unger RH, Orci L: Physiology and pathophysiology of glucagon. Physiol Rev 56:778, 1976.

Vallence-Owen J (editor): *Diabetes: Its Physiological and Biochemical Basis.* Univ Park Press, 1975.

Van Italie TB, Yang M-U: Diet and weight loss. N Engl J Med 297:1158, 1977.

Van Wyk JJ & others: The somatomedins. Am J Dis Child 126:705, 1973.

Werner SC, Ingbar SH (editors): *The Thyroid: A Fundamental and Clinical Text,* 3rd ed. Harper, 1971.

Williams RH (editor): *Textbook of Endocrinology,* 5th ed. Saunders, 1974.

Wilson JD: Sexual differentiation. Annu Rev Physiol 40:279, 1978.

Wood SC, Porte D Jr: Neural control of the endocrine pancreas. Physiol Rev 54:596, 1974.

Wortman J: Vasectomy—what are the problems? Population Reports 2:D–25, 1975.

Wurtman RJ, Moskowitz MA: The pineal organ. N Engl J Med 296:1329, 1977.

Yalow RS: Radioimmunoassay: A probe for the fine structure of biologic systems. Science 200:1236, 1978.

Yen SSC, Jaffe RB (editors): *Reproductive Endocrinology.* Saunders, 1978.

Symposium: Control of human fertility. Br Med Bull 26:1, 1970.

Symposium: Control of ovulation. Fed Proc 29:1874, 1970.

Symposium: Storage polyglucosides. Ann NY Acad Sci 210:5, 1973.

V. Gastrointestinal Function

25 | Digestion & Absorption

The gastrointestinal system is the portal through which nutritive substances, vitamins, minerals, and fluids enter the body. Proteins, fats, and complex carbohydrates are broken down into absorbable units **(digested)**, principally in the small intestine. The products of digestion and the vitamins, minerals, and water cross the mucosa and enter the lymph or the blood **(absorption)**. The digestive and absorptive processes are the subject of this chapter. The details of the function of the various parts of the gastrointestinal system are considered in Chapter 26.

Digestion of the major foodstuffs is an orderly process involving the action of a large number of **digestive enzymes** (Table 25–1). Some of these enzymes are found in the secretions of the salivary glands, the stomach, and the exocrine portion of the pancreas. Other enzymes are found in the luminal membranes of the cells that line the small intestine. The action of the enzymes is aided by the hydrochloric acid secreted by the stomach and the bile secreted by the liver.

Substances pass from the lumen of the gastroin-

Table 25–1. Principal digestive enzymes.
The corresponding proenzymes are shown in parentheses.

Source	Enzyme	Activator	Substrate	Catalytic Function or Products
Salivary glands	Salivary α-amylase	. . .	Starch	Hydrolyzes 1,4α linkages, producing α-limit dextrins, maltotriose, and maltose
Stomach	Pepsins (pepsinogens)	HCl	Proteins and polypeptides	Cleave peptide bonds adjacent to aromatic amino acids
Exocrine pancreas	Trypsin (trypsinogen)	Enterokinase	Proteins and polypeptides	Cleaves peptide bonds adjacent to arginine or lysine
	Chymotrypsins (chymotrypsinogens)	Trypsin	Proteins and polypeptides	Cleave peptide bonds adjacent to amino acids with aromatic side chains
	Elastase (proelastase)	Trypsin	Elastin, some other proteins	Cleaves bonds adjacent to amino acids with aliphatic side chains
	Carboxypeptidase A (procarboxypeptidase A)	Trypsin	Proteins and polypeptides	Cleaves carboxy terminal amino acids with aromatic or branched aliphatic side chains
	Carboxypeptidase B (procarboxypeptidase B)	Trypsin	Proteins and polypeptides	Cleaves carboxy terminal amino acids with basic side chains
	Pancreatic lipase	. . .	Triglycerides	Monoglycerides and fatty acids
	Pancreatic esterase	. . .	Cholesterol esters	Cholesterol
	Pancreatic α-amylase	Cl$^-$	Starch	Same as salivary α-amylase
	Ribonuclease	. . .	RNA	Nucleotides
	Deoxyribonuclease	. . .	DNA	Nucleotides
	Phospholipase A (prophospholipase A)	Trypsin	Lecithin	Lysolecithin
Intestinal mucosa	Enteropeptidase	. . .	Trypsinogen	Trypsin
	Aminopeptidases	. . .	Polypeptides	Cleave N-terminal amino acid from peptide
	Dipeptidases	. . .	Dipeptides	Two amino acids
	Maltase	. . .	Maltose, maltotriose	Glucose
	Lactase	. . .	Lactose	Galactose and glucose
	Sucrase*	. . .	Sucrose	Fructose and glucose
	α-Limit dextrinase	. . .	α-Limit dextrins	Glucose
	Nuclease and related enzymes	. . .	Nucleic acids	Pentoses and purine and pyrimidine bases

*Sucrase and α-limit dextrinase are linked, probably as 2 parts of a single hybrid molecule.

testinal tract to the circulation by diffusion, nonionic diffusion, facilitated diffusion, solvent drag, active transport, and endocytosis. The dynamics of transport in all parts of the body are considered in Chapter 1. The mucosal cells in the small intestine have a **brush border** made up of numerous microvilli lining their apical surface (Fig 26–22). This border is rich in enzymes and is lined on its luminal side by an amorphous layer called the **glycocalyx,** which is rich in neutral and amino sugars. Next to the brush border and glycocalyx is a 100–400 μm **unstirred water layer** (UWL) similar to the UWL adjacent to other biologic membranes (see Chapter 1). Solutes must diffuse across the UWL to reach the mucosal cells. The mucosa of the human jejunum acts as if it contained pores about 0.75 nm in diameter, whereas the mucosa of the ileum acts as if it contained pores 0.35 nm in diameter and the mucosa of the colon as if it contained pores 0.25 nm in diameter.

CARBOHYDRATES

Digestion

The principal dietary carbohydrates are polysaccharides, disaccharides, and monosaccharides. Starches (glucose polymers) and their derivatives are the only polysaccharides that are digested to any degree in the human gastrointestinal tract. In glycogen, the glucose molecules are mostly in long chains (glucose molecules in 1,4 α linkage), but there is some chain branching (produced by 1,6 α linkages; see Fig 17–13). Amylopectin, which constitutes 80–90% of dietary starch, is similar but less branched, whereas amylose is a straight chain with only 1,4 α linkages. The disaccharides **lactose** (milk sugar) and **sucrose** (table sugar) are also ingested, along with the monosaccharides fructose and glucose.

Starch is attacked by ptyalin, the α-amylase in the saliva. However, the optimal pH for this enzyme is 6.7, and its action is inhibited by the acid gastric juice when food enters the stomach. In the small intestine, the potent pancreatic α-amylase also acts on the ingested polysaccharides. Both the salivary and the pancreatic α-amylases hydrolyze 1,4 α linkages but spare 1,6 α linkages, terminal 1,4 α linkages, and the 1,4 α linkages next to branching points. Consequently, the end products of α-amylase digestion are oligosaccharides: the disaccharide **maltose,** the trisaccharide **maltotriose,** some slightly larger polymers with glucose in 1,4 α linkage, and α-**limit dextrins,** branched polymers containing an average of about 8 glucose molecules (Fig 25–1).

The oligosaccharidases responsible for the further digestion of the starch derivatives are located in the brush border on the surface of the mucosal cells, principally in the ileum. α-Limit dextrinase hydrolyzes the α-limit dextrins, and maltase splits glucose from maltose, maltotriose, and other polymers of glucose in 1,4 α linkage. Most of the glucose molecules that are

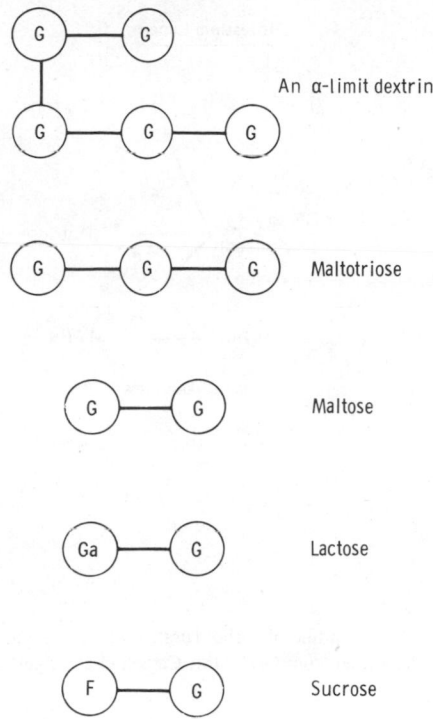

Figure 25–1. Principal end products of carbohydrate digestion in the intestinal lumen. Each circle represents a hexose molecule. G, glucose; F, fructose; Ga, galactose.

formed enter the mucosal cells, although some reenter the intestinal lumen and are absorbed farther along. Ingested disaccharides are hydrolyzed by lactase or sucrase on the luminal surface of mucosal cells (Fig 25–2). Deficiency of one or more of these disaccharidases leads to diarrhea, bloating, and flatulence after ingestion of sugar. The diarrhea is due to the increased number of osmotically active oligosaccharide molecules that remain in the intestinal lumen, causing the volume of the intestinal contents to increase. The bloating and flatulence are due to the production of gas (CO_2 and H_2) from disaccharide residues in the lower small intestine and colon.

Lactase is of interest because, in most mammals and in many races of humans, intestinal lactase activity is high at birth, declines to low levels during childhood, and remains low in adulthood. The low lactase levels are associated with intolerance to milk (lactose intolerance). However, most Western Europeans and their American descendants retain their intestinal lactase activity in adulthood. Lactose tolerance is also found in a few African tribes, but most blacks are intolerant. In the USA, 70% of the black population and only 20% of the white population are intolerant to lactose.

Absorption

Hexoses and pentoses are rapidly absorbed across the wall of the duodenum and ileum. Essentially all of

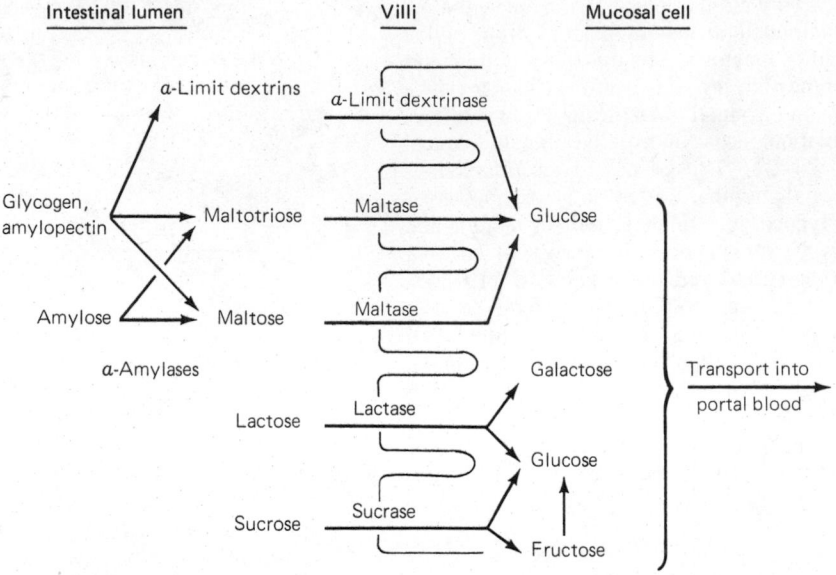

Figure 25–2. Outline of carbohydrate digestion and absorption. Some of the monosaccharides are also released into the intestinal lumen. (Modified from Gray GM: Carbohydrate digestion and absorption. N Engl J Med 292:1225, 1975.)

Table 25–2. Transport of substances by the intestine and location of maximum absorption or secretion.*

| | Location of Absorptive Capacity | | | |
| | Small Intestine | | | Colon |
	Upper†	Mid	Lower	
Absorption				
Sugars (glucose, galactose, etc)	++	+++	++	0
Neutral amino acids	++	+++	++	0
Basic amino acids	++	++	++	?
Water-soluble vitamins	+++	++	0	0
Betaine, dimethylglycine, sarcosine	+	++	++	?
Gamma globulin (newborn animals)	+	++	+++	?
Pyrimidines (thymine and uracil)	+	+	?	?
Fatty acid absorption and conversion to triglyceride	+++	++	+	0
Bile salts	0	+	+++	
Vitamin B_{12}	0	+	+++	0
Na^+	+++	++	+++	+++
H^+ (and/or HCO_3^- secretion)	0	+	++	++
Ca^{2+}	+++	++	+	?
Fe^{2+}	+++	++	+	?
Cl^-	+++	++	+	0
SO_4^{2-}	++	+	0	?
Secretion				
K^+	0	0	+	++
H^+ (and/or HCO_3^- absorption)	++	+	0	0
Sr^{2+}	0	0	+	?
Cl^- (under special conditions)	+	?	?	?
I^-	0	+	0	0

*Modified from Wilson TH: *Intestinal Absorption.* Saunders, 1962. Amount of absorption or secretion is graded + to +++.
†Upper small intestine refers primarily to jejunum, although the duodenum is similar in most cases studied (with the notable exception that the duodenum secretes HCO_3^- and shows little net absorption or secretion of NaCl).

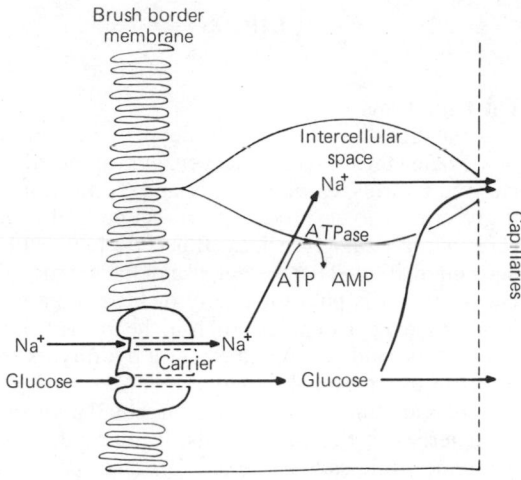

Figure 25–3. Probable mechanism for glucose transport across intestinal epithelium. Glucose transport into the intestinal cell is coupled to Na^+ transport, utilizing a common carrier. Na^+ is then actively transported out of the cell. (Reproduced, with permission, from Gray GM: Carbohydrate digestion and absorption. N Engl J Med 292:1225, 1975.)

the hexoses are removed before the remains of a meal reach the terminal part of the ileum. The sugar molecules pass from the mucosal cells to the blood in the capillaries draining into the portal vein. Some pentoses may be absorbed by diffusion, but glucose and galactose are absorbed by a process that involves active transport (Table 25–2). Fructose is absorbed by facilitated diffusion (see below). Some fructose is converted to glucose in the mucosal cells.

The transport of some sugars is uniquely affected by the amount of Na^+ in the intestinal lumen; a high concentration of Na^+ on the mucosal surface of the cells facilitates and a low concentration inhibits sugar influx into the epithelial cells. It now appears that glucose and Na^+ share the same carrier molecule (Fig 25–3). Intracellular Na^+ is low, and Na^+ moves into the cell along its concentration gradient. Glucose moves with the Na^+ and is released in the cell. The Na^+ is transported into the lateral intercellular spaces, and the glucose diffuses into the interstitium and thence to the capillaries. Thus, the energy for glucose transport is provided indirectly, by the active transport of Na^+ out of the cell. This maintains the concentration gradient across the luminal border of the cell, so that more Na^+ and consequently more glucose enter. The glucose mechanism also transports galactose. Fructose apparently utilizes a different carrier, and its absorption is independent of Na^+ or the transport of glucose and galactose. The observations on the transport of glucose and fructose that led to the idea of coupled transport were mostly made in vitro, and questions have been raised about the applicability of the findings to living humans. However, there is little evidence of any major differences.

Insulin has little effect on intestinal transport of

sugars. In this respect, intestinal absorption resembles glucose reabsorption in the proximal convoluted tubules of the kidneys (see Chapter 38); neither process requires phosphorylation, and both are essentially normal in diabetes but depressed by the drug phlorhizin. The maximal rate of glucose absorption from the intestine is about 120 g/h.

PROTEINS & NUCLEIC ACIDS

Protein Digestion

Protein digestion begins in the stomach, where pepsins cleave some of the peptide linkages. Like many of the other enzymes concerned with protein digestion, pepsins are secreted in inactive precursor, or **proenzyme,** form and activated in the intestinal tract. The pepsin precursors are called pepsinogens and are activated by gastric hydrochloric acid. Human gastric mucosa contains 3 chromatographically distinct pepsinogens, which produce 3 pepsins with slightly different properties (pepsins I, II, and III). Pepsins hydrolyze the bonds between aromatic amino acids such as phenylalanine or tyrosine and a second amino acid, so the products of peptic digestion are polypeptides of very diverse sizes. A **gelatinase** that liquefies gelatin is also found in the stomach. **Chymosin,** a gastric enzyme also known as **rennin,** clots milk. It is also found in the stomachs of young animals but is probably absent in humans.

Because pepsins have a pH optimum of 1.6–3.2, their action is terminated when the gastric contents are mixed with the alkaline pancreatic juice in the duodenum. The pH of the duodenal contents is about 6.5. In the small intestine, small peptides (oligopeptides) are formed by the action of the powerful protein-splitting enzymes trypsin, the chymotrypsins, and elastase. The formation of trypsin, the chymotrypsins, and elastase from their precursors is discussed in Chapter 26. The pancreatic carboxypeptidases and the intestinal aminopeptidases and dipeptidases split these fragments into smaller peptides and free amino acids. Some free amino acids are liberated in the intestinal lumen, but others are liberated at the cell surface by the aminopeptidases and dipeptidases in the brush border of the mucosal cells. Some di- and tripeptides are actively transported into the intestinal cells and hydrolyzed intracellularly, with the amino acids entering the bloodstream. This transport is independent of amino acid absorption from the intestinal lumen.

Absorption

After ingestion of a protein meal, there is a sharp transient rise in the amino nitrogen content of the portal blood. L-Amino acids are absorbed more rapidly than the corresponding D-isomers. The D-amino acids are apparently absorbed solely by passive diffusion, whereas most L-amino acids are actively transported out of the intestinal lumen. There are at least 3 separate transport systems: one that transports neutral amino acids, one that transports basic amino acids, and one that transports proline, hydroxyproline, and a few other compounds. Absorption of amino acids is coupled to Na^+ transport in some as yet poorly understood fashion. Amino acid transport, like sugar transport, is facilitated by a high Na^+ concentration on the mucosal side of the intestinal epithelial cells. However, the action of Na^+ is different; Na^+ increases the maximum velocity of sugar influx without affecting the apparent affinity of its carrier, whereas Na^+ does not affect the maximum velocity of amino acid influx and does seem to increase carrier affinity. The transported amino acids accumulate in the mucosal cells, and from these cells they apparently diffuse passively into the blood. It also appears that some of the absorbed di- and tripeptides enter the portal blood.

Absorption of amino acids is rapid in the duodenum and jejunum but slow in the ileum. Approximately 50% of the digested protein comes from ingested food, 25% from proteins in digestive juices, and 25% from desquamated mucosal cells. Some of the ingested protein enters the colon and is eventually digested by bacterial action. The protein in the stools is not of dietary origin but comes from bacteria and cellular debris. In humans, a congenital defect in the mechanism that transports neutral amino acids in the intestine and renal tubules causes **Hartnup disease.** A congenital defect in the transport of basic amino acids causes **cystinuria.**

In infants, some undigested proteins are also absorbed. The protein antibodies in maternal colostrum that contribute to passive immunity against infections enter the circulation from the intestine, although this transfer of antibodies is relatively minor in humans. Foreign proteins that enter the circulation provoke the formation of antibodies (see Chapter 27), and the antigen-antibody reaction occurring upon subsequent entry of more of the same protein may cause allergic symptoms. There is evidence that the mucosal cells of young animals absorb whole proteins by endocytosis and that as the cells mature they normally lose the ability to take in protein by this process. The situation is probably similar in humans, but only for the first 36 hours after birth. Some adults develop allergic symptoms after eating certain foods, and in these individuals the absorption of whole proteins may persist.

Nucleic Acids

Nucleic acids are split into nucleotides in the intestine by the pancreatic nucleases, and the nucleotides are split into the nucleosides and phosphoric acid by enzymes that appear to be located on the luminal surfaces of the mucosal cells. The nucleosides are then split into their constituent sugars and purine and pyrimidine bases. The bases are absorbed by active transport.

LIPIDS

Fat Digestion

Fat digestion begins in the duodenum, pancreatic lipase being the most important enzyme involved. This enzyme hydrolyzes only the 1- and 3- bonds of the triglycerides, so the products of its action are free fatty acids and 2-monoglycerides. It acts on fats that have been emulsified. There is a lipase in the gastric juice, but its action is physiologically of little importance. Most of the dietary cholesterol is in the form of cholesterol esters, and pancreatic esterase hydrolyzes these esters in the intestinal lumen.

Fats are finely emulsified in the small intestine by the detergent action of bile salts, lecithin, and monoglycerides; bile salts alone are relatively poor emulsifying agents, but in the presence of the phospholipid and monoglycerides, particles 200–5000 nm in diameter are formed.

When the concentration of bile salts in the intestine is high, as it is after contraction of the gallbladder, lipids and bile salts interact spontaneously to form **micelles** (Fig 25–4). These spherical aggregates are 3–10 nm in diameter with the polar hydroxy and amino portions of the bile salts facing outward and the nonpolar steroid nuclear portions forming a hydrophilic center. Although their lipid concentration varies, they generally contain fatty acids, monoglycerides, and cholesterol. Micellar formation further solubilizes the lipids and provides a mechanism for their transport to the mucosal cells. Thus, the micelles move down their concentration gradient through the unstirred water layer to the brush border of the mucosal cells. The lipids diffuse out of the micelles, and a saturated aqueous solution of the lipids is maintained in contact with the brush border of the mucosal cells (Fig 25–4). The lipids enter the cells by passive diffusion and are rapidly esterified inside the cells, maintaining a favorable concentration gradient from the lumen into the cells. Unlike the ileal mucosa, the rate of uptake of bile salts by the jejunal mucosa is low, and the bile salts diffuse back into the intestinal lumen, where they are available for the formation of new micelles. Thus, the bile salt micelles solubilize lipids, transport them across the UWL, and keep a saturated solution of lipids in contact with the mucosal cells.

Pancreatectomized animals and patients with diseases that destroy the exocrine portion of the pancreas have fatty, bulky, clay-colored stools (steatorrhea) because of the impaired digestion and absorption of fat. The steatorrhea is due in part to the lipase deficiency, but micelle formation is also depressed in pancreatic insufficiency because, in the absence of the bicarbonate that is secreted from the pancreas, the relatively acid milieu in the duodenum inhibits the incorporation of fatty acids in the micelles.

Fat Absorption

Monoglycerides, cholesterol, and fatty acids from the micelles enter the mucosal cells by passive

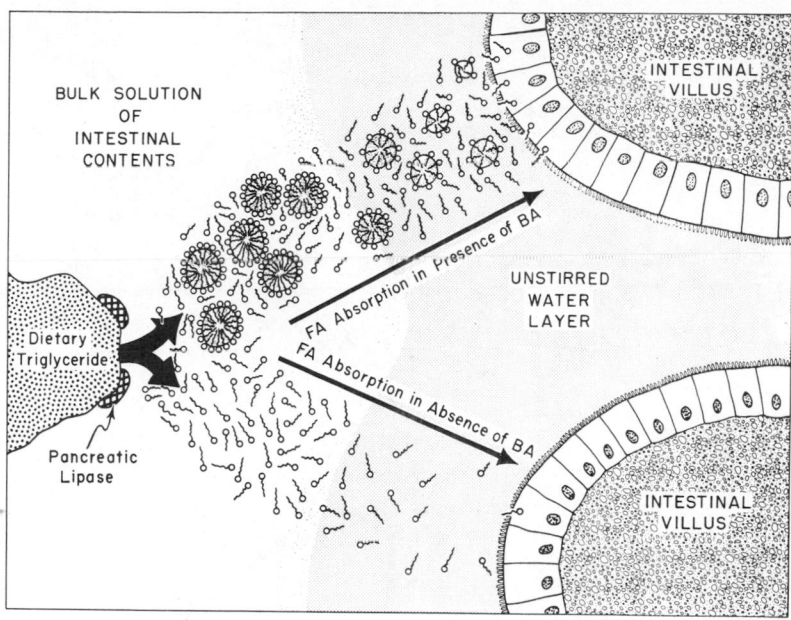

Figure 25–4. Lipid digestion and passage to intestinal mucosa. Fatty acids (FA) are liberated by the action of pancreatic lipase on dietary triglycerides, and in the presence of bile acids (BA), form micelles (the circular structures), which diffuse through the unstirred water layer to the mucosal surface. (Reproduced, with permission, from Thomson ABR: Intestinal absorption of lipids: Influence of the unstirred water layer and bile acid micelle. In: *Disturbances in Lipid and Lipoprotein Metabolism.* Dietschy JM, Gotto AM Jr, Ontko JA [editors]. American Physiological Society, 1978.)

diffusion (Fig 25–5). The subsequent fate of the fatty acids depends on their size. Fatty acids containing less than 10–12 carbon atoms pass from the mucosal cells directly into the portal blood, where they are transported as free (unesterified) fatty acids. The fatty acids containing more than 10–12 carbon atoms are reesterified to triglycerides in the mucosal cells. In addition, some of the absorbed cholesterol is esterified. The triglycerides and cholesterol esters are then coated with a layer of lipoprotein, cholesterol, and phospholipid to form chylomicrons, which leave the cell and enter the lymphatics (Fig 25–6).

In mucosal cells, most of the triglyceride is formed by the acylation of the absorbed 2-monoglycerides, primarily in the smooth endoplasmic reticulum. However, some of the triglyceride is formed from glycerophosphate, which in turn is a product of glucose catabolism. Glycerophosphate is also converted into glycerophospholipids that participate in chylomicron formation. The acylation of glycerophosphate and the formation of lipoproteins occurs in the rough endoplasmic reticulum. Carbohydrate moieties are added to the proteins in the Golgi apparatus, and the finished chylomicrons are extruded by exocytosis from the basal or lateral aspects of the cell.

Fat absorption is greatest in the upper parts of the small intestine, but appreciable amounts are also absorbed in the ileum. On a moderate fat intake, 95% or more of the ingested fat is absorbed (Fig 25–5). The stools contain 5% fat, but much of the fecal fat is probably derived from cellular debris and microorgan-

isms rather than from the diet. The processes involved in fat absorption are not fully mature at birth, and infants fail to absorb 10–15% of ingested fat. Thus, they are more susceptible to the ill effects of disease processes that reduce fat absorption.

There is evidence that the hormones of the adrenal cortex affect the absorption of the fats that appear in the lymph but not the absorption of those appearing in

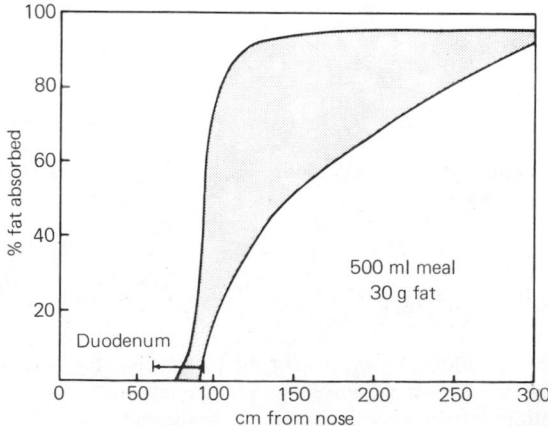

Figure 25–5. Fat absorption, based on measurement after a fat meal in humans. (Redrawn and reproduced, with permission, from Borgstrom B & others: J Clin Invest 36:1521, 1957, and Gut 3:315, 1962; redrawn from diagram in Davenport HW: *Physiology of the Digestive Tract,* 2nd ed. Year Book, 1966.)

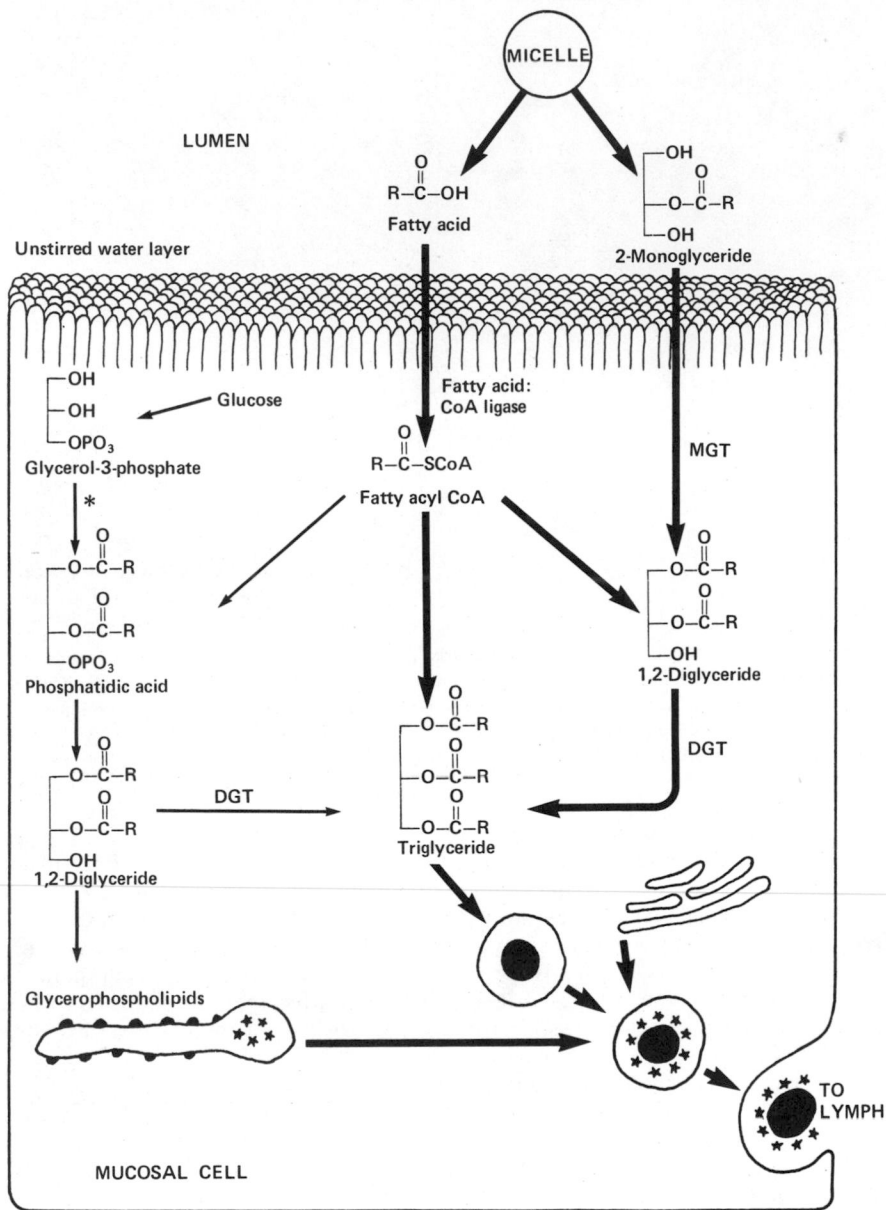

Figure 25–6. Lipid absorption. Triglycerides are formed in the mucosal cells from monoglycerides and fatty acids. Some of the glycerides also come from glucose via phosphatidic acid. The triglycerides are then converted to chylomicrons and released by exocytosis. From the extracellular space, they enter the lymph. *, reaction inhibited by monoglyceride; MGT, monoacylglycerol acyltransferase; DGT, diacylglycerol acyltransferase. (Modified and reproduced, with permission, from Johnston JM: Esterification reactions in the intestinal mucosa and lipid absorption. In: *Disturbances in Lipid and Lipoprotein Metabolism.* Dietschy JM, Gotto AM Jr, Ontko JA [editors]. American Physiological Society, 1978.)

portal blood. Absorption of the former is depressed in adrenalectomized animals and is increased by the administration of glucocorticoid hormones. In young rats, adrenocortical hormones also hasten the maturation of bile acid secretion.

Absorption of Cholesterol & Other Sterols

Cholesterol is readily absorbed from the intestine if bile, fatty acids, and pancreatic juice are present.

Closely related sterols of plant origin are poorly absorbed. Absorption of cholesterol is said to be limited to the distal portions of the small intestine. Almost all the absorbed cholesterol is incorporated into chylomicrons that enter the circulation via the lymphatics, as noted above. Nonabsorbable plant sterols such as those found in soybeans reduce the absorption of cholesterol, probably by competing with cholesterol for esterification with fatty acids.

ABSORPTION OF WATER & ELECTROLYTES

Water, Sodium, & Potassium

Overall water balance in the gastrointestinal tract is summarized in Table 25–3. The intestines are presented each day with about 2000 ml of ingested fluid plus 7000 ml of secretions from the mucosa of the gastrointestinal tract and associated glands. Ninety-eight percent of this fluid is reabsorbed, with a daily fluid loss of only 200 ml in the stools.

It should be noted that the figures for intestinal reabsorption are net rather than gross. Only small amounts of water move across the gastric mucosa, but water moves freely in both directions across the mucosa of the small and large intestines. Na^+ diffuses into and out of the small intestine depending on the salinity of the intestinal contents; it is also actively transported out of the lumen in the small intestine and colon by pumps that appear to be located on the basilateral walls of the cells (Fig 25–3). In the ileum and jejunum, Na^+ transport from intestine to blood is facilitated by aldosterone.

In the small intestine, active transport of Na^+ is important in bringing about absorption of glucose, amino acids, and other substances (see above). Conversely, the presence of glucose in the intestinal lumen facilitates the reabsorption of Na^+. This is the physiologic basis for the treatment of Na^+ and water loss in diarrhea by oral administration of solutions containing NaCl and glucose. This type of treatment has even proved to be beneficial in the treatment of cholera, a disease associated with very severe and, if untreated, frequently fatal diarrhea. The cholera vibrio stays in the intestinal lumen, but it produces a toxin that stimulates adenylate cyclase, causing a marked increase in intracellular cyclic AMP. Some strains of diarrhea-producing *E coli* produce a similar toxin. The accumulation of cyclic AMP increases Cl^- and HCO_3^-

secretion from the intestinal glands and inhibits the function of the mucosal carrier for Na^+. The resultant increase in electrolyte and water content of the intestinal contents causes the diarrhea. However, the Na^+ pump and the common carrier for glucose and Na^+ are unaffected, so coupled reabsorption of glucose and Na^+ bypasses the defect.

Water moves into or out of the stomach until the osmotic pressure of the intestinal contents equals that of the plasma. The osmolality of the duodenal contents may be hypertonic or hypotonic, depending on the meal ingested, but by the time the meal enters the jejunum, its osmolality is close to that of plasma. This osmolality is maintained throughout the rest of the small intestine; the osmotically active particles produced by digestion are removed by absorption, and water moves passively out of the gut along the osmotic gradient thus generated. In the colon, Na^+ is pumped out and water moves passively with it, again along the osmotic gradient.

There is some secretion of K^+ into the intestinal lumen, especially as a component of mucus, but for the most part, the movement of K^+ across the gastrointestinal mucosa is due to diffusion. The net movement of K^+ is proportionate to the potential difference between the blood and the intestinal lumen. In the jejunum, this potential difference is about 5 mV (lumen negative to blood), whereas in the ileum, it is about 25 mV and in the colon about 50 mV. Consequently, the concentration of K^+ on the basis of diffusion alone would be about 6 mEq/L in the jejunum, about 13 mEq/L in the ileum, and about 30 mEq/L in the colon. This is why the loss of ileal or colonic fluids in chronic diarrhea can lead to severe hypokalemia.

Chloride & Bicarbonate

In the ileum and the colon, it appears that Cl^- is actively reabsorbed in a 1 for 1 exchange for HCO_3^-. This tends to make the intestinal contents more alkaline. However, the physiologic significance of this exchange is uncertain.

Table 25–3. Daily net water turnover (ml) in the gastrointestinal tract.*

Ingested		2000
Endogenous secretions		7000
Salivary glands	1500	
Stomach	2500	
Bile	500	
Pancreas	1500	
Intestine	1000	
	7000	
Total input		9000
Reabsorbed		8800
Jejunum	5500	
Ileum	2000	
Colon	1300	
	8800	
Balance in stool		200

*Data from Moore EW: *Physiology of Intestinal Water and Electrolyte Absorption.* American Gastroenterological Society, 1976.

ABSORPTION OF VITAMINS & MINERALS

Vitamins

Absorption of water-soluble vitamins is rapid, but absorption of the fat-soluble vitamins A, D, E, and K is deficient if fat absorption is depressed because of lack of pancreatic enzymes or if bile is excluded from the intestine by obstruction of the bile duct. Most vitamins are absorbed in the upper small intestine, but vitamin B_{12} is absorbed in the ileum. This vitamin binds to intrinsic factor, a protein secreted by the stomach, and the complex is absorbed across the ileal mucosa (see Chapter 26).

Calcium

Thirty to 80% of ingested calcium is absorbed.

Active transport of Ca^{2+} out of the intestinal lumen occurs primarily in the upper small intestine. This process is facilitated by 1,25-dihydroxycholecalciferol, the metabolite of vitamin D that is produced in the kidney. The metabolite induces the synthesis of a Ca^{2+}-binding protein in the mucosal cells (see Chapter 21). The rate of production of 1,25-dihydroxycholecalciferol is increased when the plasma Ca^{2+} is decreased and reduced when the plasma Ca^{2+} is elevated (see Chapter 21). Consequently, Ca^{2+} absorption is adjusted to body needs; absorption is increased in the presence of Ca^{2+} deficiency and decreased in the presence of Ca^{2+} excess. Ca^{2+} absorption is also facilitated by lactose and protein. It is inhibited by phosphates and oxalates because these anions form insoluble salts with Ca^{2+}. Magnesium absorption is facilitated by protein.

Iron

In normal adults, very little iron is lost from the body. Men lose about 0.6 mg/d, whereas women have an average loss of about twice this value because of the additional iron lost in the blood shed during menstruation. The average daily iron intake in America and Europe is about 20 mg, but the amount absorbed is equal only to the losses; if it were any greater, iron overload would develop. Thus, the amount of iron absorbed ranges normally from about 3 to 6% of the amount ingested.

Iron is more readily absorbed in the ferrous state (Fe^{2+}), but most of the dietary iron is in the ferric form (Fe^{3+}). No more than a trace of iron is absorbed in the stomach, but the gastric secretions dissolve the iron and provide a milieu favorable to its reduction to the Fe^{2+} form. The importance of this function in humans is indicated by the fact that iron deficiency anemia is a troublesome and relatively frequent complication of partial gastrectomy. Ascorbic acid and other reducing substances in the diet facilitate conversion of ferric to ferrous iron. Heme is also absorbed, and the Fe^{2+} that it contains is released in the mucosal cells. Other dietary factors affect the availability of iron for absorption; for example, the phytic acid found in cereals reacts with iron to form insoluble compounds in the intestine. So do phosphates and oxalates. Pancreatic juice inhibits iron absorption.

Iron absorption is an active process (Table 25–2). Most of the absorption occurs in the upper part of the small intestine. Other mucosal cells can transport iron, but the duodenum and adjacent jejunum contain most of the iron suitable for absorption. The mucosal cells pass part of the iron directly into the bloodstream, but most of it is bound to **apoferritin.** This protein, which is found in many tissues, combines with iron to form **ferritin.** Apoferritin is a globular protein made up of 24 subunits. Iron forms a micelle of ferric hydroxyphosphate, and in ferritin, the subunits surround this micelle. The ferritin molecule can contain as many as 4000 atoms of iron. Ferritin is readily visible under the electron microscope and has been used as a tracer in studies of phagocytosis and related phenomena. Ferritin is the principal storage form of iron in tissues, although hemosiderin, a granular protein-iron complex, also stores iron. Seventy percent of the iron in the body is in hemoglobin, 3% in myoglobin, and the remainder in ferritin. Ferritin iron is in equilibrium with plasma iron. Ferritin is also found in plasma, but most iron is transported bound to a β_1 globulin called **transferrin** or **siderophilin.** Normally, transferrin is about 35% saturated with iron, and the normal plasma iron level is about 130 $\mu g/dl$ (23 $\mu mol/L$) in men and 110 $\mu g/dl$ (19 $\mu mol/L$) in women.

Iron absorption into the bloodstream is increased when body iron stores are depleted or when erythropoiesis is increased, and decreased in the opposite conditions. When large quantities of iron are ingested, more iron is bound in the mucosal cells, but absorption is increased very little. The iron in the mucosal cells stays bound in ferritin and is lost with the cells when they are shed into the intestinal lumen and passed in the stool. The mucosal cells also become loaded after parenteral administration of iron and reduce their uptake of dietary iron. Thus, one factor regulating iron uptake is the amount of iron in the mucosal cells, and the term "mucosal block" has been used to refer to the ability of the mucosa to prevent excess ingested iron from being absorbed.

The normal operation of the factors that maintain iron balance is essential for health. If more iron is absorbed than is excreted, iron overload results. Ferritin and hemosiderin accumulate in the tissues when the overload is prolonged. Large ferritin and hemosiderin deposits are associated with **hemochromatosis,** a syndrome characterized by pigmentation of the skin, pancreatic damage with diabetes ("bronze diabetes"), cirrhosis of the liver, a high incidence of hepatic carcinoma, and gonadal atrophy. Hemochromatosis can be produced by prolonged excessive iron intake and by a number of other conditions. Idiopathic hemochromatosis is a congenital disorder in which the mucosal regulatory mechanism behaves as if iron deficiency were present and absorbs iron at a high rate in the face of elevated rather than depleted body iron stores.

The digestive and absorptive functions of the gastrointestinal system outlined in the previous chapter depend upon a variety of mechanisms that propel the food through the gastrointestinal tract, soften it, and mix it with bile from the gallbladder and digestive enzymes secreted by the mucosal cells, salivary glands, and pancreas. Some of these mechanisms depend upon intrinsic properties of the intestinal smooth muscle. Others involve the operation of visceral reflexes or the actions of **gastrointestinal hormones.** The hormones are humoral agents secreted by parts of the mucosa and transported in the circulation to influence the functions of the stomach, the intestines, the pancreas, and the gallbladder.

The organization of the structures that make up the wall of the gastrointestinal tract from the posterior pharynx to the anus is shown in Fig 26–1. There is some local variation, but in general there are 3 layers of smooth muscle, 2 longitudinal and 1 circular. The wall is lined by mucosa and, except in the case of the

esophagus, is covered by serosa. The serosa continues onto the mesentery, which contains the nerves, lymphatics, and blood vessels supplying the tract.

Innervation of the Gastrointestinal Tract

There are 2 major networks of nerve fibers that are intrinsic to the gastrointestinal tract: the **myenteric nerve plexus** (Auerbach's plexus), between the outer longitudinal and middle circular muscle layers; and the **submucous plexus** (Meissner's plexus), between the middle circular layer and the mucosa (Fig 26–1). The plexuses contain nerve cells with processes that originate in receptors in the wall of the gut or the mucosa. The mucosal receptors are probably chemoreceptors that sense the composition of the intestinal contents or mechanoreceptors sensitive to stretch of the intestinal wall. The nerve cells innervate hormone-secreting cells and all the muscle layers in the mucosa. The plexuses are responsible for peristaltic and other contractions, and coordinated motor activity occurs in the total absence of extrinsic innervation.

The intestine receives a dual innervation from the autonomic nervous system, with parasympathetic cholinergic activity generally increasing the activity of intestinal smooth muscle and sympathetic adrenergic activity generally decreasing it. The parasympathetic fibers are preganglionic and generally end on the nerve cells of the myenteric and submucous plexuses. The sympathetic fibers are postganglionic, and most of them also end on the nerve cells, although some innervate blood vessels and others appear to end directly on intestinal smooth muscle cells. The electrical properties of intestinal smooth muscle are discussed in Chapter 3.

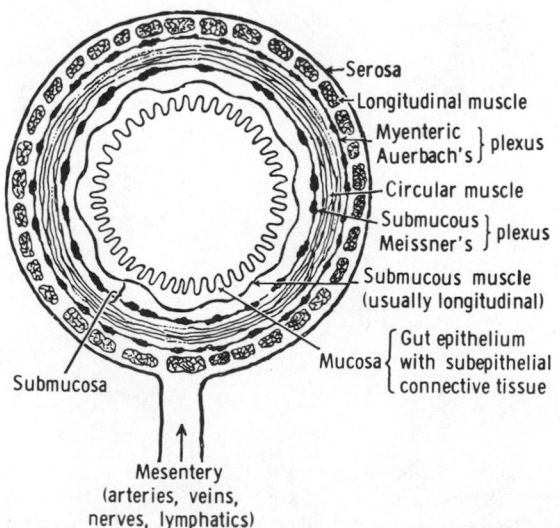

Figure 26–1. Diagrammatic representation of the layers of the wall of the stomach, small intestine, and colon. The structure of the esophagus is similar except that it has no mesentery. (Reproduced, with permission, from Bell GH, Emslie-Smith D, Paterson CR: *Textbook of Physiology and Biochemistry,* 9th ed. Churchill-Livingstone, 1976.)

GASTROINTESTINAL HORMONES

Several of the many different gastrointestinal hormones that have been postulated to exist have now been obtained in pure form and have been synthesized. Experiments with these pure hormones and measurements of hormone concentrations in blood by radioimmunoassays have provided important information about the regulation of gastrointestinal secretion and motility. When large doses of the hormones are given, their actions overlap. However, their physiologic effects appear to be relatively discrete.

Gastrin

Gastrin is a hormone produced by cells called G cells in the lateral walls of the glands in the antral portion of the gastric mucosa. G cells are flask-shaped, with a broad base containing many gastrin granules and a narrow apex that reaches the mucosal surface. Microvilli project from the apical end into the lumen. Receptors mediating gastrin responses to changes in gastric contents may be present on the microvilli. Like the other cells in the gastrointestinal tract that secrete hormones, these cells contain amines related to norepinephrine or serotonin and appear to be of neural crest origin. Because they take up amine precursors and decarboxylate them, they are sometimes called APUD cells (for amine precursor uptake and decarboxylation).

A significant amount of gastrin is also secreted by the human duodenal mucosa (Fig 26–2). Gastrin-secreting tumors called gastrinomas occur in the pancreas, but it is uncertain whether gastrin occurs in the pancreas under normal circumstances.

Three molecular forms of gastrin have been iso-

Table 26–1. Amino acid sequences of gastrointestinal peptides.*

1 CCK	2 Gastrin	3 GIP	4 Glucagon	5 Secretin	6 VIP	7 Motilin	8 Substance P	9 Bombesin	10 Somatostatin
Tyr		Tyr	His	-	-	Phe	Arg	(pyro) Glu	Ala
Ile		Ala	Ser	-	-	Val	Pro	Gln	Gly
Gln		Glu	Gln	Asp	-	Pro	Lys	Arg	Cys
Gln		Gly	-	-	Ala	Ile	Pro	Leu	Lys
Ala		Thr	-	-	Val	Phe	Gln	Gly	Asn
→Arg	(pyro) Glu	Phe	-	-	-	Thr	Gln	Asn	Phe
Lys	Leu	Ile	Thr	-	-	Tyr	Phe	Gln	Phe
Ala	Gly	Ser	-	-	Asp	Gly	Phe	Trp	Trp
Pro	Pro	Asp	-	Glu	Asn	Glu	Gly	Ala	Lys
Ser	Gln	Tyr	-	Leu	Tyr	Leu	Leu	Val	Thr
Gly	Gly	Ser	-	-	Thr	Gln	Met-NH₂	Gly	Phe
Arg	His	Ile	Lys	Arg	-	Arg		His	Thr
Val	Pro	Ala	Tyr	Leu	-	Met		Leu	Ser
Ser	Ser	Met	Leu	Arg	-	Gln		Met-NH₂	Cys
Met	Leu	Asp	-	-	Lys	Glu			
Ile	Val	Lys	Ser	-	Gln	Lys			
Lys	Ala	Ile	Arg	Ala	Met	Glu			
Asn	Asp	Arg	-	-	Ala	Arg			
Leu	Pro	Gln	Ala	Leu	Val	Asn			
Gln	Ser	Gln	-	-	Lys	Lys			
Ser	Lys	Asp	-	Arg	Lys	Gly			
Leu	→Lys	Phe	-	Leu	Tyr	Gln			
Asp	Gln	Val	-	Leu	-				
Pro	Gly	Asn	Gln	-	Asn				
Ser	→Pro	Trp	-	Gly	Ser				
His	Trp	Leu	-	-	Ile				
Arg	Leu	Leu	Met	Val-NH₂	Leu				
Ile	Glu	Ala	Asp		Asn-NH₂				
Ser	Glu	Gln	Thr						
Asp	Glu	Gln							
Arg	Glu	Lys							
Asp	Glu	Gly							
Tys	Ala	Lys							
Met	Tys	Lys							
Gly	-	Ser							
Trp	-	Asp							
Met	-	Trp							
Asp	-	Lys							
Phe-NH₂	-	His							
		Asn							
		Ile							
		Thr							
		Gln							

- = same as preceding column. → = point of cleavage to form a smaller variant. Tys = tyrosine sulfate. 1. Porcine CCK-variant. Regular CCK = C-terminal 33 residues of the variant. 2. Human big gastrin. Little gastrin = C-terminal 17 residues of big gastrin. Minigastrin = C-terminal 14 residues of big gastrin. All gastrins occur as pairs: unsulfated tyrosine = I; sulfated tyrosine = II. 3, 4, 5, 6, and 7 are all of porcine origin. 4, 9, and 10 have been identified in gut mucosa only by immunoreactivity; the exact chemical nature of this immunoreactivity has not yet been established.

*Reproduced, with permission, from Grossman MI: The gastrointestinal hormones: An overview. In: *Endocrinology*. Vol 2. James VT (editor). Excerpta Medica, 1977.

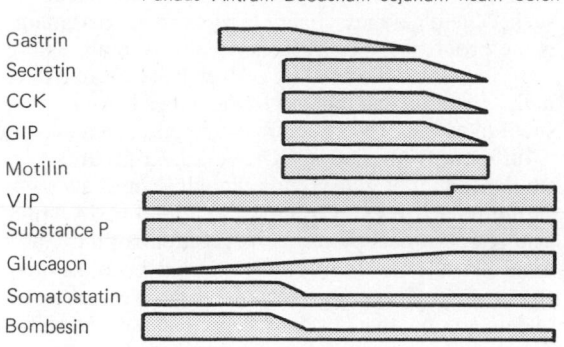

Figure 26–2. Distribution of gastrointestinal peptides along the gastrointestinal tract. The thickness of each bar is proportionate to the concentration of the peptide in the mucosa. (Reproduced, with permission, from Grossman MI: The gastrointestinal hormones: An overview. In: *Endocrinology*. Vol 1. James VT [editor]. Excerpta Medica, 1977.)

lated in pure form. All have the same C-terminal configuration. The predominant form in tissue contains 17 amino acid residues (Table 26–1) and is called G 17. It has a pyro(Glu) configuration at the N terminal. There is an increase in circulating G 17 after feeding, but the predominant form in blood at this time contains twice as many amino acid residues (G 34, or **big gastrin**). It also has a (pyro)Glu configuration at the N-terminal end but is not as active as G 17 and is not a polymer. Instead, it is probably a prohormone from which G 17 and other active fragments are derived. A tetradecapeptide, G 14, or **minigastrin,** that is less active than G 17 has been isolated from tissue and blood. To further complicate matters, all of these gastrins occur in sulfated (gastrin II) or nonsulfated (gastrin I) forms, ie, they may or may not have an $-SO_3H$ group on the tyrosine residue in position 12. The sulfated and nonsulfated forms are equally active and are generally found in blood and tissues in approximately equal amounts. Tissue and blood also contain a gastrin larger than G 34 (**big big gastrin**) and another large gastrin, but it is not known if these 2 gastrins are biologically active. A synthetic tetrapeptide made up of amino acid residues 14–17 has all the activities of gastrin, although it has only 10% of the strength of G 17. The radioimmunoassays generally used to measure gastrin measure G 17 and thus may not tell the whole story about secretion. However, they do provide valuable information about the physiology of this hormone.

G 14 and G 17 have half-lives of 2–3 minutes in the circulation, while G 34 has a half-life of 15 minutes. Gastrins are inactivated primarily in the kidney and small intestine.

In large doses, gastrin has a variety of actions, but its principal physiologic actions are stimulation of gastric acid and pepsin secretion and stimulation of the growth of the gastric mucosa. It also causes contraction of the musculature that closes the gastroesophageal junction, but this effect is of questionable

physiologic significance (see below). It stimulates insulin and glucagon secretion, but only after a protein meal and not after a carbohydrate meal does circulating endogenous gastrin reach the level necessary to stimulate the B cells. There is some evidence that gastrin stimulates calcitonin secretion (see Chapter 21), and calcitonin in turn appears to inhibit gastrin secretion.

Gastrin secretion is affected by the contents of the stomach, the rate of discharge of the vagus nerves, and blood-borne factors (Table 26–2). Secretion is increased by the presence of the products of protein digestion in the stomach and, in experimental animals, by increased vagal discharge. In dogs, the cholinergic blocking drug atropine reduces gastrin release; however, atropine does not inhibit the gastrin response to a test meal in humans. Therefore, vagal innervation may not be very important in the regulation of the secretion of human G cells. Acid in the antrum inhibits gastrin secretion. The effect of acid is the basis of a negative feedback loop regulating gastrin secretion. Increased secretion of the hormone increases acid secretion, but the acid then feeds back to inhibit further gastrin secretion.

The role of gastrin in the pathophysiology of duodenal ulcers is discussed below. In conditions such as pernicious anemia in which the acid-secreting cells of the stomach are damaged, gastrin secretion is chronically elevated.

Gastrin may also be implicated in the disease called **achalasia,** in which food accumulates in the esophagus because the gastroesophageal junction fails to relax. The normal coordinated peristalsis in the body of the esophagus also fails to occur, and the esophagus becomes massively dilated. Microscopic examination of the wall of the dilated portion of the esophagus reveals a deficient myenteric plexus. There is now some evidence that the smooth muscle at the gastroesophageal junction is hypersensitive to normal circulating levels of gastrin in this condition, and it is postulated that this is the reason for the prolonged contraction. The opposite condition is gastroesophageal reflux, in which the junction is abnor-

Table 26–2. Stimuli that affect gastrin secretion.*

Stimuli that increase gastrin secretion
Luminal
Peptides and amino acids
Distention
Neural
Increased vagal (cholinergic) discharge
Blood-borne
Calcium
Epinephrine
Stimuli that inhibit gastrin secretion
Luminal
Acid
Blood-borne
Secretin, GIP, VIP, glucagon, calcitonin

*Modified from Walsh JH, Grossman MI: Gastrin. N Engl J Med 292:1324, 1975.

mally relaxed, and it has been claimed that in patients with this disease gastrin secretion is subnormal.

Cholecystokinin-Pancreozymin

It was formerly thought that a hormone called cholecystokinin produced contraction of the gallbladder whereas a separate hormone called pancreozymin increased the secretion of pancreatic juice rich in enzymes. It is now clear that a single hormone secreted by cells in the mucosa of the upper small intestine has both activities, and the hormone has therefore been named **cholecystokinin-pancreozymin.** It is also called **CCK-PZ** or **CCK.** Porcine CCK exists in 2 forms with equal activity, one containing 39 and the other 33 amino acid residues. The last 5 residues are identical with the last 5 in gastrin (Table 26–1). There is also a sulfated tyrosine residue near the C terminal in CCK, as there is in the gastrin IIs. Removal of the $-SO_3H$ group changes the activity patterns of CCK into those of gastrin. Little is known about the metabolism of CCK. CCK is also found in the cerebral cortex (see Chapter 15).

In addition to causing contraction of the gallbladder and secretion of a pancreatic juice rich in enzymes, CCK augments the action of secretin in producing secretion of an alkaline pancreatic juice. It also inhibits gastric emptying, exerts a trophic effect on the pancreas, increases the secretion of enterokinase, and may enhance the motility of the small intestine and colon. There is some evidence that, along with secretin, it augments the contraction of the pyloric sphincter, thus preventing the reflux of duodenal contents into the stomach. Gastrin and CCK stimulate glucagon secretion, and since the secretion of both gastrointestinal hormones is increased by a protein meal, either or both may be the "gut factor" that stimulates glucagon secretion (see Chapter 19). The action of CCK on the gallbladder may be mediated via cyclic GMP (see Chapter 1).

The principal stimulus to CCK secretion is the presence in the duodenum of fatty acids containing more than 10 carbon atoms. Its secretion is also increased by amino acids, particularly tryptophan and phenylalanine, and by Ca^{2+} and H^+. Since the bile and pancreatic juice that enter the duodenum in response to CCK further the digestion of protein and fat and the products of this digestion stimulate further CCK secretion, a sort of positive feedback operates in the control of the secretion of this hormone. The positive feedback is terminated when the products of digestion move on to the lower portions of the gastrointestinal tract.

Secretin

Secretin occupies a unique position in the history of physiology. In 1902, Bayliss and Starling first demonstrated that the excitatory effect of duodenal stimulation on pancreatic secretion was due to a blood-borne factor. Their research led to the identification of secretin. They also suggested that many chemical agents might be secreted by cells in the body and passed in the circulation to affect organs some distance away, and

Starling introduced the term **hormone** to categorize such "chemical messengers." Modern endocrinology is the proof of the correctness of this hypothesis.

Secretin is secreted by cells that are located deep in the glands of the mucosa of the upper portion of the small intestine. The structure of secretin (Table 26–1) is different from that of CCK and gastrin but is very similar to that of glucagon; although secretin contains 27 amino acids and glucagon 29, a total of 14 amino acid residues occupy the same positions in the 2 hormones. Only one form of secretin has been isolated, and the fragments of the molecule that have been tested to date are inactive. Little is known about its metabolism.

Secretin increases the secretion of bicarbonate by the duct cells of the pancreas and biliary tract. It thus causes the secretion of a watery, alkaline pancreatic juice. Its action on pancreatic duct cells is mediated via cyclic AMP. It also augments the action of CCK in producing pancreatic secretion of digestive enzymes. It decreases gastric acid secretion. It may cause contraction of the pyloric sphincter, and it has been reported to increase insulin secretion. However, a glucose meal fails to increase secretin secretion, so it seems unlikely that secretin is the gut factor that augments the insulin response to a carbohydrate meal.

The only proved stimulus to secretin secretion is acid bathing the mucosa of the upper small intestine. Protein, carbohydrate, and acetylcholine are ineffective, and the effect of fat is uncertain. The release of secretin by acid is another example of feedback control: Secretin causes alkaline pancreatic juice to flood into the duodenum, neutralizing the acid from the stomach and thus stopping further secretion of the hormone.

Other Gastrointestinal Hormones

Other substances are suspected of being gastrointestinal hormones on the basis of physiologic evidence, chemical evidence, or both. **Gastric inhibitory peptide (GIP)** contains 43 amino acid residues (Table 26–1) and is found in the mucosa of the duodenum and jejunum. Its secretion is stimulated by glucose and fat in the duodenum, and it inhibits gastric secretion and motility. It also stimulates insulin secretion, and evidence is accumulating that it is the physiologic B cell–stimulating hormone of the gastrointestinal tract. **Vasoactive intestinal peptide (VIP)** has also been isolated from the intestine. It contains 28 amino acid residues (Table 26–1) and has recently been found in the brain as well as the intestine. It markedly stimulates intestinal secretion of electrolytes and hence of water. Its other actions include dilatation of peripheral blood vessels and inhibition of gastric acid secretion. VIP-secreting tumors (VIPomas) have been described in patients with severe diarrhea. Both GIP and VIP are related to secretin. Their relation to **enterogastrone,** a putative hormone that inhibits gastric acid secretion and motility, is unknown. The structures of GIP and VIP resemble those of secretin and glucagon. **Motilin,** a peptide containing 22 amino acid residues (Table

26–1), has been extracted from duodenal mucosa. It stimulates gastric acid secretion. **Chymodenin,** another peptide extracted from duodenal mucosa, has been reported to cause selective increases in the secretion of chymotrypsinogen from the pancreas, but it has not as yet been proved to exist in the circulation. Its exact structure is also unknown. **Substance P** (Table 26–1) is found in neurons in the brain and the gastrointestinal tract and in endocrine type cells in the gastrointestinal tract, but it has not been proved to enter the circulation. It increases the motility of the small intestine. **Bombesin** and **somatostatin** (Table 26–1) have not been chemically identified in the gastrointestinal mucosa, but they have been identified by immunoreactivity. Bombesin increases gastrin secretion and the motility of the small intestine and gallbladder. Somatostatin, the tetradecapeptide growth hormone–inhibiting hormone originally isolated from the hypothalamus, inhibits the secretion of gastrin, VIP, GIP, secretin, and motilin. It also inhibits pancreatic exocrine secretion, gastric acid secretion and motility, gallbladder contraction, and the absorption of glucose and xylose. However, its physiologic role in the gastrointestinal tract has not been established. Glucagon is found in the stomach and duodenum, and, as noted in Chapter 19, glucagon from the gastrointestinal tract appears to play a role in the hyperglycemia of diabetes. The relationship of this "gut glucagon" to the glucagonlike immunoreactivity (GLI) found in the mucosa of the small intestine is unknown. Other gastrointestinal hormones have been proposed to exist, but their existence has not yet been proved.

Caerulein

An interesting decapeptide isolated from the skin of the Australian frog *Hyla caerulea* has the same five C-terminal and two N-terminal amino acid residues as gastrin and also has a sulfated tyrosyl residue. This material, which has been named **caerulein,** has all the properties of gastrin and CCK in mammals and is being used in humans to contract the gallbladder during cholecystography (see below).

MOUTH & ESOPHAGUS

In the mouth, food is mixed with saliva and propelled into the esophagus. Peristaltic waves in the esophagus move the food into the stomach.

Mastication

Chewing (**mastication**) breaks up large food particles and mixes the food with the secretions of the salivary glands. This wetting and homogenizing action aids subsequent digestion. Large food particles can be digested, but they cause strong and often painful contractions of the esophageal musculature. Edentulous patients are generally restricted to a soft diet and have considerable difficulty eating dry food.

Saliva

Saliva contains the digestive enzyme **ptyalin,** or **salivary alpha-amylase** (see Chapter 25), which has a minor role in starch digestion; and **mucin,** a glycoprotein that lubricates the food. About 1500 ml of saliva are secreted per day. The pH of saliva is about 7.0. It performs a number of important functions. It facilitates swallowing, keeps the mouth moist, serves as a solvent for the molecules that stimulate the taste buds, aids speech by facilitating movements of the lips and tongue, and keeps the mouth and teeth clean. The saliva may also have some antibacterial action, and patients with deficient salivation (**xerostomia**) have a higher than normal incidence of dental caries. The buffers in saliva help maintain the oral pH at about 7.0. At this pH the saliva is saturated with calcium, and so the teeth do not lose calcium to the oral fluids. At more acid pHs, calcium loss is appreciable.

In the salivary glands, the secretory (**zymogen**) granules containing the salivary enzymes are discharged from the acinar cells into the ducts (Fig 26–3). The characteristics of each of the 3 pairs of salivary glands in humans are summarized in Table 26–3.

The concentrations of Na^+, Cl^-, and HCO_3^- in saliva increase as the amount of saliva that is secreted increases, whereas the concentration of K^+ decreases. It appears that the salivary acini elaborate a primary secretion containing these ions, with the concentrations of K^+ and HCO_3^- greater than those in plasma because of active transport. Cl^-, HCO_3^-, and Na^+ are reabsorbed in the ducts, whereas K^+ is secreted. When salivary flow rates are high, there is little time for reabsorption, so saliva contains more of the normally reabsorbed and less of the normally secreted ions.

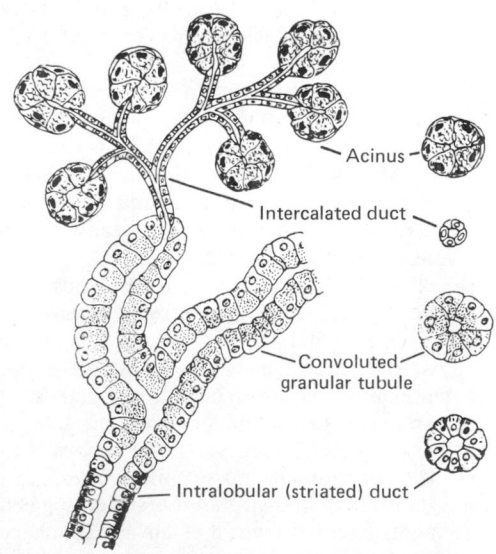

Figure 26–3. Organization of the submaxillary gland in the rat. (Reproduced, with permission, from Leeson CR: Structure of salivary glands. Volume 2, page 463, in: *Handbook of Physiology.* American Physiological Society, 1967.)

Table 26–3. Nerve supply, histologic type, and relative contribution to total salivary output of each of the pairs of salivary glands in humans. Serous cells secrete ptyalin; mucous cells secrete mucin.

Gland	Parasympathetic Nerve Supply Via	Histologic Type	Percentage of Total Salivary Secretion in Humans (1.5 L/d)
Parotid	Glossopharyngeal	Serous	25
Submaxillary	Facial	Mixed	70
Sublingual	Facial	Mucous	5

Aldosterone increases the K^+ concentration and reduces the Na^+ concentration of saliva in an action analogous to its action on the kidney (see Chapters 20 and 38), and a high salivary Na^+/K^+ ratio is seen in Addison's disease.

Control of Salivary Secretion

Salivary secretion is under neural control. Stimulation of the parasympathetic nerve supply causes profuse secretion of watery saliva with a relatively low content of organic material. Associated with this secretion is a pronounced vasodilatation in the gland, which appears to be due to the local release of the vasodilator polypeptide **bradykinin.** This nonapeptide is formed from α_2 globulins in the plasma by the action of the enzyme kallikrein (see Chapter 31), and kallikrein is released in the salivary glands by stimulation of the parasympathetic nerves. Bradykinin is also released in the exocrine portion of the pancreas and sweat glands when they are active. Atropine and other cholinergic blocking agents reduce salivary secretion. Stimulation of the sympathetic nerve supply causes vasoconstriction and, in humans, secretion of small amounts of saliva rich in organic constituents from the submaxillary glands; however, it has no effect on parotid secretion.

Food in the mouth causes reflex secretion of saliva, and so does stimulation of vagal afferent fibers at the gastric end of the esophagus. Salivary secretion is easily conditioned, as shown in Pavlov's original experiments (see Chapter 16). In humans, the sight, smell, and even thought of food causes salivary secretion ("makes the mouth water").

Like the thyroid gland, the salivary glands and the gastric mucosa concentrate iodide from the plasma, the salivary/plasma iodide ratio sometimes reaching 60. The physiologic significance of this iodide-trapping phenomenon is uncertain. The salivary glands have also been reported to contain somatostatin, glucagon, and, at least in some species, renin and various growth factors. The functions of most of these factors in the salivary glands is unknown, but it has been suggested that glucagon secreted from the salivary glands contributes to the hyperglycemia in pancreatectomized animals (see Chapter 19).

Deglutition

Swallowing (deglutition) is a reflex initiated by the voluntary action of collecting the oral contents on the tongue and propelling them backward into the pharynx. This initiates a wave of involuntary contraction in the pharyngeal muscles that pushes the material into the esophagus. Inhibition of respiration and glottic closure are part of the reflex response. Swallowing is difficult if not impossible when the mouth is open, as anyone who has spent time in the dentist's chair feeling saliva collect in the throat is well aware.

At the pharyngoesophageal junction, there is a 3 cm segment of esophagus in which the resting wall tension is high. This segment relaxes reflexly upon swallowing, permitting the swallowed material to enter the body of the esophagus. A ring contraction of the esophageal muscle forms behind the material, which is then swept down the esophagus by a peristaltic wave at a speed of approximately 4 cm/s. When humans are in an upright position, liquids and semisolid foods generally fall by gravity to the lower esophagus ahead of the peristaltic wave. The musculature of the gastroesophageal junction (lower esophageal sphincter) is tonically active but relaxes upon swallowing. The main function of this sphincter is the prevention of reflux of gastric contents into the esophagus. Large doses of the gastrointestinal hormone gastrin (see below) increase the tone of the lower esophageal sphincter, but this effect is not produced by doses of gastrin that produce circulating gastrin levels comparable to those that occur after a meal.

Nervous persons who hyperventilate sometimes swallow large amounts of air, and some air is unavoidably swallowed in the process of eating and drinking (**aerophagia**). Some of the swallowed air is regurgitated (belching), and some of the gases it contains are absorbed, but much of it passes on to the colon. Here, some of the oxygen is absorbed, and hydrogen, hydrogen sulfide, carbon dioxide, and methane formed by the colonic bacteria are added to it. It is then expelled as **flatus.** The volume of gas normally found in the human gastrointestinal tract is about 200 ml. In some individuals, gas in the intestines causes cramps, **borborygmi** (rumbling noises), and abdominal discomfort.

STOMACH

Food is stored in the stomach; mixed with acid, mucus, and pepsin; and released at a controlled, steady rate into the duodenum, where it is digested further and partially absorbed.

Anatomic Considerations

The gross anatomy of the stomach is shown in Fig 26–4. The gastric mucosa contains many deep glands. In the pyloric and cardiac regions, the glands secrete mucus. In the body of the stomach, including the fundus, the glands contain **parietal,** or **oxyntic, cells,** which secrete hydrochloric acid and intrinsic factor, and **chief, zymogen,** or **peptic cells,** which secrete pepsinogen (Fig 26–5). These secretions mix with mucus secreted by the cells in the necks of the glands. Several of the glands open on a common chamber **(gastric pit)** that opens in turn on the surface of the mucosa.

The stomach has a very rich blood and lymphatic supply. Its parasympathetic nerve supply comes from the vagi and its sympathetic supply from the celiac plexus.

Gastric Secretion

The cells of the gastric glands secrete about 3000 ml/d of **gastric juice.** This juice contains a variety of substances (Table 26–4). The gastric enzymes are discussed in Chapter 25. **Mucus** is secreted by the glands in the pyloric region and the neck cells of the glands in the rest of the stomach. It lubricates the food. The **hydrochloric acid** secreted by the glands in the body of the stomach is concentrated enough to cause tissue damage, but in normal individuals the gastric mucosa does not become irritated or digested. The gastric mucus was once thought to protect the cells, but the barrier to acid damage now appears to be the surface membranes of the mucosal cells and the tight junctions between the cells. Substances that tend to

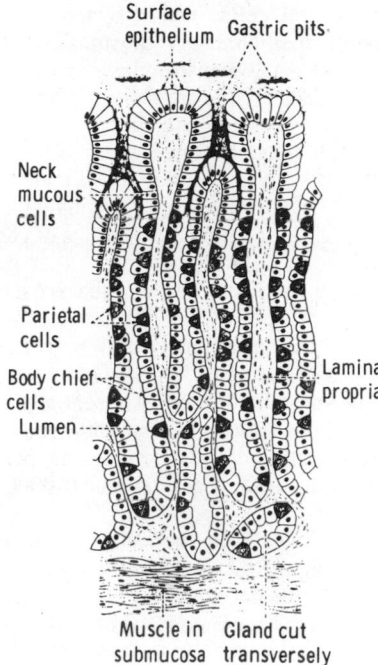

Figure 26–5. Diagram of glands in the mucosa of the body of the human stomach. (Reproduced, with permission, from Bell GH, Davidson N, Scarborough G: *Textbook of Physiology and Biochemistry,* 6th ed. Livingstone, 1965.)

disrupt the barrier and thus cause gastric irritation include aspirin, ethanol, vinegar, and bile salts.

The electrolyte content of the gastric juice varies with the rate of secretion. At low secretory rates, the Na^+ concentration is high and the H^+ concentration is low, but as acid secretion increases, Na^+ concentration falls.

Pepsinogen Secretion

The chief cells that secrete pepsinogens, the precursors of the 3 pepsins in gastric juice (see Chapter 25), contain zymogen granules. The secretory process is apparently similar to that involved in the secretion of ptyalin by the salivary glands and trypsinogen and the other pancreatic enzymes by the pancreas. Pepsinogen activity can be detected in the plasma and in the urine, where it is called **uropepsinogen.**

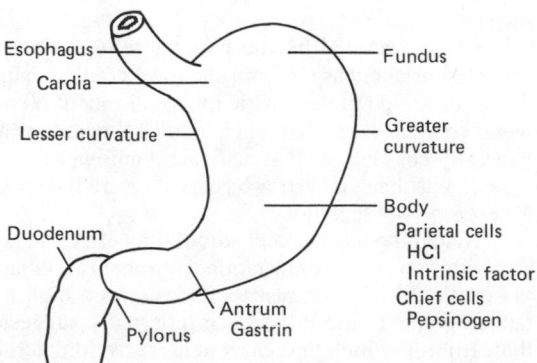

Figure 26–4. Gross anatomy of the stomach. The principal secretions are listed under the labels indicating the locations where they are produced. In addition, mucus is secreted in all parts of the stomach.

Table 26–4. Contents of normal gastric juice (fasting state).

Cations: Na^+, K^+, Mg^{2+}, H^+ (pH approximately 1.0)
Anions: Cl^-, HPO_4^{2-}, SO_4^{2-}
Pepsins I–III
Gelatinase
Mucus
Intrinsic factor
Water

Hydrochloric Acid Secretion

The parietal cells, which secrete hydrochloric acid, contain small channels, or **canaliculi,** that communicate with the lumens of the gastric glands (Fig 26–6). When these cells are stained with appropriate indicator dyes, the canaliculi have an intensely acid reaction, while the pH of the interior of the cells, like that of other body cells, is 7.0–7.2. It therefore seems likely that H^+ is secreted into the canaliculi.

It is difficult to obtain the products of parietal cell secretion free of contamination by other gastric secretions, but the purest specimens that have been analyzed are essentially isotonic. Their H^+ concentration is equivalent to approximately 0.17 N HCl, with pHs as low as 0.87. Therefore, parietal cell secretion may well be an isotonic solution of essentially pure HCl containing 150 mEq of Cl^- and 150 mEq of H^+ per liter. The comparable concentrations per liter of plasma are about 100 mEq of Cl^- and 0.00004 mEq of H^+.

The mechanism in the cells that can actively transport H^+ against a concentration gradient of this magnitude is still incompletely understood. The primary source of the secreted H^+ is unsettled. It appears to be produced by the ionization of H_2O, although some H^+ may also come from substrates such as glucose via the flavoprotein-cytochrome respiratory enzyme chain (see Chapter 17). For each H^+ secreted, an OH^- remains in the cell (Fig 26–7). The OH^- is neutralized by an H^+ formed by the dissociation of carbonic acid (carbonic acid buffer system; see Chapters 35 and 40). The HCO_3^- formed by this dissociation enters the bloodstream. The H_2CO_3 supply is replenished by the hydration of CO_2. The gastric mucosa contains an abundance of carbonic anhydrase, the enzyme that catalyzes the hydration of CO_2, and the stomach has a negative respiratory quotient (RQ)—ie, the amount of CO_2 in arterial blood is greater than the amount in gastric venous blood. Blood coming from the stomach is alkaline and has a high HCO_3^- content. When gastric acid secretion is elevated after a meal,

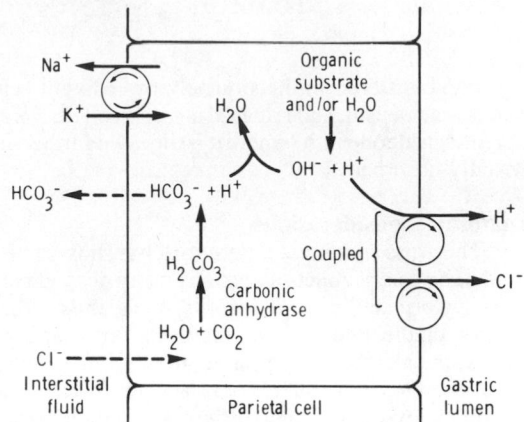

Figure 26–7. Principal chemical reactions believed to underlie HCl secretion by parietal cells in the stomach. H^+ and Cl^- are actively transported into the gastric lumen by pumps that are generally coupled in their operation. The solid arrows crossing cell membranes indicate active transport. The dashed arrows indicate diffusion. Compare with Fig 38–20.

sufficient H^+ may be secreted to raise the pH of systemic blood and make the urine alkaline. This is the probable explanation of the high pH of the urine excreted after a meal, the so-called **postprandial alkaline tide.**

The energy for the active transport of H^+ across the membrane of the parietal cell comes from aerobic glycolysis, since acid secretion ceases under anaerobic conditions. It is also inhibited by dinitrophenol, which indicates that oxidative phosphorylation is necessary for it to continue. Two moles of H^+ are secreted for each mole of O_2 consumed.

Acid secretion is stimulated by vagal discharge and by gastrin (see below). The amount of acid secreted under conditions of maximal stimulation varies with the number of parietal cells in the stomach. The maximal rate has been calculated to be 20 mEq/h/10^9 cells. Acid secretion is inhibited by gastric inhibitory peptide (GIP) and other hormones secreted from the intestinal mucosa.

Cl^- is secreted by the parietal cells against an electrical gradient as well as a chemical gradient, since the luminal side of the gastric mucosa is about 60 mV negative to the serosal side. H^+ and Cl^- secretions are generally coupled, so that equivalent amounts are secreted, but there is also a basal Cl^- secretion in the absence of H^+ secretion.

Histamine has a potent stimulating effect on acid secretion. The effect of histamine is probably mediated via cyclic AMP. The gastric mucosa has a high histamine content, and it has been repeatedly suggested that stimuli which increase acid secretion act by liberating this amine in the mucosa. There are 2 kinds of histamine receptors, H_1 and H_2 receptors, and H_2 receptors mediate the response of acid-secreting cells. The common antihistamine drugs used in the treatment of allergy block H_1 receptors and have little effect on

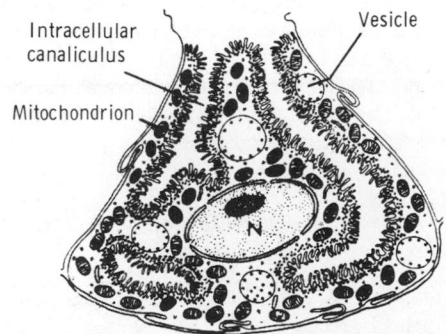

Figure 26–6. Parietal cell. Drawing of electron micrograph from mucosa of mouse after stimulation of acid secretion. In inactive parietal cells, the canaliculi are much narrower. N, nucleus. (Reproduced, with permission, from Davenport HW: *Physiology of the Digestive Tract,* 3rd ed. Year Book, 1971.)

acid secretion. However, drugs that block H_2 receptors have a marked inhibitory effect, and H_2 blocking agents such as cimetidine have proved to be very effective in the treatment of peptic ulcers. Thus, evidence is accumulating that histamine is the common mediator of the gastric acid secretory response.

Gastric Motility & Emptying

When food enters the stomach, the organ relaxes by the reflex process of **receptive relaxation.** This relaxation of the gastric musculature is triggered by movement of the pharynx and esophagus. It is followed by peristaltic contractions that mix the food and squirt food into the duodenum at a controlled rate. The peristaltic waves are most marked in the distal half of the stomach. When well developed, they occur at a rate of 3/min.

The pyloric sphincter has a limited function in the control of gastric emptying. Gastric emptying is normal if the pylorus is held open or even if it is surgically resected. The antrum, pylorus, and upper duodenum apparently function as a unit. Contraction of the antrum is followed by sequential contraction of the pyloric region and the duodenum. In the antrum, contraction ahead of the advancing gastric contents prevents solid masses from entering the duodenum. The gastric contents are thus squirted a bit at a time into the small intestine. Regurgitation from the duodenum does not occur because the contraction of the pyloric segment tends to persist slightly longer than that of the duodenum. The prevention of regurgitation may also be due to the stimulating action of CCK and secretin on the pyloric sphincter.

Gastric Slow Wave

Peristaltic contractions in the stomach are coordinated by the **gastric slow wave,** a wave of depolarization of smooth muscle cells proceeding from the fundus of the stomach to the pylorus approximately every 20 seconds. This wave is also called the **basic electric rhythm (BER).** It is the pacemaker for antral peristalsis; the wave and, consequently, peristalsis becomes chaotic and irregular after vagotomy or transection of the stomach wall. Thus, the slow wave plays a major role in the control of gastric emptying. A similar aborally directed slow wave coordinates smooth muscle contractions in the small intestine and the colon (see below).

Hunger Contractions

The musculature of the stomach is rarely inactive. Soon after the stomach is emptied, mild peristaltic contractions begin. They gradually increase in intensity over a period of hours. The more intense contractions can be felt and may even be mildly painful. These **hunger contractions** are associated with the sensation of hunger and were once thought to be an important regulator of appetite. However, it has now been demonstrated that food intake is normal in animals after denervation of the stomach and intestines (see Chapter 14).

REGULATION OF GASTRIC SECRETION & MOTILITY

Gastric motility and secretion are regulated by neural and humoral mechanisms. The neural components are local autonomic reflexes, involving cholinergic neurons, and impulses from the CNS by way of the vagus nerves. The humoral components are the hormones discussed above. At least in experimental animals, cholinergic stimulation increases gastrin secretion. Thus, the acetylcholine liberated at the endings of the postganglionic cholinergic neurons in the stomach increases gastric secretion in 2 ways: It acts directly on the cells in the fundus to increase acid and pepsin secretion; and it increases the secretion of gastrin. In their action on acid secretion, gastrin and acetylcholine potentiate each other. Stimulation of the vagus nerve in the chest or neck increases acid and pepsin secretion, but vagotomy does not abolish the secretory response to local stimuli.

For convenience, the physiologic regulation of gastric secretion is usually discussed in terms of cephalic, gastric, and intestinal influences, although these overlap. The **cephalic** influences are vagally mediated responses induced by activity in the CNS. The **gastric** influences are primarily local reflex responses and responses to gastrin. The **intestinal** influences are the reflex and hormonal feedback effects on gastric secretion initiated from the mucosa of the small intestine.

Cephalic Influences

The presence of food in the mouth reflexly stimulates gastric secretion. The efferent fibers for this reflex are in the vagus nerves. Vagally mediated increases in gastric secretion are easily conditioned. In humans, for example, the sight, smell, and thought of food increase gastric secretion. These increases are due to alimentary conditioned reflexes that become established early in life.

The neural mechanisms involved in the formation of conditioned reflexes are discussed in Chapter 16. The impulses descending in the vagi originate in part in the diencephalon and limbic system. Stimulation of the anterior hypothalamus and parts of the adjacent orbital frontal cortex increases vagal efferent activity and gastric secretion.

Emotional Responses

Psychic states have marked effects on gastric secretion and motility. These effects are principally mediated via the vagi. Among his famous observations on Alexis St. Martin, the Canadian with a permanent gastric fistula resulting from a gunshot wound, William Beaumont noted that anger and hostility were associated with turgor, hyperemia, and hypersecretion of the gastric mucosa. Similar observations have been made on other patients with gastric fistulas. Fear and depression decrease gastric secretion and blood flow and inhibit gastric motility.

Gastric Influences

Food in the stomach accelerates the increase in gastric secretion produced by the sight and smell of food and the presence of food in the mouth (Fig 26–8). Receptors in the wall of the stomach and the mucosa respond to stretch and chemical stimuli, mainly amino acids and related products of digestion. The fibers from the receptors enter Meissner's plexus, where the cell bodies of the receptor neurons are located. They synapse on postganglionic parasympathetic neurons, which end on parietal cells and stimulate acid secretion. Thus, the acid responses are produced by local reflexes in which the reflex arc is totally within the wall of the stomach. The postganglionic neurons in the local reflex arc are the same ones innervated by the descending vagal preganglionic neurons from the brain that mediate the cephalic phase of secretion. The products of protein digestion also bring about increased secretion of gastrin, and this augments the flow of acid.

Intestinal Influences

When the products of gastric protein digestion enter the duodenum, they stimulate secretion from the duodenal mucosa of additional gastrin ("intestinal gastrin"). However, fats, carbohydrates, and acid in the duodenum inhibit gastric acid and pepsin secretion and gastric motility, probably via GIP and CCK and possibly via other hormones. Gastric acid secretion is increased following removal of large parts of the small intestine. The hypersecretion, which is roughly proportionate in degree to the amount of intestine removed, may be due in part to removal of the source of hormones that inhibit acid secretion. A substance called **urogastrone**, with inhibitory effects on the stomach, has been found in urine. Its origin is unknown.

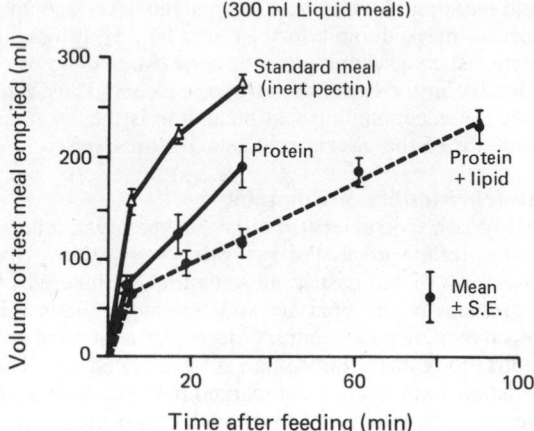

Figure 26–9. Effect of protein and fat on the rate of emptying of the human stomach. Subjects were fed 300 ml liquid meals. (Reproduced, with permission, from Brooks FP: Integrative lecture: Response of the GI tract to a meal. *Undergraduate Teaching Project.* American Gastroenterological Association, 1974.)

Other Influences

The inhibiting effect of catecholamines on gastric secretion has been discussed above. Hypoglycemia stimulates acid and pepsin secretion, and the stimulation produced by insulin is a result of hypoglycemia. Other stimulants include **alcohol** and **caffeine**, both of which act directly on the mucosa. The beneficial effects of moderate amounts of alcohol on appetite and digestion, due to this stimulatory effect on gastric secretion, have been known since ancient times.

Regulation of Gastric Motility & Emptying

The rate at which the stomach empties into the duodenum depends on the type of food ingested. Food rich in carbohydrate leaves the stomach in a few hours. Protein-rich food leaves more slowly, and emptying is slowest after a meal containing fat (Fig 26–9). Products of protein digestion and hydrogen ions bathing the duodenal mucosa initiate a neurally mediated decrease in gastric motility, the **enterogastric reflex.** Distention of the duodenum also initiates this reflex. GIP, VIP, and other hormones inhibit gastric motility and secretion. Cutting the vagus nerves slows gastric emptying. In humans, vagotomy may cause relatively severe gastric atony and distention. Excitement is said to hasten gastric emptying, and fear to slow it.

Since fats are particularly effective in inhibiting gastric emptying, some people drink milk, cream, or even olive oil before a cocktail party. The fat keeps the alcohol in the stomach for a long time, where its absorption is relatively slow, and the intoxicant enters the small intestine in a slow, steady stream so that— theoretically, at least—a sudden rise of the blood alcohol to a high level and consequent embarrassing intoxication are avoided.

Peptic Ulcer

Gastric and duodenal ulceration in humans is ap-

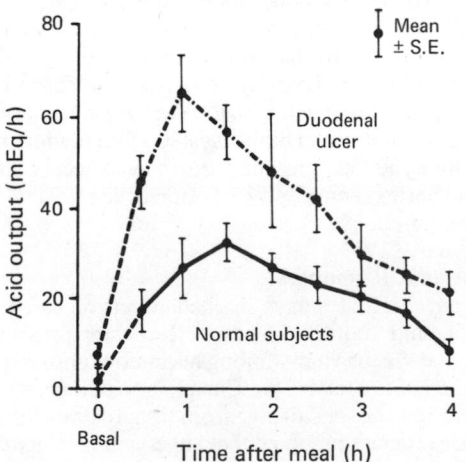

Figure 26–8. Human gastric acid secretion after a steak meal. (Reproduced, with permission, from Brooks FP: Integrative lecture: Response of the GI tract to a meal. *Undergraduate Teaching Project.* American Gastroenterological Association, 1974.)

parently related in some poorly understood way to a breakdown of the barrier that normally prevents irritation and autodigestion of the mucosa by the gastric secretions. In patients with ulcers of the duodenum and prepyloric portion of the stomach—but not in those with ulcers of other portions of the stomach—excessive acid secretion also plays a role (Fig 26–8). Another illustration of the importance of acid hypersecretion in the genesis of duodenal and prepyloric ulcers is provided by the **Zollinger-Ellison syndrome.** This syndrome is seen in patients with gastrinomas, which are tumors that secrete gastrin. These tumors can occur in the stomach and duodenum, but most of them are found in the pancreas. The gastrin causes prolonged hypersecretion of acid, and severe ulcers are produced. Resting gastrin levels do not seem to be elevated in most patients with gastric and duodenal ulcers, but their gastrin responses to feeding are greater than normal. It has been postulated that gastric ulcers are produced by damage to the mucosa when bile-containing duodenal contents reflux into the stomach. There appears to be greater reflux in ulcer patients than in normal subjects, and the greater reflux may be due to a deficient contractile response of the pylorus to CCK and secretin.

More extensive discussions of the problem of peptic ulceration can be found in textbooks of pathophysiology. However, it is pertinent to note that most of the time-honored procedures used in the treatment of ulcers are aimed at decreasing gastric secretion or neutralizing secreted acid. Thus, atropine and other anticholinergic drugs are given to inhibit vagal effects on acid secretion and motility. Antacids such as aluminum hydroxide gels are given to neutralize secreted hydrochloric acid. Frequent feedings of cream provide fat, which inhibits gastric secretion and motility via the duodenal feedback mechanism. A surgical procedure extensively used for the treatment of severe duodenal or prepyloric ulcer is vagotomy combined with removal of the gastrin-secreting antral mucosa. Vagotomy combined with a procedure such as pyloroplasty to prevent gastric stasis is popular, but the vagotomies are incomplete in about 20% of patients, and recurrent ulcers are therefore a problem. Removal of the antral mucosa circumvents this difficulty because, in the absence of the potentiating action of gastrin, the effects of a few remaining vagal fibers on acid secretion are too small to be a problem.

OTHER FUNCTIONS OF THE STOMACH

The stomach has a number of functions in addition to the storage of food and the control of its release into the duodenum. The hydrochloric acid kills many of the ingested bacteria. The parietal cells in the gastric mucosa also secrete **intrinsic factor,** a substance necessary for the absorption of **cyanocobalamin** (vitamin B_{12}) from the small intestine.

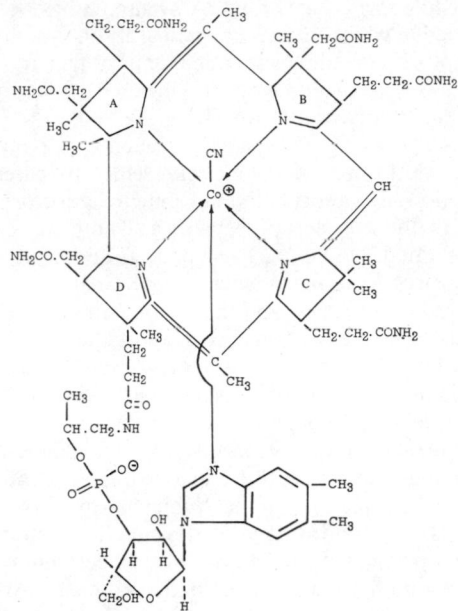

Figure 26–10. Cyanocobalamin (vitamin B_{12}). Empiric formula: $C_{63}H_{88}O_{14}N_{14}PCo$.

Cyanocobalamin (Fig 26–10) is a complex cobalt-containing vitamin that is necessary for normal erythropoiesis. Inadequate absorption of this vitamin causes an anemia characterized by the appearance in the bloodstream of large primitive red cell precursors called **megaloblasts.** A complete remission of the deficiency syndrome occurs when cyanocobalamin is injected parenterally but not when it is administered by mouth unless the intrinsic factor secreted by the gastric mucosa is present. Anemia due to an inadequate dietary intake of cyanocobalamin is very rare, apparently because the minimum daily requirements are quite low and the vitamin is found in most foods of animal origin. The deficiency states seen clinically are therefore due primarily to defective cyanocobalamin absorption. Inadequate absorption may be due to primary intestinal diseases such as sprue, or it may be caused by intrinsic factor deficiency following gastrectomy. In patients with the specific megaloblastic anemia called **pernicious anemia,** there is intrinsic factor deficiency due to an idiopathic atrophy of much of the gastric mucosa.

Intrinsic factor is a glycoprotein with a molecular weight of 60,000. Cyanocobalamin becomes firmly bound to it in the intestine. The intrinsic factor–cyanocobalamin complex then becomes bound to specific receptors in the ileum, and the cyanocobalamin is transferred across the intestinal epithelium. Trypsin is required for this process to be efficient, and absorption is sometimes decreased in patients with pancreatic insufficiency. The details of the absorptive process are uncertain, but it has been suggested that the role of intrinsic factor in the process is to stimulate endocytosis. This would explain how such a large molecule can be absorbed. A syndrome has been described in which there is congenital absence of the ileal receptors for the cyanocobalamin–intrinsic factor complex. In the bloodstream, vitamin B_{12} is bound to a protein, **transcobalamin II.**

In totally gastrectomized patients, the intrinsic factor deficiency must be circumvented by parenteral injection of cyanocobalamin. Protein digestion is normal in the absence of pepsin, and nutrition can be maintained. However, these patients are prone to develop iron deficiency anemia (see Chapter 25) and other abnormalities, and they must eat frequent small meals. Because of rapid absorption of glucose from the intestine and the resultant hyperglycemia and abrupt rise in insulin secretion, gastrectomized patients sometimes develop hypoglycemic symptoms about 2 hours after meals (see Fig 19–20). Weakness, dizziness, and sweating after meals, due in part to hypoglycemia, are part of the picture of the "dumping syndrome," a distressing syndrome that develops in patients in whom portions of the stomach have been removed or the jejunum anastomosed to the stomach. Another cause of the symptoms is rapid entry of hypertonic meals into the intestine; this provokes the movement of so much water into the gut that the resultant reduction of plasma volume is great enough to lead to a decrease in cardiac output.

EXOCRINE PORTION OF THE PANCREAS

The pancreatic juice contains enzymes that are of major importance in digestion (Table 25–1). Its secretion is controlled in part by a reflex mechanism and in part by secretin and CCK, 2 hormones secreted by the intestinal mucosa.

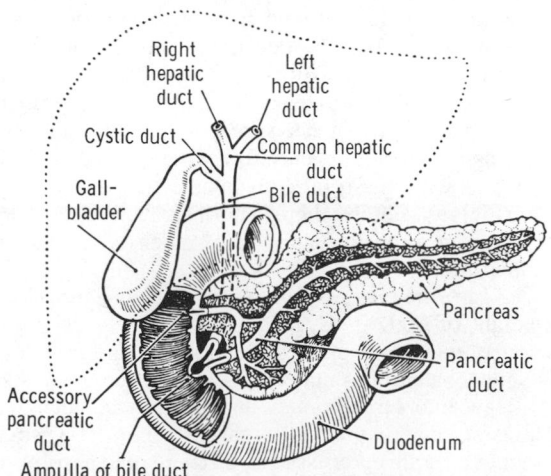

Figure 26–11. Connections of the ducts of the gallbladder, liver, and pancreas. (Reproduced, with permission, from Bell GH, Emslie-Smith D, Paterson CR: *Textbook of Physiology and Biochemistry,* 9th ed. Churchill-Livingstone, 1976.)

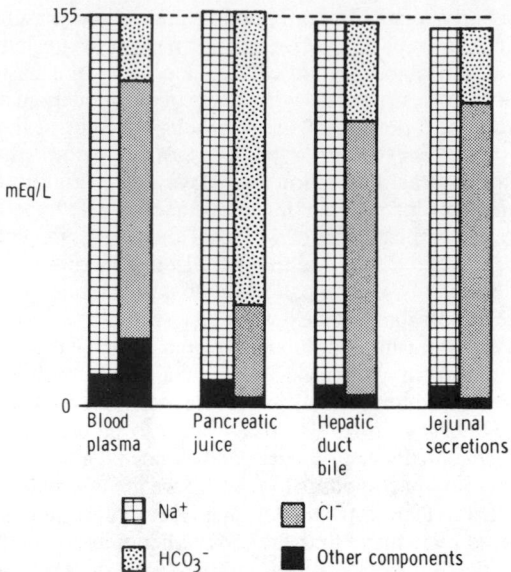

Figure 26–12. Electrolyte composition of blood plasma, pancreatic juice, bile, and intestinal juice. (Redrawn and reproduced, with permission, from Gamble JL: *Chemical Anatomy, Physiology and Pathology of the Extracellular Fluid,* 6th ed. Harvard Univ Press, 1954.)

Anatomic Considerations

The portion of the pancreas that secretes pancreatic juice is a compound alveolar gland resembling the salivary glands. Granules containing the digestive enzymes (**zymogen granules**) are formed in the cell and discharged by exocytosis (see Chapter 1) from the apexes of the cells into the lumens of the pancreatic ducts. The small duct radicles coalesce into a single duct (duct of Wirsung), which usually joins the common bile duct to form the ampulla of Vater (Fig 26–11). The ampulla opens through the duodenal papilla, and its orifice is encircled by the sphincter of Oddi. In some individuals, there is an accessory pancreatic duct (duct of Santorini) that enters the duodenum more proximally. There is said to be a high incidence of nonpatency of the accessory pancreatic duct in patients with gastric acid hypersecretion and duodenal ulcer. It is possible that failure of the alkaline pancreatic secretion to enter the upper part of the duodenum via this duct contributes to the development of the ulcer.

Composition of Pancreatic Juice

The pancreatic juice is alkaline and has a high bicarbonate content (Table 26–5 and Fig 26–12).

Table 26–5. Composition of normal human pancreatic juice.

Cations: Na^+, K^+, Ca^{2+}, Mg^{2+} (pH approximately 8.0)
Anions: HCO_3^-, Cl^-, SO_4^{2-}, HPO_4^{2-}
Digestive enzymes (see Table 25–1)
Albumin and globulin

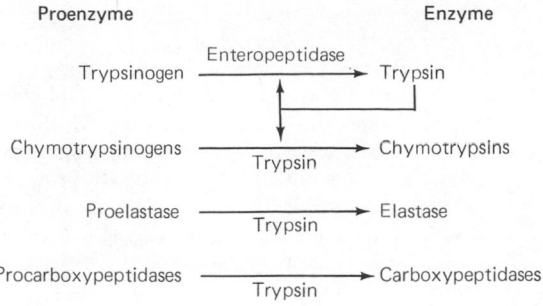

Figure 26–13. Activation of the pancreatic proteases in the duodenal lumen.

About 1500 ml of pancreatic juice are secreted per day. Bile and intestinal juices are also neutral or alkaline, and these 3 secretions neutralize the gastric acid, raising the pH of the duodenal contents to 6.0–7.0. By the time the chyme reaches the jejunum, its reaction is nearly neutral, but the intestinal contents are rarely alkaline.

The powerful protein-splitting enzymes of the pancreatic juice are secreted as inactive proenzymes. Trypsinogen is converted to the active enzyme trypsin by **enteropeptidase,** an enzyme also known as **enterokinase,** which is secreted by the duodenal mucosa. The secretion of enteropeptidase is increased by CCK. Enteropeptidase contains 41% polysaccharide, and this high polysaccharide content apparently prevents it from being digested itself before it can exert its effect. Trypsin converts chymotrypsinogens into chymotrypsins and other proenzymes into active enzymes (Fig 26–13). Trypsin can also activate trypsinogen; therefore, once some trypsin is formed, there is an autocatalytic chain reaction. Enteropeptidase deficiency occurs as a congenital abnormality and leads to protein malnutrition.

The potential danger of the release into the pancreas of a small amount of trypsin is apparent; the resulting chain reaction would produce active enzymes that could digest the pancreas. It is therefore not surprising that the pancreas normally contains a trypsin inhibitor.

Another enzyme activated by trypsin is phospholipase A. This enzyme splits a fatty acid off lecithin, forming lysolecithin. Lysolecithin damages cell membranes. In **acute pancreatitis,** a severe and sometimes fatal disease, there is evidence for activation of phospholipase in the pancreatic ducts, with the formation of lysolecithin from the lecithin that is a normal constituent of bile. This causes disruption of pancreatic tissue and necrosis of surrounding fat. A small amount of the pancreatic α-amylase normally leaks into the circulation, but in acute pancreatitis, the circulating level of this enzyme rises markedly.

Regulation of the Secretion of Pancreatic Juice

Secretion of pancreatic juice is primarily under hormonal control. Secretin causes copious secretion of a very alkaline pancreatic juice poor in enzymes, and it is believed to act on epithelial cells of the small duct radicles rather than on the acinar cells. The duct cells probably secrete water and bicarbonate. Secretin also stimulates bile secretion. CCK causes secretion of pancreatic juice rich in enzymes by causing discharge of zymogen granules from the pancreatic acinar cells. The response to intravenous secretin is shown in Fig 26–14. Note that as the volume of pancreatic secretion increases, its Cl^- concentration falls and its HCO_3^- concentration increases. Although HCO_3^- is secreted in the small ducts, it appears to be reabsorbed in the large ducts in exchange for Cl^-. The magnitude of the exchange is inversely proportionate to the rate of flow.

Secretion of pancreatic enzymes is reduced if pancreatic juice is diverted from the intestine, and it has been suggested that pancreatic enzymes are reabsorbed and recycled in a fashion similar to the bile salts (see below). However, if such a recirculation occurs, it is not known how the proteins are reabsorbed whole and reenter pancreatic cells.

Stimulation of the vagi causes secretion of a small amount of pancreatic juice rich in enzymes, an effect that is blocked by atropine and denervation of the pancreas. The effects of secretin and CCK are not. There is some evidence for vagally mediated conditioned reflex secretion of pancreatic juice in response to the sight or smell of food.

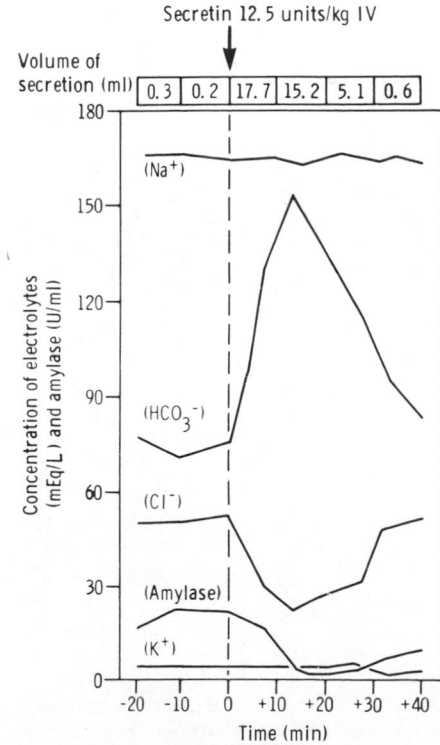

Figure 26–14. Effect of a single dose of secretin on the composition and volume of the pancreatic juice in humans. (Redrawn and reproduced, with permission, from Janowitz HD: Pancreatic secretion. Physiol Physicians 2, No. 11, Nov 1964.)

Bradykinin (see Chapter 31) is liberated during active secretion in the exocrine portion of the pancreas and may be responsible for the increased blood flow that occurs at this time.

LIVER & BILIARY SYSTEM

Bile is secreted by the cells of the liver into the bile duct, which drains into the duodenum. Between meals, the duodenal orifice of this duct is closed and bile flows into the gallbladder, where it is stored. When food enters the mouth, the sphincter around the orifice relaxes; when the gastric contents enter the duodenum, the hormone CCK from the intestinal mucosa causes the gallbladder to contract.

Anatomic Considerations

The intrahepatic portions of the biliary system are shown in Figs 26–15 and 26–16. The intrahepatic bile duct radicles coalesce to form the right and left hepatic ducts, which join outside the liver to form the common hepatic duct. The cystic duct drains the gallbladder. The hepatic duct unites with the cystic duct to form the common bile duct. The common bile duct enters the duodenum at the duodenal papilla. Its orifice is surrounded by the sphincter of Oddi, and it usually unites with the main pancreatic duct just before entering the duodenum (Fig 26–11).

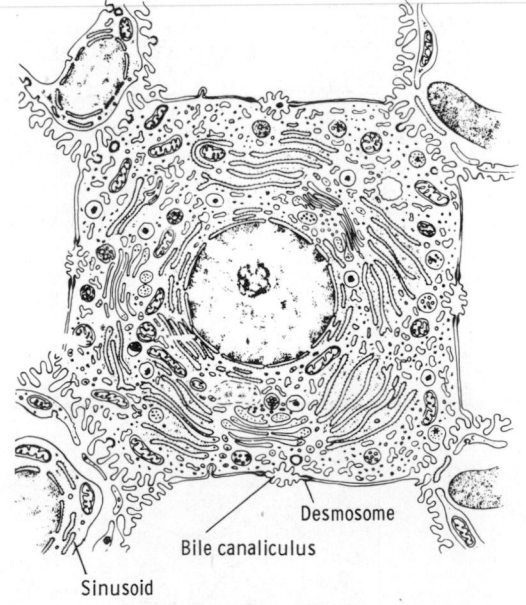

Figure 26–15. Liver cell of a rat, showing relation to blood vessels and bile canaliculi. The desmosomes are areas of membrane thickening and increased density on either side of the bile canaliculi. Notice wide openings in the endothelium of the sinusoids next to the cell. (Redrawn and reproduced, with permission, from Porter KR, Bonneville MA: *Fine Structure of Cells and Tissues,* 4th ed. Lea & Febiger, 1973.)

The walls of the extrahepatic biliary ducts and the gallbladder contain fibrous tissue and smooth muscle. The mucous membrane contains mucous glands and is lined by a layer of columnar cells. In the gallbladder, the mucous membrane is extensively folded; this increases its surface area and gives the interior of the gallbladder a honeycombed appearance. In primates, the mucous membranes of the cystic duct are also folded to form the so-called spiral valves.

Functions of the Liver

The liver, the largest gland in the body, has many complex functions. These include the formation of bile; carbohydrate storage, ketone body formation, and other functions in the control of carbohydrate metabolism; reduction and conjugation of adrenal and gonadal steroid hormones; detoxification of many drugs and toxins; manufacture of plasma proteins; inactivation of polypeptide hormones; urea formation; and many important functions in the metabolism of fat. Discussion of these functions in one place requires that they be taken out of their proper context at considerable cost in terms of clarity and integration of function. Therefore, in this book they are discussed individually in the chapters on the systems of which each is a part. However, for the convenience of the reader, all hepatic functions are also listed in the index under the heading ''liver functions.''

Composition of Bile

Bile is made up of bile salts, bile pigments, and other substances dissolved in an alkaline electrolyte solution that resembles pancreatic juice (Table 26–6, Fig 26–12). About 500 ml are secreted per day. Some of the components of the bile are reabsorbed in the intestine and then excreted again by the liver (**enterohepatic circulation**).

The glucuronides of the **bile pigments,** biliverdin and bilirubin, are responsible for the golden yellow color of bile. The formation of these breakdown products of hemoglobin is discussed in detail in Chapter 27, and their excretion is discussed below.

The **bile salts** are sodium and potassium salts of **bile acids** conjugated to glycine or taurine, a derivative of cystine. Four bile acids isolated from human bile are listed in Fig 26–17. In common with vitamin D, cholesterol, a variety of steroid hormones, and the digitalis glycosides, the bile acids contain the cyclopentanoperhydrophenanthrene nucleus (see Chapter 20). The 2 principal or primary bile acids formed in the liver are cholic acid and chenodeoxycholic acid. In the colon, bacteria convert cholic acid to deoxycholic acid and chenodeoxycholic acid to lithocholic acid. Since they are formed by bacterial action, deoxycholic acid and lithocholic acid are called secondary bile acids. Conjugation of the acids occurs in the liver, and the conjugates—eg, **glycocholic acid** and **taurocholic acid**—form sodium and potassium salts in the alkaline hepatic bile. The bile salts have a number of important actions. They combine with lipids to form micelles, water-soluble complexes from which the lipids can be

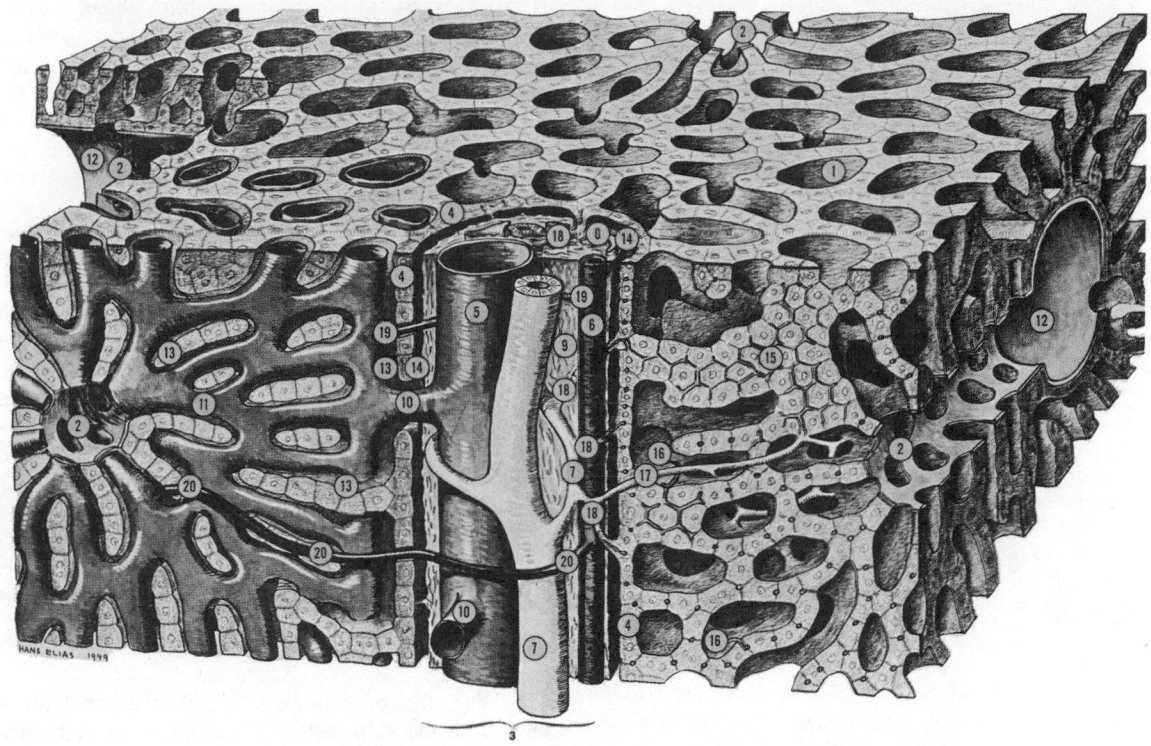

1 Lacuna	9 Periportal connective tissue	16 Bile canaliculi on the surface of
2 Central veins	10 Inlet venules	liver plates (not frequent)
3 Portal canal	11 Sinusoids	17 Intralobular cholangiole
4 Limiting plate	12 Sublobular vein	18 Cholangioles in portal canals
5 Portal vein	13 Perisinusoidal space of Disse	19 Arterial capillary emptying into
6 Hepatic artery	14 Periportal space of Mall	paraportal sinusoid
7 Bile ducts	15 Bile canaliculi within liver	20 Arterial capillary emptying into
8 Lymph vessel	plates	intralobular sinusoid

Figure 26–16. Synopsis of the structure of the normal human liver. (Reproduced, with permission, from Elias H in: *Research in the Service of Medicine*. Vol 37, 1953. Copyright © GD Searle & Co.)

more easily absorbed. This action is called their **hydrotropic** effect. They reduce surface tension and, in conjunction with phospholipids and monoglycerides, are responsible for the emulsification of fat preparatory to its digestion and absorption in the small intestine (see Chapter 25). They also play a role in activating lipases in the intestines.

Table 26–6. Composition of human hepatic duct bile.

Water	97.0%
Bile salts	0.7%
Bile pigments	0.2%
Cholesterol	0.06%
Inorganic salts	0.7%
Fatty acids	0.15%
Lecithin	0.1%
Fat	0.1%
Alkaline phosphatase	...

Cholic acid

	Group at Position			Percent in
	3	7	12	Human Bile
Cholic acid	OH	OH	OH	50
Chenodeoxycholic acid	OH	OH	H	30
Deoxycholic acid	OH	H	OH	15
Lithocholic acid	OH	H	H	5

Figure 26–17. Bile acids isolated from human bile. The numbers in the formula for cholic acid refer to the positions in the steroid ring.

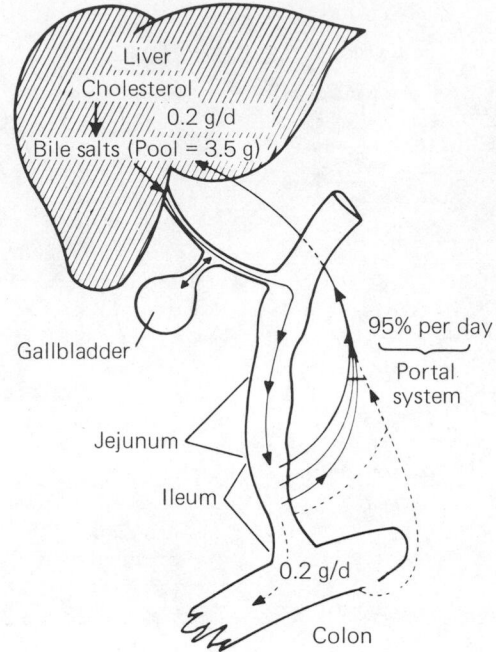

Figure 26–18. Enterohepatic circulation of bile salts. The solid lines entering the portal system represent bile salts of hepatic origin, whereas the dashed lines represent bile salts resulting from bacterial action. (Courtesy of M Tyor. Modified from Dunphy JE, Way LW [editors]: *Current Surgical Diagnosis & Treatment,* 3rd ed. Lange, 1977.)

Ninety to 95% of the bile salts are absorbed from the terminal ileum by an extremely efficient active transport process (Fig 26–18). The remaining 5% enter the colon and are converted to the salts of deoxycholic acid and lithocholic acid. Lithocholate is relatively insoluble and is mostly excreted in the stools, but deoxycholate is absorbed. The absorbed bile salts are transported back to the liver in the portal vein and reexcreted in the bile (enterohepatic circulation). The normal rate of bile salt synthesis is 0.2–0.4 g/d. The total bile salt pool of approximately 3.5 g recycles repeatedly via the enterohepatic circulation; it has been calculated that the entire pool recycles twice per meal and 6–8 times per day. When bile is excluded from the intestine, as much as 25% of ingested fat appears in the feces. There is also severe malabsorption of fat-soluble vitamins.

Bilirubin Metabolism & Excretion

Most of the bilirubin formed in the tissues by the breakdown of hemoglobin (see Chapter 27) is bound to albumin in the circulation. Free bilirubin enters liver cells, where it is bound to cytoplasmic proteins (Fig 26–19). It is next conjugated to glucuronic acid in a reaction catalyzed by the enzyme **glucuronyl transferase.** This enzyme is located primarily in the smooth endoplasmic reticulum. Each bilirubin molecule binds 2 glucuronic acid molecules. The source of the glucuronic acid is uridine diphosphoglucuronic acid

(UDPGA). The bilirubin glucuronide, which is more water-soluble than the free bilirubin, is then transported against a concentration gradient by a presumably active process into the bile canaliculi. Some of the bilirubin glucuronide escapes into the blood, where it is bound less tightly to albumin than free bilirubin, and is excreted in the urine. Most of the bilirubin glucuronide passes via the bile ducts to the intestine.

The intestinal mucosa is relatively impermeable to conjugated bilirubin but is permeable to unconjugated bilirubin and to urobilinogens, a series of colorless derivatives of bilirubin formed by the action of bacteria in the intestine. Consequently, some of the bile pigments and urobilinogens are reabsorbed in the portal circulation. Some of the reabsorbed substances are again excreted by the liver (enterohepatic circulation), but small amounts of urobilinogens enter the general circulation and are excreted in the urine.

The total plasma bilirubin normally includes free bilirubin plus conjugated bilirubin. The free bilirubin is measured as the indirect-reacting bilirubin; the conjugated bilirubin is measured as the direct-reacting bilirubin.

Jaundice

When free or conjugated bilirubin accumulates in the blood, the skin, scleras, and mucous membranes turn yellow. This yellowness is known as **jaundice** (icterus) and is usually detectable when the total plasma bilirubin is greater than 2 mg/dl. Hyperbilirubinemia may be due to (1) excess production (hemolytic anemia, etc); (2) decreased uptake of bilirubin into hepatic cells; (3) disturbed intracellular protein binding or conjugation; (4) disturbed secretion of bilirubin into the bile canaliculi; or (5) intrahepatic or extrahepatic bile duct obstruction. When it is due to processes (1)–(4), the free bilirubin rises, and it is primarily the indirect-reacting bilirubin that is elevated. When it is due to bile duct obstruction, bilirubin

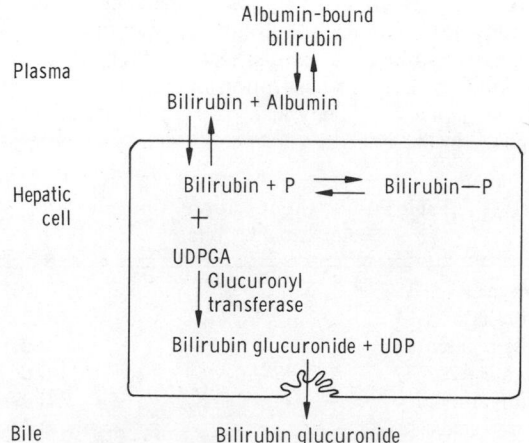

Figure 26–19. Metabolism of bilirubin in the liver. P, intracellular binding proteins; UDPGA, uridine diphosphoglucuronic acid; UDP, uridine diphosphate.

glucuronide regurgitates into the blood, and it is predominantly the direct-reacting component of the plasma bilirubin that is elevated.

Other Substances Conjugated by Glucuronyl Transferase

The glucuronyl transferase system in the smooth endoplasmic reticulum catalyzes the formation of the glucuronides of a variety of substances in addition to bilirubin. The list includes steroids (see Chapters 20 and 23) and various drugs. These other compounds can compete with bilirubin for the enzyme system when they are present in appreciable amounts. In addition, several barbiturates, antihistamines, anticonvulsants, and other compounds have been found to cause marked proliferation of the smooth endoplasmic reticulum in the hepatic cells, with a concurrent increase in hepatic glucuronyl transferase activity. Phenobarbital has been used successfully for the treatment of a congenital disease in which there is a relative deficiency of glucuronyl transferase (type 2 UDP glucuronyl transferase deficiency).

Other Substances Excreted in the Bile

Cholesterol and alkaline phosphatase are excreted in the bile. In patients with jaundice due to intra- or extrahepatic obstruction of the bile duct, the blood levels of these 2 substances usually rise; a much smaller rise is generally seen when the jaundice is due to nonobstructive hepatocellular disease. Adrenocortical and other steroid hormones and a number of drugs are excreted in the bile and subsequently reabsorbed (enterohepatic circulation). The dye sulfobromophthalein (Bromsulphalein, BSP) is removed from the bloodstream by the liver cells and excreted in the bile. Its rate of removal from the circulation is used as a test of hepatic function. This rate depends not only on the functional capacity of the liver cells but also on the hepatic blood flow.

Functions of the Gallbladder

In normal individuals, bile flows into the gallbladder when the sphincter of Oddi is closed. In the gallbladder, the bile is concentrated by absorption of water. The degree of this concentration is shown by the increase in the concentration of solids (Table 26–7); liver bile is 97% water, whereas the average water content of gallbladder bile is 89%. When the bile duct and cystic duct are clamped, the intrabiliary pressure rises to about 320 mm of bile in 30 minutes, and bile secretion stops. However, when the bile duct is

clamped and the cystic duct is left open, water is reabsorbed in the gallbladder, and the intrabiliary pressure rises only to about 100 mm of bile in several hours. Acidification of the bile appears to be another function of the gallbladder (Table 26–7).

Regulation of Biliary Secretion

When food enters the mouth, the resistance of the sphincter of Oddi decreases. Fatty acids in the duodenum release CCK, which causes gallbladder contraction. Acid, the products of protein digestion, and Ca^{2+} also stimulate the secretion of CCK. Substances that cause contraction of the gallbladder are called **cholagogues.**

The production of bile is increased by stimulation of the vagus nerves and by the hormone secretin, which increases the water and HCO_3^- content of bile. Substances that increase the secretion of bile are known as **choleretics.** Bile salts themselves are among the most important physiologic choleretics. The bile salts reabsorbed from the intestine actually inhibit the synthesis of new bile acids, but they themselves are promptly secreted, and they markedly increase bile flow.

Effects of Cholecystectomy

The periodic discharge of bile from the gallbladder aids digestion but is not essential for it. Cholecystectomized patients maintain good health and nutrition with a constant slow discharge of bile into the duodenum, although eventually the bile duct becomes somewhat dilated, and more bile tends to enter the duodenum after eating than at other times. Cholecystectomized patients can even tolerate fried foods quite well, although they generally must avoid foods that are particularly high in fat content.

Cholecystography

Certain radiopaque iodine-containing dyes such as tetraiodophenolphthalein are excreted in the bile and concentrated with the bile in the gallbladder. When the gallbladder contains an adequate concentration of such a dye, it can be visualized by x-ray (**cholecystography**). To determine if the gallbladder is capable of normal contraction, a fatty meal is fed. CCK is released and the gallbladder contracts, the size of its x-ray shadow normally decreasing to less than one-third of its original size within 30 minutes. When administered intravenously, certain other radiopaque dyes are excreted in the bile in sufficient quantities to permit x-ray visualization of the bile ducts (**intravenous cholangiography**).

Gallstones

Stones form in the gallbladder or bile ducts when a substance that is not normally present appears in the bile or when the relative composition of the bile changes so that a normal constituent precipitates. For example, calcium bilirubinate stones form if the conjugated bilirubin in the bile is deconjugated by the action of the β-glucuronidase found in certain bacteria.

Table 26–7. Comparison of human hepatic duct bile and gallbladder bile.

	Hepatic Duct Bile	Gallbladder Bile
Percent of solids	2–4	10–12
Bile salts (mmol/L)	10–20	50–200
pH	7.8–8.6	7.0–7.4

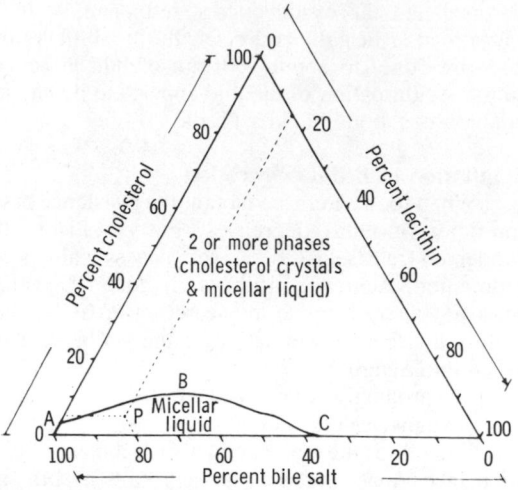

Figure 26–20. Cholesterol solubility in bile as a function of the proportions of lecithin, bile salts, and cholesterol. In bile which has a composition described by any point below line ABC (eg, point P), cholesterol is solely in micellar solution; points above line ABC describe bile in which there are cholesterol crystals as well. (Reproduced, with permission, from Small DM: Gallstones. N Engl J Med 279:588, 1968.)

The free bilirubin combines with calcium, and calcium bilirubinate is highly insoluble in bile. Cholesterol stones form when the proportions of cholesterol, lecithin, and bile salts in bile are altered. Cholesterol is normally present in bile in micelles made up of lecithin and bile salts, and relatively slight changes in bile composition lead to crystal formation (Fig 26–20). The crystals then gradually coalesce to form stones.

Gallstones occur in 10–20% of the population, and in western societies, 85% of the stones are cholesterol stones. It follows from Fig 26–20 that if the proportion of bile salts in the bile can be increased, it should be possible to dissolve cholesterol gallstones. Chenodeoxycholic acid and ursodeoxycholic acid, a bile acid isolated from polar bear bile, have been fed to patients for this purpose with encouraging results. However, the complications of bile acid treatment have not yet been fully evaluated, and the treatment must still be regarded as experimental.

SMALL INTESTINE

In the small intestine, the intestinal contents are mixed with the secretions of the mucosal cells and with pancreatic juice and bile. Digestion, which begins in the mouth and stomach, is completed in the lumen and mucosal cells of the small intestine, and the products of digestion are absorbed, along with most of the vitamins and fluid. The small intestine is presented with about 9 liters of fluid per day—2 liters from dietary sources and 7 liters of gastrointestinal secretions (Table 25–3); however, only 1–2 liters pass into the colon.

Anatomic Considerations

The general arrangement of the muscular layers, nerve plexuses, and mucosa in the small intestine is shown in Fig 26–1. The first portion of the duodenum is sometimes called the duodenal cap, or bulb. It is the region struck by the acid gastric contents squirted through the pylorus and is a common site of peptic

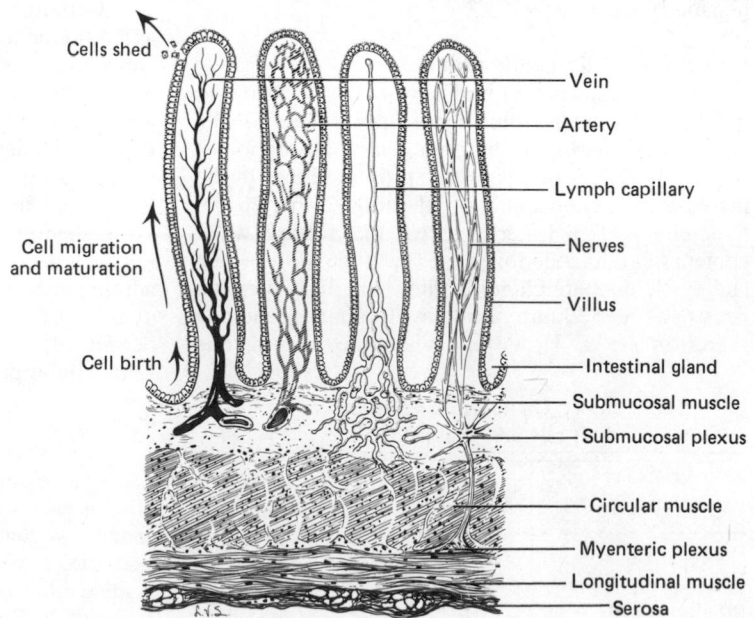

Figure 26–21. Diagrammatic section of the wall of the human small intestine. For clarity, the villi show separately, from left to right, venous drainage, arterial blood supply, lymphatic drainage, and nerve supply.

Table 26–8. Lengths of various segments of the gastrointestinal tract as measured by intubation in living humans.*

Segment	Mean Length (cm)
Duodenum	22
Jejunum and ileum	258
Colon	110

*Data from Blankenhorn DH, Hirsch J, Ahrens EH Jr: Transintestinal intubation. Proc Soc Exp Biol Med 88:356, 1955.

ulceration. At the ligament of Treitz, the duodenum becomes the jejunum. Arbitrarily, the upper 40% of the small intestine below the duodenum is called the jejunum and the lower 60% the ileum, although there is no sharp anatomic boundary between the two. The ileocecal valve marks the point where the ileum ends in the colon.

The small intestine is shorter during life than it is in cadavers because it relaxes and elongates after death. In living humans, the distance from the pylorus to the ileocecal valve is about 280 cm (Table 26–8).

The mucosa of the small intestine contains **solitary lymph nodules** and, especially in the ileum, **aggregated lymphatic nodules** (Peyer's patches) along the antimesenteric border. Throughout the small intestine there are simple tubular **intestinal glands** (crypts of Lieberkühn). In the duodenum there are, in addition, the small, coiled acinotubular **duodenal glands** (Brunner's glands). The **enterochromaffin cells** in the mucosa of the intestine secrete serotonin (see Chapter 15). These cells are often located deep in the intestinal glands. There are many valvelike folds **(valvulae conniventes)** in the mucous membrane.

Throughout the length of the small intestine, the mucous membrane is covered by **villi** (Fig 26–21). There are 20–40 villi per mm² of mucosa. Each intestinal villus is a fingerlike projection, 0.5–1 mm long, covered by a single layer of columnar epithelium and containing a network of capillaries and a lymphatic vessel **(lacteal).** Fine extensions of the smooth muscle of the submucosa run longitudinally up each villus to its tip. The free edges of the cells of the epithelium of the villi are divided into minute **microvilli** (Fig 26–22),which form a **brush border.** The cells are connected to each other by tight junctions. The outer layer of the cell membrane of the mucosal cells contains many of the enzymes involved in the digestive processes initiated by salivary, gastric, and pancreatic enzymes. Enzymes found in this membrane include various disaccharidases, peptidases, and enzymes involved in the breakdown of nucleic acids (see Chapter 25). The brush border is lined on its luminal side by an amorphous layer called the glycocalyx, which is rich in neutral and amino sugars and may serve a protective function.

The absorptive surface of the small intestine is increased about 600-fold by the valvulae conniventes, villi, and microvilli. It has been estimated that the inner surface area of a mucosal cylinder the size of the small intestine would be about 0.33 m², that the valvulae increase the surface area to 1.0 m², that the villi increase it to 10 m², and that the microvilli increase it to 200 m².

The mucosal cells in the small intestine are formed from mitotically active undifferentiated cells in the crypts of Lieberkühn. They migrate up to the tips of the villi, where they are sloughed into the intestinal lumen in large numbers (Fig 26–21). The average life of mucosal cells is 5 days, and the "secretion" of protein into the lumen due to cell sloughing has been calculated to be as great as 30 g/d. Mucosal cells are also rapidly sloughed and replaced in the stomach.

Intestinal Motility

The contractions of the small intestine are coordinated by the **small bowel slow wave,** a wave of smooth muscle depolarization that moves caudally from the duodenum in the longitudinal smooth muscle. The frequency of the slow waves decreases from about 12/min in the jejunum to about 9/min in the ileum.

The movements of the small intestine mix and churn the intestinal contents, or **chyme,** and propel it toward the large intestine. There are 2 types of movement, segmentation contractions and peristaltic waves. Both occur in the absence of extrinsic innervation but require an intact myenteric nerve plexus. **Segmentation contractions** are ringlike contractions that appear at fairly regular intervals along the gut, then disappear and are replaced by another set of ring contractions in the segments between the previous

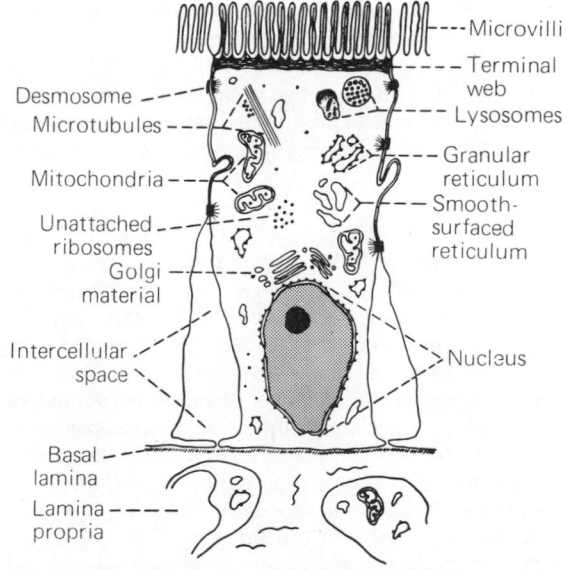

Figure 26–22. Diagram of mucosal cells from human small intestine. Note microvilli, tight connections of cells at mucosal edge (desmosomes), and space between cells at base (intercellular space). (Reproduced, with permission, from Trier JS: Structure of the mucosa of the small intestine as it relates to intestinal function. Fed Proc 26:1391, 1967.)

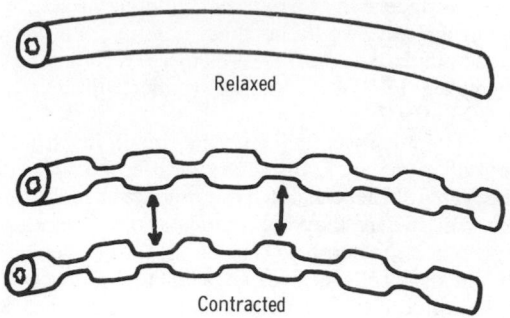

Figure 26–23. Diagram of segmentation contractions of the intestine. Arrows indicate how areas of relaxation become areas of constriction and vice versa.

contractions (Fig 26–23). They move the chyme to and fro and increase its exposure to the mucosal surface.

Peristaltic waves move the chyme along the intestine. When the intestinal wall is stretched, a deep circular contraction (peristaltic wave) forms behind the point of stimulation and passes along the intestine toward the rectum at rates varying from 2 to 25 cm/s. This response to stretch is called the **myenteric reflex.** It was originally believed that each peristaltic wave was preceded by a wave of smooth muscle relaxation, but such relaxation is often absent. Peristaltic waves differ in intensity and in the distance they travel. Very intense peristaltic waves called **peristaltic rushes** are not seen in normal individuals but do occur when the intestine is obstructed. Weak antiperistalsis is sometimes seen in the colon, but most waves pass regularly in an oral-caudal direction. Removal and resuture of a segment of intestine in its original position does not block progression, and waves will even cross a small gap where the intestine has been replaced by a plastic tube. However, if an intestinal segment is reversed and sewed back into place, peristalsis stops at the reversed segment.

Serotonin has been shown to be synthesized and bound in the myenteric plexus, and it has been suggested that it is the mediator at the junctions between neurons of the myenteric plexus. Substance P is found in high concentrations in the intestine and also may play a role as a synaptic mediator in the myenteric reflex arc. The amount of this polypeptide in the different segments of the intestine parallels the number of ganglion cells in the myenteric and submucous plexuses, and in disease states in which the number of ganglion cells is low in a particular region, there is a parallel local decline in substance P content. Enkephalins are also found in the intestine. These possible synaptic mediators are discussed in more detail and their function in the brain is considered in Chapter 15.

Regulation of Intestinal Secretion

Brunner's glands in the duodenum secrete a thick alkaline mucus that probably helps protect the duodenal mucosa from the gastric acid. The intestinal glands secrete an isotonic fluid. Most of the enzymes usually found in this secretion are in desquamated mucosal cells; cell-free intestinal juice probably contains few if any enzymes. Gastrointestinal hormones such as VIP (see above) appear to stimulate the secretion of intestinal juice. Vagal stimulation increases the secretion of Brunner's glands but probably has no effect on that of the intestinal glands.

The Malabsorption Syndrome

The digestive and absorptive functions of the small intestine are essential for life. Removal of short segments of the jejunum or ileum generally does not cause severe symptoms, and there is compensatory hypertrophy and hyperplasia of the remaining mucosa, with gradual return of the absorptive function toward normal **(intestinal adaptation).** However, when more than 50% of the small intestine is resected or bypassed, the absorption of nutrients and vitamins is so compromised that it is very difficult to prevent malnutrition and wasting. Various disease processes also impair absorption (Table 26–9). The pattern of deficiencies that results is sometimes called the **malabsorption syndrome.** This pattern varies somewhat with the cause, but it can include deficient absorption of amino acids, with marked body wasting and, eventually, hypoproteinemia and edema. Carbohydrate and fat absorption is also depressed. Because of the defective fat absorption, the fat-soluble vitamins (vitamins A, D, E, and K) are not absorbed in adequate amounts. The amount of fat and protein in the stools is increased, and the stools become bulky, pale, foul-smelling, and greasy **(steatorrhea).**

The increased gastric acid secretion produced by intestinal resection has been mentioned above. Resection of the ileum prevents the absorption of bile acids, and this leads in turn to deficient fat absorption. It also causes diarrhea because the unabsorbed bile salts enter the colon, where they inhibit the absorption of Na^+ and water. For this reason, and because the capacity of the jejunum to adapt is less than that of the ileum, distal small bowel resection causes a greater degree of malabsorption than removal of a comparable length of

Table 26–9. Disease processes associated with malabsorption.*

Abnormalities of digestion in the intestinal lumen
Inadequate lipolysis
Decreased conjugated bile salts
Abnormalities of mucosal cell transport
Nonspecific (tropical sprue, celiac disease, etc)
Specific (deficiency of various disaccharidases, etc)
Abnormalities of fat transport in intestinal lymphatics
Other
Hypoparathyroidism
Carcinoid
Dysgammaglobulinemia

*Based on Sleisenger MH, Brandborg LL: *Malabsorption.* Saunders, 1977.

proximal small bowel. Other complications of intestinal resection or bypass include hypocalcemia, arthritis, hyperuricemia, and fatty infiltration of the liver, followed by cirrhosis. Operations in which large segments of the small intestine are bypassed have been recommended for the treatment of obesity, but in view of their complications and dangers, they should not be undertaken lightly.

The defective intestinal function in tropical sprue is apparently due in part to folic acid deficiency. However, the intestinal changes in experimentally produced folic acid deficiency are less intense than those in tropical sprue, and patients with tropical sprue respond characteristically to treatment with antibiotics such as tetracycline. In celiac disease, the absorption defect is apparently caused by a congenital abnormality in the cells of the intestinal mucosa, which are harmed by the peptides formed by hydrolysis of gluten, the principal protein in wheat. When gluten is omitted from the diet, bowel function is generally restored to normal.

Adynamic Ileus

When the intestines are traumatized, there is a decrease in intestinal motility due to direct inhibition of smooth muscle. When the peritoneum is irritated, there is reflex inhibition due to increased discharge of adrenergic fibers in the splanchnic nerves. Both types of inhibition operate to cause **paralytic,** or **adynamic, ileus** after abdominal operations. Because of the diffuse decrease in peristaltic activity in the small intestine, its contents are not propelled into the colon, and it becomes irregularly distended by pockets of gas and fluid. Adynamic ileus can be relieved by passing a tube through the nose down to the small intestine and aspirating the fluid and gas for a few days until the viscera heal and peristalsis returns.

Mechanical Obstruction of the Small Intestine

Localized mechanical obstruction of the small intestine causes severe cramping pain **(intestinal colic),** whereas adynamic ileus is often painless. The segment of intestine above the point of mechanical obstruction dilates and becomes filled with fluid and gas. The pressure in the segment rises, and the blood vessels in its wall are compressed, causing local ischemia. Activity in visceral afferent nerve fibers from the distended segment causes sweating, a drop in blood pressure, and severe vomiting, with resultant metabolic alkalosis and dehydration. If the obstruction is not relieved, the condition can be fatal.

COLON

The main function of the colon is absorption of water, sodium, and other minerals. By removal of about 90% of the fluid, it converts the 1000–2000 ml of isotonic chyme that enter it each day from the ileum

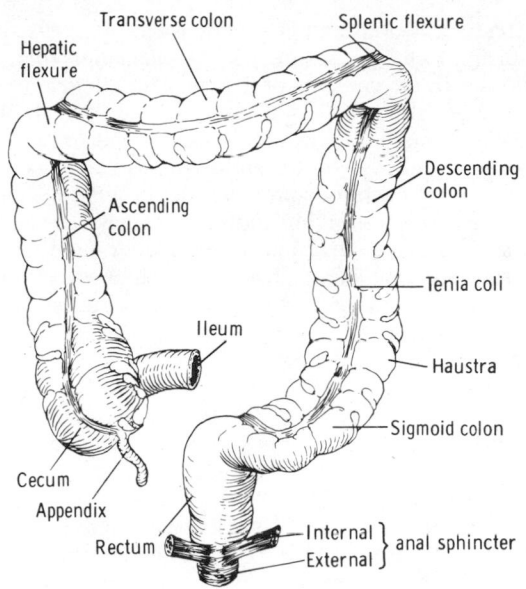

Figure 26–24. The human colon.

to about 150 g of semisolid feces. Certain vitamins are also absorbed, and some of them are synthesized by the large numbers of bacteria that grow in the colon.

Anatomic Considerations

The diameter of the colon is greater than that of the small intestine. The fibers of the external muscular layer are collected into 3 longitudinal bands, the **teniae coli.** Because these bands are shorter than the rest of the colon, the wall of the colon forms outpouchings **(haustra)** between the teniae (Fig 26–24). There are no villi on the mucosa. The colonic glands are short inward projections of the mucosa that secrete mucus. Solitary lymph follicles are present, especially in the cecum and appendix.

Motility & Secretion of the Colon

The portion of the ileum containing the ileocecal valve projects slightly into the cecum, so that increases in colonic pressure squeeze it shut whereas increases in ileal pressure open it. Therefore, it effectively prevents reflux of colonic contents into the ileum. It is normally closed. Each time a peristaltic wave reaches it, it opens briefly, permitting some of the ileal chyme to squirt into the cecum. If the valve is resected in experimental animals, the chyme enters the colon so rapidly that absorption in the small intestine is reduced; however, a significant reduction does not occur in humans. When food leaves the stomach, the cecum relaxes and the passage of chyme through the ileocecal valve increases **(gastroileal reflex).** This is presumably a vagal reflex, although there is some argument about whether vagal stimulation affects the ileocecal valve. Sympathetic stimulation increases the tonic contraction of the valve.

The movements of the colon include segmentation contractions and peristaltic waves like those occurring in the small intestine. Segmentation contractions mix the contents of the colon and, by exposing more of the contents to the mucosa, facilitate absorption. Peristaltic waves propel the contents toward the rectum, although weak antiperistalsis is sometimes seen. A third type of contraction that occurs only in the colon is the **mass action contraction,** in which there is simultaneous contraction of the smooth muscle over large confluent areas. These contractions occur in the descending and sigmoid portion and serve to empty the colon rapidly. They are the predominant contraction force during defecation.

The movements of the colon are coordinated by a slow wave of the colon. The frequency of this wave, unlike the wave in the small intestine, increases along the colon, from about 2/min at the ileocecal valve to 6/min at the sigmoid.

Mucus secretion by the colonic glands is stimulated by contact between the gland cells and the colonic contents. No hormonal or neural link is involved in the basic secretory response, although some additional secretion may be produced by local reflex responses via the pelvic and splanchnic nerves. No digestive enzymes are secreted in the colon.

Transit Time in the Small Intestine & Colon

The first part of a test meal reaches the cecum in about 4 hours, and all of the undigested portions have entered the colon in 8 or 9 hours. On the average, the first remnants of the meal reach the hepatic flexure in 6 hours, the splenic flexure in 9 hours, and the pelvic colon in 12 hours. From the pelvic colon to the anus, transport is much slower. As much as 25% of the residue of a test meal may still be in the rectum in 72 hours. When small colored beads are fed with a meal, an average of 70% of them are recovered in the stool in 72 hours; but total recovery requires more than a week.

Absorption in the Colon

The absorptive capacity of the mucosa of the large intestine is great. Na^+ is actively transported out of the colon, and water follows along the osmotic gradient thus generated. There is some net secretion of K^+ and HCO_3^- into the colon. The absorptive capacity of the colon makes rectal instillation a practical route for drug administration, especially in children. Many compounds, including anesthetics, sedatives, tranquilizers, and steroids, are absorbed rapidly by this route. Some of the water in an enema is absorbed, and if the volume of an enema is large, absorption may be rapid enough to cause water intoxication. Coma and death due to water intoxication have been reported following tap water enemas in children with megacolon.

Feces

The stools contain inorganic material, undigested plant fibers, bacteria, and water. Their composition (Table 26–10) is relatively unaffected by variations in diet because a large fraction of the fecal mass is of nondietary origin. This is why appreciable amounts of

Table 26–10. Approximate composition of feces on an average diet.

	Percentage of Total Weight
Water	75
Solids	25

	Percentage of Total Solids
Cellulose and other indigestible fiber	Variable
Bacteria	30
Inorganic material (mostly calcium and phosphates)	15
Fat and fat derivatives	5

Also desquamated mucosal cells, mucus, and small amounts of digestive enzymes

feces continue to be passed during prolonged starvation.

Intestinal Bacteria

The chyme in the jejunum normally contains few if any bacteria. There are more organisms in the ileum, but it is only the colon that regularly contains large numbers of bacteria. The reason for the relative sterility of the jejunal contents is unsettled, although gastric acid and the comparatively rapid transit of the chyme through this region may inhibit bacterial growth.

The organisms present in the colon include not only bacilli such as *Escherichia coli* and *Enterobacter aerogenes* but also pleomorphic organisms such as *Bacteroides fragilis,* cocci of various types, and organisms such as gas gangrene bacilli, which can cause serious disease in tissues outside the colon. Great masses of bacteria are passed in the stool. At birth, the colon is sterile, but the intestinal bacterial flora becomes established early in life.

The effects of the intestinal bacteria on their host are complex, some being definitely beneficial and others possibly harmful.

Antibiotics improve growth rates in a variety of species, including humans; and the addition of small amounts of antibiotics to the diets of domestic animals has become almost routine. Animals raised under sanitary but not germ-free conditions grow faster than controls. They assimilate food better and do not require certain amino acids that are essential dietary constituents in other animals. They also have larger litters and a lower neonatal death rate.

The reason for the improved growth is unsettled. Nutritionally important substances such as ascorbic acid, cyanocobalamin, and choline are utilized by some intestinal bacteria. On the other hand, some enteric organisms synthesize vitamin K and a number of B complex vitamins. Appreciable quantities of the folic acid, biotin, vitamin K, and thiamine produced in the intestine were once thought to be absorbed. However, the experiments that led to this conclusion were largely performed on rats, and rats normally eat their own feces. When such coprophagy is prevented, only the folic acid produced by the bacteria can be shown to be absorbed in significant amounts.

The brown color of the stools is due to pigments formed from the bile pigments by the intestinal bacteria. When bile fails to enter the intestine, the stools become white (**acholic stools**). Bacteria produce some of the gases in the flatus (see above). Organic acids formed from carbohydrates by the bacteria are responsible for the slightly acid reaction of the stools (pH 5.0–7.0).

A number of amines, including such potentially toxic substances as histamine and tyramine, are formed in the colon by bacterial enzymes that decarboxylate amino acids. At one time, the symptoms seen in constipated patients were blamed on absorption of these amines, but this theory of "autointoxication" has now been thoroughly discredited. Other amines formed by the intestinal bacteria, especially indole and skatole, are responsible in large part for the odor of the feces.

Ammonia is also produced in the colon and absorbed. When the liver is diseased, the ammonia is not removed from the blood, and severe neurologic symptoms result. A similar encephalopathy occurs in at least 20% of patients in whom the portal vein has been anastomosed to the vena cava in order to reduce portal pressure and stop bleeding from dilated esophageal varices. In individuals with liver disease, removal of the colon or its isolation by anastomosing the ileum to the sigmoid has been reported to bring about improvement.

Work with animals raised from birth in a germ-free environment has uncovered further interesting data on the interaction between intestinal bacteria and their hosts. In germ-free guinea pigs, rats, and mice, the cecum becomes greatly enlarged, to the point where it may account for as much as 50% of the animal's weight. There is evidence that the cecal enlargement is due to the retention in the colon of macromolecules from mucus and other sources that are normally degraded by bacterial action. The macromolecules are osmotically active, so water is retained, distending the cecum.

It is now well established that cells in the gut-associated lymphoid tissue are stimulated by intestinal antigens to proliferate and differentiate. These cells enter the circulation but return to the intestinal wall where they differentiate further into plasma cells that secrete immunoglobulins, particularly IgA and IgM (see Chapter 27). These antibodies coat the mucosa and do much to prevent pathogenic organisms from penetrating the intestinal wall.

When normal animals with the usual intestinal bacterial flora are exposed to ionizing radiation, the body defenses that prevent intestinal bacteria from invading the rest of the body break down, and a major cause of death in radiation poisoning is overwhelming sepsis. Germ-free animals have extremely hypoplastic lymphoid tissue and poorly developed immune mechanisms, probably because these mechanisms have never been challenged. However, they are much more resistant to radiation than animals with the usual intestinal flora because they have no intestinal bacteria to cause sepsis.

Dietary Fiber

Adequate nutrition in herbivorous animals depends upon the action of gastrointestinal microorganisms that break down cellulose and related plant carbohydrates. In humans, there is no appreciable digestion of these vegetable products. Cellulose, hemicellulose, and lignin in the diet are important components of the **dietary fiber,** which by definition is all ingested food that reaches the large intestine in an essentially unchanged state. However, various gums, algal polysaccharides, and pectic substances also contribute to dietary fiber.

If the amount of dietary fiber is low, the diet is said to lack **bulk.** Since the amount of material in the colon is small, the colon is inactive and bowel movements are infrequent. So-called bulk laxatives work by providing a larger volume of indigestible material to the colon. It has been claimed that some individuals with chronic constipation have a greater than normal capacity to break down cellulose and related products, thus reducing the residue in their colons.

There has been a recent upsurge of interest in dietary fiber because of epidemiologic evidence indicating that groups of people who live on a diet which contains large amounts of vegetable fiber have a low incidence of diverticulitis, cancer of the colon, diabetes mellitus, and coronary artery disease. However, the relationship between dietary fiber and the incidence of disease is still unsettled and needs further study.

Blind Loop Syndrome

Overgrowth of bacteria within the intestinal lumen can cause definite harmful effects. Such overgrowth occurs when there is stasis of the contents of the small intestine, and it causes macrocytic anemia, malabsorption of cyanocobalamin (vitamin B_{12}), and steatorrhea. Because the condition is prominent in patients with surgically created blind intestinal loops, it has acquired the name **blind loop syndrome;** however, it can occur in any condition that promotes massive bacterial contamination of the small intestine. The cause of the anemia appears to be the cyanocobalamin deficiency, and the deficiency in cyanocobalamin absorption is probably due to uptake of ingested cyanocobalamin by the bacteria. The steatorrhea is probably due to excessive hydrolysis by the bacteria of conjugated bile salts. The important role of bile salts in fat digestion is discussed in Chapter 25.

Defecation

Distention of the rectum with feces initiates reflex contractions of its musculature and the desire to defecate. In humans, the sympathetic nerve supply to the internal (involuntary) anal sphincter is excitatory, whereas the parasympathetic supply is inhibitory. This sphincter relaxes when the rectum is distended. The nerve supply to the striate muscle of the external anal sphincter comes from the pudendal nerve. The sphincter is maintained in a state of tonic contraction. It is relaxed by voluntary action, permitting the reflex contraction of the distended colon to expel the feces. Defecation is therefore a spinal reflex that can be voluntarily inhibited by keeping the external sphincter contracted or facilitated by relaxing the sphincter and contracting the abdominal muscles (straining). Reflex evacuation of the distended rectum occurs in chronic spinal animals and humans if the sacral segments of the spinal cord are intact.

Distention of the stomach by food initiates contractions of the rectum and, frequently, a desire to defecate. This response is called the **gastrocolic reflex,** although there is some evidence that it is due to an action of gastrin on the colon and is not neurally mediated. Because of the response, defecation after meals is the rule in children. In adults, habit and cultural factors play a large role in determining when defecation occurs.

Effects of Colectomy

Humans can survive after total removal of the colon if fluid and electrolyte balance is maintained. When total colectomy is performed, the ileum is brought out through the abdominal wall **(ileostomy)** and the chyme expelled from the ileum is collected in a plastic bag fastened around the opening. If the diet is carefully regulated, the volume of ileal discharge decreases and its consistency increases over a period of time, but care of an ileostomy is at best a time-consuming, difficult job.

Constipation

In bowel-conscious America, the amount of misinformation and undue apprehension about constipation probably exceeds that about any other health topic. Patients with persistent constipation, and particularly those with a recent change in bowel habits, should of course be examined carefully to rule out underlying organic disease. However, many normal humans defecate only once every 2–3 days, even though others defecate once a day and some as often as 3 times a day. Furthermore, the only symptoms caused by constipation are slight anorexia and mild abdominal discomfort and distention. These symptoms are not due to absorption of "toxic substances" because they are promptly relieved by evacuating the rectum and can be reproduced experimentally by distending the rectum with inert material. Other symptoms attributed by the lay public to constipation are due to anxiety or other causes.

Megacolon

The lack of harmful effects of infrequent bowel movements is emphasized by the relative absence for months and even years of symptoms other than abdominal distention, anorexia, and lassitude in children with **aganglionic megacolon** (Hirschsprung's disease). This disease is due to congenital absence of the ganglion cells in both the myenteric and submucous plexuses of a segment of the distal colon. The substance P content of the segment is low. Feces pass the aganglionic region with difficulty, and children with the disease may defecate as infrequently as once every 3 weeks. The condition can be cured if the aganglionic region is resected and the portion of the colon above it anastomosed to the rectum.

About 40% of patients with megacolon have dilated bladders, and 4% have dilated ureters **(megaloureters),** which suggests that some deficiency of the parasympathetic nerve supply to the urinary tract is associated with the intestinal abnormality. A few cases of aganglionic megacolon in which symptoms first developed in adulthood have been reported. In these cases, the loss of ganglion cells was presumably not a congenital defect but an acquired abnormality of unknown cause.

Diarrhea

Severe diarrhea is debilitating and can be fatal, especially in infants. Large amounts of Na^+, K^+, and water are washed out of the colon and the small intestine in the diarrheal stools, causing dehydration, hypovolemia, and, eventually, shock and cardiovascular collapse. A more insidious complication of chronic diarrhea, if fluid balance is maintained, is severe hypokalemia. The K^+ loss is appreciable because the potential difference across the mucosa is greater in the colon than in the ileum, and consequently, the steady-state K^+ concentration of the colonic contents is relatively high (see Chapter 25).

References: Section V.
Gastrointestinal Function

Alpers DH, Sectharam B: Pathophysiology of diseases involving intestinal brush-border proteins. N Engl J Med 296:1047, 1977.

Bortoff A: Myogenic control of intestinal motility. Physiol Rev 56:418, 1976.

Botelho SY, Brooks FP, Shelley WB: *The Exocrine Glands.* Univ of Pennsylvania Press, 1970.

Davenport HW: *A Digest of Digestion,* 2nd ed. Year Book, 1978.

Davenport HW: *Physiology of the Digestive Tract,* 4th ed. Year Book, 1977.

Dowling RH: Cell turnover following small bowel resection and by-pass. Digestion 8:258, 1973.

Dubos R, Schaedler RW: The digestive tract as an ecosystem. Trans Assoc Am Physicians 77:110, 1964.

Forth W, Rummel W: Iron absorption. Physiol Rev 53:724, 1973.

Frizzell RA, Field M, Schultz SG: Sodium-coupled chloride transport by epithelial tissues. Am J Physiol 236:F1, 1979.

Harvey RF: Hormonal control of gastrointestinal motility. Dig Dis 20:523, 1975.

Hofman AF, Thistle JL: Chenodeoxycholic acid: The Mayo Clinic experience. Hosp Pract 9:41, Aug 1974.

Johnson LR (editor): *Gastrointestinal Physiology.* Mosby, 1977.

Kretchmer N: Lactose and lactase. Sci Am 227:70, Oct 1972.

Levitt MD, Bond JH: Volume, composition and source of intestinal gas. Gastroenterology 59:921, 1970.

Mendeloff AI: Dietary fiber and human health. N Engl J Med 297:811, 1977.

Pearse AGE: The gut as an endocrine organ. Br J Hosp Med 11:697, 1974.

Sachs G, Heinz E, Ulrich KJ (editors): *Gastric Secretion.* Academic Press, 1972.

Sachs G, Spenney JG, Lewin M: H^+ transport: Regulation and mechanism in gastric mucosa and membrane vesicles. Physiol Rev 58:106, 1978.

Schmid R: Bilirubin metabolism in man. N Engl J Med 287:703, 1972.

Sleisenger MH, Brandborg LL: *Malabsorption.* Saunders, 1977.

Sleisenger MH, Fordtran JS (editors): *Gastrointestinal Disease: Pathophysiology, Diagnosis, Management.* Saunders, 1973.

Walker WA, Isselbacher KJ: Intestinal antibodies. N Engl J Med 297:767, 1977.

Walsh JH, Grossman MI: Gastrin. N Engl J Med 292:1324, 1975.

Williamson RCN: Intestinal adaptation. N Engl J Med 298:1393, 1978.

Symposium: Nutritional and biochemical aspects of host-microflora interaction. Fed Proc 30:1772, 1971.

Symposium: *Proceedings of the Fourth International Symposium on Gastrointestinal Motility.* Mitchell Press, 1974.

Section VI. Circulation

27 | Circulating Body Fluids

THE CIRCULATORY SYSTEM

The circulatory system is the transport system that supplies substances absorbed from the gastrointestinal tract and O_2 to the tissues, returns CO_2 to the lungs and other products of metabolism to the kidneys, functions in the regulation of body temperature, and distributes hormones and other agents that regulate cell function. The blood, the carrier of these substances, is pumped through a closed system of blood vessels by the heart, which in mammals is really 2 pumps in series with each other. From the left ventricle, blood is pumped through the arteries and arterioles to the capillaries, where the blood equilibrates with the interstitial fluid. The capillaries drain through venules into the veins and back to the right atrium. This is the **major** (or **systemic**) **circulation.** From the right atrium, blood flows to the right ventricle, which pumps it through the vessels of the lungs—the **lesser** (or **pulmonary**) **circulation**—and the left atrium to the left ventricle. In the pulmonary capillaries, the blood equilibrates with the O_2 and CO_2 in the alveolar air. Some tissue fluids enter another system of closed vessels, the lymphatics, which drain lymph via the thoracic duct and the right lymphatic duct into the venous system (the **lymphatic circulation**). The circulation is controlled by multiple regulatory systems that function in general to maintain adequate capillary blood flow—when possible, in all organs, but particularly in the heart and brain.

BLOOD

The cellular elements of the blood—white blood cells, red blood cells, and platelets—are suspended in the plasma. The normal total circulating blood volume is about 8% of the body weight, or 5600 ml in a 70 kg man. About 55% of this volume is plasma.

BONE MARROW

In the adult, red blood cells, many white blood cells, and platelets are formed in the bone marrow. In the fetus, blood cells are also formed in the liver and spleen, and in adults such **extramedullary hematopoiesis** may occur in diseases in which the bone marrow becomes destroyed or fibrosed. In children, blood cells are actively produced in the marrow cavities of all the bones. By age 20, the marrow in the cavities of the long bones, except for the upper humerus and femur, has become inactive (Fig 27–1). Active cellular marrow is called **red marrow;** inactive marrow that is infiltrated with fat is called **yellow marrow.**

The bone marrow is actually one of the largest organs in the body, approaching the size and weight of the liver. It is also one of the most active. Normally, 75% of the cells in the marrow belong to the white blood cell–producing myeloid series, and only 25% are maturing red cells, even though there are over 500 times as many red cells in the circulation as there are white cells. This difference in the marrow probably reflects the fact that the average life span of white cells is short, whereas that of red cells is long.

The bone marrow contains pluripotent uncommitted stem cells and unipotent committed stem cells. The former differentiate into the latter, but the latter, when stimulated, differentiate only into one of the differentiated cell types found in marrow and blood (Fig 27–2). It appears likely that the bone marrow contains pools of committed stem cells for granulocytes, mega-

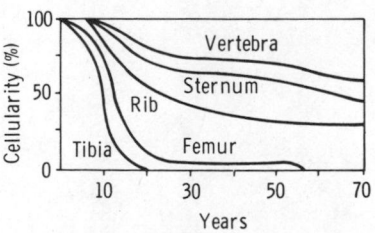

Figure 27–1. Changes in red bone marrow cellularity with age. 100% equals degree of cellularity at birth. (Reproduced, with permission, from Whitby LEH, Britton CJC: *Disorders of the Blood,* 10th ed. Churchill-Livingstone, 1969.)

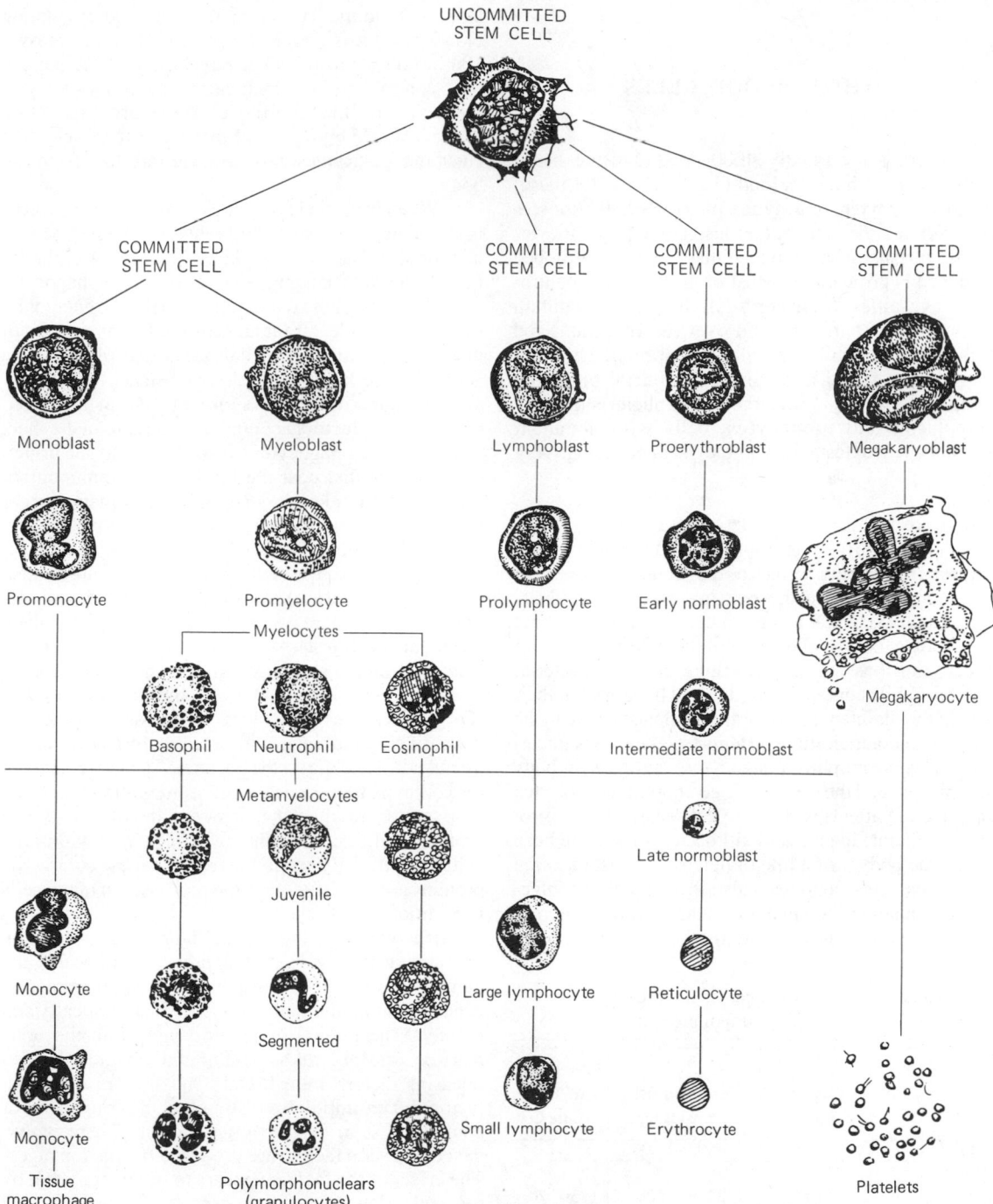

Figure 27–2. The development of the various formed elements of the blood from bone marrow cells. Cells below the horizontal line, except for the late normoblast, may be found in normal peripheral blood. (Modified from Whitby LEH, Britton CJC: *Disorders of the Blood,* 10th ed. Churchill-Livingstone, 1969.)

karyocytes, lymphocytes, and erythrocytes. Granulocytes and macrophages may arise from the same committed stem cells.

WHITE BLOOD CELLS

There are normally 4000–11,000 white blood cells per μl of human blood (Table 27–1). Of these, the **granulocytes,** or **polymorphonuclear leukocytes (PMNs),** are the most numerous. Young granulocytes have horseshoe-shaped nuclei that become multilobed as the cells grow older. Most of them contain neutrophilic granules (**neutrophils**), but a few contain granules that stain with acid dyes (**eosinophils**), and some have basophilic granules (**basophils**). The other 2 cell types found normally in peripheral blood are **lymphocytes,** cells with large, round nuclei and scanty cytoplasm; and **monocytes,** cells with abundant agranular cytoplasm and kidney-shaped nuclei (Fig 27–2).

Functions & Life Cycle of Granulocytes

Neutrophils, eosinophils, and basophils are formed from stem cells in the bone marrow. All granulocytes contain the enzyme **myeloperoxidase.** This enzyme, which has a molecular weight of about 150,000, catalyzes the formation of ClO^- and other hypohalite ions that aid in killing ingested bacteria. The basophils contain histamine and heparin, but their role in the maintenance of normal balance between the clotting and anticlotting systems (see below) is uncertain. The eosinophils phagocytose antigen-antibody complexes, and the circulating eosinophil level is often elevated in patients with allergic diseases. The neutrophils seek out, ingest, and kill bacteria and have been called the body's first line of defense against bacterial infections. The monocytes also invade areas of infection and phagocytose bacteria, other foreign material, and dead cells. They follow the neutrophils into the area of infection and constitute a second line of defense that is quantitatively of greater importance.

The average half-life of a neutrophil in the circulation is 6 hours. To maintain the normal circulating blood level, it is therefore necessary to produce over 100 billion neutrophils per day. Many of the neutrophils enter the tissues, insinuating themselves through the walls of the capillaries by a process called **diapedesis.** Many of those that leave the circulation enter the gastrointestinal tract and are lost from the body.

When bacteria invade the body, the bone marrow is stimulated to produce and release large numbers of neutrophils. Bacterial products interact with plasma factors to produce agents that attract these phagocytic cells to the infected area (**chemotaxis**). The chemotactic agents include 2 fragments formed from proteins of the complement system: kallikrein and plasminogen activator (see below). These 2 substances are breakdown products of the active form of clotting factor XII. Other plasma factors act on the bacteria to make them "tasty" to the phagocytes (**opsonization**). The principal opsonins that coat the bacteria are immunoglobulins of a particular class (IgG) and complement proteins (see below). The neutrophils then actively ingest the bacteria (**phagocytosis**), and the phagocytic vesicles thus formed fuse with the granules of the neutrophils (**degranulation**). Associated with the degranulation is a sharp increase in O_2 uptake and metabolism (**respiratory burst**), with increased activity in the hexose monophosphate shunt and the production of hydrogen peroxide (H_2O_2) and the peroxide radical (O_2^-). The latter 2 products and possibly other O_2 derivatives, combined with the lytic enzymes in the granule, kill and digest the bacteria. The movements of the cell in phagocytosis as well as migration to the site of infection involve the apparent interaction of the proteins actin and myosin (see Chapter 3) within the cell. Indeed, it is becoming clear that these contractile proteins are involved in motile processes in many cells in addition to muscle.

It is worth noting that the number of circulating granulocytes is regulated with precision. In health, the number is held at a constant level; when infection occurs, the number in the blood rises dramatically and rapidly. The release of granulocytes from the bone marrow appears to be stimulated by granulocyte-releasing factors in the blood. One or more additional factors (**granulopoietins**) stimulate the conversion of committed stem cells to granulocytes. There is evidence that such factors are produced by macrophages. The effect of the factors appears to be counteracted by prostaglandins of the E series. It also appears that mature neutrophils may generate a factor that inhibits stem cell conversion, thus providing negative feedback control of the number of circulating granulocytes. However, there is much that is still unknown about the regulation of granulocytopoiesis.

Table 27–1. Normal values for the cellular elements in human blood.

	Cells/μl (average)	Approximate Normal Range	Percentage of Total White Cells
Total WBC	9000	4000–11,000	. . .
Granulocytes			
Neutrophils	5400	3000–6000	50–70
Eosinophils	275	150–300	1–4
Basophils	35	0–100	0.4
Lymphocytes	2750	1500–4000	20–40
Monocytes	540	300–600	2–8
Erythrocytes			
Females	4.8×10^6	. . .	. . .
Males	5.4×10^6	. . .	. . .
Platelets	300,000	200,000–500,000	. . .

Monocytes

The monocytes, like neutrophilic leukocytes, are

actively phagocytic and contain peroxidase and lysosomal enzymes. They enter the circulation from the bone marrow, but after about 24 hours they enter the tissues to become **tissue macrophages.** All of the tissue macrophages, including the Kupffer cells of the liver and the alveolar macrophages in the lung, come from circulating monocytes. The tissue macrophage system has generally been called the **reticuloendothelial system.** The monocytes migrate in response to chemotactic stimuli and engulf and kill bacteria by processes that are generally similar to those occurring in neutrophils. Monocytes may also kill tumor cells after sensitization by lymphocytes, and monocytes synthesize complement and other biologically important substances.

A number of diseases are due to defects of various steps in the phagocytic process. Patients with these diseases are prone to infections that are relatively mild when only the neutrophil system is involved but severe when the monocyte–tissue macrophage system is also involved. In one syndrome (neutrophil hypomotility), actin in the neutrophils does not polymerize normally, and the neutrophils move slowly. In another more serious disease (chronic granulomatous disease), there is a failure to generate O_2^- in both the neutrophils and monocytes and consequent inability to kill many phagocytosed bacteria. In severe congenital glucose-6-phosphate dehydrogenase deficiency, there are multiple infections because of failure to generate the NADPH necessary for O_2^- production. In congenital myeloperoxidase deficiency, microbial killing power is reduced but not absent because most of the oxygen-dependent bactericidal mechanisms remain intact.

Lymphocytes

Some lymphocytes are formed in the bone marrow, but most are formed in the lymph nodes, thymus, and spleen from stem cells that originally come from the bone marrow. Lymphocytes enter the bloodstream for the most part via the lymphatics. It has been calculated that, in humans, 3.5×10^{10} lymphocytes per day enter the circulation via the thoracic duct alone; how-

ever, this count includes cells that reenter the lymphatics and thus traverse the thoracic duct more than once. The effects of adrenocortical hormones on the lymphoid organs, the circulating lymphocytes, and the granulocytes are discussed in Chapter 20. The lymphocytes play a key role in immunity.

IMMUNE MECHANISMS

Types

The body has 2 principal immune defense systems: humoral and cellular. Both react to antigens— usually proteins that are foreign to the body, such as bacteria or foreign tissue. **Humoral immunity** is immunity due to circulating antibodies in the γ globulin fraction of the plasma proteins. It is a major defense against bacterial infections. **Cellular immunity** is mediated in part by lymphocyte products of high molecular weight called **lymphokines** and is responsible for delayed allergic reactions, rejection of transplants of foreign tissue, and rejection of tumor cells. It constitutes a major defense against infections due to viruses, fungi, and a few bacteria such as the tubercle bacillus.

Development of the Immune System

Lymphocyte precursors originate in the yolk sac and migrate into the fetus. Those that populate the thymus (Fig 27–3) become transformed by the environment in this organ into the lymphocytes responsible for cellular immunity (**T lymphocytes**). In birds, the precursors that populate the bursa of Fabricius, a lymphoid structure near the cloaca, become transformed into the lymphocytes responsible for humoral immunity (**B lymphocytes**). There is no bursa in mammals, and it appears that the transformation to B lymphocytes occurs in the fetal liver and possibly the fetal spleen. After residence in the thymus or liver and spleen, many of the T and B lymphocytes migrate to the lymph nodes and bone marrow. T and B lymphocytes are mor-

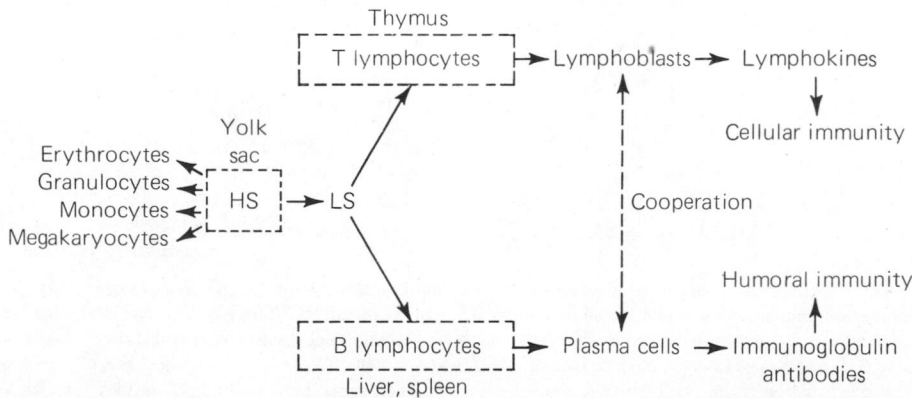

Figure 27–3. Development of the immune system. HS, hematopoietic stem cells; LS, lymphoid stem cells.

phologically indistinguishable but can be identified with special technics. Both types are present throughout life. There is evidence that the maturation of T lymphocytes is promoted by thymic hormones. One of these, a polypeptide extracted from thymic tissues, is called **thymosin.** It contains 108 amino acid residues and is rich in acidic amino acids. Other peptides that affect T cell function have also been isolated from the thymus.

Humoral Immunity

B lymphocytes have receptors on their surfaces for particular antigens. When the antigen binds to the cell, the cell is stimulated to divide, and its daughter cells are transformed into **plasma cells.** These cells secrete large quantities of antibodies into the general circulation. The antibodies circulate in the γ globulin fraction of the plasma (see below) and, like antibodies elsewhere, are called **immunoglobulins.**

The number of different antigens recognized by lymphocytes in the body is extremely large. How can so many different substances be recognized? Almost all the current evidence indicates that the ability is innate and develops without exposure to the antigen. According to this **clonal theory,** stem cells differentiate into a very large number of different B lymphocytes, each with the ability to respond to a particular antigen (Fig 27–4). When the antigen first enters the body, it binds to the appropriate B lymphocyte, and this cell is stimulated to divide, forming a **clone** of plasma cells secreting the immunoglobulin that binds to this antigen. T lymphocytes cooperate in the stimulation of the B cells, probably by processing the antigen before binding, and macrophages are also in-

volved. The T cells can also suppress B cell function. T cell development is probably similar to the development of B cells, with fewer clones (see below).

Immunoglobulins

Five general types of immunoglobulin antibodies are produced by the lymphocyte–plasma cell system (Table 27–2). The basic component of each is a symmetrical unit containing 4 polypeptide chains (Fig 27–5). The 2 long chains are called **heavy chains,** whereas the 2 short chains are called **light chains.** There are 2 types of light chains, κ or λ, and 5 types of heavy chains (see Table 27–2). The chains are joined by disulfide bridges that permit mobility, and there are intrachain disulfide bridges as well. In addition, the heavy chains are flexible in a region called the hinge. Each chain has a segment in which the amino acid sequence is variable and one or more segments in which the amino acid sequence is constant. The antigen binding sites are in the variable segments, or Fab portions of the molecule, and the differing amino acid sequences plus the flexibility of the molecule permit great variation in conformation. This variability provides the principal explanation of antibody specificity, with a unique antibody for each antigen. The constant portion of the immunoglobulin molecule (Fc portion) houses the sites where binding occurs to effectors such as complement that mediate reactions initiated by antibodies.

In IgM, 5 of the immunoglobulin units join around an additional peptide (J chain) to form a pentamer (Table 27–2). In IgA, the units form dimers and trimers with the J chain or another peptide, the SC chain.

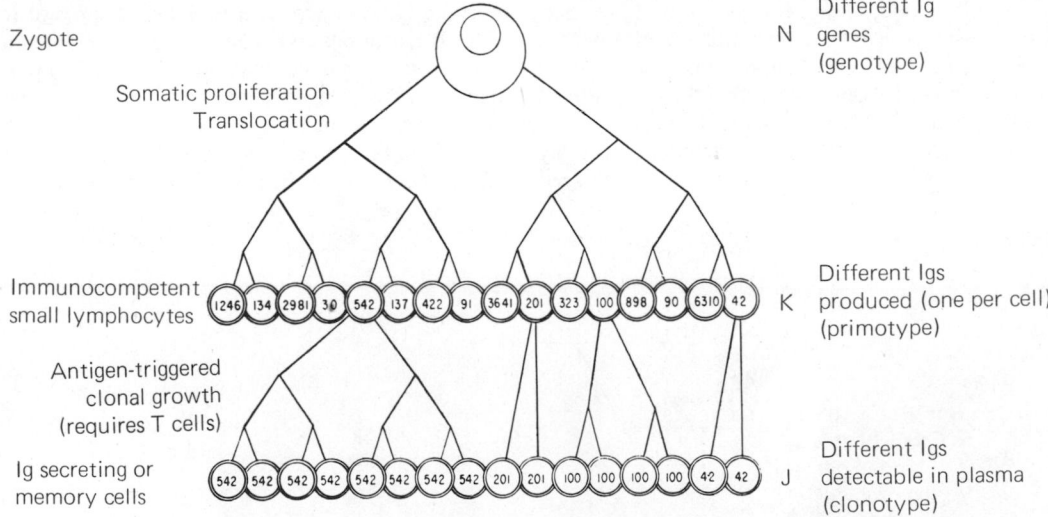

Figure 27–4. Differentiation of B lymphocytes according to the clonal selection theory. The number of Ig genes is N in the zygote but may increase during somatic growth so that in the immunologically mature animal, K different cells are formed, each committed to the synthesis of a structurally distinct Ig (indicated by the arabic number). A small proportion of these cells are stimulated by contact with antigen to form J different clones of cells, each producing a different antibody. T lymphocytes do not secrete circulating antibodies. (Reproduced, with permission, from Edelman GM: Specificity and mechanism at the lymphoid cell surface. In: *The Neurosciences, Third Study Program.* Schmitt FO, Worden FG [editors]. MIT Press, 1974.)

Table 27–2. Human immunoglobulins. In all instances, the light chains are κ or λ.

Immuno-globulin	Function	Heavy Chain	Additional Chain	Structure	Plasma Concentration (μg/ml)
IgG	Complement fixation	γ_1, γ_2, γ_3, γ_4		Monomer	12,100
IgA	Localized protection in external secretions (tears, intestinal secretions, etc)	a_1, a_2	J, SC	Monomer; dimer with J or SC chain; trimer with J chain	2600
IgM	Complement fixation	μ	J	Pentamer with J chain	930
IgD	Antigen recognition by B cells	δ		Monomer	23
IgE	Reagin activity; releases histamine from basophils and mast cells	ϵ		Monomer	0.5

The genetic mechanism responsible for the production of the immensely large number of different configurations of immunoglobulins in the body store of lymphocytes is not yet understood. However, each immunoglobulin unit appears to be specified by 3 different families of genes. One family specifies the κ light chains, another the λ light chains, and a third the various classes and subclasses of heavy chains.

The Complement System

When antigens combine with circulating antibodies, cells are lysed, bacteria are opsonized,

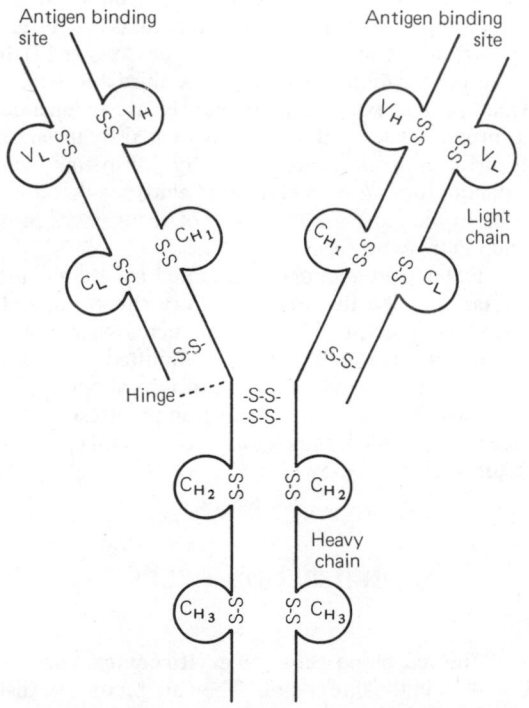

Figure 27–5. Diagrammatic representation of basic immunoglobulin molecule. V_H and V_L, variable segments; C_L, C_{H_1}, C_{H_2}, C_{H_3}, constant segments; -S-S- disulfide bridge. (Modified from Edelman GM: Antibody structure and molecular immunology. Science 180:830, 1973.)

leukocytes are attracted to the antigen, and histamine is released from elements in the blood. These effects are mediated by a system of plasma enzymes called the **complement system.** The enzymes are identified by the numbers C1 to C9. C1 is made up of 3 subunits, C1q, C1r, and C1s, so that there are actually 11 proteins in the system. C1 binds to immunoglobulins that have bound antigen, and this triggers a sequence of events that activates other components of the system. One consequence of activating the system is the formation of holes in the membranes of antibody-sensitized cells. Ions move through these membrane leaks, and the cells become lysed. Another consequence of activation is formation of the fragments C3a and C5a from C3 and C5, respectively. These fragments release histamine from granulocytes, mast cells, and platelets. The histamine dilates blood vessels and increases capillary permeability. C5a and a complex formed by C5b, C6, and C7 are chemotactic and attract leukocytes to the site of the antigen-antibody reaction. C3b is the complement component responsible for opsonization of bacteria, the step that precedes phagocytosis by neutrophils. IgG can also serve as an opsonin.

Complement-mediated cell lysis can also occur in the absence of antibodies via the **properdin pathway.** The key to this pathway is a circulating protein, **factor I,** that recognizes repetitive sugar structures such as polyglucose or polyfructose in cell membranes. These sequences are found in bacteria and viruses but not in mammalian cells. Interaction of factor I with the surface of invading cells triggers reactions that activate C3 and C5. **Properdin** is another circulating protein that stabilizes the activating enzyme complex.

Cellular Immunity

Cellular immunity is mediated by T lymphocytes, which are present throughout the body. When these cells encounter the antigens on cells from another individual or the antigens on tumor cells or viruses, they are activated. They enlarge, divide, and release **lymphokines,** substances of high molecular weight that participate in the attack on the foreign protein. In contrast to the B lymphocytes, which have primotypes capable of recognizing virtually all conceivable antigens, the T lymphocytes are specialized for recognizing antigens on living cells that distinguish self from nonself. These antigens may be the histocompatibility antigens. Once activated, the T cells enlarge, divide, and produce complement-independent lysis of the foreign cells. There are 2 kinds of cells that produce lysis: cytotoxic T lymphocytes, which attack cells with specific antigens on their surface, and K cells, which respond to the Fc portions of the IgG molecules bound to the surface of cells.

It is the T lymphocyte system that is responsible for the rejection of transplanted tissue. When tissues such as skin and kidneys are transplanted from a donor to a recipient of the same species, the transplants "take" and function for a while but then become necrotic and are "rejected" because the recipient develops an immune response to the transplanted tissue. This is true even if the donor and recipient are close relatives, and the only transplants that are not rejected are those from an identical twin. Practical methods to overcome the rejection of transplanted organs in humans are currently being developed. The transplant can be preserved by suppressing all immune responses with radiation and drugs, but this is hazardous. An antilymphocyte globulin prepared by immunizing animals with human lymphocytes is also used. This substance inhibits the lymphocytes responsible for cellular immune reactions. Additional technics are being sought.

Clinical Correlates

Disease due to defects at various stages in the development of the immune system have now been identified. Failure of the lymphocyte precursors to develop or to migrate to the thymus, liver, and spleen causes absence of cellular and humoral immunity, with marked susceptibility to infections. In individuals with congenital absence of the thymus (DiGeorge's syndrome), cellular immunity is absent but humoral immunity is normal. Conversely, in Bruton's X-linked agammaglobulinemia, the B lymphocytes fail to develop. Patients with this condition have many bacterial infections but are relatively resistant to viral and fungal diseases.

Malignant transformation can also occur at various stages of development. Most if not all cases of chronic lymphocytic leukemia are due to uncontrolled proliferation of B lymphocytes, whereas multiple myeloma is due to malignant proliferation of clones of mature plasma cells. Some cases of acute lymphocytic leukemia are T lymphocyte malignancies.

Some success has been reported in the treatment of DiGeorge's syndrome with thymosin. This hormone is also being tried in patients with tumors in an effort to facilitate rejection of the tumor by the immune system. It appears that the function of the cellular immunity mechanism declines with age in humans, and this might account for the increase in the incidence of tumors with advancing age.

PLATELETS

The platelets are small, granulated bodies 2–4 μm in diameter (Fig 27–2). There are about 300,000 per microliter of circulating blood, and they normally have a half-life of about 7 days. The **megakaryocytes,** giant cells in the bone marrow, form platelets by pinching off bits of cytoplasm and extruding them into the circulation. Platelets contain serotonin, ADP, Ca^{2+}, K^+, several clotting factors, various enzymes, and other less well characterized biologically active substances. They have an extensively invaginated membrane with an intricate canalicular system in contact with the ECF and contain 2 types of granules, one containing serotonin and ADP and the other containing lysosomal enzymes. They can change shape, collect at the site of injury **(platelet aggregation),** and discharge the contents of their granules via the canaliculi **(platelet release).** When blood vessel walls are injured, platelets adhere to the exposed collagen. Adhesion is followed by release. The secreted serotonin probably assists in the vasoconstriction produced at the site of injury, and ADP promotes release of granule contents from other platelets. The ADP makes the platelets sticky and causes more platelets to aggregate, forming the hemostatic plug (see below). In addition, many agents that cause platelet aggregation activate the phospholipase A_2 in the platelet membrane. This causes release of arachidonic acid from membrane phospholipids, and the arachidonic acid is converted to prostaglandins and thromboxanes (see Chapter 17) that cause aggregation and release. A third mechanism, which produces aggregation and release independent of thromboxanes and ADP, is activated by thrombin. Aspirin inhibits aggregation by inhibiting prostaglandin formation, and there is evidence that it is of value in reducing the incidence of recurrences in patients with some forms of stroke.

Platelet production is regulated by a circulating substance called **thrombopoietin** or **thrombopoietic stimulating factor (TSF),** which increases the formation of megakaryocytes from committed stem cells. However, the origin and nature of thrombopoietin are unknown. Normal platelet function requires the presence of von Willebrand factor, a component of clotting factor VIII (see below).

RED BLOOD CELLS

The red blood cells, or **erythrocytes,** carry hemoglobin in the circulation. They are biconcave disks (Fig 27–6) that are manufactured in the bone marrow. In mammals, they lose their nuclei before entering the circulation. In humans, they survive in the circulation for an average of 120 days. The average normal red blood cell count is 5.4 million/μl in men and 4.8 million/μl in women. Each human red blood cell is

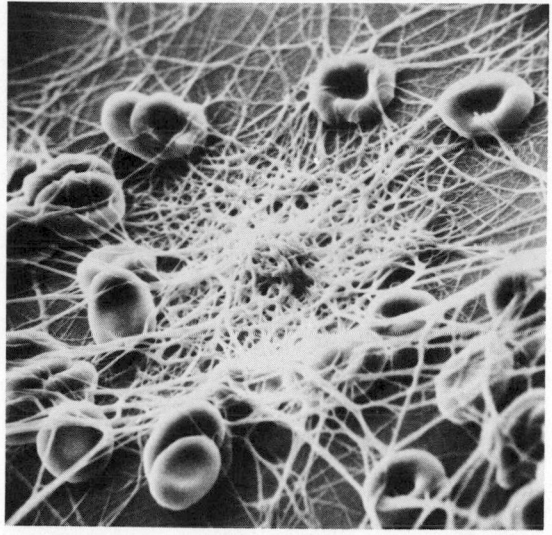

Figure 27–6. Human red blood cells and fibrin fibrils. Blood was placed on a polyvinyl chloride surface, then fixed and photographed, using a scanning electron microscope. Reduced from × 2590. (Courtesy of NF Rodman.)

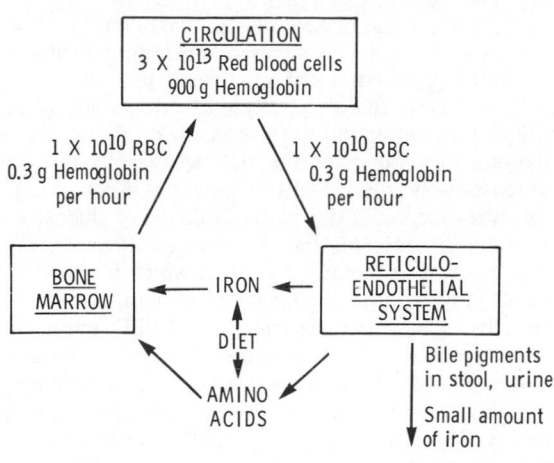

Figure 27–7. Red cell formation and destruction.

about 7.5 μm in diameter and 2 μm thick, and each contains approximately 29 pg of hemoglobin (Table 27–3). There are thus about 3×10^{13} red blood cells and about 900 g of hemoglobin in the circulating blood of an adult man (Fig 27–7).

Erythropoiesis

The formation of red blood cells (**erythropoiesis**) is subject to a feedback control. It is inhibited by a rise in the circulating red cell level to supernormal values and stimulated by anemia. It is also stimulated by hypoxia, and an increase in the number of circulating red cells is a prominent feature of acclimatization to altitude (see Chapter 37). Erythropoiesis is controlled by a circulating glycoprotein hormone called **erythropoietin,** which is formed by the action of a renal factor

on a globulin in plasma (see Chapter 24). This hormone promotes the differentiation of committed stem cells (erythropoietin-sensitive stem cells) into proerythroblasts.

Red Cell Fragility

Red blood cells, like other cells, shrink in solutions with an osmotic pressure greater than that of normal plasma. In solutions with a lower osmotic pressure, they swell, becoming spherical rather than disk-shaped, and eventually lose their hemoglobin (**hemolysis**). The hemoglobin of hemolyzed red cells dissolves in the plasma, coloring it red. A 0.9% sodium chloride solution is isotonic with plasma. When **osmotic fragility** is normal, red cells begin to hemolyze when suspended in 0.48% saline, and

Table 27–3. Characteristics of human red cells.* Cells with MCVs > 95 are called macrocytes; cells with MCVs < 80 are called microcytes; cells with MCHs < 25 are called hypochromic.

		Male	Female
Hematocrit (Hct) (%)		47	42
Red blood cells (RBC) (millions/μl)		5.4	4.8
Hemoglobin (Hb) (g/dl)		16	14
Mean corpuscular volume (MCV) (fl)	$= \dfrac{\text{Hct} \times 10}{\text{RBC } (10^6/\mu l)}$	87	87
Mean corpuscular hemoglobin (MCH) (pg)	$= \dfrac{\text{Hb} \times 10}{\text{RBC } (10^6/\mu l)}$	29	29
Mean corpuscular hemoglobin concentration (MCHC) (g/dl)	$= \dfrac{\text{Hb} \times 100}{\text{Hct}}$	34	34
Mean cell diameter (MCD) (μm)	$= $ Mean diameter of 500 cells in smear	7.5	7.5

*Values are from Wintrobe M: *Clinical Hematology,* 6th ed. Lea & Febiger, 1967.

hemolysis is complete in 0.33% saline. In **hereditary spherocytosis** (congenital hemolytic icterus), the cells are spherocytic in normal plasma and hemolyze more readily than normal cells in hypotonic sodium chloride solutions **(abnormal red cell fragility).**

Red cells can also be lysed by drugs and infections. The susceptibility of red cells to hemolysis by these agents is increased by deficiency of the enzyme glucose-6-phosphate dehydrogenase (G6PD), which catalyzes the initial step in the oxidation of glucose via the hexosemonophosphate pathway (see Chapter 17). This pathway generates NADPH, which is needed in some way for the maintenance of normal red cell fragility. Congenital deficiency of G6PD activity in the red cells due to the presence of enzyme variants is common; indeed, G6PD deficiency is the commonest known genetically determined human enzyme abnormality. More than 80 genetic variants of G6PD have been described; 40 of these do not cause appreciable decreases in enzyme activity, but the others produce decreased activity, increased sensitivity to hemolytic agents, and hemolytic anemia. Severe G6PD deficiency also inhibits the killing of bacteria by granulocytes and predisposes to severe infections (see above).

Hemoglobin

The red, oxygen-carrying pigment in the red blood cells of vertebrates is **hemoglobin,** a protein with a molecular weight of 64,450. Hemoglobin is a globular molecule made up of 4 subunits (Fig 27–8). Each subunit contains a **heme** moiety conjugated to a polypeptide. Heme is an iron-containing porphyrin derivative (Fig 27–9). The polypeptides are referred to collectively as the **globin** portion of the hemoglobin molecule. There are 2 pairs of polypeptides in each hemoglobin molecule, 2 of the subunits containing one type of polypeptide and 2 containing another. In normal adult human hemoglobin **(hemoglobin A),** the 2 types of polypeptide are called the α chains, each of

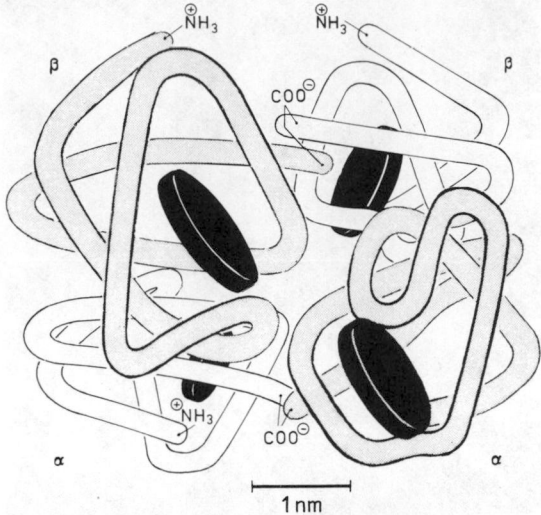

Figure 27–8. Diagrammatic representation of a molecule of hemoglobin A, showing the 4 subunits. There are 2 α and 2 β peptide chains, each containing a heme moiety. These moieties are represented by the disks. (Reproduced, with permission, from Harper HA & others: *Physiologische Chemie.* Springer-Verlag, 1975.)

which contains 141 amino acid residues, and the β chains, each of which contains 146 amino acid residues. Not all the hemoglobin in the blood of normal adults is hemoglobin A. About 2.5% of the hemoglobin is hemoglobin A_2, in which β chains are replaced by δ chains. The δ chains also contain 146 amino acid residues, but 10 individual residues differ from those in the β chains.

There are small amounts of 3 hemoglobin A derivatives closely associated with hemoglobin A that probably represent glycosylated hemoglobins. One of these, hemoglobin A_{1c} (HbA_{1c}), has a glucose attached

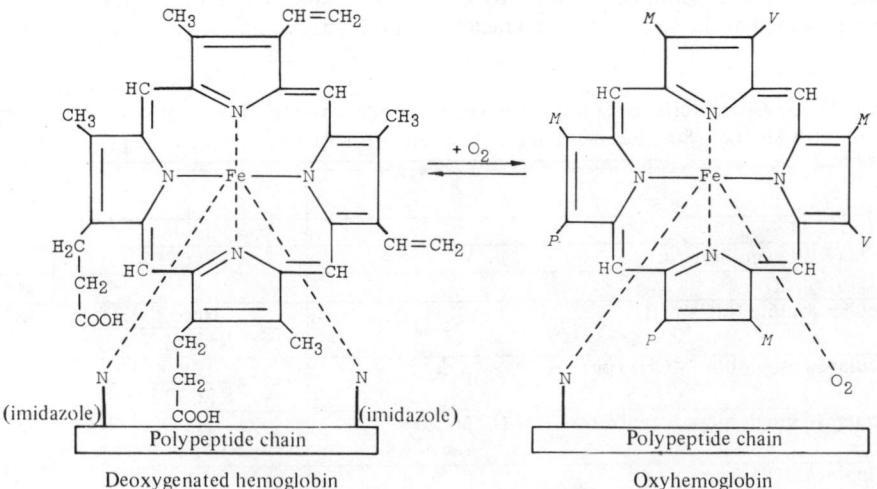

Figure 27–9. Chemistry of hemoglobin. The hemoglobin molecule is made up of 4 of the units shown on the left. The abbreviations M, V, and P stand for the groups shown on the molecule on the left.

to the terminal valine in each β chain and is of special interest because the quantity in the blood increases in poorly controlled diabetes mellitus. There is evidence that the quantity in the circulation is reduced after 5–6 weeks of good diabetic control, and thus HbA$_{1c}$ may be a convenient and valuable index of the adequacy of diabetic control.

Reactions of Hemoglobin

Hemoglobin binds O_2 to form **oxyhemoglobin,** O_2 attaching to the Fe^{2+} in the heme. The affinity of hemoglobin for O_2 is affected by pH, temperature, and the concentration in the red cells of 2,3-diphosphoglycerate (2,3-DPG). 2,3-DPG and H^+ compete with O_2 for binding to deoxygenated hemoglobin, decreasing the affinity of hemoglobin for O_2 by shifting the positions of the 4 peptide chains (quaternary structure). The details of the oxygenation and deoxygenation of hemoglobin and the physiologic role of these reactions in O_2 transport are discussed in Chapter 35. When blood is exposed to various drugs and other oxidizing agents in vitro or in vivo, the ferrous iron (Fe^{2+}) in the molecule is converted to ferric iron (Fe^{3+}), forming **methemoglobin.** Methemoglobin is dark-colored, and when it is present in large quantities in the circulation, it causes a dusky discoloration of the skin resembling cyanosis (see Chapter 37). Some oxidation of hemoglobin to methemoglobin occurs normally, but an enzyme system in the red cells, the NADH–methemoglobin reductase system, converts methemoglobin back to hemoglobin. Congenital absence of this system is one cause of hereditary methemoglobinemia.

Carbon monoxide reacts with hemoglobin to form **carbonmonoxyhemoglobin (carboxyhemoglobin).** The affinity of hemoglobin for O_2 is much less than its affinity for carbon monoxide, and carbon monoxide consequently displaces O_2 on hemoglobin, reducing the oxygen-carrying capacity of blood (see Chapter 37).

Heme is also part of the structure of **myoglobin,**

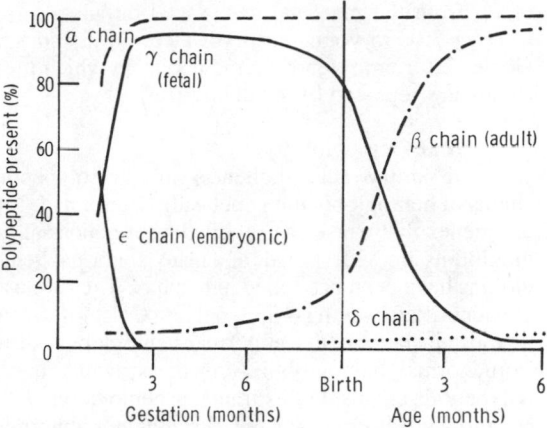

Figure 27–10. Development of human hemoglobin chains. (Reproduced, with permission, from Huens ER & others: Human embryonic hemoglobin. Cold Spring Harbor Symp Quant Biol 29:327, 1964.)

an oxygen-binding pigment found in red, or slow, muscles (see Chapter 3) and in the respiratory enzyme **cytochrome c** (see Chapter 17). Porphyrins other than that found in heme play a role in the pathogenesis of a number of metabolic diseases (congenital and acquired porphyria, etc).

Hemoglobin in the Fetus

The blood of the human fetus normally contains **fetal hemoglobin (hemoglobin F).** Its structure is similar to that of hemoglobin A except that the β chains are replaced by γ chains. The γ chains also contain 146 amino acid residues but have 37 that differ from those in the β chain. Fetal hemoglobin is normally replaced by adult hemoglobin soon after birth (Fig 27–10). In certain individuals, it fails to disappear and persists throughout life. In the body, its O_2 content at a given P_{O_2} is greater than that of adult hemoglobin because it binds 2,3-DPG less avidly. This facilitates movement

Table 27–4. Partial amino acid composition of normal human β chain, and some hemoglobins with abnormal β chains. Other hemoglobins have abnormal a chains. Hemoglobins that are very similar electrophoretically but still differ slightly in composition are indicated by the same letter and a subscript indicating the geographic location where they were first discovered; hence, M$_{Saskatoon}$ and M$_{Milwaukee}$.

Hemoglobin	Positions on β Polypeptide Chain of Hemoglobin						
	1 2 3	6 7	26	63	67	121	146
A (normal)	Val-His-Leu	Glu-Glu	Glu	His	Val	Glu	His
S (sickle cell)		Val					
C		Lys					
G$_{San Jose}$		Gly					
E			Lys				
M$_{Saskatoon}$				Tyr			
M$_{Milwaukee}$					Glu		
O$_{Arabia}$						Lys	

of O_2 from the maternal to the fetal circulation (see Chapter 32). In young embryos there is, in addition, Gower 2, or embryonic, hemoglobin, in which the β chains are replaced by ϵ chains.

Abnormal Hemoglobins

The amino acid sequences in the polypeptide chains of hemoglobin are genetically determined. Mutant genes that cause the production of abnormal hemoglobins are widespread, and many abnormal hemoglobins have been described in humans. They are usually identified by letter—hemoglobin C, E, I, J, S, etc. In most instances, the abnormal hemoglobins differ from normal hemoglobin A in the structure of the polypeptide chains. For example, in hemoglobin S, the α chains are normal but the β chains are abnormal, because among the 146 amino acid residues in each β polypeptide chain, one glutamic acid residue has been replaced by a valine residue (Table 27–4).

When an abnormal gene inherited from one parent dictates formation of an abnormal hemoglobin— ie, when the individual is heterozygous—half of the circulating hemoglobin is abnormal and half is normal. When identical abnormal genes are inherited from both parents, the individual is homozygous and all of the hemoglobin is abnormal. It is theoretically possible to inherit 2 different abnormal hemoglobins, one from the father and one from the mother. Studies of the inheritance and geographic distribution of abnormal hemoglobins have made it possible in some cases to decide where the mutant gene originated and approximately how long ago the mutation occurred. In general, harmful mutations tend to die out, but mutant genes that confer traits with survival value persist and spread in the population.

Clinical Implications

Many of the abnormal hemoglobins are harmless. However, some cause anemia. For example, hemoglobin S is very insoluble at low O_2 tensions, and this causes the red cells to become sickle-shaped. These abnormal sickle cells hemolyze, producing the severe anemia known as **sickle cell anemia.** Heterozygous individuals have the **sickle cell trait** and rarely have severe symptoms, but homozygous ones develop the full-blown disease. The sickle cell gene is an example of a gene that has persisted and spread in the population. It originated in the black population in Africa, and it confers resistance to one type of malaria. This is an important benefit in Africa, and in some parts of Africa 40% of the population have the sickle cell trait. In the American black population, its incidence is about 10%.

Other hemoglobins have abnormal O_2 equilibriums. In the various forms of M hemoglobin, for example, the structural abnormality causes the heme iron in 25% or less of the hemoglobin to be oxidized, with the production of congenital methemoglobinemia. In other abnormal hemoglobins, the affinity for O_2 is increased by changes in quaternary structure that prevent the binding of 2,3-DPG (see Chapter 35). The

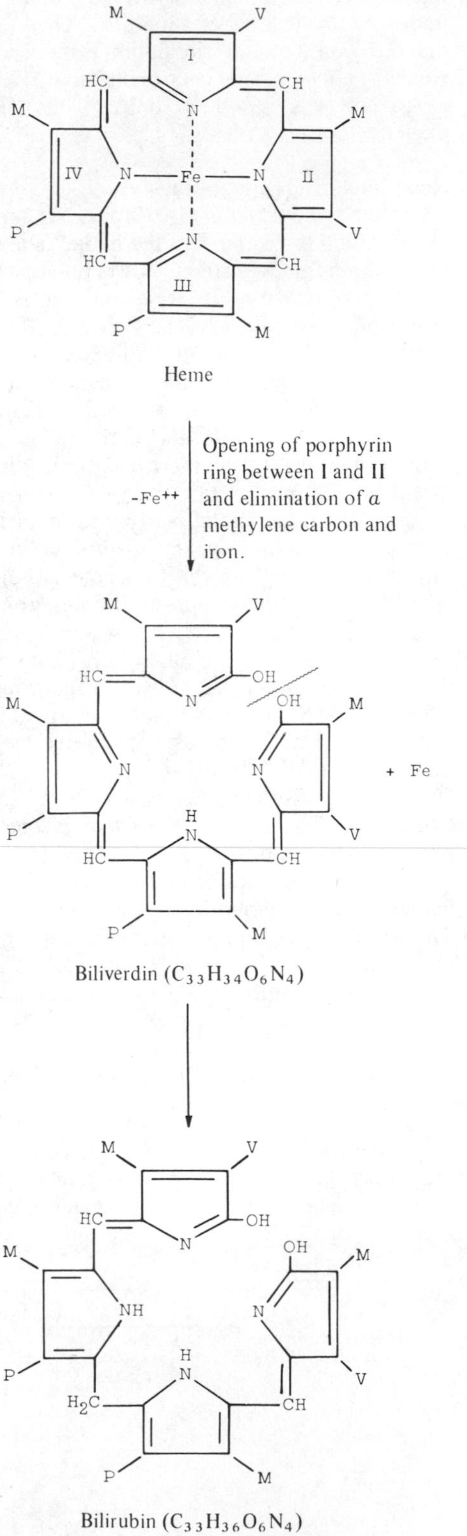

Heme

Opening of porphyrin ring between I and II and elimination of α methylene carbon and iron.

$-Fe^{++}$

Biliverdin $(C_{33}H_{34}O_6N_4)$

$+ Fe$

Bilirubin $(C_{33}H_{36}O_6N_4)$

Figure 27–11. Catabolism of heme. The abbreviations M, V, and P stand for the groups shown on the molecule on the left in Fig 27–9.

resultant mild hypoxia leads to a chronic elevation in the red cell count (**erythrocytosis**).

Synthesis of Hemoglobin

The average normal hemoglobin content of blood is 16 g/dl in men and 14 g/dl in women, all of it in red cells. In the body of a 70 kg man, there are about 900 g of hemoglobin, and 0.3 g of hemoglobin are destroyed and 0.3 g synthesized every hour (Fig 27–7). The heme portion of the hemoglobin molecule is synthesized from glycine and succinyl-CoA.

Catabolism of Hemoglobin

When old red blood cells are destroyed in the reticuloendothelial system, the globin portion of the hemoglobin molecule is split off, and the heme is converted to **biliverdin** (Fig 27–11). In humans, most of the biliverdin formed from heme is converted to **bilirubin.** The bilirubin is excreted in the bile (see Chapter 26). The iron from the heme is reused for hemoglobin synthesis. Iron is essential for hemoglobin synthesis; if blood is lost from the body and the iron deficiency is not corrected, **iron deficiency anemia** results. The metabolism of iron is discussed in Chapter 25.

BLOOD TYPES

The membranes of human red cells contain a variety of antigens called **agglutinogens.** The most important and best known of these are the A and B agglutinogens, and individuals are divided into 4 major **blood types,** types A, B, AB, and O, on the basis of the agglutinogens present in their red cells. There are A and B antigens in many tissues other than blood. They have been found in salivary glands, saliva, pancreas, kidney, liver, lungs, testes, semen, and amniotic fluid. The A and B agglutinogens are glycoproteins that differ in composition by only one sugar residue. Type A individuals have an enzyme (glycosyltransferase) that puts acetylgalactosamine on the glycoprotein skeleton, whereas type B individuals have an enzyme that puts galactose on the skeleton. Individuals with type AB blood have both enzymes.

Antibodies against agglutinogens are called **agglutinins.** They may occur naturally (ie, be inherited), or they may be produced by exposure to the red cells of another individual. This exposure may occur via a transfusion, or during pregnancy, when fetal red cells cross the placenta and enter the circulation of the mother. Agglutinins against A and B agglutinogens are inherited. Thus, individuals with type A blood (ie, those who have agglutinogen A on their red cells) always have an appreciable titer of an antibody against agglutinogen B called the β or anti-B agglutinin. When their plasma is mixed with type B cells, the agglutinins and the B cell agglutinogens react, causing the type B cells to become clumped (agglutinated) and sub-

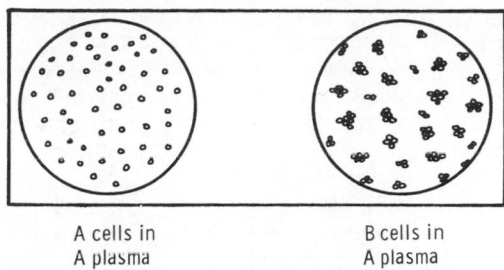

A cells in
A plasma

B cells in
A plasma

Figure 27–12. Red cell agglutination in incompatible plasma.

sequently hemolyzed (Fig 27–12). Similarly, individuals with type B blood have a circulating titer of an α, or anti-A, agglutinin. Individuals with type O blood have circulating anti-A and anti-B agglutinins, and those with type AB blood have no circulating agglutinins. **Blood typing** is performed by mixing an individual's red cells with appropriate antisera on a slide and seeing if agglutination occurs.

Some individuals with A agglutinogen have an additional agglutinogen called A_1. Thus, the A group is subdivided into types A_1 (those with both A agglutinogens) and A_2 (those with only the A agglutinogen). Therefore, there are 6 ABO groups instead of 4: B, O, A_1, A_2, A_1B, and A_2B. Individuals who lack the A_1 agglutinogen normally have little if any circulating anti-A agglutinin, but appreciable titers are sometimes found.

Transfusion Reactions

Dangerous **hemolytic transfusion reactions** occur when blood is transfused into an individual with an incompatible blood type, ie, an individual who has agglutinins against the red cells in the transfusion (Fig 27–12). The plasma in the transfusion is usually so diluted in the recipient that it rarely causes agglutination even when the titer of agglutinins against the recipient's cells is high. However, when the recipient's plasma has agglutinins against the donor's red cells, the cells agglutinate and hemolyze. Free hemoglobin is liberated into the plasma. The severity of the resulting transfusion reaction may vary from an asymptomatic minor rise in the plasma bilirubin level to severe jaundice and renal tubular damage (caused in some way by the products liberated from hemolyzed cells), with anuria and death.

Incompatibilities in the ABO blood group system are summarized in Table 27–5. Persons with type AB blood are "universal recipients" because they have no circulating agglutinins and can be given blood of any type without developing a transfusion reaction due to ABO incompatibility. Type O individuals are "universal donors" because there are no regular anti-O agglutinins, and type O blood can be given to anyone without producing a transfusion reaction due to ABO incompatibility. This does not mean, however, that blood should ever be transfused without being cross-matched except in the most extreme emergencies, since the possibility of reactions or sensitization due to

Table 27–5. Summary of ABO blood system.*

Blood Type	Agglutinins in Plasma	Frequency in USA (%)	Plasma Agglutinates Red Cells of Type
O	Anti-A, anti-B	45	A_1, A_1B, B, A_2B
A_1	Anti-B	41	B, A_1B, A_2B
A_2			B, A_1B, A_2B
B	Anti-A	10	A_1, A_1B, A_2, A_2B
A_1B	None	4	None
A_2B			

*Some type A_2 and A_2B individuals may also have sufficient anti-A_1 agglutinin to agglutinate A_1 and A_1B red cells. (Modified from Ham TH: *A Syllabus of Laboratory Examinations in Clinical Diagnosis.* Harvard Univ Press, 1953.)

incompatibilities other than those due to ABO always exists. There are also individuals with appreciable titers of the anti-A_1 agglutinin, and transfusion reactions due to this agglutinin can be prevented if blood is cross-matched. In cross-matching, donor red cells are mixed with recipient plasma on a slide and checked for agglutination (Fig 27–12). It is advisable to check the action of the donor's plasma on the recipient cells even though, as noted above, this is rarely a source of trouble.

Inheritance of A & B Antigens

The A_1, A_2, and B antigens are inherited as mendelian allelomorphs, A_1, A_2, and B being dominants. For example, an individual with type B blood may have inherited a B antigen from each parent or a B antigen from one parent and an O from the other; thus, an individual whose **phenotype** is B may have the **genotype** BB **(homozygous)** or the **genotype** BO **(heterozygous).**

When the blood types of the parents are known, the possible genotypes of their children can be stated. When both parents are type B, they could have children with genotype BB (B antigen from both parents), BO (B antigen from one parent, O from the other heterozygous parent), or OO (O antigen from both parents, both being heterozygous). When the blood types of a mother and her child are known, it is possible to state whether a man of a given blood type could or could not have been the father. This has medicolegal importance in paternity cases. It should be emphasized that typing can only prove that a man is not the father, not that he is the father. The predictive value of such determinations is increased if the blood typing of the parties concerned includes identification of antigens other than the ABO agglutinogens.

Other Agglutinogens

In addition to the 6 antigens of the ABO system in human red cells, there are other agglutinogen systems containing many individual antigens in red cells (Table 27–6). There are over 500 billion possible known blood group phenotypes, and because undiscovered antigens undoubtedly exist, it has been calculated that the number of phenotypes is actually in the trillions. For this reason, it is possible in theory to identify

people by their blood types in the way they are identified by their fingerprints.

The number of blood groups in animals is as large as it is in humans. An interesting question is why this degree of polymorphism developed and persisted through evolution. Certain diseases are more common in individuals with one blood type or another, but the differences are not great. It seems likely that the actual function of the blood group antigens is cell recognition, but the exact significance of a recognition code of this complexity is unknown.

Agglutinins against the Rh antigens occur only in individuals who lack a particular antigen and develop the antibodies as an immune response when they are exposed to red cells containing the antigen. Agglutinins against the other antigens are sometimes found without a history of sensitization by previous transfusions, but in general, anti-A and anti-B are the only agglutinins that occur in high titer without sensitization.

The Rh Group

Aside from the antigens of the ABO system, those of the Rh system are of the greatest clinical importance. The "Rh factor," named for the rhesus monkey because it was first studied in the blood of this animal, is a system composed of many antigens (Table 27–6). D is by far the most antigenic, and the term "Rh-positive" as it is generally used means that the individual has agglutinogen D. The "Rh-negative" individual has no D antigen and forms the anti-D agglutinin when injected with D-positive cells. The Rh typing serum used in routine blood typing is anti-D serum. Eighty-five percent of Caucasians are D-positive and 15% are D-negative; over 99% of Orientals are D-positive. D-negative individuals who have received a transfusion of D-positive blood (even years previously) can have appreciable anti-D titers and thus may develop transfusion reactions when transfused again with D-positive blood.

Hemolytic Disease of the Newborn

Another complication due to "Rh incompatibility" arises when an Rh-negative mother carries an Rh-positive fetus. Small amounts of fetal blood leak into the maternal circulation at the time of delivery,

Table 27–6. Human blood group antigens.*

System	Antigens Detected By	
	Positive Reactions With Specific Antibody	Positive Reaction With One Antibody, Negative With Another†
$A_1 A_2$ BO	A_1, B, ‡H	A_2, A_3, A_x, and other A and B variants
MNSs	M, N, S, s, U, M^g, M_1, M', Tm, Sj, Hu, He, Mi^a, Vw (Gr), Mur, Hil, Hut, M^v, Vr, Ri^a, St^a, Mt^a, Cl^a, Ny^a, Sul, Far	M_2, N_2, M^c, M^a, N^a, M^r, M^z, S_2
P	P_1, P^k, ‡Luke	P_2
Rh	D, C, c, C^w, C^x, E, e, e^s (VS), E^w, G, ce(f), ce^s(V), Ce, CE, cE, D^w, E^T, Go^a, hr^s, hr^H, hr^B, $\overline{\overline{R}}{}^N$, Rh33, Rh35, Be^a, ‡LW	D^u, C^u, E^u, and many other variant forms of D, C, and e
Lutheran	Lu^a, Lu^b, Lu^aLu^b (Lu3), Lu6, Lu9, §Lu4, Lu5, Lu7, Lu8, Lu10–17	
Kell	K, k, Kp^a, Kp^b, Ku, Js^a, Js^b, Ul^a, Wk^a, K11, §KL, K12–16	
Lewis	Le^a, Le^b, Le^c, Le^d, Le^x	
Duffy	Fy^a, Fy^b, Fy3, Fy4	
Kidd	Jk^a, Jk^b, Jk^aJk^b (Jk3)	
Diego	Di^a, Di^b	
Yt	Yt^a, Yt^b	
Auberger	Au^a	
Dombrock	Do^a, Do^b	
Colton	Co^a, Co^b, Co^aCo^b	
Sid	Sd^a	
Scianna	Sc1, Sc2 (Bu^a)	
Very frequent antigens	Vel, Ge, Lan, Gy^a, At^a, En^a, Wr^b, Jr^a, Kn^a, El, Dp, Gn^a, Jo^a, and many unpublished examples	
Very infrequent antigens	An^a, By, Bi, Bp^a, Bx^a, Chr^a, Evans, Good, Gf, Heibel, Hey, Hov, Ht^a, Je^a, Jn^a, Levay, Ls^a, Mo^a, Or, Pt^a, Rl^a, Rd, Re^a, Sw^a, To^a, Tr^a, Ts, Wb, Wr^a, Wu, Zd, and many unpublished examples	
Other antigens	I, i, Bg (HL-A), Chido, Cs^a, Yk^a	
Xg	Xg^a	

*Reproduced, with permission, from Race RR, Sanger R: *Blood Groups in Man*, 6th ed. Blackwell, 1975.
†Recognizable only in favorable genotypes.
‡A genetically independent part of the system.
§Place in system not yet genetically clear.

and some mothers develop significant titers of anti-Rh agglutinins during the postpartum period. During the next pregnancy, the mother's agglutinins cross the placenta to the fetus. In addition, there are some cases of fetal-maternal hemorrhage during pregnancy, and sensitization can occur during pregnancy. In any case, when anti-Rh agglutinins cross the placenta to an Rh-positive fetus, they can cause hemolysis and various forms of **hemolytic disease of the newborn (erythroblastosis fetalis).** If hemolysis in the fetus is severe, the infant may die in utero or may develop anemia, severe jaundice, and edema **(hydrops fetalis). Kernicterus,** a neurologic syndrome in which bile pigments are deposited in the basal ganglia, may also develop, especially if birth is complicated by a period of hypoxia. Bile pigments do not enter the brain in the adult, but in the fetus and newborn infant the blood-brain barrier is not developed (see Chapter 32).

About 50% of Rh-negative individuals are sensitized (develop an anti-Rh titer) by transfusion of Rh-positive blood. Since sensitization of Rh-negative mothers by carrying an Rh-positive fetus generally occurs at birth, the first child is usually normal. However, hemolytic disease occurs in about 17% of the Rh-positive fetuses born to Rh-negative mothers who have previously been pregnant one or more times with Rh-positive fetuses. Fortunately, it is possible to prevent sensitization from occurring the first time by administering a single dose of anti-Rh antibodies in the form of Rh immune globulin (RhoGAM) during the postpartum period. Such passive immunization does not harm the mother and has been demonstrated to prevent active antibody formation by the mother. In obstetric clinics, the institution of such treatment on a routine basis to unsensitized Rh-negative women who have delivered an Rh-positive baby has reduced the overall incidence of hemolytic disease by more than 90%. Treatment with a small dose during pregnancy will also prevent sensitization due to fetal-maternal hemorrhage before delivery.

Erythroblastosis can also be due to incompatibility of C, E, Kell, Duffy, Lutheran, and Kidd factors, but such cases are rare. There are cases in which ABO incompatibility between the mother and the fetus (eg, a B fetus in an A mother) has caused hemolytic disease, but such transplacental sensitization is rarely a serious problem.

PLASMA

The fluid portion of the blood, the **plasma,** is a remarkable solution containing an immense number of ions, inorganic molecules, and organic molecules that are in transit to various parts of the body or aid in the transport of other substances. The normal plasma volume is about 5% of body weight, or roughly 3500 ml in a 70 kg man. Plasma clots on standing, remaining fluid only if an anticoagulant is added. If whole blood is allowed to clot and the clot is removed, the remaining fluid is called **serum.** Serum has essentially the same composition as plasma except that its fibrinogen and clotting factors II, V, and VIII (Table 27–7) have been removed, and it has a higher serotonin content because of the breakdown of platelets during clotting. The normal plasma levels of various substances are discussed in the chapters on the systems with which the substances are concerned and summarized on the inside back cover.

Plasma Proteins

The plasma proteins consist of **albumin, globulin,** and **fibrinogen** fractions. The globulin fraction is subdivided into numerous components. One classification divides it into α_1, α_2, β_1, β_2, and γ globulins and fibrinogen. Protein fractions can be separated and characterized by their relative speed of sedimentation

Table 27–7. Numerical system for naming blood clotting factors. Factor VI is not a separate entity and has been dropped.

Factor	
I	Fibrinogen
II	Prothrombin
III	Thromboplastin
IV	Calcium
V	Proaccelerin, labile factor, accelerator globulin
VII	Proconvertin, SPCA, stable factor
VIII	Antihemophilic factor (AHF), antihemophilic factor A, antihemophilic globulin (AHG)
IX	Plasma thromboplastic component (PTC), Christmas factor, antihemophilic factor B
X	Stuart-Prower factor
XI	Plasma thromboplastin antecedent (PTA), antihemophilic factor C
XII	Hageman factor, glass factor
XIII	Fibrin-stabilizing factor, Laki-Lorand factor

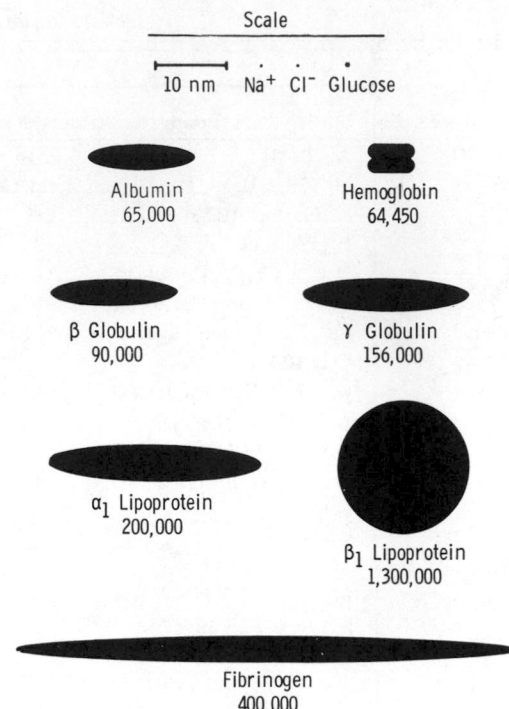

Figure 27–13. Relative dimensions and molecular weights of some of the protein molecules in the blood. (After Oncley JL. Reproduced, with permission, from Harper HA, Rodwell VW, Mayes PA: *Review of Physiological Chemistry,* 17th ed. Lange, 1979.)

in the ultracentrifuge. Electrophoresis is another technic for separating protein fractions. In this process, protein solutions in appropriate buffered solvents are placed on a medium such as paper or starch blocks and exposed to an electric current. Because of differences in electrical charge, the protein components migrate toward the anode or cathode at different rates. The molecular weights and configurations of several of the plasma proteins are shown in Fig 27–13.

The capillary walls are for the most part impermeable to the proteins in plasma, and the proteins therefore exert an osmotic force of about 25 mm Hg across the capillary wall (**oncotic pressure;** see Chapter 1) that tends to pull water into the blood. The plasma proteins are also responsible for 15% of the buffering capacity of the blood (see Chapter 35) because of the weak ionization of their substituent –COOH and –NH₂ groups. At the normal plasma pH of 7.40, the proteins are mostly in the anionic form (see Chapter 1) and constitute a significant part of the anionic complement of plasma. Plasma proteins such as the antibodies and the proteins concerned with blood clotting have specific functions. Some of the proteins function in the transport of thyroid, adrenocortical, and gonadal hormones. Binding keeps these hormones from being rapidly filtered through the glomeruli and provides a stable reservoir of hormones on which the tissues can draw. In addition, albumin serves as a carrier for metals, ions, fatty acids, amino acids, bilirubin, enzymes, and drugs.

Origin of Plasma Proteins

Circulating antibodies found in the γ globulin fraction of the plasma proteins are manufactured principally in the plasma cells of the reticuloendothelial system. The albumin fraction and the proteins concerned with blood clotting (fibrinogen, prothrombin) are manufactured in the liver. Data on the turnover of albumin provide an indication of the role played by synthesis in the maintenance of normal albumin levels. In normal adult humans, the plasma albumin level is 3.5–4.5 g/dl, and the total exchangeable albumin pool is 4.0–5.0 g/kg body weight; 38–45% of this albumin is intravascular, and much of the rest of it is in the skin. Six to 10% of the exchangeable pool is degraded per day, and the degraded albumin is replaced by hepatic synthesis of 120-200 mg/kg/d.

Hypoproteinemia

Plasma protein levels are maintained during starvation until body protein stores are markedly depleted; but in prolonged starvation and in the malabsorption syndrome due to intestinal diseases such as sprue, plasma protein levels are low (**hypoproteinemia**). They are also low in liver disease, because hepatic protein synthesis is depressed; and in nephrosis, because large amounts of albumin are lost in the urine. Because of the decrease in the plasma oncotic pressure, edema tends to develop (see Chapter 30). Rarely, there may be congenital absence of one or another plasma protein fraction. Examples of congenital protein deficiencies are **agammaglobulinemia,** a condition in which there is markedly lowered resistance to infections due to the absence of circulating antibodies; and the congenital form of **afibrinogenemia,** characterized by defective blood clotting.

HEMOSTASIS

When a small blood vessel is transected or damaged, the injury initiates a series of events that leads to the formation of a clot (**hemostasis**). This leads to sealing off of the blood vessel and prevents further blood loss. The initial event is constriction of the vessel and formation of a temporary hemostatic plug of platelets, followed by conversion of the plug into the definitive clot. The in vivo action of the clotting mechanism responsible for this conversion is balanced by limiting reactions that normally prevent clots from developing in uninjured vessels and maintain the blood in a fluid state.

Local Vasoconstriction

The constriction of an injured arteriole or small artery may be so marked that its lumen is obliterated. The vasoconstriction is probably due to serotonin and other vasoconstrictors liberated from platelets that adhere to the walls of the damaged vessels. It is claimed that, at least for a time after being divided transversely, arteries as large as the radial artery constrict and stop bleeding; however, this is no excuse for delay in ligating the damaged vessel. Furthermore, arterial walls cut longitudinally or irregularly do not constrict in such a way that the lumen of the artery is occluded, and bleeding continues.

The Temporary Hemostatic Plug

When a blood vessel is damaged, the endothelium is disrupted, and an underlying layer of collagen is exposed. Collagen attracts platelets, which adhere to it and liberate serotonin and adenosine diphosphate (ADP). The ADP in turn rapidly attracts other platelets, and a loose plug of aggregated platelets is formed. ADP from disrupted red blood cells and tissue may also contribute to the initial aggregation. Formation of this temporary plug is unaffected by clinically used doses of the anticoagulants heparin and dicumarol (see below).

The Clotting Mechanism

The loose aggregation of platelets in the temporary plug is bound together and converted into the definitive clot by **fibrin.** The clotting mechanism responsible for the formation of fibrin involves a complex series, or "cascade," of reactions. The complexity of the system has in the past been compounded by variations in nomenclature, but acceptance of a numbering system for the various clotting factors (Table 27–7) has simplified the situation.

The fundamental reaction in the clotting of blood is conversion of the soluble plasma protein fibrinogen to insoluble fibrin (Fig 27–14). The process involves the release of 2 pairs of peptides from each fibrinogen molecule. The remaining portion, **fibrin monomer,** then polymerizes with other monomer molecules to form **fibrin.** The fibrin is initially a loose mesh of interlacing strands (Fig 27–6). It is converted by the formation of covalent cross-linkages to a dense, tight aggregate. This latter reaction is catalyzed by factor XIII, the fibrin-stabilizing factor, and requires Ca^{2+}.

The conversion of fibrinogen to fibrin is catalyzed by thrombin. Thrombin is a serine protease that is formed from its circulating precursor prothrombin by the action of activated factor X. Factor X can be activated by reactions that proceed along either of 2 pathways, an intrinsic and an extrinsic pathway (Fig 27–14).

The initial reaction in the **intrinsic pathway** is conversion of inactive factor XII to active factor XII. This activation can be brought about in vitro by exposing the blood to electronegatively charged wettable surfaces such as glass, micelles of long-chain saturated fatty acids, and collagen fibers. Activation in vivo presumably occurs when blood is exposed to the collagen fibers underlying the endothelium in the blood vessels. Active factor XII then activates factor XI, and active factor XI activates factor IX. In the presence of

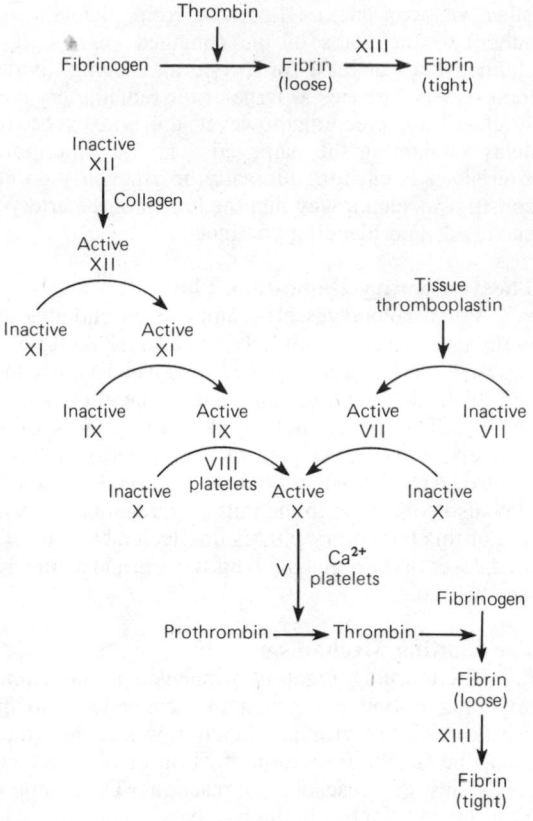

Figure 27–14. Diagrammatic summary of the clotting mechanism.

factor VIII and platelets, active factor IX activates factor X. In the presence of platelets, Ca^{2+}, and factor V, activated factor X catalyzes the conversion of prothrombin to thrombin.

The **extrinsic pathway** involves the activation of factor VII by tissue thromboplastin, a protein-lipid complex released from blood vessel walls and a variety of other tissues when they are damaged. Active factor VII activates factor X, which in turn catalyzes the conversion of prothrombin to thrombin.

Anticlotting Mechanisms

The tendency of blood to clot is balanced in vivo by a number of limiting reactions that tend to prevent clotting inside the blood vessels and to break down any clots that do form. These reactions include formation from activated factor X of an antithrombin (antithrombin III) and removal of some activated clotting factors from the circulation by the liver. The supply of clotting factors is also reduced to the degree that they are used up during clotting. Thromboxane A_2 promotes platelet aggregation and hence clotting, but its action is opposed by the simultaneous formation of PGI_2 (prostacyclin), which inhibits aggregation.

There is in addition a **fibrinolytic system** that limits clotting. The active component of this system is **plasmin**, or **fibrinolysin** (Fig 27–15). This enzyme lyses fibrin and fibrinogen, with the production of fibrinogen degradation products (FDP) that inhibit thrombin. Plasmin is formed from its inactive precursor, plasminogen, by the action of thrombin and possibly substances in tissues. There is also an **activator** in plasma that normally circulates as inactive **proactivator.** Proactivator is converted into activator by the action of proteolytic fragments of active factor XII called **prekallikrein activators.** The prekallikrein activators are also involved in the formation of kinins (see Chapter 31). They are formed by the action of plasmin on active factor XII. This positive feedback of plasmin on its own formation is limited, of course, by the available store of active factor XII and by various other limiting factors. The complex interactions between the fibrinolytic system, the coagulation system, and the kinin system are summarized in Fig 27–15, and the various processes involved in hemostasis are summarized in Fig 27–16.

Anticoagulants

Heparin, a potent anticoagulant normally found in the body, is a mixture of sulfate-containing mucopolysaccharides with a strongly acid reaction and a large electronegative charge. It acts as an anticoagulant by preventing the activation of factor IX and, in conjunction with a plasma cofactor, inhibiting the action of thrombin. It is also a cofactor for lipoprotein lipase (clearing factor; see Chapter 17). The highly basic protein protamine forms an irreversible complex with heparin and is used clinically to neutralize heparin.

Heparin and histamine are found in the granules of the circulating basophils and in the granules of the **mast cells,** wandering cells found in most tissues but most abundantly in connective tissue. Mast cells may liberate histamine in the tissues as part of the inflammatory reaction. The liver of the dog contains many mast cells that liberate their heparin into the bloodstream when anaphylactic shock is induced; but the liver of other species contains little heparin, and it has not been proved that heparin has any physiologic role in maintaining blood in the fluid state.

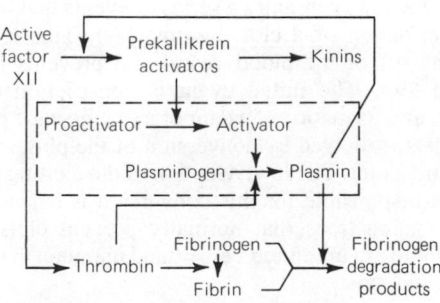

Figure 27–15. The fibrinolytic system. The immediate reactions that generate plasmin are enclosed in the dashed lines, and the interactions with the kinin system and the coagulation system are indicated above and below.

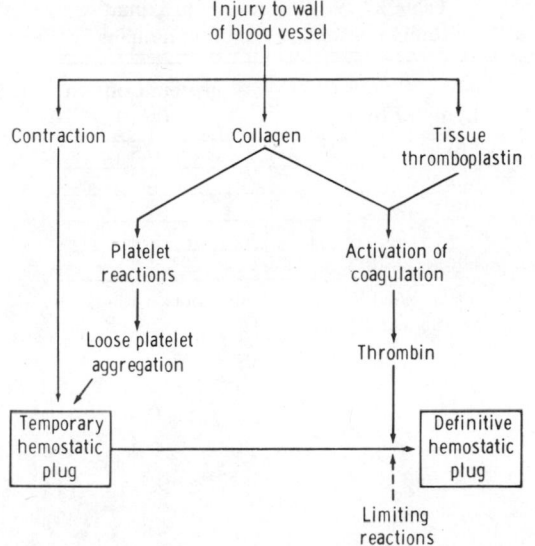

Figure 27–16. Summary of reactions involved in hemostasis. The dashed arrow indicates inhibition. (Modified and reproduced, with permission, from Deykin D: Thrombogenesis. N Engl J Med 276:622, 1967.)

Clotting can be prevented in vitro if Ca^{2+} is removed from the blood by the addition of substances such as oxalates, which form insoluble salts with Ca^{2+}, or citrate or other **chelating agents,** which bind Ca^{2+}. Coumarin derivatives such as **dicumarol** inhibit vitamin K. This vitamin catalyzes the synthesis of prothrombin and factors VII, IX, and X in the liver. Ten of the glutamic acid residues in prothrombin are normally converted to γ-carboxyglutamic acid residues by a vitamin K–dependent carboxylation in the liver. Coumarin derivatives are extensively used as anticoagulants.

Abnormalities of Hemostasis

In vivo, a plasma Ca^{2+} level low enough to interfere with blood clotting is incompatible with life, but hemorrhagic diseases due to selective deficiencies of almost all the other clotting factors have been described (Table 27–8). In some genetic conditions, normal clotting factors are replaced by abnormal factors. The absorption of the K vitamins, along with that of the other fat-soluble vitamins, is depressed in obstructive jaundice because of the lack of bile in the intestine and consequent depression of fat absorption. The resultant depression of prothrombin synthesis may cause the development of a significant bleeding tendency. Aspirin inhibits platelet aggregation by inhibiting the cyclo-oxygenase that catalyzes the formation of prostaglandins and thromboxanes. It may be of value in preventing the recurrence of strokes, but it is of little value in the prevention of venous thrombosis and rarely causes abnormal bleeding, probably because it does not inhibit aggregation to a sufficient degree.

When the platelet count is low, clot retraction is deficient and there is poor constriction of ruptured vessels. The resulting clinical syndrome (**thrombocytopenic purpura**) is characterized by easy bruisability and multiple subcutaneous hemorrhages. Purpura may also occur when the platelet count is normal, and in some of these cases, the circulating platelets are abnormal (**thrombasthenic purpura**).

Formation of clots inside blood vessels is called **thrombosis** to distinguish it from the normal extravascular clotting of blood. The functions of the fibrinolytic system and the balance between it and the clotting mechanism are under intensive investigation in an effort to shed more light on the pathogenesis of intravascular clotting. Thromboses are a major medical problem. They are particularly prone to occur where blood flow is sluggish, eg, in the veins of the calves after operations and delivery, because the slow flow permits activated clotting factors to accumulate instead of being washed away. They also occur in vessels such as the coronary and cerebral arteries at sites where the intima is damaged by arteriosclerotic plaques, and over areas of damage to the endocardium. They frequently occlude the arterial supply to the organs in which they form, and bits of thrombus (**emboli**) sometimes break off and travel in the bloodstream to distant sites, damaging other organs. Examples are obstruction of the pulmonary artery or its branches (**pulmonary embolism**) by thrombi from the leg veins, and embolism of cerebral or leg vessels by bits of clot breaking off from a thrombus in the left ventricle (**mural thrombus**) overlying a myocardial infarct.

Table 27–8. Examples of diseases due to deficiency of clotting factors.

Deficiency of Factor	Clinical Syndrome	Cause
I	Afibrinogenemia	Depletion during toxic pregnancy with premature separation of placenta; also congenital (rare)
II	Hypoprothrombinemia (hemorrhagic tendency in liver disease)	Decreased hepatic synthesis, usually secondary to vitamin K deficiency
V	Parahemophilia	Congenital
VII	Hypoconvertinemia	Congenital
VIII	Hemophilia A (classical hemophilia)	Congenital defect due to abnormal gene on X chromosome; disease is therefore inherited as sex-linked characteristic
IX	Hemophilia B (Christmas disease)	Congenital
X	Stuart-Prower factor deficiency	Congenital
XI	PTA deficiency	Congenital
XII	Hageman trait	Congenital

LYMPH

Lymph is tissue fluid that enters the lymphatic vessels. It drains into the venous blood via the thoracic and right lymphatic ducts. It contains clotting factors and clots on standing in vitro. Its protein content is generally lower than that of plasma but varies with the region from which the lymph drains (Table 27–9). It should be noted that interstitial fluid is not protein-free; it contains proteins that traverse capillary walls and return to the blood via lymph. Water-insoluble fats are absorbed from the intestine into the lymphatics, and the lymph in the thoracic duct after a meal is milky because of its high fat content (see Chapter 25). Lymphocytes enter the circulation principally through the lymphatics, and there are appreciable numbers of lymphocytes in thoracic duct lymph.

Table 27–9. Probable approximate protein content of lymph in humans.*

Lymph From	Protein Content (g/dl)
Ankle	0.5
Limbs	2
Intestine	4
Liver	6
Thoracic duct	4

*Data based on studies of various authors in humans and animals.

ORIGIN & SPREAD
OF CARDIAC EXCITATION

The parts of the heart normally beat in an orderly sequence: Contraction of the atria (**atrial systole**) is followed by contraction of the ventricles (**ventricular systole**), and during **diastole** all 4 chambers are relaxed. The heartbeat originates in a specialized **cardiac conduction system** and spreads via this system to all parts of the myocardium. The structures that make up the conduction system (Fig 28–1) are the **sinoatrial node** (SA node), the **internodal atrial pathways,** the **atrioventricular node** (AV node), the **bundle of His,** its branches, and the **Purkinje system.** The various parts of the conduction system and, under abnormal conditions, parts of the myocardium are capable of spontaneous discharge. However, the SA node normally discharges most rapidly, depolarization spreading from it to the other regions before they discharge spontaneously. The SA node is therefore the normal **cardiac pacemaker,** its rate of discharge determining the rate at which the heart beats. Impulses generated in the SA node pass through the atrial pathways to the AV node, through this node to the bundle of His, and through the branches of the bundle of His via the Purkinje system to the ventricular muscle.

Anatomic Considerations

In 4-chambered mammalian hearts, the SA node is located at the junction of the superior vena cava with the right atrium. The AV node is located in the right posterior portion of the interatrial septum (Fig 28–1). There are 3 bundles of atrial fibers that contain Purkinje type fibers and conduct impulses from the SA node to the AV node: the anterior internodal tract of Bachman, the middle internodal tract of Wenckebach, and the posterior internodal tract of Thorel. These fibers converge and interdigitate with the fibers in the AV node. The AV node is continuous with the bundle of His, which gives off a left bundle branch at the top of the interventricular septum and continues as the right bundle branch. The left bundle branch divides into an anterior fascicle and a posterior fascicle. The branches and fascicles run subendocardially down either side of the septum and come into contact with the Purkinje system, the fibers of which spread to all parts of the ventricular myocardium.

The histology of cardiac muscle is described in Chapter 3. The conduction system is composed of modified cardiac muscle that is striate but has indistinct boundaries. It is richer in glycogen and has more sarcoplasm than the rest of the cardiac muscle fibers. The atrial muscle fibers are separated from those of the ventricles by a fibrous tissue ring, and normally the only conducting tissue between the atria and ventricles is the bundle of His.

The SA node develops from structures on the right side of the embryo and the AV node from structures on the left. This is why in the adult the right vagus is distributed mainly to the SA node and the left vagus mainly to the AV node. Both areas receive adrenergic nerves from the cervical sympathetic ganglia via the cardiac nerves. Adrenergic fibers are distributed to the atrial and ventricular myocardium as well; the vagal fibers are probably distributed only to the nodal tissue and the atrial musculature.

Properties of Cardiac Muscle

The electrical responses of cardiac muscle and

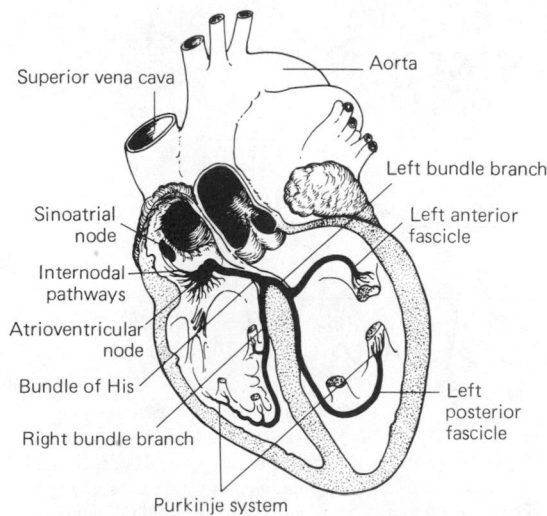

Figure 28–1. Conducting system of the heart. (Modified from Goldman MJ: *Principles of Clinical Electrocardiography,* 8th ed. Lange, 1973.)

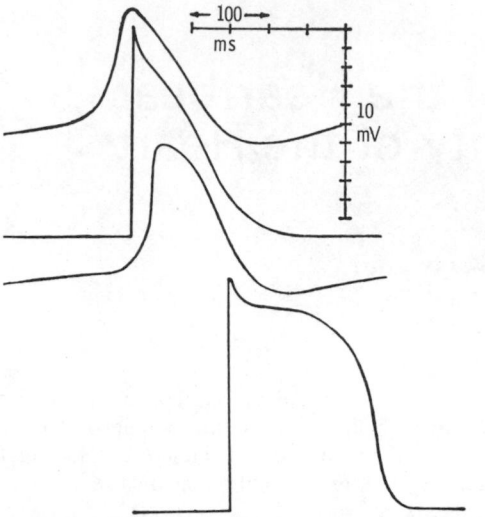

Figure 28–2. Typical transmembrane action potentials from (top to bottom) SA node, atrial muscle, AV node, and ventricular muscle fiber (all drawn on same time axis but with different zero points on the vertical scale). Note differences in configuration and sequence of activation. (Reproduced, with permission, from Hoffman EF, Cranefield J: *Electrophysiology of the Heart.* McGraw-Hill, 1960.)

nodal tissue and the ionic fluxes that underlie them are discussed in Chapter 3. Myocardial fibers have a resting membrane potential of approximately −80 mV. The individual fibers are generally separated from one another by membranes, but depolarization spreads radially through them as if they were a syncytium because of the presence of gap junctions. The transmembrane action potential of single cardiac muscle cells is characterized by rapid depolarization, a plateau, and a slow repolarization process (Figs 3–14 and 28–2). Recorded extracellularly, the action potential resembles the QRST pattern of the ECG (Fig 28–3). The initial depolarization is due to an increase in Na$^+$

permeability (increased conductance in Na$^+$ channels in the cell membrane), followed by a slower increase in Ca^{2+} permeability, which produces the plateau. Repolarization after the plateau is due to a delayed increase in K$^+$ permeability.

Rhythmically discharging cells have an unstable membrane potential that after each impulse declines to the firing level (**prepotential** or **pacemaker potential**; see Chapter 3). This triggers the next impulse. The prepotential is due to a steady decrease in K$^+$ permeability. The speed with which the membrane potential is reduced to the firing level determines the rate at which the tissue discharges. Prepotentials are normally prominent only in the SA and AV nodes (Fig 28–2), but there are "latent pacemakers" in other portions of the conduction system that can take over when the SA and AV nodes are depressed or conduction from them is blocked. Atrial and ventricular muscle fibers do not have prepotentials, and they discharge spontaneously only under abnormal conditions.

When the cholinergic vagal fibers to nodal tissue are stimulated, the slope of the prepotentials is decreased because the acetylcholine liberated at the nerve endings increases the permeability of nodal tissue to K$^+$ via muscarinic receptors. This decreases the rate of firing. In addition, acetylcholine decreases conductance in the Ca^{2+} channel via muscarinic receptors. Strong vagal stimulation may abolish spontaneous discharge for some time. Conversely, stimulation of the sympathetic cardiac nerves makes the membrane potential fall more rapidly, and the rate of spontaneous discharge increases (Fig 28–4). This is due to the adrenergic mediator norepinephrine, which, via

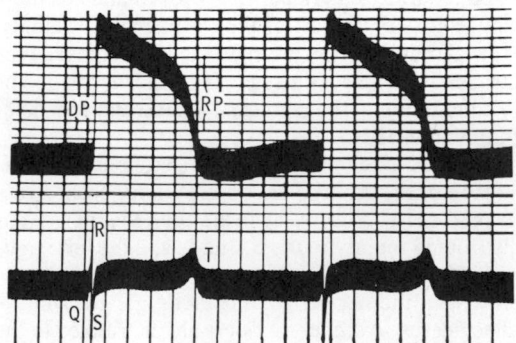

Figure 28–3. Action potential and surface ECG of cardiac muscle. Time lines, 0.1 s; DP, depolarization; RP, repolarization. (Reproduced, with permission, from Hecht HH: Normal and abnormal transmembrane potentials of the spontaneously beating heart. Ann NY Acad Sci 65:700, 1957.)

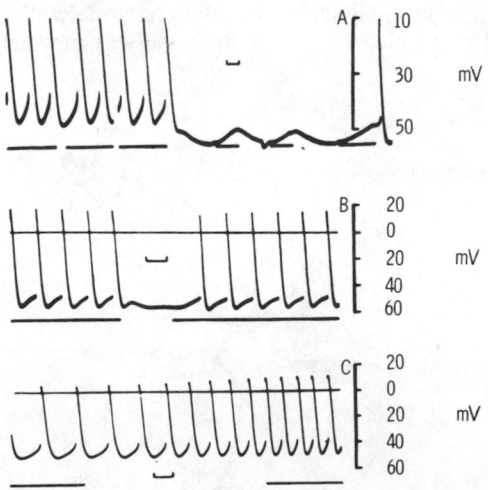

Figure 28–4. Effect of vagal stimulation (*A* and *B*) and sympathetic stimulation (*C*) on the pacemaker potentials of the sinus venosus of the frog heart. Stimulation periods are indicated by the breaks in the bottom trace in each case. Horizontal calibration marks, 1 s. (Reproduced, with permission, from Hutter OF, Trautwein W: Vagal and sympathetic effects on the pacemaker fibers in the sinus venosus of the heart. J Gen Physiol 39:715, 1956.)

Table 28–1. Conduction speeds in cardiac tissue.

Tissue	Conduction Rate (m/s)
SA node	0.05
Atrial pathways	1
AV node	0.05
Bundle of His	1
Purkinje system	4
Ventricular muscle	1

β-adrenergic receptors, produces an increase in the rate at which K^+ permeability declines between action potentials. In addition, norepinephrine acts via β-adrenergic receptors to increase conductance in the Ca^{2+} channel, thus making the action potential bigger and increasing the strength of each cardiac contraction.

The rate of discharge of the SA node and other nodal tissue is influenced by temperature and by drugs. The discharge frequency is increased when the temperature rises, and this may contribute to the tachycardia associated with fever. Digitalis depresses nodal tissue and exerts an effect like that of vagal stimulation, particularly on the AV node. The speeds of conduction in the various types of cardiac tissue are shown in Table 28–1.

Spread of Cardiac Excitation

Depolarization initiated in the SA node spreads radially through the atria, converging on the AV node. Atrial depolarization is complete in about 0.1 s. Because conduction in the AV node is slow, there is a delay of about 0.1 s (**AV nodal delay**) before excitation spreads to the ventricles. This delay is shortened by stimulation of the sympathetic nerves to the heart and lengthened by stimulation of the vagi. From the top of the septum, the wave of depolarization spreads in the rapidly conducting Purkinje fibers to all parts of the ventricles in 0.08–0.1 s. In humans, depolarization of the ventricular muscle starts at the left side of the interventricular septum and moves first to the right across the mid portion of the septum. The wave of depolarization then spreads down the septum to the apex of the heart. It returns along the ventricular walls to the AV groove, proceeding from the endocardial to the epicardial surface (Fig 28–5). The last parts of the heart to be depolarized are the posterobasal portion of the left ventricle, the pulmonary conus, and the uppermost portion of the septum.

THE ELECTROCARDIOGRAM

Because the body fluids are good conductors (ie, because the body is a **volume conductor**), fluctuations in potential that represent the algebraic sum of the action potentials of myocardial fibers can be recorded from the surface of the body. The record of these

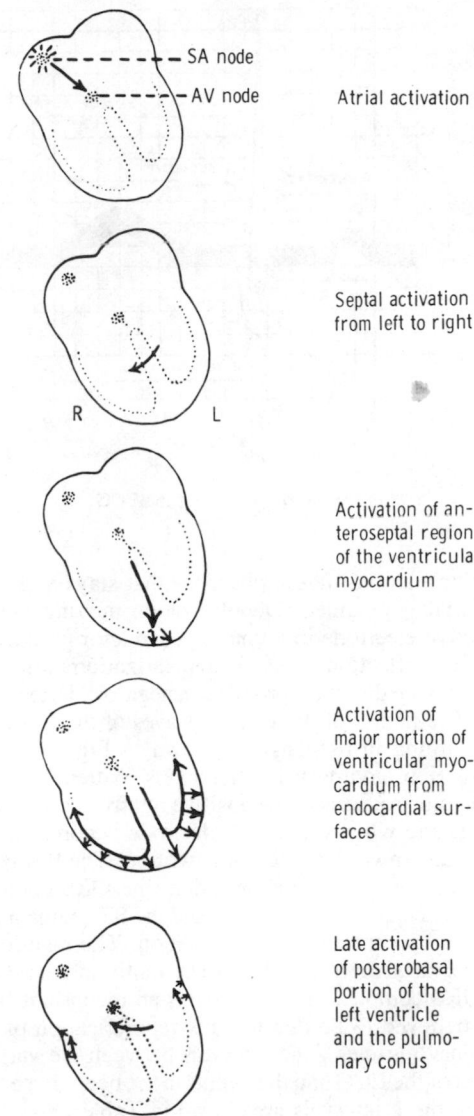

Figure 28–5. Normal spread of electrical activity in heart. (Reproduced, with permission, from Goldman MJ: *Principles of Clinical Electrocardiography,* 10th ed. Lange, 1979.)

potential fluctuations during the cardiac cycle is the **electrocardiogram (ECG).** Most electrocardiograph machines record these fluctuations on a moving strip of paper.

The ECG may be recorded using an **active** or **exploring** electrode connected to an indifferent electrode at zero potential (**unipolar** recording), or between 2 active electrodes (**bipolar** recording). In a volume conductor, the sum of the potentials at the points of an equilateral triangle with a current source in the center is zero at all times. A triangle with the heart at its center (**Einthoven's triangle**) can be approximated by placing electrodes on both arms and on the left leg. If these electrodes are connected to a common

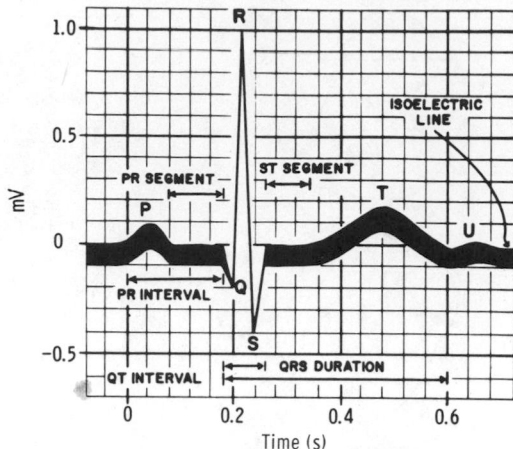

Figure 28-6. Waves of the ECG.

terminal, an indifferent electrode that stays near zero potential is obtained. Depolarization moving toward an active electrode in a volume conductor produces a positive deflection, whereas depolarization moving in the opposite direction produces a negative deflection.

The names of the various waves of the ECG and their timing in humans are shown in Fig 28-6. By convention, an upward deflection is written when the active electrode becomes positive relative to the indifferent; and when the active electrode becomes negative, a downward deflection is written. The P wave is produced by atrial depolarization, the QRS complex by ventricular depolarization, and the ST segment and T wave by ventricular repolarization. The manifestations of atrial repolarization are normally submerged in the QRS complex. The U wave is an inconstant finding, believed to be due to slow repolarization of the papillary muscles. The intervals between the various waves of the ECG and the events in the heart that occur during these intervals are shown in Table 28-2.

The magnitude and configuration of the individual waves of the ECG vary with the location of the electrodes. All of the waves are small compared with the transmembrane potentials of single fibers because the ECG is being recorded at a considerable distance from the heart.

Unipolar (V) Leads

Nine standard locations for the exploring electrode (**leads**) are used for routine clinical electrocardiography. The 6 unipolar chest leads (precordial leads) are designated V_{1-6} (Fig 28-7). The 3 unipolar limb leads are VR (right arm), VL (left arm), and VF (left foot). Since current flows only in the body fluids, unipolar limb records are those that would be obtained if the electrodes were at the points of attachment of the limbs, no matter where on the limbs the electrodes are placed. **Augmented** limb leads, designated by the letter a (aVR, aVL, aVF), are generally used. The augmented limb leads are recordings between one limb

and the other 2 limbs. This increases the size of the potentials by 50% without any change in configuration from the nonaugmented record because each augmented limb lead equals 3/2 of the unaugmented lead:

$$aVR = VR - \frac{(VL + VF)}{2}$$

$$2aVR = 2VR - (VL + VF)$$

Since VR + VL + VF = 0 (Einthoven's triangle),
$$VR = - (VL + VF)$$

Substituting for $- (VL + VF)$ in the second equation,
$$2aVR = 2VR + VR$$

Therefore, aVR = 3/2 VR

An esophageal electrode is sometimes used to study atrial activity. The electrode is inserted in a catheter and swallowed, and each esophageal lead is identified by the letter E followed by the number of centimeters from the teeth to the electrode tip. Thus, for example, lead E_{35} is a unipolar record in which the exploring electrode is 35 cm down the esophagus.

Bipolar Leads

Bipolar leads were used before unipolar leads were developed. The **standard limb leads,** leads I, II, and III, are records of the differences in potential between 2 limbs. In lead I, the electrodes are connected so that an upward deflection is inscribed when the left arm becomes positive to the right (left arm positive). In lead II, the electrodes are on the right arm and left leg, with the leg positive; and in lead III, the electrodes are on the left arm and left leg, with the leg positive.

Normal ECG

The ECG of a normal individual is shown in Fig 28-8. The sequence in which the parts of the heart are

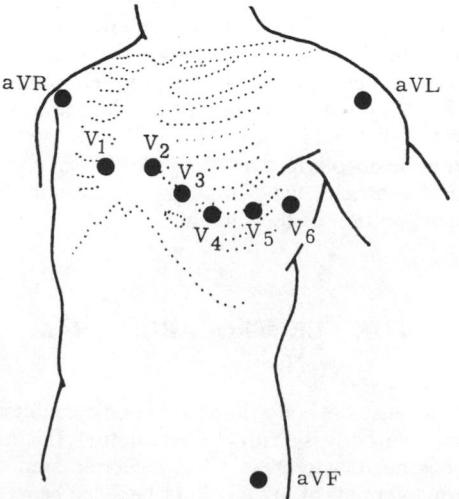

Figure 28-7. Unipolar electrocardiographic leads.

Table 28–2. ECG intervals.

	Normal Duration (s)		
	Average	Range	Events in Heart During Interval
PR interval*	0.18†	0.12–0.20	Atrial depolarization and conduction through AV node
QRS duration	0.08	to 0.10	Ventricular depolarization
QT interval	0.40	to 0.43	Ventricular depolarization plus ventricular repolarization
ST interval (QT minus QRS)	0.32	...	Ventricular repolarization

*Measured from the beginning of the P wave to the beginning of the QRS complex.
†Shortens as heart rate increases from average of 0.18 at rate of 70 to 0.14 at rate of 130.

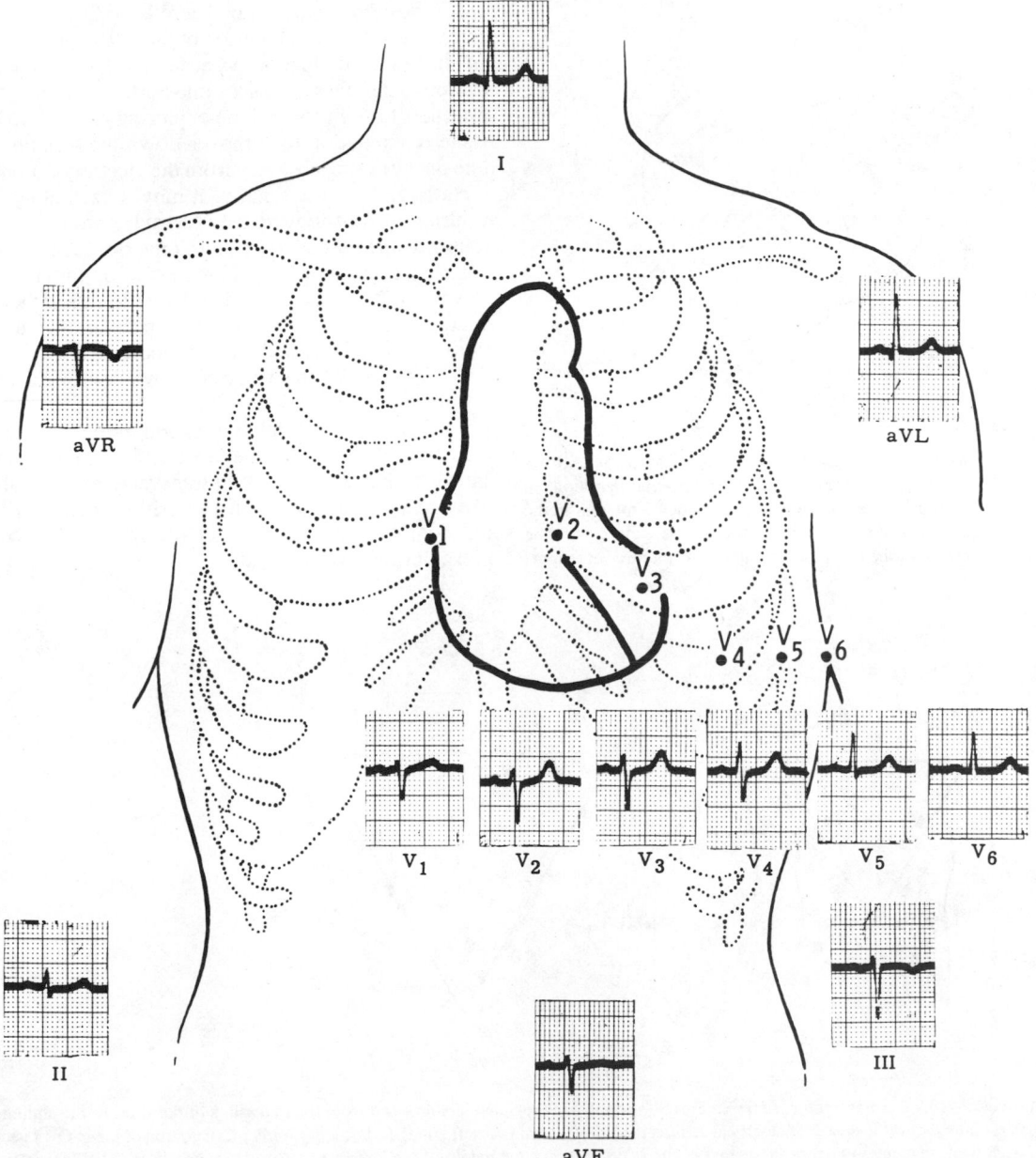

Figure 28–8. Normal ECG with heart in horizontal position. (Reproduced, with permission, from Goldman MJ: *Principles of Clinical Electrocardiography,* 10th ed. Lange, 1979.)

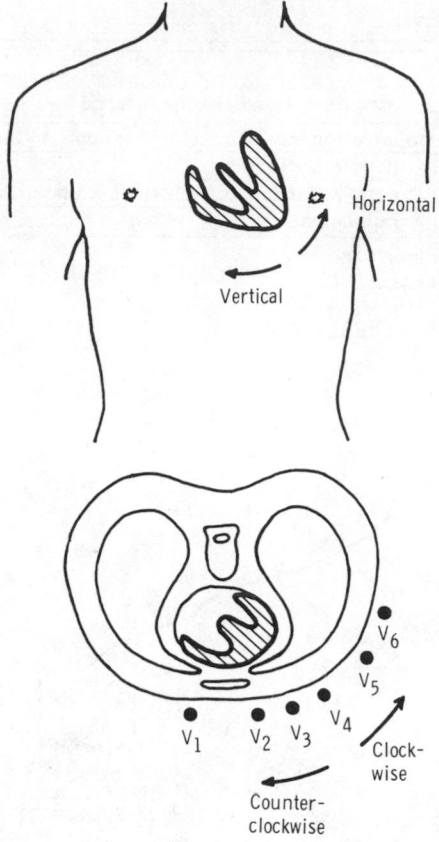

Figure 28–9. Diagram of position of heart in chest. Arrows indicate directions of cardiac rotation with normal variations in cardiac position. By convention, the direction of rotation in the horizontal plane is defined by its appearance as viewed from the inferior surface of the heart looking upward from the diaphragm.

depolarized (Fig 28–5) and the position of the heart relative to the electrodes are the important considerations in interpreting the configurations of the waves in each lead. The atria are located posteriorly in the chest. The ventricles form the base and anterior surface of the heart, and the right ventricle is anterolateral to the left (Fig 28–9). Thus, aVR "looks at" the cavities of the ventricles. Atrial depolarization, ventricular depolarization, and ventricular repolarization move away from the exploring electrode, and the P wave, QRS complex, and T wave are therefore all negative (downward) deflections; aVL and aVF look at the ventricles, and the deflections are therefore predominantly positive or biphasic. There is no Q wave in V_1 and V_2, and the initial portion of the QRS complex is a small upward deflection because ventricular depolarization first moves across the mid portion of the septum from left to right toward the exploring electrode. The wave of excitation then moves down the septum and into the left ventricle away from the electrode, producing a large S wave. Finally, it moves back along the ventricular wall toward the electrode, producing the return to the isoelectric line. Conversely, in the left ventricular leads ($V_{4–6}$), there may be an initial small Q wave (left to right septal depolarization), and there is a large R wave (septal and left ventricular depolarization) followed in V_4 and V_5 by a moderate S wave (late depolarization of the ventricular walls moving back toward the AV junction).

There is considerable variation in the position of the normal heart, since the heart rotates on the 2 axes shown in Fig 28–9 plus the transverse axis (rotation forward and backward). These position changes affect the configuration of the electrocardiographic complexes in the various leads.

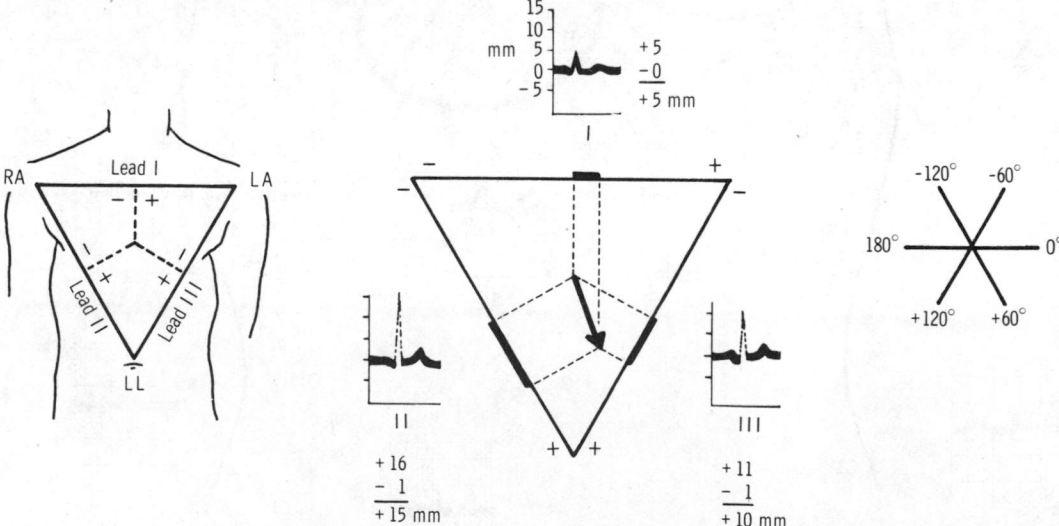

Figure 28–10. Cardiac vector. *Left:* Einthoven's triangle. Perpendiculars dropped from the midpoints of the sides of the equilateral triangle intersect at the center of electrical activity. RA, right arm; LA, left arm; LL, left leg. *Center:* Calculation of mean QRS vector. In each lead, distances equal to the height of the R wave minus the height of the largest negative deflection in the QRS complex are measured off from the midpoint of the side of the triangle representing that lead. An arrow drawn from the center of electrical activity to the point where perpendiculars extended from the distances measured off on the sides intersect represents the magnitude and direction of the mean QRS vector. *Right:* Reference axes for determining the direction of the vector.

Bipolar Limb Leads & the Cardiac Vector

Because the standard limb leads are records of the potential differences between 2 points, the deflection in each lead at any instant indicates the magnitude and direction in the axis of the lead of the electromotive force generated in the heart (**cardiac vector** or **axis**). The vector at any given moment in the 2 dimensions of the frontal plane can be calculated from any 2 standard limb leads (Fig 28–10) if it is assumed that the 3 electrode locations form the points of an equilateral triangle (Einthoven's triangle) and that the heart lies in the center of the triangle. These assumptions are not completely warranted, but calculated vectors are useful approximations. An approximate **mean QRS vector** ("electrical axis of the heart") is often plotted using the average QRS deflection in each lead as shown in Fig 28–10. This is a **mean** vector as opposed to an **instantaneous** vector, and the average QRS

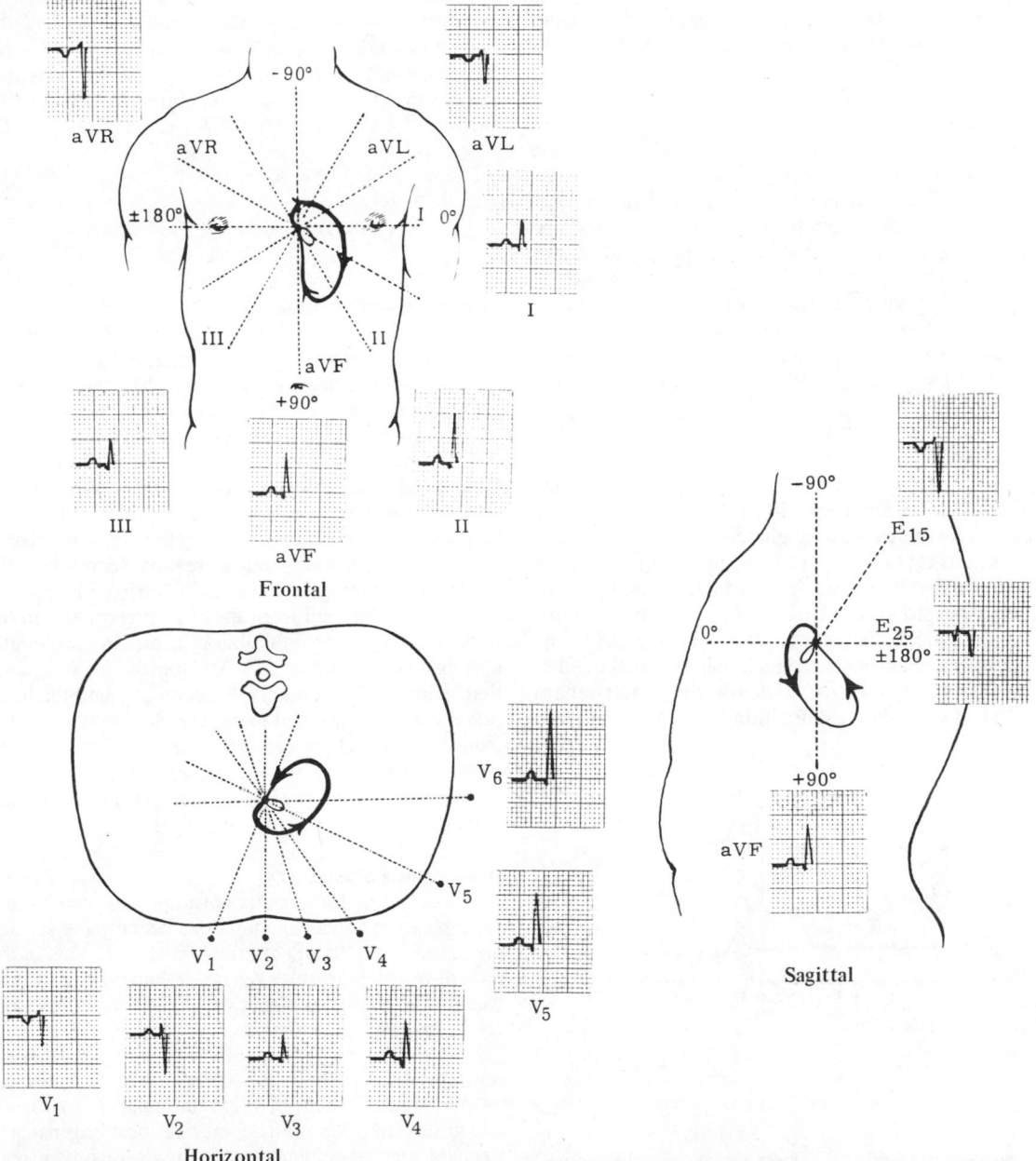

Figure 28–11. P (inner) and QRS (large outer) vectorcardiographic loops in a normal individual, with the corresponding standard and esophageal (E_{15} and E_{25}) leads of the ECG. (Reproduced, with permission, from Goldman MJ: *Principles of Clinical Electrocardiography,* 10th ed. Lange, 1979.)

deflections should be measured by integrating the QRS complexes. However, they can be approximated by measuring the net differences between the positive and negative peaks of the QRS. The normal direction of the mean QRS vector is generally said to be −30 to +110 degrees on the coordinate system shown in Fig 28–10. **Left** or **right axis deviation** is said to be present if the calculated axis falls to the left of −30 degrees or to the right of +110 degrees. Right axis deviation suggests right ventricular hypertrophy, and left axis deviation may be due to left ventricular hypertrophy. However, simple differences in heart position may produce axis values in the "abnormal" range, and there are better and more reliable electrocardiographic criteria for ventricular hypertrophy.

Vectorcardiography

If the tops of the arrows representing all of the **instantaneous** cardiac vectors in the frontal plane during the cardiac cycle are connected, from first to last, the line connecting them forms a series of 3 loops: one for the P wave, one for the QRS complex, and one for the T wave. This can be done electronically and the loops, called **vectorcardiograms,** projected on the face of a cathode ray oscilloscope. It is apparent that vectorcardiogram loops can be projected onto the horizontal and sagittal as well as the frontal planes (Fig 28–11).

His Bundle Electrogram

In patients with heart block, the electrical events in the AV node, bundle of His, and Purkinje system are frequently studied with a catheter containing ring electrodes at its tip that is passed through a vein to the right side of the heart and manipulated into a position close to the tricuspid valve. Three or more standard electrocardiographic leads are recorded simultaneously. The record of the electrical activity obtained with the catheter (Fig 28–12) is the **His bundle electrogram (HBE).** It shows an A deflection when the AV node is

activated, an H spike during transmission through the His bundle, and a V deflection during ventricular depolarization. With the HBE and the standard electrocardiographic leads, it is possible to accurately time 3 intervals (Fig 28–12): (1) the PA interval, the time from the first appearance of atrial depolarization to the A wave in the HBE, which represents conduction time from the SA node to the AV node; (2) the AH interval, from the A wave to the start of the H spike, which represents the AV nodal conduction time; and (3) the HV interval, the time from the start of the H spike to the start of the QRS deflection in the ECG, which represents conduction in the bundle of His and the bundle branches. The approximate normal values for these intervals in adults are PA, 27 ms; AH, 92 ms; and HV, 43 ms. The values serve to emphasize the relative slowness of conduction in the AV node (Table 28–1).

CARDIAC ARRHYTHMIAS

Normal Cardiac Rate

In the normal human heart, each beat originates in the SA node (**normal sinus rhythm, NSR**). The heart beats about 70 times a minute at rest. The rate is slowed (**bradycardia**) during sleep and accelerated (**tachycardia**) by emotion, exercise, fever, and many other stimuli. The control of heart rate is discussed in Chapter 31. In healthy young individuals breathing at a normal rate, the heart rate varies with the phases of respiration. The effect of respiration may be absent during quiet breathing but is readily seen when the depth of breathing is increased. During inspiration, impulses in the vagi from the stretch receptors in the lungs inhibit the cardioinhibitory center in the medulla oblongata (see Chapter 31). The tonic vagal discharge that keeps the heart rate slow decreases, and the heart rate rises. An additional factor is radiation of impulses from the inspiratory center to the cardioacceleratory center. During expiration, the rate decreases. This regular variation in rate is **sinus arrhythmia,** a normal phenomenon.

Abnormal Pacemakers

The AV node and other portions of the conduction system can in abnormal situations become the cardiac pacemaker. When an abnormal (**ectopic**) focus in the atria or ventricles discharges faster than the SA node, it can also take over as a pacemaker. Most of these foci are in or near nodal tissue.

A simple but enlightening experiment that demonstrates the hierarchy of pacemakers in the heart can be performed in cold-blooded animals such as frogs and turtles. In these animals, the heartbeat originates in a separate cardiac chamber, the **sinus venosus,** instead of in an SA node. There is no coronary circulation, the heart receiving O_2 by diffusion from the blood in the cardiac chambers. If a ligature (Stannius ligature I) is tied around the junction of the sinus venosus and right

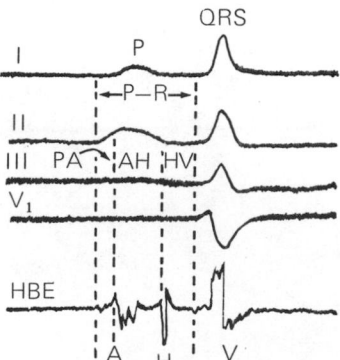

Figure 28–12. Normal His bundle electrogram (HBE). Simultaneously recorded leads I, II, III, and V_1 are also shown, and the durations of the PA, AH, and HV intervals are indicated. (Modified from Rosen KM: Catheter recording of His bundle electrograms. Mod Concepts Cardiovasc Dis 42:23, 1973.)

atrium, conduction from the sinus to the rest of the heart is prevented. The atria and ventricles stop for a moment, then resume beating at a slower rate as a focus in the atrium becomes the pacemaker for the portion of the heart below the ligature. If a second ligature (Stannius ligature II) is tied between the atria and ventricles, the ventricles stop, then resume beating at an even slower rate than the atria. With both ligatures in place, there are 3 separate regions of the heart beating at 3 different rates.

It is not possible to perform the Stannius experiment in mammals because the SA node is embedded in the atrial wall, and tying a ligature between the atria and the ventricles interrupts the coronary circulation, usually causing immediate ventricular fibrillation. However, experiments on laboratory mammals involving cooling or crushing of the SA and AV nodes and the "experiments of nature" in humans with diseased nodal tissue show that the same pacemaker hierarchy prevails.

When conduction from the atria to the ventricles is completely interrupted, complete, or third degree, heart block is said to be present, and the ventricles beat at a slow rate (**idioventricular rhythm**) independently of the atria (Fig 28–13). The block may be due to disease in the AV node (**AV nodal block**) or in the conducting system below the block (**infranodal block**). In patients with AV nodal block, the remaining nodal tissue becomes the pacemaker, and the rate of idioventricular rhythm is approximately 45 beats/min. In patients with infranodal block due to disease in the bundle of His, the ventricular pacemaker is located more peripherally in the conduction system, and the ventricular rate is slower; it averages 35 beats/min, but in individual cases it can be as slow as 15 beats/min. In such individuals, there may also be periods of asystole lasting a minute or more. The resultant cerebral ischemia causes dizziness and fainting (**Stokes-Adams syndrome**). Causes of third degree heart block include septal myocardial infarction and damage to the bundle of His during surgical correction of congenital interventricular septal defects. In infranodal block with

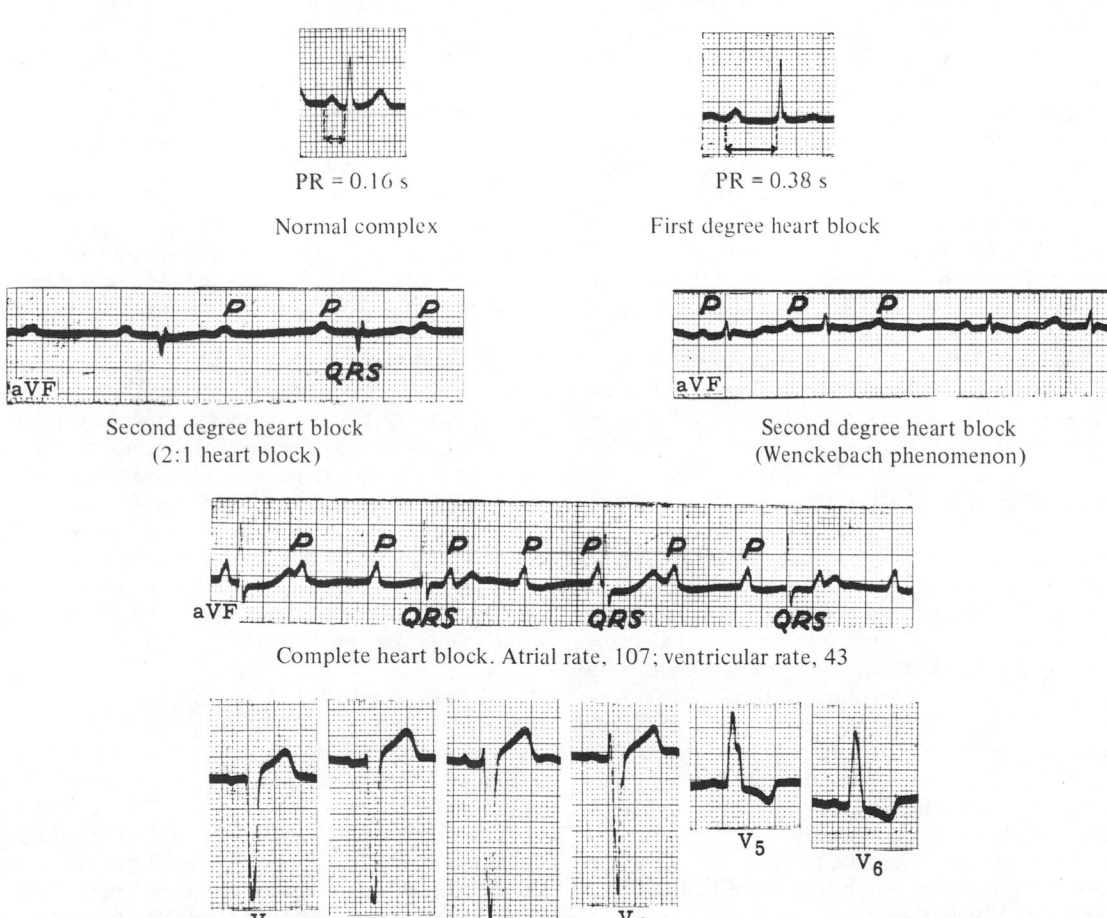

PR = 0.16 s

Normal complex

PR = 0.38 s

First degree heart block

Second degree heart block
(2:1 heart block)

Second degree heart block
(Wenckebach phenomenon)

Complete heart block. Atrial rate, 107; ventricular rate, 43

V leads in typical case of left bundle branch block

Figure 28–13. Heart block. (Tracings from Goldman MJ: *Principles of Clinical Electrocardiography,* 10th ed. Lange, 1979.)

Stokes-Adams syndrome, implantation of a permanent cardiac pacemaker is indicated in order to drive the ventricles at a more rapid, regular rate.

When conduction between the atria and ventricles is slowed but not completely interrupted, **incomplete heart block** is present. In the form called **first degree heart block,** all the atrial impulses reach the ventricles, but the PR interval is abnormally long. In the form called **second degree heart block,** not all atrial impulses are conducted to the ventricles. There may be, for example, a ventricular beat following every second or every third atrial beat (2:1 block, 3:1 block, etc). In another form of incomplete heart block, there are repeated sequences of beats in which the PR interval lengthens progressively until a ventricular beat is dropped **(Wenckebach phenomenon).** The PR interval of the cardiac cycle that follows each dropped beat is usually normal or only slightly prolonged (Fig 28–13).

Sometimes one branch of the bundle of His is interrupted, causing **right** or **left bundle branch block.** In bundle branch block, excitation passes normally down the bundle on the intact side and then sweeps back through the muscle to activate the ventricle on the blocked side. The ventricular rate is therefore normal, but the QRS complexes are prolonged and deformed (Fig 28–13). Block can also occur in the anterior or posterior fascicle of the left bundle branch, producing the condition called **hemiblock** or **fascicular block.** Left anterior hemiblock produces abnormal left axis deviation in the ECG, whereas left posterior hemiblock produces abnormal right axis deviation. It is not uncommon to find combinations of fascicle and branch blocks, and heart block can be due to combined lesions in the right bundle branch and both of the fascicles of the left bundle branch (trifascicular block). Use of the His bundle electrogram permits detailed analysis of the site of block when there is a defect in the conduction system.

Ectopic Foci of Excitation

A portion of the myocardium (or the AV node or bundle) sometimes discharges independently **(ectopic focus).** Such "irritable foci" are particularly common after an injury such as a myocardial infarction. If the focus discharges once, the result is a beat that occurs before the expected next normal beat and transiently interrupts the cardiac rhythm (atrial, nodal, or ventricular **extrasystole** or **premature beat**). If the focus discharges repetitively at a rate more rapid than that of the SA node, it produces rapid, regular tachycardia (atrial, ventricular, or nodal **paroxysmal tachycardia** or **atrial flutter**). A very rapidly and irregularly discharging focus or, more likely, group of foci in the atria or ventricles can produce **atrial fibrillation** or **ventricular fibrillation.**

Another cause of extrasystoles and rapid rhythms is a defect in conduction that causes normal depolarization to arrive late at a particular point and enter it by an abnormal route (reentry). An example of the latter mechanism involving the AV conduction system is

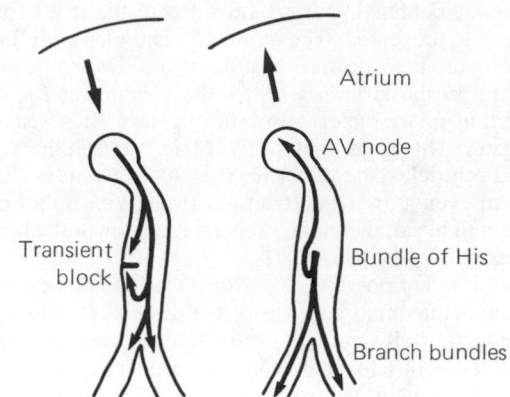

Figure 28–14. Retrograde conduction due to transient block in bundle of His. The transient block (indicated by the horizontal line) prevents anterograde conduction in a portion of the bundle, and this area is invaded from below. With generally slowed conduction, the area above the block has had time to recover and is no longer refractory. The result is reentry, retrograde conduction, and an atrial echo beat.

shown in Fig 28–14. In this example, part of the conduction system is transiently blocked by hypoxia or some other abnormality. Depolarization descends along the normal portion of the conduction system and reenters the previously blocked conduction pathway from below. Since the block has now worn off, this portion conducts in a retrograde fashion. At the normal rate of conduction, such reentrant activity tends to die out because the tissue above the block is still in the refractory period from the normal impulse. However, if the transient block is combined with generally slowed conduction resulting from the disease or some other condition causing the block, the refractory period may be over by the time the reentrant activity arrives. The reentrant activity depolarizes the atrium, and the resulting atrial beat is called an echo beat. In addition, the reentrant activity in the node can propagate back down the more normal portion of the bundle and again reenter, setting up a circular pattern of depolarization, or **circus movement.** The result in this instance would be a paroxysmal nodal tachycardia. Circus movements can also become established in the atria or ventricles.

Atrial Arrhythmias

Excitation spreading from an independently discharging focus in the atria stimulates the AV node and is conducted to the ventricles. The P waves of atrial extrasystoles are abnormal, but the QRST configurations are normal. The excitation depolarizes the SA node, which must repolarize and then depolarize to the firing level before it can initiate the next normal beat. Consequently, there is a pause between the extrasystole and the next normal beat that is usually equal in length to the interval between the normal beats preceding the extrasystole.

Atrial tachycardia occurs when an atrial focus discharges regularly at rates of 150–220/min (Table

28–3). Sometimes, especially in digitalized patients, some degree of atrioventricular block is associated with the tachycardia (**paroxysmal atrial tachycardia with block).** When the atrial rate is 200–350/min, the condition is called atrial flutter. Atrial flutter is almost always associated with 2:1 or 3:1 AV block because the normal AV node has a long refractory period and, in adults, it cannot conduct more than about 230 impulses per minute.

In atrial fibrillation, the atria beat very rapidly (300–500/min) in a completely irregular and disorganized fashion. Because the AV node discharges at irregular intervals, the ventricles beat at a completely irregular rate, usually 80–160/min (Table 28–3). Atrial fibrillation is probably due to reentrant activity in atrial muscle, with the production of a band of excitation that "chases its tail" in a continuous circular path through the atrial musculature. There appear to be, in addition, many irregularly discharging ectopic foci in the atrial muscle, and the relative contributions of the circus movement and the ectopic foci are not settled.

Consequences of Atrial Arrhythmias

Occasional atrial extrasystoles occur from time to time in most normal humans and have no pathologic significance. In paroxysmal atrial tachycardia and flutter, the ventricular rate may be so high that diastole is too short for adequate filling of the ventricles with blood between contractions. Consequently, cardiac output is reduced and symptoms of heart failure appear. The relationship between cardiac rate and cardiac output is discussed in detail in Chapter 29. Heart failure may also complicate atrial fibrillation when the ventricular rate is rapid. Acetylcholine liberated at vagal endings depresses conduction in the atrial musculature and AV node. This is why stimulating reflex vagal discharge by pressing on the eyeball (**"oculocardiac reflex"**) or massaging the carotid sinus often converts tachycardia and sometimes converts atrial flutter to normal sinus rhythm. Alternatively, vagal stimulation increases the degree of AV block, abruptly slowing the ventricular rate. Digitalis also depresses AV conduction and is used to slow a rapid ventricular rate in atrial fibrillation.

Table 28–3. Atrial arrhythmias. The tracings are portions of the continuous esophageal (E_{35}) ECG of a patient who manifested all the rhythms illustrated within a single 5-minute period.*

Rate of Discharge of Atrial Ectopic Focus	Arrhythmia
Occasional discharge at a rate slower than the basic sinus rhythm Atrial premature contractions (at arrows)	E_{35}
About 160 to about 220 Atrial tachycardia (with 1:1 conduction)	E_{35}
About 220 to about 350 Atrial flutter	E_{35}
Over 350 Atrial fibrillation	E_{35}

*Reproduced, with permission, from Goldman MJ: *Principles of Clinical Electrocardiography,* 10th ed. Lange, 1979.

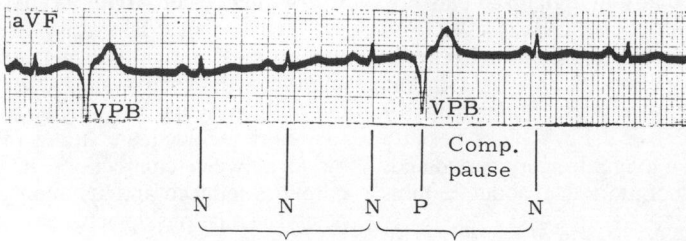

Figure 28–15. Ventricular premature beats (VPB). The lines under the tracing illustrate the compensatory pause and show that the duration of the premature beat plus the preceding normal beat is equal to the duration of 2 normal beats. (Tracing from Goldman MJ: *Principles of Clinical Electrocardiography*, 10th ed. Lange, 1979.)

Ventricular Arrhythmias

Extrasystoles that originate in an ectopic ventricular focus have bizarrely shaped prolonged QRS complexes (Fig 28–15) owing to the slow spread of the impulse from the focus through the ventricular muscle to the rest of the ventricle. They are usually incapable of exciting the bundle of His, and retrograde conduction to the atrium therefore does not occur. In the meantime, the next succeeding normal SA nodal impulse depolarizes the atria. The P wave is usually buried in the QRS of the extrasystole. If the normal impulse reaches the ventricles, they are still in the refractory period following depolarization from the ectopic focus. However, the second succeeding impulse from the SA node produces a normal beat. Thus, ventricular extrasystoles are followed by a **compensatory pause** that is longer than the pause after an atrial extrasystole. Furthermore, ventricular extrasystoles do not interrupt the regular discharge of the SA node, whereas atrial extrasystoles interrupt and "reset" the normal rhythm. These differences make it possible to distinguish between atrial and ventricular premature beats by palpation of the pulse or auscultation of the heart at the bedside. If one foot is tapped in time with the regular normal rhythm, the beats after an atrial

premature beat occur early with respect to the previous regular beats. However, the first normal beat after a ventricular premature beat occurs on the second foot tap after the premature beat because the duration of a ventricular extrasystole plus the preceding normal beat is equal to the duration of 2 normal beats (Fig 28–15).

Atrial and ventricular extrasystoles are not strong enough to produce a pulse at the wrist if they occur early in diastole, when the ventricles have not had time to fill with blood and the ventricular musculature is still in its relatively refractory period. They may not even open the aortic and pulmonary valves, in which case there is, in addition, no second heart sound (see Chapter 29).

Paroxysmal ventricular tachycardia is in effect a series of rapid, regular ventricular extrasystoles. In **ventricular fibrillation,** the ventricular muscle fibers contract in a totally irregular and ineffective way (Fig 28–16) because of the very rapid discharge of multiple ventricular ectopic foci or a circus movement. The fibrillating ventricles, like the fibrillating atria, are said to look like a quivering "bag of worms."

Ventricular extrasystoles are common and usually benign. Ventricular tachycardia is more serious because cardiac output is decreased, and ventricular

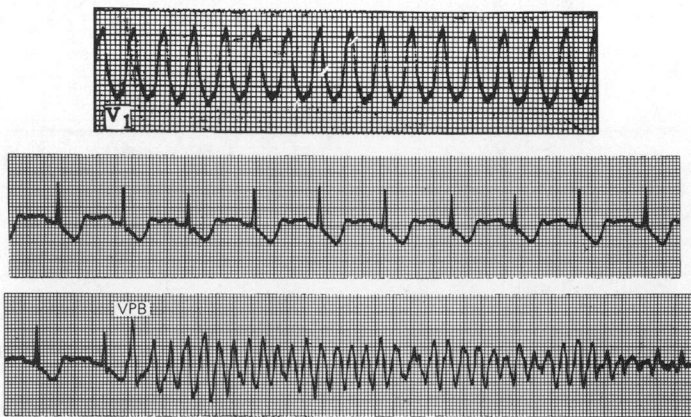

Figure 28–16. *Top:* Ventricular tachycardia. *Bottom 2 tracings:* Ventricular fibrillation triggered by a ventricular premature beat (VPB) in the vulnerable period in a patient with a myocardial infarct. The patient was immediately defibrillated electrically and made an uneventful recovery. (Tracings from Goldman MJ: *Principles of Clinical Electrocardiography*, 10th ed. Lange, 1979.)

fibrillation is an occasional complication of ventricular tachycardia. The fibrillating ventricles cannot pump blood effectively, and circulation of the blood stops. Therefore, in the absence of emergency treatment, ventricular fibrillation that lasts more than a few minutes is fatal. The most frequent cause of sudden death in patients with myocardial infarcts is ventricular fibrillation.

Ventricular fibrillation can be produced by an electric shock or an extrasystole during a critical interval, the **vulnerable period.** The vulnerable period coincides in time with the mid portion of the T wave—ie, it occurs at a time when some of the ventricular myocardium is depolarized, some is incompletely repolarized, and some is completely repolarized. These are excellent conditions in which to establish reentry and a circus movement.

Although ventricular fibrillation may be produced by electrocution, it can often be stopped and converted to normal sinus rhythm by means of electrical shocks. Electronic defibrillators are now kept in most hospital emergency rooms and should be used as rapidly as possible. Cardiac output and perfusion of the coronaries can be maintained in a patient with fibrillating ventricles by **cardiac massage.** Effective massage can be carried out without opening the chest. The person conducting external massage places the heel of one hand on the lower sternum above the xiphoid process and the heel of the other hand on top of the first (Fig 28–17). Pressure is applied straight down, depressing the sternum 4 or 5 cm toward the spine. This

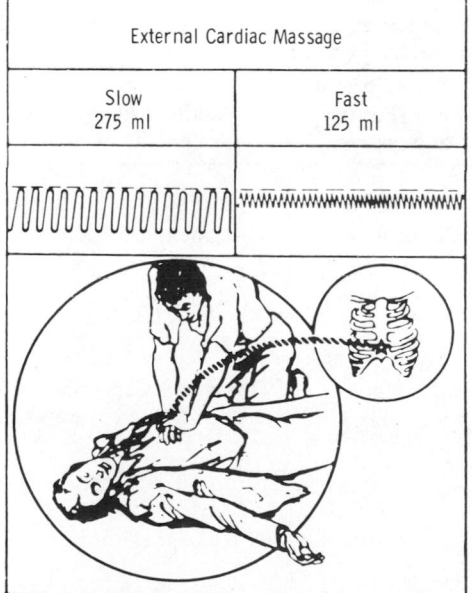

Figure 28–17. Technic of external cardiac massage. The lines above are a diagrammatic representation of the cardiac output produced by slow massage (275 ml/stroke) and fast massage (125 ml/stroke). (After Gordon AS. Reproduced, with permission, from Whittenberger JL: *Artificial Respiration: Theory and Application.* Harper & Row, 1962.)

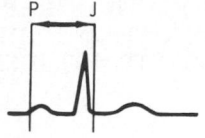

Normal sinus beat

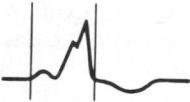

Usual accelerated conduction beat: short PR interval, wide and slurred QRS complex, normal PJ interval.

Figure 28–18. Accelerated AV conduction. (Reproduced, with permission, from Goldman MJ: *Principles of Clinical Electrocardiography,* 10th ed. Lange, 1979.)

procedure is repeated 60 times per minute. Manually squeezing the ventricles is also effective if the chest is already open, but emergency thoracotomies should not be performed.

Accelerated AV Conduction

An interesting condition seen in some otherwise normal individuals who are prone to attacks of paroxysmal atrial arrhythmias is **accelerated AV conduction (Wolff-Parkinson-White syndrome).** Normally, the only conducting pathway between the atria and the ventricles is the AV node. Individuals with Wolff-Parkinson-White syndrome probably have an additional aberrant muscular or nodal tissue connection **(bundle of Kent)** between the atria and ventricles. This conducts more rapidly than the slow-conducting AV node, and one ventricle is excited early. The manifestations of its activation merge with the normal QRS pattern, producing a short PR interval and a prolonged QRS deflection slurred on the upstroke (Fig 28–18), with a normal interval between the start of the P wave and the end of the QRS complex (''PJ interval''). The paroxysmal atrial tachycardias seen in this syndrome often follow an atrial premature beat. This beat conducts normally down the AV node but finds the aberrant bundle refractory, since the bundle has a longer refractory period than the AV node. However, when ventricular activation spreads to the aberrant bundle, it is no longer refractory, and the impulse is transmitted retrograde to the atrium. A circus movement is thus established.

Attacks of paroxysmal atrial arrhythmias are also seen in individuals with short PR intervals and normal QRS complexes **(Lown-Ganong-Levine syndrome).** In this condition, depolarization presumably passes from the atria to the ventricles via an aberrant bundle and then enters the intraventricular conducting system distal to the AV node.

ELECTROCARDIOGRAPHIC FINDINGS IN OTHER CARDIAC & SYSTEMIC DISEASES

Myocardial Ischemia

When the blood supply to a portion of myocardium is reduced and the cells are partially deprived of O_2, their repolarization becomes prolonged. The electrocardiographic manifestations of this change are negative or biphasic T waves over the ischemic area. T wave changes require careful interpretation. Many processes other than ischemia, some completely benign, cause T wave changes, and healthy patients have been made cardiac invalids by improper interpretation of minor changes.

Myocardial Infarction

When the blood supply to part of the myocardium is interrupted, there are prompt, profound changes in the myocardium that lead within minutes to hours to irreversible changes and death of muscle cells **(myocardial infarction).** The cause of myocardial infarction is usually occlusion of a coronary artery by a thrombus in a region narrowed by arteriosclerotic plaques (coronary thrombosis). The ECG is a very useful tool for diagnosing and localizing areas of infarction. The underlying electrical events and the re-

sulting electrocardiographic changes are complex, and only a brief review can be presented here.

The 3 major abnormalities that cause electrocardiographic changes in acute myocardial infarction are summarized in Table 28–4. The first change, abnormally rapid repolarization of the infarcted muscle fibers due to accelerated opening of K^+ channels, develops seconds after occlusion of a coronary artery in experimental animals. It lasts only a few minutes, but before it is over the resting membrane potential of the infarcted fibers declines because of the loss of intracellular K^+. Starting about 30 minutes later, the infarcted fibers also begin to depolarize more slowly than the surrounding normal fibers.

All 3 of these changes cause current flow that produces elevation of the ST segment in electrocardiographic leads recorded with electrodes over the infarcted area (Fig 28–19). Because of the rapid repolarization in the infarct, the membrane potential of the area is greater than it is in the normal area during the latter part of repolarization, making the normal region negative relative to the infarct. Extracellularly, current therefore flows out of the infarct into the normal area (since, by convention, current flow is from positive to negative; see Chapters 2 and 3). This current flows toward electrodes over the injured area, causing increased positivity between the S and T waves of the ECG. Similarly, the delayed depolariza-

Table 28–4. Summary of the 3 major abnormalities of membrane polarization associated with acute myocardial infarction and the ECG abnormalities they produce. Because of the characteristics of their input capacitors, ECG records show a TQ segment depression as an ST segment elevation.

Abnormality	Cause	Resultant Extra-cellular Current Flow (Positive to Negative)	Resultant ECG Change in Leads Over Infarct
During repolarization 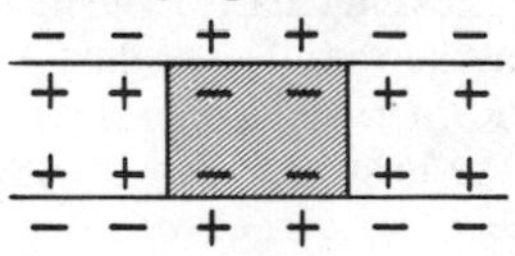	Rapid repolarization of infarcted cells	Out of infarct	ST segment elevation
At rest 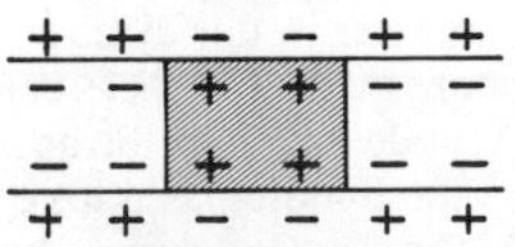	Decreased resting membrane potential of infarcted cells	Into infarct	TQ segment depression (manifest as ST segment elevation)
During repolarization 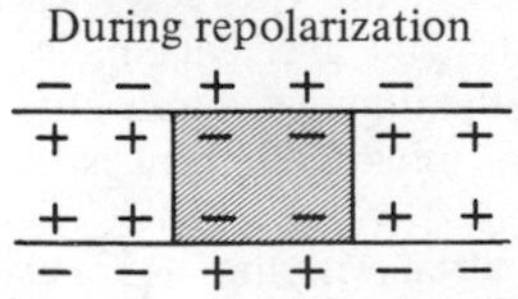	Delayed depolarization of infarcted cells	Out of infarct	ST segment elevation

Legend:

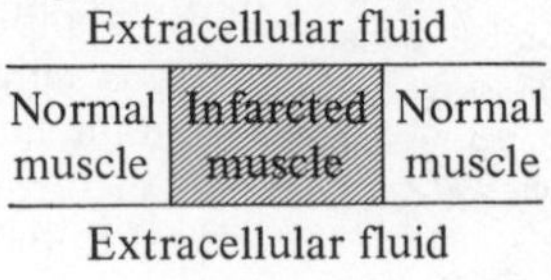

Extracellular fluid

| Normal muscle | Infarcted muscle | Normal muscle |

Extracellular fluid

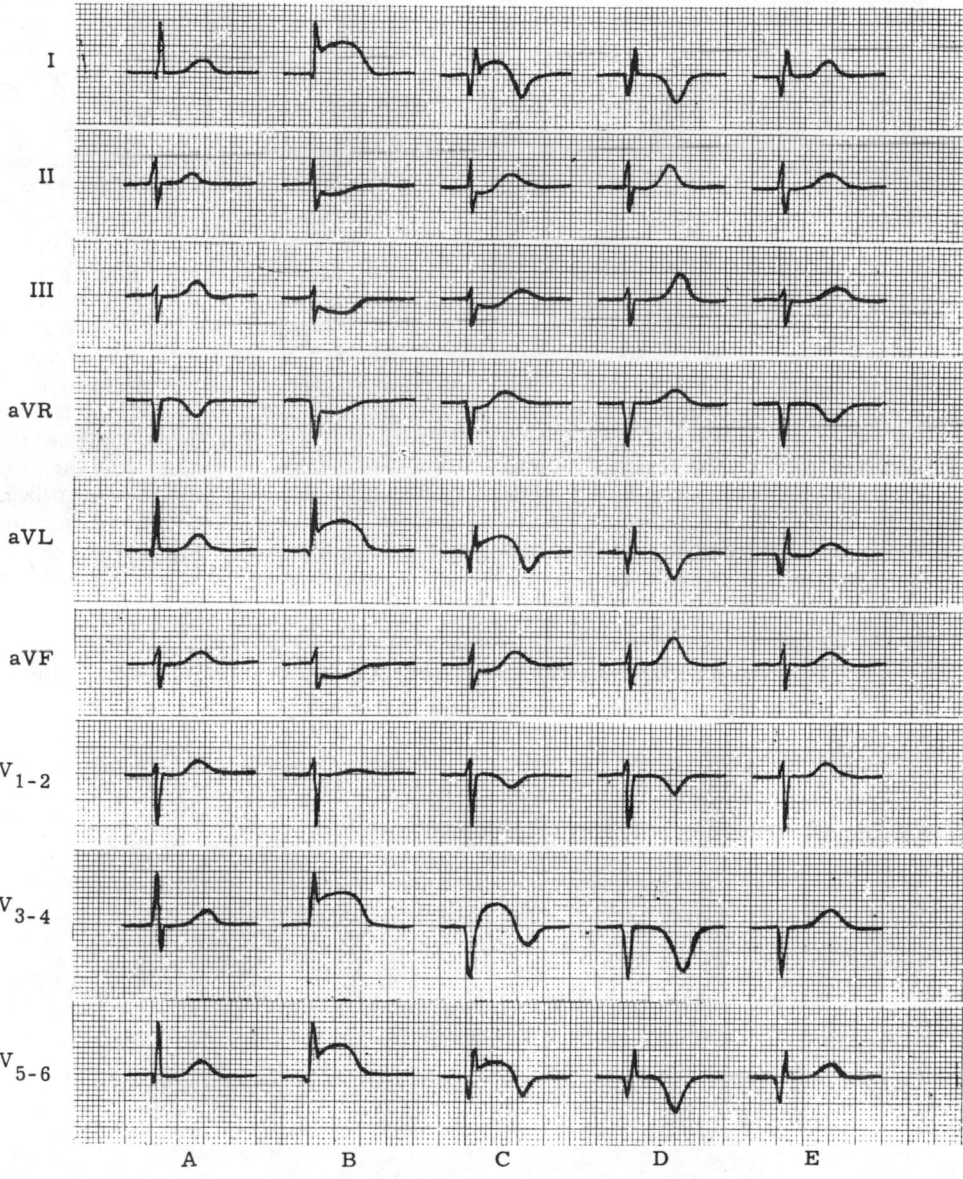

Figure 28–19. Diagrammatic illustration of serial electrocardiographic patterns in anterior infarction. *A:* Normal tracing. *B:* Very early pattern (hours after infarction): ST segment elevation in I, aVL, and V_{3-6}; reciprocal ST depression in II, III, and aVF. *C:* Later pattern (many hours to a few days): Q waves have appeared in I, aVL, and V_{5-6}. QS complexes are present in V_{3-4}. This indicates that the major transmural infarction is underlying the area recorded by V_{3-4}; ST segment changes persist but are of lesser degree, and the T waves are beginning to invert in those leads in which the ST segments are elevated. *D:* Late established pattern (many days to weeks): The Q waves and QS complexes persist; the ST segments are isoelectric; the T waves are symmetrical and deeply inverted in leads that had ST elevation and tall in leads that had ST depression. This pattern may persist for the remainder of the patient's life. *E:* Very late pattern: This may occur many months to years after the infarct. The abnormal Q waves and QS complexes persist. The T waves have gradually returned to normal. (Reproduced, with permission, from Goldman MJ: *Principles of Clinical Electrocardiography,* 10th ed. Lange, 1979.)

tion of the infarcted cells causes the infarcted area to be positive relative to the healthy tissue (Table 28–4) during the early part of repolarization, and the result is also ST segment elevation. The remaining change, the decline in resting membrane potential during diastole, causes a current flow into the infarct during ventricular diastole. The result of this current flow is a depression of the TQ segment of the ECG. However, the electronic arrangement in electrocardiographic recorders is such that a TQ segment depression is recorded as an ST segment elevation. Thus, the hallmark of acute myocardial infarction is elevation of the ST segments in the leads overlying the area of infarction (Fig 28–19). Leads on the opposite side of the heart show ST segment depression.

After some days or weeks, the ST segment abnormalities subside. The dead muscle and scar tissue become electrically silent. The infarcted area is therefore negative relative to the normal myocardium during systole, and it fails to contribute its share of positivity to the electrocardiographic complexes. The manifestations of this negativity are multiple and subtle. Common changes include the appearance of a Q wave in some of the leads in which it was not previously present and an increase in the size of the normal Q

wave in some of the other leads. Another finding in infarction of the anterior left ventricle is "failure of progression of the R wave"; the R wave fails to become successively larger in the precordial leads as the electrode is moved from right to left over the left ventricle. If the septum is infarcted, the conduction system may be damaged, causing bundle branch block or other forms of heart block.

Effects of Changes in the Ionic Composition of the Blood

Changes in ECF Na^+ and K^+ concentration would be expected to affect the potentials of the myocardial fibers because the electrical activity of the heart depends upon the distribution of these ions across the muscle cell membranes. Clinically, a fall in plasma Na^+ may be associated with low-voltage electrocardiographic complexes, but changes in the plasma K^+ level produce severe cardiac abnormalities. Hyperkalemia is a very dangerous and potentially lethal condition because of its effects on the heart. As the plasma K^+ level rises, the first change in the ECG is the appearance of tall peaked T waves, a manifestation of altered repolarization (Fig 28–20). At higher K^+ levels, there is paralysis of the atria and prolongation

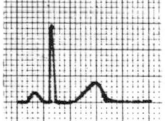

Normal tracing (plasma K^+ 4–5.5 mEq/L). PR interval = 0.16 s; QRS interval = 0.06 s; QT interval = 0.4 s (normal for an assumed heart rate of 60).

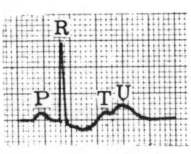

Hypokalemia (plasma K^+ ±3.5 mEq/L). PR = 0.2 s; QRS interval = 0.06 s; ST segment depression. A prominent U wave is now present immediately following the T. The actual QT interval remains 0.4 s. If the U wave is erroneously considered a part of the T, a falsely prolonged QT interval of 0.6 s will be measured.

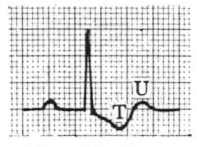

Hypokalemia (plasma K^+ ±2.5 mEq/L). The PR is lengthened to 0.32 s; the ST segment is depressed; the T wave is inverted; a prominent U wave is seen. The true QT interval remains normal.

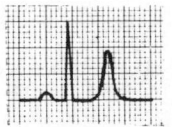

Hyperkalemia (plasma K^+ ±7.0 mEq/L). The PR and QRS intervals are within normal limits. Very tall, slender, peaked T waves are now present.

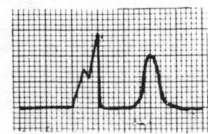

Hyperkalemia (plasma K^+ ±8.5 mEq/L). There is no evidence of atrial activity; the QRS complex is broad and slurred and the QRS interval has widened to 0.2 s. The T waves remain tall and slender. Further elevation of the plasma K^+ may result in ventricular tachycardia and ventricular fibrillation.

Figure 28–20. Correlation of plasma K^+ level and the ECG, assuming plasma Ca^{2+} is normal. The diagrammed complexes are left ventricular epicardial leads. (Reproduced, with permission, from Goldman MJ: *Principles of Clinical Electrocardiography,* 10th ed. Lange, 1979.)

of the QRS complexes. Ventricular arrhythmias may develop. The resting membrane potential of the muscle fibers decreases as the extracellular K^+ increases. The fibers eventually become unexcitable, and the heart stops in diastole. Conversely, a decrease in plasma K^+ causes prolongation of the PR interval, prominent U waves, and, occasionally, late T wave inversion in the precordial leads. If the T waves and U waves merge, the apparent QT interval is often prolonged; if the T and U waves are separated, the true QT interval is seen to be of normal duration. Hypokalemia is a serious condition, but it is not as rapidly fatal as hyperkalemia.

Increases in extracellular Ca^{2+} enhance myocardial contractility. When large amounts of Ca^{2+} are infused into experimental animals, the heart relaxes less during diastole and eventually stops in systole (**calcium rigor**). However, in clinical conditions as-sociated with hypercalcemia, the plasma Ca^{2+} level is rarely if ever high enough to affect the heart. Hypocalcemia causes prolongation of the ST segment and consequently of the QT interval, a nonspecific change also found in other clinical conditions.

Changes in plasma Ca^{2+} and K^+ levels produce relatively marked changes in the sensitivity of the heart to digitalis. Hypercalcemia enhances digitalis toxicity and hyperkalemia counteracts it. Mg^{2+}, which depresses the myocardium, also counteracts digitalis toxicity.

In experimental animals, acidosis increases the duration of diastole and decreases the strength of the heartbeat, but no electrocardiographic abnormalities specifically due to the changes in H^+ concentration of the body fluids in patients with acidosis or alkalosis have been demonstrated.

29 | The Heart as a Pump

MECHANICAL EVENTS OF THE CARDIAC CYCLE

The orderly depolarization process described in the previous chapter triggers a wave of contraction that spreads through the myocardium. In single muscle fibers, contraction starts just after depolarization and lasts until about 50 ms after repolarization is completed (Fig 3–14). Atrial systole starts after the P wave of the ECG; ventricular systole starts near the end of the R wave; and ventricular systole ends just after the T wave. The contraction produces sequential changes in pressures and flows in the heart chambers and blood vessels. It should be noted that the term **systolic pressure** in the vascular system refers to the peak pressure reached during systole, not the mean pressure; similarly, the **diastolic pressure** refers to the lowest pressure during diastole.

Events in Late Diastole

Late in diastole, the mitral and tricuspid valves between the atria and ventricles are open, and the aortic and pulmonary valves are closed. Blood flows into the heart throughout diastole, filling the atria and ventricles. The rate of filling declines as the ventricles become distended, and—especially when the heart rate is slow—the cusps of the atrioventricular (AV) valves drift toward the closed position (Fig 29–1). The pressure in the ventricles remains low.

Atrial Systole

Contraction of the atria propels some additional blood into the ventricles, but about 70% of the ventricular filling occurs passively during diastole. Contraction of the atrial muscle that surrounds the orifices of the venae cavae and pulmonary veins narrows their orifices, and the inertia of the blood moving toward the heart tends to keep blood in it; however, there is some regurgitation of blood into the veins during atrial systole.

Ventricular Systole

The initial portion of ventricular systole, the period of **isometric,** or **isovolumetric, ventricular contraction,** lasts until the aortic and pulmonary valves open. The AV valves close at the start of isometric contraction, and the ventricles contract on their contained blood. There is little muscle shortening, but the intraventricular pressure rises rapidly. This period lasts about 0.05 s. During isovolumetric contraction, the mitral and tricuspid (AV) valves bulge into the atria, causing a small but sharp rise in atrial pressure (Fig 29–2).

When the rising pressure in the left ventricle exceeds the diastolic pressure in the aorta (80 mm Hg; 10.6 kPa) and the right ventricular pressure exceeds the diastolic pressure in the pulmonary artery (10 mm Hg), the aortic and pulmonary valves open and the phase of **ventricular ejection** begins. Ejection is rapid at first, slowing down as systole progresses. The in-

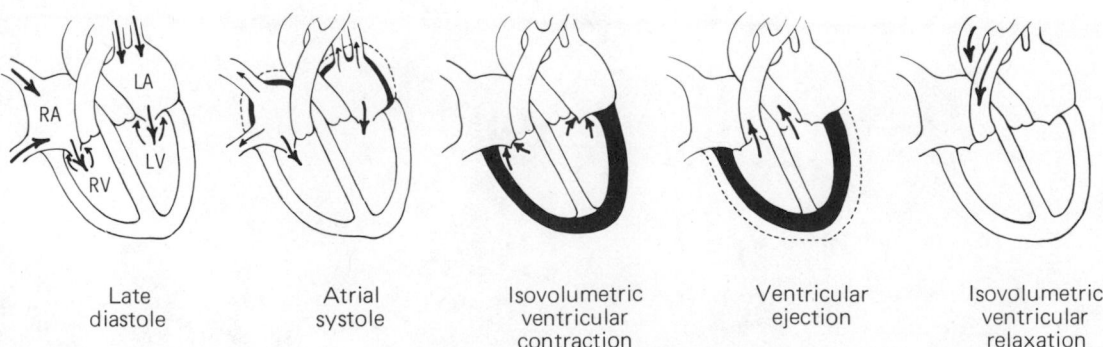

| Late diastole | Atrial systole | Isovolumetric ventricular contraction | Ventricular ejection | Isovolumetric ventricular relaxation |

Figure 29–1. Blood flow in the heart and great vessels during the cardiac cycle. The portions of the heart contracting in each phase are indicated in black. RA and LA, right and left atria; RV and LV, right and left ventricles.

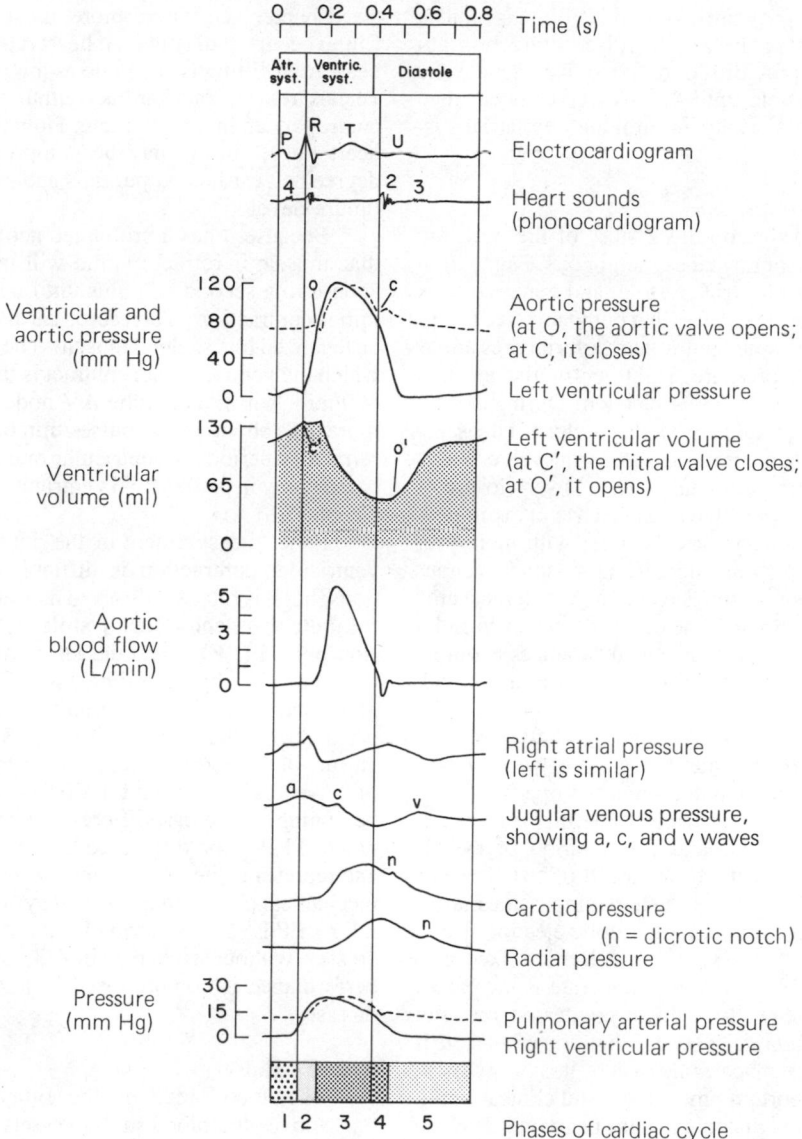

Figure 29–2. Events of the cardiac cycle at a heart rate of 75 beats/min. The phases of the cardiac cycle identified by the numbers at the bottom are as follows: 1, atrial systole; 2, isovolumetric ventricular contraction; 3, ventricular ejection; 4, isovolumetric ventricular relaxation; 5, ventricular filling. Note that late in systole, aortic pressure actually exceeds left ventricular pressure. However, the momentum of the blood keeps it flowing out of the ventricle for a short period of time. The pressure relationships in the right ventricle and pulmonary artery are similar. Atr syst, atrial systole. Ventric syst, ventricular systole.

traventricular pressure rises to a maximum and then declines somewhat before ventricular systole ends. Peak left ventricular pressure is about 120 mm Hg, and peak right ventricular pressure is 25 mm Hg or less. Late in systole, the aortic pressure actually exceeds the ventricular, but for a short period momentum keeps the blood moving forward. The AV valves are pulled down by the contractions of the ventricular muscle, and atrial pressure drops. The amount of blood ejected by each ventricle per stroke at rest is 70–90 ml. This leaves about 50 ml of blood in each ventricle at the end of systole (**end-systolic ventricular blood volume**).

Early Diastole

Once the ventricular muscle is fully contracted, the already falling ventricular pressures drop more rapidly. This is the period of **protodiastole**. It lasts about 0.04 s. It ends when the momentum of the ejected blood is overcome and the aortic and pulmonary valves close, setting up transient vibrations in the blood and blood vessel walls. After the valves are closed, pressure continues to drop rapidly during the period of **isovolumetric ventricular relaxation**. Isovolumetric relaxation ends when the ventricular pressure falls below atrial pressure and the AV valves open, permitting the ventricles to fill. Filling is rapid at first, then slows as the next cardiac contraction approaches. Atrial pressure continues to rise after the end of ventricular systole until the AV valves open, then drops and slowly rises again until the next atrial systole.

Timing

Although events on the 2 sides of the heart are similar, they are somewhat asynchronous. Right atrial systole precedes left atrial systole, and contraction of the right ventricle starts after that of the left (see Chapter 28). However, since pulmonary arterial pressure is lower than aortic pressure, right ventricular ejection begins before left ventricular ejection. During expiration, the pulmonary and aortic valves close at the same time; but during inspiration, the aortic valve closes slightly before the pulmonary. The slower closure of the pulmonary valve is due to a decrease in the impedance of the pulmonary vascular tree, with more prolonged ejection plus an increase in systemic venous return, which also prolongs ejection. When measured over a period of minutes, the output of the 2 ventricles is, of course, equal, but transient differences in output during the respiratory cycle occur in normal individuals.

Length of Systole & Diastole

Cardiac muscle has the unique property of contracting and repolarizing faster when the heart rate is rapid (see Chapter 3), and the duration of systole decreases from 0.3 s at a heart rate of 65 to 0.16 s at a rate of 200 (Table 29–1). The shortening is due mainly to a decrease in the duration of systolic ejection. However, the duration of systole is much more fixed than that of diastole, and when the heart rate is increased, diastole is shortened to a much greater degree. For example, at a heart rate of 65, the duration of diastole is 0.62 s, whereas at a heart rate of 200, it is only 0.14 s. This fact has important physiologic and clinical implications. It is during diastole that the heart muscle rests, and coronary blood flow to the subendocardial portions of the left ventricle occurs only during diastole.

Table 29–1. Variation in length of action potential and associated phenomena with cardiac rate. All values are in seconds. (Courtesy of AC Barger and GS Richardson.)

	Heart Rate 75/min	Heart Rate 200/min	Skeletal Muscle
Duration, each cardiac cycle	0.80	0.30	...
Duration of systole	0.27	0.16	...
Duration of action potential	0.25	0.15	0.005
Duration of absolute refractory period	0.20	0.13	0.004
Duration of relative refractory period	0.05	0.02	0.003
Duration of diastole	0.53	0.14	...

(see Chapter 32). Furthermore, most of the ventricular filling occurs in diastole. At heart rates up to about 180 beats/min, filling is adequate as long as there is ample venous return, and cardiac output per minute is increased by an increase in rate. However, at very rapid heart rates, filling may be compromised to such a degree that cardiac output falls and symptoms of heart failure develop.

Because it has a prolonged action potential, cardiac muscle is refractory and will not contract in response to a second stimulus until near the end of the initial contraction. Therefore, cardiac muscle cannot be tetanized like skeletal muscle. The most rapid rate at which the ventricles can contract is theoretically about 400/min, but in adults the AV node will not conduct more than about 230 impulses/min because of its long refractory period. A ventricular rate of more than 230 is seen only in paroxysmal ventricular tachycardia (see Chapter 28).

Exact measurement of the duration of isometric ventricular contraction is difficult in clinical situations, but it is relatively easy to measure the duration of **total electromechanical systole (QS_2), the preejection period (PEP),** and the **left ventricular ejection time (LVET)** by recording the ECG, phonocardiogram and carotid pulse simultaneously. QS_2 is the period from the onset of the QRS complex to the closure of the aortic valves, as determined by the onset of the second heart sound. LVET is the period from the beginning of the carotid pressure rise to the dicrotic notch. PEP is the difference between QS_2 and LVET and represents the time for the electrical as well as the mechanical events that preceed systolic ejection. The ratio PEP/LVET is normally about 0.35, and it increases without a change in QS_2 as left ventricular performance is compromised in a variety of cardiac diseases.

Arterial Pulse

The blood forced into the aorta during systole not only moves the blood in the vessels forward but also sets up a pressure wave that travels along the arteries. The pressure wave expands the arterial walls as it travels, and the expansion is palpable as the **pulse.** The rate at which the wave travels, which is independent of and much faster than the velocity of blood flow, is 5–8 m/s depending upon the age of the individual. In young adults, the pulse is felt in the radial artery at the wrist about 0.1 s after the peak of systolic ejection into the aorta (Fig 29–2). With advancing age, the arteries become more rigid, and the pulse wave moves faster.

The strength of the pulse is determined by the pulse pressure and bears little relation to the mean pressure. The pulse is weak ("thready") in shock. It is strong when stroke volume is large, eg, during exercise or after the administration of histamine. When the pulse pressure is high, the pulse waves may be large enough to be felt or even heard by the individual (palpitation, "pounding heart"). When the aortic valve is incompetent (aortic insufficiency), the pulse is particularly strong, and the force of systolic ejection may be sufficient to make the head nod with each heartbeat. The pulse in aortic insufficiency is called a **collapsing, Corrigan, or water-hammer pulse.** A water hammer is an evacuated glass tube half-filled with water that was a popular toy in the 19th century. When held in the hand and inverted, it delivers a short, hard knock.

The **dicrotic notch,** a small oscillation on the falling phase of the pulse wave caused by vibrations set up when the aortic valve snaps shut (Fig 29–2), is visible if the pressure wave is recorded but is not palpable at the wrist. There is also a dicrotic notch on the pulmonary artery pressure curve due to the closure of the pulmonary valves.

Atrial Pressure Changes & the Jugular Pulse

Atrial pressure rises during atrial systole and continues to rise during isovolumetric ventricular contraction when the AV valves bulge into the atria. When the AV valves are pulled down by the contracting ventricular muscle, pressure falls rapidly and then rises as blood flows into the atria until the AV valves open early in diastole. The return of the AV valves to their relaxed position also contributes to this pressure rise by reducing atrial capacity. The atrial pressure changes are transmitted to the great veins, producing 3 characteristic waves in the jugular pulse (Figs 29–2 and 29–3). The **a wave** is due to atrial systole. As noted above, some blood regurgitates into the great veins when the atria contract, even though the orifices of the great veins are constricted. In addition, venous inflow stops, and the resultant rise in venous pressure contributes to the a wave. The **c wave** is the transmitted manifestation of the rise in atrial pressure produced by the bulging of the tricuspid valve into the atria during

isometric ventricular contraction. The **v wave** mirrors the rise in atrial pressure before the tricuspid valve opens during diastole. The jugular pulse waves are superimposed on the respiratory fluctuations in venous pressure. Venous pressure falls during inspiration as a result of the increased negative intrathoracic pressure and rises again during expiration.

The jugular pulse can be recorded without catheterizing the vein by using a suitable transducer applied to the skin of the neck. Such recordings are rarely made today, but careful inspection at the bedside of the pulsations of the external jugular veins may give clinical information of some importance. For example, in tricuspid insufficiency there is a giant c wave with each ventricular systole. In complete heart block, when the atria and ventricles are beating at different rates, the a waves that are not synchronous with the radial pulse can be made out, and there is a giant a wave ("cannon wave") whenever the atria contract while the tricuspid valve is closed. It may also be possible to distinguish atrial from ventricular extrasystoles by inspection of the jugular pulse, because atrial premature beats produce an a wave, whereas ventricular premature beats do not.

Heart Sounds

Two sounds are normally heard through a stethoscope during each cardiac cycle: a low, slightly prolonged "lub" **(first sound),** caused by closure of the mitral and tricuspid valves at the start of ventricular systole; and a shorter, high-pitched "dup" **(second sound),** caused by closure of the aortic and pulmonary valves just after the end of ventricular systole. A soft, low-pitched **third sound** is heard about one-third of the way through diastole in many normal young individuals. It coincides with the period of rapid ventricular filling and is probably due to vibrations set up by the inrush of blood. A **fourth sound** can sometimes be heard immediately before the first sound when atrial pressure is high or the ventricle is stiff in conditions such as ventricular hypertrophy. It is due to ventricular filling and is rarely heard in normal adults.

The first sound has a duration of about 0.15 s and a frequency of 25–45 Hz. It is soft when the heart rate is slow, because the ventricles are well filled with blood and the leaflets of the AV valves float together before systole. The second sound lasts about 0.12 s, with a frequency of 50 Hz. It is loud and sharp when the diastolic pressure in the aorta or pulmonary artery is elevated, causing the respective valves to shut briskly at the end of systole. The interval between aortic and pulmonic valve closure during inspiration is frequently long enough for the second sound to be reduplicated (physiologic splitting of the second sound). Splitting also occurs in various diseases. The third sound has a duration of 0.1 s.

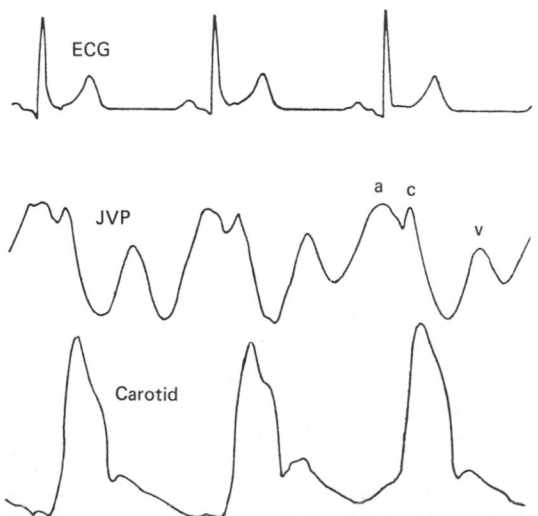

Figure 29–3. Jugular venous pressure record (JVP), showing *a, c,* and *v* waves, compared with the simultaneously recorded ECG and carotid pressure record. (Redrawn and reproduced, with permission, from Wood PW: *Diseases of the Heart.* Lippincott, 1956.)

Murmurs

Murmurs and **bruits** are abnormal sounds heard in various parts of the vascular system. Blood flows silently as long as the flow is smooth. However, if

Table 29–2. Heart murmurs.

Valve	Abnormality	Timing of Murmur
Aortic or pulmonary	Stenosis	Systolic
	Insufficiency	Diastolic
Mitral or tricuspid	Stenosis	Diastolic
	Insufficiency	Systolic

blood strikes an obstruction or passes through a narrow orifice at high speed, swirling vortices are set up that generate **vortical sounds.** Turbulent flow may also generate sound. Examples of sounds outside the heart are the bruit heard over a large, highly vascular goiter and the murmurs heard over an aneurysmal dilatation of one of the large arteries, an A-V fistula, or a patent ductus arteriosus.

The major but certainly not the only cause of cardiac murmurs is disease of the heart valves. When a valve is narrowed **(stenosis),** blood flow through it in the normal direction is turbulent. When a valve is incompetent, blood leaks through it in the wrong direction **(regurgitation** or **insufficiency).** The timing (systolic or diastolic) of a murmur due to stenosis or insufficiency of any particular valve (Table 29–2) can be predicted from a knowledge of the mechanical events of the cardiac cycle. Murmurs due to disease of a particular valve can generally be heard best when the stethoscope is over that particular valve, and there are other aspects of the duration, character, accentuation, and transmission of the sound that help localize its origin in one valve or the other. One of the loudest murmurs is that produced when blood flows backward in diastole through a hole in a cusp of the aortic valve. Most murmurs can be heard only with the aid of the stethoscope, but this high-pitched musical diastolic murmur is sometimes audible to the unaided ear several feet from the patient.

In patients with congenital interventricular septal defects, flow from the left to the right ventricle causes a systolic murmur. Soft murmurs may also be heard in patients with interatrial septal defects, although they are not a constant finding.

It should be emphasized that soft systolic murmurs are common in individuals, especially children, who have no cardiac disease. Systolic murmurs are also common in anemic patients as a result of the low viscosity of the blood and the rapid flow (see Chapter 30).

CARDIAC OUTPUT

Methods of Measurement

Two methods of measuring the output of the heart that are applicable to humans are the **direct Fick method** and the **indicator dilution method.**

The **Fick principle** states that the amount of a substance taken up by an organ (or by the whole body) per unit of time is equal to the arterial level of the substance minus the venous level (**A-V difference**) times the blood flow. This principle can be applied, of course, only in situations in which the arterial blood is the sole source of the substance taken up. The principle can be used to determine cardiac output by measuring the amount of O_2 consumed by the body in a period of time and dividing this value by the A-V difference across the lungs. Because arterial blood has the same content in all parts of the body, the arterial O_2 content can be measured in a sample obtained from any convenient artery. A sample of venous blood in the pulmonary artery is obtained by means of a cardiac catheter. Right atrial blood has been used in the past, but mixing of this blood may be incomplete, so that the sample is not representative of the whole body. An example of the calculation of cardiac output using a typical set of values is as follows:

$$\text{Output of left ventricle} = \frac{O_2 \text{ consumption (ml/min)}}{[A_{O_2}] - [V_{O_2}]}$$

$$= \frac{250 \text{ ml/min}}{\substack{190 \text{ ml/L arterial blood} - \\ 140 \text{ ml/L venous blood in} \\ \text{pulmonary artery}}}$$

$$= \frac{250 \text{ ml/min}}{50 \text{ ml/L}}$$

$$= 5 \text{ L/min}$$

It has now become commonplace to insert a long catheter through a forearm vein and to guide its tip into the heart with the aid of a fluoroscope. The idea of putting a catheter in the human heart so upset the superiors of the man who developed the technic of cardiac catheterization that he lost his job, but the procedure is now known to be essentially harmless. Catheters can be inserted not only into the right atrium but through the atrium down the inferior vena cava to the hepatic or renal vessels and through the right ventricle into the small branches of the pulmonary artery.

In the indicator dilution technic, a known amount of dye or radioactive isotope is injected into an arm vein, and the concentration of the indicator in serial samples of arterial blood is determined. The output of the heart is equal to the amount of indicator injected divided by its average concentration in arterial blood after a single circulation through the heart (Fig 29–4). The indicator must, of course, be a substance which stays in the bloodstream during the test and which has no harmful or hemodynamic effects. In practice, the log of the indicator concentration in the serial arterial samples is plotted against time as the concentration rises, falls, and then rises again as the indicator recirculates. The initial decline in concentration, linear on a semilog plot, is extrapolated to the abscissa, giving the time for first passage of the indicator through the

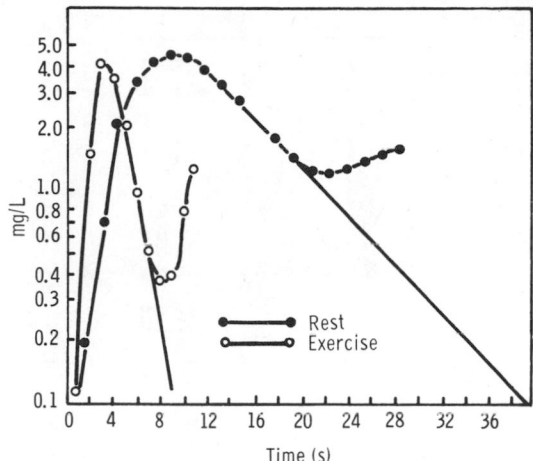

$$F = \frac{E}{\int_0^\infty Cdt}$$

F = flow
E = amount of indicator injected
C = instantaneous concentration of indicator in
      arterial blood

In the **rest** example above,

$$\frac{\text{Flow in 39 s}}{\text{(time of first passage)}} = \frac{5 \text{ mg injection}}{1.6 \text{ mg/L}}$$
$$\text{(avg concentration)}$$

Flow = 3.1 L in 39 s

$$\text{Flow (cardiac output)/min} = 3.1 \times \frac{60}{39} = 4.7 \text{ L}$$

For the **exercise** example,

$$\text{Flow in 9 s} = \frac{5 \text{ mg}}{1.51 \text{ mg/L}} = 3.3 \text{ L}$$

$$\text{Flow/min} = 3.3 \times \frac{60}{9} = 22.0 \text{ L}$$

Figure 29–4. Determination of cardiac output by indicator (dye) dilution. (Data and graph from Asmussen E, Nielsen M: The cardiac output in rest and work determined by the acetylene and the dye injection methods. Acta Physiol Scand 27:217, 1952.)

circulation. The cardiac output for that period of time is calculated (Fig 29–4) and then converted to output per minute. Similar estimates of ventricular output have been made by injecting a suitable radioactive substance (radionuclide) and monitoring radioactivity over the heart during the first pass of the radionuclide through it. Another technic involves injection of a contrast medium and serial x-ray pictures. Radionuclides are of additional interest because they can be used to demonstrate myocardial infarcts. Some radio-

nuclides are only taken up by normal tissue, whereas others are only taken up by infarcts.

Another method that has been used to measure cardiac output in humans is **ballistocardiography.** In accordance with Newton's third law of motion, the forces generated by the movements of the heart and the impact of the ejected blood on the aorta and pulmonary artery are opposed by "opposite and equal" recoil reactions. The operation of these forces has been observed by anyone who has stood on a scale and watched the pointer move with each heartbeat. The **ballistocardiogram** is a record of the to-and-fro movements of the body in the headward-footward direction when the subject lies on a suitably suspended table. However, values for stroke volume calculated from these records have proved to be unreliable.

Ventricular output and other aspects of cardiac function can be evaluated by **echocardiography,** a noninvasive technic that does not involve injections or insertion of a catheter. In echocardiography, pulses of ultrasonic waves, commonly at a frequency of 2.25 MHz, are emitted from a transducer that also functions as a receiver to detect waves reflected back from various parts of the heart. Reflections occur wherever acoustic impedance changes, and a recording of the echoes displayed against time on an oscilloscope provides a record of the movements of the ventricular wall, septum, and valves during the cardiac cycle. This technic has considerable clinical usefulness, but it is still in the stage of development, and analysis of the records obtained requires considerable skill and experience.

Cardiac Output in Various Conditions

The amount of blood pumped out of each ventricle per beat, the **stroke volume,** is about 80 ml in a resting man of average size in the supine position (80 ml from the left ventricle and 80 ml from the right, with the 2 ventricular pumps in series). The output of the heart per unit time is the **cardiac output.** In a resting,

Table 29–3. Effect of various conditions on cardiac output. Approximate percentage changes are shown in parentheses.

	Condition or Factor
No change	Sleep Moderate changes in environmental temperature
Increase	Anxiety and excitement (50–100%) Eating (30%) Exercise (up to 700%) High environmental temperature Pregnancy (late) Epinephrine Histamine
Decrease	Sitting or standing from lying position (20–30%) Rapid arrhythmias Heart disease

supine male, it averages about 5.5 L/min (80 ml × 69
beats/min). There is a correlation between resting cardiac output and body surface area. The output per
minute per square meter of body surface (the **cardiac
index**) averages 3.2 liters. The effects of various conditions on cardiac output are summarized in Table
29–3.

Factors Controlling Cardiac Output

Variations in cardiac output can be produced by
changes in cardiac rate or stroke volume (Fig 29–5).
The cardiac rate is controlled primarily by the cardiac
innervation, sympathetic stimulation increasing the
rate and parasympathetic stimulation decreasing it (see
Chapter 28). The stroke volume is also determined in
part by neural input, sympathetic stimuli making the
myocardial muscle fibers contract with greater
strength at any given length, and parasympathetic
stimuli having the opposite effect. When the strength
of contraction increases without an increase in fiber
length, more of the blood that normally remains in the
ventricles is expelled, and the end-systolic ventricular
blood volume falls. The cardiac accelerator action of
the catecholamines liberated by sympathetic stimulation is referred to as their **chronotropic action,**
whereas their effect on the strength of cardiac contraction is called their **inotropic action.** Factors which
increase the strength of cardiac contraction are said to
be positively inotropic; those which decrease it are said
to be negatively inotropic.

Stroke volume also varies with the length of the
cardiac muscle fibers (see below), and this effect is
independent of innervation. Regulation of output due
to changes in cardiac muscle fiber length is sometimes
called **heterometric regulation,** whereas regulation

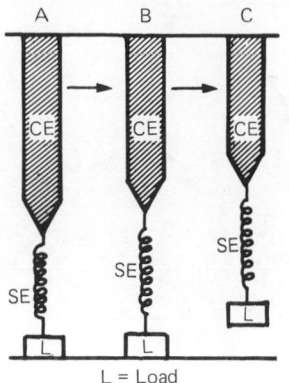

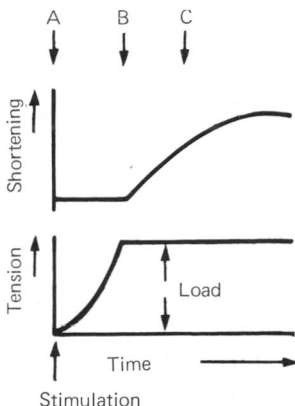

Figure 29–6. Model for isotonic contraction of afterloaded
muscles. *A:* Rest. *B:* Partial contraction of the contractile element
of the muscle (CE), with stretching of the series elastic element
(SE) but no shortening. *C:* Complete contraction, with shortening. (Reproduced, with permission, from Sonnenblick EH in: *The
Myocardial Cell: Structure, Function and Modification.* Briller
SA, Conn HL [editors]. Univ of Pennsylvania Press, 1966.)

due to changes in contractility independent of length is
sometimes called **homometric regulation.**

The force of contraction of cardiac muscle is
dependent upon its preloading and its afterloading.
These factors are illustrated in Fig 29–6, in which a
muscle strip is stretched by a load (the **preload**) that
rests on a platform. The initial phase of the contraction
is isometric; the elastic component in series with the
contractile element is stretched, and tension increases
until it is just sufficient to lift the load (**afterload**). The
muscle then contracts isotonically without developing
further tension. In vivo, the preload is the degree to
which the myocardium is stretched before it contracts
and the afterload is the resistance against which blood
is expelled.

Relation of Tension to Length in Cardiac Muscle

The length-tension relationship in cardiac muscle
(Fig 3–16) is similar to that in skeletal muscle (Fig
3–10); as the muscle is stretched, the developed tension increases to a maximum and then declines as

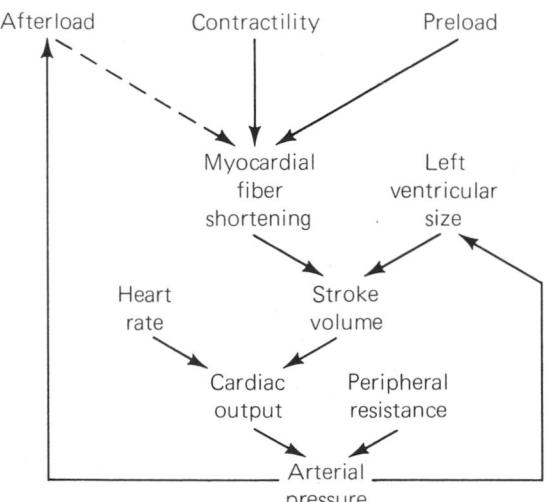

Figure 29–5. Interactions between the components that regulate cardiac output and arterial pressure. Solid lines indicate
increases, and the dashed line indicates a decrease. (Modified
from Braunwald E: Regulation of the circulation. N Engl J Med
290:1124, 1974.)

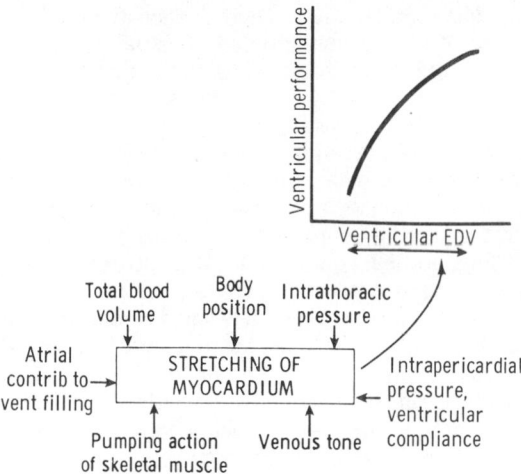

Figure 29–7. Relation between ventricular end-diastolic volume (EDV) and ventricular performance (Frank-Starling curve), with a summary of the major factors affecting EDV. (Modified from Braunwald E, Ross J, Sonnenblick EH: Mechanisms of contraction of the normal and failing heart. N Engl J Med 277:794, 1967. Courtesy of Little, Brown, Inc.)

stretch becomes more extreme. Starling pointed this out when he stated that the "energy of contraction is proportional to the initial length of the cardiac muscle fiber." This pronouncement has come to be known as **Starling's law of the heart,** or the **Frank-Starling law.** For the heart, the length of the muscle fibers (ie, the extent of the preload) is proportionate to the end-diastolic volume. The relation between ventricular performance and end-diastolic volume that is brought about through the operation of the Frank-Starling mechanism is shown in Fig 29–7. This figure also lists the principal factors that affect the end-diastolic volume. An increase in intrapericardial pressure limits the extent to which the ventricle can fill. Atrial contractions aid ventricular filling. So does a decrease in ventricular compliance, ie, an increase in ventricular stiffness produced by myocardial infarction, infiltrative disease, and other abnormalities. The other factors affect the amount of blood returning to the heart and hence the degree of cardiac filling during diastole. A reduction in total blood volume reduces venous return. Constriction of the veins reduces the size of the venous reservoirs, decreasing venous pooling and thus increasing venous return. An increase in the normal negative intrathoracic pressure increases the pressure gradient along which blood flows to the heart, whereas a decrease impedes venous return.

Effect of Changes in Aortic Impedance

The strength of cardiac contractions is also determined by the resistance, or impedance, against which the ventricles pump blood. This impedance is low in the pulmonary artery, but the aortic impedance is high. It is proportionate to the resistance to flow through the aortic valve and the systemic blood pressure.

The effect of changes in aortic impedance can be demonstrated in the **heart-lung preparation.** In this preparation, the heart and lungs of an experimental animal, usually a dog, are cannulated in such a way that blood flows from the aorta through a system of tubing and reservoirs to the right atrium, and from there through the animal's heart and lungs back to the aorta. Deprived of its blood supply, the rest of the animal dies, so that the heart is functionally denervated and the heart rate varies little if at all. By changing the caliber of the outflow tubing, the resistance against which the heart pumps (**"peripheral resistance"**) can be varied; and by raising or lowering the reservoir emptying into the right atrium, the amount of blood returning to the heart (**"venous return"**) can also be varied. One version of this preparation is shown in Fig 29–8. A **bell cardiometer** or, more recently, one of a variety of electronic devices is used to measure the volume of the heart. Cardiac volume varies with the amount of blood in the heart and is therefore a measure of the length to which the cardiac muscle fibers are stretched.

In the heart-lung preparation, when the pressure against which the heart is pumping is raised, the heart puts out less blood than it receives for several beats. Blood accumulates in the ventricles, and the size of the heart increases. The distended heart beats more forcefully, and output returns to its previous level. Conversely, when the resistance is reduced, output rises transiently but the size of the heart decreases, and output falls to the previous constant level (Fig 29–9).

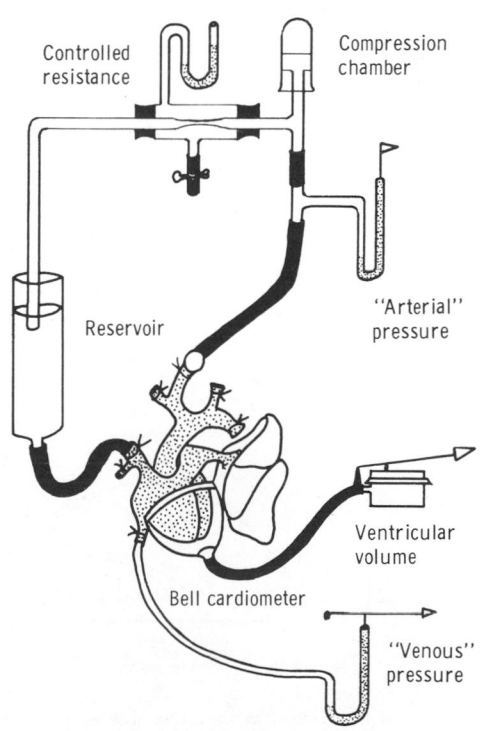

Figure 29–8. Heart-lung preparation.

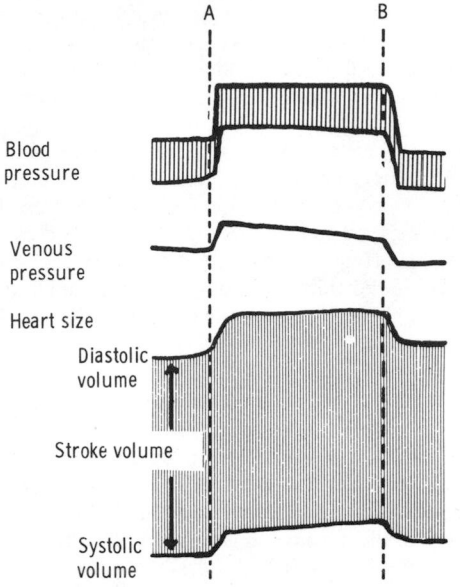

Blood pressure

Venous pressure

Heart size

Diastolic volume

Stroke volume

Systolic volume

Figure 29–9. Effect of increasing arterial resistance (at *A*) in heart-lung preparation. At *B*, the resistance was reduced to its previous level.

Myocardial Contractility

The contractility of the myocardium exerts a major influence on stroke volume. When the sympathetic nerves to the heart are stimulated, the whole length-tension curve shifts upward and to the left (Fig 29–10). The positively inotropic effect of the norepinephrine liberated at the adrenergic endings is augmented by circulating norepinephrine, and epineph-

rine has a similar effect. There is a negatively inotropic effect of vagal stimulation on the atrial muscle and a small negative inotropic effect on the ventricular muscle.

Changes in cardiac rate and rhythm also affect myocardial contractility (force-frequency relation, Fig 29–10). Ventricular extrasystoles have a unique ability to condition the myocardium in such a way that the next succeeding contraction is stronger than the preceding normal contraction. This **postextrasystolic potentiation** is at least in part independent of ventricular filling, since it occurs in isolated cardiac muscle. It has been postulated to be due to increased availability of intracellular Ca^{2+}. A sustained increment in contractility can be produced by delivering paired electrical stimuli to the heart in such a way that the second stimulus is delivered shortly after the refractory period of the first. It has also been shown that myocardial contractility increases as the heart rate increases.

The catecholamines exert their inotropic effect via an action on cardiac β-adrenergic receptors (see Chapter 3), and β-receptor effects are mediated by cyclic AMP (see Chapter 17). Xanthines such as caffeine and theophylline that inhibit the breakdown of cyclic AMP are positively inotropic. Glucagon, which increases the formation of cyclic AMP, is positively inotropic, and it has been recommended for use in the treatment of some heart diseases. It acts via a different receptor than β-adrenergic agents and may be of benefit in treating patients with β-adrenergic blocking agent toxicity. It also accelerates AV conduction. The positively inotropic effect of digitalis and related drugs (Fig 29–10) is believed to be due to their inhibitory effect on the Na^+-K^+ ATPase in the myocardium. The inhibition causes an increase in intracellular Na^+,

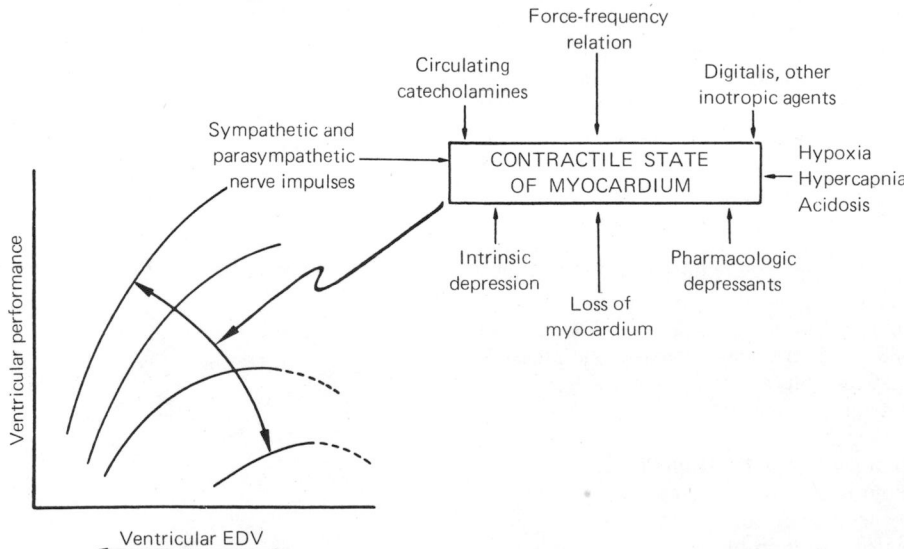

Figure 29–10. Effect of changes in myocardial contractility on the Frank-Starling curve. The major factors influencing contractility are summarized on the right. EDV, end-diastolic volume. (Reproduced, with permission, from Braunwald E, Ross J, Sonnenblick EH: Mechanisms of contraction of the normal and failing heart. N Engl J Med 277:794, 1967. Courtesy of Little, Brown, Inc.)

Table 29–4. Changes in cardiac function with exercise. Note that stroke volume levels off, then falls somewhat (as a result of the shortening of diastole) when the heart rate rises to high values.*

Work (kg-m/min)	O₂ Usage (ml/min)	Pulse Rate (per min)	Cardiac Output (L/min)	Stroke Volume (ml)	A-V O₂ Difference (ml/dl)
Rest	267	64	6.4	100	4.3
288	910	104	13.1	126	7.0
540	1430	122	15.2	125	9.4
900	2143	161	17.8	110	12.3
1260	3007	173	20.9	120	14.5

*Reproduced, with permission, from Asmussen E, Nielsen M: The cardiac output in rest and work determined by the acetylene and the dye injection methods. Acta Physiol Scand 27:217, 1952.

which in turn increases the availability of Ca^{2+} in the cell. The key role of Ca^{2+} in the initiation of contraction in skeletal and cardiac muscle is discussed in Chapter 3. Hypercapnia, hypoxia, acidosis, and drugs such as quinidine, procainamide, and barbiturates depress myocardial contractility. The contractility of the myocardium is also reduced in heart failure (intrinsic depression). This depression is associated with a reduction in the catecholamine content of the myocardium, but its exact cause is not known. If part of the myocardium becomes fibrotic and nonfunctional as the result of a myocardial infarction, total ventricular performance is reduced.

Control of Cardiac Output in Vivo

In intact animals and humans, the mechanisms listed above operate in an integrated way to maintain cardiac output. During muscular exercise, there is increased sympathetic discharge, so that myocardial contractility is increased and the heart rate rises. The increase in heart rate is particularly prominent in normal individuals, and there is little change in stroke volume (Table 29–4). However, patients with transplanted hearts are able to increase their cardiac output during exercise in the absence of cardiac innervation through the operation of the Frank-Starling mechanism (Fig 29–11). Circulating catecholamines also contribute. The increase seen in these patients is not as rapid, and their maximal increase is less than in normal individuals, but the increase is appreciable. It is important to note in this regard that the heart is the servant, rather than the master; it normally adjusts its function so that it expels all the blood that returns in the veins. If venous return increases and there is no change in sympathetic tone, venous pressure rises, diastolic inflow is greater, ventricular end-diastolic pressure increases, and the heart muscle contracts more forcefully. During muscular exercise, venous return is increased by the pumping action of the muscles and the increase in respiration (see Chapter 33). In addition, because of vasodilatation in the contracting muscles, peripheral resistance is decreased. The end result in both normal and transplanted hearts is thus a prompt and marked increase in cardiac output.

One of the differences between untrained individuals and trained athletes is that the athletes have lower heart rates, greater end-systolic ventricular volumes, and greater stroke volumes at rest. Therefore, they can potentially achieve a given increase in cardiac output without increasing their heart rate to as great a degree as an untrained individual.

Oxygen Consumption of the Heart

The O₂ consumption of the heart is determined primarily by the intramyocardial tension, the contractile state of the myocardium, and the heart rate. Additional factors exerting minor effects are the external work performed by the heart, the activational energy involved in cardiac contraction, and the basal O₂ consumption of the myocardium. Intramyocardial tension is directly proportionate to the intraventricular pressure, but it is also directly proportionate to the radius of the ventricle (law of Laplace; see Chapter 30) and inversely proportionate to the thickness of the ventricu-

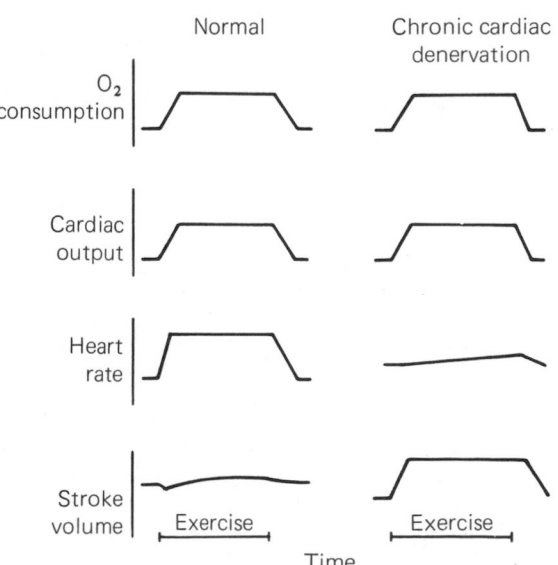

Figure 29–11. Cardiac responses to moderate supine exercise in humans. The responses labeled chronic cardiac denervation were obtained in patients with cardiac transplants. (Reproduced, with permission, from Kent KM, Cooper T: The denervated heart. N Engl J Med 291:1017, 1974.)

lar wall. Thus, $T \cong PR/h$, where T is the wall tension, P is the intraventricular pressure, R is the radius of the ventricle, and h is the thickness of the ventricular wall. Positively inotropic stimuli increase myocardial O_2 consumption both because they increase the tension the muscle can develop and because they increase the O_2 consumption for the same tension because of the energy cost of increasing contractility. The effects of heart rate on O_2 consumption depend primarily on the changes in tension development and contractile state. The increased number of beats causes more O_2 to be consumed per minute, but the stroke volume and end-diastolic volume decrease when the heart rate rises. This decreases the tension required to produce a given systolic pressure and tends to lower O_2 consumption. The work of the heart required to maintain the stroke volume against an increased aortic pressure utilizes considerably more O_2 than the work required to increase stroke volume against a constant aortic pressure. The former is "internal contractile element work," performed in stretching the series elastic elements in the myocardium; the latter is "external contractile element work," with the muscle expelling blood from the ventricle. The greater O_2 demand of expelling blood against an increased pressure explains the fact that angina pectoris, which is due to relative O_2 deficiency of the myocardium (see Chapter 7), is more common with aortic stenosis than it is with aortic regurgitation. The activation of myocardial contraction requires less than 1% of the myocardial O_2 consumption. The basal O_2 consumption of the heart is proportionate to the circulating level of thyroid hormones.

Dynamics of Blood & Lymph Flow | 30

The blood vessels are a closed system of conduits that carry blood from the heart to the tissues and back to the heart. Some of the interstitial fluid enters the lymphatics and passes via these vessels to the vascular system. Blood flows through the vessels primarily because of the forward motion imparted to it by the pumping of the heart, although, in the case of the systemic circulation, diastolic recoil of the walls of the arteries, compression of the veins by skeletal muscles during exercise, and the negative pressure in the thorax during inspiration also move the blood forward. The resistance to flow depends to a minor degree upon the viscosity of the blood but mostly upon the diameter of the vessels, principally the arterioles. The blood flow to each tissue is regulated by local chemical and general neural mechanisms that dilate or constrict the vessels of the tissue. All of the blood flows through the lungs, but the systemic circulation is made up of numerous different circuits in parallel (Fig 30–1), an arrangement that permits wide variations in regional blood flow without changing total systemic flow.

This chapter is concerned with the general principles that apply to all parts of the circulation and with pressure and flow in the systemic circulation. The homeostatic mechanisms operating to adjust flow are the subject of Chapter 31. The special characteristics of pulmonary and renal circulation are discussed in Chapters 34 and 38 and the unique features of the circulation to other organs in Chapter 32.

ANATOMIC CONSIDERATIONS

Arteries & Arterioles

The characteristics of the various types of blood vessels are shown in Table 30–1. The walls of the aorta and other arteries of large diameter contain a relatively large amount of elastic tissue. They are stretched during systole and recoil on the blood during diastole. The walls of the arterioles contain less elastic tissue but much more smooth muscle. The muscle is innervated by adrenergic nerve fibers, which are constrictor in function, and in some instances by cholinergic fibers, which dilate the vessels. The arterioles are the major site of the resistance to blood flow, and small changes in their caliber cause large changes in the total peripheral resistance.

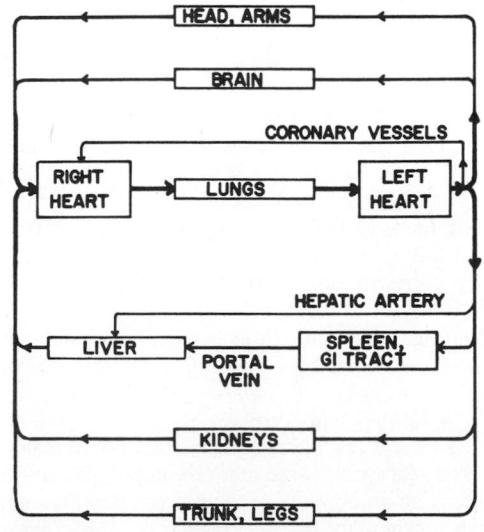

Figure 30–1. Diagram of the circulation in the adult.

Table 30–1. Characteristics of various types of blood vessels in humans.*

	Lumen Diameter	Wall Thickness	Approximate Total Cross-sectional Area (cm²)	Percentage of Blood Volume Contained†
			All Vessels of Each Type	
Aorta	2.5 cm	2 mm	4.5	2
Artery	0.4 cm	1 mm	20	8
Arteriole	30 μm	20 μm	400	1
Capillary	6 μm	1 μm	4500	5
Venule	20 μm	2 μm	4000	
Vein	0.5 cm	0.5 mm	40	54
Vena cava	3 cm	1.5 mm	18	

*Data from Gregg DE in: *The Physiological Basis of Medical Practice,* 8th ed. Best CH, Taylor NB (editors). Williams & Wilkins, 1966.

†In systemic vessels. There is an additional 12% in the heart and 18% in the pulmonary circulation.

Capillaries

The arterioles divide into smaller muscle-walled vessels, sometimes called **metarterioles,** and these in turn feed into capillaries. In some of the vascular beds that have been studied in detail, a metarteriole is connected directly with a venule by a capillary **thoroughfare vessel,** and the true capillaries are an anastomosing network of side branches of this thoroughfare vessel (Fig 30–2). The openings of the true capillaries are surrounded on the upstream side by minute smooth muscle **precapillary sphincters.** The vasoconstrictor fibers to the arterioles also innervate the metarterioles and precapillary sphincters. When the sphincters are dilated, the diameter of the capillaries is normally about 6 μm, just sufficient to permit red blood cells to squeeze through in "single file." As they pass through the capillaries, the red cells become thimble or parachute shaped, with the concavity pointing in the direction of flow. This configuration appears to be due simply to the pressure in the center of the vessel whether or not the edges of the red blood cell are in contact with the capillary walls.

The total area of all the capillary walls in the body exceeds 6300 m² in the adult. The walls, which are about 1 μm thick, are made up of a single layer of endothelial cells. The structure of the walls varies from organ to organ. In many beds, including those in skeletal, cardiac, and smooth muscle, the junctions between the endothelial cells (Fig 30–3) permit the passage of molecules up to 10 nm in diameter. It also appears that plasma and its dissolved proteins are taken up by endocytosis, transported across the endothelial cells, and discharged by exocytosis (vesicular transport; see Chapter 1). However, this process can account for only a small portion of the transport across the endothelium. In the brain, the capillaries resemble the capillaries in muscle, but the junctions between

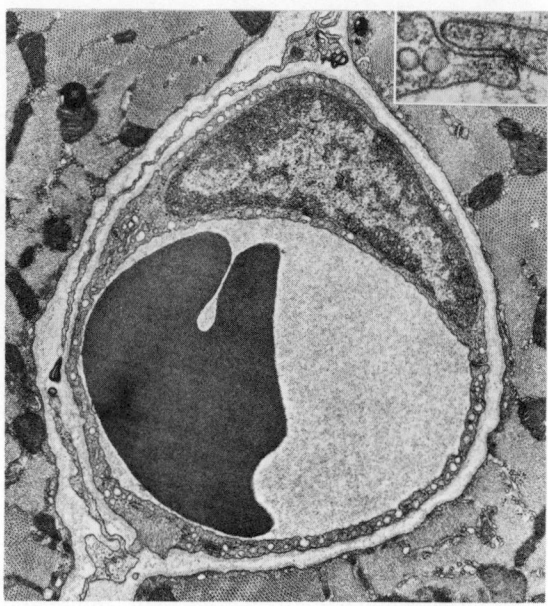

Figure 30–3. Skeletal muscle capillary in rat. Note the multiple vesicles in the endothelial cytoplasm (vesicular transport) and the large endothelial cell nucleus (× 33,000). Inset: Typical junction between 2 endothelial cells in skeletal muscle capillary (× 96,000). (Courtesy of V Bundit and M Williams.)

endothelial cells are tighter; they only permit the passage of small molecules. In most endocrine glands, the intestinal villi, and parts of the kidney, the cytoplasm of the endothelial cells is attenuated to form gaps called **fenestrations** (Fig 18–3). These fenestrations, which are closed by a thin membrane, are 20–100 nm in diameter. They permit the passage of relatively large molecules and make the capillaries porous. In the liver, where the sinusoidal capillaries are extremely porous, the endothelium is discontinuous and there are large gaps between endothelial cells (Fig 26–15).

Lymphatics

The lymphatics drain from the lungs and from the rest of the body tissues via a system of vessels that coalesce and eventually enter the right and left subclavian veins at their junctions with the respective internal jugular veins. The lymph vessels contain valves and regularly traverse lymph nodes along their course. The ultrastructure of the small lymph vessels differs from that of the capillaries in several details: There are no visible fenestrations in the lymphatic endothelium; there is very little if any basal lamina under the endothelium; and the junctions between endothelial cells are open, with no tight intercellular connections.

Arteriovenous Anastomoses

In the fingers, palms, and ear lobes of humans and the paws, ears, and some other tissues of animals there are short channels that connect arterioles to venules, bypassing the capillaries (Fig 30–2). These **arteriovenous (A-V) anastomoses,** or **shunts,** have thick,

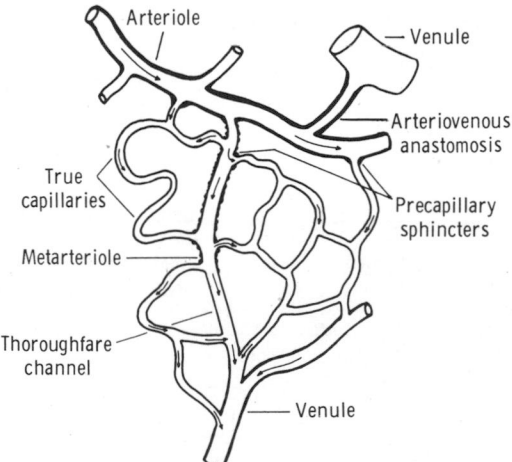

Figure 30–2. Portion of a capillary bed. In the drawing, the vessel walls are thickened in the areas where smooth muscle is found. (After Chambers R, Zweifach BW: Capillary endothelial cement in relation to permeability. J Cell Comp Physiol 15:255, 1940.)

muscular walls and are abundantly innervated, presumably by vasoconstrictor nerve fibers.

Venules & Veins

The walls of the venules are only slightly thicker than those of the capillaries. The walls of the veins are also thin and easily distended. They contain relatively little smooth muscle, but considerable venoconstriction is produced by activity in the adrenergic nerves to the veins and by chemical agents such as norepinephrine. Anyone who has had trouble making venipunctures has observed the marked local venospasm produced in superficial forearm veins by injury. Variations in venous tone are important in circulatory adjustments.

The intima of the limb veins is folded at intervals to form **venous valves** that prevent retrograde flow. The way these valves function was first demonstrated by William Harvey (Fig 30–4). There are no valves in the very small veins, the great veins, or the veins from the brain and viscera.

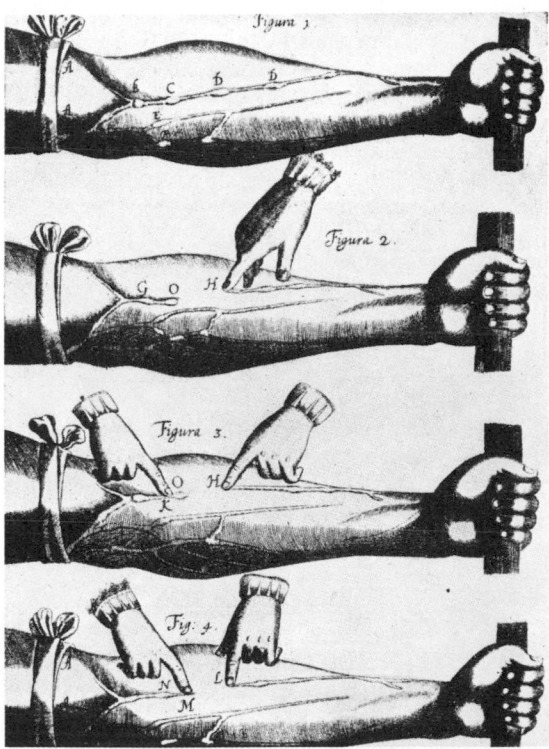

Figure 30–4. Illustration showing the function of the venous valves in the human forearm, from William Harvey's book *Exercitatio Anatomica de Motu Cordis et Sanguinis in Animalibus,* which was published in 1628. *A* is a tourniquet above the elbow, obstructing the venous return. If the vein (Fig 2) is milked from *G* to *H*, it fills from above only to the valve, *O*. If it is milked from *K* to *O* with another finger (Fig 3), it bulges above *O*, but *O* to *H* remains empty. If the vein is occluded at *L* (Fig 4) and milked with another finger *(M)* from *L* to the valve *N*, it remains empty from *L* to *N*. If the finger at *L* is removed, the vein fills from below.

BIOPHYSICAL CONSIDERATIONS

Flow, Pressure, & Resistance

Blood always flows, of course, from areas of high pressure to areas of low pressure, except in certain situations when momentum transiently sustains flow (Fig 29–2). The relationship between mean flow, mean pressure, and resistance in the blood vessels is analogous in a general way to the relationship between the current, electromotive force, and resistance in an electrical circuit expressed in Ohm's law:

$$\text{Current (I)} = \frac{\text{Electromotive force(E)}}{\text{Resistance (R)}}$$

$$\text{Flow (F)} = \frac{\text{Pressure (P)}}{\text{Resistance (R)}}$$

Flow in any portion of the vascular system is equal to the **effective perfusion pressure** in that portion divided by the **resistance.** The effective perfusion pressure is the mean intraluminal pressure at the arterial end minus the mean pressure at the venous end. The units of resistance (pressure divided by flow) are dyne-s-cm^{-5}. To avoid dealing with such complex units, resistance in the cardiovascular system is sometimes expressed in **R units** by dividing pressure in mm Hg by flow in ml/s (see also Table 32–1). Thus, for example, when the mean aortic pressure is 90 mm Hg and the left ventricular output is 90 ml/s, the total peripheral resistance is:

$$\frac{90 \text{ mm Hg}}{90 \text{ ml/s}} = 1 \text{ R unit}$$

Methods for Measuring Blood Flow

The blood flow of an organ can, of course, be measured directly by cannulating the vein draining the organ and collecting the effluent blood. The applicability of this technic is obviously limited, however, and numerous devices have been developed to measure the flow in arteries and veins without opening the vessels. All of them have limitations. **Electromagnetic flow meters** are used in many experiments. The blood vessel is placed between the poles of an electromagnet, and the flow is measured by an application of the principle that a voltage proportionate to the rate of flow is induced in a conductor (in this case, blood in a blood vessel) moving through a magnetic field at right angles to the magnetic lines of force. Sonar technics that measure the effect of velocity of flow on sound transmission through a blood vessel are also used.

The indirect methods used for measuring the blood flow of various organs in humans include adaptations of the Fick and indicator dilution technics described in Chapter 29. An ingenious example of the use of the Fick principle to measure flow in an organ is the Kety N_2O method for measuring cerebral blood flow (see Chapter 32). Another example is determination of

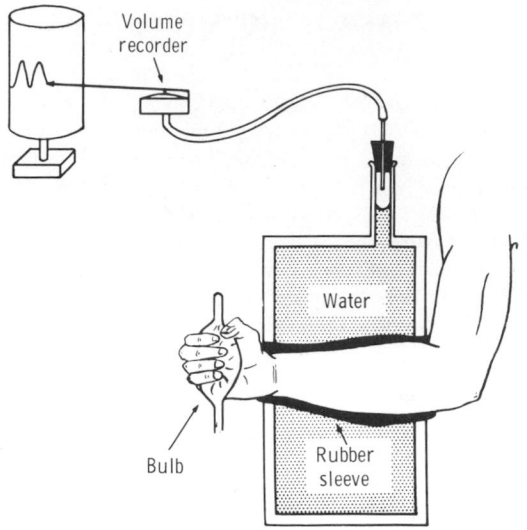

Figure 30–5. Plethysmograph. The hand is shown grasping the bulb of a dynamometer that is used to measure the strength and frequency of muscular contractions.

the renal blood flow by measuring the clearance of para-aminohippuric acid (see Chapter 38). A considerable amount of data on blood flow in the extremities has been obtained by **plethysmography** (Fig 30–5). The forearm, for example, is sealed in a watertight chamber (**plethysmograph**). Changes in the volume of the forearm, reflecting changes in the amount of blood and interstitial fluid it contains, displace the water, and this displacement is measured with a volume recorder. When the venous drainage of the forearm is occluded, the rate of increase in the volume of the forearm is a function of the arterial blood flow (**venous occlusion plethysmography**).

Applicability of Physical Principles to Flow in Blood Vessels

Physical principles and equations that are applicable to the description of the behavior of perfect fluids in rigid tubes have often been used indiscriminately to explain the behavior of blood in blood vessels. Blood vessels are not rigid tubes, and the blood is not a perfect fluid but a 2-phase system of liquid and cells. Therefore, the behavior of the circulation deviates, sometimes markedly, from that predicted by these principles. However, the physical principles are of value when used as an aid to understanding what goes on in the body rather than as an end in themselves or as a test of the memorizing ability of students.

Laminar Flow

The flow of blood in the blood vessels, like the flow of liquids in narrow rigid tubes, is normally **laminar** or **streamline.** Within the blood vessels, an infinitely thin layer of blood in contact with the wall of the vessel does not move. The next layer within the vessel has a small velocity, the next a higher velocity,

and so forth, velocity being greatest in the center of the stream (Fig 30–6). Laminar flow occurs at velocities up to a certain **critical velocity.** At or above this velocity, flow is turbulent. Streamline flow is silent, but turbulent flow creates sounds.

The probability of turbulence is also related to the diameter of the vessel and the viscosity of the blood. This probability can be expressed by the ratio of inertial to viscous forces as follows:

$$R = \frac{\rho DV}{\eta}$$

where R is the Reynolds number, named for the man who described the relationship; ρ is the density of the fluid; D is the diameter of the tube under consideration; V is the velocity of the flow; and η is the viscosity of the fluid. The higher the value of R, the greater the probability of turbulence.

In humans, critical velocity is sometimes exceeded in the ascending aorta at the peak of systolic ejection, but it is usually exceeded only when an artery is constricted. Turbulence occurs more frequently in anemia because the viscosity of the blood is lower. This may be the explanation of the systolic murmurs that are common in anemia.

Average Velocity

When considering flow in a system of tubes, it is important to distinguish between velocity, which is displacement per unit time (eg, cm/s), and flow, which is volume per unit time (eg, cm³/s). Velocity (V) is proportionate to flow (Q) divided by the area of the conduit (A):

$$V = \frac{Q}{A}$$

The average velocity of fluid movement at any point in a system of tubes is inversely proportionate to the *total* cross-sectional area at that point. Therefore, the average velocity of the blood is rapid in the aorta,

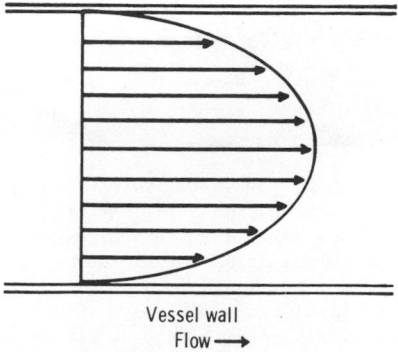

Figure 30–6. Diagram of the velocities of concentric laminas of a viscous fluid flowing in a tube, illustrating the parabolic distribution of velocities (streamline flow).

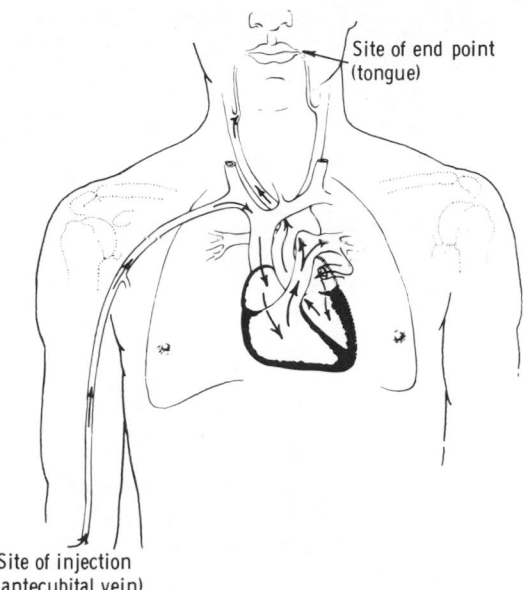

Figure 30–7. Arm to tongue circulation time.

declines steadily in the smaller vessels, and is slowest in the capillaries, which have 1000 times the *total* cross-sectional area of the aorta (Table 30–1). The average velocity of blood flow increases again as the blood enters the veins and is relatively rapid in the vena cava, although not so rapid as in the aorta. Clinically, the velocity of the circulation is often measured by injecting a bile salt preparation into an arm vein and timing the first appearance of the bitter taste it produces (Fig 30–7). The average normal arm to tongue **circulation time** is 15 s.

Poiseuille-Hagen Formula

The relation between the flow in a long narrow tube, the viscosity of the fluid, and the radius of the tube is expressed mathematically in the **Poiseuille-Hagen formula:**

$$F = (P_A - P_B) \times \left(\frac{\pi}{8}\right) \times \left(\frac{1}{\eta}\right) \times \left(\frac{r^4}{L}\right)$$

where F = flow
$P_A - P_B$ = pressure difference between the 2 ends of the tube

η = viscosity
r = radius of tube
L = length of tube

Since flow is equal to pressure difference divided by resistance (R),

$$R = \frac{8\eta L}{\pi r^4}$$

Since flow varies directly and resistance inversely with the fourth power of the radius, blood flow and resis-

tance in vivo are markedly affected by small changes in the caliber of the vessels. Thus, for example, flow through a vessel is doubled by an increase of only 16% in its radius; and when the radius is doubled, resistance is reduced to 6% of its previous value. This is why organ blood flow is so effectively regulated by small changes in the caliber of the arterioles and why variations in arteriolar diameter have such a pronounced effect on systemic arterial pressure.

Viscosity & Resistance

Blood flow varies inversely and resistance directly with the viscosity of the blood in vivo, but the relationship deviates from that predicted by the Poiseuille-Hagen formula. Viscosity depends for the most part on the **hematocrit,** ie, the percentage of the volume of blood occupied by red blood cells. In large vessels, increases in hematocrit cause appreciable increases in viscosity. However, in vessels smaller than 100 μm in diameter, ie, in arterioles, capillaries, and venules, the viscosity change per unit change in hematocrit is much less than it is in large-bore vessels. This is due to a difference in the nature of flow through the small vessels. Therefore, the net change in viscosity per unit change in hematocrit is considerably less in the body than it is in vitro (Fig 30–8). This is why hematocrit changes have relatively little effect on the peripheral resistance except when the changes are large. In severe polycythemia, the increase in resistance does increase the work of the heart. Conversely, in severe anemia, the peripheral resistance is decreased, although the decreased resistance is only partly due to the decrease in viscosity. Cardiac output is increased, and as a result, the work of the heart is also increased in anemia.

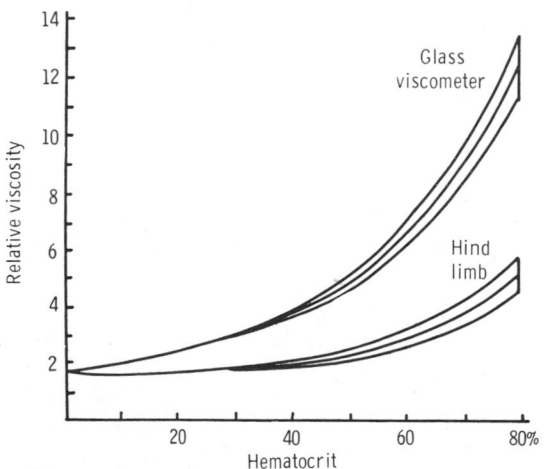

Figure 30–8. Effect of changes in hematocrit on the relative viscosity of blood measured in a glass viscometer and in the hind leg of a dog. In each case, the middle line represents the mean and the upper and lower lines the standard deviation. (Reproduced, with permission, from Whittaker SRF, Winton FR: The apparent viscosity of blood flowing in the isolated hind limb of the dog, and its variation with corpuscular concentration. J Physiol [Lond] 78:338, 1933.)

Viscosity is also affected by the composition of the plasma and the resistance of the cells to deformation. Clinically significant increases in viscosity are seen in diseases in which plasma proteins such as the immunoglobulins are markedly elevated and in diseases such as hereditary spherocytosis, in which the red blood cells are abnormally rigid.

In the vessels, red cells tend to accumulate in the center of the flowing stream. Consequently, the blood along the side of the vessels has a low hematocrit, and branches leaving a large vessel at right angles may receive a disproportionate amount of this red cell–poor blood. This phenomenon, which has been called **plasma skimming,** may be the reason the hematocrit of capillary blood is regularly about 25% lower than the whole body hematocrit.

Critical Closing Pressure

In rigid tubes, the relation between pressure and flow of homogeneous fluids is linear, but in blood vessels in vivo it is not. When the pressure in a small blood vessel is reduced, a point is reached at which there is no flow of blood even though the pressure is not zero (Fig 30–9). This is in part a manifestation of the fact that it takes some pressure to force red cells through capillaries which have diameters less than the red cells. Also, the vessels are surrounded by tissues that exert a small but definite pressure on the vessels, and when the intraluminal pressure falls below the tissue pressure the vessels collapse. In inactive tissues, for example, the pressure in many capillaries is low because the precapillary sphincters and metarterioles are constricted, and many of these capillaries are col-

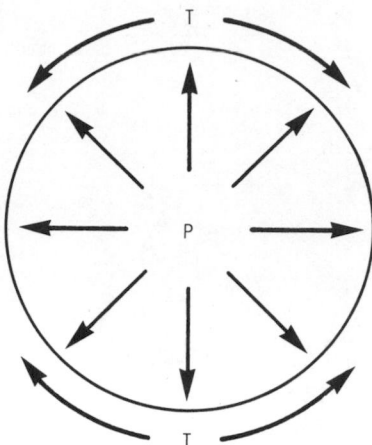

Figure 30–10. Relation between distending pressure *(P)* and wall tension *(T)* in a hollow viscus.

lapsed. The pressure at which flow ceases is called the **critical closing pressure.**

Law of Laplace

It is perhaps surprising that structures as thin-walled and delicate as the capillaries are not more prone to rupture. The principal reason for their relative invulnerability is their small diameter. The protective effect of small size in this case is an example of the operation of the **law of Laplace,** an important physical principle with several other applications in physiology. This law states that the distending pressure (P) in a distensible hollow object is equal at equilibrium to the tension in the wall (T) divided by the 2 principal radii of curvature of the object (R_1 and R_2):

$$P = T(1/R_1 + 1/R_2)$$

The relation between distending pressure and tension is shown diagrammatically in Fig 30–10.

In the equation, P is actually the **transmural pressure,** the pressure on one side of the wall minus that on the other. T is expressed in dynes/cm and R_1 and R_2 in cm, so P is expressed in dynes/cm^2. In a sphere, $R_1 = R_2$, so

$$P = 2T/R$$

In a cylinder such as a blood vessel, one radius is infinite, so

$$P = T/R$$

Consequently, the smaller the radius of a blood vessel, the less the tension in the wall necessary to balance the distending pressure. In the human aorta, for example, the tension at normal pressures is about 170,000 dynes/cm, and in the vena cava it is about 21,000 dynes/cm; but in the capillaries, it is approximately 16 dynes/cm.

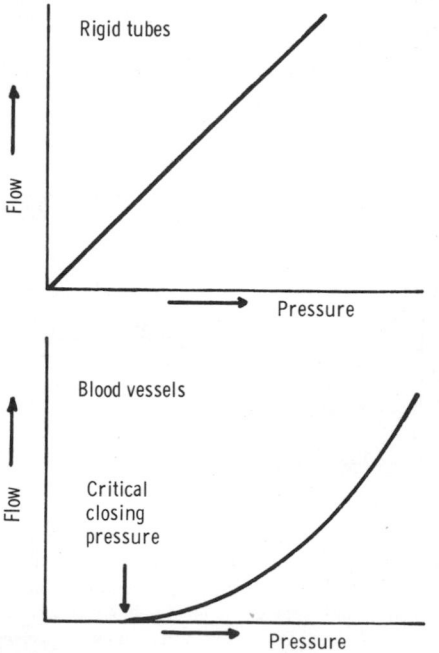

Figure 30–9. Relation of pressure to flow in a rigid-walled system *(above)* and the vascular system *(below)*.

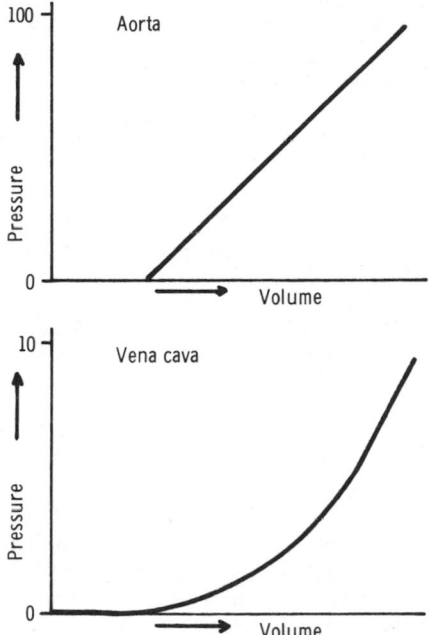

Figure 30–11. Shape of pressure-volume curves for human aorta and vena cava, based on measurements in cadavers. The curves are plotted on the same volume scale, but the pressure scale (indicated in arbitrary units) for the aorta is 10 times that for the vena cava. At pressures higher than those illustrated, the increments in volume per increment in pressure in the aorta also begin to decrease.

The law of Laplace also makes clear a disadvantage faced by dilated hearts. When the radius of a cardiac chamber is increased, a greater tension must be developed in the myocardium to produce any given pressure; consequently, a dilated heart must do more work than a nondilated heart. In the case of the lung, the radii of curvature of the alveoli become smaller during expiration, and these structures would tend to collapse because of the pull of surface tension if the tension were not reduced by the surface tension-lowering agent, surfactant (see Chapter 34). Another example of the operation of this law is seen in the urinary bladder (Chapter 39).

Pressure-Volume Relationships in Large Blood Vessels

When a segment of aorta is filled and then distended with increasing volumes of fluid, the pressure in the segment initially rises in a linear fashion (Fig 30–11). When the same experiment is carried out on a segment of the vena cava or another large distensible vein, the pressure does not rise rapidly until large volumes of fluid are injected. In vivo, the veins are an important blood reservoir. Normally they are partially collapsed and oval in cross section. A large amount of blood can be added to the venous system before the veins become distended to the point where further increments in volume produce a large rise in venous pressure. The veins are therefore called **capacitance**

vessels. The small arteries and arterioles are referred to as **resistance vessels** because they are the principal site of the peripheral resistance (see below).

At rest, at least 50% of the circulating blood volume is in the systemic veins. Twelve percent is in the heart cavities, and 18% is in the low-pressure pulmonary circulation. Only 2% is in the aorta, 8% in the arteries, 1% in the arterioles, and 5% in the capillaries (Table 30–1). When extra blood is administered by transfusion, less than 1% of it is distributed in the arterial system (the "high-pressure system"), and all the rest is found in the systemic veins, pulmonary circulation, and heart chambers other than the left ventricle (the "low-pressure system").

ARTERIAL & ARTERIOLAR CIRCULATION

The pressure and velocities of the blood in the various parts of the systemic circulation are summarized in Fig 30–12. The general relationships in the pulmonary circulation are similar, but the pressure in the pulmonary artery is 25/10 mm Hg or less.

Velocity & Flow of Blood

Although the mean velocity of the blood in the proximal portion of the aorta is 40 cm/s, the flow is phasic, and velocity ranges from 120 cm/s during systole to a negative value at the time of the transient backflow before the aortic valves close in diastole. In the distal portions of the aorta and in the arteries, velocity is also greater in systole than it is in diastole, but forward flow is continuous because of the recoil

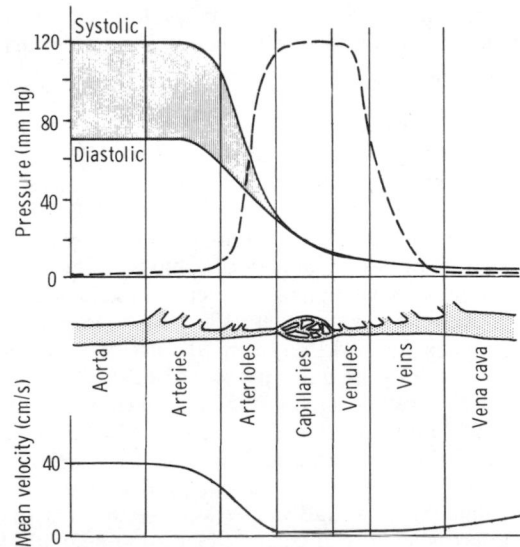

Figure 30–12. Diagram of the changes in pressure and velocity as blood flows through the systemic circulation. The dashed line indicates the total cross-sectional area of the vessels, which increases from 4.5 cm² in the aorta to 4500 cm² in the capillaries (see Table 30–1).

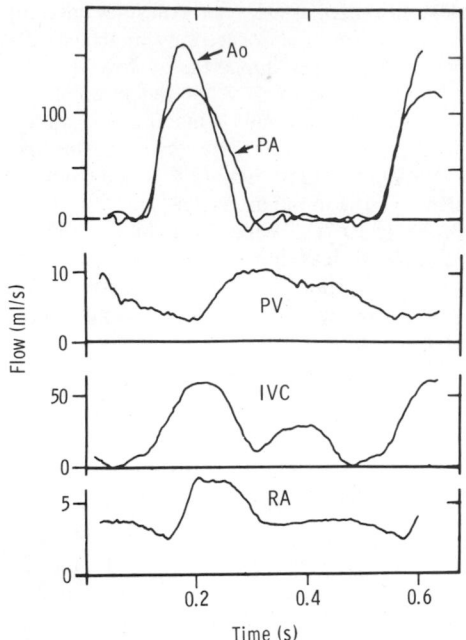

Figure 30–13. Changes in blood flow during the cardiac cycle in the dog. Systole at 0.2 and 0.6 s. Flow patterns in humans are similar. Ao, aorta; PA, pulmonary artery; PV, pulmonary vein; IVC, inferior vena cava; RA, renal artery. (Reproduced, with permission, from Milnor WR: Pulsatile blood flow. N Engl J Med 287:27, 1972.)

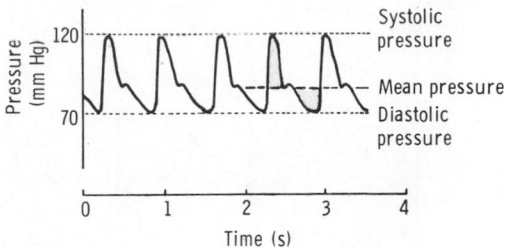

Figure 30–14. Brachial artery pressure curve of normal young human, showing the relation of systolic and diastolic pressure to mean pressure. The shaded area above the mean pressure line is equal to the shaded area below it.

during diastole of the vessel walls that have been stretched during systole (Fig 30–13). Pulsatile flow appears in some poorly understood way to maintain optimal function of the tissues. If an organ is perfused with a pump that delivers a nonpulsatile flow, there is a gradual rise in vascular resistance, and tissue perfusion fails.

Arterial Pressure

The pressure in the aorta and in the brachial and other large arteries in a young adult human rises to a peak value **(systolic pressure)** of about 120 mm Hg during each heart cycle and falls to a minimum value **(diastolic pressure)** of about 70 mm Hg. The arterial pressure is conventionally written as systolic pressure over diastolic pressure—eg, 120/70 mm Hg. One mm Hg equals 0.133 kPa, so in SI units this value is 16.0/9.3 kPa. The **pulse pressure,** the difference between the systolic and diastolic pressures, is normally about 50 mm Hg. The **mean pressure** is the average pressure throughout the cardiac cycle. Because systole is shorter than diastole, the mean pressure is slightly less than the value halfway between systolic and diastolic pressure. It can actually be determined only by integrating the area of the pressure curve (Fig 30–14); however, as an approximation, the diastolic pressure plus one-third of the pulse pressure is reasonably accurate.

The pressure falls very slightly in the large and medium sized arteries because their resistance to flow is small, but it falls rapidly in the small arteries and arterioles, which are the main sites of the peripheral resistance against which the heart pumps. The mean pressure at the end of the arterioles is 30–38 mm Hg. Pulse pressure also declines rapidly to about 5 mm Hg at the ends of the arterioles (Fig 30–12). The magnitude of the pressure drop along the arterioles varies considerably depending upon whether they are constricted or dilated.

Effect of Gravity

The pressures in Fig 30–12 are those in blood vessels at heart level. The pressure in any vessel below heart level is increased and that in any vessel above heart level is decreased by the effect of gravity. The magnitude of the gravitational effect—the product of the density of the blood, the acceleration due to gravity (980 cm/s/s), and the vertical distance above or below the heart—is 0.77 mm Hg/cm at the density of normal blood. Thus, in the upright position, when the mean arterial pressure at heart level is 100 mm Hg, the mean pressure in a large artery in the head (50 cm above the heart) is 62 mm Hg (100 − [0.77 × 50]) and the pressure in a large artery in the foot (105 cm below the heart) is 180 mm Hg (100 + [0.77 × 105]) (Fig 30–15). The effect of gravity on venous pressure is similar (see below).

Methods of Measuring Blood Pressure

If a cannula is inserted into an artery, the arterial pressure can be measured directly with a mercury manometer or a suitably calibrated strain gauge and an oscillograph arranged to write directly on a moving strip of paper. When an artery is tied off beyond the point at which the cannula is inserted, an **end pressure** is recorded. Flow in the artery is interrupted, and all the kinetic energy of flow is converted into pressure energy. If, alternatively, a T tube is inserted into a vessel and the pressure is measured in the side arm of the tube, under conditions where pressure drop due to resistance is negligible, the recorded **side pressure** is less than the end pressure by the kinetic energy of flow. This is because in a tube or a blood vessel the total

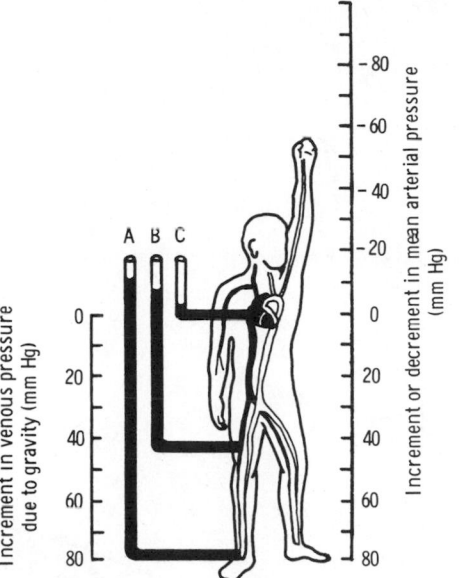

Figure 30–15. Effects of gravity on arterial and venous pressure. The scale on the right indicates the increment (or decrement) in mean pressure in a large artery at each level. The mean pressure in all large arteries is approximately 100 mm Hg when they are at the level of the left ventricle. The scale on the left indicates the increment in venous pressure at each level due to gravity. The manometers on the left of the figure indicate the height to which a column of blood in a tube would rise if connected to an ankle vein (*A*), the femoral vein (*B*), or the right atrium (*C*), with the subject in the standing position. The approximate pressures in these locations in the recumbent position—ie, when the ankle, thigh, and right atrium are at the same level—are (*A*), 10 mm Hg; (*B*), 7.5 mm Hg; and (*C*), 4.6 mm Hg.

energy—the sum of the kinetic energy of flow and the pressure energy—is constant **(Bernoulli's principle).**

It is worth noting that the pressure drop in any segment of the arterial system is due both to resistance and to conversion of potential into kinetic energy. The pressure drop due to energy lost in overcoming resistance is irreversible, since the energy is dissipated as heat; but the pressure drop due to conversion of potential to kinetic energy as a vessel narrows is reversed when the vessel widens out again.

Bernoulli's principle also has a significant application in pathophysiology. According to the principle, the greater the velocity of flow in a vessel, the less the lateral pressure distending its walls. When a vessel is narrowed, the velocity of flow in the narrowed portion increases and the distending pressure decreases. Therefore, when a vessel is narrowed by a pathologic process such as an arteriosclerotic plaque, the lateral pressure at the constriction is decreased and the narrowing tends to maintain itself.

Auscultatory Method

The arterial blood pressure in humans is routinely measured by the **auscultatory method.** An inflatable cuff **(Riva-Rocci cuff)** attached to a mercury manome-

ter **(sphygmomanometer)** is wrapped around the arm and a stethoscope is placed over the brachial artery at the elbow (Fig 30–16). The cuff is rapidly inflated until the pressure in it is well above the expected systolic pressure in the brachial artery. The artery is occluded by the cuff, and no sound is heard with the stethoscope. The pressure in the cuff is then lowered slowly. At the point at which systolic pressure in the artery just exceeds the cuff pressure, a spurt of blood passes through with each heartbeat and, synchronously with each beat, a tapping sound is heard below the cuff. The cuff pressure at which the sounds are first heard is the systolic pressure. As the cuff pressure is lowered further, the sounds become louder, then dull and muffled, and finally, in most individuals, they disappear. These are the **sounds of Korotkow.** When direct and indirect blood pressure measurements are made simultaneously, the diastolic pressure correlates better with the pressure at which the sounds become muffled than with the pressure at which they disappear.

The sounds of Korotkow are produced by turbulent flow in the brachial artery. The streamline flow in the unconstricted artery is silent, but when the artery is narrowed, the velocity of flow through the constriction exceeds the **critical velocity** (see above), and turbulent flow results. At cuff pressures just below the systolic pressure, flow through the artery occurs only at the peak of systole, and the intermittent turbulence produces a tapping sound. As long as the pressure in the cuff is above the diastolic pressure in the artery, flow is interrupted at least during part of diastole, and the intermittent sounds have a staccato quality. When the cuff pressure is just below the arterial diastolic pressure, the vessel is still constricted, but the turbulent flow is continuous. Continuous sounds have a muffled rather than a staccato quality.

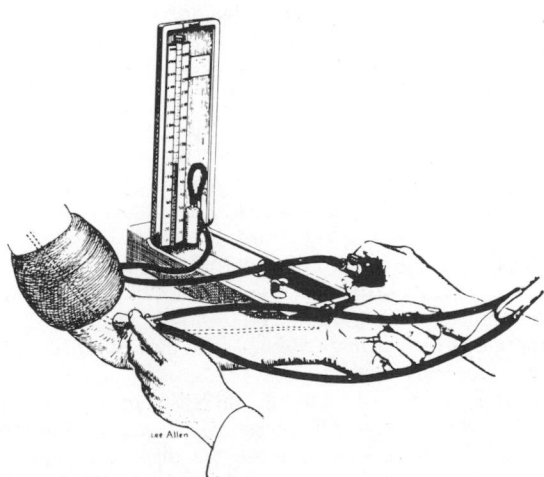

Figure 30–16. Determination of blood pressure by the auscultatory method. (Reproduced, with permission, from Schottelius BA, Schottelius D: *Textbook of Physiology,* 17th ed. Mosby, 1973.)

The auscultatory method is accurate when used properly, but a number of precautions must be observed. The cuff must be at heart level to obtain a pressure that is uninfluenced by gravity. The blood pressure in the thighs can be measured with the cuff around the thigh and the stethoscope over the popliteal artery, but there is more tissue between the cuff and the artery in the leg than there is in the arm, and some of the cuff pressure is dissipated. Therefore, pressures obtained using the standard arm cuff are falsely high. The same thing is true when brachial arterial pressures are measured in individuals with obese arms, because the blanket of fat dissipates some of the cuff pressure. In both situations, accurate pressures can be obtained by using a cuff that is wider than the standard arm cuff. If the cuff is left inflated for some time, the discomfort may cause generalized reflex vasoconstriction, raising the blood pressure. It is always wise to compare the blood pressure in both arms when examining an individual for the first time. Persistent major differences between the pressure on the 2 sides indicate the presence of vascular obstruction.

Palpation Method

The systolic pressure can be determined by inflating an arm cuff and then letting the pressure fall and determining the pressure at which the radial pulse first becomes palpable. Because of the difficulty in determining exactly when the first beat is felt, pressures obtained by this **palpation method** are usually 2–5 mm Hg lower than those measured by the auscultatory method.

It is wise to form a habit of palpating the radial pulse while inflating the blood pressure cuff during measurement of the blood pressure by the auscultatory method. When the cuff pressure is lowered, the sounds of Korotkow sometimes disappear at pressures well above diastolic pressure, then reappear at lower pressures ("auscultatory gap"). If the cuff is initially inflated until the radial pulse disappears, the examiner can be sure that the cuff pressure is above systolic pressure, and falsely low pressure values will be avoided.

Normal Arterial Blood Pressure

The blood pressure in the brachial artery in young adults in the sitting or lying position at rest is approximately 120/70 mm Hg. Since the arterial pressure is the product of the cardiac output and the peripheral resistance, it is affected by conditions that affect either or both of these parameters. Emotion, for example, increases the cardiac output, and it may be difficult to obtain a truly resting blood pressure in an excited or tense individual. In general, increases in cardiac output increase the systolic pressure, whereas increases in peripheral resistance increase the diastolic pressure. There is a good deal of controversy about where to draw the line between normal and elevated blood pressure levels (**hypertension**), particularly in older patients. However, the evidence seems incontrovertible that in apparently healthy humans both the systolic and

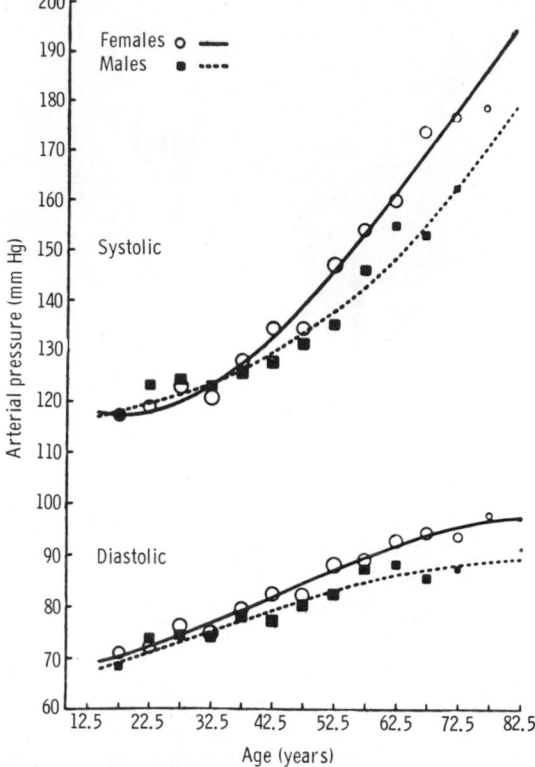

Figure 30–17. Arterial pressure as a function of age in the general population. The size of the squares and the circles is proportionate to the number of subjects studied in that age group. (Reproduced, with permission, from Hamilton M & others: The aetiology of essential hypertension. 1. The arterial pressure in the general population. Clin Sci 13:11, 1954.)

the diastolic pressure rise with age (Fig 30–17). The systolic pressure increase is greater than the diastolic. An important cause of the rise in systolic pressure is decreased distensibility of the arteries as their walls become increasingly more rigid. At the same level of cardiac output, the systolic pressure is higher in old subjects than in young ones because there is less increase in the volume of the arterial system during systole to accommodate the same amount of blood.

CAPILLARY CIRCULATION

At any one time, only 5% of the circulating blood is in the capillaries, but this 5% is in a sense the most important part of the blood volume because it is across the systemic capillary walls that O_2 and nutrients enter the interstitial fluid and CO_2 and waste products enter the bloodstream. The exchange across the capillary walls is essential to the survival of the tissues.

Methods of Study

It is difficult to obtain accurate measurements of

capillary pressures and flows. The capillaries in the mesentery of experimental animals and the fingernail beds of humans are readily visible under the dissecting microscope, and observations on flow patterns under various conditions have been made in these and in some other tissues. Capillary pressure has been estimated by determining the amount of external pressure necessary to occlude the capillaries or the amount of pressure necessary to make saline start to flow through a micropipette inserted so that its tip faces the arteriolar end of the capillary.

Capillary Pressure & Flow

Capillary pressures vary considerably, but typical values in human nail bed capillaries are 32 mm Hg at the arteriolar end and 15 mm Hg at the venous end. The pulse pressure is approximately 5 mm Hg at the arteriolar end and zero at the venous end. The capillaries are short, but blood moves slowly (about 0.07 cm/s) because the total cross-sectional area of the capillary bed is large. Transit time from the arteriolar to the venular end of an average sized capillary is 1–2 s.

Equilibration With Interstitial Fluid

As noted above, the capillary wall is a thin membrane made up of endothelial cells. Substances pass through the junctions between endothelial cells, and some may also pass through the cells by vesicular transport or, in the case of lipid-soluble substances, by diffusion.

The factors other than vesicular transport that are responsible for transport across the capillary wall are diffusion and filtration (see Chapter 1). Diffusion is quantitatively much more important in terms of the exchange of nutrients and waste materials between blood and tissue. O_2 and glucose are in higher concentration in the bloodstream than in the interstitial fluid and diffuse into the interstitial fluid, whereas CO_2 diffuses in the opposite direction. Lipid-soluble substances diffuse across the capillary walls with greater ease than lipid-insoluble substances, probably by passing directly through the endothelial cells.

The rate of filtration at any point along a capillary depends upon a balance of forces sometimes called the **Starling forces** after the physiologist who first described their operation in detail. One of these forces is the **filtration pressure** (the hydrostatic pressure in the capillary minus the hydrostatic pressure of the interstitial fluid) at that point. The other is the **osmotic pressure gradient** across the capillary wall (colloid osmotic pressure of plasma minus colloid osmotic pressure of interstitial fluid). This component is directed inward, and since the colloid osmotic pressure of the interstitial fluid is usually negligible, the gradient equals the oncotic pressure. The magnitude of these forces along a typical muscle capillary is shown in Fig 30–18. Fluid moves into the interstitial space at the arteriolar end of the capillary, where the filtration pressure across its wall exceeds the oncotic pressure; and into the capillary at the venular end, where the oncotic pressure exceeds the filtration pressure.

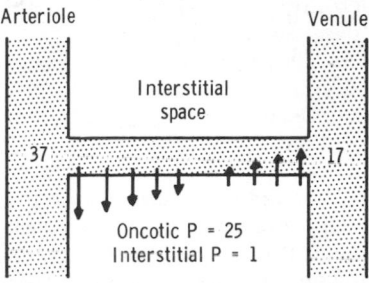

Figure 30–18. Schematic representation of pressure gradients across the wall of a muscle capillary. The figures at the arteriolar and venular ends of the capillary are the hydrostatic pressures in mm Hg in these locations. The arrows indicate the approximate magnitude and direction of fluid movement. In this example, the pressure differential at the arteriolar end of the capillary is 11 mm Hg ([37 − 1] − 25) outward; at the opposite end, it is 9 mm Hg (25 − [17 − 1]) inward.

The amount of fluid that moves across the capillary walls is enormous. It is said that every minute an amount equal to the entire plasma volume enters the tissues from the capillaries and an equal amount enters the capillaries and lymphatics.

Active & Inactive Capillaries

In resting tissues, most of the capillaries are collapsed, and blood flows for the most part through the thoroughfare vessels from the arterioles to the venules. In active tissues, the metarterioles and the precapillary sphincters dilate. The intracapillary pressure rises, overcoming the critical closing pressure of the vessels, and blood flows through all the capillaries. Relaxation of the smooth muscle of the metarterioles and precapillary sphincters is due to the action of vasodilator metabolites formed in active tissue (see Chapter 31) and possibly also to a decrease in the activity of the sympathetic vasoconstrictor nerves that innervate the smooth muscle.

In injured tissue, a substance is released that increases capillary permeability ("H substance"; see Chapter 32). Bradykinin and histamine also increase capillary permeability. When capillaries are stimulated mechanically, they empty (white reaction; see Chapter 32), but this is probably due to contraction of the precapillary sphincters.

LYMPHATIC CIRCULATION & INTERSTITIAL FLUID VOLUME

Lymphatic Circulation

Fluid efflux normally exceeds influx across the capillary walls, but the extra fluid enters the lymphatics and drains through them back into the blood. This keeps the interstitial fluid pressure from rising and promotes the turnover of tissue fluid. The normal 24-

hour lymph flow is 2–4 liters. The composition of lymph is discussed in Chapter 27.

Movements of skeletal muscles and pulsations transmitted from arteries undoubtedly compress lymphatics, and since the valves in the lymph vessels prevent backflow, the compression propels the lymph toward the heart. The negative intrathoracic pressure during inspiration probably also aids lymphatic flow. However, it has now been demonstrated that the lymph vessels contract rhythmically. Furthermore, the rate of these contractions increases in direct proportion to the volume of lymph in the vessels. Evidence is now accumulating that the passive extralymphatic forces contribute relatively little to lymph flow and that the principal factor propelling the lymph is contraction of the vessels.

Agents that increase lymph flow are called **lymphagogues.** They include a variety of agents that increase capillary permeability. Agents that cause contraction of smooth muscle also increase lymph flow from the intestines.

Other Functions of the Lymphatic System

Appreciable quantities of protein enter the interstitial fluid in the liver and intestine, and smaller quantities enter from the blood in other tissues. These proteins are returned to the bloodstream via the lymphatics. The amount of protein returned in this fashion in 1 day is equal to 25–50% of the total circulating plasma protein. In the kidneys, formation of a maximally concentrated urine depends upon an intact lymphatic circulation; removal of reabsorbed water from the medullary pyramids is essential for the efficient operation of the countercurrent mechanism (see Chapter 38), and water enters the vasa recta only if an appreciable osmotic gradient is maintained between the medullary interstitium and the vasa recta blood by drainage of protein-containing interstitial fluid into the renal lymphatics. Some large enzymes—notably histaminase and lipase—may reach the circulation largely or even exclusively via the lymphatics after their secretion from cells into the interstitial fluid. The transport of absorbed long-chain fatty acids and cholesterol from the intestine via the lymphatics has been discussed in Chapter 25.

Interstitial Fluid Volume

The amount of fluid in the interstitial spaces depends upon the capillary pressure, the interstitial fluid pressure, the oncotic pressure, the permeability of the capillaries, the number of active capillaries, the lymph flow, and the total ECF volume. The ratio of precapillary to postcapillary venular resistance is also important. Precapillary constriction lowers filtration pressure, whereas postcapillary constriction raises it. Changes in any of these parameters lead to changes in the volume of interstitial fluid. Factors promoting an increase in this volume are summarized in Table 30–2. **Edema** is the accumulation of interstitial fluid in abnormally large amounts.

In active tissues, capillary pressure rises, often to

Table 30–2. Causes of increased interstitial fluid volume and edema.

Increased filtration pressure
  Arteriolar dilatation
  Venular constriction
  Increased venous pressure (heart failure, incompetent valves, venous obstruction, increased total ECF volume, effect of gravity, etc)

Decreased osmotic pressure gradient across capillary
  Decreased plasma protein level
  Accumulation of osmotically active substances in interstitial space

Increased capillary permeability
  Histamine and related substances
  Kinins, etc

Inadequate lymph flow

the point where it exceeds the oncotic pressure throughout the length of the capillary. In addition, osmotically active metabolites may temporarily accumulate in the interstitial fluid because they cannot be washed away as rapidly as they are formed. To the extent that they accumulate, they exert an osmotic effect that decreases the magnitude of the osmotic gradient due to the oncotic pressure. The amount of fluid leaving the capillaries is therefore markedly increased and the amount entering them reduced. Lymph flow is increased, decreasing the degree to which the fluid would otherwise accumulate, but exercising muscle, for example, still increases in volume by as much as 25%.

Interstitial fluid tends to accumulate in dependent parts because of the effect of gravity. In the upright position, the capillaries in the legs are protected from the high arterial pressure by the arterioles, but the high venous pressure is transmitted to them through the venules. Skeletal muscle contractions keep the venous pressure low by pumping blood toward the heart (see below) when the individual moves about; but if one stands still for long periods, fluid accumulates and edema eventually develops. The ankles also swell during long trips when travelers sit for prolonged periods with their feet in a dependent position. Venous obstruction may contribute to the edema in these situations.

Whenever there is abnormal retention of salt in the body, water is also retained. The salt and water are distributed throughout the ECF, and since the interstitial fluid volume is therefore increased, there is a predisposition to edema. Salt and water retention is a factor in the edema seen in heart failure, nephrosis, and cirrhosis, but there are also variations in the mechanisms that govern fluid movement across the capillary walls in these diseases. In congestive heart failure, for example, there is usually an elevation in venous pressure, and capillary pressure is consequently elevated.

In cirrhosis of the liver, oncotic pressure is low because hepatic synthesis of plasma proteins is depressed; and in nephrosis, oncotic pressure is low because large amounts of protein are lost in the urine.

Another cause of edema is inadequate lymphatic drainage. A not infrequent complication of **radical mastectomy,** an operation for cancer of the breast in which the axillary lymph nodes are also removed, is edema of the arm due to interruption of its lymph drainage. In filariasis, parasitic worms migrate into the lymphatics and obstruct them. Fluid accumulation plus tissue reaction lead in time to massive swelling, usually of the legs or scrotum **(elephantiasis).** The extent of the reaction is perhaps most graphically illustrated by the remarkable account of the man with elephantiasis whose scrotum was so edematous that he had to place it in a wheelbarrow and wheel it along with him when he walked.

VENOUS CIRCULATION

Blood flows through the blood vessels, including the veins, primarily because of the pumping action of the heart, although venous flow is aided by the heartbeat, the increase in the negative intrathoracic pressure during each inspiration, and contractions of skeletal muscles that compress the veins **(muscle pump).**

Venous Pressures & Flow

The pressure in the venules is 12–18 mm Hg. It falls steadily in the larger veins to about 5.5 mm Hg in the great veins outside the thorax. The pressure in the great veins at their entrance into the right atrium **(central venous pressure)** averages 4.6 mm Hg but fluctuates with respiration and heart action.

The peripheral venous pressures, like the arterial, are affected by gravity. They are increased by 0.77 mm Hg for each cm below the right atrium and decreased a like amount for each cm above the right atrium the pressures are measured (Fig 30–15).

When blood flows from the venules to the large veins, its average velocity increases as the total cross-sectional area of the vessels decreases. In the great veins, the velocity of blood is about one-fourth as great as that in the aorta, averaging about 10 cm/s.

Thoracic Pump

During inspiration, the intrapleural pressure falls from −2.5 mm Hg to −6 mm Hg. This negative pressure is transmitted to the great veins and, to a lesser extent, the atria, so that central venous pressure fluctuates from about 6 mm Hg during expiration to approximately 2 mm Hg during quiet inspiration. The drop in venous pressure during inspiration aids venous return. When the diaphragm descends during inspiration, intra-abdominal pressure rises, and this also squeezes blood toward the heart because backflow into the leg veins is prevented by the venous valves.

Effects of Heartbeat

The variations in atrial pressure are transmitted to the great veins to produce the **a, c,** and **v waves** of the venous pressure–pulse curve (see Chapter 29). Atrial pressure drops sharply during the ejection phase of ventricular systole because the atrioventricular valves are pulled downward, increasing the capacity of the atria. This action sucks blood into the atria from the great veins. The sucking of the blood into the atria during systole contributes appreciably to the venous return, especially at rapid heart rates.

Close to the heart, venous flow becomes pulsatile. When the heart rate is slow, 2 periods of peak flow are detectable, one during ventricular systole, due to pulling down of the atrioventricular valves, and one in early diastole, during the period of rapid ventricular filling (Fig 30–13).

Muscle Pump

In the limbs, the veins are surrounded by skeletal muscles, and contraction of these muscles during activity compresses the veins. Pulsations of nearby arteries may also compress veins. Since the venous valves prevent reverse flow, the blood moves toward the heart. During quiet standing, when the full effect of gravity is manifest, venous pressure at the ankle is 85–90 mm Hg (Fig 30–15). Pooling of blood in the leg veins reduces venous return, with the result that cardiac output is reduced, sometimes to the point where fainting occurs. Rhythmic contractions of the leg muscles while the person is standing serve to lower the venous pressure in the legs to less than 30 mm Hg by propelling blood toward the heart. This heartward movement of the blood is decreased in patients with **varicose veins,** whose valves are incompetent, and such patients may have venous stasis and ankle edema. However, even when the valves are incompetent, muscle contractions will continue to produce a basic heartward movement of the blood because the resistance of the larger veins in the direction of the heart is less than the resistance of the small vessels away from the heart.

Venous Pressure in the Head

In the upright position, the venous pressure in the parts of the body above the heart is decreased by the force of gravity. The neck veins collapse above the point where the venous pressure is zero, and the pressure all along the collapsed segments is zero rather than subatmospheric. However, the dural sinuses have rigid walls and cannot collapse. The pressure in them in the standing or sitting position is therefore subatmospheric. The magnitude of the negative pressure is proportionate to the vertical distance above the top of the collapsed neck veins and in the superior sagittal sinus may be as much as −10 mm Hg. This fact must be kept in mind by neurosurgeons. Neurosurgical procedures are sometimes performed with the patient in the sitting position, and if one of the sinuses is opened during such a procedure it sucks air, causing **air embolism.**

Air Embolism

Because air, unlike fluid, is compressible, its presence in the circulation has serious consequences. The forward movement of the blood depends upon the fact that blood is incompressible. Large amounts of air fill the heart and effectively stop the circulation, causing sudden death, because most of the air is compressed by the contracting ventricles rather than propelled into the arteries. Small amounts of air are swept through the heart with the blood, but the bubbles lodge in the small blood vessels. The surface capillarity of the bubbles markedly increases the resistance to blood flow, and flow is reduced or abolished. Blockage of small vessels in the brain leads to serious and even fatal neurologic abnormalities. In experimental animals, the amount of air that produces fatal air embolism varies considerably, depending in part upon the rate at which it enters the veins. Sometimes as much as 100 ml can be injected without ill effects, whereas at other times as little as 5 ml is lethal.

Measuring Venous Pressure

Central venous pressure can be measured directly by inserting a catheter into the thoracic great veins. **Peripheral venous pressure** correlates well with central venous pressure in most conditions. To measure peripheral venous pressure, a needle attached to a manometer containing sterile saline is inserted into an arm vein (Fig 30–19). The peripheral vein should be at the level of the right atrium (a point 10 cm or half the chest diameter from the back). The values obtained in mm of saline can be converted into mm Hg by dividing by 13.6 (the density of mercury). The amount by which peripheral venous pressure exceeds central venous pressure increases with the distance from the heart along the veins. The mean pressure in the antecubital vein is normally 7.1 mm Hg, compared with a mean pressure of 4.6 mm Hg in the central veins.

A fairly accurate estimate of central venous pressure can be made without any equipment by simply noting the height to which the external jugular veins are distended when the subject lies with the head slightly above the heart. The vertical distance between the right atrium and the place the vein collapses (the

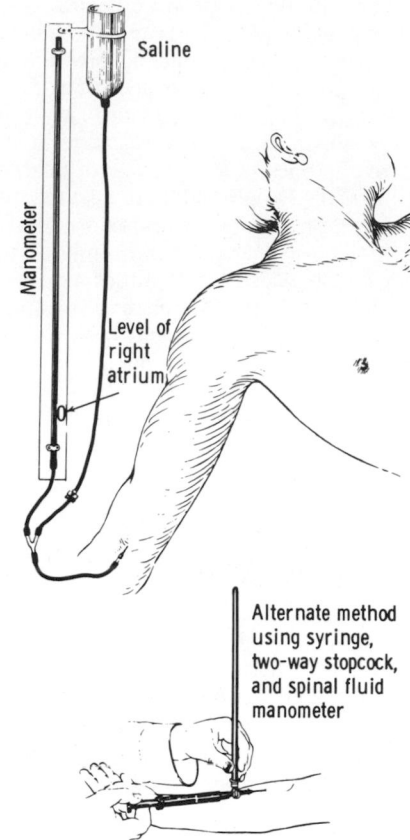

Figure 30–19. Two technics of measuring peripheral venous pressure.

place where the pressure in it is zero) is the venous pressure in mm of blood.

Central venous pressure is decreased during negative pressure breathing and shock. It is increased by positive pressure breathing, straining, expansion of the blood volume, and heart failure. In advanced congestive heart failure or obstruction of the superior vena cava, the pressure in the antecubital vein may reach values of 20 mm Hg or more.

Cardiovascular Regulatory Mechanisms | 31

In humans and other mammals, multiple cardiovascular regulatory mechanisms have evolved. These mechanisms increase the blood supply to active tissues and increase or decrease heat loss from the body by redistributing the blood. In the face of challenges such as hemorrhage, they maintain the blood flow to the heart and brain. When the challenge faced is severe, flow to these vital organs is maintained at the expense of the circulation to the rest of the body.

Circulatory adjustments are effected by local and systemic mechanisms that change the caliber of the arterioles and other resistance vessels and thus alter hydrostatic pressure in the capillaries. The systemic mechanisms are both chemical and neural. In addition to varying the caliber of the arteries, they increase or decrease blood storage in venous reservoirs and vary the rate and stroke output of the heart. In some situations, the capillaries may also be involved. The local autoregulatory mechanisms operate to maintain blood flow despite fluctuations in perfusion pressure and to dilate the arterioles and precapillary sphincters in active tissues. The systemic mechanisms synergize with the local mechanisms and adjust vascular responses throughout the body.

The terms vasoconstriction and vasodilatation are generally used to refer to constriction and dilatation of the resistance vessels. Changes in the caliber of the veins are referred to specifically as venoconstriction or venodilatation.

LOCAL REGULATORY MECHANISMS

Autoregulation

The capacity of tissues to regulate their own blood flow is referred to as **autoregulation.** Most vascular beds have an intrinsic capacity to compensate for moderate changes in perfusion pressure by changes in vascular resistance so that blood flow remains relatively constant. This capacity is well developed in the kidney (see Chapter 38), but it has also been observed in the mesentery, skeletal muscle, brain, liver, and myocardium. It is probably due in part to the intrinsic contractile response of smooth muscle to stretch: As the pres-

sure rises, the blood vessels are distended, and the vascular smooth muscle fibers that surround the vessels contract (**myogenic theory of autoregulation**). If it is postulated that the muscle responds to the tension in the vessel wall, this theory could explain the greater degree of contraction at higher pressures; the wall tension is proportionate to the distending pressure times the radius of the vessel (law of Laplace; see Chapter 30), and the maintenance of a given wall tension as the pressure rises would require a decrease in radius. Vasodilator substances tend to accumulate in active tissues, and these "metabolites" also contribute to autoregulation (**metabolic theory of autoregulation**); when blood flow decreases, they accumulate and the vessels dilate; whereas when blood flow increases, they tend to be washed away. It has also been argued that as blood flow increases, the accumulation of interstitial fluid compresses the capillaries and venules; but the bulk of the available evidence is against this **tissue pressure hypothesis of autoregulation.**

"Vasodilator Metabolites"

The metabolic changes that produce vasodilatation include, in most tissues, decreases in O_2 tension and pH. These changes cause relaxation of the arterioles and precapillary sphincters. A rise in CO_2 tension also dilates the vessels. The direct dilator action of CO_2 is most pronounced in the skin and brain. The neurally mediated vasoconstrictor effects of systemic as opposed to local hypoxia and hypercapnia are discussed below. A rise in temperature exerts a direct vasodilator effect, and the temperature rise in active tissues (due to the heat of metabolism) may contribute to the vasodilatation. K^+ is another substance that accumulates locally, has demonstrated dilator activity, and probably plays a role in the dilatation that occurs in skeletal muscle. In injured tissues, histamine released from damaged cells increases capillary permeability. Adenosine may play a role in cardiac muscle but not in skeletal muscle.

Local Vasoconstrictors

Injured arteries and arterioles constrict strongly. The constriction appears to be due in part to the local liberation of serotonin from platelets that stick to the vessel wall in the injured area (see Chapter 27).

SYSTEMIC REGULATORY MECHANISMS

Kinins

Three related vasodilator peptides called **kinins** are found in the body. Two of these, the nonapeptide **bradykinin** and the decapeptide **lysylbradykinin** (kallidin), are formed in the plasma (Fig 31–1). The third, **methionyllysylbradykinin,** has been found in human urine and is presumably formed in a similar fashion. The kinins are formed from a number of circulating globulins called **kininogens** by the action of proteolytic enzymes called **kallikreins.** In at least one of the kininogens, the 11 amino acids shown in Fig 31–1 constitute the carboxyl end of the protein. The kallikrein in plasma splits the Lys-Arg bond, forming bradykinin, whereas the kallikrein in tissue splits the Met-Lys bond, forming lysylbradykinin. An aminopeptidase in plasma rapidly removes the lysyl residue, but lysylbradykinin is also active by itself.

Plasma kallikrein is formed from an inactive precursor, prekallikrein (Fig 31–2). The prekallikrein is converted to kallikrein in the presence of prekallikrein activators, which are proteolytic fragments of the active form of clotting factor XII. The formation of prekallikrein activators from active factor XII is catalyzed by plasmin (see Chapter 27) and in a positive feedback fashion by plasma kallikrein itself.

Kinins are converted to inactive peptides by 2 kininases. One of these, kininase I, is a carboxypeptidase that removes the C-terminal amino acid residue. The other, kininase II, is also known as converting enzyme and is the peptidase that converts angiotensin I to angiotensin II (see Chapter 24). It is found in highest concentration in the lung, and the lung is particularly active in removing kinins from the circulation.

The actions of the kinins resemble those of histamine. They cause contraction of visceral smooth muscle, but they relax vascular smooth muscle and increase capillary permeability. They also attract leukocytes and cause pain upon injection under the skin. They are potent vasodilators and appear to be

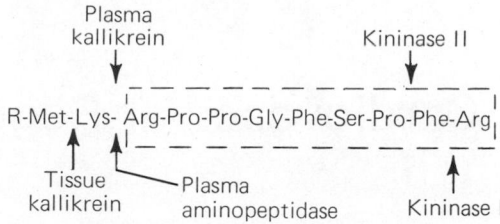

Figure 31–1. Structure of kinins. The amino acid sequence shown is the C-terminal portion of a kininogen. R, rest of protein. The structure of bradykinin is shown within the dashed lines, and the sites of action of various enzymes are indicated by the arrows.

formed during active secretion in sweat glands, salivary glands, and the exocrine portion of the pancreas (see Chapter 26). Thus, they may be responsible for the increase in blood flow in these tissues. They are probably involved in the production of local vasodilatation in other active tissues as well. A role in thermoregulatory vascular adjustments is suggested by experiments on human volunteers in whom cutaneous vasodilatation was produced by warming the body while the subcutaneous tissue of the forearm was being perfused with saline. As the forearm vessels dilated, bradykinin appeared in the perfusate.

Kinin release is inhibited by adrenal glucocorticoids. A kininlike peptide has been implicated as a possible cause of migraine, and the kinins appear to be responsible for some episodes of vasodilatation in patients with carcinoid tumors.

Circulating Vasoconstrictors

Norepinephrine, epinephrine, and angiotensin II are vasoconstrictor agents found in the circulation of normal individuals. Vasopressin is not normally secreted in amounts sufficient to produce appreciable vasoconstriction. Norepinephrine has a generalized vasoconstrictor action, whereas epinephrine dilates the vessels in skeletal muscle and the liver. The relative unimportance of circulating catecholamines in mediat-

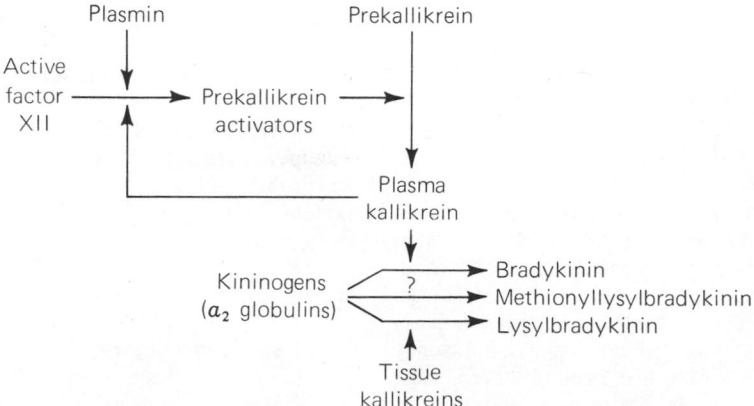

Figure 31–2. Formation of kinins. The details of the formation of methionyllysylbradykinin are unsettled.

ing cardiovascular (as opposed to metabolic) adjustments is pointed out in Chapter 20, in which their cardiovascular actions are discussed in detail.

The octapeptide angiotensin II has a generalized vasoconstrictor action. It is formed from angiotensin I liberated by the action of renin from the kidney on circulating angiotensinogen (see Chapter 24). Its formation is increased when the blood pressure falls or ECF volume is reduced, and it helps maintain blood pressure. Angiotensin II also stimulates aldosterone secretion, and increased formation of angiotensin II is part of a homeostatic mechanism that operates to maintain ECF volume (see Chapter 20).

Neural Regulatory Mechanisms

Although the arterioles and the other resistance vessels are most densely innervated, all blood vessels except capillaries contain smooth muscle and receive motor nerve fibers from the sympathetic division of the autonomic nervous system. The fibers to the resistance vessels regulate tissue blood flow and arterial pressure. The fibers to the venous capacitance vessels vary the volume of blood ''stored'' in the veins. Venoconstriction is produced by stimuli that also activate the vasoconstrictor nerves to the arterioles. The resultant decrease in venous capacity increases venous return, shifting blood to the arterial side of the circulation. In addition, increased vasoconstrictor discharge mobilizes blood from the splanchnic area because constriction of the arterioles of the gastrointestinal tract decreases inflow into the portal venous system, and changes that occur in the liver increase portal runoff (see Chapter 32).

Innervation of the Blood Vessels

Adrenergic fibers end on vessels in all parts of the body, although the fibers from the sympathetic ganglia to the cerebral vessels are of little functional importance. The adrenergic fibers are vasoconstrictor in function. In addition to their vasoconstrictor innervation, the resistance vessels of the skeletal muscles are innervated by vasodilator fibers that, although they travel with the sympathetic nerves, are cholinergic (the **sympathetic vasodilator system**).

There is no tonic discharge in the vasodilator fibers, but the vasoconstrictor fibers to most vascular beds have some tonic activity. When the sympathetic nerves are cut **(sympathectomy),** the blood vessels dilate. In most tissues, vasodilatation is produced by decreasing the rate of tonic discharge in the vasoconstrictor nerves, although in skeletal muscles it can also be produced by activating the sympathetic vasodilator system (Table 31–1).

There is evidence that afferent impulses in sensory nerves from the skin are relayed antidromically down branches of the sensory nerves which innervate blood vessels and that these impulses produce vasodilatation. This local neural mechanism is called the **axon reflex** (Fig 32–12). Other cardiovascular reflexes are integrated in the CNS.

Cardiac Innervation

Impulses in the adrenergic sympathetic nerves to the heart increase the cardiac rate (chronotropic effect) and the force of cardiac contraction (inotropic effect). Impulses in the cholinergic vagal cardiac fibers decrease heart rate. Although there is some tonic discharge in the cardiac sympathetic nerves at rest, there is a good deal of tonic vagal discharge (**vagal tone**) in humans and other large animals. When the vagi are cut in experimental animals, the heart rate rises, and after the administration of parasympatholytic drugs such as atropine, the cardiac rate in humans increases from its normal resting value of 70 to 150–180 beats per minute. In humans in whom both adrenergic and cholinergic systems are blocked, the heart rate is approximately 100.

Cardioinhibitory Center

The nucleus ambiguus in the medulla is the **cardioinhibitory center** that initiates the tonic vagal discharge at rest (Fig 31–3). The tachycardia produced by excitement and emotional states is due to discharge in the sympathetic nerves to the heart, although there is no ''cardioacceleratory center'' per se. On the other hand, the afferents from the baroreceptors in the heart and great vessels (see below) pass directly to the cardioinhibitory center. The reflex bradycardia initiated by a rise in systemic arterial pressure is due to stimulation of the cardioinhibitory center, whereas the tachycardia produced by a fall in pressure is due to decreased vagal tone and increased discharge in the sympathetic cardiac nerves. It is possible that other afferents converge on the cardioinhibitory center.

The Vasomotor Center

The discharge rate in the sympathetic vasoconstrictor nerves is influenced to a minor degree by spinal reflex activity but is controlled for the most part by the **vasomotor center** in the medulla oblongata. This center is a large diffuse area in the reticular formation, extending from just below the obex to the

Table 31–1. Summary of factors affecting the caliber of the arterioles.

Constriction	Dilatation
Increased adrenergic discharge	Decreased adrenergic discharge
Circulating catecholamines (except epinephrine in skeletal muscle and liver)	Circulating epinephrine in skeletal muscle and liver
Circulating angiotensin II	Activation of cholinergic dilators in skeletal muscle
Locally released serotonin	Histamine
Decreased local temperature	Kinins
	''Axon reflex''
	Decreased O_2 tension
	Increased CO_2 tension
	Decreased pH
	Lactic acid, K^+, adenosine, etc
	Increased local temperature

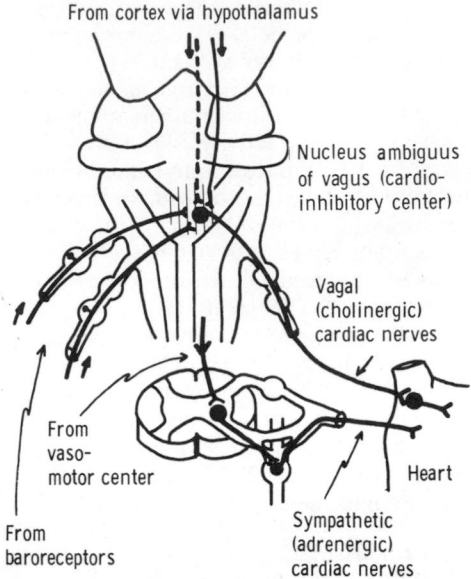

Figure 31–3. Neural mechanisms regulating the heart. The cholinergic fibers slow the heart, whereas the adrenergic fibers accelerate it and increase the force of contraction of cardiac muscle. Inhibitory pathways are indicated by the dashed neuron. The vasomotor center in the medulla is not shown.

region of the vestibular nuclei and from the floor of the fourth ventricle ventrally almost to the pyramids. Stimulation of the rostral and lateral portions of this center causes a rise in blood pressure and tachycardia, whereas stimulation of a smaller portion around the obex produces a fall in blood pressure and bradycardia (Fig 31–4). On the basis of these observations, it was originally postulated that there were separate vasoconstrictor and vasodilator centers with different

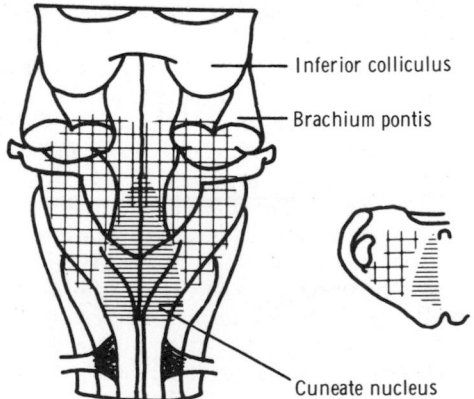

Figure 31–4. The vasomotor center in the cat, showing the location of pressor (cross-hatched) and depressor (horizontal lined) areas. *Left:* Dorsal view of brain stem with cerebellum removed. *Right:* Transverse section of medulla just above obex. (Modified, redrawn, and reproduced, with permission, from Alexander RS: Tonic and reflex functions of medullary sympathetic cardiovascular centers. J Neurophysiol 9:205, 1946.)

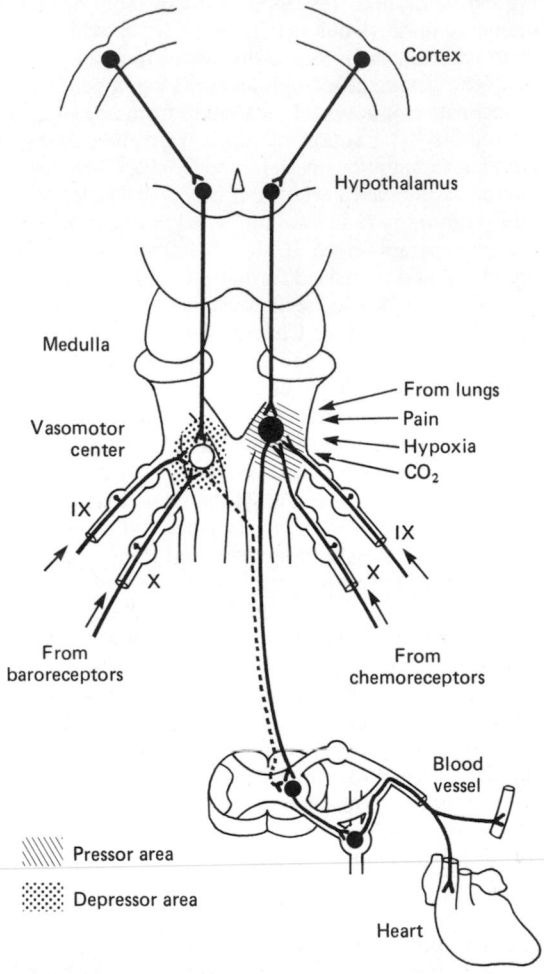

Figure 31–5. Simplified diagram of the vasomotor center, showing the principal factors affecting its activity. The inhibitory fibers are indicated by the neuron with the dashed axon. The excitatory fibers from the pressor area are mostly ipsilateral and travel in the ventrolateral portion of the cord. The inhibitory fibers from the depressor area cross extensively in the medulla.

efferent mechanisms, but it now seems clear that medullary influences are exerted solely through variations in the rate of tonic discharge in the vasoconstrictor nerves. The terms **pressor** and **depressor areas** within a single vasomotor center are therefore more accurate. The details of the interaction between the 2 areas are unsettled, but it is known that excitatory fibers from the pressor area and inhibitory fibers from the depressor area descend in different portions of the spinal cord. These fibers presumably converge on and control the rate of discharge of the preganglionic vasoconstrictor neurons, the final common path to the blood vessels (Fig 31–5).

Summary of Effects of Variations in the Activity of the Vasomotor Center

When vasoconstrictor tone is increased by a decrease in the activity of the depressor area or an increase in the activity of the pressor area of the vasomotor center, there is increased arteriolar constriction and a rise in blood pressure. Venoconstriction and a decrease in the stores of blood in the venous reservoirs usually accompany these changes, although changes in the capacitance vessels do not always parallel changes in the resistance vessels. Heart rate and stroke volume are increased because of activity in the sympathetic nerves to the heart, and cardiac output is increased. There is usually an associated but separate decrease in the tonic activity of vagal fibers to the heart. Conversely, a decrease in the discharge rate of the vasoconstrictor fibers causes vasodilatation, a fall in blood pressure, and an increase in the storage of blood in the venous capacitance vessels. There is usually a concomitant decrease in heart rate, but this is mostly due to a separate direct stimulation of the cardioinhibitory center. There is relatively little tonic discharge in the cardiac sympathetic nerves at rest.

Afferents to the Vasomotor Center

The afferents that converge on the vasomotor center are summarized in Fig 31–5. They include not only the very important fibers from arterial baroreceptors but fibers from other parts of the nervous system and from the carotid and aortic chemoreceptors as well. In addition, some stimuli act directly on the vasomotor center.

There are descending tracts to the vasomotor center from the cerebral cortex (particularly the limbic cortex) that relay in the hypothalamus and possibly also in the mesencephalon. These fibers are responsible for the blood pressure rise and tachycardia produced by emotions such as sexual excitement and anger.

Inflation of the lungs causes vasodilatation and a decrease in blood pressure. This response is mediated via vagal afferents from the lungs that inhibit the vasomotor center. Pain usually causes a rise in blood pressure, presumably as a result of afferent impulses in the reticular formation converging on the vasomotor center. However, prolonged severe pain may cause vasodilatation and fainting.

Afferents from the chemoreceptors in the carotid and aortic bodies exert their main effect on respiration, and their function is discussed in Chapter 36. However, they also converge on the vasomotor center. The cardiovascular response to chemoreceptor stimulation is peripheral vasoconstriction and bradycardia. However, hypoxia also produces increased catecholamine secretion from the adrenal medulla and hyperpnea, both of which produce tachycardia and an increase in cardiac output. Hemorrhage that produces hypotension leads to chemoreceptor stimulation. This is due to decreased blood flow to the chemoreceptors and consequent stagnant anoxia of these organs (see Chapter 37). In hypotensive animals, baroreceptor discharge is low (see below), and section of the glossopharyngeal and vagus nerves leads to a fall rather than a rise in blood pressure because the chemoreceptor drive to the

vasomotor center is removed. Chemoreceptor discharge may also contribute to the production of **Mayer waves.** These should not be confused with **Traube-Hering waves,** which are fluctuations in blood pressure synchronized with respiration. The Mayer waves are slow regular oscillations in arterial pressure that occur at the rate of about one per 20–40 s during hypotension. Under these conditions, hypoxia stimulates the chemoreceptors. The stimulation raises the blood pressure, which improves the blood flow in the receptor organs and eliminates the stimulus to the chemoreceptors, so that the pressure falls and a new cycle is initiated. However, Mayer waves are reduced but not abolished by chemoreceptor denervation and are sometimes present in spinal animals, so oscillation in spinal vasopressor reflexes is also involved.

Hypoxia and hypercapnia both stimulate the vasomotor center directly, although the direct effect of hypoxia is small. When intracranial pressure is increased, the blood supply to the vasomotor center is compromised, and the local hypoxia and hypercapnia increase its discharge. The resultant rise in systemic arterial pressure (**Cushing reflex**) tends to restore the blood flow to the medulla. The rise in blood pressure causes a reflex decrease in heart rate via the arterial baroreceptors (see below), and this is why bradycardia rather than tachycardia is characteristically seen in patients with increased intracranial pressure.

A rise in arterial P_{CO_2} stimulates the vasomotor center, but, as noted above, the direct peripheral effect of hypercapnia is vasodilation. Therefore, the peripheral and central actions tend to cancel each other. Moderate hyperventilation, which significantly lowers the CO_2 tension of the blood, causes cutaneous and cerebral vasoconstriction in humans, but there is little change in blood pressure. Exposure to high concentrations of CO_2 is associated with marked cutaneous and cerebral vasodilatation, but there is vasoconstriction elsewhere and usually a slow rise in blood pressure.

Baroreceptors

The **baroreceptors** are stretch receptors in the walls of the heart and blood vessels. The **carotid sinus** and **aortic arch** receptors monitor the arterial circulation. Receptors are also located in the walls of the right and left atria at the entrance of the superior and inferior venae cavae and the pulmonary veins, in the wall of the left ventricle, and in the pulmonary circulation. The receptors are stimulated by distention of the structures in which they are located, and so they discharge at an increased rate when the pressure in these structures rises. Their afferent fibers pass via the glossopharyngeal and vagus nerves to the vasomotor center and the cardioinhibitory center. Impulses generated in the baroreceptors *inhibit* the tonic discharge of the vasoconstrictor nerves and *excite* the cardioinhibitory center, producing vasodilatation, a drop in blood pressure, bradycardia, and a decrease in cardiac output. The effects on cardiac rate are blocked by atropine. Some venodilatation also occurs, although it is still uncertain which receptors are responsible for reflex changes in venomotor tone.

Carotid Sinus & Aortic Arch

The carotid sinus is a small dilatation of the internal carotid artery just above the bifurcation of the common carotid into external and internal carotid branches (Fig 31–6). Baroreceptors are located in this dilatation and are also found in the wall of the arch of the aorta. The receptors are located in the adventitia of the vessels. They are extensively branched, knobby, coiled and intertwined ends of myelinated nerve fibers that resemble Golgi tendon organs (Fig 6–5). Similar receptors have been found in various other parts of the large arteries of the thorax and neck in some species. The afferent nerve fibers from the carotid sinus and carotid body form a distinct branch of the glossopharyngeal nerve, the **carotid sinus nerve,** but the fibers from the aortic arch form a separate distinct branch of the vagus only in the rabbit. The carotid sinus nerves and vagal fibers from the aortic arch are commonly called the **buffer nerves.**

Buffer Nerve Activity

At normal blood pressure levels, the fibers of the buffer nerves discharge at a slow rate (Fig 31–7). When the pressure in the sinus and aortic arch rises, the discharge rate increases; and when the pressure falls, the rate declines. The compensatory response produced by increased discharge is a fall in blood pressure because activity in the baroreceptor afferents inhibits

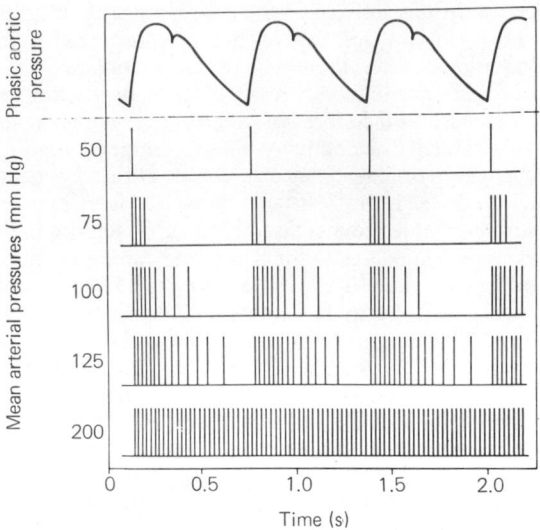

Figure 31–7. Discharges (vertical lines) in a single afferent nerve fiber from the carotid sinus at various arterial pressures. (Reproduced, with permission, from Berne RM, Levy MN: *Cardiovascular Physiology,* 3rd ed. Mosby, 1977.)

the tonic discharge in the vasoconstrictor nerves.

When one carotid sinus of a dog is isolated and perfused and the other baroreceptors are denervated, there is no discharge in the afferent fibers from the perfused sinus and no drop in the animal's arterial pressure or heart rate when the perfusion pressure is below 70 mm Hg. At perfusion pressures of 70–150 mm Hg, there is an essentially linear relation between the perfusion pressure and the fall in blood pressure and heart rate produced in the dog. At perfusion pressures above 150 mm Hg there is no further increase in response (Fig 31–8), presumably because the rate of baroreceptor discharge and the degree of inhibition of the vasomotor center are maximal.

The carotid receptors respond both to sustained pressure and to pulse pressure. A decline in carotid pulse pressure without any change in mean pressure decreases the rate of baroreceptor discharge and provokes a rise in blood pressure and tachycardia. The receptors also respond to changes in pressure as well as steady pressure; when the pressure is fluctuating, they sometimes discharge during the rises and are silent during the falls (Fig 31–7) at mean pressures high enough so that, if there were no fluctuations, there would be a steady discharge.

The aortic receptors have not been studied in as great detail, but there is no reason to believe that their responses differ significantly from those of the receptors in the carotid sinus.

Function of the Arterial Baroreceptors

From the foregoing discussion, it is apparent that the baroreceptors on the arterial side of the circulation, their afferent fibers to the vasomotor and cardioinhibitory centers, and the efferent pathways from

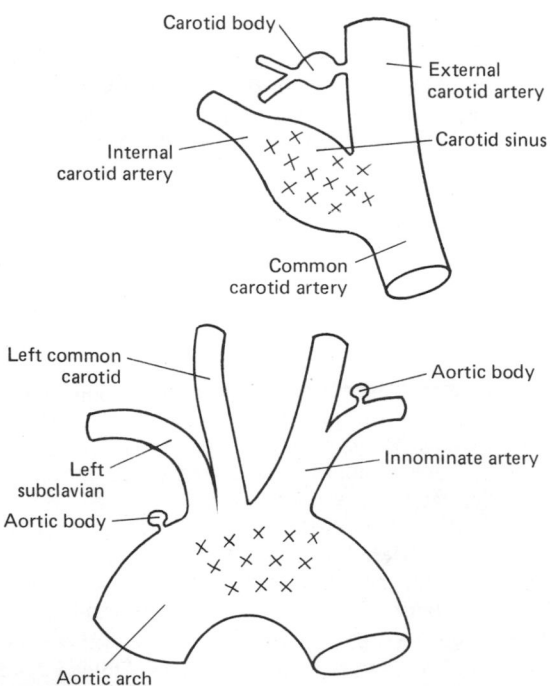

Figure 31–6. Baroreceptor areas in carotid sinus and aortic arch. The Xs identify sites where receptors are located.

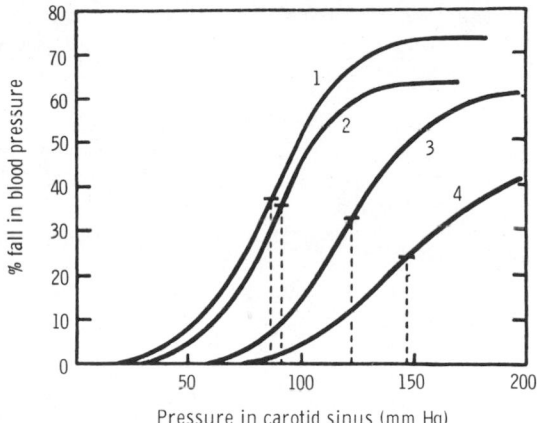

Figure 31–8. Relationships between pressure in the isolated carotid sinus and change in systemic blood pressure in the monkey (1), rabbit (2), dog (3), and cat (4). The horizontal line on each curve represents the normal mean blood pressure for that species. Note that in each case the normal blood pressure is in the mid portion of the curve, where variations in pressure produce the greatest reflex changes. (After Koch E. Reproduced, with permission, from Keele CA, Neil E: *Samson Wright's Applied Physiology,* 10th ed. Oxford Univ Press, 1961.)

these centers constitute a reflex feedback mechanism that operates to stabilize the blood pressure and heart rate. Any drop in systemic arterial pressure decreases the inhibitory discharge in the buffer nerves, and there is a compensatory rise in blood pressure and cardiac output. Any rise in pressure produces dilatation of the arterioles and decreases cardiac output until the blood pressure returns to its previous normal level.

In chronic hypertension, the baroreceptor reflex mechanism is "reset" to maintain an elevated rather than a normal blood pressure. In perfusion studies on hypertensive experimental animals, raising the pressure in the isolated carotid sinus lowers the systemic pressure and decreasing the perfusion pressure raises the systemic pressure. Little is known about how and why this resetting occurs. Since some forms of hypertension are curable, and since circulatory reflexes as well as blood pressure are apparently normal after treatment, it appears that the resetting is reversible.

If norepinephrine is painted on the carotid sinus, baroreceptor discharge increases and blood pressure falls. According to some investigators, stimulation of the sympathetic nerves to the sinus has a similar effect. The increased discharge is probably due to distortion of the receptors produced by contraction of the smooth muscle in the wall. However, there is considerable evidence that variations in the rate of sympathetic discharge and catecholamine secretion in intact animals have little if any effect on the sensitivity of the carotid sinus mechanism.

Effect of Carotid Clamping & Buffer Nerve Section

Bilateral clamping of the carotid arteries below

the carotid sinuses elevates the blood pressure and heart rate because the procedure lowers the pressure in the sinuses. Cutting the carotid sinus nerves on each side has the same effect. The pressor response following these 2 procedures is moderate because the aortic baroreceptors are still functioning normally, and they buffer the rise. If baroreceptor afferents in the vagi are also interrupted, blood pressure rises to 300/200 mm Hg or higher. The baroreceptor afferents end in the nucleus of the tractus solitarius in the medulla, and in animals lesions of this nucleus cause severe hypertension that can be fatal. These forms of experimental hypertension are called "neurogenic hypertension."

Atrial Stretch Receptors

The stretch receptors in the atria are of 2 types: those which discharge primarily during atrial systole (type A), and those which discharge primarily late in diastole, at the time of peak atrial filling (type B). The discharge of type B baroreceptors is increased when venous return is increased and decreased by positive pressure breathing, indicating that they respond primarily to distention of the atrial walls. The reflex circulatory adjustments initiated by increased discharge from most if not all of these receptors include tachycardia rather than bradycardia plus vasodilatation and a fall in blood pressure. The atrial baroreceptors are therefore probably part of a reflex mechanism that combats excessive rises in central venous pressure and venous return.

Bainbridge Reflex

Rapid infusion of blood or saline in anesthetized animals sometimes produces a rise in heart rate if the initial heart rate is low. This effect was described by Bainbridge in 1915, and since then it has been known as the **Bainbridge reflex.** It appears to be a true reflex rather than a response to local stretch, since infusion of fluids in animals with transplanted hearts increases the rate of the recipient's atrial remnant but fails to affect the rate of the transplanted heart. The receptors may be the tachycardia-producing atrial receptors mentioned above. The reflex is diminished or absent when the initial heart rate is high. There has been much debate about its significance, and an increase in heart rate can sometimes be produced in an isolated heart-lung preparation if the venous return is increased rapidly. Thus, the Bainbridge reflex is an inconstant phenomenon of uncertain physiologic significance.

Left Ventricular Receptors

When the left ventricle is distended in experimental animals, there is a fall in systemic arterial pressure and heart rate. It takes considerable ventricular distention to produce this response, and its physiologic significance is uncertain. However, left ventricular stretch receptors may play a role in the maintenance of the vagal tone that keeps the heart rate slow at rest.

In experimental animals, injections of the drug **veratridine** into the branches of the coronary arteries that supply the left ventricle cause apnea, hypotension, and bradycardia (the **coronary chemoreflex**, or **Bezold-Jarisch reflex**). The response is prevented by vagotomy. Injections into the coronary arteries supplying the right ventricle and atria are ineffective. Nicotine produces a similar response when it is injected into the arterial supply of the left ventricle or applied to the surface of the left ventricle near the apex of the heart on pieces of filter paper. The response to nicotine by both routes is absent if procaine is first injected into the pericardial sac. The coronary chemoreflex might be triggered by chemical stimulation of the stretch receptors in the ventricular wall, or it might be due to stimulation of as yet unidentified chemoreceptors in the myocardium. There has been speculation that in patients with myocardial infarcts, substances released from the infarcted tissue stimulate ventricular receptors, contributing to the hypotension that is not infrequently a stubborn complication of this disease.

Pulmonary Receptors

Distention of the pulmonary vascular bed causes reflex bradycardia and systemic hypotension. The location of the receptors involved is not settled.

Injections of veratridine, phenyl biguanide, and serotonin into the pulmonary artery produce apnea, hypotension, and bradycardia (**pulmonary chemoreflex**). The response, which is blocked by vagotomy, is essentially the same as that produced by injection of veratridine into the arterial supply of the left ventricle, but it occurs too rapidly to be caused by the drugs reaching the left ventricular receptors. The receptors are probably in the pulmonary veins, but their exact location has not been determined, and it is not now known whether they are different from the receptors for the response to distention of the pulmonary circulation.

Mesenteric Baroreceptors

There is some evidence that the pacinian corpuscles in the mesentery function as baroreceptors. They probably initiate reflexes that control the local blood flow in the viscera.

Other Effects of Baroreceptor Stimulation

Increased activity in baroreceptor afferents inhibits respiration, but this effect is slight and of little physiologic importance.

There is considerable evidence that impulses initiated in atrial stretch receptors are relayed to the hypothalamus, where they inhibit vasopressin secretion (see Chapter 14). The resultant diuresis helps reduce the venous distention that caused the stimulation. Atrial distention also tends to lower renin secretion, but the effect on aldosterone secretion is slight. A drop in systemic arterial pressure stimulates vasopressin secretion. The increase is inhibited if the carotid sinus nerves and the vagi are cut, but not by vagotomy alone. Constriction of the carotid arteries increases renin secretion, but not to the degree that it regularly increases aldosterone secretion. Thus, the baroreceptors influence water metabolism with lesser effects on Na^+ metabolism.

Clinical Testing & Stimulation

The changes in pulse rate and blood pressure that occur in humans on standing up or lying down (see Chapter 33) are due for the most part to baroreceptor reflexes. The function of the receptors can be tested by monitoring the changes in pulse and blood pressure that occur in response to brief periods of straining (forced expiration against a closed glottis: the **Valsalva maneuver**). The blood pressure rises at the onset of straining (Fig 31–9) because the increase in intrathoracic pressure is added to the pressure of the blood in the aorta. It then falls because the high intrathoracic pressure compresses the veins, decreasing venous return and cardiac output. The decreases in arterial pressure and pulse pressure inhibit the

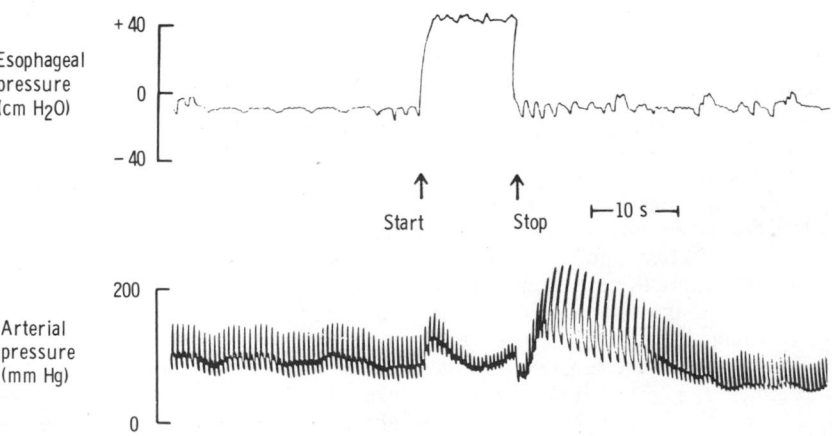

Figure 31–9. Diagram of the response to straining (the Valsalva maneuver) in a normal man, recorded with a needle in the brachial artery. (Courtesy of M McIlroy.)

baroreceptors, causing tachycardia and a rise in peripheral resistance. When the glottis is opened and the intrathoracic pressure returns to normal, cardiac output is restored but the peripheral vessels are constricted. The blood pressure therefore rises above normal, and this stimulates the baroreceptors, causing bradycardia and a drop in pressure to normal levels.

In sympathectomized patients, heart rate changes still occur because the baroreceptors and the vagi are intact. However, in patients with autonomic insufficiency, a disease of unknown cause in which there is widespread disruption of autonomic function, the heart rate changes are absent. For reasons that are still obscure, patients with primary hyperaldosteronism also fail to show the heart rate changes and the blood pressure rise when the intrathoracic pressure returns to normal. Their response to the Valsalva maneuver returns to normal after removal of the aldosterone-secreting tumor.

Stimulation of the carotid sinus nerves by means

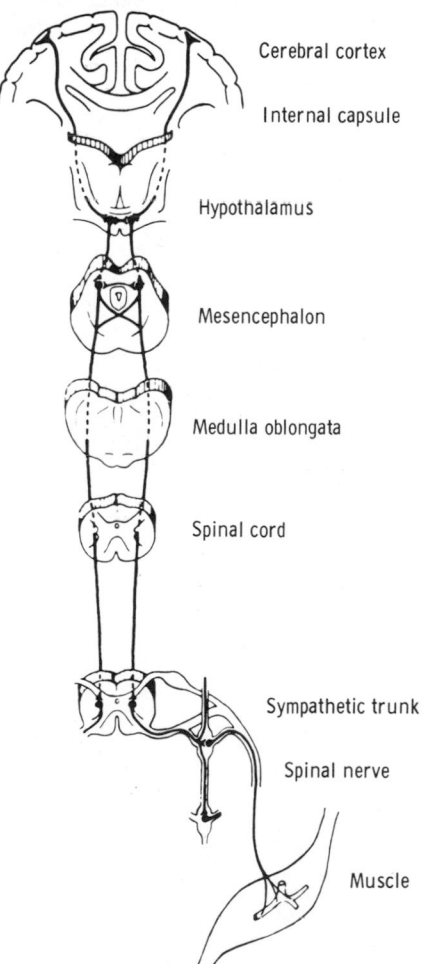

Figure 31–10. The sympathetic vasodilator pathways. (Reproduced, with permission, from Lindgren P: The mesencephalic and vascular system. Acta Physiol Scand 35:Suppl 121, 1955.)

Cerebral cortex

Internal capsule

Hypothalamus

Mesencephalon

Medulla oblongata

Spinal cord

Sympathetic trunk

Spinal nerve

Muscle

of a chronically implanted radiofrequency stimulator has been used with considerable success in the treatment of angina pectoris. The pain in this condition is due to the accumulation of a pain-producing substance in the myocardium when it is ischemic (see Chapter 7). When the patient feels pain coming on, the stimulator is switched on. The resulting decrease in cardiac rate and output reduces the load on the heart, relieving the attack.

Sympathetic Vasodilator System

The cholinergic sympathetic vasodilator fibers are part of a regulatory system that originates in the cerebral cortex, relays in the hypothalamus and mesencephalon, and passes through the medulla without interruption to the intermediate gray column of the spinal cord, where the preganglionic sympathetic vasodilator fibers as well as the vasoconstrictor fibers originate (Fig 31–10). Stimulation of this system produces vasodilatation in skeletal muscle, but the resultant increase in blood flow is associated with a decrease rather than an increase in muscle O_2 consumption. This suggests that the blood is being diverted through thoroughfare channels rather than capillaries. Adrenal medullary secretion of norepinephrine and epinephrine is apparently increased when this system is stimulated, the epinephrine probably reinforcing the dilatation of muscle blood vessels. In cats and dogs, the system has been shown to discharge in response to emotional stimuli such as fear, apprehension, and rage. Its role in humans is uncertain, but it has been suggested that the sympathetic vasodilator system is responsible for fainting in emotional situations. It has also been argued that this system is responsible for the increase in muscle blood flow that occurs at or even before the start of muscular exercise (see Chapter 33). However, it now appears that the vasodilatation before the start of exercise is not a constant or marked phenomenon.

Control of Heart Rate

Various conditions that affect the heart rate are listed in Table 31–2. The sympathetic and parasympathetic nerves to the heart and the centers in the medulla that regulate the cardiac rate have been described above. Baroreceptor-mediated reflex changes in heart rate have also been considered in detail in preceding sections of this chapter. It is worth noting that, in general, stimuli which increase the heart rate also increase the blood pressure, whereas those which decrease the heart rate lower the blood pressure. Thus, for example, anger and excitement are associated with tachycardia and a rise in blood pressure, whereas fear and grief are usually associated with bradycardia and hypotension. The major exception to this generalization is the occurrence of hypertension and bradycardia when the intracranial pressure is increased. The 2 occur together in this condition because, as noted above, there is hypercapnic stimulation of the vasomotor center and reflex bradycardia. When the body temperature rises, the heart rate is increased, but

Table 31−2. Factors affecting heart rate. Norepinephrine has a direct chronotropic effect on the heart, but
in the intact animal its pressor action stimulates the
baroreceptors, leading to enough reflex increase in
vagal tone to overcome the direct effect and produce
bradycardia.

Heart rate **accelerated** by:

    Decreased activity of baroreceptors in the arter-
       ies, left ventricle, and pulmonary circulation*
    Inspiration†
    Excitement*
    Anger*
    Most painful stimuli*
    Hypoxia*
    Exercise*
    Norepinephrine*
    Epinephrine
    Thyroid hormones
    Fever
    Bainbridge reflex

Heart rate **slowed** by:

    Increased activity of baroreceptors in the arter-
       ies, left ventricle, and pulmonary circulation†
    Expiration*
    Fear†
    Grief†
    Stimulation of pain fibers in trigeminal nerve
    Increased intracranial pressure*

*Also produces a rise in blood pressure.
†Also produces a fall in blood pressure.

the cutaneous vessels dilate and blood pressure is unchanged or lowered. When the sinoatrial node is
warmed, its rate of discharge increases, and the effect
of fever on the heart rate is probably due in part to the
rise in cardiac temperature. Thyroid hormones increase the pulse pressure and accelerate the heart by
potentiating the action of catecholamines and possibly
by a direct action on the heart. Epinephrine and norepinephrine both act directly on the heart to increase its
rate, but the marked pressor response produced by
norepinephrine stimulates the arterial baroreceptors,
and the reflex bradycardia obscures the cardioacceleratory action.

The acceleration of the heart during inspiration
(sinus arrhythmia; see Chapter 28) is partly due to
impulses in afferents from vagal stretch receptors in
the lung that inhibit the cardioinhibitory center, although increased sympathetic activity due to radiation
of impulses from the inspiratory center to the
vasomotor center also contributes to the tachycardia.

Emotional stimuli converge through the hypothalamus on the cardioinhibitory center and probably
exert their effects on heart rate by increasing or decreasing its rate of tonic discharge.

The heart rate increases promptly at the start of
exercise and sometimes even in anticipation of it. The
mechanisms responsible for the rapid onset of
tachycardia are unsettled, although the increased heart
rate is probably due to impulses from the cerebral
cortex relayed via the hypothalamus to the cardioinhibitory and vasomotor centers. Increased activity in the cardiac sympathetic nerves as well as a
decrease in vagal tone appears to be involved.

Circulation Through Special Regions | 32

The distribution of the cardiac output to various parts of the body at rest in a normal man is shown in Table 32–1. The general principles described in preceding chapters apply to the circulation of all these regions, but the vascular supplies of most organs have additional special features. The portal circulation of the anterior pituitary is discussed in Chapter 14, the renal circulation in Chapter 38, and the pulmonary circulation in Chapter 34. The circulation of skeletal muscle is discussed with the physiology of exercise in Chapter 33. This chapter is concerned with the circulation of the brain, the heart, the splanchnic area, the skin, the placenta, and the fetus.

CEREBRAL CIRCULATION

ANATOMIC CONSIDERATIONS

Vessels

Except for a small contribution from the anterior spinal artery to the medulla, the entire arterial inflow to the brain in humans is via 4 arteries: 2 internal carotids and 2 vertebrals. The vertebral arteries unite to form the basilar artery; and the circle of Willis, formed by the carotids and the basilar artery, is the origin of the 6 large vessels supplying the cerebral cortex. In some animals the vertebrals are large and the internal carotids small, but in humans a relatively small fraction of the total arterial flow is carried by the vertebral arteries. Substances injected into one carotid artery are distributed almost exclusively to the cerebral hemisphere on that side. There is normally no crossing over, probably because the pressure is equal on both sides. Even when it is not, the anastomotic channels in the circle do not permit a very large flow. Occlusion of one carotid artery, particularly in older patients, often causes serious symptoms of cerebral ischemia. There are precapillary anastomoses between the cerebral arterioles in humans and some other species, but flow through these channels is generally insufficient to maintain the circulation and prevent infarction when a cerebral artery is occluded.

Venous drainage from the brain by way of the deep veins and dural sinuses empties principally into the internal jugular veins in humans, although a small amount of venous blood drains through the ophthalmic and pterygoid venous plexuses, through emissary veins to the scalp, and down the system of paravertebral veins in the spinal canal. In other species, the internal jugular veins are small, and the venous blood from the brain mixes with blood from other structures.

The cerebral vessels have a number of unique anatomic features. In the choroid plexuses there are gaps between the endothelial cells of the capillary

Table 32–1. Blood flow and O_2 consumption of various organs in a 63 kg adult human with a mean arterial blood pressure of 90 mm Hg and an O_2 consumption of 250 ml/min. R units are pressure (mm Hg) divided by blood flow (ml/s).*

Region	Mass (kg)	Blood Flow ml/min	Blood Flow ml/100 g/min	Arteriovenous Oxygen Difference (ml/L)	Oxygen Consumption ml/min	Oxygen Consumption ml/100 g/min	Resistance in R units Absolute	Resistance in R units per kg	Percentage of Total Cardiac Output	Percentage of Total Oxygen Consumption
Liver	2.6	1500	57.7	34	51	2.0	3.6	9.4	27.8	20.4
Kidneys	0.3	1260	420.0	14	18	6.0	4.3	1.3	23.3	7.2
Brain	1.4	750	54.0	62	46	3.3	7.2	10.1	13.9	18.4
Skin	3.6	462	12.8	25	12	0.3	11.7	42.1	8.6	4.8
Skeletal muscle	31.0	840	2.7	60	50	0.2	6.4	198.4	15.6	20.0
Heart muscle	0.3	250	84.0	114	29	9.7	21.4	6.4	4.7	11.6
Rest of body	23.8	336	1.4	129	44	0.2	16.1	383.2	6.2	17.6
Whole body	63.0	5400	8.6	46	250	0.4	1.0	63.0	100.0	100.0

*Reproduced, with permission, from Bard P (editor): *Medical Physiology,* 11th ed. Mosby, 1961.

wall, but the choroid epithelial cells are densely inter-meshed and interlocked. The capillaries in the brain substance resemble nonfenestrated capillaries in muscle and other parts of the body (see Chapter 30). However, there are tight junctions between the endothelial cells that do not permit the passage of substances which pass through the junctions between endothelial cells in other tissues. In addition, there are relatively few vesicles in the endothelial cytoplasm, and presumably there is little vesicular transport. The brain capillaries are surrounded by the end-feet of astrocytes (Fig 32–1). These end-feet are closely applied to the basal lamina of the capillaries, but they do not cover the entire capillary wall. The protoplasm of astrocytes is also found around synapses, where it appears to isolate the synapses in the brain from one another.

Innervation

There are numerous myelinated and unmyelinated nerve fibers on the cerebral vessels. The sympathetic fibers on the pial arteries and arterioles come from the cervical ganglia of the sympathetic ganglion chain. However, the vessels in brain tissue appear to be innervated by intracerebral noradrenergic neurons that have their cell bodies in the brain stem (see Chapter 15). The parasympathetic fibers pass to the cerebral

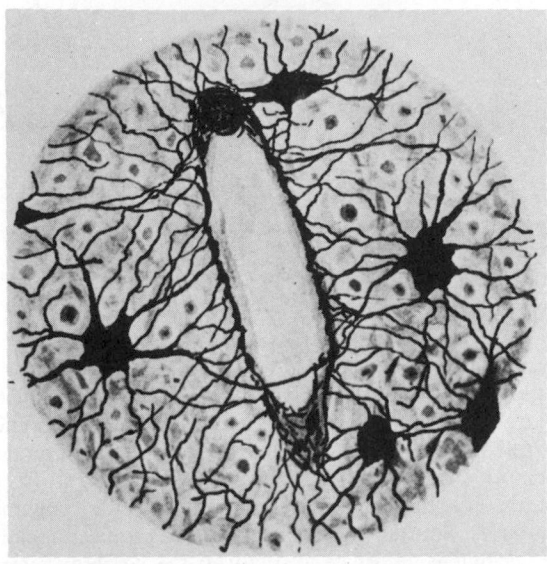

Figure 32–1. Membrane of end-feet of fibrous astrocytes (large dark cells) around a cerebral capillary. From occipital cortex of a monkey, silver carbonate stain. (Reproduced, with permission, from Glees P: *Neuroglia, Morphology and Function.* Blackwell, 1955.)

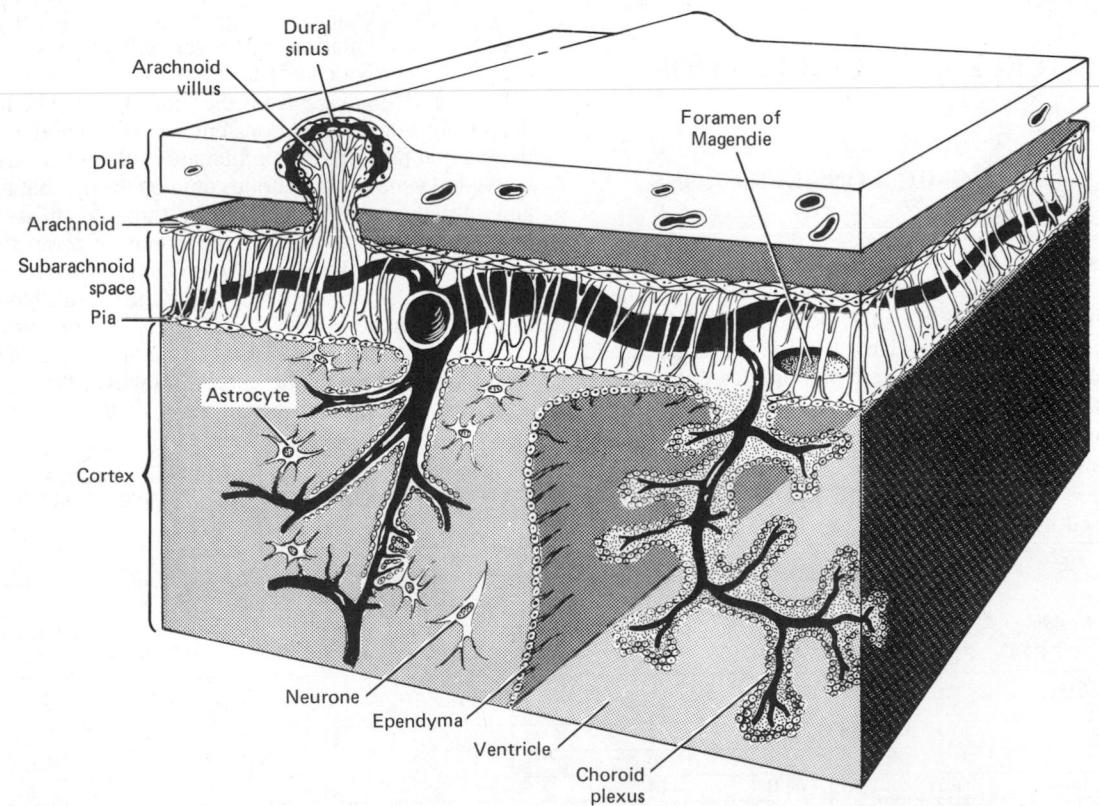

Figure 32–2. Section of the brain and investing membranes. (Reproduced, with permission, from Tschirgi R in: *Handbook of Physiology.* Field J, Magoun HW [editors]. Washington: The American Physiological Society, 1960. Section 1, pages 1865–1890.)

vessels from the facial nerve via the greater superficial petrosal nerve. The myelinated fibers are probably sensory in function, since touching or pulling on the cerebral vessels causes pain.

CEREBROSPINAL FLUID

Formation & Absorption

About 50% of the cerebrospinal fluid (CSF) that fills the cerebral ventricles and subarachnoid space is formed in the choroid plexuses (Fig 32–2); the remaining 50% is formed around the cerebral vessels and along the ventricular walls. The composition of the CSF depends on filtration and diffusion from the blood, along with facilitated diffusion and active transport, much of it across the choroid plexus. The composition (Table 32–2) is essentially the same as brain ECF, and there appears to be free communication between the brain extracellular space, the ventricles, and the subarachnoid space. The CSF flows out through the foramens of Magendie and Luschka and is absorbed through the arachnoid villi into the cerebral venous sinuses. Bulk flow via the villi is 500 ml/d in humans. Substances also leave the CSF by diffusion across adjacent membranes, and there is facilitated diffusion of glucose and active transport of cations and organic acids out of the CSF.

The rate of CSF formation is independent of intraventricular pressure, but the absorption, which takes place largely by bulk flow, is proportionate to the pressure (Fig 32–3). Below a pressure of approximately 68 mm CSF, absorption stops. Large amounts of fluid accumulate when the reabsorptive capacity of

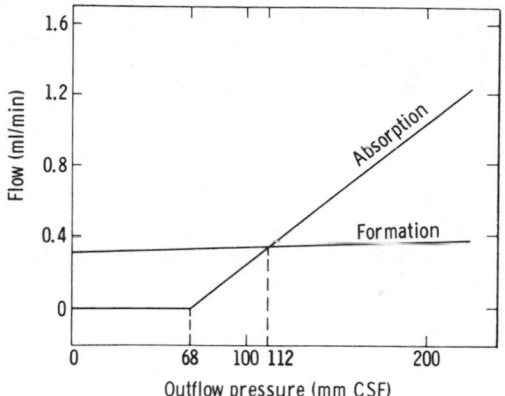

Figure 32–3. CSF formation and absorption in humans at various CSF pressures. Note that at 112 mm CSF, formation and absorption are equal, and at 68 mm CSF, absorption is zero. (Modified and reproduced, with permission, from Cutler RWP & others: Formation and absorption of cerebrospinal fluid in man. Brain 91:707, 1968.)

the arachnoid villi is decreased (**external, or communicating, hydrocephalus**). Fluid also accumulates proximal to the block and distends the ventricles when the foramens of Luschka and Magendie are blocked or there is obstruction within the ventricular system (**internal hydrocephalus**).

Brain Extracellular Space

There has been considerable controversy about the size of the brain extracellular space. The Na^+ space in brain tissue is about 35% of brain volume and the Cl^- space is about 30%, but both ions are known to be present inside as well as outside of brain cells. Inulin

Table 32–2. Concentration of various substances in human CSF and plasma.*

Substance		CSF	Plasma	Ratio CSF/Plasma
Na^+	(mEq/kg H_2O)	147.0	150.0	0.98
K^+	(mEq/kg H_2O)	2.9	4.6	0.62
Mg^{2+}	(mEq/kg H_2O)	2.2	1.6	1.39
Ca^{2+}	(mEq/kg H_2O)	2.3	4.7	0.49
Cl^-	(mEq/kg H_2O)	113.0	99.0	1.14
HCO_3^-	(mEq/L)	25.1	24.8	1.01
P_{CO_2}	(mm Hg)	50.2	39.5	1.28
pH		7.33	7.40	. . .
Osmolality	(mOsm/kg H_2O)	289.0	289.0	1.00
Protein	(mg/dl)	20.0	6000.0	0.003
Glucose	(mg/dl)	64.0	100.0	0.64
Inorganic P	(mg/dl)	3.4	4.7	0.73
Urea	(mg/dl)	12.0	15.0	0.80
Creatinine	(mg/dl)	1.5	1.2	1.25
Uric acid	(mg/dl)	1.5	5.0	0.30
Lactic acid	(mg/dl)	18.0	21.0	0.86
Cholesterol	(mg/dl)	0.2	175.0	0.001

*Data partly from Davson H: *Physiology of the Cerebrospinal Fluid,* Churchill, 1967; and partly courtesy of R Mitchell & associates.

and ferrocyanide, which do not enter cells, distribute in about 15% of brain volume. Under the electron microscope, brain cells appear very close together, and some electron microscopists have argued that the volume of the brain extracellular space could not be more than 4% of brain volume. However, asphyxia makes brain cells swell, and the brain extracellular space shrinks to 4% or less of brain volume when the brain is exposed to approximately the same amount of asphyxia as brain tissue prepared for electron photomicrography. These and other data indicate that the extracellular space in the living human occupies about 15% of brain volume.

Protective Function

The meninges and the CSF protect the brain. The dura is attached firmly to bone. There is normally no "subdural space," the arachnoid being held to the dura by the surface tension of the thin layer of fluid between the 2 membranes. The brain itself is supported within the arachnoid by the blood vessels and nerve roots and by the multiple, fine fibrous **arachnoid trabeculae** (Fig 32–2). The brain weighs about 1400 g in air, but in its "water bath" of CSF it has a net weight of only 50 g. The buoyancy of the brain in the CSF permits its relatively flimsy attachments to suspend it very effectively. When the head receives a blow, the arachnoid slides on the dura and the brain moves, but its motion is gently checked by the CSF cushion and by the arachnoid trabeculae.

The pain produced by spinal fluid deficiency illustrates the importance of spinal fluid in supporting the brain. As a diagnostic procedure in patients suspected of having brain tumors, spinal fluid is removed and replaced by air to make the outline of the ventricles visible by x-ray (**pneumoencephalography**). This procedure causes a severe headache after the fluid is removed because the brain hangs on the vessels and nerve roots, and traction on them stimulates pain fibers. The pain can be relieved by intrathecal injection of sterile isotonic saline.

Head Injuries

Without the protection of the spinal fluid and the meninges, the brain would probably be unable to withstand even the minor traumas of everyday living; but with the protection afforded, it takes a fairly severe blow to produce cerebral damage. The brain is damaged most commonly when the skull is fractured and bone is driven into neural tissue (depressed skull fracture), when the brain moves far enough to tear the delicate bridging veins from the cortex to the bone, or when the brain is accelerated by a blow on the head and is driven against the skull or the tentorium at a point opposite where the blow was struck (**contrecoup injury**).

THE BLOOD–BRAIN BARRIER

Over 50 years ago, it was first demonstrated that when acidic dyes such as trypan blue are injected into living animals all the tissues are stained except most of the brain and spinal cord. To explain the failure of the neural tissue to stain, the existence of a **blood-brain barrier** was postulated. The work with dyes has been criticized, but subsequent research has established the fact that only water, CO_2, and O_2 cross the cerebral capillaries with ease, and the exchange of other substances is slow.

The general features of exchange across capillary walls between the plasma and the interstitial fluid are described in Chapter 30. There is considerable variation in capillary permeability from organ to organ in the body. However, the exchange across the cerebral vessels is so different from that in other capillary beds—and the rate of exchange of many physiologically important substances is so slow—that it seems justifiable to speak specifically of a blood-brain barrier.

Penetration of Substances Into Brain

As noted above, brain ECF is essentially identical to CSF, and substances enter the CSF by filtration, diffusion, facilitated diffusion, and active transport. There is an H^+ gradient between brain ECF and blood; the pH of brain ECF is 7.33, whereas that of blood is 7.40.

In general, the rapidity with which substances penetrate brain tissue is inversely related to their molecular size and directly related to their lipid solubility; water-soluble polar compounds generally cross slowly. Water, CO_2, and O_2 cross the blood-brain barrier readily, whereas glucose crosses more slowly. Na^+, K^+, Mg^{2+}, Cl^-, HCO_3^-, and HPO_4^{2-} in plasma

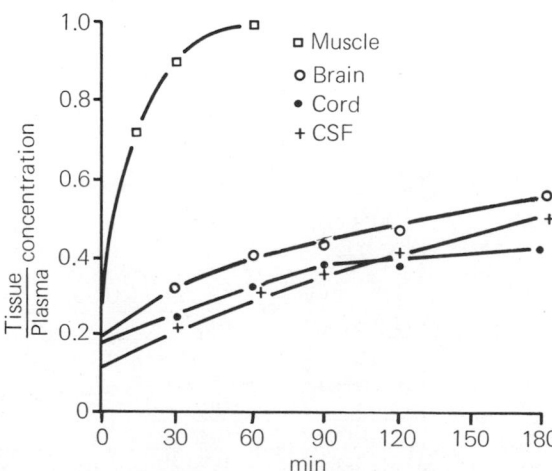

Figure 32–4. Penetration of urea into muscle, brain, spinal cord, and cerebrospinal fluid. (Modified and reproduced, with permission, from Kleeman CR, Davson H, Levin E: Urea transport in the central nervous system. Am J Physiol 203:739, 1962.)

require 3–30 times as long to equilibrate with spinal fluid as they do with other portions of the interstitial fluid. The relatively slow penetration of urea into brain and the cerebrospinal fluid is illustrated in Fig 32–4. Bile salts and catecholamines do not enter the adult brain in more than minute amounts. Proteins cross the barrier to a very limited extent, and it is because they are bound to protein that acidic dyes fail to stain neural tissue. It is worth noting that no substance is completely excluded from the brain, and the important consideration is the rate of transfer of the substance. Certain compounds cross the blood-brain barrier slowly, whereas closely related compounds enter rapidly. For example, the amines dopamine and serotonin penetrate to a very limited degree, but their corresponding acids, L-dopa and 5-hydroxytryptophan, enter with relative ease (see Chapter 15).

Development of the Blood-Brain Barrier

The cerebral capillaries are much more permeable at birth than in adulthood, and the blood-brain barrier develops during the early years of life. In severely jaundiced infants, bile pigments penetrate into the nervous system and, in the presence of asphyxia, damage the basal ganglia (kernicterus). However, in jaundiced adults, the nervous system is unstained and not directly affected.

Circumventricular Organs

When an acidic dye is injected into an animal, 5 small areas in or near the brain stain like the tissues outside the brain. These areas are (1) the **pineal gland,** (2) the **posterior pituitary** (neurohypophysis) and the adjacent ventral part of the median eminence of the hypothalamus, (3) the **area postrema,** (4) the **supraoptic crest** (organum vasculosum of the lamina terminalis, OVLT), and (5) the **subfornical organ** (intercolumnar tubercle).

These areas are referred to collectively as the **circumventricular organs** (Fig 32–5). All have fenestrated capillaries, and because of their permeability they are said to be "outside the blood-brain barrier." Many appear to contain hypothalamic hormones. Some of them function as **neurohemal organs,** ie, areas in which substances secreted by neurons enter the circulation; for example, oxytocin and vasopressin enter the general circulation in the posterior pituitary, and hypothalamic hypophyseotropic hormones enter the portal hypophyseal circulation in the median eminence. Other circumventricular organs function as chemoreceptor zones, ie, areas in which substances in the circulating blood can act to trigger changes in brain function without penetrating the blood-brain barrier. The area postrema is a chemoreceptor zone that initiates vomiting in response to chemical changes in the plasma (Chapter 14). In some species, circulating angiotensin II acts on the area postrema to trigger an increase in blood pressure. Angiotensin II also acts on the subfornical organ and possibly on the OVLT to increase water intake (Fig 14–9). The subcommissural organ (Fig 32–5) is

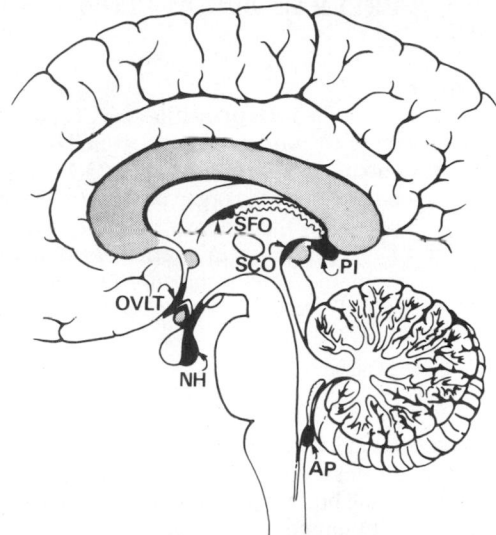

Figure 32–5. Circumventricular organs. The neurohypophysis (NH), organum vasculosum of the lamina terminalis (OVLT, supraoptic crest), subfornical organ (SFO), pineal (PI), and area postrema (AP) are shown projected on a sagittal section of the human brain. SCO, subcommissural organ.

closely associated with the pineal and histologically resembles the circumventricular organs. However, it does not have fenestrated capillaries, is less permeable, and has no established function.

Function of the Blood-Brain Barrier

The blood-brain barrier probably functions to maintain the constancy of the environment of the neurons in the CNS. These neurons are so dependent upon the ionic composition of the fluid bathing them that even minor variations have far-reaching consequences. The constancy of the composition of the ECF in all parts of the body is maintained by multiple homeostatic mechanisms (see Chapters 1 and 40), but because of the sensitivity of the cortical neurons to ionic change it is not surprising that an additional defense has evolved to protect them.

Clinical Implications

The physician must know the permeability of the blood-brain barrier to drugs in order to treat diseases of the nervous system intelligently. For example, among the antibiotics, penicillin and chlortetracycline enter the brain to a very limited degree. Sulfadiazine and erythromycin, on the other hand, enter quite readily.

Another important clinical consideration is the fact that the blood-brain barrier breaks down in areas of the brain that are irradiated, infected, or the site of tumors. The breakdown makes it possible to localize tumors with considerable accuracy. Substances such as radioactive iodine–labeled albumin penetrate normal brain tissue very slowly, but they enter rapidly into tumor tissue, making the tumor stand out as an island of radioactivity in the surrounding normal brain.

CEREBRAL BLOOD FLOW

Kety Method

According to the **Fick principle** (see Chapter 29), the blood flow of any organ can be measured by determining the amount of a given substance (Q_x) removed from the bloodstream by the organ per unit of time and dividing that value by the difference between the concentration of the substance in arterial blood and the concentration in the venous blood from the organ ($[A_x]) - [V_x]$). Thus:

$$\text{Cerebral blood flow (CBF)} = \frac{Q_x}{[A_x] - [V_x]}$$

When an individual inhales small subanesthetic amounts of nitrous oxide (N_2O), this gas is taken up by the brain, and the brain N_2O equilibrates with the N_2O in blood in 9–11 minutes. After equilibration, the N_2O concentration in cerebral venous blood is equal to the concentration in the brain because the brain-blood partition coefficient for N_2O is 1. Therefore, the level in cerebral venous blood after equilibration divided by the mean arteriovenous N_2O difference during equilibration equals the cerebral blood flow per unit of brain:

$$\text{CBF (ml/100 g brain/min)} = \frac{100\ V_u S}{\displaystyle\int_0^u (A-V)dt}$$

where V = Cerebral venous N_2O concentration (vol/100 g)

  u = Time of equilibrium (minutes)

  S = Partition coefficient of N_2O in blood and brain (= 1)

  A = Arterial N_2O concentration (vol/100 g)

The mean arteriovenous difference can also be estimated from a plot of the differences at various times during equilibration (Fig 32–6). When blood N_2O concentrations are expressed in volumes per deciliter of blood or, more accurately, in volumes per 100 g of blood, the cerebral blood flow values obtained are in ml/100 g of brain per minute. The value per unit of brain tissue can be converted to an approximate value for total cerebral blood flow by multiplying by 1400 g, an average figure for brain weight in adult humans.

When the N_2O method (**Kety method**) is used to determine the cerebral blood flow in intact humans, arterial blood samples can be obtained from any convenient artery, since the concentration of substances in systemic arterial blood is uniform throughout the body. To obtain cerebral venous blood, a needle is inserted into the jugular bulb. This blood is not significantly diluted with blood from other sources in 95% of humans. The jugular bulb is readily penetrated if the needle is inserted in a slightly headward direction halfway between the mastoid process and the angle of the mandible. The subject inhales the gas for 10 min-

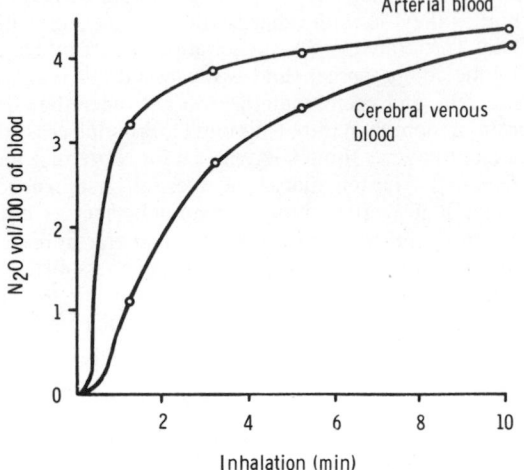

Figure 32–6. Arterial and cerebral venous blood N_2O levels while inhaling N_2O. (Redrawn and reproduced, with permission, from Kety S in: *Methods in Medical Research.* Vol 1. Potter VR [editor]. Year Book, 1948.)

utes, and arterial and jugular venous blood samples are obtained repeatedly during this time. The gas content of the samples is determined, and the mean arteriovenous gas difference is calculated. The average value for cerebral blood flow (CBF) in young adults with this method is 54 ml/100 g/min (750 ml/min for the whole brain), with a range of approximately 40–67 ml/100 g/min.

The value obtained with the Kety method is, of course, an average value for the flow during the 10-minute equilibration period. Values for total CBF give no information about the relative blood flow in the various parts of the brain. Indeed, trying to draw conclusions about regional blood flow from total CBF measurements has been likened to trying to analyze the activity of individual tenants in a large apartment house by sampling the flow in the main water pipe and sewer pipe outside the apartment house. A reduction in flow to one part of the brain may be compensated by an increase in flow to another part, so that CBF remains unchanged. An uncompensated decrease in the blood flow to part of the brain results in decreased CBF, but the Kety method does not detect the decrease in total CBF produced by complete occlusion of the vessels supplying part of the brain. This is true because the method measures only the flow per unit of brain, and the nonperfused area takes up no N_2O. The remaining normal brain extracts normal amounts, so that the CBF per unit of brain tissues is unaffected.

Blood Flow in Various Parts of the Brain

By determining the distribution of an inert radioactive gas in frozen sections of the brains of experimental animals and comparing these values with the level of the gas in the blood, it is possible to measure regional blood flow in the brain. The flow in

Table 32–3. Blood flow of representative areas of the brain of unanesthetized cats.*

Area	Mean Blood Flow (ml/g/min)
Inferior colliculus	1.80
Sensorimotor cortex	1.38
Auditory cortex	1.30
Visual cortex	1.25
Medial geniculate body	1.22
Lateral geniculate body	1.21
Superior colliculus	1.15
Caudate nucleus	1.10
Thalamus	1.03
Association cortex	0.88
Cerebellar nuclei	0.87
Cerebellar white matter	0.24
Cerebral white matter	0.23
Spinal cord white matter	0.14

*Data from Landau WM & others: The local circulation of the living brain: Values in the unanesthetized cat. Trans Am Neurol Assoc 80:125, 1955.

the cerebral and cerebellar cortex is large, but the part of the brain with the highest blood flow is the inferior colliculus (Table 32–3). The blood flow in gray matter is about 6 times the flow in white matter.

The blood flow of different regions of the cerebral cortex can be measured in conscious humans by injecting a radioactive gas such as ^{133}Xe dissolved in saline into one carotid artery. The arrival and clearance of the gas in various regions is then monitored by a battery of 254 scintillation detectors placed over the head. Each detector is collimated to scan about 1 cm^2 of brain surface. The output from the detectors is processed in a computer and displayed on a color television screen in such a way that the color corresponding to the location of each detector is proportionate to the flow it is detecting. With this technic, only the radioactivity from the superficial layers of the cerebral cortex is detected. The visual cortex is left out, since it is supplied primarily by branches of the vertebral rather than the carotid arteries. However, the technic makes it possible not only to visualize regional cortical blood flow at rest but also to determine changes in this flow with various mental and other activities (Fig 32–7).

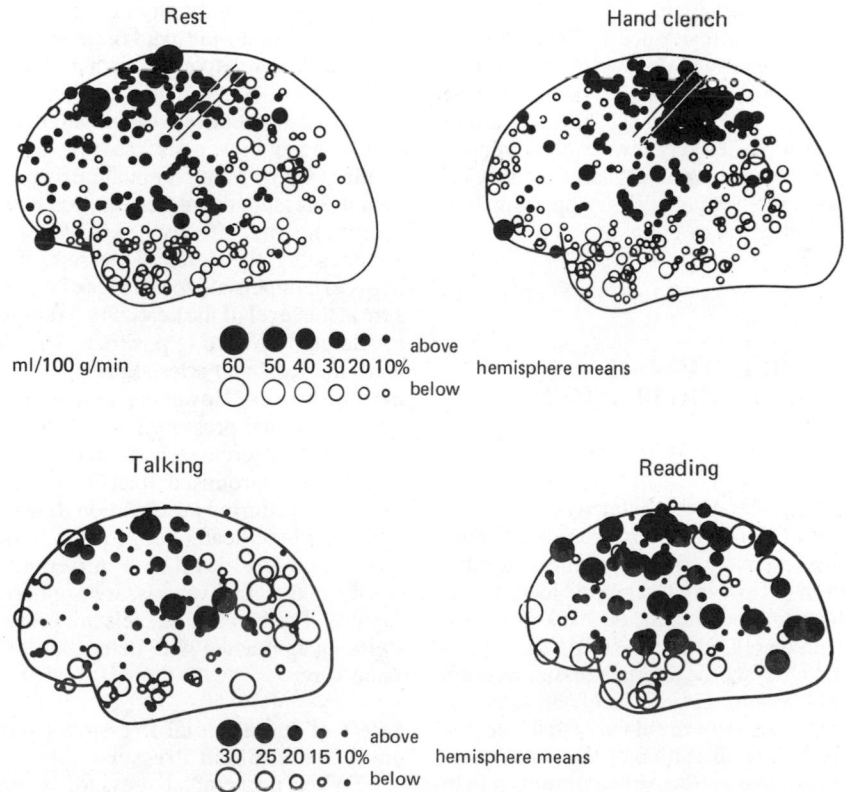

Figure 32–7. Local blood flow in the left cerebral hemisphere of conscious humans, determined by the ^{133}Xe method. Values are expressed as percentage differences from hemispheric mean flow. The values shown were obtained at rest, during voluntary clenching of the right hand, during talking, and during reading. Note that the scale for the bottom 2 diagrams is different from the scale for ones at top. (Reproduced from Ingvar DH: Functional landscapes in the brain in normal and patients with brain disorders. Curr Concepts Cerebrovascular Dis 12:1, 1977. By permission of the American Heart Association, Inc.)

Studies with this technic make it clear that in the brain, as in other organs, there are increases in blood flow associated with increases in activity. The local increases are presumably mediated by vasodilator metabolites. In subjects who are awake but at rest, blood flow is greatest in the premotor and frontal regions (Fig 32–7). During voluntary clenching of the right hand, flow is increased in the hand area of the left motor cortex and the corresponding sensory areas in the postcentral gyrus. When subjects talk, there is a bilateral increase in blood flow in the face, tongue, and mouth sensory and motor areas and the upper premotor cortex as well as an increase in Broca's area in the categorical (usually the left) hemisphere. Reading produces widespread increases in blood flow. Problem solving, reasoning, and motor ideation without movement produce increases in the premotor and frontal regions.

The ^{133}Xe technic is now being applied to the study of various diseases. Epileptic foci are hyperemic, whereas there is decreased temporal lobe flow in patients with memory deficits and decreased parieto-occipital flow in patients with agnostic symptoms (see Chapter 16). In chronic schizophrenia, there is decreased blood flow at rest in the dominant hemisphere.

Cerebral Vascular Resistance

The cerebral vascular resistance (CVR) is equal to the cerebral perfusion pressure divided by the cerebral blood flow. The CVR in the supine position can be calculated on the basis of the mean brachial artery pressure (ignoring the relatively low cerebral venous pressure) without introducing a very large error. Calculated in this way, the normal CVR is approximately 10 "R units" per kilogram of brain, or 7.2 R units for the whole brain (Table 32–1).

REGULATION OF CEREBRAL CIRCULATION

Normal Flow

The cerebral circulation is regulated in such a way that a constant total CBF is generally maintained under varying conditions. For example, despite extensive shifts in the pattern of flow, total cerebral blood flow is not increased by strenuous mental activity. It is also unchanged or even increased during sleep. The factors affecting the total CBF are the arterial pressure at brain level, the venous pressure at brain level, the intracranial pressure, the viscosity of the blood, and the degree of active constriction or dilatation of the cerebral arterioles (Fig 32–8). The caliber of the arterioles is in turn controlled by vasomotor nerves, cerebral metabolism, and autoregulation.

Role of Intracranial Pressure

In adults, the brain, spinal cord, and spinal fluid are encased, along with the cerebral vessels, in a rigid

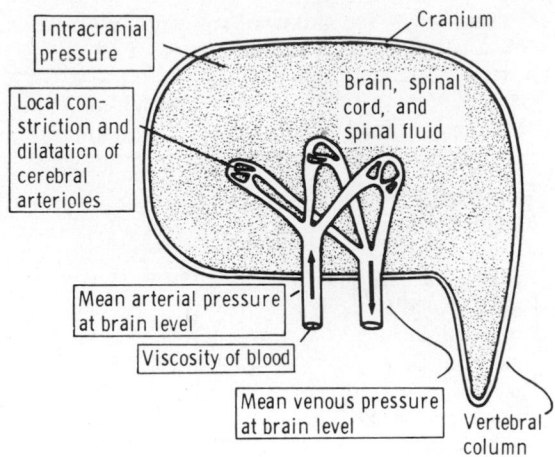

Figure 32–8. Diagrammatic summary of the factors affecting cerebral blood flow. (Modified from Patterson JL Jr in: *Physiology and Biophysics,* 19th ed. Ruch TC, Patton HD [editors]. Saunders, 1965.)

bony enclosure. The cranial cavity normally contains a brain weighing approximately 1400 g, 75 ml of blood, and 75 ml of spinal fluid. Because brain tissue and spinal fluid are essentially incompressible, the volume of blood, spinal fluid, and brain in the cranium at any time must be relatively constant (**Monro-Kellie doctrine**). More importantly, the cerebral vessels are compressed whenever the intracranial pressure rises. Any change in venous pressure promptly causes a similar change in intracranial pressure. Thus, a rise in venous pressure decreases cerebral blood flow both by decreasing the effective perfusion pressure and by compressing the cerebral vessels. This relationship helps to compensate for changes in arterial blood pressure at the level of the head. For example, if the body is accelerated upward ("positive *g*"), blood moves toward the feet, and arterial pressure at the level of the head decreases. However, venous pressure also falls and intracranial pressure falls, so that the pressure on the vessels decreases and blood flow is much less severely compromised than it would otherwise be. Conversely, during acceleration downward, force acting toward the head ("negative *g*") increases arterial pressure at head level, but intracranial pressure also rises, so that the vessels are supported and do not rupture. The cerebral vessels are protected during the straining associated with defecation or delivery in the same way.

Effect of Intracranial Pressure Changes on Systemic Blood Pressure

When intracranial pressure is elevated to more than 450 mm of water (33 mm Hg) over a short period of time, cerebral blood flow is significantly reduced. The resultant ischemia stimulates the vasomotor center (see Chapter 31), and systemic blood pressure rises. Stimulation of the cardioinhibitory center produces bradycardia, and respiration is slowed. The blood pressure rise, which was described by Cushing and is sometimes called the **Cushing reflex,** helps to maintain the cerebral blood flow. Over a considerable range, the rise in systemic blood pressure is proportionate to the rise in intracranial pressure, although eventually a point is reached where the intracranial pressure exceeds the arterial pressure, and cerebral circulation ceases.

Role of Vasomotor Nerves

The bulk of the evidence presently available indicates that even though cerebral vessels are innervated by adrenergic vasoconstrictor fibers and parasympathetic vasodilator fibers, vasomotor reflexes play little if any part in the regulation of cerebral blood flow in humans. Stimulation of the cervical sympathetics does cause some constriction of pial vessels in animals, and injecting procaine into the stellate ganglion has had a considerable vogue in the treatment of cerebral thrombosis on the theory that the vasospasm associated with the thrombosis is mediated via vasoconstrictor nerves. However, careful measurements clearly show that blocking the stellate ganglion has no effect on cerebral blood flow, and the therapeutic value of stellate ganglion block is questionable. Of course, stellate ganglion block does not affect the intracerebral noradrenergic neurons that innervate the arterioles in the substance of the brain, but the functional role of this system is presently unknown.

Effects of Brain Metabolism on
Cerebral Vessels

The arterioles in the brain, like those in other parts of the body, are directly affected by local changes in CO_2 and O_2 tension. A rise in P_{CO_2} exerts a particularly potent dilator effect on the cerebral vessels. A fall in P_{CO_2} has a constrictor effect, and cerebral vasoconstriction is an important factor in the production of the cerebral symptoms seen when the arterial P_{CO_2} falls during hyperventilation. Hydrogen ions also exert a vasodilator effect, and a fall in pH is associated with increased flow whereas a rise in pH is associated with decreased flow. Changes in P_{CO_2} lead to corresponding changes in H^+ concentration in the brain, and current evidence indicates that the effects of CO_2 are mediated via changes in pH. The vasodilator effect of H^+ appears to be due to a direct local action on the blood vessels.

Changes in local O_2 tension also affect the cerebral arterioles; a low P_{O_2} is associated with vasodilatation and a high P_{O_2} with mild vasoconstriction. In addition, adenosine and other vasoactive metabolites may produce local vasodilatation in active cerebral tissue.

Autoregulation

Autoregulation is prominent in the brain. This process, by which the flow to many tissues is maintained at relatively constant levels despite variations in perfusion pressure, is discussed in Chapter 31. As in other tissues, cerebral autoregulation may depend upon an inherent capacity of vascular smooth muscle to contract when it is stretched or upon the washing away of CO_2 and other vasodilator metabolites when the perfusion pressure and hence the blood flow is increased—or upon both mechanisms.

Integrated Operation of Regulatory Mechanisms

Several examples of the way the regulatory mechanisms discussed above maintain cerebral blood flow are discussed in Chapter 33. It is worth remembering that these mechanisms operate together to overcome such formidable challenges as the effect of gravity on the cerebral blood flow, not only in humans but also in giraffes when these animals stoop to drink water and when they raise their heads to nibble leaves from the tops of trees.

BRAIN METABOLISM
& OXYGEN REQUIREMENTS

Uptake & Release of Substances by the Brain

If the cerebral blood flow is known, it is possible to calculate the consumption or production by the brain of O_2, CO_2, glucose, or any other substance present in the bloodstream by multiplying the cerebral blood flow by the difference between the concentration of the substance in arterial blood and its concentration in cerebral venous blood. When calculated in this fashion, a negative value indicates that the brain is producing the substance (Table 32–4).

Oxygen Consumption

The O_2 consumption of human brain, or **cerebral metabolic rate for O_2 (CMRO$_2$),** averages about 3.5 ml/100 g brain/min, or 49 ml/min for the whole brain in an adult. This figure represents approximately 20% of the total resting O_2 consumption (Table 32–1). The

Table 32–4. Utilization and production of substances by adult human brain in vivo.*

	Uptake (+) or output (−) per 100 g brain/min	Total/min
Substances utilized		
Oxygen	+3.5 ml	+49 ml
Glucose	+5.5 mg	+77 mg
Glutamic acid	+0.4 mg	+ 5.6 mg
Substances produced		
Carbon dioxide	−3.5 ml	−49 ml
Glutamine	−0.6 mg	− 8.4 mg

Substances not utilized or produced in the fed state: lactic acid, pyruvic acid, total ketones, α-ketoglutarate.

*From data compiled by Sokoloff L in: *Handbook of Physiology*. Field J, Magoun HW (editors). Washington: The American Physiological Society, 1960. Section 1, pages 1843–1865.

Table 32–5. Oxygen consumption of parts of adult dog brain in vitro.*

	Oxygen Consumption (μl/100 mg/h)
Caudate nucleus	136
Cerebral cortex	116
Cerebellum	107
Thalamus	101
Midbrain	92
Medulla	69
Spinal cord	50

*Data from Himwich NE, Fazekas JF: Comparative studies of the metabolism of the brain. Am J Physiol 132:454, 1941.

brain is extremely sensitive to hypoxia, and occlusion of its blood supply produces unconsciousness in as short a period as 10 s. The vegetative structures in the brain stem are more resistant to hypoxia than the cerebral cortex, and patients may recover from accidents such as cardiac arrest and other conditions causing fairly prolonged hypoxia with normal vegetative functions but severe, permanent intellectual deficiencies. The basal ganglia also use O_2 at a very rapid rate. The values for in vitro O_2 consumption of various parts of the dog brain are shown in Table 32–5. The metabolic rate of the cerebral cortex relative to that of the basal ganglia may be higher in humans than in dogs, but it is well to remember that the basal ganglia are sensitive to hypoxia in humans and that symptoms of Parkinson's disease as well as intellectual deficits can be produced by chronic hypoxia. The thalamus and the inferior colliculus are also very susceptible to hypoxic damage.

Energy Sources

Glucose is the major ultimate source of energy for the brain under normal conditions. It is taken up from the blood in large amounts, and the RQ (respiratory quotient; see Chapter 17) of cerebral tissue is 0.95–0.99 in normal individuals. This does not mean that the total source of energy is always glucose. During prolonged starvation, there is appreciable utilization of other substances. Indeed, there is evidence that as much as 30% of the glucose taken up under normal conditions is converted to amino acids, lipids, and proteins, and that substances other than glucose are metabolized for energy during convulsions. There may also be some utilization of amino acids from the circulation even though the amino acid arteriovenous difference across the brain is normally minute. Insulin is not required for most cerebral cells to utilize glucose.

Glucose uptake is increased in active neurons, and 2-deoxyglucose is taken up like glucose but is not metabolized. Therefore, the uptake of radioactive 2-deoxyglucose can be used to map the activity of neurons on a microscopic scale. For example, illumination of one eye in monkeys causes an increase in the amount of 2-deoxyglucose, as determined by radioautography, in columns of cells in the visual cortex that are less than 1 mm apart.

Hypoglycemia

The symptoms of hypoglycemia are mental changes, ataxia, confusion, sweating, coma, and convulsions (see Chapter 19). The total glycogen content of the brain is about 1.6 mg/g in fasted animals, but the available glycogen and glucose are used up in 2 minutes if the blood supply is totally occluded. Thus, the brain can withstand hypoglycemia for somewhat longer periods than it can withstand hypoxia, but glucose and O_2 are both needed for survival. The cortical regions are more sensitive to hypoglycemia than the vegetative centers in the brain stem, and sublethal exposures to hypoglycemia, like similar exposures to hypoxia, may cause irreversible cortical changes.

Glutamic Acid & Ammonia Removal

The brain uptake of glutamic acid is approximately balanced by its output of glutamine. It is probable that the glutamic acid entering the brain takes up ammonia and leaves as glutamine (see Chapter 17). The glutamic acid–glutamine conversion in the brain—the opposite of the reaction in the kidney that produces some of the ammonia entering the tubules—probably serves as a detoxifying mechanism to keep the brain free of ammonia. Ammonia is very toxic to nerve cells, and ammonia intoxication is believed to be a major cause of the bizarre neurologic symptoms in hepatic coma.

CORONARY CIRCULATION

Anatomic Considerations

The 2 coronary arteries that supply the myocardium arise from the sinuses behind the cusps of the aortic valve at the root of the aorta (Fig 32–9). Eddy currents keep the valves away from the orifices of the arteries, and they are patent throughout the cardiac cycle. The right coronary artery has a greater flow in 50% of individuals, the left has a greater flow in 20%, and the flow is equal in 30%. There are 2 venous drainage systems: a superficial system, ending in the coronary sinus and anterior cardiac veins, that drains the left ventricle; and a deep system draining the rest of the heart (Fig 32–10). The deep system is made up in large part of the **arteriosinusoidal vessels,** sinusoidal capillary–like vessels that empty directly into the heart chambers. There are also direct connections to the atria and ventricles from the coronary arterioles (**arterioluminal vessels**) and the veins (**thebesian veins**). There are a few anastomoses between the coronary arterioles and extracardiac arterioles, especially around the mouths of the great veins. Anastomoses between coronary arterioles in humans only pass particles less than 40 μm in diameter, but there is evidence that these channels enlarge and increase in number in patients with coronary artery disease.

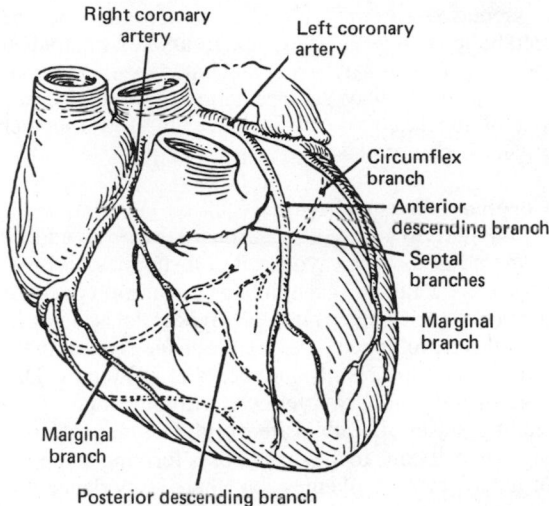

Figure 32–9. Coronary arteries and their principal branches in humans. (Reproduced, with permission, from Ross G: The cardiovascular system. In Ross G [editor]: *Essentials of Human Physiology.* Copyright © 1978 by Year Book Medical Publishers, Inc., Chicago.)

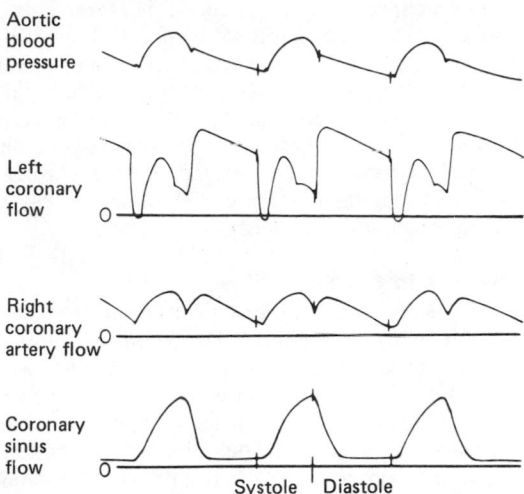

Figure 32–11. Schematic representation of blood flow in the left and right coronary arteries and the coronary sinus of dogs during phases of the cardiac cycle. (After Gregg DE. Reproduced, with permission, from Ruch TC, Patton HD [editors]: *Physiology and Biophysics,* 19th ed. Saunders, 1965.)

Pressure Gradients & Flow in the Coronary Vessels

The heart is a muscle that, like skeletal muscle, compresses its blood vessels when it contracts. The pressure inside the left ventricle is slightly greater than in the aorta during systole (Table 32–6). Consequently, flow occurs in the arteries supplying the subendocardial portion of the left ventricle only during diastole, although the force is sufficiently dissipated in the more superficial portions of the left ventricular myocardium to permit some flow in this region throughout the cardiac cycle. Since diastole is shorter when the heart rate is rapid, left ventricular coronary flow is reduced during tachycardia. On the other hand, the pressure differential between the aorta and the right ventricle, and the differential between the aorta and the atria, is somewhat greater during systole than during diastole. Consequently, coronary flow in those parts of the heart is not appreciably reduced during systole.

Flow in the right and left coronary arteries of dogs is shown in Fig 32–11. Because there is no blood flow during systole in the subendocardial portion of the left ventricle, this region is prone to ischemic damage and is the most common site of myocardial infarction. Blood flow to the left ventricle is decreased in patients with stenotic aortic valves because in aortic stenosis the pressure in the left ventricle must be much greater than that in the aorta to eject the blood. Consequently, the coronary vessels are severely compressed during systole. Patients with this disease are particularly prone to develop symptoms of myocardial ischemia, in part because of this compression and in part because the myocardium requires more O_2 to expel blood through the stenotic aortic valve. Coronary flow is also decreased when the aortic diastolic pressure is low. The rise in venous pressure in conditions such as congestive heart failure reduces coronary flow because it decreases effective coronary perfusion pressure.

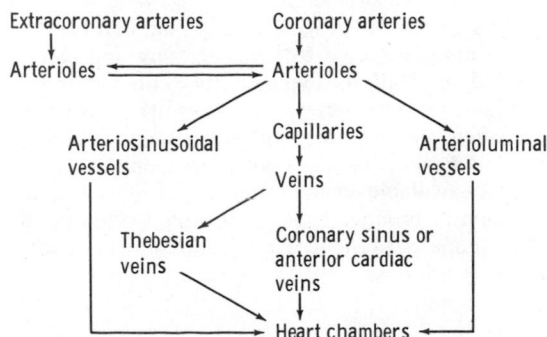

Figure 32–10. Diagram of the coronary circulation

Table 32–6. Pressures in aorta and left and right ventricles in systole and diastole.

	Pressure (mm Hg) in			Pressure Differential (mm Hg) Between Aorta and	
	Aorta	Left Vent	Right Vent	Left Vent	Right Vent
Systole	120	121	25	−1	95
Diastole	80	0	0	80	80

For technical reasons, accurate measurements of coronary flow are difficult to obtain. In humans, a venous catheter can be slipped into the coronary sinus without ill effects and the Kety method applied to the heart, on the assumption that the N_2O content of coronary venous blood is typical of the entire myocardial effluent. The most reliable data indicate that coronary flow at rest in humans is about 250 ml/min, or 5% of the cardiac output (Table 32–1).

Variations in Coronary Flow

The heart extracts large amounts of O_2 from each unit of blood at rest (Table 32–1). O_2 consumption can be increased significantly only by increasing blood flow. Therefore, it is not surprising that there is an increase in blood flow when the metabolism of the myocardium is increased. The caliber of the coronary vessels, and consequently the rate of coronary blood flow, is influenced not only by pressure changes in the aorta but also by chemical and neural factors. The coronary circulation shows considerable autoregulation.

Chemical Factors

The close relationship between coronary blood flow and myocardial O_2 consumption suggests that one or more of the products of metabolism cause coronary vasodilatation. Factors suspected of playing this role include O_2 lack and increased local concentrations of CO_2, H^+, K^+, lactic acid, prostaglandins, adenine nucleotides, and adenosine. More than one of these vasodilator metabolites could be involved. Asphyxia, hypoxia, and intracoronary injections of cyanide all increase coronary blood flow 200–300% in denervated as well as intact hearts, and the feature common to these 3 stimuli is hypoxia of the myocardial fibers. A similar increase in flow is produced in the area supplied by a coronary artery if the artery is occluded and then released. This **reactive hyperemia** is similar to that seen in the skin (see below).

Neural Factors

The coronary arterioles contain α-adrenergic receptors, which mediate vasoconstriction, and β-adrenergic receptors, which mediate vasodilatation. Activity in the adrenergic nerves to the heart and injections of norepinephrine cause coronary vasodilatation. However, adrenergic mediators increase the heart rate and the force of cardiac contraction, and the vasodilatation is probably produced by chemical changes in the myocardium secondary to the increase in its activity. When the inotropic and chronotropic effects of adrenergic discharge are blocked by a β-adrenergic blocking drug, stimulation of the adrenergic nerves or injection of norepinephrine in unanesthetized animals elicits coronary vasoconstriction. Thus, the direct effect of adrenergic stimulation is constriction rather than dilatation of the coronary vessels. Stimulation of vagal fibers to the heart dilates the coronaries.

When the systemic blood pressure falls, the overall effect of the reflex increase in adrenergic discharge is increased coronary blood flow secondary to the metabolic changes in the myocardium at a time when the cutaneous, renal, and splanchnic vessels are constricted. In this way the circulation of the heart, like that of the brain, is preserved when flow to other organs is compromised.

Coronary Artery Disease

When flow through a coronary artery is reduced to the point that the myocardium it supplies becomes hypoxic, "P factor" accumulates and **angina pectoris** develops (see Chapter 7). If the myocardial ischemia is severe and prolonged, irreversible changes occur in the muscle, and the result is myocardial infarction. Disease of the coronary arteries is currently one of the leading causes of death in the world. Coronary narrowing is usually due to the thromboses forming at the site of atherosclerotic plaques, but there is evidence that α-adrenergically mediated spasm of coronary arteries can also cause angina, myocardial infarction, and sudden death.

The electrical events produced by myocardial ischemia and infarction and the resulting changes produced in the ECG are discussed in Chapter 28. It is interesting that before the ischemic muscle cells die, they cease contracting, and this cessation of contraction has the homeostatic effect of prolonging the period before the onset of irreversible changes. The cause of the loss of contractile activity is uncertain, but toxic metabolites accumulating in the cells, intracellular acidosis, and precipitation of intracellular Ca^{2+} by liberated phosphates may all play a role.

Damaged cells leak enzymes into the circulation, and the rise in the serum enzymes and isoenzymes produced by myocardial infarction plays an important ancillary role in the diagnosis of this disease. The enzymes most commonly measured are glutamic oxaloacetic transaminase (GOT), creatine phosphokinase (CPK), and lactic dehydrogenase (LDH). However, these enzymes are released by injury to many different tissues, and a rise in any of them is not specific for myocardial infarction. LDH and CPK have isoenzymes that are found in higher concentrations in heart muscle than in many other organs, and measurement of the serum concentration of the particular isoenzymes helps improve the diagnostic specificity of the enzyme measurement.

Discrete areas of narrowing in the coronary arteries can be detected by arteriography and can be removed surgically or bypassed by implantation of a graft (aortocoronary artery bypass graft). This procedure often produces marked and sustained relief of intractable angina but does not appear, on the basis of presently available data, to protect against myocardial infarction or produce significant prolongation of life when compared to modern medical treatment of coronary artery disease.

SPLANCHNIC CIRCULATION

The blood from the intestines, the pancreas, and the spleen drains via the portal vein and hepatic veins through the liver into the inferior vena cava. This large splanchnic vascular bed is a blood reservoir that plays an important role in homeostatic adjustments within the circulatory system.

Hepatic Circulation

The way the intrahepatic branches of the hepatic artery and portal vein converge on the sinusoids and drain into the central lobular veins of the liver is shown in Fig 26–16. The lobular veins drain via the hepatic veins to the inferior vena cava. Portal venous pressure is normally about 10 mm Hg in humans and hepatic venous pressure approximately 5 mm Hg. The mean pressure in the hepatic artery branches that converge on the sinusoids is about 90 mm Hg, but the pressure in the sinusoids is less than portal venous pressure, so there is a marked pressure drop along the hepatic arterioles. This pressure drop is adjusted so that there is an inverse relationship between hepatic arterial and portal venous blood flow. This inverse relationship is maintained in part by nerve fibers to α-adrenergic receptors on sphincters in the hepatic arterial system, but additional factors are also involved. These probably involve intrinsic myogenic responses of the vascular smooth muscle and the production of vasodilator metabolites in the liver when its blood flow is reduced.

The endothelium of the hepatic sinusoids is more permeable to protein than the capillary endothelium elsewhere in the body. The liver receives about one-fourth of the cardiac output in resting adults (1500 ml/min; Table 32–1). Eighty percent of its flow reaches the liver via the portal vein and 20% via the hepatic artery.

The intrahepatic portal vein radicles have smooth muscle in their walls that is innervated by adrenergic vasoconstrictor nerve fibers reaching the liver via the third to eleventh thoracic ventral roots and the splanchnic nerves. The vasoconstrictor innervation of the hepatic artery comes from the hepatic sympathetic plexus. There are no known vasodilator fibers reaching the liver. The hepatic veins are supplied with smooth muscle in dogs, but there is no good evidence for functioning "hepatic vein sphincters" in humans. At rest, circulation in the peripheral portions of the liver is sluggish, and only a portion of the organ is actively perfused. When systemic venous pressure rises, the portal vein radicles are dilated passively, and the amount of blood in the liver increases. In congestive heart failure, this hepatic venous congestion may be extreme. Conversely, when there is diffuse adrenergic discharge in response to a drop in systemic blood pressure, the intrahepatic portal radicles constrict, portal pressure rises, and blood flow through the liver is brisk, bypassing most of the organ. Most of the blood in the liver enters the systemic circulation. Constric-

tion of the hepatic arterioles diverts blood from the liver, and constriction of the mesenteric arterioles reduces portal inflow. In severe shock, hepatic blood flow may be reduced to such a degree that there is patchy necrosis of the liver.

Reservoir Function of the Spleen

In dogs and other carnivores, there is a large amount of smooth muscle in the capsule of the spleen. The spleen traps blood, and rhythmic contractions of its capsule pump plasma into the lymphatics. The spleen therefore contains a reservoir of blood rich in cells. Adrenergic nerve discharge and epinephrine make the spleen contract strongly, discharging the blood into the circulation. However, this function of the spleen is quantitatively unimportant in humans. Other functions of the spleen are discussed in Chapter 24.

Other blood reservoirs that contain a large volume of blood at rest are the skin and lungs. During severe exercise, constriction of the vessels in these organs and decreased blood "storage" in the liver and other portions of the splanchnic bed, the skin, and the lungs may increase the volume of actively circulating blood perfusing the muscles by as much as 30%.

CIRCULATION OF THE SKIN

The amount of heat lost from the body is regulated to a large extent by varying the amount of blood flowing through the skin (see Chapter 14). The fingers, toes, palms, and ear lobes contain well-innervated anastomotic connections between arterioles and venules (arteriovenous anastomoses; Fig 30–2). Blood flow in response to thermoregulatory stimuli can vary from 1 to as much as 150 ml/100 g of skin per minute, and it has been postulated that these variations are possible because blood can be shunted through the anastomoses. The subdermal capillary and venous plexus is a blood reservoir of some importance, and the skin is one of the few places where the reactions of blood vessels can be observed visually.

White Reaction

When a pointed object is drawn lightly over the skin, the stroke lines become pale (**white reaction**). The mechanical stimulus apparently initiates contraction of the precapillary sphincters, and blood drains out of the capillaries and small veins. The response appears in about 15 seconds.

Triple Response

When the skin is stroked more firmly with a pointed instrument, instead of the white reaction there is reddening at the site that appears in about 10 seconds (**red reaction**). This is followed in a few minutes by local swelling and diffuse, mottled reddening around the injury. The initial redness is due to capillary dilatation, a direct response of the capillaries to pressure. The swelling, or **wheal,** is local edema due to increased permeability of the capillaries and postcapillary venules. The redness spreading out from the injury **(flare)** is due to arteriolar dilatation. This three-part response, the red reaction, wheal, and flare, is called the **triple response** and is part of the normal reaction to injury (see Chapter 20). It is present after total sympathectomy. The increase in vascular permeability responsible for wheal formation is produced by a substance ("H substance") or substances released locally. Histamine produces a wheal and is probably one of the substances liberated. The flare is absent in locally anesthetized skin and in denervated skin after the nerves have degenerated, but it is present immediately after nerve block or section above the site of injury. Therefore, the flare is generally held to be due to an **axon reflex,** a response in which impulses initiated in sensory nerves by the injury are relayed antidromically down other branches of the sensory nerves (Fig 32–12). This is the one situation in the body where there is substantial evidence for a physiologic effect due to antidromic conduction. The transmitter that is released at the central terminations of these neurons is substance P (see Chapter 15), and this peptide dilates arterioles. In addition, the presence of substance P in nerve endings in the skin has been demonstrated by immunohistochemical technics. Consequently, it seems likely that the antidromic impulses release substance P at the endings near the cutaneous arterioles.

Reactive Hyperemia

A response of the blood vessels that occurs in many organs but is visible in the skin is **reactive hyperemia,** an increase in the amount of blood in a region when its circulation is reestablished after a period of occlusion. When the blood supply to a limb is occluded, the cutaneous arterioles below the occlusion dilate; and when the circulation is reestablished, blood flowing into the dilated vessels makes the skin become fiery red. O_2 diffuses a short distance through the skin, and reactive hyperemia is prevented if the circulation of the limb is occluded in an atmosphere of 100% O_2. Therefore, the arteriolar dilatation is apparently due to a local effect of hypoxia, and it is believed to be effected by the release of a chemical substance.

Generalized Responses

Adrenergic nerve stimulation and circulating epinephrine and norepinephrine constrict cutaneous blood vessels. There are no known vasodilator nerve fibers to the cutaneous vessels, and vasodilatation is brought about by decreasing constrictor tone. Skin color and temperature also depend on the state of the capillaries and venules. A cold blue or gray skin is one in which the arterioles are constricted and the capillaries dilated; a warm red skin is one in which both are dilated.

Because painful stimuli cause diffuse adrenergic discharge, a painful injury causes generalized cutaneous vasoconstriction in addition to the local triple response. When the body temperature rises during exercise, the cutaneous blood vessels dilate in spite of continuing adrenergic discharge in other parts of the body. Dilatation of cutaneous vessels in response to a rise in hypothalamic temperature (see Chapter 14) is a prepotent reflex response that overcomes other reflex activity. The vasodilatation may be due in part to the local liberation of the nonapeptide bradykinin (see Chapter 31). Cold causes cutaneous vasoconstriction; however, with severe cold, superficial vasodilatation may supervene. This vasodilatation is the cause of the ruddy complexions seen on a cold day.

Shock is more profound in patients with elevated temperatures because of the cutaneous vasodilatation, and patients in shock should not be warmed to the point that their body temperature rises. This is sometimes a problem because well-meaning laymen have read in first-aid books that "injured patients should be kept warm," and they pile blankets on accident victims who are in shock.

PLACENTAL & FETAL CIRCULATION

Uterine Circulation

The blood flow of the uterus parallels the metabolic activity of the myometrium and endometrium and undergoes cyclic fluctuations that correlate well with the menstrual cycle in the nonpregnant woman. The function of the spiral and basal arteries of the endometrium in menstruation is discussed in Chapter 23. During pregnancy, blood flow increases rapidly as

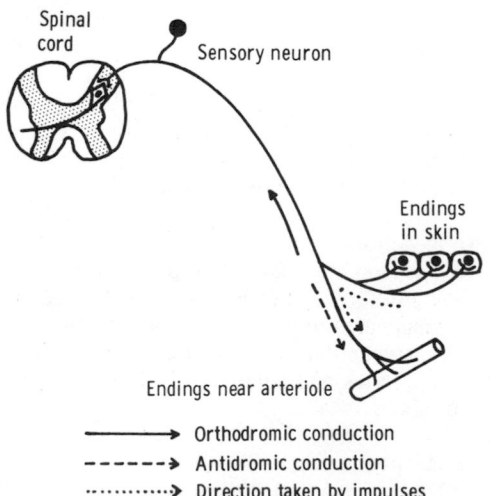

Figure 32–12. Axon reflex. Hypothetical pathway involved in the flare response.

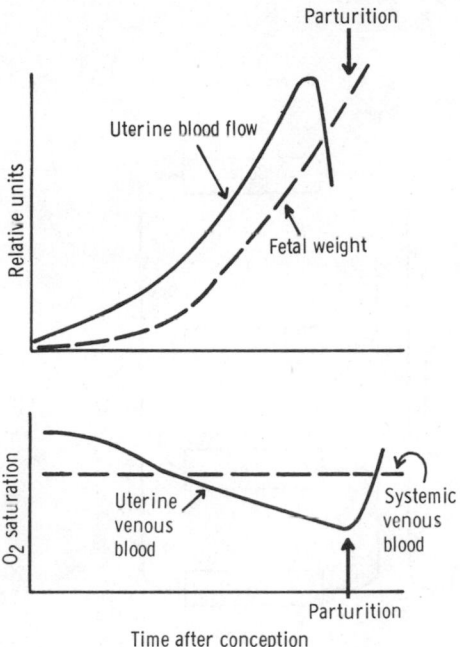

Figure 32–13. Changes in uterine blood flow and the amount of O_2 in uterine venous blood during pregnancy. (After Barcroft H. Modified and redrawn, with permission, from Keele CA, Neil E: *Samson Wright's Applied Physiology,* 12th ed. Oxford Univ Press, 1971.)

the uterus increases in size (Fig 32–13). Metabolites with a vasodilator action are undoubtedly produced in the uterus, as they are in other active tissues; but in early pregnancy the arteriovenous O_2 difference across the uterus is small, and it has been suggested that estrogens act on the blood vessels to increase uterine blood flow in excess of tissue O_2 needs. However, even though uterine blood flow increases 20-fold during pregnancy, the size of the conceptus increases much more, changing from a single cell to a fetus plus a placenta that weigh 4–5 kg at term in humans. Consequently, more O_2 is extracted from the uterine blood during the latter part of pregnancy, and the O_2 saturation of uterine blood falls. Just before parturition there is a sharp decline in uterine blood flow, but the significance of this is not clear.

Placenta

The placenta is the "fetal lung." Its maternal portion is in effect a large blood sinus. Into this "lake" project the villi of the fetal portion containing the small branches of the fetal umbilical arteries and vein (Fig 32–14). O_2 is taken up by the fetal blood and CO_2 is discharged into the maternal circulation across the walls of the villi in a fashion analogous to O_2 and CO_2 exchange in the lungs (see Chapter 35), but the cellular layers covering the villi are thicker and less permeable than the alveolar membranes in the lung, and exchange is much less efficient. The placenta is also the route by which all nutritive materials enter the fetus and by

which fetal wastes are discharged to the maternal blood.

Fetal Circulation

The arrangement of the circulation in the fetus is shown diagrammatically in Fig 32–15. Fifty-five percent of the fetal cardiac output goes through the placenta. The blood in the umbilical vein in humans is believed to be about 80% saturated with O_2, compared with 98% saturation in the arterial circulation of the adult. The **ductus venosus** (Fig 32–16) diverts some of this blood directly to the inferior vena cava, and the remainder mixes with the portal blood of the fetus. The portal and systemic venous blood of the fetus is only 26% saturated, and the saturation of the mixed blood in the inferior vena cava is approximately 67%. Most of the blood entering the heart through the inferior vena cava is diverted directly to the left atrium via the patent foramen ovale. Most of the blood from the superior vena cava enters the right ventricle and is expelled into the pulmonary artery. The resistance of the collapsed lungs is high, and the pressure in the pulmonary artery is several mm Hg higher than it is in the aorta, so that most of the blood in the pulmonary artery passes through the **ductus arteriosus** to the aorta. In this fashion, the relatively unsaturated blood from the right

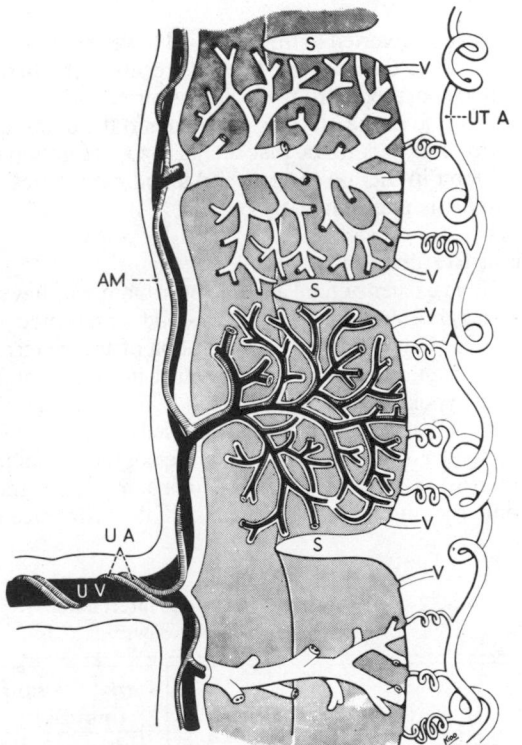

Figure 32–14. Diagram of a section through the human placenta. AM, amnion; S, septa; UA, umbilical arteries; UV, umbilical vein; UT A, uterine artery; V, veins. (Reproduced, with permission, from Harrison RG: *Textbook of Human Embryology,* 2nd ed. Blackwell, 1964.)

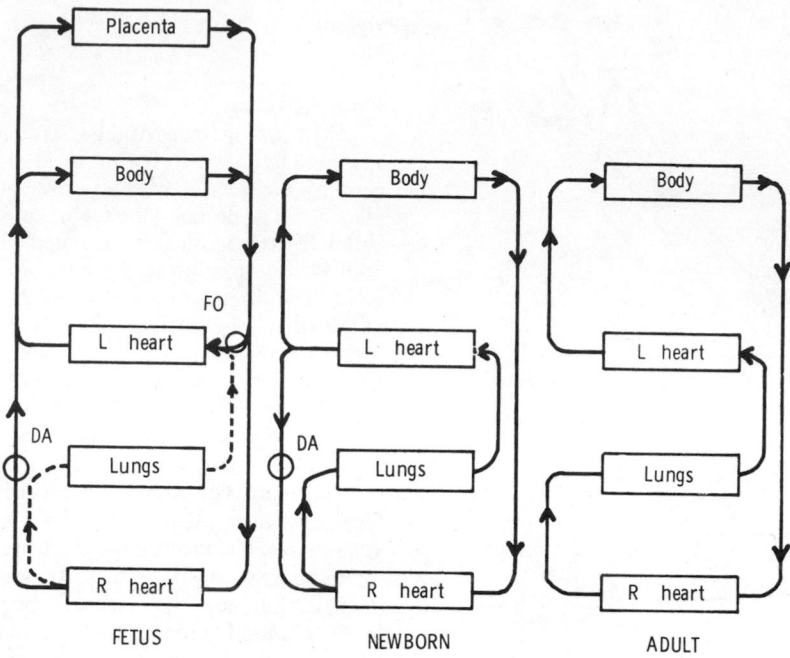

Figure 32–15. Diagram of the circulation in the fetus, the newborn infant, and the adult. DA, ductus arteriosus; FO, foramen ovale. (Redrawn and reproduced, with permission, from Born GVR & others: Changes in the heart and lungs at birth. Cold Spring Harbor Symp Quant Biol 19:102, 1954.)

ventricle is diverted to the trunk and lower body of the fetus, while the head of the fetus receives the better oxygenated blood from the left ventricle. From the aorta, some of the blood is pumped into the umbilical arteries and back to the placenta. The O_2 saturation of the blood in the lower aorta and umbilical arteries of the fetus is approximately 60%.

Fetal Respiration

The tissues of fetal and newborn mammals have a remarkable but poorly understood resistance to hypoxia. However, the O_2 saturation of the maternal blood in the placenta is so low that the fetus might suffer hypoxic damage if fetal red cells did not have a greater O_2 affinity than adult red cells (Fig 32–17). The fetal red cells contain fetal hemoglobin (hemoglobin F), while the adult cells contain adult hemoglobin (hemoglobin A). The cause of the difference in

O_2 affinity between the 2 is that hemoglobin F binds 2,3-DPG less effectively than hemoglobin A. The decrease in O_2 affinity due to the binding of 2,3-DPG is discussed in detail in Chapter 35. The quantitative aspects of gas exchange across the placenta, based on experiments on the cow, are shown in Table 32–7.

In humans, hemoglobin A first appears in the fetal circulation at about the 20th week, when the bone marrow first begins to function (Fig 27–10). At birth, only 20% of the circulating hemoglobin is of the adult type. However, no more hemoglobin F is normally formed after birth, and by the age of 4 months 90% of the circulating hemoglobin is hemoglobin A.

Changes in Fetal Circulation & Respiration at Birth

Because of the patent ductus arteriosus and foramen ovale (Fig 32–16), the left and right heart pump in parallel in the fetus rather than in series as they do in the adult. At birth, the placental circulation is cut off and the peripheral resistance suddenly rises. The pressure in the aorta rises until it exceeds that in the pulmonary artery. Meanwhile, because the placental circulation has been cut off, the infant becomes increasingly asphyxic. Finally, the infant gasps several times, and the lungs expand. The markedly negative intrapleural pressure (-30 to -50 mm Hg) during the gasps contributes to the expansion of the lungs, but other poorly understood factors are also involved. The sucking action of the first breath plus constriction of the umbilical veins squeezes as much as 100 ml of blood from the placenta (the "placental transfusion").

Table 32–7. Summary of gaseous interchange across the placenta in the cow.*

	Hemoglobin % Saturation	Partial Pressure (mm Hg)	
		O_2	CO_2
Maternal artery	90	70	41
Uterine vein	70	41.5	46.5
Umbilical vein		11.5	48
Umbilical artery		5.5	50

*Data of Roos J, Romijn C: J Physiol (Lond) 92:261, 1938.

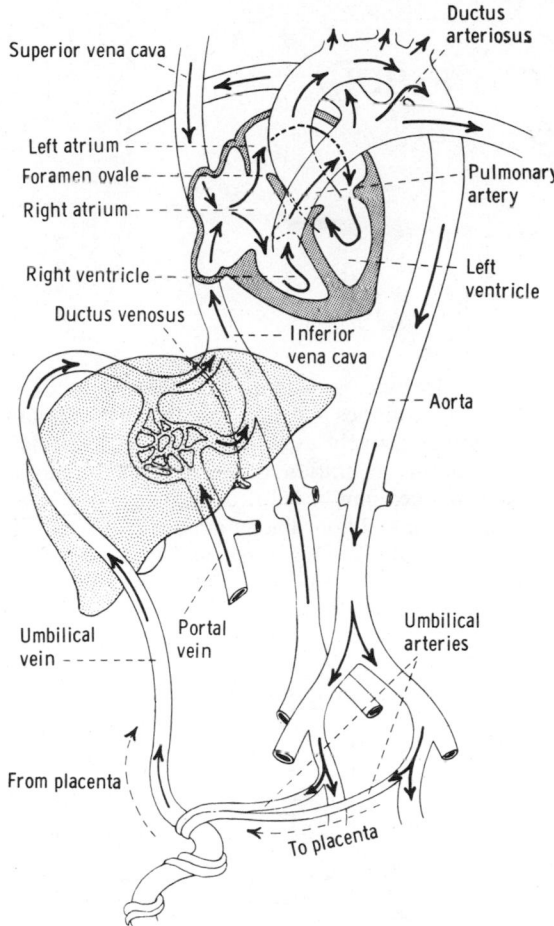

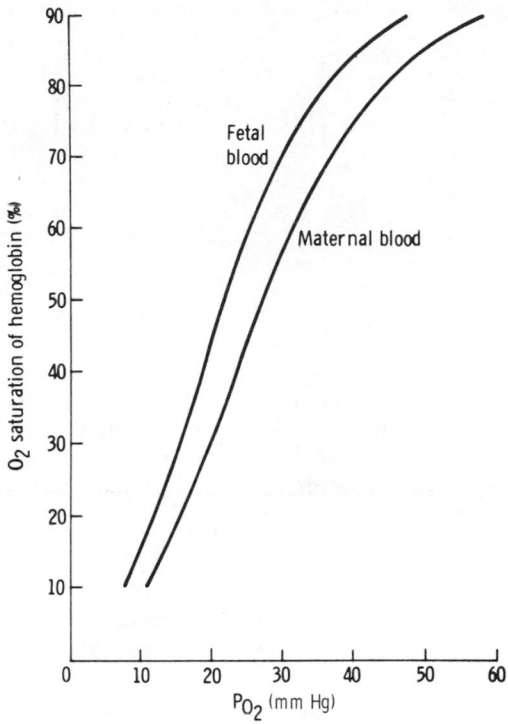

Figure 32–17. Dissociation curves for hemoglobin in fetal and adult blood in the human. (Reproduced, with permission, from Darling RC & others: Some properties of human fetal and maternal blood. J Clin Invest 20:739, 1941.)

Figure 32–16. Circulation in the fetus. Most of the oxygenated blood reaching the heart via the umbilical vein and inferior vena cava is diverted through the foramen ovale and pumped out the aorta to the head, while the deoxygenated blood returned via the superior vena cava is mostly pumped through the pulmonary artery and ductus arteriosus to the feet and the umbilical arteries.

Once the lungs are expanded, the pulmonary vascular resistance falls to less than 20% of the in utero value, and pulmonary blood flow increases markedly. Blood returning from the lungs raises the pressure in the left atrium, closing the foramen ovale by pushing the valve that guards it against the interatrial septum. The ductus arteriosus constricts within a few minutes after birth but, at least in sheep, does not close completely for 24–48 hours. Eventually, the foramen ovale and the ductus arteriosus both fuse shut in normal infants, and by the end of the first few days of life the adult circulatory pattern is established. The mechanism responsible for obliteration of the ductus arteriosus, like that responsible for expansion of the lungs, is incompletely understood, although there is evidence that a rise in arterial P_{O_2} and asphyxia are both capable of making the ductus constrict. Bradykinin has been shown to constrict the umbilical vessels and the ductus arteriosus while dilating the pulmonary vascular bed. Recent evidence indicates a role for prostaglandins in maintaining the patency of the ductus arteriosus before birth. Indeed, it has been reported that rectal administration of a single small dose of indomethacin, a drug that inhibits prostaglandin synthesis (see Chapter 17), closes the ductus in infants who would otherwise require surgical closure. On the other hand, closure of the ductus before birth causes pulmonary hypertension, and there is some evidence for an increased incidence of this abnormality in the children of women given prostaglandin inhibitors to delay the onset of labor.

33 | Cardiovascular Homeostasis in Health & Disease

The compensatory adjustments of the cardiovascular system to the challenges the circulation faces normally in everyday life and abnormally in disease illustrate the integrated operation of the cardiovascular regulatory mechanisms described in the preceding chapters.

COMPENSATIONS FOR GRAVITATIONAL EFFECTS

In the standing position, as a result of the effect of gravity on the blood (see Chapter 30), the mean arterial blood pressure in the feet of a normal adult is 180–200 mm Hg and venous pressure is 85–90 mm Hg. The arterial pressure at head level is 60–75 mm Hg and the venous pressure is zero. Blood pools in the venous capacitance vessels of the lower extremities, and stroke volume is decreased up to 40%. Symptoms of cerebral ischemia develop when the cerebral blood flow decreases to less than about 60% of the flow in the recumbent position. If there were no compensatory cardiovascular changes, the reduction in cardiac output due to pooling on standing would lead to a reduction of cerebral flow of this magnitude, and consciousness would be lost.

The major compensations on assuming the upright position are triggered by the drop in blood pressure in the carotid sinus and aortic arch. The heart rate increases, helping to maintain cardiac output. There is little if any venoconstriction, but there is a prompt increase in the circulating levels of renin and aldosterone. The arterioles constrict, helping to maintain blood pressure. The actual blood pressure change at heart level is variable, depending upon the balance between the degree of arteriolar constriction and the drop in cardiac output (Fig 33–1).

In the cerebral circulation there are additional compensatory changes. The arterial pressure at head level drops 20–30 mm Hg, but jugular venous pressure falls 5–8 mm Hg, reducing the drop in perfusion pressure (arterial pressure minus venous pressure). Cerebral vascular resistance is reduced because intracranial pressure falls as venous pressure falls, decreasing the pressure on the cerebral vessels. The decline in cere-

bral blood flow increases the partial pressure of CO_2 (P_{CO_2}) and decreases the P_{O_2} and the pH in brain tissue, further actively dilating the cerebral vessels. Because of the operation of these autoregulatory mechanisms, cerebral blood flow declines only 20% on standing. In addition, the amount of O_2 extracted from each unit of blood increases, and the net effect is that cerebral O_2 consumption is about the same in the supine and the upright position.

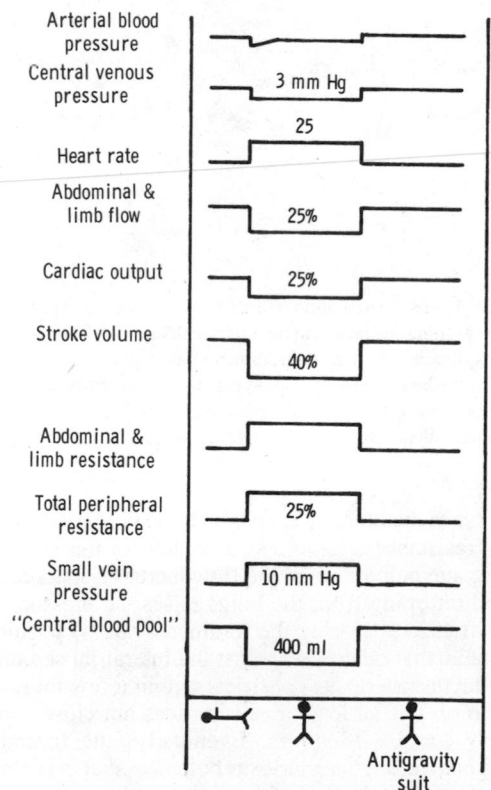

Figure 33–1. Effect on the cardiovascular system of rising from the supine to the upright position. Figures shown are average changes. Changes in abdominal and limb resistance and in blood pressure are variable from individual to individual. (Redrawn and reproduced, with permission, from Brobeck JR [editor]: *Best and Taylor's Physiological Basis of Medical Practice,* 9th ed. Williams & Wilkins, 1973.)

Prolonged standing presents an additional problem because of increasing interstitial fluid volume in the lower extremities. Plasma volume decreases about 15% in the standing position. As long as the individual moves about, the operation of the muscle pump (see Chapter 30) keeps the venous pressure below 30 mm Hg in the feet, and venous return is adequate. However, with prolonged quiet standing (eg, in military personnel standing at attention for long periods) fainting may result. In a sense, the fainting is a "homeostatic mechanism" because falling to the horizontal position promptly restores venous return, cardiac output, and cerebral blood flow to adequate levels.

The effects of gravity on the circulation in humans depend in part upon the blood volume. When the blood volume is low, these effects are marked; when it is high, they are minimal.

The compensatory mechanisms that operate on assumption of the erect posture are better developed in humans than in quadrupeds even though these animals have sensitive carotid sinus mechanisms. Quadrupeds tolerate tilting to the upright position poorly.

Postural Hypotension

In some individuals, sudden standing causes a fall in blood pressure, dizziness, dimness of vision, and even fainting. Such **orthostatic,** or **postural, hypotension** is common after surgical sympathectomy and in patients receiving sympatholytic drugs. It also occurs in diseases such as diabetes and syphilis, in which there is damage to the sympathetic nervous system, underscoring the importance of the sympathetic vasoconstrictor fibers in compensating for the effects of gravity on the circulation. Another cause of postural hypotension is **autonomic insufficiency.** In one form of this disease, the defect is in the CNS, and resting plasma norepinephrine values are normal but fail to rise with standing. In another form, the defect is peripheral, and resting norepinephrine values are low with little or no response to baroreceptor stimulation. Baroreceptor reflexes are also abnormal in patients with primary hyperaldosteronism. However, these patients generally do not have postural hypotension because their blood volumes are expanded sufficiently to maintain cardiac output in spite of changes in position. Indeed, mineralocorticoids are used to treat patients with postural hypotension.

Effects of Acceleration

The effects of gravity on the circulation are multiplied during acceleration or deceleration in vehicles that in modern civilization range from elevators to rockets. Force acting on the body as a result of acceleration is commonly expressed in *g* units, 1 *g* being the force of gravity on the earth's surface. "Positive *g* " is force due to acceleration acting in the long axis of the body, from head to foot; "negative *g* " is force due to acceleration acting in the opposite direction. During exposure to positive *g,* blood is "thrown" into the lower part of the body. The cerebral circulation is protected by the fall in venous pressure and intracranial

pressure. Cardiac output is maintained for a time because blood is drawn from the pulmonary venous reservoir and because the force of cardiac contraction is increased. At accelerations producing more than 5 *g,* however, vision fails ("blackout") in about 5 s and unconsciousness follows almost immediately thereafter. The effects of positive *g* are effectively cushioned by the use of "*g* suits," double-walled pressure suits containing water or compressed air and regulated in such a way that they compress the abdomen and legs with a force proportionate to the positive *g.* This decreases venous pooling and helps maintain venous return (Fig 33–1).

Negative *g* causes increased cardiac output, a rise in cerebral arterial pressure, intense congestion of the head and neck vessels, ecchymoses around the eyes, severe throbbing head pain, and, eventually, mental confusion ("red-out"). In spite of the great rise in cerebral arterial pressure, the vessels in the brain do not rupture because there is a corresponding increase in intracranial pressure and their walls are supported in the same way as during straining (see Chapter 32). The tolerance for *g* forces exerted across the body is much greater than it is for axial *g.* Men tolerate 11 *g* acting in a back-to-chest direction for 3 minutes and 17 *g* acting in a chest-to-back direction for 4 minutes. Astronauts are therefore positioned to take the *g* forces of rocket flight in the chest-to-back direction. The tolerances in this position are sufficiently large to permit acceleration to orbital or escape velocity and deceleration back into the earth's atmosphere without ill effects.

Effects of Zero Gravity

From the data available to date, weightlessness for up to 139 days appears to have only transient adverse effects on the circulation. One would expect that the circulation in zero gravity would be essentially similar to that in the recumbent position at sea level, with possible minor variations due to changes in the position of viscera. Transient postural hypotension has been present after return to earth from orbital flights. There has been speculation that prolonged weightlessness during future trips to the planets may lead to more severe "disuse atrophy" of the cardiovascular and somatic reflex mechanisms (see Chapter 12) responsible for postural adjustments. Muscular effort will, of course, be much reduced when the objects to be moved are weightless, and the decrease in the extensive normal proprioceptive input due to the action of gravity on the body may lead to flaccidity of skeletal muscles. In the absence of the increases in cardiac output normally occasioned by the efforts of everyday living, it is possible that there may even be some atrophy of the myocardium. A program of regular exercises against resistance, eg, pushing against a wall or stretching a heavy rubber band, might prevent this.

Other changes that have been observed during long space flights include extreme bradycardia, with heart rates as low as 35 beats/min during sleep; bone demineralization; diuresis; and a decrease in red blood cell volume.

EXERCISE

Muscle Blood Flow

The blood flow of resting skeletal muscle is low (2–4 ml/100 g/min). When a muscle contracts, it compresses the vessels in it if it develops more than 10% of its maximal tension (Fig 33–2); when it develops more than 70% of its maximal tension, blood flow is completely stopped. Between contractions, however, flow is so greatly increased that blood flow per unit of time in a rhythmically contracting muscle is increased as much as 30-fold. Blood flow sometimes increases at or even before the start of exercise, so the initial rise is probably a neurally mediated response. Impulses in the sympathetic vasodilator system (see Chapter 31) may be involved. The blood flow in resting muscle doubles after sympathectomy, and so some decrease in tonic vasoconstrictor discharge may also be involved. However, once exercise has started, local mechanisms maintain the high blood flow, and there is no difference in flow in normal and sympathectomized animals.

Local mechanisms maintaining a high blood flow in exercising muscle include a fall in tissue P_{O_2}, a rise in tissue P_{CO_2}, and accumulation of "vasodilator metabolites" (see Chapter 31). The temperature rises in active muscle, and this further dilates the vessels. Dilatation of the arterioles, metarterioles, and precapillary sphincters causes a 10–100-fold increase in the number of open capillaries. The average distance between the blood and the active cells—and the distance O_2 and metabolic products must diffuse—is thus greatly decreased. The dilatation increases the cross-sectional area of the vascular bed, and the velocity of flow therefore decreases. The capillary pressure increases until it exceeds the oncotic pressure throughout the length of the capillaries. In addition, the accumulation of osmotically active metabolites at a more rapid

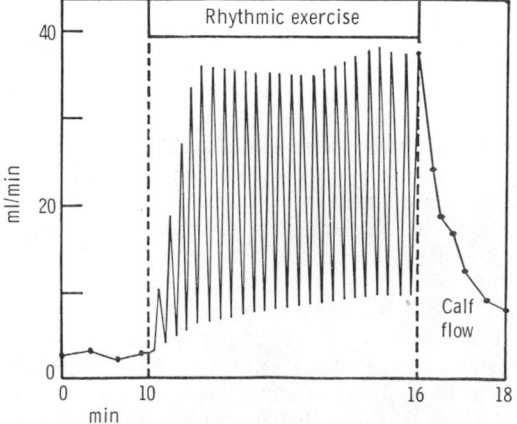

Figure 33–2. Blood flow through a portion of the calf muscles during rhythmic contraction. (Reproduced, with permission, from Barcroft H, Swan HJC: *Sympathetic Control of Human Blood Vessels.* Arnold, 1953.)

rate than they can be carried away decreases the osmotic gradient across the capillary walls. Therefore, fluid transudation into the interstitial spaces is tremendously increased. Lymph flow is also greatly increased, limiting the accumulation of interstitial fluid and in effect greatly increasing its turnover. The decreased pH and increased temperature shift the dissociation curve for hemoglobin to the right, so that more O_2 is given up by the blood. Increased concentration of 2,3-DPG in the red blood cells has been reported, and this would further decrease the O_2 affinity of hemoglobin (see Chapters 27 and 35). The net result is an up to 3-fold increase in the arteriovenous O_2 difference, and the transport of CO_2 out of the tissue is also facilitated. All of these changes combine to make it possible for the O_2 consumption of skeletal muscle to increase 100-fold during exercise. An even greater increase in energy output is possible for short periods during which the energy stores are replenished by anaerobic metabolism of glucose and the muscle incurs an O_2 debt (see Chapter 3). The overall changes in intermediary metabolism during exercise are discussed in Chapter 17.

Evidence is accumulating that potassium ions are among the most important "vasodilator metabolites" that dilate arterioles in exercising muscle, at least during the early part of exercise. Muscle blood flow increases to a lesser degree during exercise in potassium-depleted individuals, and there is a greater tendency for severe disintegration of muscle (**exertional rhabdomyolysis**) to occur.

Systemic Circulatory Changes

The systemic cardiovascular response to exercise depends on whether the muscle contractions are primarily isometric or primarily isotonic with the performance of external work. With the start of an isometric muscle contraction, heart rate rises. This increase still occurs if the muscle contraction is prevented by local infusion of a neuromuscular blocking drug. It also occurs with just the thought of performing a muscle contraction, so it is probably the result of psychic stimuli acting on the medulla oblongata. The increase is largely due to decreased vagal tone, although increased discharge of the cardiac sympathetic nerves plays some role. Within a few seconds of the onset of an isometric muscle contraction, systolic and diastolic blood pressures rise sharply. Stroke volume changes relatively little, and blood flow to the steadily contracting muscles is reduced as a result of compression of their blood vessels.

The response to exercise involving isotonic muscle contraction is similar in that there is a prompt increase in heart rate but different in that there is a marked increase in stroke volume. In addition, there is a fall in total peripheral resistance (Fig 33–3) due to vasodilatation in exercising muscles (Table 33–1). Consequently, systolic blood pressure rises only moderately, whereas diastolic pressure may remain unchanged or even fall.

Cardiac output is increased during isotonic exer-

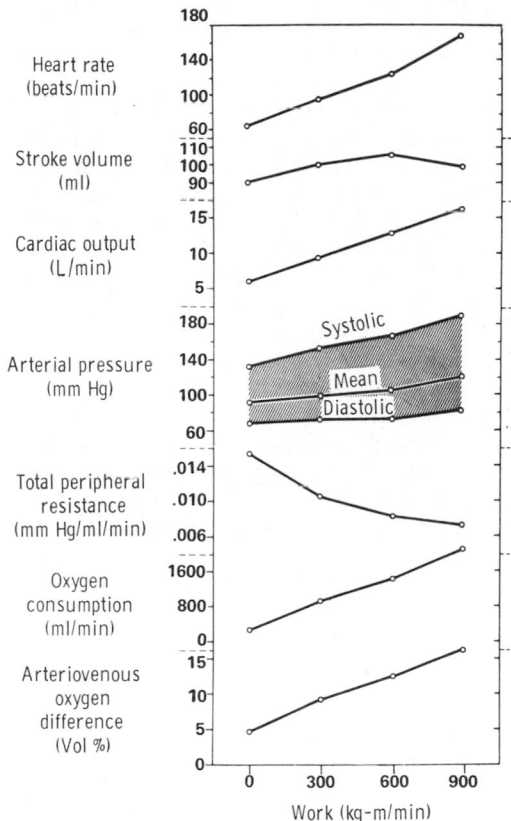

Figure 33–3. Effects of different levels of isotonic exercise on cardiovascular function. (Reproduced, with permission, from Berne RM, Levy MN: *Cardiovascular Physiology*, 3rd ed. Mosby, 1977; data from Carlsten A, Grimby G: *The Circulatory Response to Muscular Exercise in Man*. Thomas, 1966.)

cise to values that may exceed 35 L/min, the amount being proportionate to the increase in O_2 consumption. The mechanisms responsible for this increase are discussed in Chapter 29. The increase is due to an increase in heart rate and stroke volume, the heart muscle contracting more forcibly and discharging more of the end-systolic volume of blood in the ventricles. These chronotropic and inotropic effects on the heart are both due to increased activity in the adrenergic sympathetic nerves to the heart. The activity is apparently initiated by psychic stimuli. Decreased vagal tone also contributes to the increase in heart rate. The increase in heart rate is sustained by the autonomic changes plus the stimulatory effect of the increase in P_{CO_2} on the medulla. To the extent that it operates, the Bainbridge reflex may also contribute to the increase in heart rate. The maximal heart rate achieved during exercise decreases with age. In children, it rises to 200 or more beats per minute; in adults it rarely exceeds 195 beats per minute, and in elderly individuals the rise is even less.

A great increase in venous return is necessary to supply the extra blood put out by the heart, although the increase in venous return is not, as was once thought, the cause of the increase in cardiac output (see Chapter 29). Venous return is increased by the great increase in the activity of the muscle and thoracic pumps; by mobilization of blood from the viscera; by increased pressure transmitted through the dilated arterioles to the veins; and by adrenergically mediated venoconstriction, which decreases the volume of blood in the veins. The amount of blood mobilized from the splanchnic area and other reservoirs may increase the amount of blood in the arterial portion of the circulation by as much as 30% during strenuous exercise.

After exercise, the blood pressure may transiently drop to subnormal levels, presumably because accumulated metabolites keep the muscle vessels dilated for a short period. However, it soon returns to the preexercise level. The heart rate returns to normal more slowly.

Temperature Regulation

The quantitative aspects of heat dissipation during exercise are summarized in Fig 33–4. In many locations, the skin is supplied by branches of muscle arteries, so that some of the blood warmed in the muscles is transported directly to the skin, where some of the heat is radiated to the environment. There is a marked increase in ventilation (see Chapter 37), and some heat is lost in the expired air. The body temperature rises and the hypothalamic centers that control heat-dissipating mechanisms are activated. The temperature increase is due in part to inability of the heat-dissipating mechanism to handle the great increase in heat production, but there is evidence that during exercise there is in addition a "resetting of the thermostat"—ie, an increase in the body temperature at which the heat-dissipating mechanisms are activated. Sweat secretion is greatly increased, and vaporization of this sweat is the major path for heat loss. The cutaneous vessels also dilate. In some regions, this

Table 33–1. Cardiac output and regional blood flow in a sedentary man.* Values are at rest and during isotonic exercise at maximal oxygen uptake.

	ml/min	
	Quiet Standing	Exercise
Cardiac output	5900	24,000
Blood flow to:		
Heart	250	1000
Brain	750	750
Active skeletal muscle	650	20,850
Inactive skeletal muscle	650	300
Skin	500	500
Kidney, liver, gastrointestinal tract, etc	3100	600

*Data from Mitchell JH, Blomqvist G: Maximal oxygen uptake. N Engl J Med 284:1018, 1971.

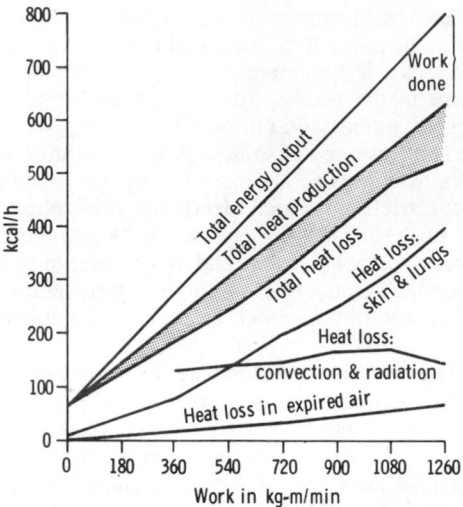

Figure 33–4. Energy exchange in muscular exercise. The shaded area represents the excess of heat production over heat loss. The total energy output equals the heat production plus the work done. (Redrawn and reproduced, with permission, from Nielsen M: *Die Regulation der Korpertemperatur bei Muskelarbeit.* Skand Arch Physiol 79:193, 1938.)

dilatation is due to inhibition of vasoconstrictor tone; but in the forearms and possibly elsewhere it appears to be due to local release of the vasodilator peptide bradykinin (see Chapter 31).

Training

Trained athletes have a larger stroke volume and slower heart rate at rest than untrained individuals, and they tend to have larger hearts (see Chapter 29). Training increases the maximal oxygen consumption (VO_2 max) that can be produced by exercise in an individual. In active healthy men, VO_2 max averages about 38 ml/kg/min, and in active healthy women, it averages about 29 ml/kg/min. It is lower in sedentary individuals. VO_2 max is the product of maximal cardiac output and maximal O_2 extraction by the tissues, and both increase with training. Heart rate increases linearly with the percentage of VO_2 max produced by the exercise, so trained athletes have lower increases in heart rate for a given amount of work.

In view of the current vogue for jogging and other forms of exercise, it is worth noting that one of the clear-cut benefits of exercise regimens is psychologic; patients who exercise regularly ''feel better.'' Regular physical exertion also increases the probability that an individual can remain active past the standard age of retirement. In addition, there is evidence that exercise decreases the incidence and severity of myocardial infarctions, but this beneficial effect cannot as yet be regarded as established. The exercise should be primarily isotonic rather than isometric, because isometric exercise produces a greater increase in cardiac pressure work. Exercise training under medical supervision is being used with increasing frequency in the treatment of patients with coronary artery disease.

HEMORRHAGE & HEMORRHAGIC SHOCK

Effects of Hemorrhage

The decline in blood volume produced by bleeding decreases venous return, and cardiac output falls. Numerous compensatory mechanisms are activated (Table 33–2). The heart rate is increased, and with severe hemorrhage, there is always a fall in blood pressure. With moderate hemorrhage (5–15 ml/kg body weight), pulse pressure is reduced, but mean arterial pressure may be normal. The blood pressure changes vary from individual to individual, even when exactly the same amount of blood is lost. The skin is cool and pale and may have a grayish tinge because of stasis in the capillaries and a small amount of cyanosis. Respiration is rapid, and intense thirst is a prominent symptom. This combination of findings constitutes the clinical syndrome known as **hypovolemic shock.** **Hemorrhagic shock** is the form of hypovolemic shock due to hemorrhage. Other causes of this type of shock are discussed below.

In hypovolemic and other forms of shock, the inadequate perfusion of the tissue leads to increased anaerobic glycolysis with the production of large amounts of lactic acid. In severe cases, the blood lactic acid level rises from the normal value of about 1 mmol/L to 9 mmol/L or more. The resulting **lactic acidosis** depresses the myocardium, decreases peripheral vascular responsiveness to catecholamines, and may be severe enough to cause coma.

Immediate Compensatory Reactions

When blood volume is reduced and venous return is decreased, the arterial baroreceptors are stretched to a lesser degree, and sympathetic outflow is increased. Even if there is no drop in mean arterial pressure, the decrease in pulse pressure decreases the rate of discharge in the arterial baroreceptors, and reflex tachycardia and vasoconstriction result.

The vasoconstriction is generalized, sparing only the vessels of the brain and heart. The vasoconstrictor innervation of the cerebral arterioles is probably insig-

Table 33–2. Compensatory reactions activated by hemorrhage.

Vasoconstriction
Tachycardia
Venoconstriction
Increased thoracic pumping
Increased skeletal muscle pumping (in some cases)
Increased movement of interstitial fluid into capillaries
Increased secretion of norepinephrine and epinephrine
Increased secretion of vasopressin
Increased secretion of glucocorticoids
Increased secretion of renin and aldosterone
Increased plasma protein synthesis
Increased formation of erythropoietin

nificant from a functional point of view, and the coronary vessels are dilated because of the increased myocardial metabolism secondary to the increase in heart rate (see Chapter 32). Vasoconstriction is most marked in the skin, where it accounts for the coolness and pallor, and in the kidneys and viscera.

Hemorrhage also evokes a widespread reflex venoconstriction that helps maintain the filling pressure of the heart, although the receptors that initiate the venoconstriction are unsettled. The intense vasoconstriction in the splanchnic area shifts blood from the visceral reservoir into the systemic circulation. Blood is also shifted out of the subcutaneous and pulmonary veins. Contraction of the spleen discharges more "stored" blood into the circulation, although the volume mobilized in humans is small.

In the kidneys, both afferent and efferent arterioles are constricted, but the efferent vessels are constricted to a greater degree. Glomerular filtration rate is depressed, but renal plasma flow is decreased to a greater extent, so that the filtration fraction (glomerular filtration rate/renal plasma flow) increases. There may be shunting of the blood through the medullary portions of the kidneys, bypassing the cortical glomeruli. Very little urine is formed. Sodium retention is marked, and there is retention of the nitrogenous products of metabolism in the blood (**azotemia** or **uremia**). Especially when the hypotension is prolonged, there may be severe renal tubular damage (**lower nephron nephrosis**).

Hemorrhage is a potent stimulus to adrenal medullary secretion (see Chapter 20). Circulating norepinephrine is also increased because of the increased discharge of sympathetic adrenergic neurons. The increase in circulating catecholamines probably contributes relatively little to the generalized vasoconstriction, but it may lead to stimulation of the reticular formation (see Chapter 11). Possibly because of such reticular stimulation, some patients in hemorrhagic shock are restless and apprehensive. Others are quiet and apathetic, and their sensorium is dulled, probably because of cerebral ischemia and acidosis. When restlessness is present, increased motor activity and increased respiratory movements increase the muscular and thoracic pumping of venous blood.

The loss of red cells decreases the O_2-carrying power of the blood, and the blood flow in the carotid and aortic bodies is reduced. The resultant anemia and stagnant hypoxia (see Chapter 37) as well as the acidosis stimulate the chemoreceptors. Increased activity in chemoreceptor afferents is probably the main cause of respiratory stimulation in shock. Chemoreceptor activity also excites the vasomotor center, increasing vasoconstrictor discharge. In fact, in hemorrhaged dogs with arterial pressures of less than 70 mm Hg, cutting the nerves to the carotid baroreceptors and chemoreceptors may cause a further fall in blood pressure rather than a rise. This paradoxic result is due to the fact that there is no baroreceptor discharge at pressures below 70 mm Hg and activity in fibers from the carotid chemoreceptors is driving the vasomotor center beyond the maximal rate produced by release of baroreceptor inhibition.

Long-Term Compensatory Reactions

When the arterioles constrict and the venous pressure falls because of the decrease in blood volume, capillary pressure drops. Fluid moves into the capillaries along most of their course, helping to maintain the circulating blood volume. This dehydrates the interstitial tissues, and fluid moves out of the cells. Decreased ECF volume has been shown to cause thirst, and thirst is intense in patients in shock. Thirst can occur without any change in plasma osmolality after hemorrhage and appears to be caused, at least in part, by increased circulating angiotensin II acting on the subfornical organ (see Chapter 14).

After a moderate hemorrhage, the circulating plasma volume is restored in 12–72 hours (Fig 33–5). There is also a rapid entry of preformed albumin from extravascular stores, but most of the tissue fluids that are mobilized are protein-free. They dilute the plasma proteins and cells, but when whole blood is lost, the hematocrit may not fall for several hours after the onset of bleeding. After the initial influx of preformed albumin, the rest of the plasma protein losses are replaced, presumably by hepatic synthesis, over a period of 3–4 days. Erythropoietin appears in the circulation and the

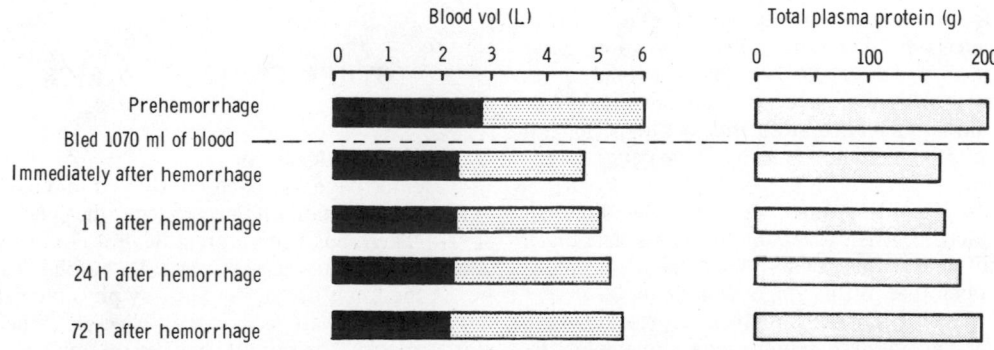

Figure 33–5. Changes in plasma volume (dotted bars), red cell volume (black bars), and total plasma protein following hemorrhage in a normal human subject. (From data in Keele CA, Neil E: *Samson Wright's Applied Physiology*, 11th ed. Oxford Univ Press, 1965.)

reticulocyte count increases, reaching a peak in 10 days. The red cell mass is restored to normal in 4–8 weeks. However, a low hematocrit is remarkably well tolerated because of various compensatory mechanisms. One of these is an increase in the concentration of 2,3-DPG in the red blood cells, which causes hemoglobin to give up more O_2 to the tissues (see Chapters 27 and 35). In long-standing anemia in otherwise healthy individuals, exertional dyspnea is not observed until the hemoglobin concentration is about 7.5 g/dl. Weakness becomes appreciable at about 6 g/dl; dyspnea at rest appears at about 3 g/dl; and the heart fails when the hemoglobin level falls to 2 g/dl.

Hemorrhage causes an increase in aldosterone secretion, due in part to increased secretion of renin and in part to increased secretion of ACTH (see Chapter 20). It also produces a marked rise in vasopressin secretion that is triggered by the decrease in discharge from the arterial and atrial baroreceptors (see Chapters 14 and 31). The increased circulating levels of aldosterone and vasopressin cause retention of Na^+ and water, which helps reexpand the blood volume. However, the initial decline in urine volume and Na^+ excretion is certainly due for the most part to the hemodynamic alterations in the kidney.

The angiotensin II liberated during hemorrhage plays a role in maintaining blood pressure. The blood pressure fall produced by removal of a given volume of blood is greater in animals infused with drugs that block angiotensin II receptors than it is in controls. Vasopressin also raises blood pressure when administered in large doses, but infusion in normal dogs of doses that produce the same plasma vasopressin levels produced by hemorrhage causes little, if any, increase in blood pressure. In addition, the fall in blood pressure produced by a standard hemorrhage in dogs is not increased by hypophysectomy. Thus, it appears unlikely that vasopressin contributes significantly to the restoration of blood pressure in shock.

Irreversible Shock

Depending largely upon the amount of blood lost, some patients die soon after hemorrhage and others recover as the compensatory mechanisms, aided by appropriate treatment, gradually restore the circulation to normal. In an intermediate group of patients, shock persists for hours and gradually progresses to a state in which there is no longer any response to vasopressor drugs and in which, even if the blood volume is returned to normal, cardiac output remains depressed. This is known as **irreversible shock.** The peripheral resistance falls, the heart slows, and the patient eventually dies.

There has been much discussion about what makes shock become irreversible. It seems clear that a number of deleterious positive feedback mechanisms become operative in this stage. For example, severe cerebral ischemia leads eventually to depression of the vasomotor and cardiac center, with slowing of the heart rate and vasodilatation. These both make the blood pressure drop further, with a further reduction in

cerebral blood flow and further depression of the vasomotor and cardiac centers.

Another important example of this type of positive feedback is myocardial depression. In severe shock, the coronary blood flow is reduced because of the hypotension and tachycardia (see Chapter 32), even though the coronary vessels are dilated. The myocardial failure makes the shock and the acidosis worse, and this in turn leads to further depression of myocardial function. If the reduction is marked and prolonged, the myocardium may be damaged to the point where cardiac output cannot be restored to normal in spite of reexpansion of the blood volume.

Spasm of the precapillary sphincters and venules, especially in the splanchnic region, is apparently a prominent feature of reversible shock. The reduced capillary perfusion due to the constriction of the precapillary sphincters leads to hypoxic tissue damage. Irreversible shock begins to develop when, after 3–5 hours, the precapillary sphincters dilate while the venules remain constricted. Blood now enters the capillaries but stagnates in these vessels, so that the tissue hypoxia continues. Capillary hydrostatic pressure rises, and fluid leaves the vascular system in increasing amounts. The capillary walls eventually lose their integrity and slough, permitting whole blood to enter the tissues. At this stage, administered fluids leak out of the vascular system almost as fast as they can be given. Circulating bacterial toxins may contribute to the paralysis of the precapillary sphincters. There is evidence that, presumably as a result of stagnant hypoxia in the gastrointestinal tract, the barriers to the entry of bacteria into the circulation from the intestinal tract break down.

On the theory that the imbalance between precapillary sphincter and venular tone is the key to the development of the irreversibility, treatment of shock with adrenergic blocking agents such as phenoxybenzamine to reduce the vascular spasm has been recommended. Results with such treatment are striking in dogs, but there is some uncertainty about the value of the blocking agents in the treatment of shock in humans. It is also claimed that glucocorticoids in very large doses are beneficial and may prevent the development of the abnormalities in the capillary bed.

OTHER FORMS OF SHOCK

General Considerations

Hemorrhage has been considered in detail as an example of a condition that produces the syndrome of shock. There has been a great deal of confusion and controversy about this syndrome. Part of the difficulty lies in the loose use of the term by physiologists and physicians as well as laymen. **Electric shock** and **spinal shock,** for example, bear no resemblance to the condition produced by hemorrhage. Shock, in the restricted sense of "circulatory shock," is still a collection of different entities that share certain common features. The feature that appears to be common to all cases is inadequate tissue perfusion. The cardiac output may be inadequate because the heart is damaged, or the volume of circulating blood may be less than the capacity of the circulation, either because the blood volume is reduced or because the capacity is increased. On this basis, 3 general types of shock are often delineated: (1) **hypovolemic shock,** in which blood or plasma has been lost from the circulation to the exterior or into the tissues; (2) **cardiogenic shock,** in which the pumping action of the heart is inadequate; and (3) **low-resistance shock,** in which there is vasodilatation in the face of a normal cardiac output and blood volume.

Hypovolemic Shock

Hypovolemic shock is also called "cold shock." It is characterized in the typical case by hypotension; a rapid thready pulse; a cold, pale, clammy skin; intense thirst; rapid respiration; and restlessness or, alternatively, torpor. None of these findings, however, are invariably present. The hypotension may be relative. A hypertensive patient whose blood pressure is regularly 240/140, for example, may be in severe shock when the blood pressure is 120/90.

Hypovolemic shock is commonly subdivided into categories on the basis of cause. The use of terms such as hemorrhagic shock, wound shock, surgical shock, traumatic shock, and burn shock is of some benefit because, although there are similarities between these various forms of shock, there are important features that are unique to each type. Hemorrhagic shock is discussed above.

Traumatic shock develops when there is severe damage to muscle and bone. This is the type of shock seen in battle casualties and automobile accident victims. Frank bleeding into the injured areas is the principal cause of the shock, although some plasma also enters the tissues. The amount of blood which can be lost into an injury that appears relatively minor is remarkable; the thigh muscles can accommodate 1 liter of extravasated blood, for example, with an increase in the diameter of the thigh of only 1 cm.

When there is extensive soft tissue and muscle crushing, myoglobin leaks into the circulation. It is said to precipitate in the renal tubules, causing renal damage, and the combination of traumatic shock and renal damage due to myoglobinuria has been called the **crush syndrome.** However, myoglobinuria is only one of the factors causing renal damage, and in all forms of shock renal insufficiency is a potential complication.

Surgical shock and **wound shock** are due to the combination in various proportions of external hemorrhage, bleeding into injured tissues, and dehydration.

In **burn shock** the most apparent abnormality is loss of plasma as exudate from the burned surfaces. Since the loss in this situation is plasma rather than whole blood, the hematocrit rises and **hemoconcentration** is a prominent finding. Burns also cause complex, poorly understood metabolic changes in addition to fluid loss. For example, there is a 50% rise in metabolic rate of nonthyroidal origin, and some burned patients develop hemolytic anemia. Because of these complications, plus the severity of the shock and the problems of sepsis and kidney damage, the mortality rate when third degree burns cover more than 75% of the body is still essentially 100%.

Cardiogenic Shock

When there is a gross decline in cardiac output due to disease of the heart rather than to inadequate blood volume, the condition that results is called cardiogenic shock. The symptoms are those of shock plus congestion of the lungs and viscera due to failure of the heart to put out all the venous blood returned to it. Consequently, the condition is sometimes called "congested shock." The incidence of this type of shock in patients with myocardial infarction is about 10%, and it usually occurs when there is extensive damage to the left ventricular myocardium. It has been suggested that release of chemical agents such as serotonin from the infarcted area activates ventricular receptors which trigger a reflex inhibition of the vasomotor center (Bezold-Jarisch reflex; see Chapter 31). This limits the compensatory vasoconstrictor responses and makes the shock worse.

Low-Resistance Shock

Low-resistance shock includes a number of entities in which the blood volume is normal while the capacity of the circulation is increased by massive vasodilatation. For this reason, it is also called "warm shock." Examples include fainting in response to strong emotion and the reaction produced by overwhelming fear and grief. Another form is the poorly understood, immediate, stunned reaction in injured individuals. The most common form, however, is that produced by endotoxin from gram-negative bacteria. This toxin may be liberated in the body in large amounts in certain infections.

Anaphylactic shock is a rapidly developing, severe allergic reaction that sometimes occurs when an individual who has previously been sensitized to an antigen is subsequently reexposed to it. The resultant antigen-antibody reaction releases large quantities of histamine, causing increased capillary permeability and widespread dilatation of arterioles and capillaries. Various other circulatory abnormalities contribute to the shock in animals, but in humans, phenomena such as bronchospasm and changes in hepatic blood flow are not prominent.

Shock is a complication of various metabolic and infectious diseases. Low vascular resistance is a factor in these cases, but there is also an element of hypovolemia. For example, although the mechanism is different in each case, adrenal insufficiency, diabetic ketoacidosis, and severe diarrhea are all characterized by loss of Na^+ from the circulation. The resultant decline in plasma volume may be severe enough to precipitate cardiovascular collapse. In severe infections, shock may occur as a result of diffuse vasculitis with leakage of plasma into the tissues (Rocky Mountain spotted fever, Korean hemorrhagic fever), circulating "toxins" that paralyze vascular smooth muscle, dehydration, or, very rarely, bilateral hemorrhage into the adrenal glands and acute adrenal insufficiency. In febrile patients, shock is apt to be more severe because the cutaneous blood vessels are often dilated (see Chapter 32), increasing the disparity between the capacity of the vascular system and the available circulating blood volume.

Treatment of Shock

The treatment of shock should be aimed at correcting the cause and helping the physiologic compensatory mechanisms to restore an adequate level of tissue perfusion. In hemorrhagic, traumatic, wound, and surgical shock, for example, the cause of the shock is blood loss, and the treatment should include early and rapid transfusion of adequate amounts of compatible whole blood. Saline is of limited temporary value. The immediate goal is restoration of an adequate circulating blood volume, and since saline is distributed in ECF, only 25% of the amount administered stays in the vascular system. In burn shock and other conditions in which there is hemoconcentration, plasma is the treatment of choice to restore the fundamental defect, the loss of plasma. "Plasma expanders," solutions of sugars of high molecular weight and related substances that do not cross capillary walls, have some merit. Concentrated human serum albumin and other hypertonic solutions expand the blood volume by drawing fluid out of the interstitial spaces. They are valuable in emergency treatment but have the disadvantage of further dehydrating the tissues of an already dehydrated patient.

In anaphylactic shock, epinephrine has a highly beneficial and almost specific effect that must represent more than just constriction of the dilated vessels. In all types of shock, restoration of an adequate arterial pressure is important to maintain coronary blood flow. Vasopressor agents such as norepinephrine are of value for this purpose, but their use should be discontinued as soon as possible.

A number of measures sometimes used in the treatment of shock inhibit the operation of the physiologic compensatory mechanisms. Sedatives and other drugs that depress the CNS should be used as sparingly as possible because they depress the discharge of the vasomotor center. Alcohol is particularly unphysiologic because it depresses the CNS and, through a central action, dilates cutaneous vessels. Care should be taken to avoid overheating and resultant cutaneous vasodilatation. Further compromising the circulation by permitting the patient to sit or stand is, of course, detrimental, and gravity should be put to work to help rather than hinder the compensatory mechanisms. Raising the foot of the bed 6–12 inches (15–30 cm) with "shock blocks" is a simple but valuable therapeutic maneuver that aids venous return from the lower half of the body and improves cerebral

blood flow. However, the head-down position also causes the abdominal viscera to press on the diaphragm, making adequate ventilation more difficult to maintain and favoring the development of pulmonary complications. Consequently, it should not be used for prolonged periods.

FAINTING

Sudden loss of consciousness due to cerebral ischemia has many causes. Probably the most common cause of fainting, or **syncope,** is hypotension due to sudden diffuse vasodilatation and bradycardia, often in association with a strong emotion. The attacks are short-lived, and consciousness is restored in a few minutes. The term **vasovagal syncope** has been coined to denote this entity. The fall in blood pressure is due in part to the decreased cardiac output caused by the marked bradycardia. However, diffuse discharge of the sympathetic vasodilator system also occurs, decreasing the vascular resistance in skeletal muscle. Sudden loss of consciousness due to decreased cardiac output also occurs in patients who have short runs of ventricular fibrillation or episodes of cardiac asystole (Stokes-Adams syndrome; see Chapter 28). **Postural syncope** is fainting due to pooling of blood in the dependent parts of the body on standing. **Micturition syncope,** fainting during urination, occurs in patients with orthostatic hypotension. It is due to the combination of the orthostasis and reflex bradycardia induced by voiding in these patients. Pressure on the carotid sinus, produced, for example, by a tight collar, can cause such marked bradycardia and vasodilatation that fainting results **(carotid sinus syncope). Cough syncope** occurs when the increase in intrathoracic pressure during straining or coughing is sufficient to block venous return. **Effort syncope** is fainting on exertion due to inability to increase the cardiac output to meet the increased demands of the tissues and is particularly common in patients with aortic or pulmonary stenosis.

HEART FAILURE

Manifestations

The manifestations of heart failure range from sudden death (eg, in ventricular fibrillation or air embolism), through the shocklike state called cardiogenic shock, to chronic **congestive heart failure,** depending upon the degree of circulatory inadequacy and the rapidity with which it develops. The principal symptoms and signs of congestive failure are cardiac enlargement, weakness, edema (particularly of the dependent portions of the body), a prolonged circulation time, hepatic enlargement **(hepatomegaly),** a sensation of shortness of breath and suffocation **(dyspnea),** and distention of the neck veins. Dyspnea on exertion is a prominent symptom. In advanced cases, a common finding is dyspnea that is precipitated by lying flat and relieved by sitting up **(orthopnea).** The dyspnea may be paroxysmal and sometimes progresses to frank **pulmonary edema.** Some of these abnormalities are due to "backward failure"—failure of the left and right heart pumps to put out all the blood returned to them in the veins, with a resultant rise in venous pressure and congestion of the lungs and viscera. Others are due to "forward failure"—failure of the heart to maintain a cardiac output that is adequate for normal perfusion of all the tissues (Table 33–3). The decline in cardiac output may be relative rather than absolute. In thyrotoxicosis and thiamine deficiency, for example, output may be elevated in absolute terms, but when it is inadequate relative to the needs of the tissues, heart failure is present ("high-output failure").

Pathogenesis & Pathophysiology

The pathophysiology of heart failure is a complex and, in some areas, controversial subject. One of the earliest and most constant findings in chronic congestive failure is abnormal retention of Na^+ and water (Fig 33–6). This expands the ECF, predisposing to the formation of edema and increasing the load on the heart by increasing venous return.

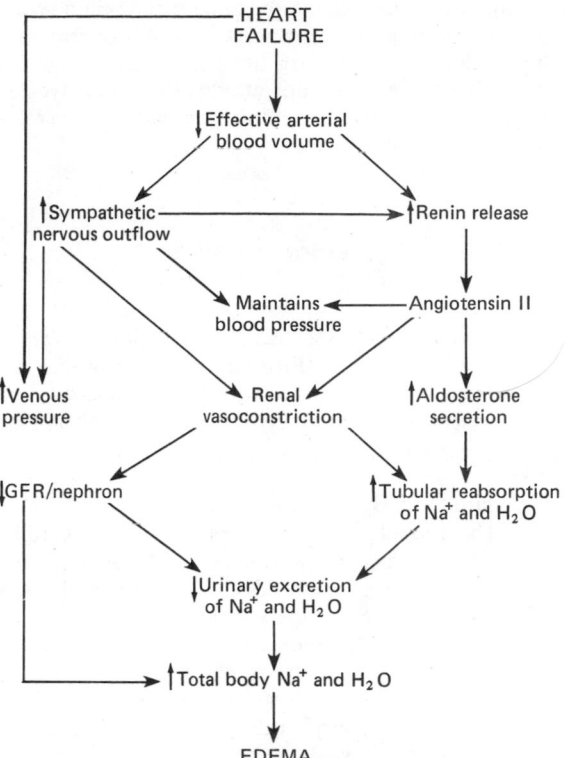

Figure 33–6. Summary of major mechanisms leading to the formation of edema in heart failure. (Modified from Cannon PJ: The kidney in heart failure. N Engl J Med 296:26, 1977.)

The key to the abnormal Na^+ retention in early heart failure may be the circulatory abnormalities that occur during exercise. At this stage, cardiac output, venous pressure, glomerular filtration rate, and renal blood flow are normal at rest. However, when the patient exercises, the increase in cardiac output is subnormal. This initiates, probably via the baroreceptors, reflex changes in the circulation that include constriction of the cutaneous, splanchnic, and renal vessels and a marked decline in renal blood flow.

Circulating renin levels are increased in congestive heart failure, and the aldosterone secretion rate is elevated in some patients. However, it now seems clear that in most cases of heart failure aldosterone secretion remains unchanged. Furthermore, salt retention occurs when the heart fails in bilaterally adrenalectomized animals maintained on constant doses of desoxycorticosterone. On the other hand, mineralocorticoids are metabolized at an abnormally slow rate in patients with heart failure, and the plasma aldosterone level is often high even when the secretion rate is normal. Other possible mechanisms for the Na^+ retention have been suggested, but the cause of the abnormal Na^+ retention in early congestive failure remains unsettled.

Treatment of heart failure includes positively inotropic agents such as digitalis glycosides and the use

Table 33–3. Simplified summary of pathogenesis of major findings in congestive heart failure.

Abnormality	Cause
Ankle, sacral edema	"Backward failure" of right ventricle → increased venous pressure → fluid transudation.
Hepatomegaly	Increased venous pressure → increased resistance to portal flow.
Pulmonary congestion	"Backward failure" of left ventricle → increased pulmonary venous pressure → pulmonary venous distention and transudation of fluid into air spaces.
Dyspnea on exertion	Failure of left ventricular output to rise during exercise → increased pulmonary venous pressure.
Paroxysmal dyspnea, pulmonary edema	Probably sudden failure of left heart output to keep up with right heart output → acute rise in pulmonary venous and capillary pressure → transudation of fluid into air spaces.
Orthopnea	Normal pooling of blood in lungs in supine position added to already congested pulmonary vascular system; increased venous return not put out by left ventricle. (Relieved by sitting up, raising head of bed, lying on extra pillows.)
Weakness, exercise intolerance	"Forward failure"; cardiac output inadequate to perfuse muscles; especially, failure of output to rise with exercise.
Cardiac dilatation	Greater ventricular end-diastolic volume.

of diuretics to overcome the abnormal sodium retention. In addition, judicious use of vasodilator drugs has been demonstrated to be beneficial. Arterial vasodilators decrease the afterload on the myocardium, and venodilators diminish preload, thus decreasing the work of the heart.

HYPERTENSION

Hypertension is a sustained elevation of the systemic arterial pressure. **Pulmonary hypertension** can also occur, but the pressure in the pulmonary artery (see Chapter 34) is relatively independent of that in the systemic arteries.

Experimental Hypertension

The arterial pressure is determined by the cardiac output and the peripheral resistance (pressure = flow × resistance; see Chapter 30). The peripheral resistance is determined by the viscosity of the blood and, more importantly, by the caliber of the resistance vessels. Hypertension can be produced by elevating the cardiac output, but sustained hypertension is usually due to increased peripheral resistance. Some of the procedures that have been reported to produce sustained hypertension in experimental animals are listed in Table 33–4. For the most part, the procedures involve manipulation of the kidneys, the nervous system, or the adrenals. There are in addition a number of strains of rats that develop hypertension either spontaneously or when fed a high-sodium diet.

The hypertension that follows constriction of the renal arterial blood supply or compression of the kidney is called **renal hypertension.** The role of renin in its pathogenesis is discussed in Chapter 24. The kid-

Table 33–4. Procedures that produce sustained hypertension in experimental animals.

1. Interference with renal blood flow (renal hypertension)
   a. Constriction of one renal artery; other kidney removed (one-kidney Goldblatt hypertension)
   b. Constriction of one renal artery; other kidney intact (2-kidney Goldblatt hypertension)
   c. Constriction of both renal arteries or aorta
   d. Compression of kidney by rubber capsules, production of perinephritis, etc
2. Interruptions of afferent input from arterial baroreceptors (neurogenic hypertension)
   a. Denervation of carotid sinuses and aortic arch
   b. Lesions of nucleus tractus solitarius
3. Treatment with corticosteroids
   a. Desoxycorticosterone and salt
   b. Other mineralocorticoids
4. Partial adrenalectomy (adrenal regeneration hypertension)
5. Genetic
   a. Spontaneous hypertension in various strains of rats
   b. Salt-induced hypertension in genetically sensitive rats

Table 33–5. Principal causes of sustained diastolic hypertension in humans. The conditions marked by the asterisk are quite often curable. In all of them except Cushing's syndrome, sustained hypertension may be the only physical finding.

1. Unknown (essential hypertension)
2. Adrenocortical diseases
   a. Hypersecretion of aldosterone (Conn's syndrome)*
   b. Hypersecretion of other mineralocorticoids (hypertensive form of congenital virilizing adrenal hyperplasia; 17a-hydroxylase deficiency)
   c. Hypersecretion of glucocorticoids (Cushing's syndrome)*
3. Tumor of adrenal medullary or paraganglionic origin (pheochromocytoma)*
4. Tumor of juxtaglomerular cells*
5. Narrowing of one or both renal arteries (renal hypertension)*
6. Renal disease
   a. Glomerulonephritis
   b. Pyelonephritis
   c. Polycystic disease
7. Narrowing (coarctation) of the aorta*
8. Severe polycythemia
9. Oral contraceptives*

neys may also secrete a vasodepressor agent, and the hypertension produced by compromising the renal circulation could be due to decreased secretion of this substance. Extracts of the renal medulla have depressor activity, and medullary tissue has been shown to contain prostaglandins with vasodepressor activity. Other renal vasodepressor substances have been reported, but the function of all such agents remains obscure. Neurogenic hypertension is discussed in Chapter 31. Provided salt intake is normal or high, desoxycorticosterone causes hypertension that may persist after treatment is stopped. The hypertension is more severe in unilaterally nephrectomized animals.

Hypertension in Humans

Hypertension is a very common abnormality in humans. It can be produced by many diseases (Table 33–5). It is also a prominent symptom of **toxemia of pregnancy,** a condition that may be caused by a pressor polypeptide secreted by the placenta.

Hypertension causes a number of serious disorders. When the resistance against which the left ventricle must pump (afterload) is elevated for a long period, the cardiac muscle hypertrophies. The total O_2 consumption of the heart, already increased by the work of expelling blood against a raised pressure (see Chapter 29), is increased further because there is more muscle. Therefore, any decrease in coronary blood flow has more serious consequences in hypertensive patients than it does in normal individuals, and degrees of coronary narrowing that do not produce symptoms when the size of the heart is normal may produce myocardial infarction when the heart is enlarged. There is an increased incidence of arteriosclerosis in hypertension, and myocardial infarcts are common even when the heart is not enlarged. The "Starling mechanism" (see Chapter 29) operates in hypertension, dilatation of the heart stretching the muscle fibers and increasing their strength of contraction. However, the ability to compensate for the high peripheral resistance is eventually exceeded, and the heart fails. Hypertensive individuals are also predisposed to thromboses of cerebral vessels and cerebral hemorrhage.

Malignant Hypertension

Chronic hypertension can enter an accelerated phase in which necrotic arteriolar lesions develop and there is a rapid downhill course with papilledema, cerebral symptoms, and progressive renal failure. This syndrome is known as **malignant hypertension,** and without vigorous treatment it is fatal in less than 2 years. It appears to be due to a pathologic process that can be triggered by hypertension due to any cause, but the nature of this process and why it develops are not known.

Essential Hypertension

In 90% of patients with elevated blood pressure, the cause of the hypertension is unknown, and they are said to have **essential hypertension.** The remainder have blood pressure elevations due to a variety of different diseases (Table 33–5). Early in the course of essential hypertension, the blood pressure elevations are intermittent and there is an exaggerated pressor response to stimuli such as cold and excitement that produce only a moderate blood pressure elevation in normal individuals. This suggests that overactive autonomic reactions are responsible for the arteriolar spasm, and treatment with drugs that block sympathetic outflow markedly slows the progress of the disease. Later on, the blood pressure elevation becomes sustained. The baroreceptor mechanism becomes "reset," so that the blood pressure is maintained at the elevated level (see Chapter 31). The spasm of the arterioles leads to hypertrophy of their musculature, and there is some degree of organic narrowing of the vessels. At this stage, even a normal rate of autonomic discharge is associated with an elevated pressure.

The progression of untreated essential hypertension is variable. Particularly in women, it is often benign, with elevated pressure being the only finding for many years. However, it may also progress rapidly into the malignant phase.

Essential hypertension is not at present a curable disease, although even after it has entered the malignant phase its progression can be stopped with modern drug treatment. On the other hand, several of the other disease processes that cause hypertension in humans are curable. It is therefore important to recognize these latter diseases and institute appropriate definitive treatment.

Other Causes of Hypertension

In humans, deoxycorticosterone and aldosterone both elevate the blood pressure, and hypertension is a prominent feature of primary hyperaldosteronism. It is also seen in patients who secrete excess deoxycorticos-

terone (see Chapter 20). The hypokalemia that these hormones produce damages the kidneys **(hypokalemic nephropathy),** and the hypertension may be partly renal in origin. Expansion of the blood volume due to Na^+ retention may also play a role.

Plasma renin activity is low in the forms of hypertension that are due to excess secretion of aldosterone and deoxycorticosterone. It has also been found to be low in the presence of normal or low aldosterone and deoxycorticosterone secretion rates in 10–15% of patients with what otherwise appears to be essential hypertension **("low-renin hypertension").** This raises the interesting possibility that an as yet unidentified mineralocorticoid is being secreted in excess in these patients.

Hypertension is also seen in Cushing's syndrome, in which aldosterone secretion is usually normal. The cause of the hypertension in this syndrome is uncertain; it may be due to the increased secretion of deoxycorticosterone produced by increased circulating ACTH, or it may be due to a direct action of glucocorticoids on the arterioles.

Pheochromocytomas—tumors of the adrenal medulla or of catecholamine-secreting tissue elsewhere in the body—also produce hypertension. The hypertension is often episodic, and, particularly when the tumors secrete predominantly epinephrine, the blood glucose level and the metabolic rate are intermittently elevated. However, in some patients with pheochromocytomas, sustained hypertension is the only finding.

Renal hypertension due to narrowing of the renal arteries is discussed above and in Chapter 24. Various other types of renal disease are associated with hypertension, but it is not known whether the association is due to renin secretion, to secretion of other vasoactive substances of renal origin, or to nonhumoral mechanisms. **Coarctation of the aorta,** a congenital narrowing of a segment of the thoracic aorta, increases the resistance to flow, producing severe hypertension in the upper part of the body. The blood pressure in the lower part of the body is usually normal.

Increased cardiac output is sometimes a cause of diastolic as well as systolic hypertension. The elevated blood pressure seen in thyrotoxicosis and in anxious, tense patients is explained on this basis. In severe polycythemia, the increase in blood viscosity may raise the peripheral resistance enough to cause significant hypertension.

Chronic treatment with oral contraceptives containing progestins and estrogens produces significant hypertension in some women. The hypertension is due, at least in part, to an increase in circulating levels of angiotensinogen, the production of which is stimulated by estrogens (see Chapter 24). There is some evidence that women developing "pill hypertension" are those predisposed to hypertension in any case. Certainly the occurrence of hypertension is not a reason for normotensive women to avoid oral contraceptives, but it would seem wise for them to have their blood pressures checked at 6-month intervals.

References: Section VI.
Circulation

Babior BM: Oxygen-dependent microbial killing by phagocytes. N Engl J Med 298:659, 1978.

Benson H: Systemic hypertension and relaxation response. N Engl J Med 296:1152, 1977.

Braunwald E, Ross J, Sonnenblick EH: *Mechanisms of Contraction of the Normal and Failing Heart,* 2nd ed. Little, Brown, 1976.

Bunn F, Forget BG, Ranney HM: *Human Hemoglobins.* Saunders, 1977.

Clausen JP: Effect of physical training on cardiovascular adjustments to exercise in man. Physiol Rev 57:779, 1977.

Colman RW: Formation of human plasma kinin. N Engl J Med 291:509, 1974.

Cranefield PF: *The Conduction of the Cardiac Impulse: The Slow Response and Cardiac Arrhythmias.* Futura, 1975.

Cross KW (editor): Perinatal research. Br Med Bull 31:1, 1975.

Dietschy JM, Gotto AM Jr, Ontko JA (editors): *Disturbances in Lipid and Lipoprotein Metabolism.* American Physiological Society, 1978.

Doyle JT: Mechanisms and prevention of sudden death. Mod Concepts Cardiovasc Dis 45:111, 1976.

Edelman GM: Antibody structure and molecular immunology. Science 180:830, 1973.

Edvinsson L, MacKenzie ET: Amine mechanisms in the cerebral circulation. Pharmacol Rev 28:275, 1976.

Freda VJ, Pollack W, Gorman JG: Rh disease: How near the end? Hosp Pract 13:61, June 1978.

Genest J, Koiw E, Kuchel O (editors): *Hypertension.* McGraw-Hill, 1977.

Gibbs CL: Cardiac energies. Physiol Rev 58:174, 1978.

Goldmann MJ: *Principles of Clinical Electrocardiography,* 10th ed. Lange, 1979.

Hillis LD, Braunwald E: Coronary artery spasm. N Engl J Med 299:695, 1978.

Hoffman BF (editor): *Brief Reviews from Circulation Research 1978.* American Heart Association, 1978.

Katz AM: *Physiology of the Heart.* Raven, 1977.

Kent KM, Cooper T: The denervated heart: A model for studying the autonomic control of the heart. N Engl J Med 291:1017, 1974.

Krayenbuehl HP, Hess OM, Turina J: Assessment of left ventricular function. Cardiovasc Med 3:883, 1978.

Kuschinsky W, Wahl M: Local chemical and neurogenic regulation of cerebral vascular resistance. Physiol Rev 58:656, 1978.

Laragh JH, Sealey JE: Renin-sodium profiling: Why, how, and when in clinical practice. Cardiovasc Med 2:1052, 1977.

Lassen NA, Ingvar DH, Skinhoj E: Brain function and blood flow. Sci Am 239:62, Oct 1978.

Lown B, Verrier RL: Neural activity and ventricular fibrillation. N Engl J Med 294:1165, 1976.

Metcalf J & others: Gas exchange in the pregnant uterus. Physiol Rev 47:782, 1967.

Milhorat TH: Structure and function of the choroid plexus and other sites of cerebrospinal fluid formation. Int Rev Cytol 47:225, 1976.

Mills E & others: Role of carotid body catecholamines in chemoreceptor function. Neuroscience 3:1137, 1978.

Moss GS, Saletta JD: Traumatic shock in man. N Engl J Med 290:724, 1974.

Müler-Eberhard HJ: Chemistry and function of the complement system. Hosp Pract 12:33, Aug 1977.

Nieuhuis AW, Benz EJ Jr: Regulation of hemoglobin synthesis during the development of red cell. N Engl J Med 297:1318, 1977.

Pace N: Weightlessness: A matter of gravity. N Engl J Med 297:32, 1977.

Parisi AF & others: Noninvasive cardiac diagnosis. N Engl J Med 296:316, 1977.

Parker CW: Control of lymphocyte function. N Engl J Med 295:1180, 1976.

Paul WE, Benacerraf B: Functional specificity of thymus-dependent lymphocytes. Science 195:1293, 1977.

Putnam FW (editor): *The Plasma Proteins: Structure, Function and Genetic Control,* 2nd ed. Academic Press, 1975.

Rapaport SI: *Blood-Brain Barrier in Physiology and Medicine.* Raven, 1976.

Ratnoff OD, Bennett B: The genetics of hereditary disorders of blood coagulation. Science 179:1291, 1973.

Resenkov L: Mechanical assistance for the failing ventricle. Mod Concepts Cardiovasc Dis 43:81, 1974.

Rhodin JAG: Fine structure of capillaries. In: *Topics in the Study of Life.* Kramer A (editor). Harper, 1971.

Rothschild MA, Oratz M, Schreiber SS: Albumin synthesis. N Engl J Med 286:748, 1972.

Rudolph AM, Heyman MA: Fetal and neonatal circulation and respiration. Annu Rev Physiol 36:187, 1974.

Scheer E: Enzymatic changes and myocardial infarction: A nursing update. Cardiovasc Nurs 14:5, 1978.

Scheuer J, Greenberg MA, Zohman LR: Exercise training in patients with coronary artery disease. Mod Concepts Cardiovasc Dis 47:85, 1978.

Shepherd JT, Vanhoutte PM: *Veins and Their Control.* Saunders, 1977.

Smith TW, Haber E: Digitalis. N Engl J Med 289:945, 1973.

Sonnenblick EH, Skelton CC: Oxygen consumption of the heart: Physiological principles and clinical implications. Mod Concepts Cardiovasc Dis 40:9, 1971.

Sparks HV, Belloni FL: The peripheral circulation: Local regulation. Physiol Rev 40:67, 1978.

Surgenor DM (editor): *The Red Blood Cell.* 2 vols. Academic Press, 1975.

Talbot L, Berger SA: Fluid-mechanical aspects of the human circulation. Am Sci 62:671, 1974.

Temini BA, Lee Y-C: *Essentials of Echocardiography.* Medical Economics Co, 1976.

Vassalle M: Cardiac automaticity and its control. Am J Physiol 233:H625, 1977.

Vatner SF, Braunwald E: Cardiovascular control mechanisms in the conscious state. N Engl J Med 293:970, 1976.

Yoshida A: Hemolytic anemia and G6PD deficiency. Science 179:532, 1973.

Zweifach BW, Grant L, McCluskey RT (editors): *The Inflammatory Process,* 2nd ed. 3 vols. Academic Press, 1973, 1974.

Symposium: Blood cell differentiation. Fed Proc 34:2271, 1975.

Symposium: The hepatic circulation and portal hypertension. Ann NY Acad Sci 170:1, 1970.

Symposium: Macrophage function and immunity. Fed Proc 37:77, 1978.

Respiration, as the term is generally used, includes 2 processes: **external respiration,** the absorption of O_2 and removal of CO_2 from the body as a whole; and **internal respiration,** the gaseous exchanges between the cells and their fluid medium. Details of the uptake of O_2 by cells and the formation and liberation of CO_2 by cells are considered in the section on intermediary metabolism (see Chapter 17). This chapter is concerned with the processes responsible for the uptake of O_2 and excretion of CO_2 in the lungs. Chapter 35 is concerned with the transport of O_2 and CO_2 to and from the tissues.

At rest, a normal human breathes 12–15 times a minute. Five hundred ml of air per breath, or 6–8 L/min, are inspired and expired. This air mixes with the gas in the alveoli and, by simple diffusion, O_2 enters the blood in the pulmonary capillaries while CO_2 enters the alveoli. In this manner, 250 ml of O_2 enter the body per minute and 200 ml of CO_2 are excreted.

Traces of other gases such as methane from the intestines are also found in expired air. Alcohol and acetone are expired when present in appreciable quantities in the body. Indeed, over 250 different volatile substances have been identified in human breath.

PROPERTIES OF GASES

Partial Pressures

Unlike liquids, gases expand to fill the volume available to them, and the volume occupied by a given number of gas molecules at a given temperature and pressure is (ideally) the same regardless of the composition of the gas.

$$P = \frac{nRT}{V} \qquad \text{(from equation of state of ideal gas)}$$

P = Pressure
n = Number of moles
R = Gas constant
T = Absolute temperature
V = Volume

Therefore, the pressure exerted by any one gas in a mixture of gases (its **partial pressure**) is equal to the total pressure times the fraction of the total amount of gas it represents.

The composition of dry air is 20.98% O_2, 0.04% CO_2, 78.06% N_2, and 0.92% other inert constituents such as argon and helium. The barometric pressure (P_B) at sea level is 760 mm Hg (one atmosphere). The partial pressure (indicated by the symbol P) of O_2 in dry air is therefore 0.21×760, or 160 mm Hg at sea level. The partial pressure of N_2 and the other inert gases is 0.79×760, or 600 mm Hg; and the P_{CO_2} is 0.0004×760, or 0.3 mm Hg. The water vapor in the air in most climates reduces these percentages, and therefore the partial pressures, to a slight degree. Air equilibrated with water is saturated with water vapor, and inspired air is saturated by the time it reaches the lungs. The P_{H_2O} at body temperature (37 C) is 47 mm Hg. Therefore, the partial pressures at sea level of the other gases in the air reaching the lungs are P_{O_2}, 149 mm Hg; P_{CO_2}, 0.3 mm Hg; and P_{N_2} (including the other inert gases), 564 mm Hg.

Gas diffuses from areas of high pressure to areas of low pressure, the rate of diffusion depending upon the concentration gradient and the nature of the barrier between the 2 areas. When a mixture of gases is in contact with and permitted to equilibrate with a liquid, each gas in the mixture dissolves in the liquid to an extent determined by its partial pressure and its solubility in the fluid. The partial pressure of a gas in a liquid is that pressure which in the gaseous phase in equilibrium with the liquid would produce the concentration of gas molecules found in the liquid.

Methods of Quantitating Respiratory Phenomena

Respiratory excursions can be recorded, using devices that measure chest expansion or recording spirometers (Fig 17–2), which also permit measurement of gas intake and output. Since gas volumes vary with temperature and pressure and since the amount of water vapor in them varies, it is important to correct respiratory measurements involving volume to a stated set of standard conditions. The 3 most commonly used standards and their abbreviations are shown in Table 34–1. Modern refinements of standard technics for gas analysis make possible rapid, reliable measurements of the composition of gas mixtures and the gas content of body fluids. N_2, for example, emits light in an

Table 34—1. Standard conditions to which measurements involving gas volumes are corrected.

STPD	0 C, 760 mm Hg, dry (standard temperature and pressure, dry)
BTPS	Body temperature and pressure, saturated with water vapor
ATPS	Ambient temperature and pressure, saturated with water vapor

electrical field in vacuo, and by using a meter that continuously measures and records the light emitted, it is possible to obtain a graphic record of the fluctuations in P_{N_2} of the expired air while various gas mixtures are breathed. O_2 and CO_2 electrodes, small probes sensitive to O_2 or CO_2, can be inserted into the airway or into blood vessels or tissues and the P_{O_2} and P_{CO_2} recorded continuously. CO_2, carbon monoxide (CO), and many anesthetic gases can be measured rapidly by infrared absorption spectroscopy. Gases can also be measured by gas chromatography or mass spectrometry.

MECHANICS OF RESPIRATION

Inspiration & Expiration

The lungs and the chest wall are elastic structures. Normally, there is no more than a thin layer of fluid between the lungs and the chest wall. The lungs slide easily on the chest wall but resist being pulled away from it in the same way that 2 moist pieces of glass slide on each other but resist separation. The pressure in the "space" between the lungs and chest wall (intrapleural pressure) is subatmospheric (Fig 34–1). The lungs are stretched when they are expanded at birth, and at the end of quiet expiration their tendency to recoil from the chest wall is just balanced by the tendency of the chest wall to recoil in the opposite direction. If the chest wall is opened, the lungs collapse; and if the lungs lose their elasticity, the chest expands and becomes barrel-shaped.

Inspiration is an active process. The contraction of the inspiratory muscles increases intrathoracic volume. During quiet breathing, the intrapleural pressure, which is about −2.5 mm Hg (relative to atmospheric) at the start of inspiration, decreases to about −6 mm Hg, and the lungs are pulled into a more expanded position. The pressure in the airway becomes slightly negative, and air flows into the lungs (Fig 34–1). At the end of inspiration, the lung recoil pulls the chest back to the expiratory position, where the recoil pres-

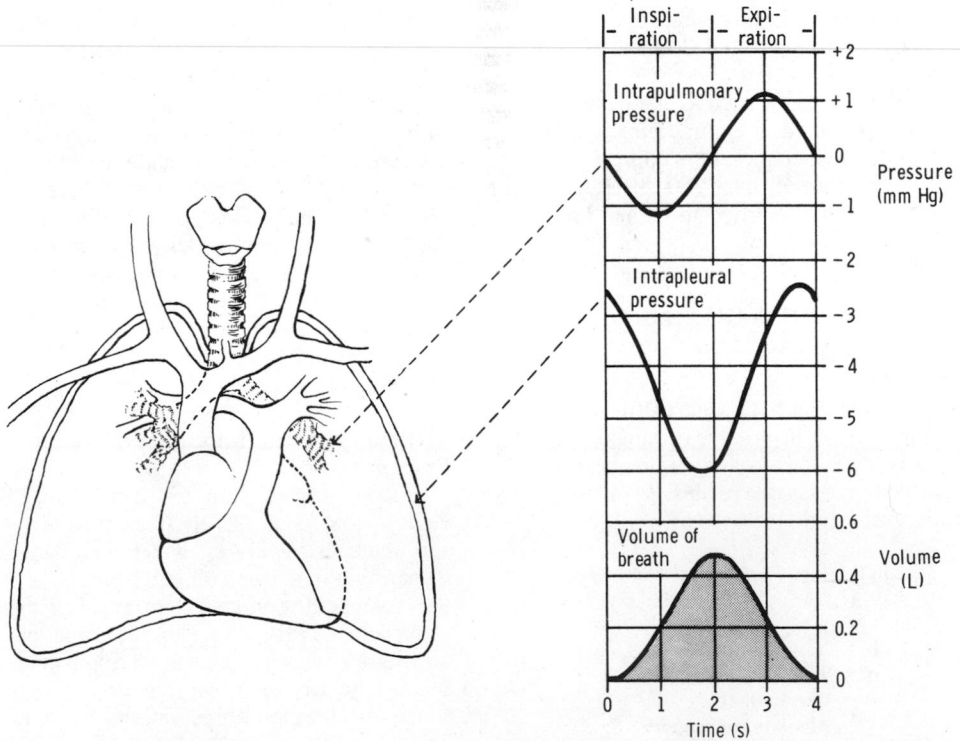

Figure 34—1. Changes in intrapleural (intrathoracic) and intrapulmonary pressure relative to atmospheric pressure during inspiration and expiration. (Based in part on data in Perkins J: Respiration. *Encyclopaedia Britannica,* 1961.)

sures of the lungs and chest wall balance. The pressure in the airway becomes slightly positive, and air flows out of the lungs. Expiration during quiet breathing is passive in the sense that no muscles which decrease intrathoracic volume contract. However, there is some contraction of the inspiratory muscles in the early part of expiration. This contraction exerts a braking action on the recoil forces and slows expiration.

Strong inspiratory efforts reduce intrapleural pressure to values as low as −30 mm Hg, producing correspondingly greater degrees of lung inflation. When ventilation is increased, the extent of lung deflation is also increased by active contraction of expiratory muscles that decrease intrathoracic volume.

Because of gravitational forces, intrapleural pressure in the standing position is about 5 mm Hg greater at the bases of the lungs than at the apexes. Consequently, the transmural pressure (the difference between intrapulmonary and intrapleural pressure) is less and, at the end of forced expiration, may become negative, causing airways at the bases to close. It is for the same reason that during the first part of inspiration more of the inspired gas goes to the apexes than the bases of the lungs (see below).

Air Passages

After passing through the nasal passages and pharynx, where it is warmed and takes up water vapor, the inspired air passes down the trachea and through the bronchioles, respiratory bronchioles, and alveolar ducts to the alveoli (Fig 34–2).

Between the trachea and the alveolar sacs, the airways divide 23 times. The first 16 generations of passages form the conducting zone of the airways and are made up of bronchi, bronchioles, and terminal bronchioles. The remaining 7 form the transitional and respiratory zones where gas exchange occurs and are made up of respiratory bronchioles, alveolar ducts, and alveolar sacs. These multiple divisions greatly increase the total cross-sectional area of the airways. Consequently, the velocity of air flow in the small airways declines to very low values. It has been calculated that the aggregate circumference of the 16th generation of air passages (terminal bronchioles) is 2000 times the circumference of the trachea.

The alveoli are surrounded by pulmonary capillaries, and in most areas the structures between the air and the capillary blood across which O_2 and CO_2 diffuse are exceedingly thin (Fig 34–3). There are 300

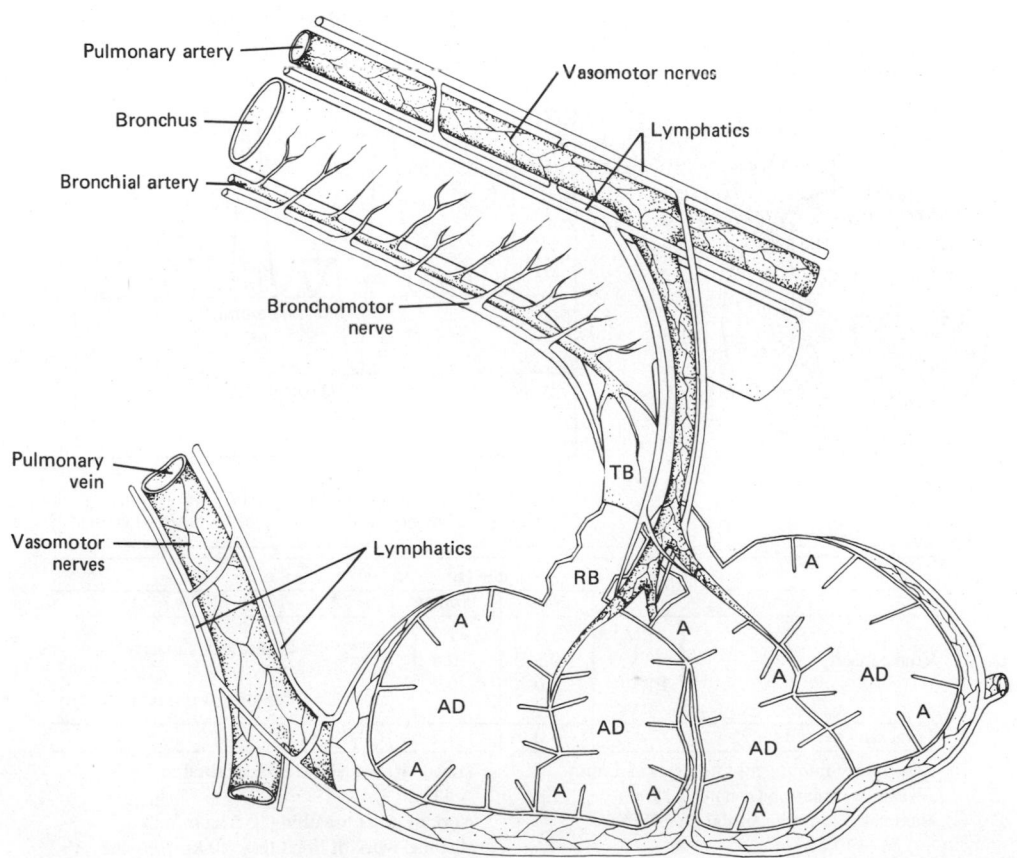

Figure 34–2. Structure of the lung. A, anatomic alveolus; AD, alveolar duct; RB, respiratory bronchiole; TB, terminal bronchiole. (Reproduced, with permission, from Staub NC: The pathophysiology of pulmonary edema. Hum Pathol 1:419, 1970.)

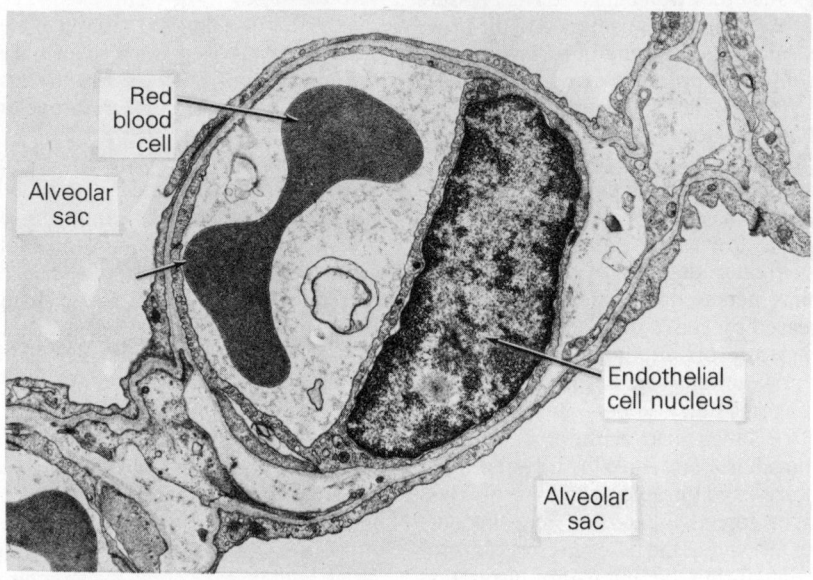

Figure 34–3. Electron photomicrograph of monkey lung, showing a red blood cell in a pulmonary capillary between 2 alveolar sacs. The arrow indicates the diffusion path from alveolar gas to the erythrocyte. (Reproduced, with permission, from Weibel ER: Morphometric estimation of pulmonary diffusion capacity. Respir Physiol 11:54, 1970.)

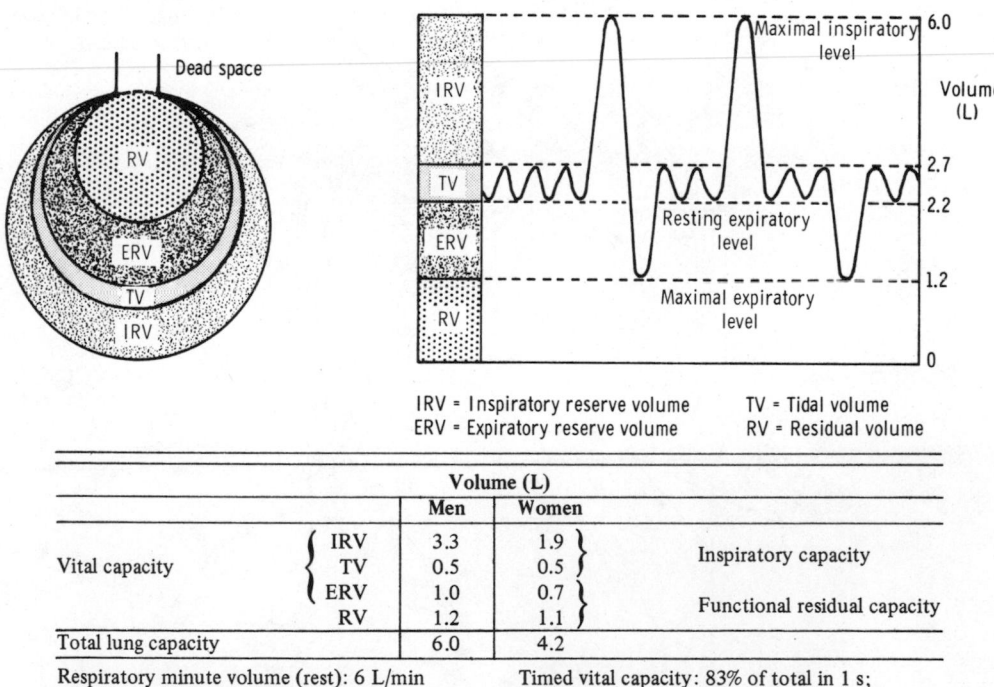

IRV = Inspiratory reserve volume   TV = Tidal volume
ERV = Expiratory reserve volume   RV = Residual volume

		Volume (L)		
		Men	**Women**	
Vital capacity	IRV	3.3	1.9	Inspiratory capacity
	TV	0.5	0.5	
	ERV	1.0	0.7	Functional residual capacity
	RV	1.2	1.1	
Total lung capacity		6.0	4.2	

Respiratory minute volume (rest): 6 L/min   Timed vital capacity: 83% of total in 1 s;
Alveolar ventilation (rest): 4.2 L/min   97% in 3 s
Maximal voluntary ventilation (BTPS):   Work of quiet breathing: 0.5 kg-m/min
    125–170 L/min   Maximal work of breathing: 10 kg-m/breath

Figure 34–4. Lung volumes and some measurements related to the mechanics of breathing. The diagram at the upper right represents the excursions of a spirometer plotted against time. (Data and graph, slightly modified, from Comroe JH Jr & others: *The Lung: Clinical Physiology and Pulmonary Function Tests,* 2nd ed. Year Book, 1962.)

million alveoli in humans, and the total area of the alveolar walls in contact with capillaries in both lungs is about 70 m².

The alveoli are lined by 2 types of epithelial cells. **Type I cells** are flat cells with large cytoplasmic extensions and are the primary lining cells. **Type II cells,** or **granular pneumocytes,** are thicker and contain numerous lamellar inclusion bodies. These cells secrete surfactant (see below). There may be other special types of epithelial cells, and the lung also contains alveolar macrophages, lymphocytes, plasma cells, and mast cells. The mast cells contain heparin, various lipids, histamine, and polypeptides that participate in allergic reactions.

The bronchi and bronchioles contain smooth muscle and are innervated by the autonomic nervous system. In general, parasympatholytic drugs dilate large airways whereas β-adrenergic agonists such as isoproterenol dilate small airways (see Chapter 13). This accounts for the value of isoproterenol in the treatment of asthma.

Lung Volumes

The amount of air that moves into the lungs with each inspiration (or the amount that moves out with each expiration) is called the **tidal volume.** The air inspired with a maximal inspiratory effort in excess of the tidal volume is the **inspiratory reserve volume.** The volume expelled by an active expiratory effort after passive expiration is the **expiratory reserve volume,** and the air left in the lungs after a maximal expiratory effort is the **residual volume.** Normal values for these lung volumes, and names applied to

combinations of them, are shown in Fig 34–4. The space in the conducting zone of the airways occupied by gas that does not exchange with blood in the pulmonary vessels is the **respiratory dead space.** The **vital capacity,** the greatest amount of air that can be expired after a maximal inspiratory effort, is frequently measured clinically as an index of pulmonary function. The fraction of the vital capacity expired in 1 s (**timed vital capacity;** also called forced expired volume in 1 s, or FEV 1″) gives additional valuable information. The vital capacity may be normal but the timed vital capacity greatly reduced in diseases such as asthma, in which, due to bronchial constriction, the resistance of the airways is increased. The amount of air inspired per minute (**pulmonary ventilation,** or **respiratory minute volume**) is normally about 6 L (500 ml/breath × 12 breaths/min). The **maximal voluntary ventilation (MVV),** or, as it was formerly called, the **maximal breathing capacity,** is the largest volume of gas that can be moved into and out of the lungs in one minute by voluntary effort. The normal MVV is 125–170 L/min.

Respiratory Muscles

Movement of the **diaphragm** accounts for 75% of the change in intrathoracic volume during quiet inspiration. Attached around the bottom of the thoracic cage, this muscle arches over the liver and moves downward like a piston when it contracts. The distance it moves ranges from 1.5 cm to as much as 7 cm with deep inspiration (Fig 34–5). The other major **inspiratory muscles** are the **external intercostal muscles,** which run obliquely downward and forward from rib to rib. The ribs pivot as if hinged at the back, so that when

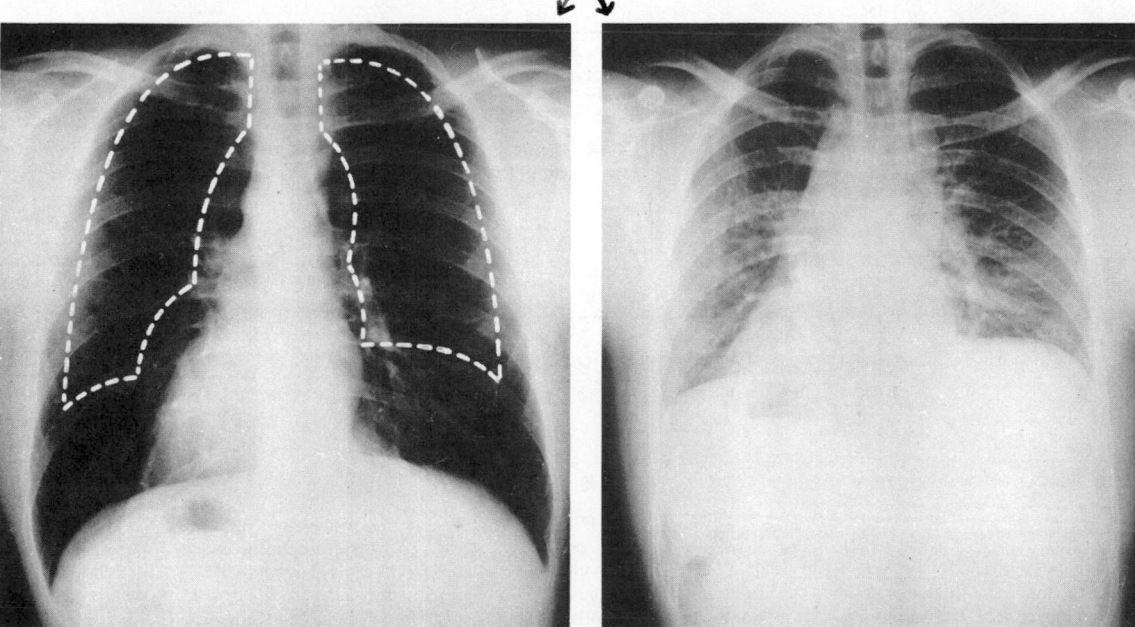

Figure 34–5. X-ray of chest in full expiration *(left)* and full inspiration *(right).* Dashed white line on right is outline of lungs in full expiration. (From Comroe JH Jr: *Physiology of Respiration,* 2nd ed. Copyright © 1974 by Year Book Medical Publishers, Inc., Chicago. Used by permission.)

the external intercostals contract they elevate the lower ribs. This pushes the sternum outward and increases the anteroposterior diameter of the chest. The transverse diameter is actually changed little if at all. Either the diaphragm or the external intercostal muscles alone can maintain adequate ventilation at rest. Transection of the spinal cord above the third cervical segment is fatal without artificial respiration, but transection below the origin of the phrenic nerves that innervate the diaphragm (third to fifth cervical segments) is not; conversely, in patients with bilateral phrenic nerve palsy, respiration is adequate to maintain life. The scalene and sternocleidomastoid muscles in the neck are accessory inspiratory muscles that help to elevate the thoracic cage during deep labored respiration.

A decrease in intrathoracic volume and forced expiration result when the **expiratory muscles** contract. The internal intercostals have this action because they pass obliquely downward and posteriorly from rib to rib and therefore pull the rib cage downward when they contract. Contractions of the muscles of the anterior abdominal wall also aid expiration by pulling the rib cage downward and inward, and by increasing the intra-abdominal pressure, which pushes the diaphragm upward.

Glottis

The abductor muscles in the larynx contract early in inspiration, pulling the vocal cords apart and opening the glottis. During swallowing or gagging, there is reflex contraction of the adductor muscles that closes the glottis and prevents aspiration of food, fluid, or vomitus into the lungs. In unconscious or anesthetized patients, glottic closure may be incomplete and vomitus may enter the trachea, causing an inflammatory reaction in the lung (**aspiration pneumonia**).

The laryngeal muscles are supplied by the vagi. When the abductors are paralyzed, there is inspiratory stridor. When the adductors are paralyzed, food and fluid enter the trachea, causing aspiration pneumonia and edema. Bilateral cervical vagotomy in animals causes the slow development of fatal pulmonary congestion and edema. The edema is due at least in part to aspiration, although some edema develops even if a tracheostomy is performed before the vagotomy.

Compliance of the Lungs & Chest Wall

The interaction between the recoil of the lungs and recoil of the chest can be demonstrated in living subjects. The nostrils are clipped shut and the subject breathes through an apparatus that contains a valve just beyond the mouthpiece. The mouthpiece contains a pressure-measuring device. After the subject inhales a given amount, the valve is shut, closing off the airway. The respiratory muscles are then relaxed while the pressure in the airway is recorded. The procedure is repeated after inhaling or actively exhaling various volumes. The curve of airway pressure obtained in this way, plotted against volume, is the relaxation pressure curve of the total respiratory system (Fig 34–6). The pressure is zero at a lung volume that corresponds to the volume of gas in the lungs at the end of quiet expiration (functional residual capacity; see below), positive at greater volumes, and negative at smaller

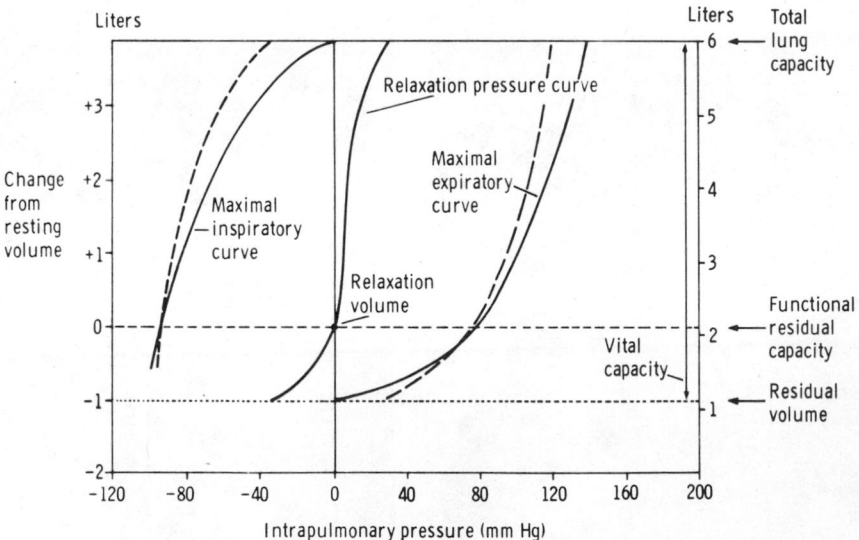

Figure 34–6. Relation between intrapulmonary pressure and volume. The middle curve is the static pressure curve of values obtained when the lungs are inflated or deflated by various amounts and the intrapulmonary pressure (elastic recoil pressure) is measured with the airway closed. The relaxation volume is the point where the recoil of the chest and the recoil of the lungs balance. The slope of the curve is the compliance of the lungs and chest wall. The maximal inspiratory and expiratory curves are the airway pressures that can be developed during maximal inspiratory and expiratory efforts. The dashed lines, the horizontal distances between the inspiratory and expiratory curves and the relaxation pressure curve, represent the net pressure exerted by the inspiratory and expiratory muscles. (Modified from Lambertsen CJ in: *Medical Physiology,* 12th ed. Mountcastle VB [editor]. Mosby, 1968.)

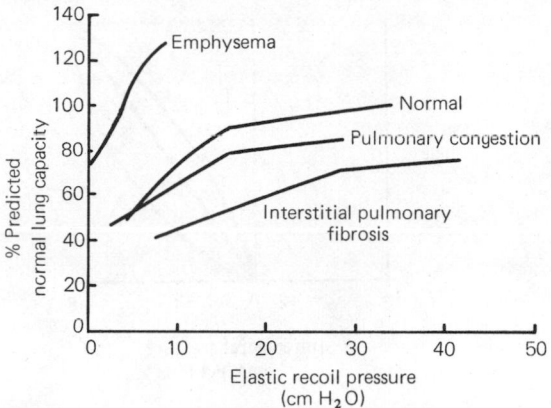

Figure 34–7. Static deflation pressure-volume curves (relaxation pressure curves) in various states. (Modified from Bates DV, Macklem PT, Christie RV: *Respiratory Function in Disease.* Saunders, 1971.)

volumes. The change in lung volume per unit change in airway pressure ($\Delta V/\Delta P$) is the stretchability, or **compliance,** of the lungs and chest wall. It is normally measured in the pressure range where the relaxation pressure curve is steepest, and the normal value is approximately 0.2 L/cm H_2O. However, compliance depends on lung volume; an individual with only one lung has approximately half the ΔV for a given ΔP. Compliance is also slightly greater when measured during deflation than when measured during inflation. Consequently, it is more informative to examine the whole pressure-volume curve. The curve is shifted downward and to the right (compliance is decreased) by pulmonary congestion and interstitial pulmonary fibrosis (Fig 34–7). It is shifted upward and to the left (compliance is increased) in emphysema. It should be noted that compliance is a static measure of lung and chest recoil. The **resistance** of the lung and chest is the pressure difference required for a unit of air flow, and this measurement, which is dynamic rather than static, also takes into account the resistance to air flow in the airways.

Alveolar Surface Tension

An important factor affecting the compliance of the lungs is the surface tension of the film of fluid that lines the alveoli. The magnitude of this component at various lung volumes can be measured by removing the lungs from the body and distending them alternately with saline and with air while measuring the intrapulmonary pressure. Because saline reduces the surface tension to nearly zero, the pressure-volume curve obtained with saline measures the tissue elasticity (Fig 34–8), while the curve obtained with air measures both components. The difference between the 2 curves, the elasticity due to surface tension, is much smaller at small than at large lung volumes. The surface tension is also much less than the expected surface tension at a water-air interface of the same dimensions.

The low surface tension when the alveoli are small is due to the presence in the fluid lining the alveoli of **surfactant,** a lipid surface tension–lowering agent. Surfactant is a complex 2-phase mixture of protein and lipids, but the major component is dipalmitoylphosphatidylcholine (DPPC). This phospholipid has a hydrophilic "head" and 2 parallel hydrophobic fatty acid "tails" like phospholipids in cell membranes (see Chapters 1 and 17). Presumably, the molecules are parallelly oriented at the air-fluid interface in the alveoli, and surface tension is inversely proportionate to their concentration. The molecules of surfactant are spread apart as alveolar size increases during inspiration but move together during expiration, thus adjusting surface tension during breathing. If the surface tension is not kept low when the alveoli become smaller during expiration, they collapse in accordance with the law of Laplace (see Chapter 30). In spherical structures like the alveoli, the distending pressure equals 2 times the tension divided by the radius ($P = 2T/R$); if T is not reduced as R is reduced, the tension overcomes the distending pressure. Surfactant also helps to prevent pulmonary edema. It has been calculated that if it were not present the unopposed surface tension in the alveoli would produce a 20 mm Hg force favoring transudation of fluid from the blood into the alveoli.

Surfactant is produced by type II alveolar epithelial cells. The lamellar inclusions of these cells are believed to be surfactant that is secreted by exocytosis. Surfactant is removed, at least in part, by alveolar macrophages.

Surfactant is important at birth. The fetus makes respiratory movements in utero, but the lungs remain collapsed until birth. After birth, the infant makes several strong inspiratory movements and the lungs expand. Surfactant keeps them from collapsing again. Surfactant deficiency is the cause of **hyaline mem-**

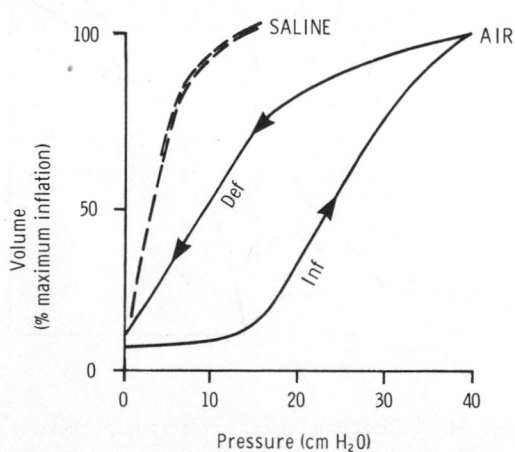

Figure 34–8. Pressure-volume relations in the lungs of a cat after removal from the body. *Air:* lungs inflated (Inf) and deflated (Def) with air. *Saline:* lungs inflated and deflated with saline. (Reproduced, with permission, from Morgan TE: Pulmonary surfactant. N Engl J Med 284:1185, 1971.)

brane disease, (respiratory distress syndrome, RDS), the serious pulmonary disease that develops in infants born before their surfactant system is functional. Surface tension in the lungs of these infants is high, and there are many areas in which the alveoli are collapsed (atelectasis).

The size and number of inclusions in type II cells are increased by thyroid hormones, and RDS is more common and more severe in infants with low plasma levels of thyroid hormones than in those with normal plasma levels. Maturation of surfactant in the lungs is also accelerated by adrenocortical hormones. There is an increase in fetal and maternal cortisol near term, and the lung is rich in glucocorticoid receptors.

Patchy atelectasis is also associated with surfactant deficiency in patients who have undergone cardiac surgery during which a pump oxygenator was used and the pulmonary circulation was interrupted. In addition, surfactant deficiency may also play a role in some of the abnormalities that develop following occlusion of a main bronchus, occlusion of one pulmonary artery, and long-term inhalation of 100% O_2. There is a decrease in surfactant in the lungs of cigarette smokers.

Work of Breathing

Work is performed by the respiratory muscles in stretching the elastic tissues of the chest wall and lungs, moving inelastic tissues, and moving air through the respiratory passages. Since pressure times volume ($g/cm^2 \times cm^3 = g \times cm$) has the same dimensions as work (force $\times$ distance), the work of breathing can be calculated from the relaxation pressure curve (Figs 34–6 and 34–9). In Fig 34–9, the total elastic work required for inspiration is area ABCA. It is worth

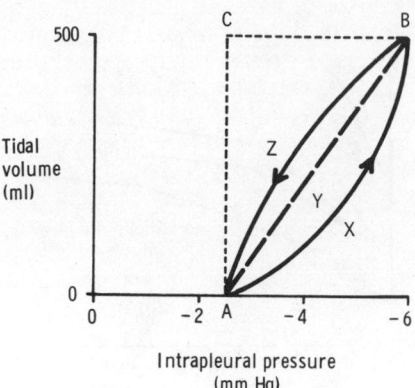

Figure 34–10. Diagrammatic representation of pressure and volume changes during quiet inspiration (line AXB) and expiration (line BZA). Line AYB is the compliance line.

noting that the relaxation pressure curve of the total respiratory system differs from that of the lungs alone. The actual elastic work required to increase the volume of the lungs alone is area ABDEA. The amount of elastic work required to inflate the whole respiratory system is less than the amount required to inflate the lungs alone because part of the work comes from elastic energy stored in the thorax. The elastic energy lost from the thorax (area AFGBA) is equal to that gained by the lungs (area AEDCA).

The frictional resistance to air movement is relatively small during quiet breathing, but it does cause the intrapleural pressure changes to lead the lung volume changes during inspiration and expiration, producing a **hysteresis loop** rather than a straight line when pressure is plotted against volume (Fig 34–10). In this diagram, area AXBYA represents the work done to overcome airway resistance and lung viscosity.

Estimates of the total work of quiet breathing range from 0.3 up to 0.8 kg-m/min. The value rises markedly during exercise, but the energy cost of breathing in normal individuals represents less than 3% of the total energy expenditure during exercise. The work of breathing is greatly increased in diseases such as emphysema, asthma, and congestive heart failure with dyspnea and orthopnea.

Dead Space & Uneven Ventilation

Since gaseous exchange in the respiratory system occurs only in the terminal portions of the airways, the gas that occupies the rest of the respiratory system is not available for gas exchange with pulmonary capillary blood. Normally, the volume of this dead space is approximately equal to the body weight in pounds. Thus, in a man who weighs 150 lb (68 kg), only the first 350 ml of the 500 ml inspired with each breath at rest mixes with the air in the alveoli. Conversely, with each expiration, the first 150 ml expired is gas that occupied the dead space, and only the last 350 ml is gas from the alveoli.

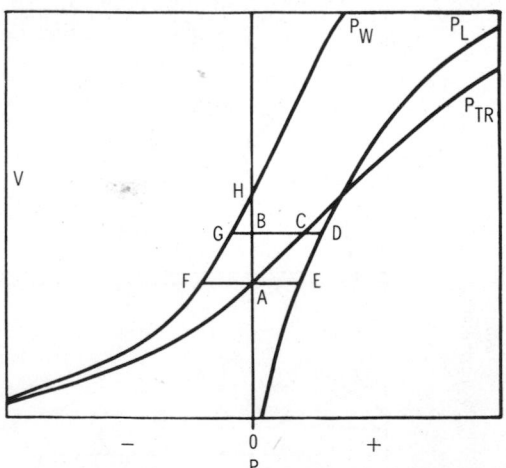

Figure 34–9. Relaxation pressure curve of total respiratory system (PTR) and its components, the relaxation pressure curve of the lungs (PL) and the chest (PW). (Reproduced, with permission, from Otis AB: The work of breathing. In: *Handbook of Physiology.* Fenn WO, Rahn H [editors]. Washington: The American Physiological Society, 1964. Section 3, vol 1, pages 463–476.)

It is wise to distinguish between the anatomic dead space (volume of the respiratory system exclusive of alveoli) and the **total,** or **physiologic, dead space** (volume of gas not equilibrating with blood, ie, wasted ventilation). In health, the 2 dead spaces are identical; but in disease states, there may be no exchange between the gas in some of the alveoli and the blood, and some of the alveoli may be overventilated. The volume of gas in nonperfused alveoli and any volume of air in the alveoli in excess of that necessary to arterialize the blood in the alveolar capillaries is part of the dead space (nonequilibrating) gas volume. The anatomic dead space can be measured by analysis of the single breath N_2 curves (Fig 34–11). From mid inspiration, the subject takes as deep a breath as possible of pure O_2, then exhales steadily while the N_2 content of the expired gas is continuously measured. The initial gas exhaled (phase I) is the gas that filled the dead space and that consequently contains no N_2. This is followed by a mixture of dead space and alveolar gas (phase II) and then by alveolar gas (phase III). The volume of the dead space is the volume of the gas expired from peak inspiration to the mid portion of phase II (Fig 34–11).

Phase III of the single breath N_2 curve terminates at the **closing volume (CV)** and is followed by phase IV, during which the N_2 content of the expired gas is increased. The CV is the lung volume above residual volume at which airways in the lower, dependent parts of the lungs begin to close off because of the lesser transmural pressure in these areas (see above). The gas in the upper portions of the lungs is richer in N_2 than the gas in the lower, dependent portions because during the early part of the preceding inspiration the upper portions received more gas than the lower, and most of this gas was N_2-rich dead space gas rather than the pure O_2 the subject inspired. It is also worth noting that in most normal individuals phase III has a slight positive slope even before phase IV is reached. This indicates that even during phase III there is a gradual increase in the proportion of the expired gas coming from the relatively N_2-rich upper portions of the lungs. The pattern of ventilation in the lungs can be assessed by having the subject inhale a radioactive isotope of the inert gas xenon (^{133}Xe) while the chest is monitored with a battery of radiation detectors. Areas that show little radioactivity are poorly ventilated.

The total dead space can be calculated from the P_{CO_2} of expired air, the P_{CO_2} of alveolar gas, and the tidal volume. The tidal volume (V_T) times the P_{CO_2} of the expired gas (P_{ECO_2}) equals the alveolar P_{CO_2} (P_{ACO_2}) times the difference between the tidal volume and the dead space (V_D) plus the P_{CO_2} of inspired air (P_{ICO_2}) times V_D:

$$P_{ECO_2} \times V_T = P_{ACO_2} \times (V_T - V_D) +$$

$$P_{ICO_2} \times V_D \text{ (Bohr's equation)}.$$

However, the term $P_{ICO_2} \times V_D$ is so small that it can be ignored and the equation solved for V_D. If, for example,

$$P_{ECO_2} = 28 \text{ mm Hg}$$

$$P_{ACO_2} = 40 \text{ mm Hg}$$

$$V_T = 500 \text{ ml}$$

then, $\qquad V_D = 150 \text{ ml}$

Although it is possible to stand underwater and breathe through a tube that projects above the surface, it may be worth noting that such a tube is in effect an extension of the respiratory dead space. For each ml of tube volume, the depth of inspiration would have to be increased 1 ml to supply the same volume of air to the alveoli. Thus, if the volume of the tube were at all large, breathing would become very laborious. Additional effort is also required to expand the chest against the pressure of the surrounding water.

Alveolar Ventilation

Because of the dead space, the amount of air reaching the alveoli (**alveolar ventilation**) at a respiratory minute volume of 6 L/min is 500–150 ml times 12 breath/min, or 4.2 L/min. Because of the dead space, rapid, shallow respiration produces much less alveolar ventilation than slow, deep respiration at the same respiratory minute volume (Table 34–2).

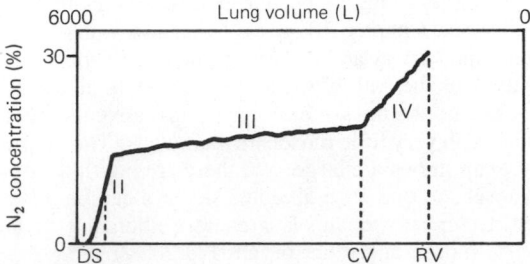

Figure 34–11. Single breath N_2 curve. From mid inspiration, the subject takes a deep breath of pure O_2, then exhales steadily. The changes in the N_2 concentration of expired gas during expiration are shown, with the various phases of the curve indicated by roman numerals. DS, dead space; CV, closing volume; RV, residual volume. (Modified from Buist AS: New tests to assess lung function: The single-breath nitrogen test. N Engl J Med 293:438, 1975.)

Table 34–2. Effect of variations in respiratory rate and depth on alveolar ventilation.

Respiratory rate	30/min	10/min
Tidal volume	200 ml	600 ml
Minute volume	6 L	6 L
Alveolar ventilation	(200–150) × 30 = 1500 ml	(600–150) × 10 = 4500 ml

GAS EXCHANGE IN THE LUNG

Composition of Alveolar Air

Oxygen continuously diffuses out of the gas in the alveoli (**alveolar gas**) into the bloodstream, and CO_2 continuously diffuses into the alveoli from the blood. In the steady state, inspired air mixes with the alveolar gas, replacing the O_2 that has entered the blood and diluting the CO_2 that has entered the alveoli. Part of this mixture is expired. The O_2 content of the alveolar gas then falls and its CO_2 content rises until the next inspiration. Since the volume of gas in the alveoli is about 2 liters at the end of expiration (functional residual capacity; Fig 34–4), each 350 ml increment of inspired and expired air changes the P_{O_2} and P_{CO_2} very little. Indeed, the composition of alveolar gas remains remarkably constant, not only at rest but in a variety of other conditions as well (see Chapter 36).

Sampling Alveolar Air

Theoretically, all but the first 150 ml expired with each expiration is alveolar air, but there is always some mixing at the interface between the dead space gas and the alveolar air (Fig 34–11). A later portion of expired air is therefore the portion taken for analysis. Using modern apparatus with a suitable automatic valve, it is possible to collect the last 10 ml expired during quiet breathing. The composition of alveolar gas is compared with that of inspired and expired air in Fig 34–12.

Diffusion Capacity

The P_{O_2} of alveolar air is 100 mm Hg, whereas that in the venous blood in the pulmonary artery is 40 mm Hg (Fig 34–12). There is no evidence that any process other than passive diffusion is involved in the movement of O_2 into the blood along this pressure gradient. O_2 dissolves in the plasma and enters the red cells, where it combines with hemoglobin, a reaction considered in detail in the next chapter. Diffusion into the blood must be very rapid, since the time each ml of blood is in the capillaries is short. Nevertheless, O_2 diffusion is adequate in health to raise the P_{O_2} of the blood to 97 mm Hg, a value just under the alveolar P_{O_2}.

The **diffusion capacity** of the lungs for O_2 is the amount of O_2 that crosses the alveolar membrane per minute per mm Hg difference in P_{O_2} between the alveolar gas and the blood in the pulmonary capillaries. Expressed in terms of STPD (Table 34–1), it is normally about 20 ml/min/mm Hg at rest. As a result of capillary dilatation and an increase in the number of active capillaries, it rises to values of 65 or more during exercise. The diffusion capacity for O_2 is decreased in diseases such as sarcoidosis and beryllium poisoning (berylliosis) that cause fibrosis of the alveolar walls and produce **alveolar-capillary block.**

The P_{CO_2} of venous blood is 46 mm Hg, whereas that of alveolar air is 40 mm Hg, and CO_2 diffuses from the blood into the alveoli along this gradient. The P_{CO_2}

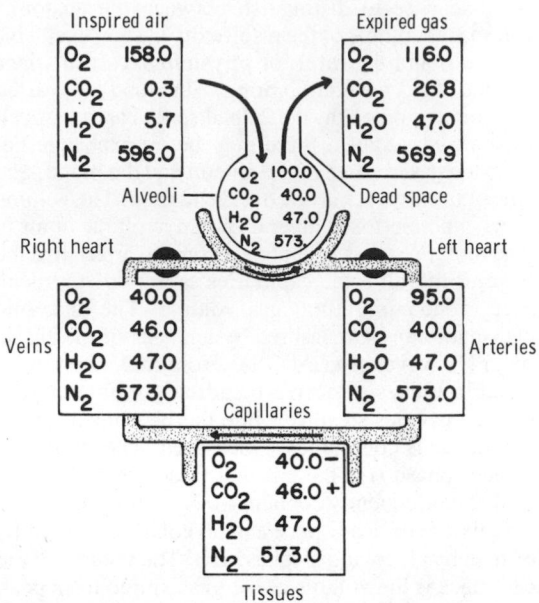

Figure 34–12. Partial pressures of gases (mm Hg). (Values [modified slightly] from Lambertsen CJ in: *Medical Physiology,* 13th ed. Mountcastle VB [editor]. Mosby, 1974.)

of blood leaving the lungs is 40 mm Hg. CO_2 passes through all biologic membranes with ease, and the pulmonary diffusion capacity for CO_2 is much greater than the capacity for O_2. It is for this reason that CO_2 retention is rarely a problem in patients with alveolar-capillary block even when the reduction in diffusion capacity for O_2 is severe.

PULMONARY CIRCULATION

Anatomic Considerations

The pulmonary vascular bed resembles the systemic (see Chapter 30) except that the walls of the pulmonary artery and its large branches are about 30% as thick as the wall of the aorta, and the small arterial vessels, unlike the systemic arterioles, are endothelial tubes with very little muscle in their walls. The pulmonary capillaries are large, and there are multiple anastomoses, so that each alveolus sits in a capillary basket. Lymphatic channels are more abundant in the lungs than in any other organ (Fig 34–2).

Pressure, Volume, & Flow

The output per minute of the right ventricle is, of course, equal to that of the left ventricle and, like that of the left ventricle, averages 5.5 L/min at rest. The ratio of alveolar ventilation to pulmonary blood flow at rest is therefore about 0.8 (4.2/5.5). It should be noted that this ratio may be normal in patients with severe hypoxia because in disease states there may be

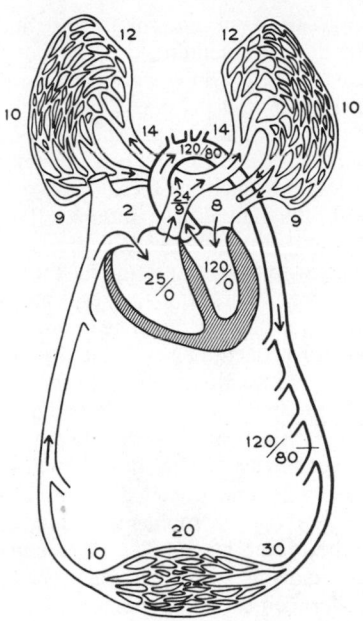

Figure 34–13. Blood pressures (mm Hg) in the pulmonary and systemic circulation. (From Comroe JH, Jr: *Physiology of Respiration,* 2nd ed. Copyright © 1974 by Year Book Medical Publishers, Inc., Chicago. Used by permission.)

nonuniform ventilation and nonuniform perfusion of alveoli. The extreme case of such nonuniformity would be that in which all the ventilation went to one lung and all the blood flow to the other, a state which would, of course, be rapidly fatal even though the ventilation/blood flow ratio would be normal.

The entire pulmonary vascular system is a distensible low-pressure system. The pulmonary arterial pressure is about 24/9 mm Hg and the mean pressure is about 15 mm Hg. The pressure in the left atrium is about 8 mm Hg during diastole, so that the pressure gradient in the pulmonary system is about 7 mm Hg, compared with a gradient of about 90 mm Hg in the systemic circulation (Fig 34–13).

The volume of blood in the pulmonary vessels at any one time is about 1 liter, of which less than 100 ml are in the capillaries. The mean velocity of the blood in the root of the pulmonary artery is the same as that in the aorta (about 40 cm/s). It falls off rapidly, then rises slightly again in the larger pulmonary veins. It takes a red cell about 0.75 s to traverse the pulmonary capillaries at rest, and 0.3 s or less during exercise.

"Physiologic Shunt"

About 2% of the blood in the systemic arteries is blood that has bypassed the pulmonary capillaries. The bronchial arteries, branches of the thoracic aorta, provide blood that nourishes parts of the lung parenchyma, and some of this blood returns to the heart via the pulmonary veins. There is further dilution of the oxygenated blood in the heart by blood that flows from the coronary arteries directly into the chambers of the

left side of the heart (see Chapter 32). It is because of this small "physiologic shunt" that the blood in the systemic arteries contains less O_2 per deciliter than the blood that has equilibrated with the alveolar air.

Capillary Pressure

Pulmonary capillary pressure is about 10 mm Hg, whereas the oncotic pressure is 25 mm Hg, so that there is an inward-directed pressure gradient of about 15 mm Hg which keeps the alveoli free of fluid. When the pulmonary capillary pressure is more than 25 mm Hg—as it may be, for example, when there is "backward failure" of the left ventricle—pulmonary congestion and edema result. Patients with mitral stenosis also have a chronic, progressive rise in pulmonary capillary pressure and extensive fibrotic changes in the pulmonary vessels. Pulmonary edema is not as prominent a symptom in mitral stenosis as in frank congestive heart failure, probably because the fibrosis and constriction of the pulmonary arterial vessels "protect" the capillaries.

Pulmonary Reservoir

Because of their distensibility, the pulmonary veins are an important blood reservoir. When a normal individual lies down, the pulmonary blood volume increases by up to 400 ml, and on standing up this blood is discharged into the general circulation. This shift is the cause of the decrease in vital capacity in the supine position and is responsible for the occurrence of orthopnea in heart failure (see Chapter 33).

Dilatation & Constriction of the Pulmonary Vessels

The pulmonary vessels are capable of considerable passive dilatation. When the blood supply to one normal lung is obstructed by inflating a balloon in a main branch of the pulmonary artery, the flow through the other lung is doubled, but there is only a small rise in pulmonary arterial pressure. Pulmonary arterioles are constricted by norepinephrine, epinephrine, angiotensin II, and some prostaglandins; they are dilated by isoproterenol and acetylcholine. Pulmonary venules are constricted by serotonin, histamine, and *E coli* endotoxin. The vessels are plentifully supplied with sympathetic vasoconstrictor nerve fibers, and stimulation of the cervical sympathetic ganglia decreases pulmonary blood flow by as much as 30%. The fibers serve in part to decrease the capacity of the pulmonary circulation, thus mobilizing blood from the pulmonary reservoir. Pressure in the pulmonary artery is increased by hypoxia, possibly because of the release of a prostaglandin. It is little affected by stimuli that alter the systemic pressure. In exercise, for example, pulmonary blood flow increases by the same amount as systemic blood flow (as much as 7-fold), but pulmonary arterial pressure changes very little. The pulmonary arterial pressure is usually normal in essential hypertension.

When a bronchus is obstructed, the vessels supplying the poorly ventilated alveoli constrict, and blood is shunted to other areas. The constriction is due to a local effect of the low alveolar P_{O_2} on the vessels. Accumulation of CO_2 leads to a drop in pH in the area, and a decline in pH also produces constriction. Conversely, reduction of the blood flow to a portion of the lung lowers the alveolar P_{CO_2} in that area, and this leads to constriction of the bronchi supplying it, shifting ventilation away from the poorly perfused area.

^{133}Xe can also be used to survey pulmonary blood flow by injecting a saline solution of the gas intravenously while monitoring the chest. The gas rapidly enters the alveoli which are perfused normally but fails to enter those which are not perfused. Another technic for locating poorly perfused areas is injection of macroaggregates of albumin labeled with radioactive iodine. These aggregates are large enough to block capillaries and small arterioles, and they lodge only in vessels in which blood was flowing when they reached the lungs. Although it seems paradoxic to study patients with pulmonary vascular obstruction by producing additional obstruction, the technic is safe because relatively few particles are injected. The particles block only a small number of pulmonary vessels and are rapidly removed by the body.

Pulmonary Embolization

One of the normal functions of the lungs is to filter out small blood clots, and this occurs without any symptoms. When emboli block larger branches of the pulmonary artery, they provoke a rise in pulmonary arterial pressure and rapid, shallow respiration **(tachypnea).** The rise in pulmonary arterial pressure is apparently due to reflex vasoconstriction via the sympathetic nerve fibers, although there is controversy on this point and reflex vasoconstriction appears to be absent when large branches of the pulmonary artery are blocked. The tachypnea is a reflex response to activation of vagally innervated pulmonary deflation receptors close to the vessel walls. There is some evidence that serotonin is released from platelets at the site of embolization and that serotonin stimulates or "sensitizes" these receptors.

OTHER FUNCTIONS
OF THE RESPIRATORY SYSTEM

Lung Defense Mechanisms

The respiratory passages that lead from the exterior to the alveoli do more than serve as gas conduits. They humidify and cool or warm the inspired air so that even very hot or very cold air is at or near body temperature by the time it reaches the alveoli. Bronchial secretions contain substances that help resist infections and maintain the integrity of the mucosa. They also contain mechanisms that do much to prevent foreign matter from reaching the alveoli. The hairs in the nostrils strain out many particles larger than 10 μm in diameter. Most of the remaining particles of this size

settle on mucous membranes in the nose and pharynx; because of their momentum, they do not follow the airstream as it curves downward into the lungs, and they impact on or near the tonsils and adenoids, large collections of immunologically active lymphoid tissue. Particles 2–10 μm in diameter generally fall on the walls of the bronchi as the air flow slows in the smaller passages. There they initiate reflex bronchial constriction and coughing (see Chapter 14). They are also moved away from the lungs by the "ciliary escalator." The epithelium of the respiratory passages from the anterior third of the nose to the beginning of the respiratory bronchioles is ciliated, and the cilia, which are covered with mucus, beat in a coordinated fashion at a frequency of 1000–1500 cycles per minute. The ciliary mechanism is capable of moving particles at a rate of at least 16 mm/min. Particles less than 2 μm in diameter generally reach the alveoli, where they are ingested by the macrophages ("dust cells") and carried to the lymph nodes. The importance of these defense mechanisms is evident when one remembers that in modern cities, each liter of air may contain several million particles of dust and irritants.

In **Kartagener's syndrome,** ciliary motility is defective and mucus transport virtually absent. Patients with this syndrome have chronic sinusitis and bronchiectasis.

Metabolic Functions of the Lungs

In addition to their functions in gas exchange, the lungs have a number of metabolic functions. They manufacture surfactant for local use as noted above. They also release a variety of substances that enter the systemic arterial blood (Table 34–3) and remove other substances from the systemic venous blood that reaches them via the pulmonary artery. Prostaglandins are removed from the circulation, but they are also synthesized in the lungs and released into the blood when lung tissue is stretched. Prostaglandin $F_{2\alpha}$ may be the agent responsible for pulmonary vasoconstriction during hypoxia.

Table 34–3. Biologically active substances
metabolized by the lung.

Synthesized and used in the lung
Surfactant
Synthesized or stored and released into the blood
Prostaglandins
Histamine
Kallikrein
Partially removed from the blood
Prostaglandins
Bradykinin
Adenine nucleotides
Serotonin
Norepinephrine
Acetylcholine
Activated in the lung
Angiotensin I → angiotensin II

The lungs also activate one hormone; the physiologically inactive decapeptide angiotensin I is converted to the pressor, aldosterone-stimulating octapeptide angiotensin II in the pulmonary circulation (see Chapter 24). The converting enzyme responsible for this activation is located on the surface of the endothelial cells of the pulmonary capillaries and particularly in small pits, or **caveolae,** on the vascular surface of these cells. The converting enzyme also inactivates bradykinin. Circulation time through the pulmonary capillaries is less than 1 second, yet 70% of the angiotensin I reaching the lungs is converted to angiotensin II in a single trip through the capillaries. Removal of serotonin and norepinephrine reduces the amounts of these vasoactive substances reaching the systemic circulation. However, many other vasoactive hormones pass through the lungs without being metabolized. These include epinephrine, dopamine, oxytocin, vasopressin, angiotensin II, substance P, and vasoactive intestinal peptide (VIP). The lungs also contain a fibrinolytic system that lyses clots in the pulmonary vessels.

35 | Gas Transport Between the Lungs & the Tissues

The partial pressure gradients for O_2 and CO_2 have been plotted in graphic form in Fig 35–1 to emphasize that they are the key to gas movement and that O_2 "flows downhill" from the air through the alveoli and blood into the tissues whereas CO_2 "flows downhill" from the tissues to the alveoli. However, the amount of both of these gases transported to and from the tissues would be grossly inadequate if it were not that the O_2 which dissolves in the blood combines with the O_2-carrying protein hemoglobin and that the CO_2 which dissolves enters into a series of reversible chemical reactions which convert it into other compounds. The presence of hemoglobin increases the O_2-carrying capacity of the blood 70-fold, and the reactions of CO_2 increase the blood CO_2 content 17-fold (Table 35–1).

Table 35–1. Gas content of blood.

Gas	ml/dl of Blood Containing 15 g of Hemoglobin			
	Arterial Blood (P_{O_2} 95 mm Hg; P_{CO_2} 40 mm Hg; Hb 97% Saturated)		Venous Blood (P_{O_2} 40 mm Hg; P_{CO_2} 46 mm Hg; Hb 75% Saturated)	
	Dissolved	Combined	Dissolved	Combined
O_2	0.29	19.5	0.12	15.1
CO_2	2.62	46.4	2.98	49.7
N_2	0.98	0	0.98	0

OXYGEN TRANSPORT

Oxygen Delivery to the Tissues

The O_2 delivery system in the body consists of the lungs and the cardiovascular system. O_2 delivery to a particular tissue depends on the amount of O_2 entering the lungs, the adequacy of pulmonary gas exchange, the blood flow to the tissue, and the capacity of the blood to carry O_2. The blood flow depends on the degree of constriction of the vascular bed in the tissue and the cardiac output. The amount of O_2 in the blood is determined by the amount of dissolved O_2, the amount of hemoglobin in the blood, and the affinity of the hemoglobin for O_2.

Reaction of Hemoglobin & Oxygen

The dynamics of the reaction of hemoglobin with O_2 make it a particularly suitable O_2 carrier. Hemoglobin (see Chapter 27) is a protein made up of 4 subunits, each of which contains a **heme** moiety attached to a polypeptide chain. Heme (Fig 27–11) is a complex made up of a porphyrin and one atom of ferrous iron. Each of the 4 iron atoms can bind reversibly one O_2 molecule. The iron stays in the ferrous state, so that the reaction is an **oxygenation,** not an oxidation. It has been customary to write the reaction of hemoglobin with O_2 as $Hb + O_2 \leftrightarrows HbO_2$. Since it contains 4 Hb units, the hemoglobin molecule can also be represented as Hb_4, and it actually reacts with 4 molecules of O_2 to form Hb_4O_8.

$$Hb_4 + O_2 \leftrightarrows Hb_4O_2$$
$$Hb_4O_2 + O_2 \leftrightarrows Hb_4O_4$$
$$Hb_4O_4 + O_2 \rightleftarrows Hb_4O_6$$
$$Hb_4O_6 + O_2 \rightleftarrows Hb_4O_8$$

The reaction is rapid, requiring less than 0.01 s. The deoxygenation (reduction) of Hb_4O_8 is also very rapid.

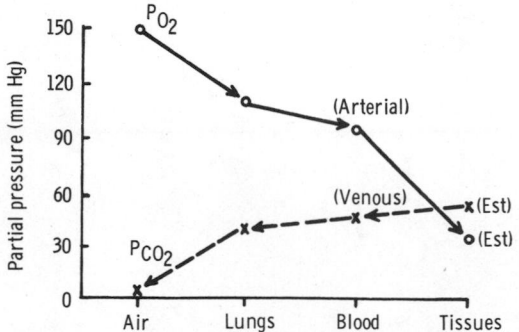

Figure 35–1. Summary of P_{O_2} and P_{CO_2} values in air, lungs, blood, and tissues, graphed to emphasize the fact that both O_2 and CO_2 diffuse "downhill" along gradients of decreasing partial pressure. (Redrawn and reproduced, with permission, from Kinney JM: Transport of carbon dioxide in blood. Anesthesiology 21:615, 1960.)

The quaternary structure of hemoglobin determines its affinity for O_2; by shifting the relationship of its 4 component peptide chains, the molecule fosters either O_2 uptake or O_2 delivery. The movement of the chains is associated with a change in the position of the heme moieties, which assume a relaxed or **R state,** which favors O_2 binding, or a tense or **T state,** which decreases O_2 binding. The transition from one state to another involves breaking or forming salt bridges between the peptide chains, and it has been calculated that these shifts occur about 10^8 times in the life of a red blood cell.

When hemoglobin takes up a small amount of O_2, the R state, and uptake of additional O_2, is favored. This is why the **oxygen hemoglobin dissociation curve,** the curve relating percentage saturation of the O_2-carrying power of hemoglobin to the P_{O_2} (Fig 35–2), has a characteristic sigmoid shape. Combination of the first heme in the Hb molecule with O_2 increases the affinity of the second heme for O_2, and oxygenation of the second increases the affinity of the third, etc, so that the affinity of Hb for the fourth O_2 molecule is many times that for the first. When hemoglobin takes up O_2, the 2 β chains move closer together; when O_2 is given up, they move farther apart. This shift is essential for the shift in affinity for O_2 to occur.

When blood is equilibrated with 100% O_2 (P_{O_2} = 760 mm Hg), the hemoglobin becomes 100% saturated. When fully saturated, each gram of hemoglobin contains 1.34 ml of O_2. The hemoglobin concentration in normal blood is about 15 g/dl (14 g/dl in women and 16 g/dl in men; see Chapter 27). Therefore, 1 dl of blood contains 20.1 ml (1.34 ml × 15) of O_2 bound to hemoglobin when the hemoglobin is 100% saturated. The amount of dissolved O_2 is a linear function of the P_{O_2} (0.003 ml/dl blood/mm Hg P_{O_2}).

In vivo, the hemoglobin in the blood at the ends of the pulmonary capillaries is about 97.5% saturated with O_2 (P_{O_2} = 97 mm Hg). Because of a slight admixture with venous blood that bypasses the lungs (''physiologic shunt''), the hemoglobin in systemic

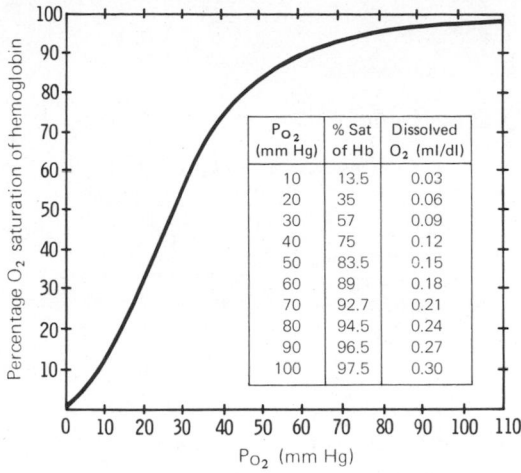

Figure 35–2. Oxygen hemoglobin dissociation curve. pH 7.40, temperature 38 C. (Redrawn and reproduced, with permission, from Comroe JH Jr & others: *The Lung: Clinical Physiology and Pulmonary Function Tests,* 2nd ed. Year Book, 1962.)

arterial blood is only 97% saturated. The arterial blood therefore contains a total of about 19.8 ml of O_2 per dl; 0.29 ml in solution and 19.5 ml bound to hemoglobin. In venous blood at rest, the hemoglobin is 75% saturated, and the total O_2 content is about 15.2 ml/dl. Thus, at rest the tissues remove about 4.6 ml of O_2 from each dl of blood passing through them (Table 35–1); 0.17 ml of this total represents O_2 that was in solution in the blood, and the remainder represents O_2 that was liberated from hemoglobin. In this way, 250 ml of O_2 per minute are transported from the blood to the tissues at rest.

Factors Affecting the Affinity of Hemoglobin for Oxygen

Three important conditions affect the oxygen-hemoglobin dissociation curve: the pH, the temperature, and the concentration of 2,3-diphosphoglycerate (**DPG, 2,3-DPG**). A rise in temperature or a fall in pH

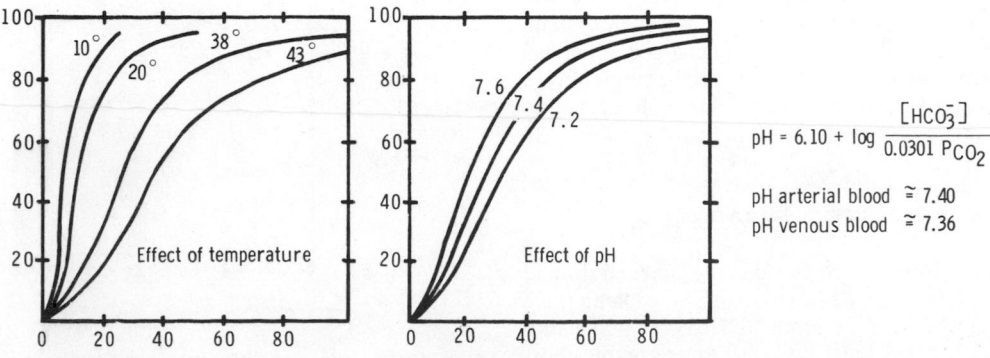

$$pH = 6.10 + \log \frac{[HCO_3^-]}{0.0301\ P_{CO_2}}$$

pH arterial blood $\cong$ 7.40
pH venous blood $\cong$ 7.36

Figure 35–3. Effect of temperature and pH on hemoglobin dissociation curve. Ordinates and abscissas as in Fig 35–2. (Redrawn and reproduced, with permission, from Comroe JH Jr & others: *The Lung: Clinical Physiology and Pulmonary Function Tests,* 2nd ed. Year Book, 1962.)

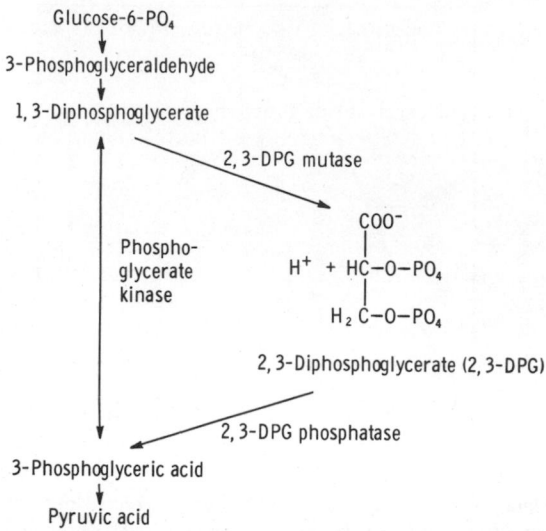

Figure 35-4. Formation and catabolism of 2,3-DPG.

shifts the curve to the right (Fig 35–3). When the curve is shifted in this direction, a higher P_{O_2} is required for hemoglobin to bind a given amount of O_2. Conversely, a fall in temperature or a rise in pH shifts the curve to the left, and a lower P_{O_2} is required to bind a given amount of O_2. A convenient index of such shifts is the P_{50}, the P_{O_2} at which the hemoglobin is half-saturated with O_2; the higher the P_{50}, the lower the affinity of hemoglobin for O_2.

The decrease in O_2 affinity of hemoglobin when the pH of blood falls is called the **Bohr effect** and is closely related to the fact that deoxyhemoglobin binds H^+ more actively than oxyhemoglobin. The pH of blood falls as its CO_2 content increases (see below), so that when the P_{CO_2} rises, the curve shifts to the right and the P_{50} rises. Most of the unsaturation of hemoglobin that occurs in the tissues is secondary to the decline in the P_{O_2}, but an extra 1–2% unsaturation is due to the rise in P_{CO_2} and consequent shift of the dissociation curve to the right.

2,3-DPG is very plentiful in red cells. It is formed (Fig 35–4) from 3-phosphoglyceraldehyde, which is a product of glycolysis via the Embden-Meyerhof pathway (see Chapter 17). It is a highly charged anion that binds to the β chains of deoxygenated hemoglobin but not to those of oxyhemoglobin. One mole of deoxygenated hemoglobin binds 1 mole of 2,3-DPG. In effect:

$$HbO_2 + 2,3\text{-DPG} \rightleftharpoons Hb\text{-}2,3\text{-DPG} + O_2$$

In this equilibrium, an increase in the concentration of 2,3-DPG shifts the reaction to the right, causing more O_2 to be liberated. ATP binds to deoxygenated hemoglobin to a lesser extent, and some other organic phosphates bind to a minor degree.

Factors affecting the concentration of 2,3-DPG in the red cells include pH. Because acidosis inhibits red

cell glycolysis, the 2,3-DPG concentration falls when the pH is low. Thyroid hormones, growth hormone, and androgens increase the concentration of 2,3-DPG and the P_{50}.

Exercise has been reported to produce an increase in 2,3-DPG within 60 minutes, although the rise may not occur in trained athletes. The P_{50} is also increased during exercise because the temperature rises in active tissues and CO_2 and metabolites accumulate, lowering the pH. In addition, much more O_2 is removed from each unit of blood flowing through active tissues because the tissue P_{O_2} declines. Finally, at low P_{O_2} values, the oxygen-hemoglobin dissociation curve is steep, and large amounts of O_2 are liberated per unit drop in P_{O_2}.

Ascent to high altitude triggers a substantial rise in red cell 2,3-DPG concentration, with a consequent increase in P_{50} and increase in the availability of O_2 to tissues. The rise in 2,3-DPG, which has a half-life of 6 hours, is secondary to the rise in blood pH (see Chapter 37). 2,3-DPG levels drop to normal upon return to sea level.

The greater affinity of fetal hemoglobin (hemoglobin F) than adult hemoglobin (hemoglobin A) for O_2 facilitates the movement of O_2 from the mother to the fetus (see Chapters 27 and 32). The cause of this greater affinity is the poor binding of 2,3-DPG by the γ polypeptide chains that replace β chains in fetal hemoglobin. The changes in P_{50} produced by 2,3-DPG in hemoglobin F and hemoglobin A are shown in Fig 35–5. Some abnormal hemoglobins found in adults also have low P_{50} values, and the resulting high O_2 affinity of the hemoglobin causes enough tissue hypoxia to stimulate increased red cell formation, with resulting polycythemia (see Chapter 24). It is interesting to speculate that these hemoglobins may not bind 2,3-DPG.

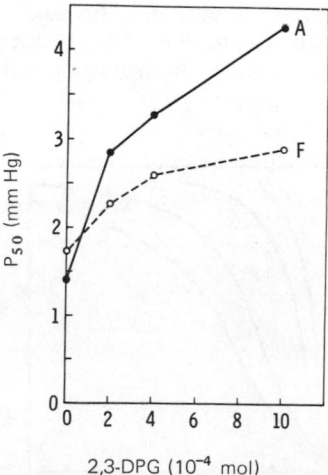

Figure 35-5. Effect of 2,3-DPG on P_{50} values for human fetal (F) and adult (A) hemoglobin. (Reproduced, with permission, from Bunn HF, Jandl JH: Control of hemoglobin function within the red cell. N Engl J Med 282:1414, 1970.)

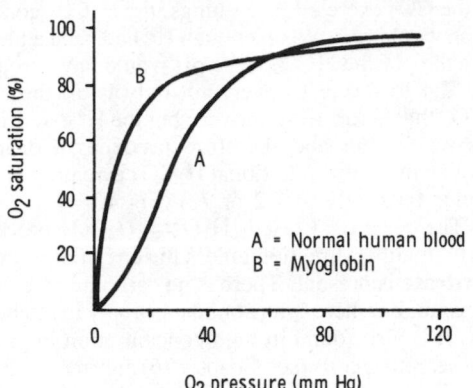

Figure 35–6. Dissociation curve of oxyhemoglobin and myoglobin at 38 C, pH 7.40. (Redrawn and reproduced, with permission, from Roughton FJW: *Handbook of Respiratory Physiology.* USAF School of Aviation Medicine, 1954.)

Red cell 2,3-DPG concentration is increased in anemia and in a variety of diseases in which there is chronic hypoxia. This facilitates the delivery of O_2 to the tissues by raising the P_{O_2} at which O_2 is released in peripheral capillaries. In bank blood that is stored, the 2,3-DPG level falls, and the ability of this blood to release O_2 to the tissues is consequently reduced. This decrease, which obviously limits the benefit of the blood if it is transfused into a hypoxic patient, is less if the blood is stored in citrate-phosphate-dextrose solution rather than the usual acid-citrate-dextrose solution.

Other aspects of the chemistry of hemoglobin are discussed in Chapter 27. Fetal hemoglobin and transplacental O_2 exchange are discussed in Chapter 32.

Myoglobin

Myoglobin is an iron-containing pigment found in skeletal muscle. It resembles hemoglobin but binds one rather than 4 mol of O_2 per mole. Its dissociation curve is a rectangular hyperbola rather than a sigmoid curve. Because its curve is to the left of the hemoglobin curve (Fig 35–6), it takes up O_2 from hemoglobin in the blood. It releases O_2 only at low P_{O_2} values, but the P_{O_2} in exercising muscle is close to zero. The myoglobin content is greatest in muscles specialized for sustained contraction. The muscle blood supply is compressed during such contractions, and myoglobin may provide O_2 when blood flow is cut off. There is also evidence that myoglobin facilitates the diffusion of O_2 from the blood to the mitochondria, where the oxidative reactions occur.

BUFFERS IN BLOOD

Since CO_2 forms carbonic acid in the blood, a discussion of the buffer systems in the blood is a necessary preliminary to a consideration of CO_2 transport.

The Henderson-Hasselbalch Equation

The general equation for a buffer system is

$$HA \rightleftharpoons H^+ + A^-$$

A^- represents any anion, and HA the undissociated acid. If an acid stronger than HA is added to a solution containing this system, the equilibrium is shifted to the left. Hydrogen ions are "tied up" in the formation of more undissociated HA, so the increase in H^+ concentration is much less than it would otherwise be. Conversely, if a base is added to the solution, H^+ and OH^- react to form H_2O; but more HA dissociates, limiting the decrease in H^+ concentration. By the law of mass action, the product of the concentrations of the products in a chemical reaction divided by the product of the concentration of the reactants at equilibrium is a constant.

$$\frac{[H^+]\,[A^-]}{[HA]} = K$$

If this equation is solved for H^+ and put in pH notation (pH is the negative log of $[H^+]$), the resulting equation is that originally derived by Henderson and Hasselbalch to describe the pH changes resulting from addition of H^+ or OH^- to any buffer system (**Henderson-Hasselbalch equation**):

$$pH = pK + \log\frac{[A^-]}{[HA]}$$

It is apparent from these equations that the buffering capacity of a system is greatest when the amount of free anion is equal to the amount of undissociated HA, ie, when $[A^-]/[HA] = 1$, so that $\log [A^-]/[HA] = 0$ and pH = pK. This is why the most effective buffers in the body would be expected to be those with pKs close to the pH in which they operate. The pH of the blood is normally 7.40; that of the cells is probably about 7.2; and that of the urine varies from 4.5 to 8.0.

Buffers in Blood

In the blood, proteins—particularly the **plasma proteins**—are effective buffers because both their free carboxyl and their free amino groups dissociate.

$$RCOOH \rightleftharpoons RCOO^- + H^+$$

$$pH = pK_{RCOOH} + \log\frac{[RCOO^-]}{[RCOOH]}$$

$$RNH_3^+ \rightleftharpoons RNH_2 + H^+$$

$$pH = pK_{RNH_3^+} + \log\frac{[RNH_2]}{[RNH_3^+]}$$

Another important buffer system is provided by the dissociation of the imidazole groups of the histidine residues in **hemoglobin**.

Indeed, in the pH 7.0–7.7 range, the free carboxyl and amino groups of hemoglobin contribute relatively little to its buffering capacity. However, the hemoglobin molecule contains 38 histidine residues, and on this basis—plus the fact that it is present in large amounts—the hemoglobin in blood has 6 times the buffering capacity of the plasma proteins. In addition, the action of hemoglobin is unique because the imidazole groups of deoxygenated hemoglobin dissociate less than those of oxyhemoglobin, making Hb a weaker acid and therefore a better buffer than HbO_2. Titration curves for Hb and HbO_2 are shown in Fig 35–7.

The third major buffer system in blood is the **carbonic acid–bicarbonate** system:

$$H_2CO_3 \rightleftarrows H^+ + HCO_3^-$$

$$pH = pK_{H_2CO_3} + \log \frac{[HCO_3^-]}{[H_2CO_3]}$$

The pK of this system is low relative to blood pH, and yet it is one of the most effective systems because the H_2CO_3 level in plasma is in equilibrium with dissolved CO_2, and the amount of dissolved CO_2 is controlled by respiration:

$$H_2CO_3 \rightleftarrows CO_2 + H_2O$$

In addition, the plasma concentration of HCO_3^- is regulated by the kidneys. When H^+ is added to the blood, HCO_3^- declines as more H_2CO_3 is formed. If the extra H_2CO_3 were not converted to CO_2 and H_2O

and the CO_2 excreted in the lungs, the H_2CO_3 concentration would rise. When enough H^+ had been added to halve the plasma HCO_3^-, the pH would have dropped from 7.4 to 6.0. However, not only is all the extra H_2CO_3 that is formed removed, but the H^+ rise stimulates respiration and therefore produces a drop in P_{CO_2}, so that some additional H_2CO_3 is removed. The pH thus falls only to 7.2 or 7.3 (Fig 40–4).

The reaction $CO_2 + H_2O \rightleftarrows H_2CO_3$ proceeds slowly in either direction unless the enzyme **carbonic anhydrase** is present. There is no carbonic anhydrase in plasma, but there is an abundant supply in red blood cells. It is also found in high concentration in gastric acid–secreting cells (see Chapter 26) and in renal tubular cells (see Chapter 38). Carbonic anhydrase is a protein with a molecular weight of 30,000 that contains an atom of zinc in each molecule. It is inhibited by cyanide, azide, and sulfide. The sulfonamides also inhibit this enzyme, and sulfonamide derivatives have been used clinically as diuretics because of their inhibitory effects on carbonic anhydrase in the kidney (see Chapter 38).

The system $H_2PO_4^- \rightleftarrows H^+ + HPO_4^{2-}$ has a pK of 6.80. In the plasma, the phosphate concentration is too low for this system to be a quantitatively important buffer, but in the urine it frequently plays a significant role (see Chapter 38).

Buffering in Vivo

Buffering in vivo is of course not limited to the blood. Indeed, in metabolic acidosis, only 15–20% of the acid load is buffered by the H_2CO_3-HCO_3^- system in the interstitial fluid, and the remainder is buffered in cells. The principal intracellular buffers are proteins and organic phosphates. They bind H^+ and liberate Na^+ and K^+; thus, in acidosis, the total extracellular Na^+ and K^+ rise. In metabolic alkalosis, about 30–35% of the OH^- load is buffered in cells, whereas in respiratory acidosis and alkalosis (see Chapter 40) almost all the buffering is intracellular.

Summary

When a strong acid is added to the blood, the 3 major buffer reactions are driven to the left.

$$\begin{aligned}
HHb &\rightleftarrows H^+ + Hb^- \\
HProt &\rightleftarrows H^+ + Prot^- \\
H_2CO_3 &\rightleftarrows H^+ + HCO_3^-
\end{aligned}$$

The blood levels of the 3 "buffer anions"—Hb^- (hemoglobin), $Prot^-$ (protein), and HCO_3^-—consequently drop (Fig 35–8). The anions of the added acid are filtered into the renal tubules. They are accompanied ("covered") by cations, particularly Na^+, because electrochemical neutrality is maintained. By processes that are discussed in Chapter 38, the tubules replace the Na^+ with H^+ and in so doing reabsorb equimolar amounts of Na^+ and HCO_3^-, thus conserving the cations, eliminating the acid, and restoring the supply of buffer anions to normal. When CO_2 is added

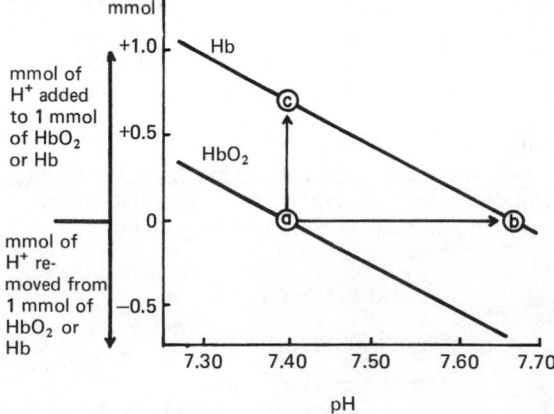

Figure 35–7. Titration curves of Hb and HbO_2. The arrow from *a* to *c* indicates the mmol of H^+ that can be added without pH shift. The arrow from *a* to *b* indicates the pH shift on deoxygenation. (Modified from Davenport HW: *The ABC of Acid-Base Chemistry*, 6th ed. Univ of Chicago Press, 1974.)

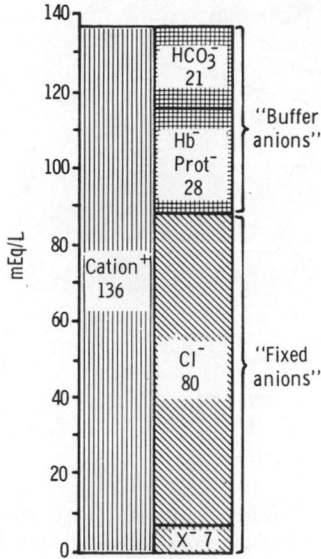

Figure 35–8. Distribution of cations and anions in whole blood, pH 7.39, P_{CO_2} 41 mm Hg. Hb⁻, hemoglobin; Prot⁻, plasma protein; X⁻, remaining anions. (Reproduced, with permission, from Singer RB, in Altman PL & others: *Handbook of Respiration.* Saunders, 1958.)

to the blood, similar reactions occur, except that since it is H_2CO_3 that is formed, the plasma HCO_3^- rises rather than falls.

CARBON DIOXIDE TRANSPORT

Fate of Carbon Dioxide in Blood

The solubility of CO_2 in blood is about 20 times that of O_2, so that there is considerably more CO_2 than O_2 in simple solution. The CO_2 that diffuses into red blood cells is rapidly hydrated to H_2CO_3 because of the presence of carbonic anhydrase. The H_2CO_3 dissociates to H^+ and HCO_3^-, and the H^+ is buffered, primarily by hemoglobin, while the HCO_3^- diffuses into the plasma. The decline in the O_2 saturation of the hemoglobin as the blood passes through the tissue capillaries improves its buffering capacity because deoxygenated hemoglobin binds more H^+ than oxyhemoglobin (see above). Some of the CO_2 in the red cells reacts with the amino groups of proteins, principally hemoglobin, to form **carbamino compounds:**

$$CO_2 + R-N\begin{matrix}H\\ \\H\end{matrix} \rightleftharpoons R-N\begin{matrix}H\\ \\COOH\end{matrix}$$

At P_{CO_2} values above 10 mm Hg, the amount of carbamino-Hb formed is relatively constant and inde-

pendent of the P_{CO_2} because the tendency to form more as the amount of available CO_2 increases is offset by the formation of more H^+, which ties up RNH_2 groups by forming RNH_3^+. Since deoxygenated hemoglobin forms carbamino compounds much more readily than HbO_2, transport of CO_2 is facilitated in venous blood. About 20% of the CO_2 added to the blood in the systemic capillaries is carried to the lungs as carbamino-CO_2.

In the plasma, CO_2 reacts with plasma proteins to form small amounts of carbamino compounds, and small amounts of CO_2 are hydrated; but the hydration reaction is slow in the absence of carbonic anhydrase.

Chloride Shift

Since the rise in the HCO_3^- content of red cells is much greater than that in plasma as the blood passes through the capillaries, HCO_3^- diffuses into the plasma. About 70% of the HCO_3^- formed in the red cells enters the plasma. Normally, the protein anions cannot cross the cell membrane, and owing to the operation of the sodium-potassium pump, Na^+ and K^+ do not diffuse freely. Electrochemical neutrality is maintained by diffusion of Cl^- into the red cells (the **chloride shift**). The Cl^- content of the red cells in venous blood is therefore significantly greater than in arterial blood. The chloride shift occurs rapidly and is essentially complete in 1 s.

Because there are many negative charges on each protein molecule but only one on each HCO_3^- and Cl^-, the number of osmotically active particles in the red cells increases as the hydrogen ions are buffered and the HCO_3^- accumulates (Fig 35–9). The red cells take up water, and the resultant increase in red cell size is the reason the hematocrit of venous blood is normally 3% greater than that of the arterial blood. In the lungs, the Cl^- moves out of the cells and they shrink.

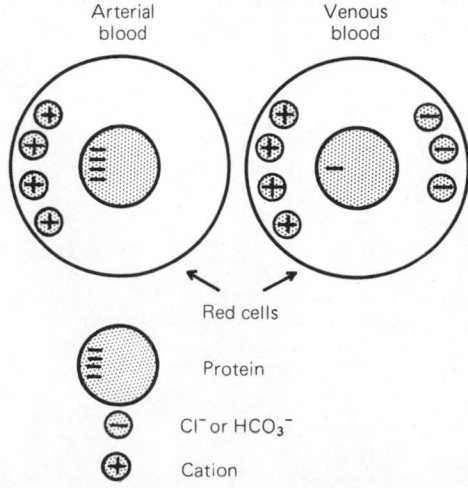

Figure 35–9. Simplified scheme showing why there are more osmotically active particles in the red cells in venous blood than in arterial blood. For explanation, see text.

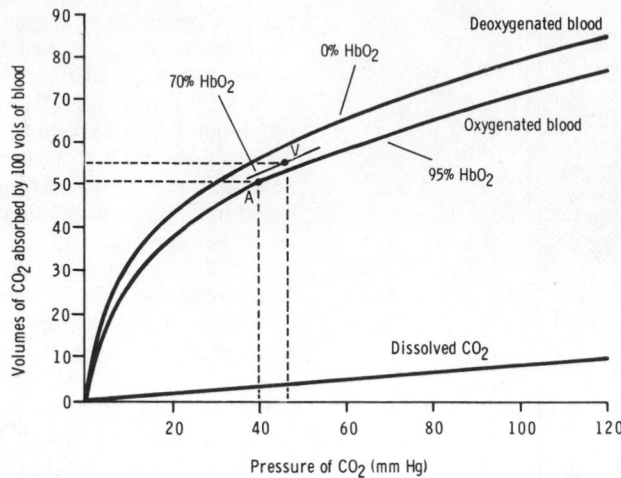

Figure 35–10. CO_2 dissociation curves. The arterial point (A) and the venous point (V) indicate the total CO_2 content found in arterial blood and venous blood of normal resting humans. (Modified and reproduced, with permission, from Kinney JM: Transport of carbon dioxide in blood. Anesthesiology 21:615, 1960.)

Summary of Carbon Dioxide Transport

For convenience, the various fates of CO_2 in the plasma and red cells are summarized in Table 35–2. The extent to which they increase the capacity of the blood to carry CO_2 is indicated by the difference between the dissolved CO_2 line and the total CO_2 content lines in the dissociation curves for CO_2 shown in Fig 35–10.

Of the approximately 49 ml of CO_2 in each dl of arterial blood (Table 35–1), 2.6 ml are dissolved, 2.6 ml are in carbamino compounds, and 43.8 ml are in HCO_3^-. In the tissues, 3.7 ml of CO_2 per dl of blood are added; 0.4 ml stays in solution, 0.8 ml forms carbamino compounds, and 2.5 ml form HCO_3^-. The pH of the blood drops from 7.40 to 7.36. In the lungs, the processes are reversed, and the 3.7 ml of CO_2 are discharged into the alveoli. In this fashion, 200 ml of CO_2 per minute at rest and much larger amounts during exercise are transported from the tissues to the lungs and excreted. It is worth noting that this amount of CO_2 is equivalent in 24 hours to over 12,500 mEq of H^+.

Table 35–2. Fate of CO_2 in blood.

In plasma
  1. Dissolved
  2. Formation of carbamino compounds with plasma protein
  3. Hydration, H^+ buffered, HCO_3^- in plasma
In red blood cells
  1. Dissolved
  2. Formation of carbamino-Hb
  3. Hydration, H^+ buffered, 70% of HCO_3^- diffuses into plasma
  4. Cl^- shifts into cells; mOsm/L in cells increases

NEURAL CONTROL OF BREATHING

Control Systems

Spontaneous respiration is produced by rhythmic discharge of the motor neurons that innervate the respiratory muscles. This discharge is totally dependent on nerve impulses from the brain; breathing stops if the spinal cord is transected above the origin of the phrenic nerves.

Two separate neural mechanisms regulate respiration. One is responsible for voluntary control and the other for automatic control. The voluntary system is located in the cerebral cortex and sends impulses to the respiratory motor neurons via the corticospinal tracts. The automatic system is located in the pons and medulla, and the motor outflow from this system to the respiratory motor neurons is located in the lateral and ventral portions of the spinal cord.

The motor neurons to the expiratory muscles are inhibited when those supplying the inspiratory muscles are active, and vice versa. This **reciprocal innervation** is not due to spinal reflexes and in this regard differs from the reciprocal innervation of the limb flexors and extensors (see Chapter 6). Instead, impulses in descending pathways that excite agonists also produce inhibition of antagonists, probably by exciting inhibitory interneurons.

Medullary Centers

Rhythmic discharge of neurons in the medulla oblongata produces automatic respiration. The area in the medulla that is concerned with respiration has classically been called the **respiratory center,** but there are actually 2 groups of respiratory neurons (Figs 36–1 and 36–2). The **dorsal group** of neurons near the nucleus of the tractus solitarius is the source of rhythmic drive to the contralateral phrenic motor

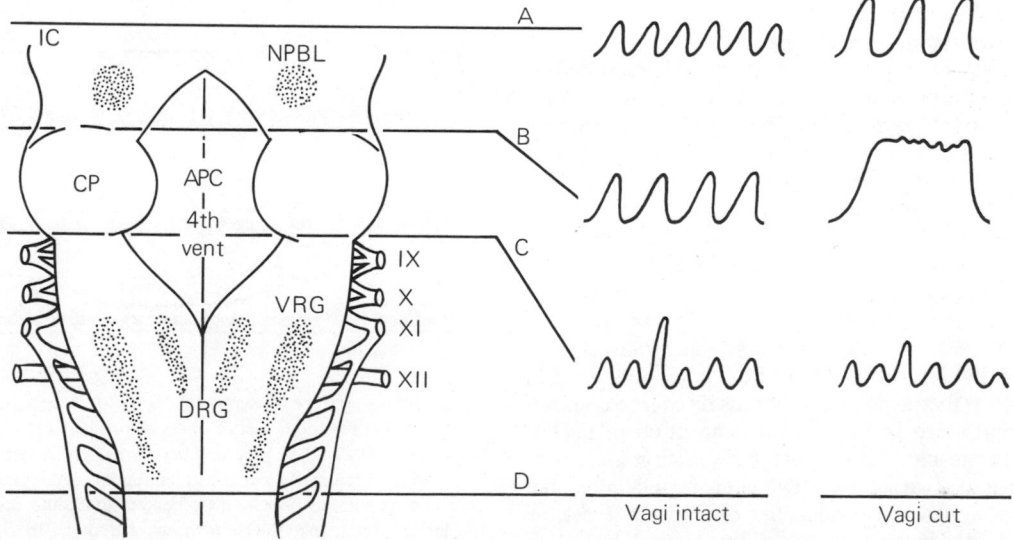

Figure 36–1. Respiratory neurons in the brain stem. Dorsal view of brain stem; cerebellum removed. The effects of transecting the brain stem at various levels are also shown. The spirometer tracings at the right indicate the depth and rate of breathing, and the letters identify the level of transection. DRG, dorsal group of respiratory neurons; VRG, ventral group of respiratory neurons; NPBL, nucleus parabrachialis (pneumotaxic center); APC, apneustic center; 4th vent, fourth ventricle; IC, inferior colliculus; CP, middle cerebellar peduncle. (Modified and reproduced, with permission, from Mitchell RA, Berger A: State of the art: Review of neural regulation of respiration. Am Rev Respir Dis 111.206, 1975.)

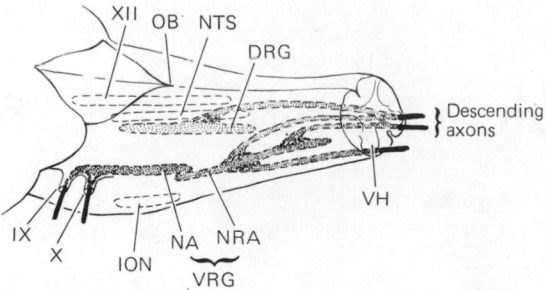

Figure 36-2. Schematic representation of dorsal (DRG) and ventral (VRG) groups of respiratory neurons and their efferent paths in the cat. ION, inferior olivary nucleus; NA, nucleus ambiguus; NRA, nucleus retroambigualis; NTS, nucleus tractus solitarius; OB, obex; VH, ventral horn; IX, X, glossopharyngeal and vagus nerves; XII, hypoglossal nucleus. (Reproduced, with permission, from Mitchell RA, Berger A: State of the art: Review of neural regulation of respiration. Am Rev Respir Dis 111:206, 1975.)

neurons. These neurons also project to and drive the **ventral group.** This group has 2 divisions. The cranial division is made up of neurons in the nucleus ambiguus that innervate the ipsilateral accessory muscles of respiration, principally via the vagus nerves. The caudal division is made up of neurons in the nucleus retroambigualis that provide the inspiratory and expiratory drive to the motor neurons supplying the intercostal muscles. The paths from these neurons to expiratory motor neurons are crossed, but those to inspiratory motor neurons are both crossed and uncrossed (Fig 36-2).

Pontine & Vagal Influences

The rhythmic discharge of the neurons in the respiratory center is spontaneous, but it is modified by centers in the pons and by afferents in the vagus nerves from receptors in the lungs. The interactions of these components can be analyzed by evaluating the results of the experiments summarized diagrammatically in Fig 36-1. Complete transection of the brain stem below the medulla (section D in Fig 36-1) stops all respiration. When all of the cranial nerves (including the vagi) are cut and the brain stem is transected above the pons (section A in Fig 36-1), regular breathing continues. However, when an additional transection is made in the inferior portion of the pons (section B in Fig 36-1), the inspiratory neurons discharge continuously and there is a sustained contraction of the inspiratory muscles. This arrest of respiration in inspiration is called **apneusis.** The area in the pons that prevents apneusis is called the **pneumotaxic center** and is located in the nucleus parabrachialis. The area in the caudal pons responsible for apneusis is called the **apneustic center.**

When the brain stem is transected in the inferior portion of the pons and the vagus nerves are left intact, regular respiration continues. In an apneustic animal, stimulation of the proximal stump of one of the cut vagi

produces, after a moderate latent period, a relatively prolonged inhibition of inspiratory neuron discharge (Fig 36-3). There are stretch receptors in the lung parenchyma that relay to the medulla via afferents in the vagi, and rapid inflation of the lung inhibits inspiratory discharge (Hering-Breuer reflex; see below). Thus, stretching of the lungs during inspiration reflexly inhibits inspiratory drive, reinforcing the action of the pneumotaxic center in producing intermittency of inspiratory neuron discharge. This is why the depth of inspiration is increased after vagotomy in otherwise intact experimental animals, although breathing continues as long as the pneumotaxic center is intact.

When all pontine tissue is separated from the medulla (section C in Fig 36-1), respiration continues whether or not the vagi are intact. This respiration is somewhat irregular and gasping, but it is rhythmic. Its occurrence demonstrates that the respiratory center neurons are capable of spontaneous rhythmic discharge.

The precise physiologic role of the pontine respiratory areas is uncertain, but they apparently make the rhythmic discharge of the medullary neurons smooth and regular. It appears that there are tonically discharging neurons in the apneustic center which drive inspiratory neurons in the medulla, and these neurons are intermittently inhibited by impulses in afferents from the pneumotaxic center and vagal afferents.

Genesis & Regulation of Rhythmicity

The exact mechanism responsible for the spontaneous discharge of the medullary neurons is also uncertain, although recurrent collateral inhibition and a mechanism similar to that producing synchronous discharge of thalamic neurons may be involved (see

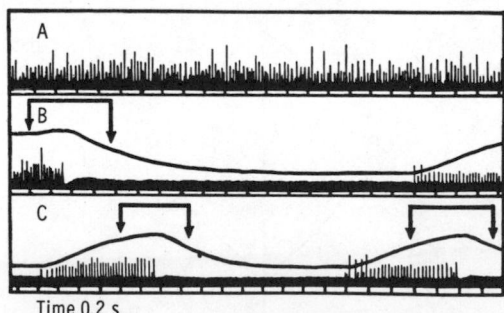

Time 0.2 s

Figure 36-3. Effect of vagal stimulation (between arrows) on discharge rate in phrenic nerve fibers in an "isolated inspiratory center preparation." The cat had been prepared by cutting both vagi and transecting the medulla at the caudal border of the pons, thus cutting off the pneumotaxic center. In *A*, the continuous discharge of the inspiratory neurons is shown. In *B* and *C*, stimulation of the proximal stump of one vagus produces, after a considerable latent period, inhibition of inspiratory discharge. The animal exhales when the inspiratory discharge stops, as is shown by the record of respiratory excursions (upper line in *B* and *C*; inspiration upward). (Reproduced, with permission, from Pitts RF: The function of components of the respiratory complex. J Neurophysiol 5:407, 1942.)

Chapter 11). The neurons of the ventral respiratory group are driven by neurons in the dorsal respiratory group, so respiratory rhythmicity does not originate in the ventral group. In intact animals, the inspiratory neurons are characterized by bursts of activity interspersed with periods of quiescence 12–15 times per minute. Unlike the inspiratory neurons, the expiratory neurons do not discharge spontaneously, but they can be excited via afferents that converge on them and the inspiratory neurons from many sources.

When the activity of the inspiratory neurons is increased in intact animals, the rate and the depth of breathing are increased. The depth of respiration is increased because the lungs are stretched to a greater degree before the amount of vagal and pneumotaxic center inhibitory activity is sufficient to overcome the more intense inspiratory neuron discharge. The respiratory rate is increased because the after-discharge in the vagal and pneumotaxic afferents is rapidly overcome.

REGULATION OF RESPIRATORY CENTER ACTIVITY

A rise in the P_{CO_2} or H^+ concentration of arterial blood or a drop in its P_{O_2} increases the level of respiratory center activity, and changes in the opposite direction have a slight inhibitory effect. The effects of variations in blood chemistry on ventilation are mediated via respiratory **chemoreceptors**—receptor cells in the medulla and the carotid and aortic bodies sensitive to changes in the chemistry of the blood which initiate impulses that stimulate the respiratory center. Superimposed on this basic **chemical control of respiration,** other afferents provide nonchemical controls for the ''fine adjustments'' that affect breathing in particular situations (Table 36–1).

CHEMICAL CONTROL OF BREATHING

The chemical regulatory mechanisms adjust ventilation in such a way that the alveolar P_{CO_2} is normally held constant, the effects of excess H^+ in the blood are combated, and the P_{O_2} is raised when it falls to a potentially dangerous level. The respiratory minute volume is proportionate to the metabolic rate, but the link between metabolism and ventilation is CO_2, not O_2. The receptors in the carotid and aortic bodies are stimulated by a rise in the P_{CO_2} or H^+ concentration of arterial blood or a decline in its P_{O_2}. After denervation of the carotid chemoreceptors, the response to a drop in P_{O_2} is abolished; the predominant effect of hypoxia after denervation of the carotid bodies is a direct depression of the respiratory center. The response to

Table 36–1. Stimuli affecting the respiratory center.

Chemical control

CO_2 (via CSF H^+ concentration)

$\left.\begin{array}{l} O_2 \\ H^+ \end{array}\right\}$ (via carotid and aortic bodies)

Nonchemical control

Afferents from proprioceptors

Afferents for sneezing, coughing, swallowing, yawning

Vagal afferents from inflation and deflation receptors

Afferents from baroreceptors: arterial, atrial, ventricular, pulmonary

changes in arterial blood H^+ concentration in the pH 7.3–7.5 range is also abolished, although larger changes do exert some effect. The response to changes in arterial P_{CO_2}, on the other hand, is affected only slightly; it is reduced no more than 20%.

Carotid & Aortic Bodies

There is a carotid body near the carotid bifurca-

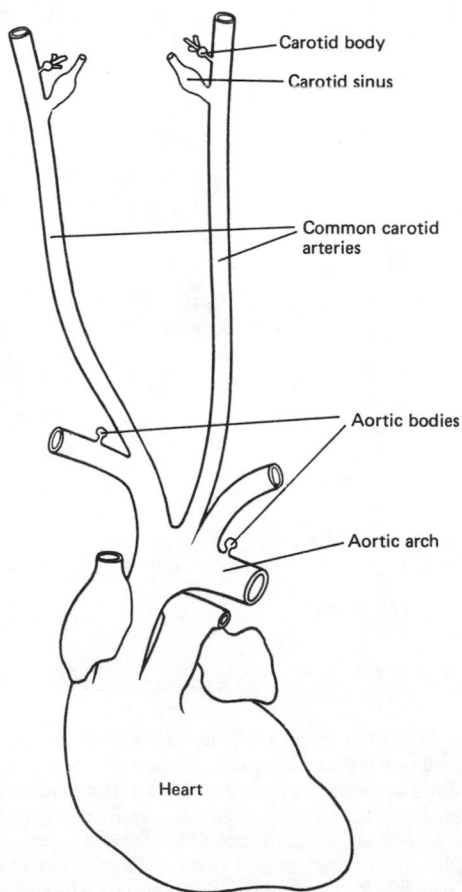

Figure 36–4. Location of carotid and aortic bodies.

tion on each side, and there are usually 2 or more aortic bodies near the arch of the aorta (Fig 36–4). Each carotid and aortic body, or **glomus,** contains islands of 2 types of cells, surrounded by sinusoidal vessels. The cell types have received various names, but it seems wise to simply refer to them as type I and type II cells. The type II cells, which are probably glial cells, surround the type I cells. Unmyelinated endings of glossopharyngeal nerve fibers are found at intervals between the type I and type II cells. There is reason to believe that the chemoreceptors which sense O_2 tension are these nerve endings. The type I cells contain a catecholamine, probably dopamine, and may make reciprocal synaptic connections with the nerve endings (Fig 36–5). Dopamine inhibits discharge in the carotid body nerves, and it is postulated that the type I cells modulate the responses of the nerve endings to hypoxia. However, the glomus cells are not necessary for carotid body function, since the neuroma that forms on the stump of the glossopharyngeal nerve after the carotid body is removed is sensitive to hypoxia and increased CO_2 in the absence of glomus cells.

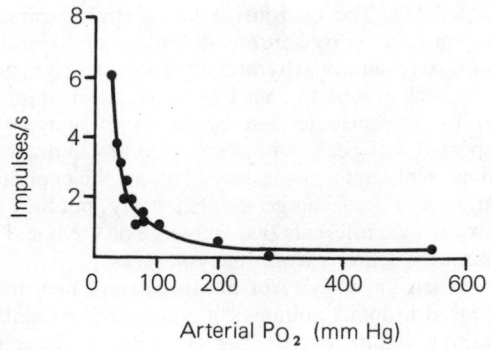

Figure 36–6. Change in rate of discharge of a single afferent fiber from the carotid body when $P_{A_{O_2}}$ is reduced. (Courtesy of S Sampson.)

Outside the capsule of each body, the nerve fibers acquire a myelin sheath; however, they are only 2–5 μm in diameter and conduct at the relatively slow rate of 7–12 m/s. Afferents from the carotid bodies ascend to the medulla via the carotid sinus and glossopharyngeal nerves, and fibers from the aortic bodies ascend in the vagi. Studies in which one carotid body has been isolated and perfused while recordings are being taken from its afferent nerve fibers show that there is a graded increase in impulse traffic in these afferent fibers as the P_{O_2} of the perfusing blood is lowered (Fig 36–6) or the P_{CO_2} raised.

The blood flow in each 2 mg carotid body is about 0.04 ml/min, or 2000 ml/100 g of tissue per minute, compared with a blood flow per 100 g/min of 54 ml in the brain and 420 ml in the kidney (Table 32–1). Because the blood flow per unit of tissue is so enormous, the O_2 needs of the cells can be met largely by dissolved O_2 alone. Therefore, the receptors are not stimulated in conditions such as anemia and carbon monoxide poisoning, in which the amount of dissolved O_2 in the blood reaching the receptors is generally normal even though the combined O_2 in the blood is markedly decreased. The receptors are stimulated when the arterial P_{O_2} is low or when, because of vascular stasis, the amount of O_2 delivered to the receptors per unit of time is decreased. Powerful stimulation is also produced by drugs such as cyanide, which prevent O_2 utilization at the tissue level. In sufficient doses, nicotine and lobeline activate the chemoreceptors.

Because of their anatomic location, the aortic bodies have not been studied in as great detail as the carotid bodies. Their responses are probably similar but of lesser magnitude. In humans in whom both carotid bodies have been removed but the aortic bodies have been left intact, the responses are essentially the same as those following denervation of both carotid and aortic bodies in animals; there is little change in ventilation at rest, but the ventilatory response to hypoxia is lost and there is a 30% reduction in the ventilatory responses to CO_2. The humans who were studied had their carotid bodies removed in an effort to

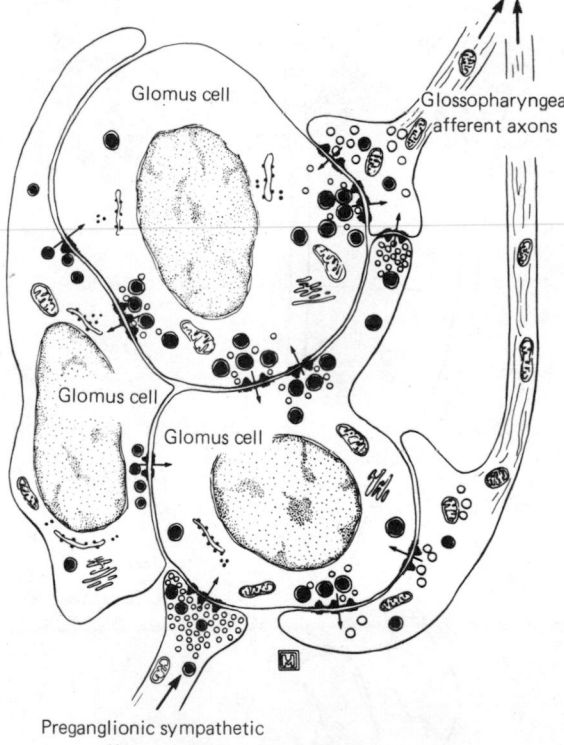

Figure 36–5. Organization of the carotid body. According to the view illustrated here, which is based on studies in the rat, there are reciprocal synapses (arrows) between the afferent neurons and the glomus cells. The glomus cells also receive a preganglionic sympathetic innervation. (Reproduced from McDonald DM, Mitchell RA: The innervation of glomus cells, ganglion cells, and blood vessels in the rat carotid body: A quantitative ultrastructural study. J Neurocytol 4:177, 1975. By permission from Chapman & Hall Ltd.)

relieve severe asthma, but it now appears that bilateral carotid body resection is of little benefit in this disease. It is interesting that subjects without carotid bodies can hold their breath longer than normal individuals. This suggests that impulses from the peripheral chemoreceptors contribute to the sensations that determine the breaking point when breath can be held no longer.

Chemoreceptors in the Brain Stem

The chemoreceptors that mediate the hyperventilation produced by increases in arterial P_{CO_2} after the carotid and aortic bodies are denervated are located near the respiratory center itself but separate from it. The response to CO_2, for example, is depressed during anesthesia and natural sleep, but the response to hypoxia is unchanged. This experimental observation indicates that CO_2 does not act directly on the inspiratory neurons.

The medullary chemoreceptors are now believed to be located on the ventral surface of the brain stem (Fig 36–7) and to monitor the H^+ concentration of the cerebrospinal fluid or, possibly, the brain interstitial fluid. CO_2 readily penetrates membranes, including the blood-brain and blood-CSF barriers, whereas H^+ and HCO_3^- penetrate slowly. The CO_2 that enters the brain and CSF is promptly hydrated. The H_2CO_3 dissociates, so that the local H^+ concentration rises. The spinal fluid H^+ concentration parallels the arterial P_{CO_2}. Experimentally produced changes in the P_{CO_2} of spinal fluid have minor, variable effects on respiration as long as the H^+ is held constant, but any increase in spinal fluid H^+ concentration stimulates respiration. The magnitude of the stimulation is proportionate to the rise in H^+. Thus, the effects of CO_2 on respiration

are mainly due to its movement into the spinal fluid, where it increases the H^+ concentration and stimulates receptors sensitive to H^+.

Pulmonary & Myocardial "Chemoreceptors"

Bradycardia and hypotension produced by injections of veratridine and nicotine into the coronary circulation (Bezold-Jarisch reflex) and the pulmonary circulation are due to stimulation of "chemoreceptors" of some type in the coronary and pulmonary vessels (see Chapter 31). Such injections also produce brief periods of respiratory arrest **(apnea),** but the effects on respiration of stimuli from these receptors in physiologic situations are probably insignificant.

Ventilatory Responses to Changes in Acid-Base Balance

In metabolic acidosis due, for example, to the accumulation of the acid ketone bodies in the circulation in diabetes mellitus, there is pronounced respiratory stimulation (Kussmaul breathing; see Chapter 19). The hyperventilation decreases alveolar P_{CO_2} ("blows off CO_2") and thus produces a compensatory fall in blood H^+ concentration (see Chapter 40). Conversely, in metabolic alkalosis due, for example, to protracted vomiting with loss of HCl from the body, ventilation is depressed and the arterial P_{CO_2} rises, raising the H^+ concentration toward normal (see Chapter 40). If there is an increase in ventilation that is not secondary to a rise in arterial H^+ concentration, the drop in P_{CO_2} lowers the H^+ concentration below normal **(respiratory alkalosis);** conversely, hypoventilation that is not secondary to a fall in plasma H^+ concentration causes **respiratory acidosis.**

Ventilatory Responses to CO_2

When there is a rise in arterial P_{CO_2} due to increased tissue metabolism, ventilation is stimulated and the rate of pulmonary excretion of CO_2 is increased until the arterial P_{CO_2} falls to normal, shutting off the stimulus. The operation of this feedback mechanism keeps CO_2 excretion and production in balance.

When a gas mixture containing CO_2 is inhaled, the alveolar P_{CO_2} rises, elevating the arterial P_{CO_2} and stimulating ventilation as soon as the blood that contains more CO_2 reaches the medulla. CO_2 elimination is increased, and the alveolar P_{CO_2} drops toward normal. This is why relatively large increments in the P_{CO_2} of inspired air (eg, 15 mm Hg) produce relatively slight increments in alveolar P_{CO_2} (eg, 3 mm Hg). However, the P_{CO_2} does not drop to normal, and a new equilibrium is reached at which the alveolar P_{CO_2} is slightly elevated and the hyperventilation persists as long as CO_2 is inhaled. The essentially linear relationship between respiratory minute volume and the alveolar P_{CO_2} is shown in Fig 36–8.

There is, of course, an upper limit to this linearity. When the P_{CO_2} of the inspired gas is close to the alveolar P_{CO_2}, elimination of CO_2 becomes difficult. When the CO_2 content of the inspired gas is more than 7%, the alveolar and arterial P_{CO_2} begin to rise

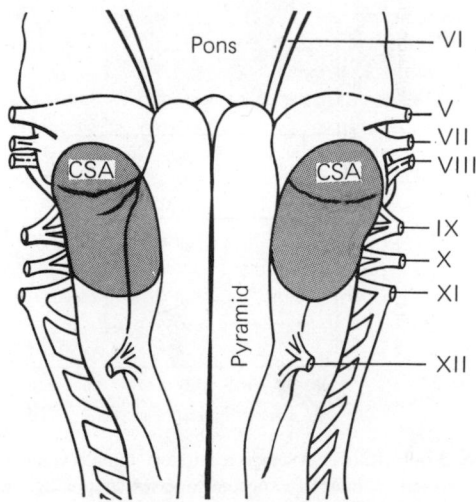

Figure 36–7. Chemosensitive areas (CSA) on the ventral surface of the medulla. (Modified and reproduced, with permission, from Mitchell RA, Severinghaus JW: Cerebrospinal fluid and regulation of respiration. Physiol Physicians, Vol 3, No. 3, 1965.)

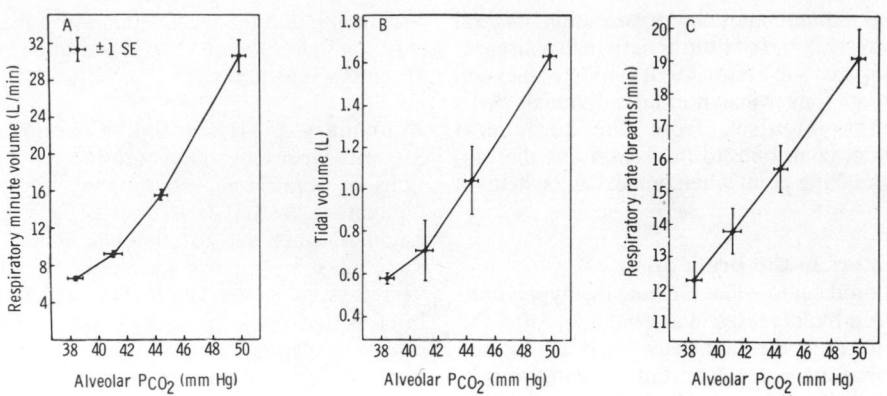

Figure 36–8. Responses of normal subjects to inhaling 0 and approximately 2, 4, and 6% CO_2. Note that the increase in respiratory minute volume *(A)* is due to an increase in both the depth *(B)* and rate *(C)* of respiration. (Reproduced, with permission, from Lambertsen CJ in: *Medical Physiology,* 13th ed. Mountcastle VB [editor]. Mosby, 1974.)

abruptly in spite of hyperventilation. The resultant accumulation of CO_2 in the body **(hypercapnia)** depresses the CNS, including the respiratory center, and produces headache, confusion, and, eventually, coma **(CO_2 narcosis).**

Ventilatory Response to Oxygen Lack

When the O_2 content of the inspired air is decreased, there is an increase in respiratory minute volume. The stimulation is slight when the P_{O_2} of the inspired air is more than 60 mm Hg, and marked stimulation of respiration occurs only at lower P_{O_2} values (Fig 36–9). However, any decline in arterial P_{O_2} below 100 mm Hg produces increased discharge in the nerves from the carotid and aortic chemoreceptors. There are 2 reasons why in normal individuals this increase in impulse traffic does not increase ventilation to any extent until the P_{O_2} is less than 60 mm Hg. Because Hb is a weaker acid than HbO_2 (see Chapter 35), there is a slight decrease in the H^+ concentration of arterial blood when the arterial P_{O_2} falls and hemoglobin becomes less saturated with O_2. The fall in H^+ concentration tends to inhibit respiration. In addition, any increase in ventilation that does occur lowers the alveolar P_{CO_2}, and this also tends to inhibit respiration. Therefore, the stimulatory effects of hypoxia on ventilation are not clearly manifest until they become strong enough to override the counterbalancing inhibitory effects of a decline in arterial H^+ concentration and P_{CO_2}.

The effects on ventilation of decreasing the alveolar P_{O_2} while holding the alveolar P_{CO_2} constant are shown in Fig 36–10. When the alveolar P_{CO_2} is stabilized at a level 2–3 mm Hg above normal, there is an inverse relationship between ventilation and the alveolar P_{O_2} even in the 90–110 mm Hg range; but when the alveolar P_{CO_2} is fixed at lower than normal values there is no stimulation of ventilation by hypoxia until the alveolar P_{O_2} falls below 60 mm Hg.

Effects of Hypoxia on the CO_2 Response Curve

When the converse experiment is performed, ie, when the alveolar P_{O_2} is held constant while the response to varying amounts of inspired CO_2 is tested, it is found that the slope of the CO_2 response curve increases when the alveolar P_{O_2} is decreased (Fig 36–11). In other words, hypoxia makes the individual more sensitive to increases in arterial P_{CO_2}. However, the alveolar P_{CO_2} level at which the curves in Fig 36–11 intersect is unaffected. In the normal individual, this threshold value is just below the normal alveo-

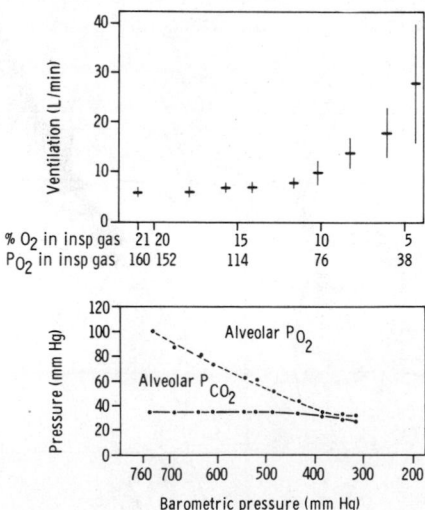

Figure 36–9. *Above:* Average respiratory minute volume during the first half hour of exposure to gases containing various amounts of O_2. The horizontal line in each case indicates the mean; the vertical bar indicates one standard deviation. *Below:* Alveolar P_{O_2} and P_{CO_2} values when breathing air at various barometric pressures. The 2 graphs are aligned so that the P_{O_2}s of the inspired gas mixtures in the upper graph correspond to the P_{O_2}s at the various barometric pressures in the lower graph. (Data from various authors, compiled by RH Kellogg.)

lar P_{CO_2}, indicating that normally there is a very slight but definite "CO_2 drive" of the respiratory center.

Effect of H$^+$ on the CO$_2$ Response

The stimulatory effects of H^+ and CO_2 on respiration appear to be additive and not, like those of CO_2 and O_2, complexly interrelated. Fig 36–11 shows this additive effect; when the subject became acidotic by ingesting NH_4Cl, the CO_2 response curves "shifted to the left" without a change in slope. In other words, the same amount of respiratory stimulation was produced by lower arterial P_{CO_2} levels. It has been calculated that the CO_2 response curve shifts 0.8 mm Hg to the left for each nanomole rise in arterial H^+. About 40% of the ventilatory response to CO_2 is removed if the increase in arterial H^+ produced by CO_2 is prevented. As noted above, the remaining 60% is probably due to the effect of CO_2 on spinal fluid or brain interstitial fluid H^+ concentration.

Breath Holding

Respiration can be voluntarily inhibited for some time, but eventually the voluntary control is overridden. The point at which breathing can no longer be voluntarily inhibited is called the **breaking point.** Breaking is due to the rise in arterial P_{CO_2} and the fall in P_{O_2}. Individuals can hold their breath longer after removal of the carotid bodies (see above). Breathing 100% oxygen before breath holding raises alveolar P_{O_2} initially, so that the breaking point is delayed. The

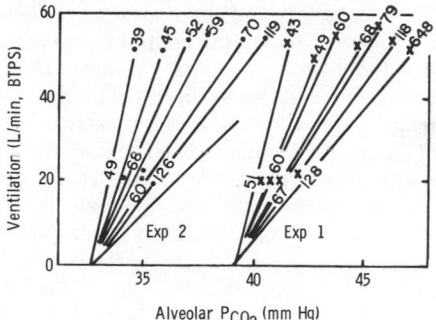

Figure 36-11. Fan of lines representing linear segments of CO_2 response curves at the alveolar P_{O_2} values indicated by the small figures near each line. *Experiment 1:* Control. *Experiment 2:* Metabolic acidosis. (Redrawn and reproduced, with permission, from Cunningham DJC & others: The effect of maintained ammonium chloride acidosis on the relation between pulmonary ventilation and alveolar oxygen and carbon dioxide in man. Q J Exp Physiol 46:323, 1961.)

same is true of hyperventilating room air, because CO_2 is blown off and arterial P_{CO_2} is lower at the start. Reflex or mechanical factors appear to influence the breaking point, since subjects who hold their breath as long as possible and then breathe a gas mixture low in O_2 and high in CO_2 can hold their breath for an additional 20 s or more. Psychic factors also play a role, and subjects can hold their breath longer when they are told their performance is very good than when they are not.

Sudden Infant Death Syndrome

A syndrome that has attracted a great deal of attention in recent years is sudden death in apparently healthy infants **(sudden infant death syndrome).** Characteristically, these children are found dead in their cribs. Apneic spells are common in premature infants and less common in normal term infants, but some healthy infants develop periods of apnea several months after birth. However, it is not known if the apneic spells of either type are related to sudden death. None of the known tests of chemoresponsiveness distinguish premature infants who have apneic spells from those who do not, and the cause of sudden infant death syndrome remains unknown.

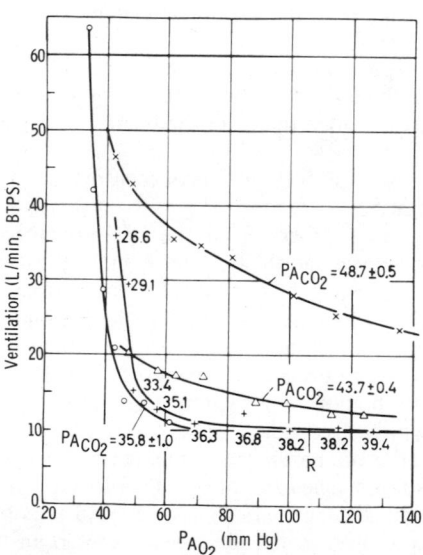

Figure 36–10. Ventilation at various alveolar P_{O_2} values in a subject in whom the alveolar P_{CO_2} was held constant at 48.7, 43.7, and 35.8 mm Hg and, in one experiment, varied as shown by the individual values along this curve *(R)*. (Slightly modified and reproduced, with permission, from Loeschke HH, Gertz KH: Einfluss des O$_2$-Druckes in der Einatmungsluft auf die Atemtätigkeit des Menschen, geprüft unter Konstanthaltung des alveolaren CO$_2$-Druckes. Arch Ges Physiol Pflügers 267:460, 1958.)

NONCHEMICAL INFLUENCES ON RESPIRATION

Afferents From "Higher Centers"

There are afferents from the neocortex to the motor neurons innervating the respiratory muscles, and even though breathing is not usually a conscious event, both inspiration and expiration are under voluntary control. Pain and emotional stimuli affect respiration, so there must also be afferents from the limbic system and hypothalamus.

Since voluntary and automatic control of respiration are separate, automatic control is sometimes disrupted without loss of voluntary control. The clinical condition that results has been called **Ondine's curse.** In German legend, Ondine was a water nymph who had an unfaithful mortal lover. The king of the water nymphs punished the lover by casting a curse upon him that took away all his automatic functions. In this state, he could stay alive only by staying awake and remembering to breathe. He eventually fell asleep from sheer exhaustion and his respiration stopped. Patients with this intriguing condition generally have disease processes that compress the medulla or bulbar poliomyelitis. The condition has also been produced, however, in patients who have been subjected to bilateral anterolateral cervical cordotomy for pain (see Chapter 7). This cuts the pathways that bring about automatic respiration while leaving the voluntary efferent pathways in the corticospinal and rubrospinal tracts intact. However, it also cuts ascending fibers carrying proprioceptive inputs, and there is evidence that the absence of these inputs also tends to produce apnea.

Afferents From Proprioceptors

Carefully controlled experiments have shown that active and passive movements of joints stimulate respiration, presumably because impulses in afferent pathways from proprioceptors in muscles, tendons, and joints stimulate the respiratory center. This effect probably helps increase ventilation during exercise.

Responses to Irritation of the Air Passages

Sneezing and coughing are reflex responses to irritation of receptors in the mucosa of the large respiratory passages (see Chapter 14). Irritation of the walls of the trachea or large bronchi produces coughing, which begins with a deep inspiration followed by forced expiration against a closed glottis. This increases intrapleural pressure to 100 mm Hg or more. The glottis is then suddenly opened, producing an explosive outflow of air at velocities up to 965 km (600 miles) per hour. Sneezing is a similar expiratory effort with a continuously open glottis. These reflexes help expel irritants and keep the airways clear.

Other Pulmonary Receptors

The vagally mediated inhibition of inspiration produced by inflation of the lung has been mentioned above. The response is due to stimulation of stretch receptors located in the smooth muscle of the airways. Pulmonary deflation receptors that trigger inflation

have also been described, and the expiratory and inspiratory reflex responses to pulmonary inflation and deflation, respectively, have been known as the **Hering-Breuer reflexes.** However, the deflation receptors respond better to pulmonary congestion and embolization, producing shallow, rapid breathing, and they have come to be called **type J receptors** instead, because of their juxtacapillary location. There are also **lung irritant receptors** located between the epithelial cells in the bronchi and bronchioles. When stimulated, they initiate hyperventilation and bronchoconstriction, but their function in normal breathing is not known.

Respiratory Components of Other Visceral Reflexes

The respiratory adjustments during vomiting, swallowing, and gagging are discussed in Chapters 14 and 26. Inhibition of respiration and closure of the glottis during these activities not only prevent the aspiration of food or vomitus into the trachea but, in the case of vomiting, fix the chest so that contraction of the abdominal muscles increases the intra-abdominal pressure. Similar glottic closure and inhibition of respiration occur during voluntary and involuntary straining.

Hiccup is a spasmodic contraction of the diaphragm that produces an inspiration during which the glottis suddenly closes. The glottic closure is responsible for the characteristic sensation and sound. Yawning is a peculiar "infectious" respiratory act the physiologic basis and significance of which are uncertain. However, underventilated alveoli have a tendency to collapse, and it has been suggested that the deep inspiration and stretching open up alveoli and prevent the development of atelectasis. Yawning also increases venous return to the heart.

Respiratory Effects of Baroreceptor Stimulation

Afferent fibers from the baroreceptors in the carotid sinuses, aortic arch, atria, and ventricles relay to the respiratory center as well as the vasomotor and cardioinhibitory centers. Impulses in them inhibit respiration, but the inhibitory effect is slight and of little physiologic importance. The hyperventilation in shock is due to chemoreceptor stimulation caused by acidosis and hypoxia secondary to local stagnation of blood flow and is not baroreceptor mediated. The activity of the inspiratory neurons affects the blood pressure and heart rate (see Chapters 28 and 31), and activity in the vasomotor center and the cardiac centers in the medulla may have minor effects on respiration.

Respiratory Adjustments in Health & Disease | 37

EFFECTS OF EXERCISE

Many cardiovascular respiratory mechanisms must operate in an integrated fashion if the O_2 needs of the active tissues are to be met and the extra CO_2 and heat removed from the body during exercise. There is an increase in ventilation that provides extra O_2, eliminates some of the heat, and excretes extra CO_2; there are circulatory changes that increase tissue blood flow while maintaining an adequate circulation in the rest of the body (see Chapter 33); and there is an increase in the extraction of O_2 from the blood in the tissues.

Changes in Ventilation

During exercise, the amount of O_2 entering the blood in the lungs is increased because the amount of O_2 added to each unit of blood and the pulmonary blood flow per minute is increased. The P_{O_2} of blood flowing into the pulmonary capillaries falls from 40 mm Hg to 25 mm Hg or less, so that the alveolar-capillary P_{O_2} gradient is increased and more O_2 enters the blood. Blood flow per minute is increased from 5.5 L/min to as much as 20–35 L/min. The total amount of

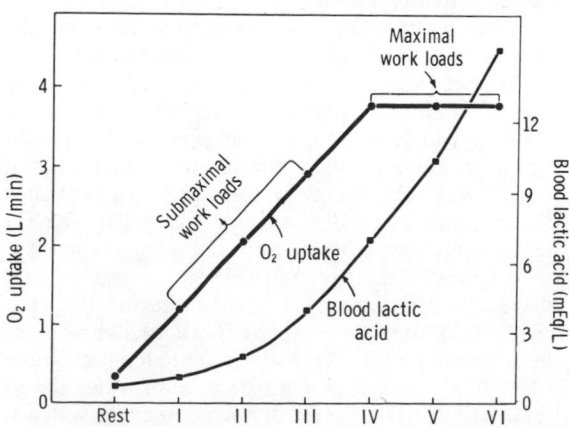

Figure 37–1. Relation between work load, blood lactic acid, and O_2 uptake. I–VI, increasing work loads produced by increasing the speed and grade of a treadmill on which the subjects worked. (Reproduced, with permission, from Mitchell JH, Blomqvist G: Maximal oxygen uptake. N Engl J Med 284:1018, 1971.)

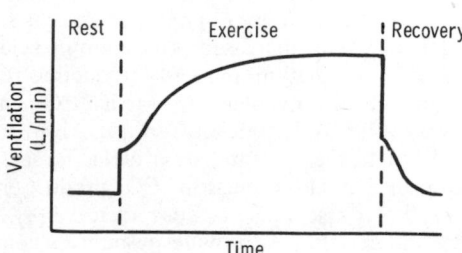

Figure 37–2. Changes in ventilation during exercise. (Reproduced, with permission, from Dejours P in: *Regulation of Human Respiration*. Cunningham DJC, Lloyd BB [editors]. Blackwell, 1963.)

O_2 entering the blood therefore increases from 250 ml/min at rest to values as high as 4000 ml/min. The amount of CO_2 removed from each unit of blood is increased, and CO_2 excretion increases from 200 ml/min to as much as 8000 ml/min. The increase in O_2 uptake is proportionate to work load up to a maximum. Above this maximum, O_2 consumption levels off and blood lactic acid rises precipitously (Fig 37–1). The lactic acid comes from muscles in which aerobic resynthesis of energy stores cannot keep pace with their utilization and an **oxygen debt** is being incurred (see Chapter 3).

There is an abrupt increase in ventilation with the onset of exercise, followed by a further, more gradual increase (Fig 37–2). With moderate exercise, the increase is due mostly to an increase in the depth of respiration; this is accompanied by an increase in the respiratory rate when the exercise is more strenuous. There is an abrupt decrease in ventilation when exercise ceases, followed by a more gradual decline to preexercise values. The abrupt increase at the start of exercise is presumably due to psychic stimuli and afferent impulses from proprioceptors in muscles, tendons, and joints. The more gradual increase is presumably humoral even though arterial pH, P_{CO_2}, and P_{O_2} remain constant during moderate exercise. The increase in ventilation is proportionate to the increase in O_2 consumption, but the mechanisms responsible for the stimulation of respiration are still the subject of much debate. The increase in body temperature may play a role. In addition, it may be that the sensitivity of the respiratory center to CO_2 is increased or that the respiratory fluctuations in arterial P_{CO_2} increase so that, even though the mean arterial P_{CO_2} does not rise, it is CO_2 that is responsible for the increase in ventilation. O_2 also seems to play some role despite the lack of a decrease in arterial P_{O_2}, since, during the performance of a given amount of work, the increase in ventilation while breathing 100% O_2 is 10–20% less than the increase while breathing air (Fig 37–3). Thus, it currently appears that a number of different factors combine to produce the increase in ventilation seen during moderate exercise.

When exercise becomes more severe, buffering of the increased amounts of lactic acid that are produced liberates more CO_2, and this further increases ventilation. The response to graded exercise is shown in Fig 37–4. With increased production of acid, the increases in ventilation and CO_2 production remain proportionate, so alveolar and arterial CO_2 change relatively little (**isocapnic buffering**). Alveolar P_{O_2} falls. With further accumulation of lactic acid, the increase in ventilation outstrips CO_2 production and alveolar P_{CO_2} also falls, as does arterial P_{CO_2}. The decline in arterial P_{CO_2} provides respiratory compensation (see Chapter 40) for the metabolic acidosis produced by the additional lactic acid. The additional increase in ventilation produced by the acidosis is dependent on the carotid bodies and does not occur if they are removed.

The respiratory rate after exercise does not reach basal levels until the O_2 debt is repaid. This may take as long as 90 minutes. The stimulus to ventilation is not the arterial P_{CO_2}, which is normal or low, or the arterial P_{O_2}, which is normal or high, but the elevated arterial H^+ concentration due to the lactic acidemia. The magnitude of the O_2 debt is the amount by which O_2 consumption exceeds basal consumption from the end of exertion until the O_2 consumption has returned to preexercise basal levels. Because of the extra CO_2 produced by the buffering of lactic acid during strenu-

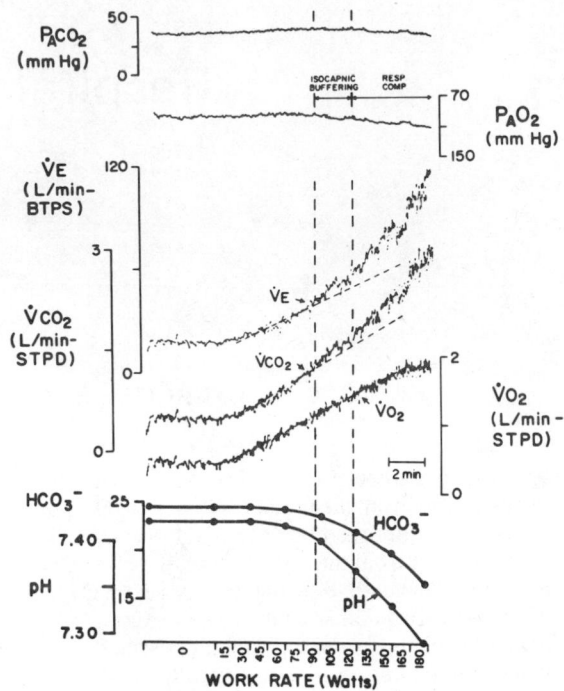

Figure 37–4. Changes in alveolar P_{CO_2}, alveolar P_{O_2}, ventilation ($\dot{V}_E$), CO_2 production ($\dot{V}_{CO_2}$), O_2 consumption ($\dot{V}_{O_2}$), arterial HCO_3^-, and arterial pH with graded increases in work on a bicycle ergometer. The subject was a normal adult male. (Reproduced, with permission, from Wasserman K: Breathing during exercise. N Engl J Med 298:780, 1978.)

ous exercise, the RQ rises, values reaching 1.5–2.0. After exertion, while the O_2 debt is being repaid, the RQ falls to 0.5 or less.

Changes in the Tissues

During exercise, the contracting muscles use more O_2 and the tissue P_{O_2} falls nearly to zero. More O_2 diffuses from the blood, the blood P_{O_2} drops, and more O_2 is removed from hemoglobin. Because the capillary bed is dilated and many previously closed capillaries are open, the mean distance from the blood to the tissue cells is greatly decreased; this facilitates the movement of O_2 from blood to cells. The O_2 hemoglobin dissociation curve is steep in the P_{O_2} range below 60 mm Hg, and a relatively large amount of O_2 is supplied for each mm Hg drop in P_{O_2} (Fig 35–2). Additional O_2 is supplied because, as a result of the accumulation of CO_2 and the rise in temperature in active tissues—and perhaps because of a rise in red blood cell 2,3-DPG—the dissociation curve shifts to the right (Fig 35–3). The net effect is a 3-fold increase in O_2 extraction from each unit of blood (Table 37–1). Since this increase is accompanied by a 30-fold or greater increase in blood flow, it permits the metabolic rate of muscle to rise as much as 100-fold during exercise (see Chapter 3).

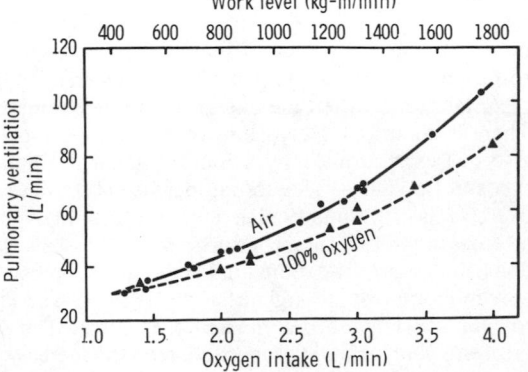

Figure 37–3. Effect of 100% O_2 on ventilation during work at various levels on the bicycle ergometer. (Reproduced, with permission, from Astrand P-O: The respiratory activity in man exposed to prolonged hypoxia. Acta Physiol Scand 30:343, 1954.)

Table 37–1. Oxygen in venous blood
from resting and exercising muscle.

	Rest	Strenuous Exercise
P_{O_2} (mm Hg)	40	15
Percentage saturation of Hb	70	16
O_2 content (ml/dl)	15	3
O_2 extracted (ml/dl)	5	17

Fatigue

Fatigue is a poorly understood phenomenon to which, undoubtedly, many factors contribute. The subjective hardness or ''heaviness'' of exercise correlates with the rate of O_2 consumption, not with the actual work performed in kg-m/min. Barrages of impulses in afferents from proprioceptors in muscles are said to make one feel ''tired.'' The effects of the acidosis on the brain may contribute to the sensation of fatigue. Sustained muscle contractions are painful because the muscle becomes ischemic, and a substance that stimulates pain endings accumulates (''P substance''; see Chapter 7), but intermittent contractions are not painful because the P substance is washed away. Muscle stiffness may be due in part to the accumulation of interstitial fluid in the muscles during exertion.

Heat dissipation during exercise is discussed in Chapter 33 and summarized in Fig 33–4.

HYPOXIA

Hypoxia is O_2 deficiency at the tissue level. It is a more correct term than **anoxia,** there rarely being no O_2 at all left in the tissues.

Traditionally, hypoxia has been divided into 4 types. Numerous other classifications are currently in use, but the 4-type system still has considerable utility if the definitions of the terms are kept clearly in mind. The 4 categories are as follows: (1) **hypoxic hypoxia (anoxic anoxia),** in which the P_{O_2} of the arterial blood is reduced; (2) **anemic hypoxia,** in which the arterial P_{O_2} is normal but the amount of hemoglobin available to carry O_2 is reduced; (3) **stagnant** or **ischemic hypoxia,** in which the blood flow to a tissue is so low that adequate O_2 is not delivered to it despite a normal P_{O_2} and hemoglobin concentration; and (4) **histotoxic hypoxia,** in which the amount of O_2 delivered to a tissue is adequate but, because of the action of a toxic agent, the tissue cells cannot make use of the O_2 supplied to them.

Effects of Hypoxia

The effects of stagnant hypoxia depend upon the tissue affected. In hypoxic hypoxia and the other generalized forms of hypoxia, the brain is affected first. A sudden drop in the inspired P_{O_2} to less than 20

mm Hg, which occurs, for example, when cabin pressure is suddenly lost in a plane flying above 16,000 m, causes loss of consciousness in about 20 s and death in 4–5 min. Less severe hypoxia causes a variety of mental aberrations not unlike those produced by alcohol: impaired judgment, drowsiness, dulled pain sensibility, excitement, disorientation, loss of time sense, and headache. Other symptoms include anorexia, nausea, vomiting, tachycardia, and, when the hypoxia is severe, hypertension. The rate of ventilation is increased in proportion to the severity of the hypoxia of the carotid chemoreceptor cells.

Respiratory Stimulation

Dyspnea is by definition breathing in which the subject is conscious of shortness of breath; **hyperpnea** is the general term for an increase in the rate or depth of breathing regardless of the patient's subjective sensations. **Tachypnea** is rapid, shallow breathing. In general, a normal individual is not conscious of respiration until ventilation is doubled, and breathing is not uncomfortable (ie, the **dyspnea point** is not reached) until ventilation is tripled or quadrupled. Whether or not a given level of ventilation is uncomfortable also depends upon the respiratory reserve. This factor is taken into account in the **dyspneic index.** This index measures the fraction of the respiratory capacity that is not being used at a given respiratory minute volume. When the dyspneic index is less than about 0.7, dyspnea is usually present. An additional factor is the effort involved in moving the air in and out of the lungs (the work of breathing). In asthma, for example, the bronchi are constricted, especially during expiration, and breathing against this increased airway resistance is uncomfortable work. Another factor producing dyspnea may be increased discharge in vagal afferents from lung irritant receptors.

$$\text{Dyspneic Index} = \% \text{ Breathing Reserve} = \frac{MVV - RMV}{MVV} \times 100$$

MVV = Maximal voluntary ventilation, L/min
(see Chapter 34)
RMV = Respiratory minute volume, L/min,
in state under consideration

Cyanosis

Reduced hemoglobin has a dark color, and a dusky bluish discoloration of the tissues called **cyanosis** appears when the reduced hemoglobin concentration of the blood in the capillaries is more than 5 g/dl. Cyanosis is most easily seen in the nail beds and mucous membranes and in the ear lobes, lips, and fingers, where the skin is thin. Its occurrence depends upon the total amount of hemoglobin in the blood, the degree of hemoglobin unsaturation, and the state of the capillary circulation.

One might think that cyanosis would be more marked when the cutaneous vessels were dilated. However, when there is cutaneous arteriolar and venous constriction, blood flow through the capillaries is very slow and more O_2 is removed from the hemoglobin. This is why moderate cold causes cyanosis in exposed areas even in normal individuals. In very cold weather cyanosis does not develop because the drop in skin temperature inhibits the dissociation of oxyhemoglobin and the O_2 consumption of the cold tissues is decreased. Cyanosis does not occur in anemic hypoxia when the total hemoglobin content is low; in carbon monoxide poisoning, because the color of reduced hemoglobin is obscured by the cherry-red color of carbonmonoxyhemoglobin (see below); or in histotoxic hypoxia, because the blood gas content is normal. A discoloration of the skin and mucous membranes similar to cyanosis is produced by high circulating levels of methemoglobin (see Chapter 27).

HYPOXIC HYPOXIA

Hypoxic hypoxia is a problem in normal individuals at high altitudes and is a complication of pneumonia and a number of other common diseases (Table 37–2).

Effects of Decreased Barometric Pressure

The composition of air stays the same, but the total barometric pressure falls with increasing altitude (Fig 37–5). Therefore, the P_{O_2} also falls. At 3000 m

Table 37–2. Causes of hypoxic hypoxia.

1. Decreased P_{O_2} in inspired air (high altitude, breathing O_2-poor gas mixture)
2. Hypoventilation
   Airway obstruction (foreign body, etc)
   Paralysis of respiratory muscles (poliomyelitis)
   Skeletal deformities (kyphoscoliosis)
   Depression of respiratory center (morphine, etc)
   Shallow breathing (pain on inspiration due to pleurisy)
   Increased airway resistance (asthma, emphysema)
   Increased pulmonary tissue resistance (pulmonary sarcoidosis)
   Decreased elastic recoil (emphysema)
   Large pneumothorax
3. Alveolar-capillary diffusion block
   Decrease in total area of normal alveolar membrane (pneumonia, pulmonary congestion)
   Fibrosis of alveolar or pulmonary capillary walls (pulmonary fibrosis, berylliosis)
4. Abnormal ventilation-perfusion ratio or ventilation-perfusion imbalance
   Areas of underventilation and overperfusion of alveoli (emphysema)
   Perfusion of completely unventilated alveoli (emphysema, atelectasis)
   Shunting of venous blood into the arterial circulation, bypassing the lungs (cyanotic congenital heart disease)

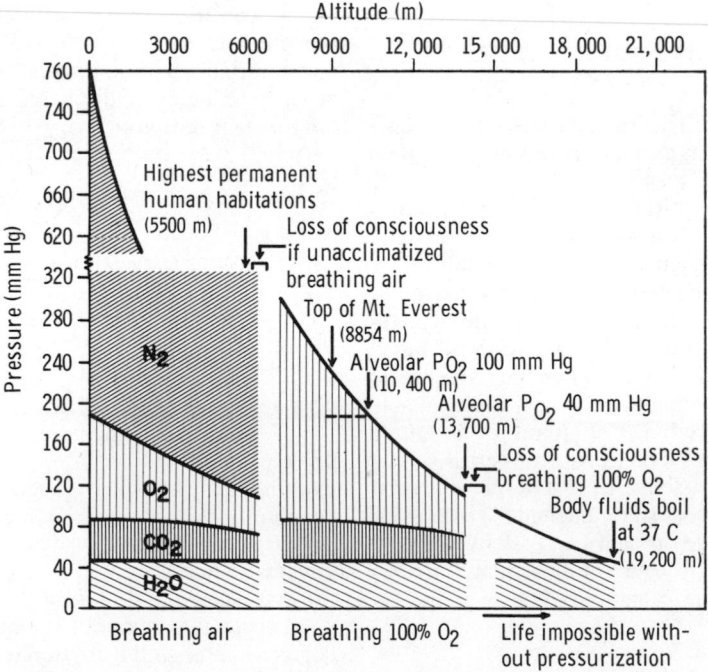

Figure 37–5. Composition of alveolar air breathing air (0–6100 m) and 100% O_2 (6100–13,700 m). The minimal alveolar P_{O_2} that an unacclimatized subject can tolerate without loss of consciousness is about 35–40 mm Hg. Note that with increasing altitude, the alveolar P_{CO_2} drops because of the hyperventilation due to hypoxic stimulation of the carotid and aortic chemoreceptors. The fall in barometric pressure with increasing altitude is not linear because air is compressible.

(approximately 10,000 ft) above sea level, the alveolar P_{O_2} is about 60 mm Hg and there is enough hypoxic stimulation of the chemoreceptors to definitely increase ventilation. As one ascends higher, the alveolar P_{O_2} falls less rapidly and the alveolar P_{CO_2} declines somewhat because of the hyperventilation. The resulting fall in arterial P_{CO_2} produces respiratory alkalosis.

Hypoxic Symptoms Breathing Air

There are a number of compensatory mechanisms that operate over a period of time to increase altitude tolerance (**acclimatization**), but in unacclimatized subjects, mental symptoms such as irritability appear at about 3700 m. At 5500 m, the hypoxic symptoms are severe; and at altitudes above 6100 m (20,000 ft), consciousness is usually lost (Fig 37–6).

Hypoxic Symptoms Breathing Oxygen

The total atmospheric pressure becomes the limiting factor in altitude tolerance when breathing 100% O_2. The partial pressure of water vapor in the alveolar air is constant at 47 mm Hg, and that of CO_2 is normally 40 mm Hg, so that the lowest barometric pressure at which a normal alveolar P_{O_2} of 100 mm Hg is possible is 187 mm Hg, the pressure at about 10,400 m (34,000 ft). At greater altitudes, the increased ventilation due to the decline in alveolar P_{O_2} lowers the alveolar P_{CO_2} somewhat, but the maximal alveolar P_{O_2} that can be attained breathing 100% O_2 at the ambient barometric pressure of 100 mm Hg at 13,700 m is about 40 mm Hg. At about 14,000 m, consciousness is lost in spite of the administration of 100% O_2 (Fig 37–7). It is possible, however, to create an artificial atmosphere around an individual; in a pressurized suit or cabin supplied with O_2 and a system to remove CO_2, ascent to any altitude is possible.

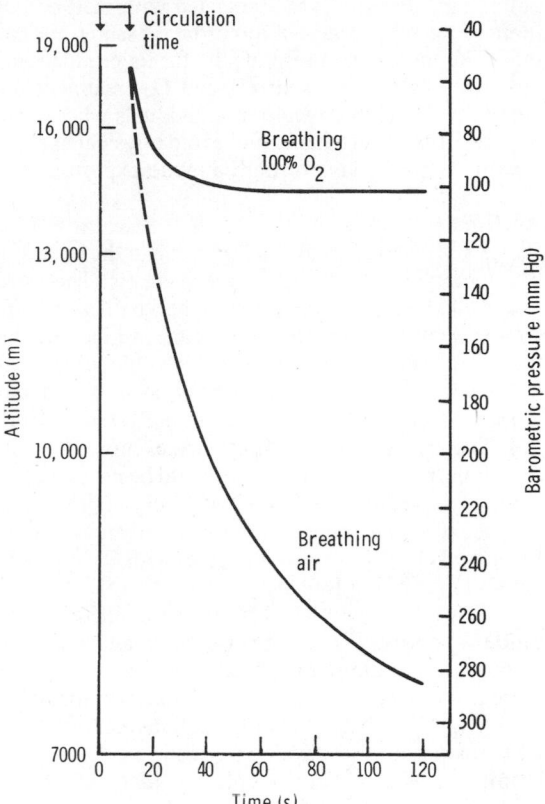

Figure 37–7. Duration of useful consciousness upon sudden exposure to the ambient pressure at various altitudes. Note that 10 s is the approximate lung-to-brain circulation time. (After Benzinger TH & others, from: *Flight Surgeon's Manual*, USAF Manual No. 160–5, 1954.)

At 19,200 m, the barometric pressure is 47 mm Hg, and at or below this pressure the body fluids boil at body temperature. The point is largely academic, however, because any individual exposed to such a low pressure would be dead of hypoxia before the bubbles of steam could cause death.

Delayed Effects of High Altitude

Many individuals, when they first arrive at a high altitude, develop transient "mountain sickness." This syndrome develops 8–24 hours after arrival at altitude and lasts 4–8 days. It is characterized by headache, irritability, insomnia, breathlessness, and nausea and vomiting. Its cause is unknown, but the symptoms are reduced or prevented if alkalosis is reduced by procedures such as treatment with acetazolamide.

High altitude pulmonary edema and cerebral edema are serious forms of mountain sickness. Pulmonary edema is prone to occur in individuals who ascend quickly to altitudes above 2500 m and engage in heavy physical activity during the first 3 days after arrival. It is also seen in individuals acclimatized to high altitudes who spend 2 weeks or more at sea level and then reascend. It occurs in the absence of cardiovascular or

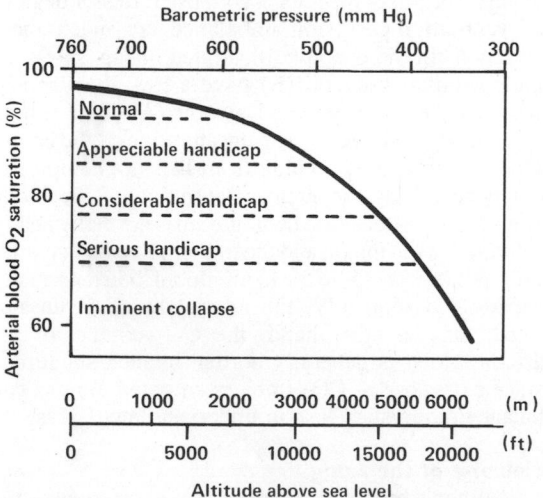

Figure 37–6. Acute effects of hypoxia at various arterial O_2 saturation levels. (Modified and reproduced, with permission, from Pace N in: *The Air We Breathe: A Study of Man and His Environment*. Farber SM, Wilson RHL [editors]. Thomas, 1961.)

pulmonary disease. It is associated with marked pulmonary hypertension, but left atrial pressures are normal. The mechanism responsible for its production is unknown. It responds to rest and O_2 treatment and generally does not develop in individuals who ascend to high altitudes gradually and avoid physical exertion for the first few days of high altitude exposure.

Acclimatization

Acclimatization to altitude is due to the operation of a variety of compensatory mechanisms. The respiratory alkalosis produced by the hyperventilation shifts the O_2-hemoglobin dissociation curve to the left, but there is a concomitant increase in red blood cell 2,3-DPG, which tends to decrease the O_2 affinity of hemoglobin. The net effect is an increase in P_{50} (see Chapter 35). The decrease in O_2 affinity makes more O_2 available to the tissues. However, it should be noted that the value of the increase in P_{50} is lost at very high altitudes because when the arterial P_{O_2} is markedly reduced, the decreased O_2 affinity also interferes with O_2 uptake by hemoglobin in the lungs.

The initial ventilatory response to increased altitude is relatively small because the alkalosis tends to counteract the stimulating effect of hypoxia. However, there is a steady increase in ventilation over the next 4 days (Fig 37–8) because the active transport of H^+ into CSF, or possibly a developing lactic acidosis in the brain, causes a fall in CSF pH that increases the response to hypoxia. After 4 days, the ventilatory response begins to decline slowly, but it takes years of residence at higher altitudes for it to decline to the initial level. Associated with this decline is a gradual desensitization to the stimulatory effects of hypoxia.

Erythropoietin secretion increases promptly on ascent to high altitude (see Chapter 24) and then falls somewhat over the following 4 days as the ventilatory response increases and the arterial P_{O_2} rises. The increase in circulating red blood cells triggered by the erythropoietin begins in 2–3 days and is sustained as long as the individual remains at high altitude.

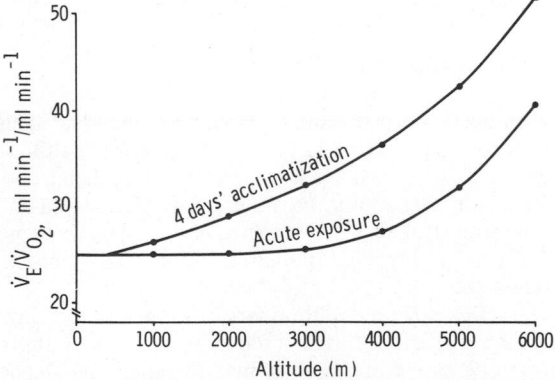

Figure 37–8. Effect of acclimatization on the ventilatory response at various altitudes. $\dot{V}_E/\dot{V}_{O_2}$ is the ventilatory equivalent, the ratio of expired minute volume ($\dot{V}_E$) to the O_2 consumption ($\dot{V}_{O_2}$). (Reproduced, with permission, from Lenfant C, Sullivan K: Adaptation to high altitude. N Engl J Med 284:1298, 1971.)

There are also compensatory changes in the tissues. The mitochondria, which are the site of oxidative reactions, increase in number, and there is an increase in myoglobin (see Chapter 35) which facilitates the movement of O_2 in the tissues. There is also an increase in the tissue content of cytochrome oxidase.

The effectiveness of the acclimatization processes is indicated by the fact that in the Andes and Himalayas there are permanent human habitations at elevations above 5500 m (18,000 ft). The natives who live in these villages are markedly polycythemic and have low alveolar P_{O_2} values, but in most other ways they are remarkably normal.

Diseases Causing Hypoxic Hypoxia

Hypoxic hypoxia is the most common form of hypoxia seen clinically. The diseases that cause it can be roughly divided into those in which inadequate amounts of O_2 reach the alveoli; those in which there is uneven ventilation in relation to blood flow; those in which diffusion from the alveoli to the capillaries is blocked; and those in which venous blood bypasses the lungs (Table 37–2). However, there is a good deal of overlap.

Ventilation-Perfusion Imbalance

In disease processes that prevent ventilation of some of the alveoli, the ventilation/blood flow ratios in different parts of the lung determine the extent to which systemic arterial P_{O_2} declines. If nonventilated alveoli are perfused, the nonventilated but perfused portion of the lung is in effect a right-to-left shunt, dumping unoxygenated blood into the left side of the heart; but if blood is diverted from the diseased areas to better ventilated portions of the lung, the arterial P_{O_2} may remain essentially normal. Such shifts occur when a portion of the lung is collapsed. Lesser degrees of ventilation-perfusion imbalance are much more common. In the example illustrated in Fig 37–9, the underventilated alveoli (B) have a low alveolar P_{O_2} whereas the overventilated alveoli (A) have a high alveolar P_{O_2}. However, the unsaturation of the hemoglobin of the blood coming from B is not completely compensated by the greater saturation of the blood coming from A because hemoglobin is normally nearly saturated in the lungs, and the higher alveolar P_{O_2} adds only a little more O_2 to the hemoglobin than it normally carries. Consequently, the arterial blood is unsaturated. On the other hand, the CO_2 content of the arterial blood is generally normal in such situations, since extra loss of CO_2 in overventilated regions can balance diminished loss in underventilated areas.

Collapse of the Lung

When a bronchus or bronchiole is obstructed, the gas in the alveoli beyond the obstruction is absorbed and the lung segment collapses. Collapse of alveoli is called **atelectasis.** The atelectic area may range in size from a small patch to a whole lung. When a large part of the lung is collapsed, there is an appreciable

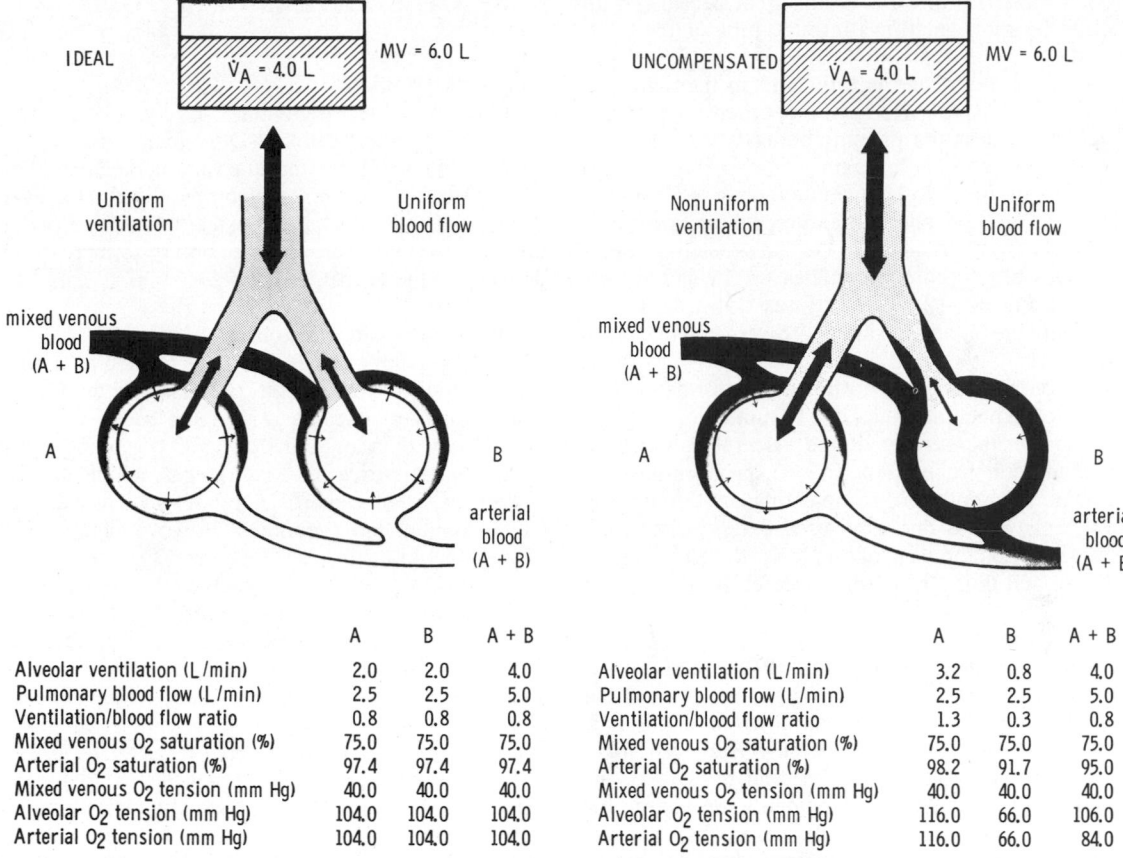

	A	B	A + B			A	B	A + B
Alveolar ventilation (L/min)	2.0	2.0	4.0	Alveolar ventilation (L/min)		3.2	0.8	4.0
Pulmonary blood flow (L/min)	2.5	2.5	5.0	Pulmonary blood flow (L/min)		2.5	2.5	5.0
Ventilation/blood flow ratio	0.8	0.8	0.8	Ventilation/blood flow ratio		1.3	0.3	0.8
Mixed venous O_2 saturation (%)	75.0	75.0	75.0	Mixed venous O_2 saturation (%)		75.0	75.0	75.0
Arterial O_2 saturation (%)	97.4	97.4	97.4	Arterial O_2 saturation (%)		98.2	91.7	95.0
Mixed venous O_2 tension (mm Hg)	40.0	40.0	40.0	Mixed venous O_2 tension (mm Hg)		40.0	40.0	40.0
Alveolar O_2 tension (mm Hg)	104.0	104.0	104.0	Alveolar O_2 tension (mm Hg)		116.0	66.0	106.0
Arterial O_2 tension (mm Hg)	104.0	104.0	104.0	Arterial O_2 tension (mm Hg)		116.0	66.0	84.0

Figure 37–9. *Left:* "Ideal" ventilation/blood flow relationship. *Right:* Nonuniform ventilation and uniform blood flow, uncompensated. $\dot{V}_A$, alveolar ventilation; MV, respiratory minute volume. (Reproduced, with permission, from Comroe JH Jr & others: *The Lung: Clinical Physiology and Pulmonary Function Tests,* 2nd ed. Year Book, 1962.)

decrease in lung volume. The intrapleural pressure therefore becomes more negative and pulls the mediastinum, which in humans is a fairly flexible structure, to the affected side.

Another cause of atelectasis is absence or inactivation of surfactant, the surface tension–depressing agent normally found in the thin fluid lining the alveoli (see Chapter 34). This abnormality is a major cause of failure of the lungs to expand normally at birth.

Collapse of the lung may also be due to the presence in the pleural space of air (**pneumothorax**), tissue fluids (**hydrothorax, chylothorax**), or blood (**hemothorax**).

Pneumothorax

When air is admitted to the pleural space, through either a rupture in the lung or a hole in the chest wall, the lung on the affected side collapses because of its elastic recoil. Since the intrapleural pressure on the affected side is atmospheric, the mediastinum shifts toward the normal side. If the communication between the pleural space and the exterior remains open (**open** or **sucking pneumothorax**), more air moves in and out of the pleural space each time the patient breathes.

If the hole is large, the resistance to air flow into the pleural cavity is less than the resistance to air flow into the intact lung, and little air enters the lung during inspiration. The mediastinum shifts farther to the intact side, kinking the great vessels until it flaps back during expiration. There is marked stimulation of respiration due to hypoxia, hypercapnia, and activation of pulmonary deflation receptors, and respiratory distress is severe.

If there is a flap of tissue over the hole in the lung or chest wall that acts as a flutter valve, permitting air to enter during inspiration but preventing its exit during expiration, the pressure in the pleural space rises above atmospheric (**tension pneumothorax**). The hypoxic stimulus to respiration causes deeper inspiratory efforts, which further increase the pressure in the pleural cavity, kinking the great veins and causing further hypoxia. Intrapleural pressure in such cases may rise to 20–30 mm Hg. The peripheral veins become distended, there is intense cyanosis, and the condition is potentially fatal if the pneumothorax is not decompressed by removing the air.

On the other hand, if the hole through which air enters the pleural space seals off (**closed pneumotho-**

rax), respiratory distress is not great because, with each inspiration, air flows into the lung on the unaffected side rather than into the pleural space. Because the vascular resistance is increased in the collapsed lung, blood is diverted to the other lung. Consequently, unless the pneumothorax is very large, it does not cause much hypoxia.

The air in a closed pneumothorax is absorbed. Since it is at atmospheric pressure, its total pressure, P_{O_2}, and P_{N_2} are greater than the corresponding values in venous blood (compare values for air and venous blood in Fig 34–12). Gas diffuses down these gradients into the blood, and after 1–2 weeks all of the gas disappears.

Spontaneous pneumothorax, the formation of a small closed pneumothorax due to rupture of congenital blebs on the surface of the visceral pleura, is a common benign condition. Indeed, production of an artificial pneumothorax by injecting air through the chest wall was at one time used extensively in the treatment of pulmonary tuberculosis, the aim being to collapse and thus "rest" the diseased lung.

Emphysema

In the degenerative pulmonary disease called **emphysema,** the lungs lose their elasticity and the walls between the alveoli break down so that the alveoli are replaced by large air sacs. The physiologic dead space is greatly increased, and because of inadequate and uneven alveolar ventilation and perfusion of underventilated alveoli, severe hypoxia develops. Hypercapnia also develops. Inspiration and expiration are labored, and the work of breathing is greatly increased. The changes in lung compliance are shown in Fig 34–7. The chest becomes enlarged and barrel-shaped because the chest wall expands as the opposing elastic recoil of the lungs declines (see Chapter 34). The hypoxia leads to polycythemia. Pulmonary hypertension develops, and the right side of the heart enlarges (**cor pulmonale),** then fails.

Venous to Arterial Shunts

When a cardiovascular abnormality such as an interatrial septal defect permits large amounts of unoxygenated venous blood to bypass the pulmonary capillaries and dilute the oxygenated blood in the systemic arteries ("right-to-left shunt"), chronic hypoxic hypoxia and cyanosis (**cyanotic congenital heart disease)** result. Administration of 100% O_2 raises the O_2 content of alveolar air and improves the hypoxia due to hypoventilation, impaired diffusion, or ventilation-perfusion imbalance (short of perfusion of totally unventilated segments) by increasing the amount of O_2 in the blood leaving the lungs. However, in patients with venous to arterial shunts and normal lungs, any beneficial effect of 100% O_2 is slight and due solely to an increase in the amount of dissolved O_2 in the blood.

OTHER FORMS OF HYPOXIA

Anemic Hypoxia

Hypoxia due to anemia is rarely severe at rest because red blood cell 2,3-DPG increases, and the hemoglobin deficiency must be very marked before the tissue O_2 supplies at rest are compromised. However, anemic patients may have considerable difficulty during exercise because of limited ability to increase O_2 delivery to the active tissues.

Carbon Monoxide Poisoning

Carbon monoxide (CO), a gas formed by incomplete combustion of carbon, was used by the Greeks and Romans to execute criminals. Today it causes more deaths than any other gas. CO poisoning is less common in America since natural gas, which does not contain CO, replaced artificial gases such as coal gas, which contains large amounts. However, the exhaust of gasoline engines is 6% or more CO.

CO is toxic because it reacts with hemoglobin to form **carbonmonoxyhemoglobin (carboxyhemoglobin, COHb),** and COHb cannot take up O_2. Carbon monoxide poisoning is often listed as a form of anemic hypoxia because there is a deficiency of hemoglobin that can carry O_2, but the total hemoglobin content of the blood is unaffected by CO. The affinity of hemoglobin for CO is 210 times its affinity for O_2, but COHb liberates CO very slowly. An additional difficulty is that when COHb is present the dissociation curve of the remaining HbO_2 shifts to the left, decreasing the amount of O_2 released. This is why an anemic individual who has 50% of the normal amount of HbO_2 may be able to perform moderate work, whereas an individual whose HbO_2 is reduced to the same level because of the formation of COHb is seriously incapacitated.

Because of the affinity of CO for hemoglobin, there is progressive COHb formation when the alveolar P_{CO} is greater than 0.4 mm Hg. However, the amount of COHb formed depends upon the duration of exposure to CO as well as the concentration of CO in the inspired air and the alveolar ventilation.

CO is also toxic to the cytochromes in the tissues, but the amount of CO required to poison the cytochromes is 1000 times the lethal dose; tissue toxicity thus plays no role in clinical CO poisoning.

The symptoms of CO poisoning are those of any type of hypoxia, especially headache and nausea, but there is little stimulation of respiration, since the arterial P_{O_2} remains normal and the carotid and aortic chemoreceptors are not stimulated (see Chapter 36). The cherry-red color of COHb is visible in the skin, nail beds, and mucous membranes. Death results when about 70–80% of the circulating hemoglobin is converted to COHb. The symptoms produced by chronic exposure to sublethal concentrations of CO are those of progressive brain damage, including mental changes and, sometimes, a parkinsonianlike state (see Chapter 32).

Treatment of CO poisoning consists of immediate termination of the exposure and adequate ventilation, by artificial respiration if necessary. Ventilation with O_2 is preferable to ventilation with fresh air, since O_2 hastens the dissociation of COHb, and hyperbaric oxygenation (see below) is useful.

Stagnant Hypoxia

Hypoxia due to slow circulation is a problem in organs such as the kidneys and heart during shock (see Chapter 33). The liver and possibly the brain are damaged by stagnant hypoxia in congestive heart failure. The blood flow to the lung is normally very large, and it takes prolonged hypotension to produce significant damage. However, **shock lung** can develop in prolonged circulatory collapse, particularly in those areas of the lung that are higher than the heart. In this condition, production of surfactant is decreased in the underperfused areas.

Histotoxic Hypoxia

Hypoxia due to inhibition of tissue oxidative processes is most commonly the result of cyanide poisoning. Cyanide inhibits cytochrome oxidase and possibly other enzymes. Methylene blue or nitrites are used to treat cyanide poisoning. They act by forming **methemoglobin,** which then reacts with cyanide to form **cyanmethemoglobin,** a nontoxic compound. The extent of treatment with these compounds is, of course, limited by the amount of methemoglobin that can be safely formed. Hyperbaric oxygenation may also be useful.

OXYGEN TREATMENT

Administration of oxygen-rich gas mixtures is of very limited value in stagnant, anemic, and histotoxic hypoxia because all that can be accomplished in this way is an increase in the amount of dissolved O_2 in the arterial blood. This is also true in hypoxic hypoxia when it is due to shunting of unoxygenated venous blood past the lungs. In other forms of hypoxic hypoxia, O_2 is of great benefit. However, it must be remembered that in hypercapnic patients in severe pulmonary failure the CO_2 level may be so high that it depresses rather than stimulates respiration. Some of these patients keep breathing only because the carotid and aortic chemoreceptors drive the respiratory center. If the hypoxic drive is withdrawn by administering O_2, breathing may stop. During the resultant apnea, the arterial P_{O_2} drops, but breathing may not start again because the increase in P_{CO_2} further depresses the respiratory center. Therefore, O_2 therapy in this situation may be fatal.

When 100% O_2 is first inhaled, there may be a slight decrease in respiration in normal individuals, suggesting that there is normally some hypoxic chemoreceptor drive. However, the effect is minor and can only be demonstrated by special technics. In addition, it is offset by a slight accumulation of H^+ ions, since the concentration of deoxygenated hemoglobin in the blood is reduced and Hb is a better buffer than HbO_2 (see Chapter 35).

Oxygen Toxicity

It is interesting that while O_2 is necessary for life in aerobic organisms, it is also toxic. Indeed, hyperbaric O_2 has been demonstrated to exert toxic effects on bacteria, fungi, and plants as well as animals. The toxicity seems to be due to the production of the superoxide anion (O_2^-) and H_2O_2. When 80–100% O_2 is administered to humans for periods of 8 hours or more the respiratory passages become irritated, causing substernal distress, nasal congestion, sore throat, and coughing. The reason O_2 produces the irritation is not completely understood, although O_2 treatment appears to inhibit the ability of lung macrophages to kill bacteria, and surfactant production is reduced. In animals, more prolonged administration without irritation is possible if treatment is briefly interrupted from time to time, but it is not certain that periodic interruptions are of benefit in humans. In some infants treated with O_2 for respiratory distress syndrome, a chronic condition characterized by lung cysts and densities develops **(bronchopulmonary dysplasia),** and there is evidence that this syndrome is a manifestation of O_2 toxicity.

No other untoward symptoms have been reported from the administration of 100% O_2 to adult humans at atmospheric pressure; but 100% O_2 administered at pressures greater than atmospheric produces muscle twitching, ringing in the ears, dizziness, convulsions, and coma. The speed with which these symptoms develop is proportionate to the pressure at which the O_2 is administered; eg, at 4 atmospheres, symptoms develop in half the subjects in 30 minutes, whereas at 6 atmospheres, convulsions develop in a few minutes. Administration of other gases at increased pressure also causes CNS symptoms (see below). Administration of O_2 to rats at elevated pressures decreases their brain γ-aminobutyric acid (GABA) content (see Chapter 15) and their brain, liver, and kidney ATP content. Succinate has been reported to protect animals from this type of oxygen toxicity.

Exposure to O_2 at increased pressures **(hyperbaric oxygenation)** can produce marked increases in the dissolved O_2 in blood. It has proved useful during surgery for certain forms of congenital heart disease. It is also of value in the treatment of gas gangrene, carbon monoxide poisoning, and probably cyanide poisoning. However, oxygen toxicity limits exposures to less than 5 hours and pressures to 3 atmospheres or less.

HYPERCAPNIA & HYPOCAPNIA

Hypercapnia

Retention of CO_2 in the body (hypercapnia) is characterized by symptoms due to depression of the CNS: confusion, diminished sensory acuity, and, eventually, coma with respiratory depression and death. In patients with these symptoms, the P_{CO_2} is markedly elevated, there is severe respiratory acidosis, and the plasma HCO_3^- may exceed 40 mEq/L. Large amounts of HCO_3^- are excreted, partially compensating for the acidosis (see Chapter 40).

CO_2 is so much more soluble than O_2 that hypercapnia is rarely a problem in patients with hypoxia due to alveolar-capillary block, but it is a problem when for any reason alveolar ventilation is inadequate.

Asphyxia

In asphyxia produced by occlusion of the airway, acute hypercapnia and hypoxia develop together. There is pronounced stimulation of respiration, with violent respiratory efforts. Blood pressure and heart rate rise sharply, and blood pH drops. Catecholamine secretion is stimulated, the stimulation of norepinephrine secretion being proportionately greater than the stimulation of epinephrine secretion. Eventually the respiratory efforts cease, the blood pressure falls, and the heart slows. Asphyxiated animals can still be revived at this point by artificial respiration, although they are prone to ventricular fibrillation, probably owing to the combination of hypoxic myocardial damage and high circulating catecholamine levels. If artificial respiration is not started, cardiac arrest occurs in 4–5 minutes.

Drowning

In about 10% of drownings, the first gasp of water after the losing struggle not to breathe triggers laryngospasm, and death results from asphyxia without any water in the lungs. In the remaining cases, the glottic muscles eventually relax and the lungs are flooded. Fresh water is rapidly absorbed, diluting the plasma and causing intravascular hemolysis. Ocean water is markedly hypertonic and draws fluid from the vascular system into the lungs, decreasing plasma volume. The immediate goal in the treatment of drowning is, of course, resuscitation, but long-term treatment must also take into account the circulatory effects of the water in the lungs.

Hypocapnia

Hypocapnia is the result of hyperventilation. During voluntary hyperventilation, the arterial P_{CO_2} falls from 40 to as low as 15 mm Hg while the alveolar P_{O_2} rises to 120–140 mm Hg.

The acute effects of voluntary hyperventilation demonstrate the interaction of the chemical respiratory regulating mechanisms. When an individual hyperventilates for 2–3 minutes, then stops and permits respiration to continue without exerting any voluntary control

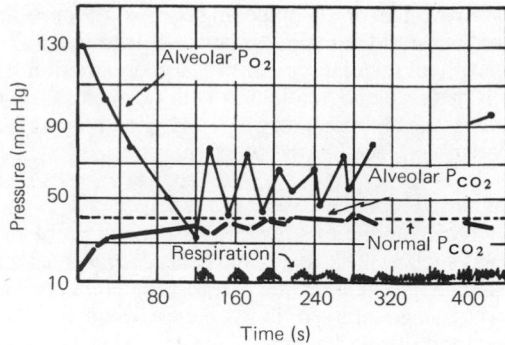

Figure 37–10. Changes in breathing and composition of alveolar air after forced hyperventilation for 2 minutes. (Redrawn and reproduced, with permission, from Douglas CG, Haldane JBS: The causes of periodic or Cheyne-Stokes breathing. J Physiol [Lond] 38:401, 1909.)

over it, there is a period of apnea. This is followed by a few shallow breaths and then by another period of apnea, followed again by a few breaths (**periodic breathing**). The cycles may last for some time before normal breathing is resumed (Fig 37–10). The apnea apparently is due to CO_2 lack because it does not occur following hyperventilation with gas mixtures containing 5% CO_2. During the apnea, the alveolar P_{O_2} falls and the P_{CO_2} rises. Breathing resumes because of hypoxic stimulation of the carotid and aortic chemoreceptors before the CO_2 level has returned to normal. A few breaths eliminate the hypoxic stimulus, and breathing stops until the alveolar P_{O_2} falls again. Gradually, however, the P_{CO_2} returns to normal, and normal breathing resumes.

Cheyne-Stokes Respiration

Periodic breathing in disease states is called **Cheyne-Stokes respiration.** It is seen most commonly in congestive heart failure and uremia, but it occurs also in patients with brain disease and during sleep in some normal individuals at high altitudes. Some of the patients with Cheyne-Stokes respiration have been shown to have increased sensitivity to CO_2. The increased response is apparently due to disruption of neural pathways that normally inhibit respiration. In these individuals, CO_2 causes relative hyperventilation, lowering the arterial P_{CO_2}. During the resultant apnea, the arterial P_{CO_2} again rises to normal, but the respiratory mechanism again overresponds to CO_2. Breathing ceases, and the cycle repeats.

Another cause of periodic breathing in patients with cardiac disease is prolongation of the lung-to-brain circulation time, so that it takes longer for changes in arterial gas tensions to affect the respiratory center. When individuals with a slower circulation hyperventilate, they lower the P_{CO_2} of the blood in their lungs, but it takes longer than normal for the blood with a low P_{CO_2} to reach the brain. During this time, the P_{CO_2} in the pulmonary capillary blood continues to be lowered, and when this blood reaches the brain, the low P_{CO_2} inhibits the respiratory center, producing apnea. In other words, the respiratory control system oscillates because the negative feedback loop from lungs to brain is abnormally long.

Other Effects of Hypocapnia

The more chronic effects of hypocapnia are seen in neurotic patients who chronically hyperventilate. Cerebral blood flow may be reduced 30% or more because of the direct constrictor effect of hypocapnia on the cerebral vessels (see Chapter 32). The cerebral ischemia causes lightheadedness, dizziness, and paresthesias. Hypocapnia also increases cardiac output. It has a direct constrictor effect on many vessels, but it depresses the vasomotor center, so that the blood pressure is usually unchanged or only slightly elevated.

Other consequences of hypocapnia are due to the associated respiratory alkalosis, the blood pH being increased to 7.5 or 7.6. The plasma HCO_3^- is low, but bicarbonate reabsorption is decreased because of the inhibition of renal acid secretion by the low P_{CO_2}. The plasma total calcium level does not change, but the plasma ionized calcium level falls and hypocapnic individuals develop carpopedal spasm, a positive Chvostek sign, and the other manifestations of tetany (see Chapter 21).

EFFECTS OF INCREASED BAROMETRIC PRESSURE

The ambient pressure increases by 1 atmosphere for every 10 m of depth in sea water and every 10.4 m of depth in fresh water. Therefore, at a depth of 31 m (100 ft) in the ocean, a diver is exposed to a pressure of 4 atmospheres. Those who dig underwater tunnels are also exposed to the same hazards because the pressure in the chambers (caissons) in which they work is increased to keep out the water.

The hazards of exposure to increased barometric pressure used to be the concern largely of the specialists who cared for deep sea divers and tunnel workers. However, the invention of SCUBA gear (self-contained underwater breathing apparatus, a tank and valve system carried by the diver) has transformed diving from a business into a sport. The popularity of skin diving is so great that all physicians should be aware of its potential dangers. The interest in performing certain surgical procedures in high-pressure tanks (see above) also focuses attention on the effects of increased barometric pressure.

Nitrogen Narcosis & the High-Pressure Nervous Syndrome

A diver must breathe air or other gases at increased pressure to equalize the increased pressure on the chest wall and abdomen. CO_2 is routinely removed to prevent its accumulation. 100% O_2 at increased pressure causes CNS symptoms of oxygen toxicity

Table 37–3. Potential problems associated with exposure to increased barometric pressure.

Oxygen toxicity
Lung damage
Convulsions
Nitrogen narcosis
Euphoria
Impaired performance
High-pressure nervous syndrome
Tremors
Somnolence
Decompression sickness
Pain
Paralyses
Air embolism
Sudden death

(Table 37–3). Since the harmful effects of breathing O_2 (see above) are proportionate to the P_{O_2}, they can be prevented by decreasing the concentration of O_2 in the gas mixture to 20% or less.

If a diver breathes compressed air, the increased P_{N_2} can cause **nitrogen narcosis,** a condition also known as "rapture of the deep" (Table 37–3). At pressures of 4–5 atmospheres (ie, at depths of 30–40 m in the ocean), 80% N_2 produces definite euphoria. At greater pressures, the symptoms resemble alcohol intoxication. Manual dexterity is maintained, but intellectual functions are impaired.

The problem of nitrogen narcosis can be avoided by breathing mixtures of O_2 and helium, and deeper dives can be made. However, the **high-pressure nervous syndrome** (HPNS) develops during deep dives with such mixtures. This condition is characterized by tremors, drowsiness, and a depression of the α activity in the EEG. Unlike nitrogen narcosis, intellectual functions are not severely affected but manual dexterity is impaired. The cause of HPNS is not settled, but it is worth noting that a variety of gases that are physiologically inert at atmospheric pressure are anesthetics at increased pressure. This is true of N_2 and is also true of xenon, krypton, argon, neon, and helium. Their anesthetic activity parallels their lipid solubility, and the anesthesia may be due to an action on nerve cell membranes.

Decompression Sickness

As a diver breathing 80% N_2 ascends from a dive, the elevated alveolar P_{N_2} falls. N_2 diffuses from the tissues into the bloodstream and from the bloodstream into the lungs along the partial pressure gradient. If the return to atmospheric pressure (decompression) is gradual, no harmful effects are observed; but if the ascent is rapid, N_2 escapes from solution. Bubbles form in the tissues and blood, causing the symptoms of **decompression sickness (the bends, caisson disease).** Bubbles in the tissues cause severe pains, particularly around joints, and neurologic symptoms that include paresthesias and itching. Bubbles in the bloodstream, which occur in more severe cases, obstruct the arteries to the brain, causing major paralyses and respiratory failure. Bubbles in the pulmonary capillaries are apparently responsible for the dyspnea that divers call the "chokes," and bubbles in the coronary arteries may cause myocardial damage.

Treatment of this disease is prompt recompression in a pressure chamber, followed by slow decompression. Recompression is frequently lifesaving. Recovery is often complete, but there may be residual neurologic sequelae due to irreversible damage to the nervous system.

It should be noted that ascent in an airplane is equivalent to ascent from a dive. The decompression during a climb from sea level to 8550 m in the unpressurized cabin of an airplane (pressure drop from 1 down to one-third atmosphere) is the same as that during ascent to the surface after spending a period of time in 20 m of sea water (pressure drop from 3 down to 1 atmosphere). A rapid ascent in either situation can cause decompression sickness.

Air Embolism

If, during a dive, a diver breathing from a tank at increased pressure takes and holds a breath and suddenly heads for the surface—as may occur if the diver gets into trouble and panics—the gas in the lungs may expand rapidly enough to rupture the pulmonary veins. This drives air into the vessels, causing air embolism. Fatal air embolism has occurred during rapid ascent from as shallow a depth as 5 m. The consequences of air in the circulatory system are discussed in Chapter 30. This cannot happen, of course, to an individual who takes a breath on the surface, dives, and returns to the surface still holding that breath, no matter how deep the dive.

Air embolism also occurs as a result of rapid expansion of the gas in the lungs when the external pressure is suddenly reduced from atmospheric to subatmospheric, as it is when the wall of the pressurized cabin of an airplane or rocket at high altitude is breached (**explosive decompression**).

ARTIFICIAL RESPIRATION

In acute asphyxia due to drowning, CO or other forms of gas poisoning, electrocution, anesthetic accidents, and other similar causes, artificial respiration after breathing has ceased may be lifesaving. It should always be attempted because the respiratory center fails before the vasomotor center and heart. There are numerous methods of emergency artificial respiration, but the method presently recommended to produce adequate ventilation in all cases is mouth-to-mouth breathing.

Mouth-to-Mouth Breathing

In this form of resuscitation, the operator first places the victim in the supine position and opens the

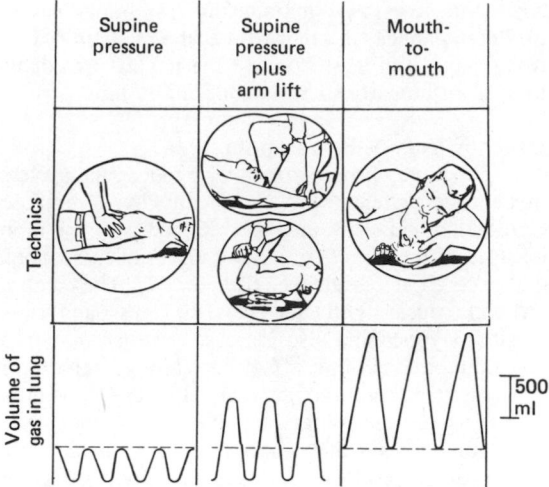

Figure 37–11. Technics of artificial respiration. The prone pressure plus arm lift method moves about the same amount of air as the supine pressure plus arm lift method. The dotted line indicates the volume of gas in the lung in the subject whose respiration has ceased. (Modified and reproduced, with permission, from Gordon AS, in Whittenberger JL: *Artificial Respiration: Theory and Applications*. Harper, 1962.)

airway by placing a hand under the neck and lifting, while keeping pressure with the other hand on the victim's forehead. This extends the neck and lifts the tongue away from the back of the throat. The hand already on the forehead occludes the nostrils, and the victim's mouth is covered by the operator's. The operator blows into the victim's mouth a volume about twice the tidal volume, then permits the elastic recoil of the victim's lungs to produce passive expiration. The victim's neck is kept extended. The nostrils can also be occluded by the operator's cheek as shown in Fig 37–11, or they can be held shut with the operator's other hand. Any gas blown into the stomach can be expelled by applying upward pressure on the abdomen from time to time. The advantages of mouth-to-mouth resuscitation lie not only in its simplicity but also in the fact that it works by expanding the lungs. In the prone or supine pressure methods of artificial respiration, the lungs are compressed by pressure on the thorax, and passive recoil of the chest wall pulls air into them (Fig 37–11). Some expansion of the lungs can be achieved by raising the arms, but even when arm raising and pressure are alternated, the effective ventilation is not so great as that produced by the mouth-to-mouth method.

Mechanical Respirators

For treatment of chronic respiratory insufficiency due to inadequate ventilation in such conditions as bulbar poliomyelitis, mechanical respirators such as the Drinker tank respirator are available. These are airtight metal or plastic containers enclosing the body except for the head. By means of a motor, negative pressure is applied to the chest at regular intervals, moving the chest wall in a way that resembles normal breathing. Modern portable models that cover only the chest are now in use. Intermittent positive pressure breathing machines are also used. These machines produce intermittent increases in intrapulmonary pressure by means of "pulses" of air delivered via a face mask.

References: Section VII.
Respiration

Agostoni E: Mechanics of the pleural space. Physiol Rev 52:57, 1972.

Bakhle YS, Vane JR: Pharmacokinetic function of the pulmonary circulation. Physiol Rev 54:1007, 1974.

Berger AJ, Mitchell RA, Severinghaus JW: Regulation of respiration. N Engl J Med 297:92, 1977.

Cherniack NS, Longobardo GS: Cheyne-Stokes breathing. N Engl J Med 288:952, 1973.

Clark JM, Lambertson CJ: Pulmonary oxygen toxicity: A review. Pharmacol Rev 23:37, 1971.

Davenport HW: *The ABC of Acid-Base Chemistry,* 6th ed. Univ of Chicago Press, 1974.

Finch CA, Lenfant C: Oxygen transport in man. N Engl J Med 286:407, 1972.

Fishman AP, Renkin EM (editors): *Pulmonary Edema.* American Physiological Society, 1979.

Fridovich I: Oxygen is toxic. Bioscience 27:462, 1977.

Goerke J: Lung surfactant. Biochim Biophys Acta 344:241, 1974.

James LH: Perinatal events and respiratory-distress syndrome. N Engl J Med 292:1291, 1975.

Kellog RH: Oxygen and carbon dioxide in the regulation of respiration. Fed Proc 36:1658, 1977.

Kilmartin JN, Rossi-Bernardini L: Interaction of hemoglobin with hydrogen ions, carbon dioxide, and organic phosphates. Physiol Rev 53:836, 1973.

Lambertsen CJ (editor): *Underwater Physiology.* Academic Press, 1971.

Leusen I: Regulation of cerebrospinal fluid composition with reference to breathing. Physiol Rev 52:1, 1972.

Marklem PT: Respiratory mechanics. Annu Rev Physiol 40:157, 1978.

Murray JF: *The Normal Lung: The Basis for Diagnosis and Treatment of Pulmonary Disease.* Saunders, 1976.

Newhouse M, Sanchis J, Bienenstock J: Lung defense mechanisms. N Engl J Med 295:990, 1976.

Perutz FM: Hemoglobin structure and respiratory transport. Sci Am 239:92, Dec 1978.

Staub NC: Pulmonary edema. Physiol Rev 54:679, 1974.

Sugar O: In search of Ondine's curse. JAMA 240:236, 1978.

Wagner PD: Diffusion and chemical reaction in pulmonary gas exchange. Physiol Rev 57:257, 1977.

Wasserman K: Breathing during exercise. N Engl J Med 298:780, 1978.

West JB: *Respiratory Physiology: The Essentials.* Williams & Wilkins, 1974.

Whittenberger JL: Myoglobin-facilitated oxygen diffusion: Role of myoglobin in oxygen entry into muscle. Physiol Rev 50:559, 1970.

Widdicombe JG (editor): *Respiratory Physiology II.* Univ Park Press, 1977.

Winter PM, Lowenstein E: Acute respiratory failure. Sci Am 221:23, Nov 1969.

Symposium: The meaning of physical fitness. Proc R Soc Med 62:1155, 1969.

Symposium: Nonrespiratory aspects of lung physiology. Fed Proc 36:2651, 1977.

Section VIII. Formation & Excretion of Urine

38 | Renal Function

In the kidneys, a fluid that resembles plasma is filtered through the glomerular capillaries into the renal tubules (**glomerular filtration**). As this glomerular filtrate passes down the tubules, its volume is reduced and its composition altered by the processes of **tubular reabsorption** (removal of water and solutes from the tubular fluid) and **tubular secretion** (secretion of solutes into the tubular fluid) to form urine. A comparison of the composition of the plasma and an average urine specimen illustrates the magnitude of some of these changes (Table 38–1) and emphasizes the manner in which wastes are eliminated while water and important electrolytes and metabolites are conserved. Furthermore, the composition of the urine can be varied, and many homeostatic regulatory mechanisms minimize or prevent changes in the composition of the ECF by changing the amount of water and various specific solutes in the urine. The kidneys are also endocrine organs, secreting renin (see Chapter 24) and the renal erythropoietic factor (see Chapters 24 and 27).

FUNCTIONAL ANATOMY

The Nephron

Each individual renal tubule and its glomerulus is a unit, or **nephron.** The size of the kidneys in various species is largely determined by the number of nephrons they contain. There are approximately 1 million nephrons in each human kidney. The parts of the nephron are illustrated in Fig 38–1.

The glomerulus, which is about 200 μm in diameter, is formed by the invagination of a tuft of capillaries

into the dilated, blind end of the nephron (**Bowman's capsule**). The capillaries are supplied by an **afferent arteriole** and drained by a slightly smaller **efferent arteriole** (Fig 38–1). There are 2 cellular layers separating the blood from the glomerular filtrate in Bowman's capsule: the capillary endothelium and the epithelium of the tubule. These layers are separated by a basal lamina (Fig 38–2). The endothelium is fenestrated, with pores that are approximately 100 nm in diameter. The pseudopodia of the epithelial cells (**podocytes**) form slits along the capillary wall that are approximately 25 nm wide. The basal lamina does not contain visible gaps or pores. Functionally, the glomerular membrane permits the free passage of neutral substances up to 4 nm in diameter and almost totally excludes those with diameters greater than 8 nm.

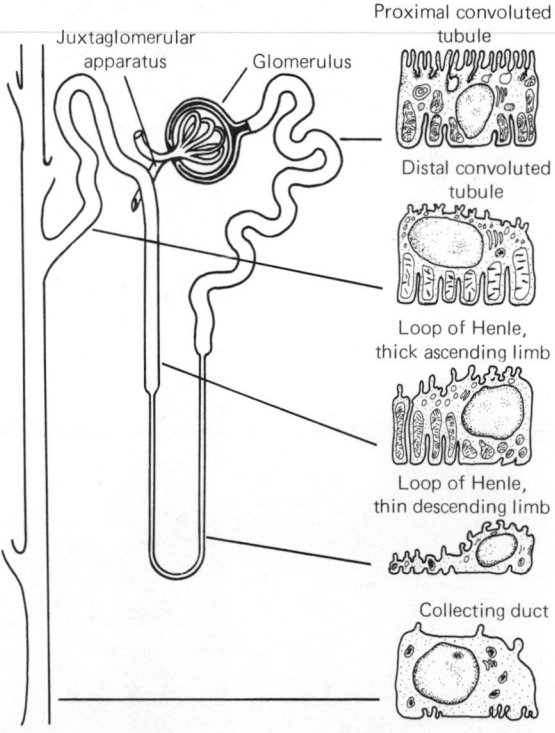

Figure 38–1. Diagram of a juxtamedullary nephron. Below each label on the right is a drawing of the type of cell that makes up that segment.

Table 38–1. Urinary and plasma concentrations of some physiologically important substances.

Substance	Concentration in Urine (U)	Plasma (P)	U/P Ratio
Glucose (mg/dl)	0	100	0
Na$^+$ (mEq/L)	150	150	1
Urea (mg/dl)	900	15	60
Creatinine (mg/dl)	150	1	150

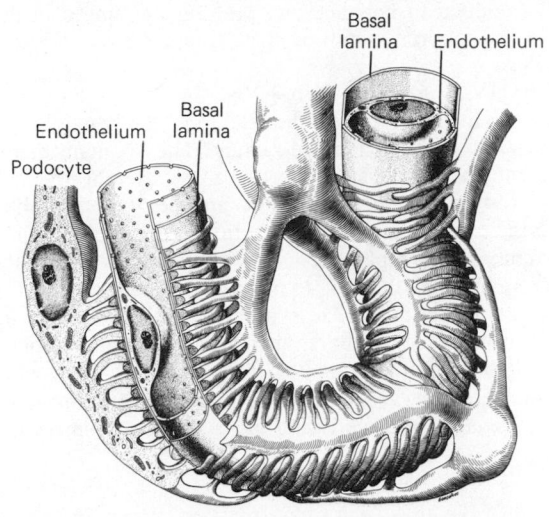

Figure 38–2. Ultrastructure of glomerular capillary and visceral layer of Bowman's capsule formed by podocytes. (Redrawn and modified after Gordon L. Reproduced, with permission, from Ham AW: *Histology,* 7th ed. Lippincott, 1974.)

However, the charges on molecules as well as their diameters affect their passage into Bowman's capsule (see below). The average capillary area in each glomerulus is about 0.4 mm^2, and the total area of glomerular capillary endothelium across which filtration occurs in humans is about 0.8 m^2.

The human **proximal convoluted tubule** is about 15 mm long and 55 μm in diameter. Its wall is made up of a single layer of cells that interdigitate with one another. The luminal edges of the cells have a striate **brush border** due to the presence of innumerable 1×0.7 μm microvilli.

The convoluted portion of the proximal tubule (pars convoluta) drains into the straight portion (pars recta), which forms the first part of the **loop of Henle** (Figs 38–1 and 38–3). The proximal tubule terminates in the thin segment of the descending limb of the loop of Henle, which has an epithelium made up of attenuated, flat cells. The nephrons with glomeruli in the outer portions of the renal cortex have short loops of Henle (Fig 38–3), whereas those with glomeruli in the juxtamedullary region of the cortex have long loops extending down into the medullary pyramids. In humans, only 15% of the nephrons have long loops. The total length of the thin segment of the loop varies from

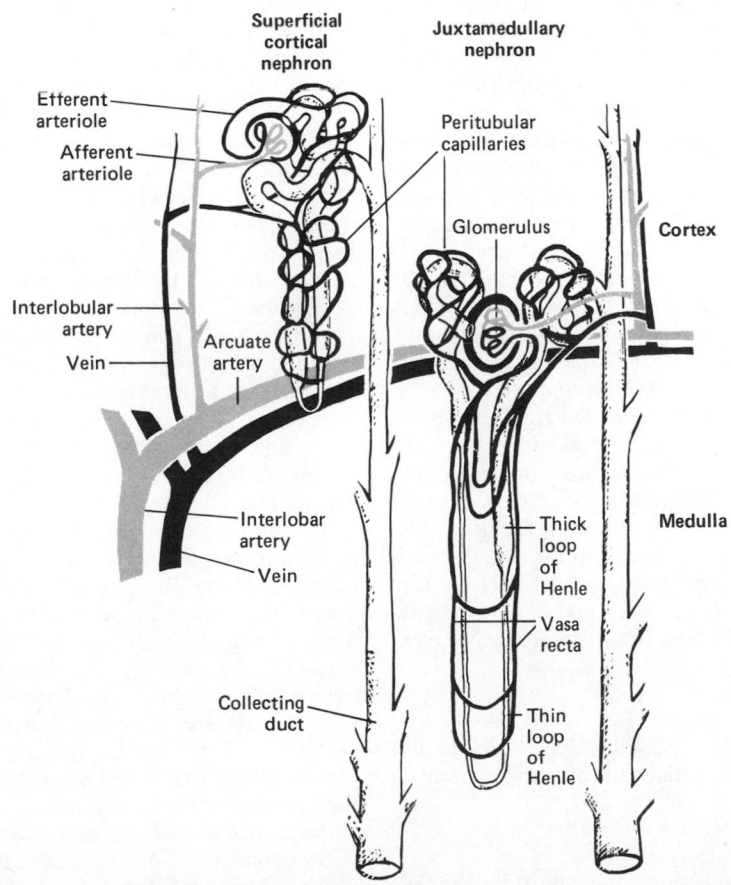

Figure 38–3. Diagram of renal circulation. Note difference in circulation to tubules of cortical nephrons and juxtamedullary nephrons. (Modified from Vander AJ: *Renal Physiology.* McGraw-Hill, 1975.)

2 to 14 mm in length. It ends in the thick segment of the ascending limb, which is about 12 mm in length.

The thick ascending limb of the loop of Henle reaches the glomerulus of the nephron from which the tubule arose and passes close to its afferent arteriole, the wall of which contains the renin-secreting juxtaglomerular cells. At this point, the tubular epithelium is modified histologically to form the **macula densa** (see Chapter 24). The macula densa is arbitrarily designated as the point where the loop of Henle ends and the distal convoluted tubule begins. The juxtaglomerular cells, the macula densa, and a few granulated cells between them are known collectively as the **juxtaglomerular apparatus.**

The **distal convoluted tubule** is about 5 mm long. Its epithelium is lower than that of the proximal tubule, and although there are a few microvilli, there is no distinct brush border. The distal tubules coalesce to form **collecting ducts** that are about 20 mm long and pass through the renal cortex and medulla to empty into the pelvis of the kidney at the apexes of the medullary pyramids. The total length of the nephrons, including the collecting ducts, ranges from 45 to 65 mm.

Blood Vessels

The renal circulation is diagrammed in Fig 38–3. The afferent arterioles are short, straight branches of the interlobular arteries. Each divides into multiple capillary branches to form the tuft of vessels in the glomerulus. The capillaries coalesce to form the efferent arterioles, which in turn break up into capillaries that supply the tubules before draining into the interlobular veins. The arterial segments between glomeruli and tubules are thus technically a portal system, and the glomerular capillaries are the only capillaries in the body that drain into arterioles.

The capillaries draining the tubules of the cortical nephrons form a peritubular network, but the efferent arterioles from the juxtamedullary glomeruli drain into a network of vessels that form hairpin loops (the **vasa recta**). These loops dip into the medullary pyramids alongside the loops of Henle (Fig 38–3). The efferent arteriole from each glomerulus breaks up into capillaries that supply a number of different nephrons. Thus, the tubule of each nephron does not necessarily receive blood solely from the efferent arteriole of that nephron. In humans, the total surface of the renal capillaries is approximately equal to the total surface area of the tubules, both being about 12 m^2. The volume of blood in the renal capillaries at any given time is 30–40 ml.

Lymphatics

The kidneys have an abundant lymphatic supply that drains via the thoracic duct into the venous circulation in the thorax.

Capsule

The renal capsule is thin but tough. If the kidney becomes edematous, the capsule limits the swelling, and the tissue pressure (**renal interstitial pressure**)

rises. This decreases the glomerular filtration rate and is claimed to enhance and prolong the anuria in the lower nephron syndrome (see Chapter 33).

Innervation of the Renal Vessels

The renal nerves travel along the renal blood vessels as they enter the kidney. They contain many sympathetic efferent fibers and a few afferent fibers of unknown function. There also appears to be a cholinergic component, but its function is uncertain. In humans, the sympathetic innervation comes primarily from the 12th thoracic to the second lumbar segments of the spinal cord. The sympathetic fibers are in part vasoconstrictor in function and are distributed particularly to the afferent and efferent arterioles. However, adrenergic nerve fibers also end in close proximity to the renal tubular cells and the juxtaglomerular cells.

RENAL CIRCULATION

Blood Flow

In a resting adult, the kidneys receive 1.2–1.3 L of blood per minute, or just under 25% of the cardiac output (Table 32–1). Renal blood flow can be measured with electromagnetic or other types of flow meters, or it can be determined by applying the Fick principle (see Chapter 29) to the kidney—ie, by measuring the amount of a given substance taken up per unit of time and dividing this value by the arteriovenous difference for the substance across the kidney. Since the kidney filters plasma, the **renal plasma flow** equals the amount of a substance excreted per unit of time divided by the renal arteriovenous difference as long as the amount in the red cells is unaltered during passage through the kidney. Any excreted substance can be used if its concentration in arterial and renal venous plasma can be measured and if it is not metabolized, not stored or produced by the kidney, and does not itself affect blood flow.

Renal plasma flow is commonly measured by infusing para-aminohippuric acid (PAH) or iodopyracet (Diodrast) and determining their urine and plasma concentrations. These substances are filtered by the glomeruli and secreted by the tubular cells, so that their **extraction ratio** (arterial concentration minus renal venous concentration/arterial concentration) is high. For example, when PAH is infused at low doses, 90% of the PAH in arterial blood is removed in a single circulation through the kidney. It has therefore become commonplace to calculate the "renal plasma flow" by dividing the amount of PAH in the urine by the plasma PAH level, ignoring the level in renal venous blood. Peripheral venous plasma can be used because its PAH concentration is essentially identical to that in the arterial plasma reaching the kidney. The value obtained should be called the **effective renal plasma flow (ERPF)** to indicate that the level in renal venous plasma was not measured. In humans, ERPF averages about 625 ml/min.

Effective renal plasma flow (ERPF) =

$$\frac{U_{PAH}V}{P_{PAH}} = \text{Clearance of PAH (C}_{PAH}\text{)}$$

Example:

Concentration of PAH in urine (U_{PAH}): 14 mg/ml

Urine volume (V): 0.9 ml/min

Concentration of PAH in plasma (P_{PAH}): 0.02 mg/ml

$$ERPF = \frac{14 \times 0.9}{0.02} = 630 \text{ ml/min}$$

It should be noted that the ERPF determined in this way is the **clearance** of PAH. The concept of clearance is discussed in detail below.

ERPF can be converted to actual renal plasma flow (RPF):

Average PAH extraction ratio: 0.9

$$\frac{ERPF}{\text{Extraction ratio}} = \frac{630}{0.9} = \text{Actual RPF} = 700 \text{ ml/min}$$

From the renal plasma flow, the renal blood flow can be calculated by dividing by one minus the hematocrit.

Hematocrit (Hct): 45%

$$\text{Renal blood flow} = \text{RPF} \times \frac{1}{1-\text{Hct}} =$$

$$700 \times \frac{1}{0.55} = 1273 \text{ ml/min}$$

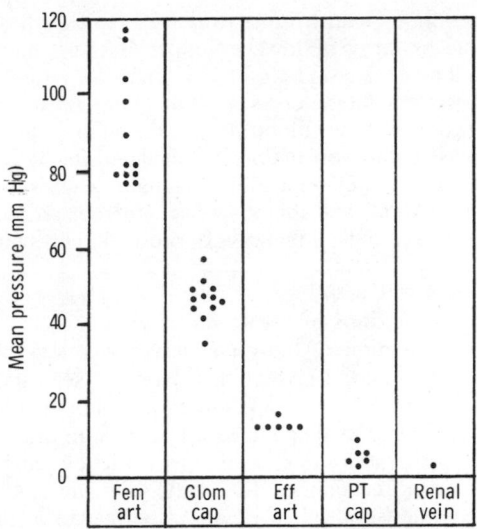

Figure 38–4. Mean pressures in the blood vessels of rats. Dots represent individual values in the femoral artery (Fem art), glomerular capillaries (Glom cap), efferent arterioles (Eff art), peritubular capillaries (PT cap), and renal vein. (Reproduced, with permission, from Brenner BM, Troy JL, Daugharty TM: The dynamics of glomerular filtration in the rat. J Clin Invest 50:1176, 1971.)

Regional Blood Flow

The blood flow in the renal cortex is much greater than in the medulla. Values obtained in dogs are 4–5 ml/g of kidney tissue per minute in the cortex, 1–2 ml/g/min in the outer medulla, and 0.3–0.6 ml/g/min in the inner medulla. However, the renal blood flow per gram of tissue is very large, and even the medullary flow is relatively large on a tissue weight basis. For comparison, the normal blood flow of the brain is 0.5 ml/g/min (see Chapter 32).

Pressure in Renal Vessels

The pressure in the glomerular capillaries has now been measured directly in rats and has been found to be considerably lower than predicted on the basis of indirect measurements. Directly measured values in a systemic artery, glomerular capillaries, efferent arterioles, peritubular capillaries, and the renal vein are shown in Fig 38–4. Pressure gradients are similar in the squirrel monkey and presumably in humans, with a glomerular capillary pressure that is about 50% of systemic arterial pressure and a peritubular capillary pressure of about 15 mm Hg.

Renal Vasoconstriction

Stimulation of the renal nerves causes a marked decrease in renal blood flow. Similar renal vasoconstriction can be produced by stimulating the vasomotor center in the medulla, parts of the brain stem, and the cerebral cortex, especially the anterior tip of the temporal lobe. There is some tonic discharge in the renal nerves at rest in animals and humans, however; and when systemic blood pressure falls, the vasoconstrictor response produced by decreased discharge in the baroreceptor nerves includes renal vasoconstriction.

Hypoxia is another stimulus to renal vasoconstriction, but only when the arterial O_2 content falls to less than 50% of normal. The response is mediated via the chemoreceptors, which stimulate the vasomotor center to produce renal vasoconstriction when the renal nerves are intact. Catecholamines constrict the renal vessels. Small doses of epinephrine and norepinephrine have a greater effect on the efferent than on the afferent arterioles, so that glomerular capillary pressure and, consequently, the glomerular filtration rate are maintained while renal blood flow is decreased; large doses depress the glomerular filtration rate. Renal blood flow is decreased during exercise and, to a lesser extent, on rising from the supine to the standing position.

Renal Vasodilatation

Bacterial pyrogens cause renal vasodilatation. The response is not due to the fever they produce, because it occurs when the febrile response is blocked by the administration of antipyretic drugs. In fact, fever due to other causes is usually associated with moderate renal vasoconstriction. Hydralazine

(Apresoline), a drug used to treat hypertension, has the unique property of lowering blood pressure and increasing renal blood flow. For unknown reasons, a high-protein diet increases renal blood flow. Prostaglandins increase blood flow in the renal cortex and decrease blood flow in the renal medulla. In conscious dogs, moderate hemorrhage actually causes renal vasodilatation, and this response is prevented by indomethacin, a drug that blocks prostaglandin synthesis.

Other Functions of the Renal Nerves

Stimulation of the renal nerves increases renin secretion from the juxtaglomerular cells (see Chapter 24). There are a number of observations in the literature that suggest that increased activity in the renal nerves decreases salt excretion by an action independent of its effect on the afferent arterioles and hence on glomerular filtration. This could be due to a direct effect on the tubular cells or could be secondary to changes in medullary blood flow. It could also be due to stimulation of the juxtaglomerular cells, with increased secretion of renin and consequently of aldosterone. However, most renal functions appear to be normal in patients with transplanted kidneys, and those kidneys do not acquire a functional innervation for long periods of time.

Autoregulation of Renal Blood Flow

When the kidney is perfused at moderate pressures (90–220 mm Hg in the dog), the renal vascular resistance varies with the pressure so that renal blood flow is relatively constant (Fig 38–5). Autoregulation of this type occurs in other organs, and many theories have been advanced to explain it (see Chapter 31). Renal autoregulation is present in denervated and in isolated, perfused kidneys but is prevented by the administration of drugs that paralyze vascular smooth muscle. It is probably produced by a direct contractile response of the smooth muscle of the afferent arteriole to stretch.

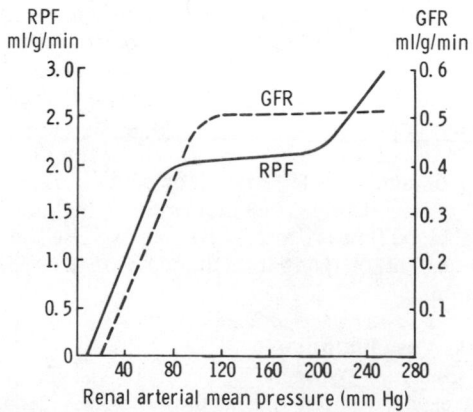

Figure 38–5. Autoregulation in the dog kidney. GFR, glomerular filtration rate; RPF, renal plasma flow. (Modified and reproduced, with permission, from Shipley RE, Study RS: Changes in renal blood flow. Am J Physiol 167:676, 1951.)

Renal Oxygen Consumption

The O_2 consumption of the human kidney is about 18 ml/min. The renal blood flow per gram of tissue is very large, and it is therefore not surprising that the arteriovenous O_2 difference is only 14 ml/L of blood, compared with 62 ml/L for the brain and 114 ml/L for the heart (Table 32–1). The renal function with which the O_2 consumption correlates best is the rate of active transport of Na^+. The O_2 consumption of the cortex is about 9 ml/100 g/min, whereas that of the inner medulla is only 0.4 ml/100 g/min. The tubular fluid passes through the medulla on its way to the renal pelvis, and the P_{O_2} of the urine is also low.

GLOMERULAR FILTRATION

Measuring GFR

The **glomerular filtration rate (GFR)** can be measured in intact animals and humans by measuring the excretion and plasma level of a substance that is freely filtered through the glomeruli and neither secreted nor reabsorbed by the tubules. The amount of such a substance in the urine per unit of time must have been provided by filtering exactly the number of ml of plasma that contained this amount. Therefore, if the substance is designated by the letter x, the GFR is equal to the **concentration** of x in urine (U_X) times the **urine flow** per unit of time (V) divided by the **arterial plasma level** of x (P_X), or $U_X V/P_X$. This value is called the **clearance** of x (C_X). P_X is, of course, the same in all parts of the arterial circulation, and if x is not metabolized to any extent in the tissues, the level of x in peripheral venous plasma can be substituted for the arterial plasma level.

Substances Used to Measure GFR

In addition to the requirement that it be freely filtered and neither reabsorbed nor secreted in the tubules, a substance suitable for measuring the GFR should meet other criteria (Table 38–2). Inulin, a polymer of fructose with a molecular weight of 5200 that is found in dahlia tubers, meets these criteria in humans and most animals and is extensively used to measure GFR. In practice, a loading dose of inulin is

Table 38–2. Characteristics of a substance suitable for measuring the GFR by determining its clearance.

Freely filtered

Not reabsorbed or secreted by tubules

Not metabolized

Not stored in kidney

Not protein-bound (substances bound to albumin and globulin not filtered)

Not toxic

Has no effect on filtration rate

Preferably easy to measure in plasma and urine

administered intravenously, followed by a sustaining infusion to keep the arterial plasma level constant. After the inulin has equilibrated with body fluids, an accurately timed urine specimen is collected and a plasma sample obtained halfway through the collection. Plasma and urinary inulin concentrations are determined and the clearance calculated.

Example:

$$U_{In} = 29 \text{ mg/ml}$$

$$V = 1.1 \text{ ml/min}$$

$$P_{In} = 0.25 \text{ mg/ml}$$

$$C_{In} = \frac{U_{In}V}{P_{In}} = \frac{29 \times 1.1}{0.25}$$

$$C_{In} = 128 \text{ ml/min}$$

In dogs, cats, rabbits, and a number of other mammalian species, clearance of creatinine (C_{Cr}) can also be used to determine the GFR, but in primates, including humans, some creatinine is secreted by the tubules, and some may be reabsorbed. In addition, plasma creatinine determinations are inaccurate at low creatinine levels because the method for determining creatinine measures small amounts of other plasma constituents. In spite of this, the clearance of endogenous creatinine is frequently measured in patients. The values agree quite well with the GFR values measured with inulin because, although the value for $U_{Cr}V$ is high as a result of tubular secretion, the value for P_{Cr} is also high as a result of nonspecific chromogens and the errors thus tend to cancel. Endogenous creatinine clearance is easy to measure and is a worthwhile index of renal function, but when precise measurements of GFR are needed it seems unwise to rely on a method that owes what accuracy it has to compensating errors.

Normal GFR

The GFR in an average-sized normal man is approximately 125 ml/min. Its magnitude correlates fairly well with surface area, but values in women are 10% lower than those in men even after correction for surface area. It should be noted that 125 ml/min is 7.5 L/h, or 180 L/d, whereas the normal urine volume is about 1 L/d. Thus, 99% or more of the filtrate is normally reabsorbed. At the rate of 125 ml/min, the kidneys filter in 1 day an amount of fluid equal to 4 times the total body water, 15 times the ECF volume, and 60 times the plasma volume.

Control of GFR

The factors governing filtration across the glomerular capillaries are the same as those governing filtration across all other capillaries (see Chapter 30), ie, the size of the capillary bed, the permeability of the capillaries, and the hydrostatic and osmotic pressure gradients across the capillary wall. Thus, for each nephron:

$$GFR = kS[(P_{GC} - P_T) - (\Pi_{GC} - \Pi_T)]$$

where k is the capillary permeability, S the size of the capillary bed, P_{GC} the mean hydrostatic pressure in the glomerular capillaries, P_T the mean hydrostatic pressure in the tubule, Π_{GC} the osmotic pressure of the plasma in the glomerular capillaries, and Π_T the osmotic pressure of the filtrate in the tubule.

Permeability

The permeability of the glomerular capillaries is about 50 times that of the capillaries in skeletal muscle. Neutral substances with effective molecular diameters of less than 4 nm are freely filtered, and the filtration of neutral substances with diameters of more than 8 nm approaches zero (Fig 38–6). Between these values, filtration is inversely proportionate to diameter. However, sialoproteins in the endothelium and basement membrane are negatively charged, and studies with anionically charged and cationically charged dextrans indicate that the endothelial and membrane charges repel negatively charged substances in blood, with the result that filtration of anionic substances 4 nm in diameter is less than half that of neutral substances of the same size. Filtration of cationic substances is slightly greater than that of neutral substances. This probably explains why albumin, with an effective molecular radius of approximately 7.2 nm, normally has a glomerular concentration only 0.2% of its plasma concentration rather than the higher concentration that would be expected on the basis of diameter alone; circulating albumin is negatively charged.

The presence of albumin in the urine is called **albuminuria.** There is evidence that in nephritis the negative charges in the glomerular wall are dissipated and that albuminuria can occur for this reason without an increase in the size of the "pores" in the membrane.

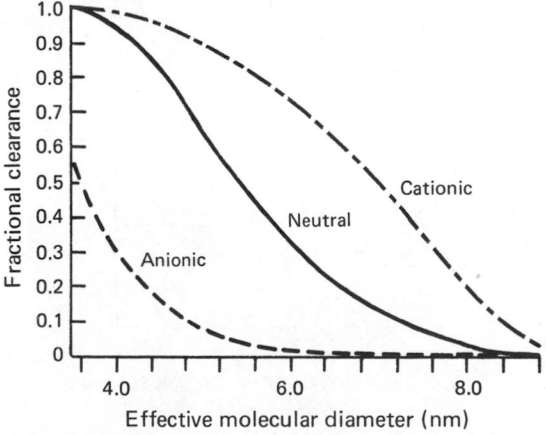

Figure 38–6. Effect of electrical charge on the fractional clearance of dextran molecules of various sizes in rats. The negative charges in the glomerular membrane retard the passage of negatively charged molecules (anionic dextran) and facilitate the passage of positively charged molecules (cationic dextran). (Reproduced, with permission, from Brenner BM, Beeuwkes R: Renal circulations. Hosp Pract 13:35, July 1978.)

Because of the nondiffusibility of plasma proteins, there is a Donnan effect (see Chapter 1) on the monovalent diffusible ion distribution, the concentration of anions being about 5% greater in the glomerular filtrate than in plasma and the concentration of monovalent cations 5% less. However, for most purposes this effect can be ignored, and in other respects the composition of the filtrate is similar to that of plasma.

Hydrostatic & Osmotic Pressure

The pressure in the glomerular capillaries is higher than that in other capillary beds because the afferent arterioles are short, straight branches of the interlobular arteries. Furthermore, the vessels "downstream" from the glomeruli, the efferent arterioles, have a relatively high resistance. The capillary hydrostatic pressure is opposed by the hydrostatic pressure in Bowman's capsule. It is also opposed by the osmotic pressure gradient across the glomerular capillaries ($\Pi_{GC} - \Pi_T$). Π_T is normally negligible, and the gradient is equal to the oncotic pressure of the plasma proteins.

The actual pressures in rats are shown in Fig 38–7. The corresponding pressures in humans are unknown, but it is significant that the pressures have been measured in the squirrel monkey and are comparable to those in the rat. The net filtration pressure in the rat (P_{UF}) is 15 mm Hg at the afferent end of the glomerular capillaries, but it falls to 0—ie, **filtration equilibrium** is reached—proximal to the efferent end of the glomerular capillaries. This is because fluid leaves the

Table 38–3. Factors affecting the glomerular filtration rate.

1. Changes in renal blood flow
2. Changes in glomerular capillary hydrostatic pressure
   a. Changes in systemic blood pressure
   b. Afferent or efferent arteriolar constriction
3. Changes in hydrostatic pressure in Bowman's capsule
   a. Ureteral obstruction
   b. Edema of kidney inside tight renal capsule
4. Changes in concentration of plasma proteins: dehydration, hypoproteinemia, etc (minor factors)
5. Increased permeability of glomerular filter: various diseases
6. Decrease in total area of glomerular capillary bed
   a. Diseases that destroy glomeruli with or without destruction of tubules
   b. Partial nephrectomy

plasma and the oncotic pressure rises as blood passes through the glomerular capillaries. The calculated change in $\Delta\Pi$ along an idealized glomerular capillary is shown in Fig 38–7. It is apparent that portions of the glomerular capillaries do not normally contribute to the formation of the glomerular ultrafiltrate. It is also apparent that a decrease in the rate of rise of the $\Delta\Pi$ curve would increase filtration without any change in ΔP because it would increase the distance along the capillary in which filtration was taking place.

Changes in GFR

Variations in the factors listed in the preceding paragraphs have predictable effects on the GFR (Table 38–3). Increases in glomerular plasma flow consequent to increased renal blood flow can increase GFR without any change in perfusion pressure because they displace the point at which filtration equilibrium is reached closer to the efferent end of the glomerular capillaries. The area between the ΔP and $\Delta\Pi$ curves is therefore increased and the ultrafiltration pressure is increased. Conversely, decreases in glomerular plasma flow lower GFR.

Changes in renal vascular resistance due to autoregulation tend to stabilize filtration pressure, but when the mean systemic arterial pressure drops below 90 mm Hg, there is a sharp drop in GFR. The GFR tends to be maintained when efferent arteriolar constriction is greater than afferent constriction, but either type of constriction decreases the tubular blood flow.

Filtration Fraction

The ratio of the GFR to the renal plasma flow (RPF), the **filtration fraction,** is normally 0.16–0.20. The GFR varies less than the RPF. When there is a fall in systemic blood pressure, GFR falls less than the RPF because of efferent arteriolar constriction, and consequently the filtration fraction rises.

	(mm Hg)	
	Afferent End	Efferent End
P_{GC}	45	45
P_T	10	10
Π_{GC}	20	35
$P_{UF} = P_{GC} - P_T - \Pi_{GC}$	15	0

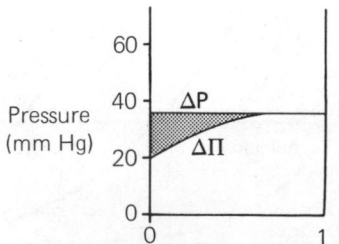

Dimensionless distance along idealized glomerular capillary

Figure 38–7. Hydrostatic pressure (P_{GC}) and osmotic pressure (Π_{GC}) in a glomerular capillary in the rat. P_T, pressure in tubule; P_{UF}, net filtration pressure. Since Π_T is negligible (see text), $\Delta\Pi = \Pi_{GC}$. $\Delta P = P_{GC} - P_T$. (Reproduced, with permission, from Mercer PF, Maddox DA, Brenner BM: Current concepts of sodium chloride and water transport by the mammalian nephron. West J Med 120:33, 1974.)

TUBULAR FUNCTION

General Considerations

The amount of any substance that is filtered is the product of the GFR and the plasma level of the substance ($C_{In}P_X$). The tubular cells may add more of the substance to the filtrate (tubular secretion), may remove some or all of the substance from the filtrate (tubular reabsorption), or may do both. The amount of the substance excreted (U_XV) equals the amount filtered plus the **net amount transferred** by the tubules. This latter quantity is conveniently indicated by the symbol T_X. When there is net tubular secretion, T_X is positive; when there is net tubular reabsorption, T_X is negative (Fig 38–8).

Since the clearance of any substance is UV/P, the clearance equals the GFR if there is no net tubular secretion or reabsorption; exceeds the GFR if there is net tubular secretion; and is less than the GFR if there is net tubular reabsorption. It should be noted that in the latter 2 cases the clearance is a "virtual volume," an index of renal function, rather than an actual volume.

Much of our knowledge about glomerular filtration and tubular function has been obtained by the use of micropuncture technics. It was first demonstrated some years ago that micropipettes could be inserted into the tubules of the living kidney and the composition of aspirated tubular fluid determined by the use of microchemical technics. Recent technical advances have made it possible to study in this way the kidneys of a variety of mammals. In the rat, data are now available on samples from the glomerulus, the first 70% of the proximal tubule, the tip of the loop of Henle, and all parts of the distal tubule and collecting ducts as well as all parts of the renal vasculature. Using microelectrodes, it has been possible to measure the membrane potentials of the tubular cells. The potential difference of -70 mV between the tubular lumen and the interior of proximal tubular cells is the same, or nearly the same, as that between the cells and the ECF. Consequently, the potential between the tubular lumen and the ECF is -2 mV (tubular lumen negative) in the first quarter of the proximal tubule, and, according to some investigators, $+2$ mV (tubular lumen positive) in the remainder of the proximal tubule. The lumen of the loop of Henle is negative to the ECF except for the thick ascending limb, where the potential difference is $+7$ mV. In the distal tubule, the potential difference again becomes lumen negative, and it increases to a peak of -45 mV in the late portion. The potential difference in the collecting duct is -35 mV (lumen negative).

Mechanisms of Tubular Reabsorption & Secretion

Substances are secreted or reabsorbed in the tubules by passive diffusion down chemical or electrical gradients or actively transported against such gradients (see Chapter 1). Like transport systems elsewhere, each renal active transport system has a maximal rate, or **transport maximum (Tm)** at which it can transport a particular solute. Thus, the amount of a particular solute transported is proportionate to the amount present up to the Tm for the solute, but at higher concentrations, the transport mechanism is **saturated** and there is no appreciable increment in the amount transported. However, the Tm for some systems is so high that it is almost impossible to saturate them.

Glucose Reabsorption

Glucose is typical of substances removed from the urine by active transport. It is filtered at a rate of approximately 100 mg/min (80 mg/dl of plasma × 125

$$GFR \times P_X + T_X = U_XV$$

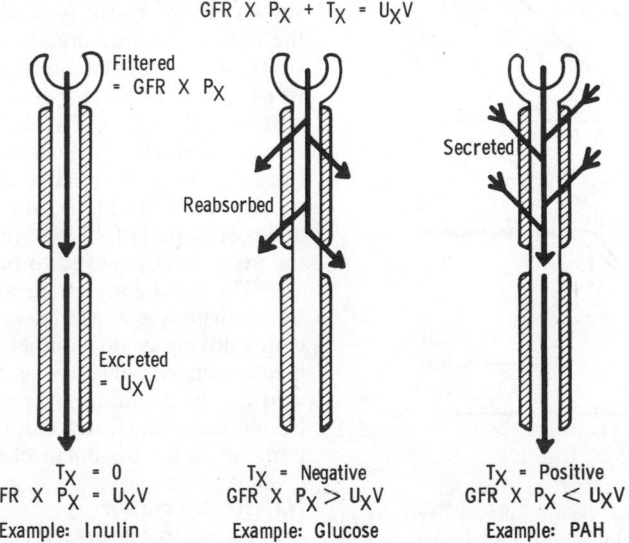

Figure 38–8. Tubular function. For explanation of symbols, see text.

ml/min). Micropuncture studies demonstrate that reabsorption occurs in the first part of the proximal tubule. Essentially all of the glucose is reabsorbed, and no more than a few milligrams appear in the urine per 24 hours. The amount reabsorbed is proportionate to the amount filtered and hence to the plasma glucose level (P_G) up to the transfer maximum (Tm_G); but when the Tm_G is exceeded, the amount of glucose in the urine rises (Fig 38–9). The Tm_G is about 375 mg/min in men and 300 mg/min in women.

The **renal threshold** for glucose is the plasma level at which the glucose first appears in the urine in more than the normal minute amounts. One would predict that the renal threshold would be about 300 mg/dl—ie, 375 mg/min (Tm_G) divided by 125 ml/min (GFR). However, the actual renal threshold is about 200 mg/dl of arterial plasma, which corresponds to a venous level of about 180 mg/dl.

Fig 38–9 shows why the actual renal threshold is less than the predicted threshold. The ''ideal'' curve shown in this diagram would be obtained if the Tm_Gs in all the tubules were identical and if all the glucose were removed from each tubule when the amount filtered was below the Tm_G. The curve of data actually obtained in humans is not sharply angulated and deviates considerably from the ''ideal'' curve. This deviation is called **splay.** It is present for 2 reasons. In the first place, not all of the 2 million nephrons in the kidneys have exactly the same Tm_G or filtration rate; in some, Tm_G is exceeded at low levels of P_G. In the second place, some glucose escapes reabsorption when the amount filtered is below the Tm_G because the reactions involved in glucose transport are not completely irreversible. Indeed, the dynamics of all the active transport systems that remove substances from the tubules are probably such that for each, the curve relating amount transported to the plasma level of the substance is rounded rather than sharply angulated. The degree of rounding is inversely proportionate to the avidity with which the transport mechanism binds the substance it transports.

Glucose Transport Mechanism

The details of the operation of the renal glucose transport mechanism are still obscure. The same mechanism transports fructose, galactose, and xylose. It is unaffected by insulin, Tm_G being normal in diabetes; but it is inhibited, as is the transport of glucose across the intestinal mucosa, by the plant glycoside **phlorhizin.**

Other Substances Reabsorbed Actively

Other substances that are actively reabsorbed include Na^+, K^+, Cl^-, PO_4^{3-}, amino acids, creatine, sulfate, uric acid, ascorbic acid, and the ketone bodies acetoacetic acid and β-hydroxybutyric acid. The Tm's of these substances range from very low values to values so high that they have not yet been accurately measured. Some of the transport mechanisms appear to share a common step. Some transport in either direction, depending on circumstances, and some may exchange one substance for another. There are several different systems that transport amino acids. It appears that Na^+ is necessary for the binding of most amino acids to their carriers, and K^+ is also necessary.

Most of the active transport mechanisms responsible for reabsorbing particular solutes are located in the proximal tubules. Na^+ is also actively transported out of the tubular fluid in the distal tubule and collecting ducts. There is active transport of Cl^- in the thick ascending limb of the loop of Henle.

A profile of transport along the proximal tubule is shown in Fig 38–10. According to this view, most of the reabsorption of organic molecules occurs in the first quarter of the tubule and may be coupled, at least in part, to active transport of Na^+. In the remaining portion of the tubule, Cl^- diffuses down its concentration gradient out of the tubular fluid. Since the tubular lumen is positive relative to the interstitium, Na^+ moves out of the tubule along its electrical gradient, and at least part of the Na^+ reabsorption in this part of the nephron is believed to be passive.

The renal active transport mechanisms, like active transport systems elsewhere, can be inhibited competitively or noncompetitively. For example, the mechanism responsible for the reabsorption of uric acid can be inhibited by probenecid (Benemid) and phenylbutazone (Butazolidin), a fact of practical importance in the treatment of gout (see Chapter 17).

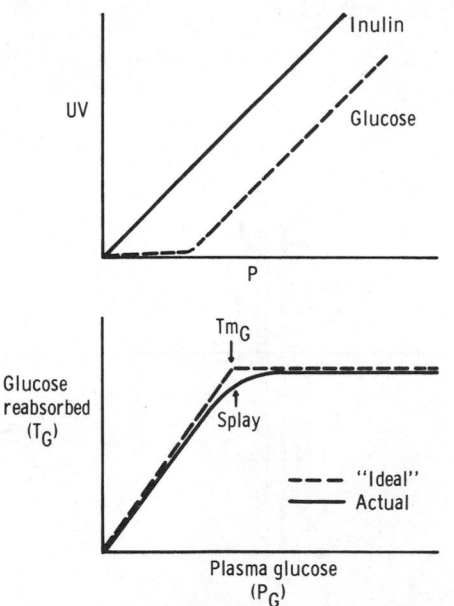

Figure 38–9. *Above:* Relation between plasma level (P) and excretion (UV) of glucose and inulin. *Below:* Relation between plasma glucose level (P_G) and amount of glucose reabsorbed (T_G).

Na$^+$ Reabsorption

Na^+ diffuses passively from the tubular lumen into tubular epithelial cells and is pumped actively from them into the interstitial space. The tubular cells

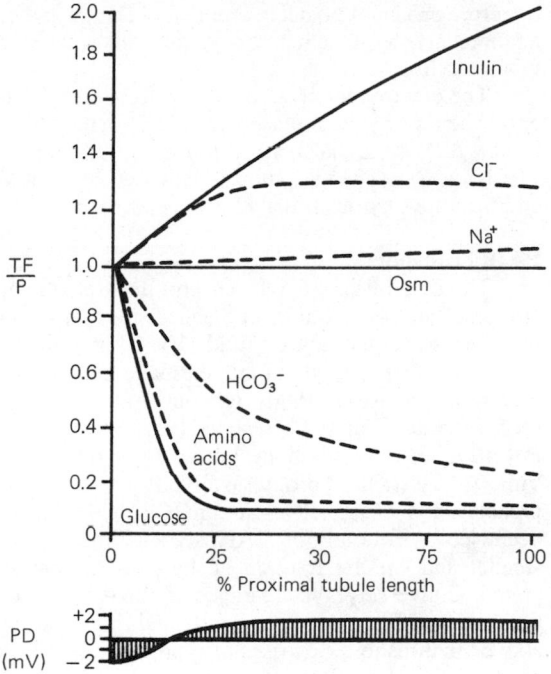

Figure 38–10. Reabsorption of various solutes in the proximal tubule in relation to the potential difference (PD) along the tubule. TF/P, tubular fluid to plasma concentration ratio. (Courtesy of FC Rector Jr.)

are connected at their luminal surface by tight junctions, but there is space between the cells along the rest of their lateral borders. Much of the Na^+ is actively transported into these extensions of the interstitial space, which are called the **lateral intercellular spaces** (Fig 38–11). This creates a hyperosmotic local environment in the spaces, and water moves passively into it from cells. From the lateral intercellular spaces and the rest of the interstitium, the rate at which solutes and water move into the capillaries is determined by the Starling forces determining movement across the walls of all capillaries, ie, the hydrostatic and osmotic pressures in the interstitium and the capillaries (see Chapter 30). When the capillary hydrostatic pressure is increased or the plasma protein pressure is decreased, the movement of solute and water into the capillaries slows, and the lateral intercellular spaces expand (Fig 38–11, right). There is evidence that some salt and water leaks across the tight junctions to the tubular lumen even in the hydropenic state, and when the lateral intercellular spaces are expanded, this "leak" back into the tubules is large. Thus, net Na^+ reabsorption is decreased.

There appear to be 2 separate Na^+ pumps in the renal tubules. One (pump A in Fig 38–12) extrudes Na^+ into the interstitium, and Cl^- moves passively with the Na^+. The Cl^- in the cells is replenished by diffusion from the tubular fluid. This pump is an **electrogenic Na^+ pump** in that it extrudes positively charged Na^+ ions and consequently contributes to the maintenance of the electronegativity of the cell interior. The other pump (pump B in Fig 38–12) is a coupled exchange pump that transports a K^+ into the cell for each Na^+ it transports into the interstitium. It

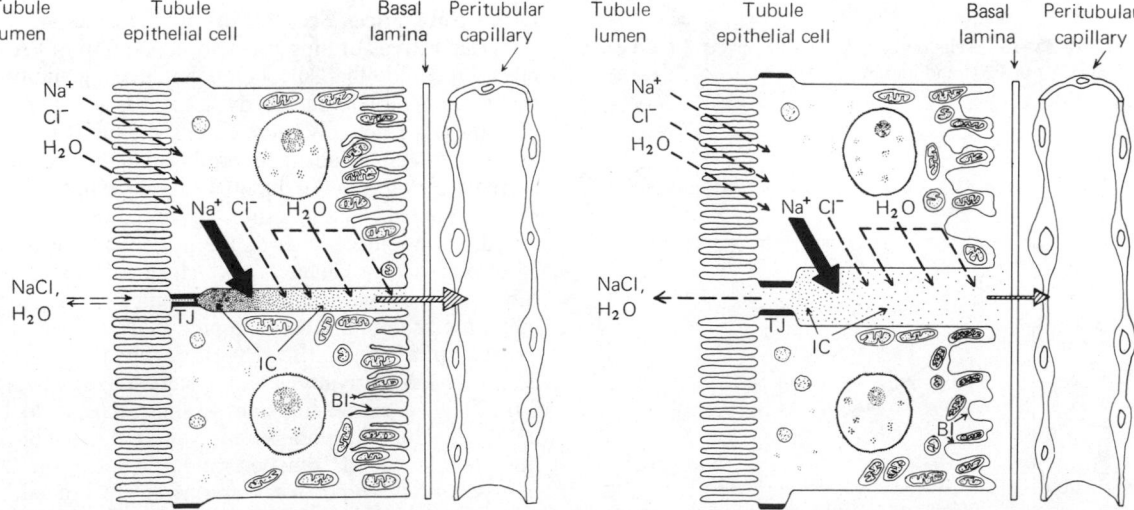

Figure 38–11. Diagrammatic summary of the movement of Na^+ from the tubular lumen to the renal capillaries in locations where it is actively transported. **Left:** Situation in hydropenic state. **Right:** Situation when capillary uptake is reduced by increasing capillary pressure or decreasing plasma protein concentration. Heavy solid arrow indicates active transport; dashed arrows indicate passive movement; hatched arrow indicates movement into renal capillaries as a function of the Starling forces across these capillaries. TJ, tight junction; IC, lateral intercellular space; BI, basilar infoldings. (Reproduced, with permission, from Mercer PF, Maddox DA, Brenner BM: Current concepts of sodium chloride and water transport by the mammalian nephron. West J Med 120:33, 1974.)

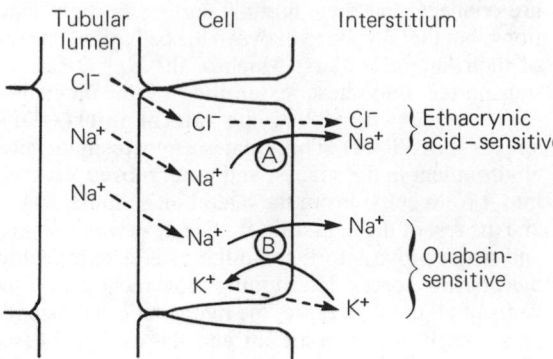

Figure 38–12. Two mechanisms that actively transport Na^+ from renal tubular cells into the lateral intercellular spaces and the other parts of the interstitium. Solid arrows represent active transport; dashed arrows, passive movement. Pump A transports only Na^+, whereas pump B is a coupled Na^+-K^+ exchange pump. (Modified and reproduced, with permission, from Giebisch G: Coupled ion and fluid transport in the kidney. N Engl J Med 287:913, 1972.)

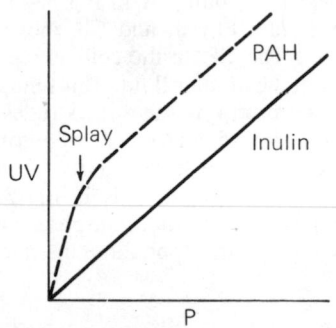

Figure 38–13. Relation between plasma levels (P) and excretion (UV) of PAH and inulin.

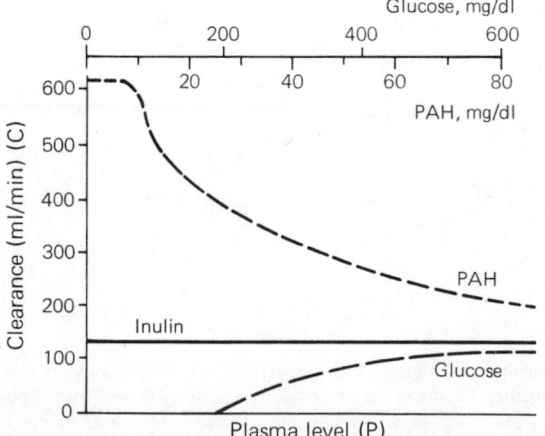

Figure 38–14. Clearance of inulin, glucose, and PAH at various plasma levels of each substance in humans.

therefore produces no net movement of charge and has no direct effect on the membrane potential of the renal tubular cells.

The electrogenic Na^+ pump is inhibited by ethacrynic acid or by the replacement of Cl^- in the tubular fluid with anions that penetrate tubular cells poorly. The Na^+-K^+ exchange pump is inhibited by ouabain and by a low extracellular K^+ concentration.

PAH Transport

The dynamics of PAH transport illustrate the operation of the active transport mechanisms that secrete substances into the tubular fluid. The filtered load of PAH is a linear function of the plasma level, but PAH secretion increases as P_{PAH} rises only until a maximal secretion rate (Tm_{PAH}) is reached (Fig 38–13). When P_{PAH} is low, C_{PAH} is high; but as P_{PAH} rises above Tm_{PAH}, C_{PAH} falls progressively. It eventually approaches the clearance of inulin (C_{In}) (Fig 38–14) because the amount of PAH secreted becomes a smaller and smaller fraction of the total amount excreted. Conversely, the clearance of glucose is essentially zero at P_G levels below the renal threshold; but above the threshold, C_G rises to approach C_{In} as P_G is raised.

The use of C_{PAH} to measure effective renal plasma flow (ERPF) is discussed above. It should again be emphasized that the excretion of any substance that is not stored or metabolized in the kidney can be used to measure renal plasma flow if the level in arterial and renal venous plasma can be measured, and the only advantage of PAH is that its extraction ratio is so high that renal plasma flow can be approximated without measuring the PAH concentration in renal venous blood.

Other Substances Secreted by the Tubules

Derivatives of hippuric acid in addition to PAH, phenol red and other sulfonphthalein dyes, penicillin, and a variety of iodinated dyes such as iodopyracet (Diodrast) are actively secreted into the tubular fluid. Substances that are normally produced in the body and secreted by the tubules include various ethereal sulfates, steroid and other glucuronides, and 5-hydroxyindoleacetic acid, the principal metabolite of serotonin (see Chapter 15). All of these secreted substances are weak anions and compete with each other for secretion; for example, PAH reduces the excretion of both the 18-glucuronide and the 3-glucuronide derivatives of aldosterone (see Chapter 20). Thus, a single transport system appears to be involved. This transport system is limited to the proximal tubule. PAH transport and, presumably, the transport of the other weak anions are facilitated by acetate and lactate and inhibited by various Krebs cycle intermediates, probenecid, phenylbutazone, dinitrophenol, and mercurial diuretics. Probenecid has been used clinically to inhibit penicillin excretion and thus to maintain the blood levels after a given dose for a longer period of time. A separate proximal tubular transport mechanism secretes certain drugs that are

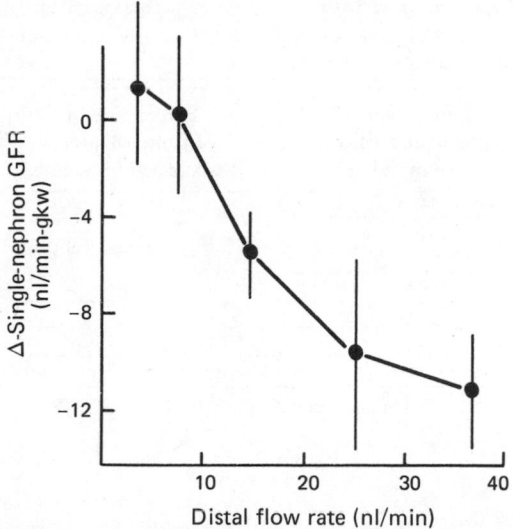

Figure 38–15. Changes (Δ) in single nephron GFR with changes in rate of perfusion of the distal portion of the loop of Henle (distal flow rate) in the same nephron. gkw, grams kidney weight. Vertical lines indicate ± standard error of the mean. (Modified from Wright FS: Regulation of glomerular filtration rate and renal salt excretion by a single-nephron feedback pathway. Cardiovasc Med 3:731, 1978.)

organic bases. A third, which secretes ethylenediaminetetraacetic acid (EDTA), has also been described.

Tubuloglomerular Feedback

Convincing evidence has now accumulated that signals from the renal tubules feed back to affect glomerular filtration. As the rate of flow through the ascending limb of the loop of Henle and first part of the distal tubule increases, glomerular filtration in the same nephron decreases, and, conversely, a decrease in flow increases GFR (Fig 38–15). This tends to maintain the constancy of the load delivered to the distal tubule. The sensor for the response appears to be the macula densa, and GFR is probably adjusted by constriction or dilatation of the afferent arteriole. Constriction may be mediated by the renin-angiotensin system, prostaglandins, or cyclic AMP. The urinary component responsible for the feedback is Cl^-, and the degree of constriction is probably proportionate to the rate of Cl^- reabsorption across the macula densa. The sensitivity of the feedback may be increased when ECF volume is decreased and is decreased when ECF volume is expanded.

WATER EXCRETION

Normally, 180 L of fluid are filtered through the glomeruli each day, while the average daily urine volume is about 1 L. The same load of solute can be excreted per 24 h in a urine volume of 500 ml with a concentration of 1400 mOsm/L; or in a volume of 23.3 L, with a concentration of 30 mOsm/L (Table 38–4). These figures demonstrate 2 important facts: first, that at least 88% of the filtered water is reabsorbed, even when the urine volume is 23 L; and second, that the reabsorption of the remainder of the filtered water can be varied without affecting total solute excretion. Therefore, when the urine is concentrated, water is retained in excess of solute; and when it is dilute, water is lost from the body in excess of solute. Both facts have great importance in the body economy and the regulation of the osmolality of the body fluids.

Proximal Tubule

Many substances are actively transported out of the fluid in the proximal tubule, but fluid obtained from the first 70% of the proximal tubule by micropuncture is isosmotic with plasma, and it presumably remains isosmotic to the end of the proximal tubule (Fig 38–10). Therefore, in the proximal tubule, water moves passively out of the tubule along the osmotic gradients set up by active transport of solutes, and isotonicity is maintained. Since the ratio of the concentration in tubular fluid to the concentration in plasma (TF/P) of the nonreabsorbable substance inulin is approximately 4 at the end of the proximal tubule, it follows that approximately 75% of the filtered solute and 75% of the filtered water have been removed by the time the filtrate reaches this point (Table 38–5).

Loop of Henle

As noted above, the loops of Henle of the jux-

Table 38–4. Alterations in water metabolism produced by vasopressin in humans. In each case, the osmotic load excreted is 700 mOsm/d.

	GFR (ml/min)	Percentage of Filtered Water Reabsorbed	24-Hour Urine Volume	Urine Concentration (mOsm/L)	Gain or Loss of Water in Excess of Solute (L/d)
Urine isotonic to plasma	125	98.7	2.4	290	. . .
Vasopressin (maximal antidiuresis)	125	99.7	0.5	1400	1.9 gain
No vasopressin ("complete" diabetes insipidus)	125	88	23.3	30	20.9 loss

Table 38–5. Water reabsorption in various portions of the nephron in hydropenic rats (maximal anti-diuresis), based on micropuncture studies in which the tubular fluid/plasma ratio of ^{14}C inulin was determined. The values for "end proximal tubule" are calculated rather than observed.*

Location	Ratio of ^{14}C Inulin, Tubular Fluid/Plasma	Percentage of Glomerular Filtrate Remaining	Percentage of Filtered Water Reabsorbed in Segment
Bowman's capsule	1	100	
Junction middle and distal third of proximal tubule	3	33	75 in proximal tubule
End proximal tubule (calculated)	4	25	
Start distal tubule	5	20	5 in loop
End distal tubule	20	5	15 in distal tubule
Ureter	690	0.14	4.86 in collecting ducts

*Based on data of Gottschalk C: Micropuncture studies of tubular function in the mammalian kidney. Physiologist 4:35, 1961.

tamedullary nephrons dip deeply into the medullary pyramids before draining into the distal convoluted tubules in the cortex, and all of the collecting ducts descend back through the medullary pyramids to drain at the tips of the pyramids into the renal pelvis. It is now established that there is a graded increase in the osmolality of the interstitium of the pyramids, the osmolality at the tips of the papillae normally being many times that of plasma. The descending limb of the loop of Henle is permeable to water, but the ascending limb is relatively impermeable. Cl^- is actively pumped out of the thick segment of the ascending limb, with

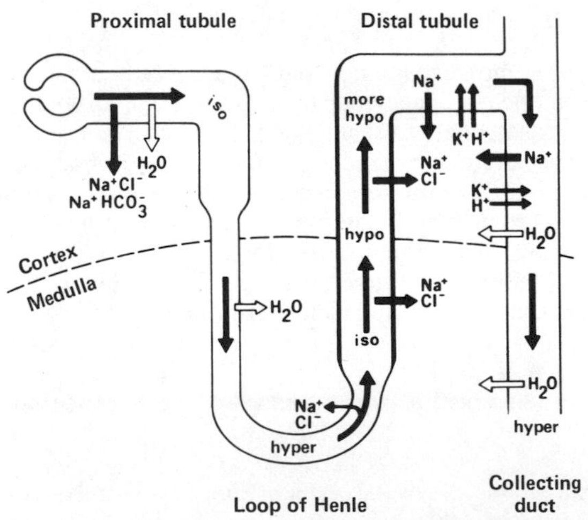

Figure 38–16. Summary of changes in urine osmolality in various parts of the nephron. The thickened wall of the ascending limb of the loop of Henle indicates relative impermeability of the tubular epithelium to water. In the presence of vasopressin, the fluid in the collecting ducts becomes hypertonic, whereas in the absence of this hormone, the fluid remains hypotonic throughout the distal tubule and collecting duct. Aldosterone promotes reabsorption of Na^+ and secretion of H^+ and K^+ in the distal convoluted tubule. (Reproduced, with permission, from Cannon PJ: The kidney in heart failure. N Engl J Med 296:26, 1977.)

Na^+ diffusing out along with the anion. Therefore, the fluid in the descending limb of the loop of Henle becomes hypertonic as water moves into the hypertonic interstitium. In the ascending limb, it becomes more dilute, and when it reaches the top, it is hypotonic to plasma because of the movement of Na^+ and Cl^- out of the tubular lumen (Fig 38–16). In passing through the loop of Henle, there is a net reduction of the volume of fluid of about 5%, so that when the fluid enters the distal tubule about 80% of the amount originally filtered has been reabsorbed (Table 38–5).

Distal Tubule & Collecting Duct

The changes in the osmolality and volume of the fluid in the distal tubule and collecting duct depend upon whether or not vasopressin, the antidiuretic hormone of the posterior pituitary (see Chapter 14), is present. This hormone increases the permeability of the epithelium of the collecting ducts to water. In monkeys and presumably in humans, it acts only on the collecting ducts, but in other species, it also increases the permeability of the distal tubule. When it is present, small volumes of concentrated urine are excreted; but when it is absent, large volumes of dilute urine are excreted.

In the presence of vasopressin in rats, water leaves the distal tubule, and the fluid in it is isosmotic from the mid portion of the tubule on (Fig 38–16). Na^+ is pumped out, and water moves with it, further reducing the volume of filtrate. The isotonic fluid then enters the collecting duct system and passes down through the hypertonic medullary pyramids, where water moves out of the lumen along the osmotic gradient, making the fluid concentrated. Fifteen percent of the filtrate is reabsorbed in the distal tubule by isosmotic reabsorption. A final 4+% is reabsorbed from the collecting ducts, forming a concentrated urine. The total amount of water reabsorbed during maximal antidiuresis is therefore 99.86% in the water-deprived rat (Table 38–5), and the urine is 6.4 times as concentrated as the plasma. The concentrating process presumably occurs only in the cortical and medullary portions of the collecting ducts in humans, and the concentrating power is not quite so great; however, 99.7% of the filtered water can be reabsorbed, and the final urine can contain 1400 mOsm/L, a concentration that is almost 5 times that of plasma. Maximal urine osmolality in dogs is about 2500 mOsm/L; in laboratory rats, about 3200 mOsm/L; and in certain desert rodents, as high as 5000 mOsm/L.

When vasopressin is absent, the distal tubule and collecting duct epithelium is relatively impermeable to water. The fluid therefore remains hypotonic, and large amounts flow into the renal pelvis. In humans, the urine osmolality may be as low as 30 mOsm/L. The impermeability of the distal portions of the nephron is not absolute; along with the salt that is pumped out of the distal tubular and collecting duct fluid, about 8% of the filtered fluid is reabsorbed in the absence of vasopressin. However, as much as 12% of the filtered fluid may be excreted, and urine flow may reach 15 ml/min or more. The effects on daily water metabolism of the absence and the presence of vasopressin are summarized in Table 38–4.

Since it is much easier to drop a hydrometer into a urine specimen than to determine its osmolality, the **specific gravity** is still measured clinically as an index of urine concentration. The specific gravity of an ultrafiltrate of plasma is 1.010, while that of a maximally concentrated urine specimen is about 1.035. However, it should be remembered that the specific gravity of a solution depends upon the nature as well as the number of solute particles in it. Thus, for example, a subject excreting radiographic contrast medium may have a specific gravity at 1.040–1.050, with relatively little increase in osmolality. Consequently, it is more accurate to measure osmolality.

The Countercurrent Mechanism

The concentrating mechanism depends upon the maintenance of a gradient of increasing osmolality along the medullary pyramids. This gradient exists because of the operation of the loops of Henle as **countercurrent multipliers** and the vasa recta as **countercurrent exchangers.** A countercurrent system is a system in which the inflow runs parallel to, counter to, and in close proximity to the outflow for some distance. The operation of such a system in increasing the heating at the apex of a loop of pipe is shown in Fig 38–17. The heat in the outgoing fluid heats the incoming fluid so that by the time it reaches the heater its temperature is 90 degrees instead of 30 degrees, and the heater therefore raises the fluid temperature from 90 degrees to 100 degrees rather than from 30 degrees to 40 degrees. The loop of Henle operates in an analogous fashion. The descending limb of the loop of Henle is relatively impermeable to solute but highly permeable to water. Consequently, water moves into the interstitium, and the concentration of Na^+ in the tubular fluid rises markedly (Fig 38–18). The thin ascending limb of the loop is relatively impermeable to water and relatively permeable to Na^+ and urea, but more permeable to Na^+ than to urea.

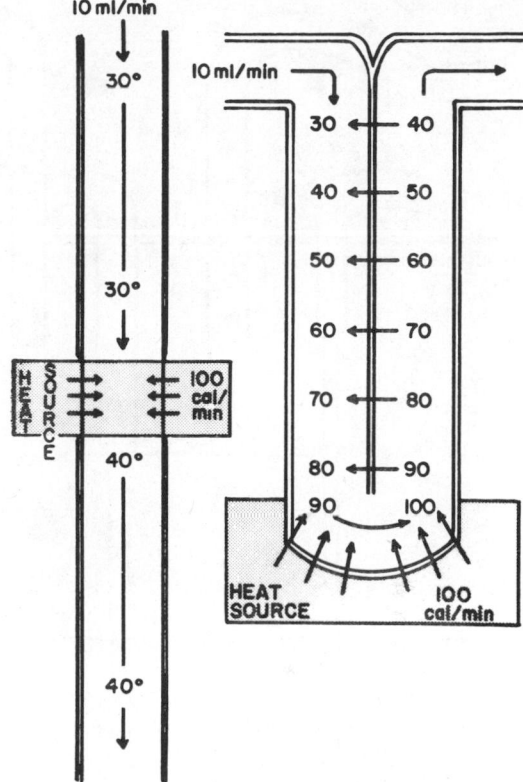

Figure 38–17. Operation of a countercurrent system. On the left, a heater surrounds a pipe and raises the temperature of the water flowing in it 10 degrees. On the right, the same heater is applied to a pipe bent to form a U, with the inflow close to the outflow. The heater still raises the temperature of the water 10 degrees, but the heater water flowing away from the heater warms the inflow. A gradient of temperature is thus set up along the pipe, so that at the bend the temperature is raised not from 30 to 40 degrees but from 90 to 100 degrees. (Reproduced, with permission, from Berliner RW: Dilution and concentration of the urine and the action of antidiuretic hormone. Am J Med 24:730, 1958.)

Consequently, Na^+ moves passively into the interstitium along a concentration gradient. The thick ascending limb is relatively impermeable to both water and solute, but in this segment, Cl^- is actively transported out of the tubular fluid. Na^+ passively follows Cl^- out of the tubular lumen. The distal tubule and outer portions of the collecting duct are relatively impermeable to urea but permeable to water in the presence of vasopressin. Consequently, water leaves the lumen, and the urea concentration of the fluid increases markedly. Finally, the inner medullary portion of the collecting duct is permeable to urea and, in the presence of vasopressin, to water. Urea moves passively into the interstitium, maintaining the high osmolality of the medullary pyramid. Additional water is also removed, and the fluid in the tubule becomes highly concentrated. The action of vasopressin on the kidney and the effects of demeclocycline, a drug that antagonizes this action, are discussed in Chapter 14.

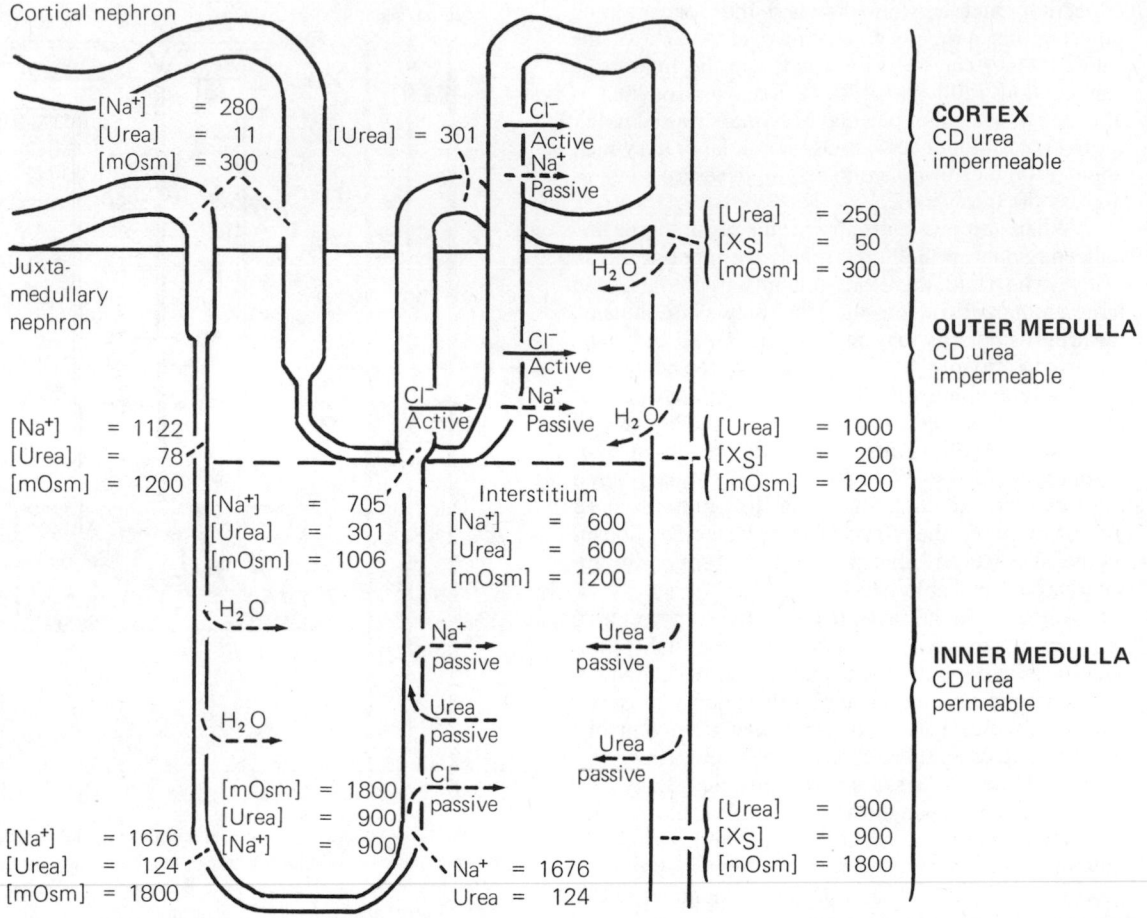

Figure 38–18. Diagrammatic summary of the operation of the countercurrent mechanism in the renal medulla. All concentrations ([]) are in mOsm/L. CD, collecting duct; X, nonreabsorbable solute. (Modified and reproduced, with permission, from Kokko JP, Rector FC Jr: Countercurrent multiplication system without active transport in inner medulla. Kidney Int 2:214, 1972.)

The osmotic gradient in the medullary pyramids would not last long if the Na^+ and urea in the interstitial spaces were removed by the circulation. These solutes remain in the pyramids primarily because the vasa recta operate as countercurrent exchangers. The solutes diffuse out of the vessels conducting blood toward the cortex and into the vessels descending into the pyramid. Conversely, water diffuses out of the descending vessels and into the ascending vessels. Therefore, the solutes tend to recirculate in the medulla and water tends to bypass it, so that the hypertonicity is maintained. The water removed from the collecting ducts in the pyramids is also removed by the vasa recta and enters the general circulation. It should be noted that countercurrent exchange is a passive process; it depends upon diffusion of water and solutes in both directions across the permeable walls of the vasa recta and could not maintain the osmotic gradient along the pyramids if the process of countercurrent multiplication in the loops of Henle were to cease.

It is also worth noting that there is a very large osmotic gradient in the renal tubules, and it is the

countercurrent system that makes this gradient possible by spreading it along a system of tubules 1 cm or more in length rather than across a single layer of cells that is only a few μm thick. There are other examples of the operation of countercurrent systems in animals. One is the heat exchange between the arteries and venae comitantes of the limbs. To a minor degree in humans but to a major degree in mammals living in cold water, heat is transferred from the arterial blood flowing into the limbs to the adjacent veins draining blood back into the body, making the tips of the limbs cold while conserving body heat.

Role of Urea

Although active transport of urea apparently occurs in some species, it has not been demonstrated in humans. However, the urea in the glomerular filtrate diffuses out of the tubules as its concentration is increased by the progressive reduction of filtrate volume. This is hardly surprising, since urea diffuses rapidly through most membranes in the body except the blood-brain barrier. When urine flows are low, there is more opportunity for urea to leave the tubules, and only 10–20% of the filtered urea is excreted; at high urine flows, 50–70% is excreted.

Urea accumulates in the interstitium of the medullary pyramids, where it tends to remain trapped by the countercurrent exchange in the vasa recta. The urea concentration of the tubular fluid as it issues from the collecting ducts is still much higher than it would be if the fluid passed only through tissue with the low urea content of the rest of the kidney. Because the walls of the collecting ducts are very permeable to urea in the presence of vasopressin, relatively little difference in urea concentration develops across them, and urea exerts only a slight inhibitory effect on the reabsorption of water from the collecting ducts. Therefore, the nonurea solutes can be concentrated almost as if urea were not present. The amount of urea in the medullary interstitium and, consequently, in the urine varies with the amount of urea filtered, and this in turn varies with the dietary intake of protein. Therefore, a high-protein diet increases the ability of the kidney to concentrate the urine.

Water Diuresis

The feedback mechanism controlling vasopressin secretion and the way vasopressin secretion is stimulated by a rise and inhibited by a drop in the effective osmotic pressure of the plasma are discussed in Chapter 14. The **water diuresis** produced by drinking large amounts of hypotonic fluids begins about 15 minutes after ingestion of a water load and reaches its maximum in about 40 minutes. The delay represents the time required for the water to be absorbed, the vasopressin secretory mechanism inhibited, and the previously circulating vasopressin metabolized.

Water Intoxication

While excreting an average osmotic load, the maximal urine flow that can be produced during a water diuresis is about 16 ml/min. If water is ingested at a more rapid rate than this for any length of time, swelling of the cells because of the uptake of water from the hypotonic ECF becomes severe, and the symptoms of **water intoxication** develop. Swelling of the cells in the brain causes convulsions and coma and leads eventually to death. Water intoxication can also occur when water intake is not reduced after administration of exogenous vasopressin or secretion of endogenous vasopressin in response to nonosmotic stimuli such as surgical trauma.

Osmotic Diuresis

The presence of large quantities of unreabsorbed solutes in the renal tubules causes an increase in urine volume called **osmotic diuresis.** Solutes that are not reabsorbed in the proximal tubules exert an appreciable osmotic effect as the volume of tubular fluid decreases and their concentration rises. They therefore "hold water in the tubules." In addition, there is a limit to the concentration gradient against which Na^+ can be pumped out of the proximal tubules. Normally,

the movement of water out of the proximal tubule prevents any appreciable gradient from developing, but Na^+ concentration in the fluid falls when water reabsorption is decreased because of the presence in the tubular fluid of increased amounts of unreabsorbable solutes. The limiting concentration gradient is reached, and further proximal reabsorption of Na^+ is prevented; more Na^+ remains in the tubule, and water stays with it. The result is that the loop of Henle is presented with a greatly increased volume of isotonic fluid. This fluid has a somewhat decreased Na^+ concentration, but the total amount of Na^+ reaching the loop per unit time is increased. In the loop, the reabsorption of water and Na^+ is decreased because the medullary hypertonicity is decreased. Several factors contribute to this reduction, but the principal cause is an increase in medullary blood flow. The cause of the increased medullary blood flow is unknown. More fluid passes through the distal tubule, and because of the decrease in the osmotic gradient along the medullary pyramids, less water is reabsorbed in the collecting ducts. The result is a marked increase in urine volume and Na^+ excretion and in excretion of other electrolytes.

Osmotic diuresis is produced by the administration of compounds such as mannitol and related polysaccharides that are filtered but not reabsorbed. It is also produced by naturally occurring substances when they are present in amounts exceeding the capacity of the tubules to reabsorb them. In diabetes, for example, the glucose that remains in the tubules when the filtered load exceeds the Tm_G causes polyuria. Osmotic diuresis can also be produced by the infusion of large amounts of sodium chloride or urea.

It is important to recognize the difference between osmotic diuresis and water diuresis. In water diuresis, the amount of water reabsorbed in the proximal portions of the nephron is normal, and the maximal urine flow that can be produced is about 16 ml/min. In osmotic diuresis, increased urine flow is due to decreased water reabsorption in the proximal tubules and loops, and very large urine flows can be produced. As the load of excreted solute is increased, the concentration of the urine approaches that of plasma (Fig 38–19) in spite of maximal vasopressin secretion because an increasingly large fraction of the excreted urine is isotonic proximal tubular fluid. If osmotic diuresis is produced in an animal with diabetes insipidus, the urine concentration rises for the same reason.

Relation of Urine Concentration to GFR

The magnitude of the osmotic gradient along the medullary pyramids is increased when the rate of flow of fluid through the loops of Henle is decreased. A reduction in GFR such as that caused by dehydration produces a decrease in the volume of fluid presented to the countercurrent mechanism, so that the rate of flow in the loops declines and the urine becomes more concentrated. When the GFR is low, the urine can become quite concentrated in the absence of

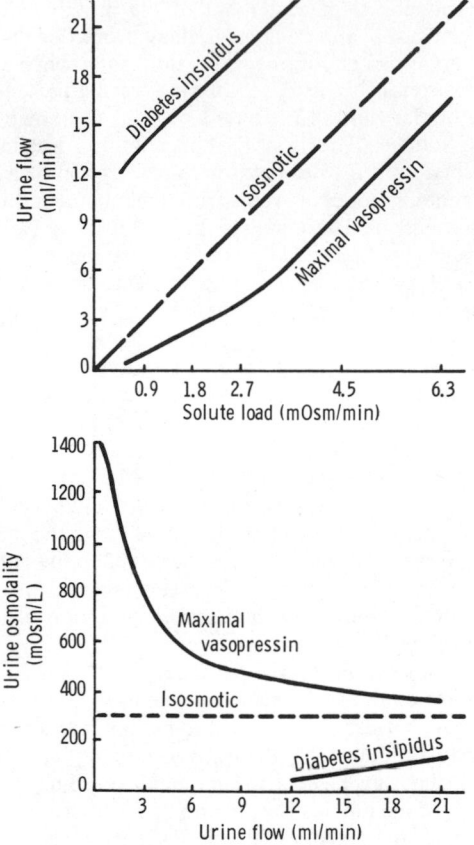

Figure 38–19. Approximate relationship between urine concentration and urine flow in osmotic diuresis in humans. The dashed line in the lower diagram indicates the concentration at which the urine is isosmotic with plasma. (Slightly modified, redrawn, and reproduced, with permission, from Berliner RW in: *Best and Taylor's Physiological Basis of Medical Practice*, 9th ed. Brobeck JR [editor]. Williams & Wilkins, 1973.)

vasopressin; if one renal artery is constricted in an animal with diabetes insipidus, the urine excreted on the side of the constriction becomes hypertonic because of the reduction in GFR, whereas that excreted on the opposite side remains hypotonic.

Disruption of the renal lymphatics decreases renal concentrating ability, presumably because it permits protein to accumulate in the interstitium of the medullary pyramids, reducing the osmotic gradient along which reabsorbed water moves into the vasa recta for return to the general circulation (see Chapter 30). For unknown reasons, hypercalcemia and hypokalemia are also associated with polyuria, polydipsia, and decreased concentrating ability.

"Free Water Clearance"

In order to quantitate the gain or loss of water by excretion of a concentrated or dilute urine, the "free water clearance" (C_{H_2O}) is sometimes calculated. This is the difference between the urine volume and the clearance of osmoles (C_{Osm}):

$$C_{H_2O} = V - \frac{U_{Osm}V}{P_{Osm}}$$

where V is the urine volume and U_{Osm} and P_{Osm} the urine and plasma osmolality. C_{Osm} is the amount of water necessary to excrete the osmotic load in a urine that is isotonic with plasma. Therefore, C_{H_2O} is negative when the urine is hypertonic and positive when the urine is hypotonic. In Table 38–4, for example, the values for C_{H_2O} are −1.3 ml/min (−1.9 L/d) during maximal antidiuresis and 14.5 ml/min (20.9 L/d) in the absence of vasopressin.

ACIDIFICATION OF THE URINE & BICARBONATE EXCRETION

H⁺ Secretion

The cells of the proximal and distal tubules, like the cells of the gastric glands, secrete hydrogen ions (see Chapter 26). Acidification also occurs in the collecting ducts. The reactions believed to occur in the cells are shown in Fig 38–20. Like other cells, the renal tubular cells have a Na⁺-K⁺ exchange pump (see Chapter 1), but this pump is believed to be absent from the membrane that faces the tubular lumen. H⁺ is actively transported across the luminal membrane, and for each H⁺ secreted an Na⁺ enters the cell. In this case, Na⁺ is moving down its electrical and chemical gradients. There is no evidence that H⁺ efflux and Na⁺ influx are linked by utilization of a common carrier, and it appears that Na⁺ simply diffuses into the cell to maintain electroneutrality. Na⁺ is then pumped into the interstitial fluid in exchange for K⁺. Thus, for each H⁺ secreted, one HCO_3^- and one Na⁺ enter the inter-

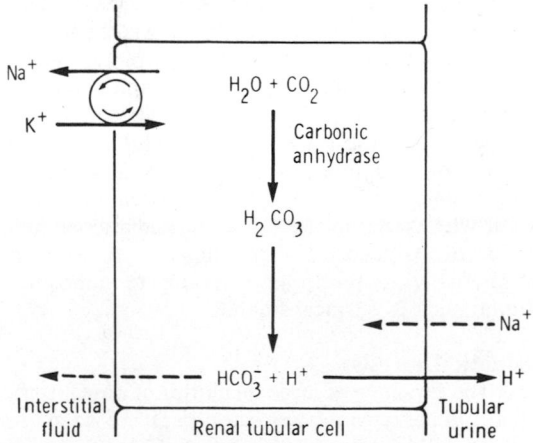

Figure 38–20. Probable chemical reactions involved in secretion of H⁺ by proximal and distal tubular cells in the kidney. Solid arrows crossing cell membranes indicate active transport. Dashed arrows indicate diffusion. The circle containing arrows in the cell wall represents a coupled active transport mechanism. Compare with Fig 26–7.

stitial fluid and diffuse from there into the bloodstream.

The source of the H^+ secreted by the tubular cells is uncertain. It may be produced simply by dissociation of H_2CO_3, as shown in Fig 38–20, or it may be produced by the ionization of H_2O or more complex reactions such as those postulated to occur in the stomach, with the H^+ from H_2CO_3 buffering the OH^- that is formed. The acid-secreting cells contain the enzyme **carbonic anhydrase,** which catalyzes the reaction $CO_2 + H_2O \rightleftharpoons H_2CO_3$. This makes possible the rapid formation of H_2CO_3 (see Chapter 35). Drugs that inhibit carbonic anhydrase depress renal acid secretion and the reactions in the kidney which depend on it.

Fate of H^+ in the Urine

The amount of acid secreted depends upon the subsequent events in the tubular urine. The maximal H^+ gradient against which the transport mechanism can secrete in humans corresponds to a urine pH of about 4.5, which is thus the **limiting pH.** If there were no buffers or other substances that "tied up" H^+ in the urine, this pH would be reached rapidly, and H^+ secretion would stop. However, 3 important reactions in the tubular fluid remove free H^+, permitting more acid to be secreted (Fig 38–21). These are the reactions with HCO_3^- to form CO_2 and H_2O, with HPO_4^{2-} to form $H_2PO_4^-$, and with NH_3 to form NH_4^+.

Reaction With Buffers

The dynamics of buffering are discussed in Chapter 35. The major buffers in the glomerular filtrate are the bicarbonate (pK 6.1) and dibasic phosphate (pK

6.8) systems. The concentration of HCO_3^- in the plasma, and consequently in the glomerular filtrate, is normally about 24 mEq/L, whereas that of phosphate is only 1.5 mEq/L. Therefore, in the proximal tubule, most of the secreted H^+ reacts with HCO_3^- to form H_2CO_3 (Fig 38–21). The H_2CO_3 breaks down to form CO_2 and H_2O. In the proximal (but not in the distal) tubule, there is carbonic anhydrase in the brush border of the cells; this facilitates the formation of CO_2 and H_2O in the tubular fluid. The CO_2, which diffuses readily across all biologic membranes, enters the tubular cells, where it adds to the pool of CO_2 available to form H_2CO_3. Since the H^+ is removed from the tubule, the pH of the fluid is unchanged. This is the mechanism by which HCO_3^- is reabsorbed; for each mole of HCO_3^- removed from the tubular fluid, 1 mol of HCO_3^- diffuses from the tubular cells into the blood, even though it is not the same mole that disappeared from the tubular fluid.

Secreted H^+ also reacts with dibasic phosphate (HPO_4^{2-}) to form monobasic phosphate ($H_2PO_4^-$). This happens to the greatest extent in the distal tubules and collecting ducts because it is here that the phosphate which escapes proximal reabsorption is greatly concentrated by the reabsorption of water. H^+ also combines to a minor degree with other buffer anions.

Each H^+ that reacts with buffer anions other than HCO_3^- contributes to the urinary **titratable acidity,** which is measured by determining the amount of alkali that must be added to the urine to return its pH to 7.4, the pH of the glomerular filtrate. The titratable acidity obviously measures only a fraction of the acid secreted, since it does not measure the H^+ that combines with HCO_3^- or that which combines with NH_3.

Ammonia Secretion

NH_3 is secreted in the proximal and distal tubules and the collecting ducts. The reactions forming NH_3 in the cells are summarized in Fig 38–22. Glutamine is converted to glutamic acid and ammonia (Fig 17–22). This reaction is catalyzed by the enzyme **glutaminase,** which is abundant in tubular cells. More NH_3 is formed by the deamination of glutamic acid and small amounts by deamination of other amino acids. In addition, some comes directly from arterial blood. The NH_3 diffuses into the tubular fluid because it is lipid-soluble and crosses the lipid-containing membranes of the cells with ease. In the fluid, it reacts with secreted H^+ to form ammonium ions (NH_4^+). Unlike NH_3, NH_4^+ is relatively lipid-insoluble and thus stays in the tubular fluid.

The amount of NH_4^+ formed depends upon the pH of the tubular fluid and the rate of NH_3 production. At any given rate of NH_3 production, the amount of NH_4^+ formed is proportionate to the amount of H^+ available and therefore to the rate of H^+ secretion. Thus, the NH_4^+ content of an alkaline urine is nil whereas that of a maximally acid urine is high.

The production of NH_3 is gradually increased over a period of 3–5 days in chronic acidosis. This **adaptation** of NH_3 production is brought about by an

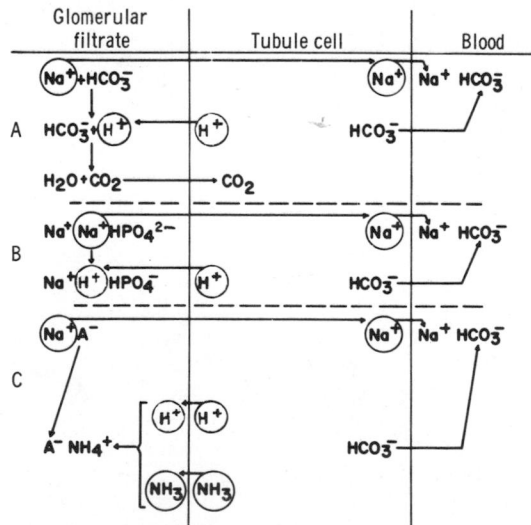

Figure 38–21. Fate of H^+ secreted into tubule in exchange for Na^+. *A:* Reabsorption of filtered bicarbonate. *B:* Formation of titratable acid. *C:* Ammonium formation. Note that in each instance one Na^+ and one HCO_3^- enter the bloodstream for each H^+ secreted. A^-, anion.

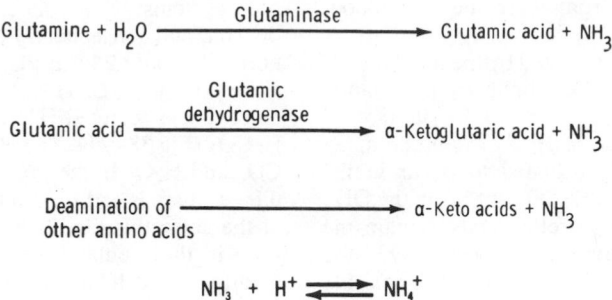

Figure 38–22. Major reactions involved in ammonia production in the kidney. See also Figs 17–21 and 17–22.

increase in tissue glutaminase activity, but the mechanism responsible for this increase is not known. The increase is independent of changes in urinary pH and occurs even in compensated acidosis in which the pH of the plasma is nearly normal (see Chapter 40).

The process by which NH_3 is secreted is called **nonionic diffusion** (see Chapter 1). Salicylates and a number of other drugs that are weak bases or weak acids are also secreted by nonionic diffusion. They diffuse into the tubular fluid at a rate that is dependent upon the urine pH, and the amount of each drug excreted therefore varies with the pH of the urine.

pH Changes Along the Nephrons

Micropuncture studies indicate that an appreciable drop in pH occurs in the proximal tubule in mammalian kidneys, although there is further acidification in the distal tubule. Since most of the HCO_3^- is absorbed in the proximal tubule and the H^+ secretion responsible for its reabsorption does not change the pH of the fluid, it is apparent that there is considerably more acid secretion in the proximal than in the distal tubule. The acid-secreting mechanism in the distal tubules, and particularly in the collecting ducts, has a lower secretory capacity but is capable of generating a large pH difference between the tubular lumen and the cells. The pH of the tubular urine also depends upon the relation between the amount of HCO_3^- reabsorbed and the reduction in the volume of the filtrate. The urinary pH, like that of the blood, depends upon the ratio $[HCO_3^-]/[H_2CO_3]$, since

$$pH = pK_{H_2CO_3} + \log \frac{[HCO_3^-]}{[H_2CO_3]}$$

and $[H_2CO_3]$ is proportionate to P_{CO_2}. Therefore, if the amount of fluid in the tubule decreases less rapidly than the amount of HCO_3^- at any given P_{CO_2}, the **concentration** of HCO_3^- falls and so does the pH. Conversely, when the HCO_3^- concentration rises, the pH rises.

Factors Affecting Acid Secretion

Renal acid secretion is altered by changes in the intracellular P_{CO_2}, K^+ concentration, carbonic anhydrase level, and adrenocortical hormone concentra-

tion. When the P_{CO_2} is high (respiratory acidosis), more intracellular H_2CO_3 is available to buffer the hydroxyl ions and acid secretion is enhanced, whereas the reverse is true when the P_{CO_2} falls. K^+ depletion enhances acid secretion, apparently because the loss of K^+ causes intracellular acidosis even though the plasma pH may be elevated. Conversely, K^+ excess in the cells inhibits acid secretion. When carbonic anhydrase is inhibited, acid secretion is inhibited because the formation of H_2CO_3 is decreased. Aldosterone and the other adrenocortical steroids that enhance tubular reabsorption of Na^+ also increase the secretion of H^+ and K^+.

Bicarbonate Excretion

Although the process of HCO_3^- reabsorption does not actually involve transport of this ion into the tubular cells, HCO_3^- behaves as if it had a Tm that is exceeded when the plasma HCO_3^- concentration exceeds 28 mEq/L (mmol/L). At lower HCO_3^- levels, all the HCO_3^- is reabsorbed; but at values above this threshold, HCO_3^- appears in the urine and urine becomes alkaline (Fig 38–23).

When the plasma HCO_3^- is 28 mEq/L, H^+ is being secreted at its maximal rate and all of it is being used to reabsorb HCO_3^-; but as the plasma HCO_3^- drops, more H^+ becomes available to appear as titratable acidity and NH_4. Therefore, the further the plasma HCO_3^- drops, the more acid the urine becomes and the greater its NH_4^+ content. For unknown reasons, the capacity of the tubules to reabsorb HCO_3^- rises when the GFR rises.

Implications of Urinary pH Changes

Depending upon the rates of the interrelated processes of acid secretion, NH_4^+ production, and HCO_3^- excretion, the pH of the urine in humans varies from an extreme of 4.5 to about 8.0. Excretion of a urine that is at a pH different from that of the body fluids has important implications for the body's electrolyte and acid-base economy which are discussed in detail in Chapter 40. Acids are buffered in the plasma and cells, the overall reaction being $HA + NaHCO_3 \rightleftharpoons NaA + H_2CO_3$. The H_2CO_3 forms CO_2 and H_2O, and the CO_2 is expired, while the NaA appears in the glomerular filtrate. To the extent that the Na^+ is replaced by H^+ as

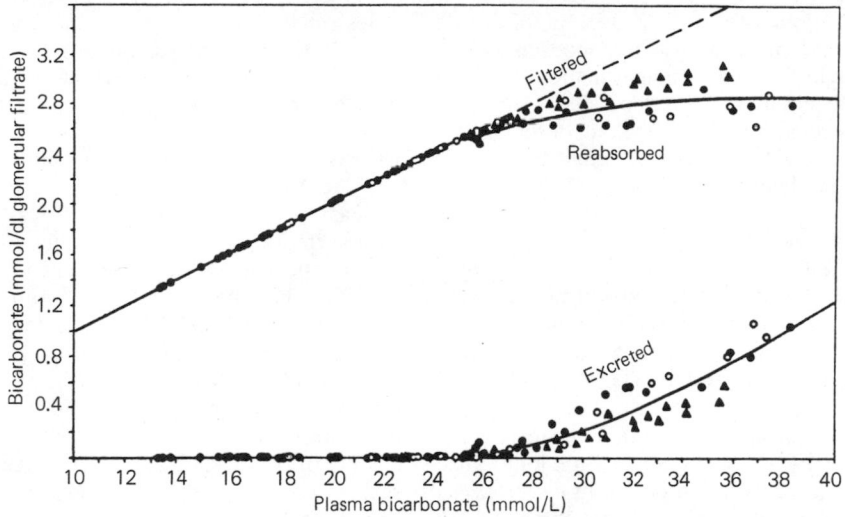

Figure 38–23. Reabsorption and excretion of bicarbonate at various plasma bicarbonate levels in humans. The different symbols represent values from different subjects. (Reproduced, with permission, from Pitts RW, Ayer JL, Scheiss WA: The renal regulation of acid-base balance in man. 3. The reabsorption and excretion of bicarbonate. J Clin Invest 28:35, 1949.)

titratable acidity or NH_4^+, Na^+ is conserved in the body. Furthermore, for each H^+ excreted as titratable acidity or NH_4^+, there is a net gain of one HCO_3^- in the blood, replenishing the supply of this important buffer anion. Conversely, when base is added to the body fluids, the OH^- ions are buffered, raising the plasma HCO_3^-. When the plasma level exceeds 28 mEq/L, the urine becomes alkaline and the extra HCO_3^- is excreted in the urine. Because the rate of maximum H^+ secretion by the tubules varies directly with the arterial P_{CO_2}, HCO_3^- reabsorption also is affected by the P_{CO_2}. This relationship is discussed in detail in Chapter 40.

SODIUM & CHLORIDE EXCRETION

Na^+ is filtered in large amounts, but it appears to be actively transported out of the proximal tubules, the distal tubules, and the collecting ducts. Normally, 96% to well over 99% of the filtered Na^+ is reabsorbed. Most of the Na^+ is reabsorbed with Cl^- (Table 38–6), but some is reabsorbed in the processes by which one Na^+ enters the bloodstream for each H^+ secreted by the tubules, and in the distal tubules, a small amount is actively reabsorbed in association with the secretion of K^+.

Regulation of Na^+ Excretion

Because Na^+ is the most abundant cation in ECF and because sodium salts account for over 90% of the osmotically active solute in the plasma and interstitial fluid, the amount of Na^+ in the body is a prime determinant of the ECF volume. Therefore, it is not surprising that multiple regulatory mechanisms have evolved

in terrestrial animals to control the excretion of this ion. Through the operation of these regulatory mechanisms, the amount of Na^+ excreted is adjusted to equal the amount ingested over a wide range of dietary intakes, and the individual stays in Na^+ balance. Thus, urinary Na^+ output ranges from less than 1 mEq/d on a low-salt diet to 400 mEq/d or more when the dietary Na^+ intake is high. In addition, there is a natriuresis when saline is infused intravenously and a decrease in Na^+ excretion when ECF volume is reduced. Variations in Na^+ excretion are effected by changes in the amount filtered and the amount reabsorbed in the

Table 38–6. Quantitative aspects of Na^+ reabsorption in a normal man.

GFR = 125 ml/min	
Plasma HCO_3^- = 27 mEq/L	
Plasma Na^+ = 145 mEq/L	
Na^+ filtered per minute	18,125 µEq
Reabsorbed with Cl^-	14,585 µEq
Reabsorbed while reabsorbing 3375 µEq HCO_3^- }	3,375 µEq
Reabsorbed in association with formation of titratable acidity and ammonia }	50 µEq
Reabsorbed in association with secretion of K^+	50 µEq
Total Na^+ reabsorbed per minute	18,060 µEq

tubules. The factors affecting the GFR are discussed above. The factors affecting Na^+ reabsorption include the oncotic and hydrostatic pressures in the peritubular capillaries, the circulating level of aldosterone and other adrenocortical hormones, the rate of tubular secretion of H^+ and K^+, and possibly other factors that are as yet incompletely identified.

Glomerulotubular Balance

The amount of Na^+ filtered is so large (over 26,000 mEq/d) that if the total amount of Na^+ reabsorbed stayed constant, a rise in GFR of only 2 ml/min would more than double the amount excreted (Table 38–7). Conversely, a small fall in GFR would reduce Na^+ excretion to zero. These figures are theoretical rather than actual, because the total amount reabsorbed rises when the GFR rises and falls when it falls. Most of the change in reabsorption occurs in the proximal tubule. The compensation is usually not complete, but it is appreciable. The proximal tubular reabsorption of a number of other substances is also proportionate to the load delivered to the tubule by filtration. The proportionality, which is especially apparent in the case of Na^+ reabsorption, has come to be referred to as **glomerulotubular balance.** The mechanism by which the change in proximal reabsorption is brought about is currently the subject of intensive research. The change in Na^+ reabsorption occurs within seconds after a change in filtration, so it seems unlikely that an extrarenal humoral factor is involved. One factor is the oncotic pressure in the peritubular capillaries. When the GFR is high, there is a relatively large increase in the oncotic pressure of the plasma by the time it reaches the efferent arterioles and their capillary branches. This increases the reabsorption of Na^+ from the tubule. However, all the intrarenal mechanisms that bring about the change have not as yet been identified.

Hemodynamic Effects on Tubular Reabsorption

Changes in renal capillary hydrostatic and oncotic pressure appear to be important in the response to salt loading. Intravenous saline produces a natriuresis with decreased Na^+ reabsorption in the proximal tubule. Saline dilutes the blood, lowering the oncotic pressure, and volume expansion also appears to decrease renal vascular resistance, with a consequent increase in hydrostatic pressure. Conversely, conditions that reduce ECF volume cause renal vasoconstriction, with a consequent reduction in hydrostatic pressure in the capillaries, and proximal tubular Na^+ reabsorption is increased. Changes in hydrostatic and osmotic pressures may also play a role in glomerulotubular balance and in the "escape phenomenon" (see Chapter 20).

Effects of Adrenocortical Steroids

Adrenal mineralocorticoids such as aldosterone increase tubular reabsorption of Na^+ in association with secretion of K^+ and H^+ in the distal tubule (Fig 38–16) and also Na^+ reabsorption with Cl^- (see Chapter 20). When these hormones are injected into adrenalectomized animals, there is a latent period of 10–30 minutes before their effects on Na^+ reabsorption become manifest. They act on the distal convoluted tubules and collecting ducts, and there is some evidence that they cause the reabsorption of a small amount of Na^+ from the bladder. The glucocorticoids such as cortisol also increase Na^+ reabsorption; but, unlike the mineralocorticoids, they increase the GFR. They may therefore increase rather than decrease Na^+ excretion because the increase they produce in the filtered load of Na^+ may exceed the increase in reabsorption.

Reduction of the dietary intake of salt increases aldosterone secretion (Fig 20–30). Changes in aldosterone secretion can explain changes in Na^+ excretion that occur over days or even hours, but, because of the latent period before its effects are manifest, rapid changes in Na^+ excretion cannot be attributed to this hormone.

Relation to Acid & K^+ Secretion

Na^+ excretion is increased by drugs that decrease renal acid secretion by inhibiting carbonic anhydrase. After CO_2 or acid is buffered in the blood, Na^+ filtered with acid anions is lost in the urine if the amount in the filtrate exceeds the capacity of the tubules to exchange the Na^+ for H^+. Changes in Na^+ excretion due to changes in the rate of K^+ secretion are small (Table 38–6).

Other Factors

The factors affecting proximal Na^+ reabsorption are important because proximal reabsorption is increased when ECF volume is reduced and decreased when it is expanded. The role of hydrostatic and oncotic pressures in mediating these changes is discussed above. Other investigators argue that an as yet unisolated hormone, an elusive **"third factor,"** acts along with the adrenocortical hormones and the GFR to regu-

Table 38–7. Changes in Na^+ excretion that would occur as a result of changes in GFR if there were no concomitant changes in Na^+ reabsorption.

GFR (ml/min)	Plasma Na^+ ($\mu Eq/ml$)	Amount Filtered ($\mu Eq/min$)	Amount Reabsorbed ($\mu Eq/min$)	Amount Excreted ($\mu Eq/min$)
125	145	18,125	18,000	125
127	145	18,415	18,000	415
124.1	145	18,000	18,000	0

late Na$^+$ excretion. It has been suggested that such a hormone acts primarily on proximal Na$^+$ reabsorption. There is some evidence that the renal nerves affect Na$^+$ reabsorption (see above). However, the elucidation of the role of each of these factors, if any, must await further research.

Chloride Excretion

Chloride reabsorption is increased when HCO$_3^-$ reabsorption is decreased, and vice versa, so that Cl$^-$ concentration in plasma varies inversely with the HCO$_3^-$ concentration, keeping the total anion concentration constant. Passive diffusion can explain the movements of Cl$^-$ in some situations. However, Cl$^-$ is actively transported out of the tubular lumen in the thick ascending limb of the loop of Henle.

POTASSIUM EXCRETION

Much of the filtered K$^+$ is removed from the tubular fluid by active reabsorption in the proximal tubules (Table 38–8), and K$^+$ is then secreted into the fluid by the distal tubular cells. In the absence of complicating factors, the amount secreted is approximately equal to the K$^+$ intake, and K$^+$ balance is maintained. In the distal tubules, Na$^+$ is generally reabsorbed and K$^+$ is secreted. There is no rigid one-for-one exchange, and much of the movement of K$^+$ is passive. However, there is electrical coupling in the sense that intracellular migration of Na$^+$ tends to lower the potential difference across the tubular cell, and this favors movement of K$^+$ into the tubular lumen. Since Na$^+$ is also reabsorbed in association with H$^+$ secretion, there is competition for the Na$^+$ in the distal tubular fluid. K$^+$ excretion is decreased when the amount of Na$^+$ reaching the distal tubule is low, and K$^+$ excretion is also decreased when H$^+$ secretion is increased. When total body K$^+$ is high, H$^+$ secretion is

inhibited, apparently because of intracellular alkalosis; and K$^+$ secretion and excretion are therefore facilitated. Conversely, the cells are acid in K$^+$ depletion, and K$^+$ secretion declines. Apparently the K$^+$ secretory mechanism is capable of "adaptation," because the amount of K$^+$ excreted gradually increases when a constant large dose of a potassium salt is administered for a prolonged period of time.

DIURETICS

Although a detailed discussion of diuretic agents is outside the scope of this book, consideration of their mechanisms of action constitutes an informative review of the factors affecting urine volume and electrolyte excretion. These mechanisms are summarized in Table 38–9. Water, alcohol, osmotic diuretics, xanthines, and acidifying salts have limited clinical usefulness, but the other agents on the list are used extensively in medical practice.

Water diuresis and osmotic diuresis have been discussed above. Ethyl alcohol acts directly on the hypothalamus. The diuretic action of the xanthines is weak. When NH$_4$Cl is ingested, the NH$_4^+$ dissociates to H$^+$ and NH$_3$ and the NH$_3$ is converted to urea, so that ingesting NH$_4$Cl is equivalent to adding HCl to the body. The H$^+$ is buffered and the Cl$^-$ filtered along with Na$^+$, thus maintaining electrical neutrality. To the extent that any of the Na$^+$ is not replaced by H$^+$ from the renal tubules, Na$^+$ and water are lost in the urine. Other acidifying salts produce diuresis in a similar way.

The carbonic anhydrase–inhibiting drugs are only moderately effective as diuretic agents, but because they inhibit acid secretion by decreasing the supply of carbonic acid, they have far-reaching effects. Not only is Na$^+$ excretion increased because H$^+$ secretion is decreased, but HCO$_3^-$ reabsorption is also

Table 38–8. Renal handling of various plasma constituents in a normal adult human on an average diet. P, proximal tubules; L, loops of Henle; D, distal tubules; C, collecting ducts.

Substance	Per 24 Hours				Percentage Reabsorbed	Location
	Filtered	Reabsorbed	Secreted	Excreted		
Na$^+$ (mEq)	26,000	25,850		150	99.4	P, L, D, C
K$^+$ (mEq)	900	900*	100	100	100*	P, D*
Cl$^-$ (mEq)	18,000	17,850		150	99.2	P, L, D, C
HCO$_3^-$ (mEq)	4,900	4,900		0	100	P, D
Urea (mmol)	870	460†		410	53	P, L, D, C
Creatinine (mmol)	12	1‡	1‡	12	. . .	. . .
Uric acid (mmol)	50	49	4	5	98	P
Glucose (mmol)	800	800		0	100	P
Total solute (mOsm)	54,000	53,400	100	700	87	P, L, D, C
Water (ml)	180,000	179,000		1000	99.4	P, L, D, C

*K$^+$ is reabsorbed proximally and secreted distally. It is not certain that all of the filtered K$^+$ is reabsorbed proximally.

†Urea diffuses into as well as out of some portions of the nephron.

‡Variable secretion and probable reabsorption of creatinine in humans.

Table 38–9. Mechanism of action
of various diuretics.

Agent	Mechanism of Action
Water	Inhibits vasopressin secretion.
Ethyl alcohol	Inhibits vasopressin secretion.
Large quantities of osmotically active substances such as mannitol and glucose	Produce osmotic diuresis.
Xanthines such as caffeine and theophylline	Probably decrease tubular reabsorption of Na^+ and increase GFR.
Acidifying salts such as $CaCl_2$ and NH_4Cl	Supply acid load; H^+ is buffered, and anion is excreted with Na^+ when the ability of the kidney to replace Na^+ with H^+ is exceeded.
Organic salts of mercury such as mercaptomerin (Thiomerin) and meralluride (Mercuhydrin)	Inhibit Cl^- reabsorption in the medullary thick ascending limb of the loop of Henle; inhibit K^+ secretion.
Carbonic anhydrase inhibitors such as acetazolamide (Diamox)	Decrease H^+ secretion throughout nephron, with resultant increase in Na^+ and K^+ excretion.
Metolazone (Zaroxolyn), thiazides such as chlorothiazide (Diuril)	Inhibit Cl^- reabsorption in the distal cortical portion of the loop of Henle and proximal portion of the distal tubule.
Furosemide (Lasix), ethacrynic acid (Edecrin), and bumetanide	Inhibit Cl^- reabsorption in the medullary thick ascending limb of the loop of Henle.
K^+-retaining natriuretics such as spironolactone (Aldactone), triamterene (Dyrenium), and amiloride (Colectril)	Inhibit Na^+-K^+ "exchange" in the distal portion of the distal tubule by inhibiting the action of aldosterone (spironolactone) or by inhibiting K^+ secretion (triamterene, amiloride).

depressed; and because H^+ and K^+ compete with each other and with Na^+, the decrease in H^+ secretion facilitates the secretion and excretion of K^+.

Another determinant of the rate of K^+ secretion is the amount of Na^+ delivered to the Na^+-K^+ "exchange" site in the distal tubule. Thiazides, furosemide, ethacrynic acid, and bumetanide act proximal to this site, and the resultant increase in Na^+ delivery increases K^+ secretion. The K^+ loss is appreciable, and K^+ depletion is one of the common complications of treatment with these agents. The thiazides inhibit Cl^- transport at a site in the terminal cortical portion of the thick ascending limb of the loop of Henle and the proximal portion of the distal tubule. Furosemide, ethacrynic acid, and bumetanide inhibit Cl^- transport in the medullary thick ascending limb of the loop of Henle. The mercurial diuretics also act in the medullary thick ascending limb, but they have the additional action of inhibiting K^+ secretion, so that K^+ depletion is not marked. Spironolactone, triamterene,

and amiloride act on the exchange mechanism itself, causing K^+ retention and, in some cases, mild hyperkalemia.

EFFECTS OF DISORDERED RENAL FUNCTION

A number of abnormalities are common to many different types of renal disease. The secretion of renin by the kidneys and the relation of the kidneys to hypertension are discussed in Chapters 24 and 33. A frequent finding in various forms of renal disease is the presence in the urine of protein, leukocytes, red cells, and **casts,** which are bits of proteinaceous material precipitated in the tubules and washed into the bladder. Other important consequences of renal disease are loss of the ability to concentrate or dilute the urine, uremia, acidosis, and abnormal retention of Na^+.

Proteinuria

In many renal diseases and in one benign condition, the permeability of the glomerular capillaries is increased, and protein is found in the urine in more than the usual trace amounts (**proteinuria**). Most of this protein is albumin, and the defect is commonly called **albuminuria.** The relation of charges on the glomerular membrane to albuminuria is discussed above. The amount of protein in the urine may be very large, and, especially in nephrosis, the urinary protein loss may exceed the rate at which the liver can synthesize plasma proteins. The resulting hypoproteinemia reduces the oncotic pressure, and the plasma volume declines, sometimes to dangerously low levels, while edema fluid accumulates in the tissues.

A benign condition that causes proteinuria is a poorly understood change in renal hemodynamics which in some otherwise normal individuals causes protein to appear in urine formed when they are in the standing position (**orthostatic albuminuria**). Urine formed when these individuals are lying down is protein-free.

Loss of Concentrating & Diluting Ability

In renal disease, the urine becomes less concentrated, and urine volume is often increased, producing the symptoms of **polyuria** and **nocturia** (waking up at night to void). The ability to form a dilute urine is often retained, but in advanced renal disease, the osmolality of the urine becomes fixed at about that of plasma, indicating that the diluting and concentrating functions of the kidney have both been lost. The loss is due in part to disruption of the countercurrent mechanism, but a more important cause is a loss of functioning nephrons. When one kidney is removed surgically, the number of functioning nephrons is halved. The number of osmoles excreted is not reduced to this extent, and so the remaining nephrons must each be filtering and excreting more osmotically active substances, producing what is in effect an osmotic diuresis. In osmotic diuresis, the osmolality of the urine approaches that of plasma (see above); the same thing happens when the number of functioning nephrons is reduced by disease. Of course, when most of the nephrons are destroyed, urine volume falls and **oliguria** or even **anuria** is present.

Uremia

When the breakdown products of protein metabolism accumulate in the blood, the syndrome known as **uremia** develops. The symptoms of uremia include lethargy, anorexia, nausea and vomiting, mental deterioration and confusion, muscle twitching, convulsions, and coma. Because erythropoiesis is depressed, anemia is a prominent feature of chronic uremia. The blood urea nitrogen (BUN), nonprotein nitrogen (NPN), and creatinine levels are high, and the blood levels of these substances are used as an index of the severity of the uremia. It is often stated that it is not the accumulation of urea and creatinine per se but rather the accumulation of other toxic substances—possibly organic acids or phenols—that produces the symptoms of uremia. Because urea crosses the blood-brain barrier slowly, it is administered intravenously to neurosurgical patients to make the ECF outside the brain hypertonic and shrink the brain during surgery. However, urea infusions cause changes in the electrical activity of the brain in experimental animals and may not be as innocuous as they appear to be. In dogs, prolonged infusions of urea cause anorexia, weakness, vomiting, and diarrhea.

The toxic substances that cause the symptoms of uremia can be removed by dialyzing the blood of uremic patients against a bath of suitable composition in an artificial kidney. By repeated dialysis, patients can be kept alive and in reasonable health for many months, even when they are completely anuric or have had both kidneys removed.

Acidosis

Acidosis is common in chronic renal disease due to failure to excrete the acid products of digestion and metabolism (see Chapter 40). In the rare syndrome of **renal tubular acidosis,** there is specific impairment of the ability to make the urine acid, and other renal functions are usually normal. However, in most cases of chronic renal disease, the urine is maximally acidified, and acidosis develops because the total amount of H^+ that can be secreted is reduced because of impaired renal tubular production of NH_3.

Abnormal Na$^+$ Metabolism

Many patients with renal disease retain excessive amounts of Na^+ and become edematous. There are at least 3 causes of Na^+ retention in renal disease. In acute glomerulonephritis, a disease that primarily affects the glomeruli, there is a marked decrease in the amount of Na^+ filtered without a corresponding decrease in Na^+ reabsorption. In nephrosis, an increase in aldosterone secretion contributes to the salt retention. The plasma protein is low in this condition, and so fluid moves from the plasma into the interstitial spaces and the plasma volume falls. The decline in plasma volume triggers the increase in aldosterone secretion via the renin-angiotensin system.

A third cause of Na^+ retention and edema in renal disease is **heart failure.** The relationship between heart failure and abnormal salt retention is discussed in Chapter 33. Renal disease predisposes to heart failure, partly because of the hypertension it frequently produces.

A rare but interesting syndrome is **salt-losing nephritis.** In this condition there is marked loss of Na^+ in the urine, unresponsiveness to endogenous and exogenous mineralocorticoids, and symptoms and signs of hypovolemia that may lead to the mistaken diagnosis of adrenocortical insufficiency. The syndrome is apparently the result of relatively selective damage to the Na^+-reabsorbing mechanisms. In patients with this condition, a very high salt intake is necessary to prevent cardiovascular collapse.

Variations in the Response to Aldosterone

An interesting problem is why aldosterone-treated normal individuals and patients with primary hyperaldosteronism become severely K^+ depleted, whereas edematous patients with nephrosis, cirrhosis, or heart failure who have secondary hyperaldosteronism do not. One factor seems to be the amount of Na^+ reaching the distal tubule; Na^+ in the tubular fluid helps maintain the potential difference between the tubular lumen and the cells, and this favors K^+ secretion. In patients with primary hyperaldosteronism, "escape" has taken place and proximal tubular Na^+ reabsorption is decreased, so that large quantities of Na^+ reach the distal tubule. In patients with edema, the filtered Na^+ load may be small because the plasma Na^+ is low as a result of "dilutional hyponatremia," or the GFR is low, or both. However, the amount of Na^+ reaching the distal tubules may be low even when the plasma Na^+ and GFR are apparently normal because there is increased Na^+ reabsorption in the more proximal portions of the nephron. Another factor in patients with edema is the flow of fluid in the distal tubule. K^+ excretion appears to be flow-limited, and in these patients, the amount of fluid reaching the distal tubules is often reduced.

39 | Micturition

FILLING OF THE BLADDER

The walls of the ureters contain smooth muscle arranged in spiral, longitudinal, and circular bundles, but distinct layers of muscle are not seen. Regular peristaltic contractions occurring 1–5 times per minute move the urine from the renal pelvis to the bladder, where it enters in spurts synchronous with each peristaltic wave. The ureters pass obliquely through the bladder wall and, although there are no ureteral sphincters as such, the oblique passage tends to keep the ureters closed except during peristaltic waves, preventing reflex of urine from the bladder.

EMPTYING OF THE BLADDER

Anatomic Considerations

The smooth muscle of the bladder, like that of the ureters, is arranged in spiral, longitudinal, and circular bundles. Contraction of this muscle, which is called the **detrusor muscle,** is mainly responsible for emptying the bladder during urination (micturition). Muscle bundles pass on either side of the urethra, and these fibers are sometimes called the **internal urethral sphincter** although they do not encircle the urethra. Farther along the urethra is a sphincter of skeletal muscle, the sphincter of the membranous urethra, or **external urethral sphincter.** The bladder epithelium is made up of a superficial layer of flat cells and a deep layer of cuboidal cells. The innervation of the bladder is summarized in Fig 39–1.

Micturition

The physiology of micturition and its disorders are subjects about which there is much confusion. Micturition is fundamentally a spinal reflex facilitated and inhibited by higher brain centers and, like defecation, subject to voluntary facilitation and inhibition. Urine enters the bladder without producing much increase in intravesical pressure until the viscus is well filled. In addition, like other types of smooth muscle, the bladder muscle has the property of plasticity; when it is stretched, the tension initially produced is not

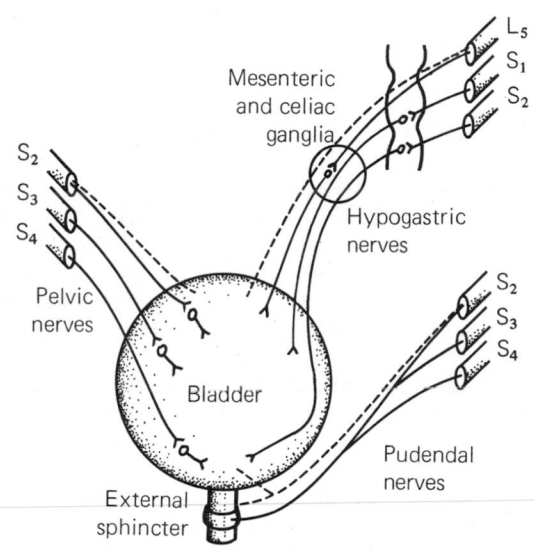

Figure 39–1. Innervation of the bladder. Dashed lines indicate sensory nerves. Parasympathetic innervation is shown at left, sympathetic at upper right, and somatic at lower right.

maintained. The relation between intravesical pressure and volume can be studied by inserting a catheter and emptying the bladder, then recording the pressure while the bladder is filled with 50 ml increments of water or air **(cystometry).** A plot of intravesical pressure against the volume of fluid in the bladder is called a **cystometrogram** (Fig 39–2). The curve shows an initial slight rise in pressure when the first increments in volume are produced; a long, nearly flat segment as further increments are produced; and a sudden, sharp rise in pressure as the micturition reflex is triggered. These 3 components are sometimes called segments Ia, Ib, and II (Fig 39–2). The first urge to void is felt at a bladder volume of about 150 ml, and a marked sense of fullness at about 400 ml. The flatness of segment Ib is a manifestation of the law of Laplace (see Chapter 30). This law states that the pressure in a spherical viscus is equal to twice the wall tension divided by the radius. In the case of the bladder, the tension increases as the organ fills—but so does the radius, so that, until the organ is relatively full, the pressure increase is slight.

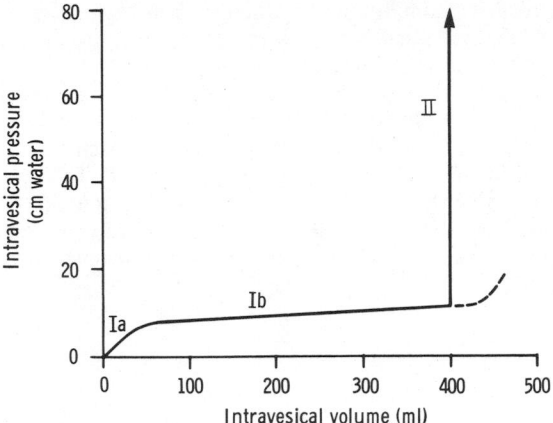

Figure 39–2. Cystometrogram in normal human. The numerals identify the 3 components of the curve described in the text. The dotted line indicates the pressure-volume relations that would have been found had micturition not occurred and produced component II. (Modified and reproduced, with permission, from Smith DR: *General Urology,* 9th ed. Lange, 1978.)

During micturition, the perineal muscles and external urethral sphincter are relaxed; the detrusor muscle contracts; and urine passes out through the urethra. The bands of smooth muscle on either side of the urethra apparently play no role in micturition, and their main function is believed to be the prevention of reflux of semen into the bladder during ejaculation.

The mechanism by which voluntary urination is initiated remains unsettled. One of the initial events is relaxation of the muscles of the pelvic floor, and this may cause a sufficient downward tug on the detrusor muscle to initiate its contraction. The perineal muscles and external sphincter can be contracted voluntarily, preventing urine from passing down the urethra or interrupting the flow once urination has begun. It is through the learned ability to maintain the external sphincter in a contracted state that adults are able to delay urination until the opportunity to void presents itself. After urination, the female urethra empties by gravity. Urine remaining in the urethra of the male is expelled by several contractions of the bulbocavernosus muscle.

Reflex Control

The bladder smooth muscle has some inherent contractile activity; however, when its nerve supply is intact, stretch receptors in the bladder wall initiate a reflex contraction that has a lower threshold than the inherent contractile response of the muscle. Fibers in the pelvic nerves are the afferent limb of the voiding reflex, and the efferent parasympathetic fibers to the bladder also travel in these nerves. The reflex is integrated in the sacral portion of the spinal cord. In the adult, the volume of urine in the bladder that normally initiates a reflex contraction is about 300–400 ml. The sympathetic nerves to the bladder play no part in micturition, but they do mediate the contraction of the bladder muscle that prevents semen from entering the bladder during ejaculation (see Chapter 22).

There is no small motor nerve system to the stretch receptors in the bladder wall; but the threshold for the voiding reflex, like the stretch reflexes, is adjusted by the activity of facilitatory and inhibitory centers in the brain stem. There is a facilitatory area in the pontine region and an inhibitory area in the midbrain. After transection of the brain stem just above the pons, the threshold is lowered, and less bladder filling is required to trigger it; whereas after transection at the top of the midbrain, the threshold for the reflex is essentially normal. There is another facilitatory area in the posterior hypothalamus. In humans with lesions in the superior frontal gyrus, the desire to urinate is reduced, and there is also difficulty in stopping micturition once it has commenced. However, stimulation experiments in animals indicate that other cortical areas also affect the process. The bladder can be made to contract when it contains only a few ml of urine by voluntary facilitation of the spinal voiding reflex. Voluntary contraction of the abdominal muscles aids the expulsion of urine by increasing the intra-abdominal pressure, but voiding can be initiated without straining even when the bladder is nearly empty.

ABNORMALITIES OF MICTURITION

There are 3 major types of bladder dysfunction due to neural lesions: (1) the type due to interruption of the afferent nerves from the bladder; (2) the type due to interruption of both afferent and efferent nerves; and (3) the type due to interruption of facilitatory and inhibitory pathways descending from the brain. In all 3 types the bladder contracts, but the contractions are generally not sufficient to empty the viscus completely, and residual urine is left in the bladder.

Effects of Deafferentation

When the sacral dorsal roots are cut in experimental animals or interrupted by diseases of the dorsal roots such as **tabes dorsalis** in humans, all reflex contractions of the bladder are abolished. The bladder becomes distended, thin-walled, and hypotonic, but there are some contractions because of the intrinsic response of the smooth muscle to stretch.

Effects of Denervation

When the afferent and efferent nerves are both destroyed, as they may be by tumors of the cauda equina or filum terminale, the bladder is flaccid and distended for a while. Gradually, however, the muscle of the "decentralized bladder" becomes active, with many contraction waves that expel dribbles of urine out of the urethra. The bladder becomes shrunken and the bladder wall hypertrophied. The reason for the difference between the small, hypertrophic bladder seen in this condition and the distended, hypotonic bladder seen when only the afferent nerves are interrupted is not known. The hyperactive state in the former condition suggests the development of denervation hypersensitization even though the neurons interrupted are preganglionic rather than postganglionic.

Effects of Spinal Cord Transection

During spinal shock, the bladder is flaccid and unresponsive. It becomes overfilled, and urine dribbles through the sphincters (overflow incontinence). After spinal shock has passed, the voiding reflex returns, although there is, of course, no voluntary control and no inhibition or facilitation from higher centers when the spinal cord is transected. Some paraplegic patients train themselves to initiate voiding by pinching or stroking their thighs, provoking a mild mass reflex (see Chapter 12). In some instances, the voiding reflex becomes hyperactive. Bladder capacity is reduced, and the wall becomes hypertrophied. This type of bladder is sometimes called the **spastic neurogenic bladder.** The reflex hyperactivity is made worse by, and may possibly be caused by, infection in the bladder wall.

Regulation of Extracellular Fluid Composition & Volume | 40

This chapter is a review of the major homeostatic mechanisms that operate, primarily through the kidneys, to maintain the **tonicity,** the **volume,** and the **specific ionic composition,** particularly the **H⁺ concentration,** of the ECF. The interstitial portion of this fluid is the fluid environment of the cells, and life depends upon the constancy of this ''internal sea'' (see Chapter 1).

DEFENSE OF TONICITY

The defense of the tonicity of the ECF is primarily the function of the vasopressin-secreting and thirst mechanisms. The total body osmolality is directly proportionate to the total body sodium plus the total body potassium divided by the total body water, so that changes in the osmolality of the body fluids occur when there is a disproportion between the amount of these electrolytes and the amount of water ingested or lost from the body (see Chapter 1). When the effective osmotic pressure of the plasma rises, vasopressin secretion is increased and the thirst mechanism is stimulated. Water is retained in the body, diluting the hypertonic plasma, and water intake is increased (Fig 40–1). Conversely, when the plasma becomes hypotonic, vasopressin secretion is decreased and ''solute-free water'' (water in excess of solute) is excreted. In this way, the tonicity of the body fluids is maintained within a narrow normal range. In health, plasma osmolality ranges from 280 to 295 mOsm/L, with vasopressin secretion completely inhibited at 280 mOsm/L and maximally stimulated at 295 mOsm/L. The details of the way the regulatory mechanisms operate and the disorders that result when their function is disrupted are considered in Chapters 14 and 38.

DEFENSE OF VOLUME

The volume of the ECF is determined primarily by the total amount of osmotically active solute in the ECF. The composition of the ECF is discussed in Chapter 1. Since Na⁺ and Cl⁻ are by far the most abundant osmotically active solutes in ECF, and since changes in Cl⁻ are to a great extent secondary to changes in Na⁺, the amount of Na⁺ in the ECF is the most important determinant of ECF volume, and the mechanisms that control Na⁺ balance are the major mechanisms defending ECF volume. There is, however, a volume control of water excretion as well; a rise in ECF volume inhibits vasopressin secretion, and a decline in ECF volume produces an increase in the secretion of this hormone. Volume stimuli override the osmotic regulation of vasopressin secretion. Angiotensin II stimulates aldosterone and vasopressin secretion. It also causes thirst and constricts blood vessels, which help to maintain blood pressure. Thus, angiotensin II plays a key role in the body's response to hypovolemia (Fig 40–2).

In disease states, loss of water from the body **(dehydration)** causes a moderate decrease in ECF volume because water is lost from both the intracellular and extracellular fluid compartments; but loss of Na⁺ in the stools (diarrhea), urine (severe acidosis, adrenal insufficiency), or sweat (heat prostration) decreases ECF volume markedly and eventually leads to shock. The immediate compensations in shock operate principally to maintain intravascular volume (see Chapter 33), but the long-term mechanisms affect Na⁺ balance. In adrenal insufficiency, the decline in ECF volume is due not only to loss of Na⁺ in the urine but also to its movement into cells (see Chapter 20).

Because of the key position of Na⁺ in volume homeostasis, it is not surprising that more than one

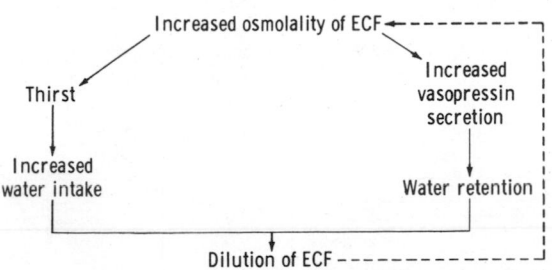

Figure 40–1. Mechanisms defending ECF tonicity. The dashed arrow indicates inhibition. (Courtesy of J Fitzsimons.)

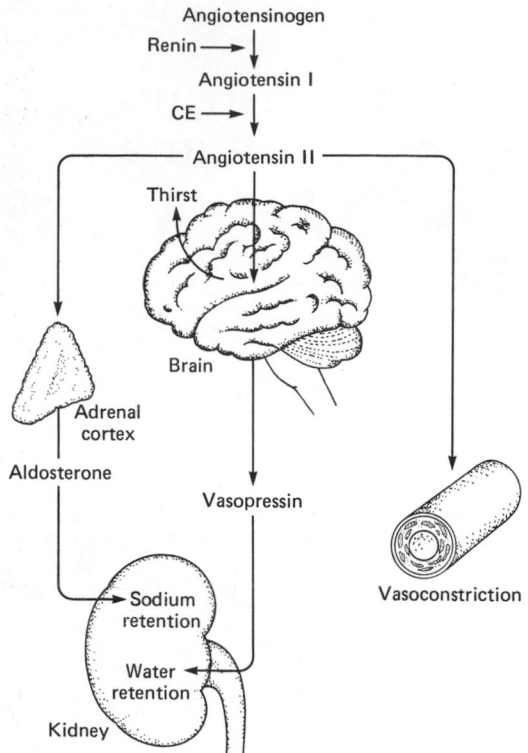

Figure 40–2. Role of angiotensin II in defense of ECF volume. CE, converting enzyme. (Modified from Ramsey DJ, Ganong WF: CNS regulation of salt and water intake. Hosp Pract 12:63, March 1977.)

mechanism operates to control the excretion of this ion. The filtration and reabsorption of Na^+ in the kidneys and the effects of these processes on Na^+ excretion are discussed in Chapter 38. When ECF volume is decreased, blood pressure falls. Glomerular capillary pressure declines, and the GFR therefore falls, reducing the amount of Na^+ filtered. Tubular reabsorption of Na^+ is increased, in part because the secretion of aldosterone is increased but in part also because hemodynamic changes and possibly other poorly understood mechanisms increase its transport out of the tubular fluid. Aldosterone secretion is controlled in part by a feedback system in which the change that initiates increased secretion is a decline in mean intravascular pressure (see Chapters 20 and 24). Other changes in Na^+ excretion occur too rapidly to be due solely to changes in aldosterone secretion. For example, rising from the supine to the standing position increases aldosterone secretion. However, Na^+ excretion is decreased within a few minutes, and this rapid change in Na^+ excretion occurs in adrenalectomized subjects. Some investigators believe that the effect of standing is due to a slight decrease in GFR, but others have presented evidence that an increase in tubular reabsorption is also involved. For reasons that remain obscure, a patient who has re-

ceived a water load up to 24 hours before a salt load excretes the salt load more rapidly than a control who has not received a water load, even though the administered water has long since been excreted.

DEFENSE OF SPECIFIC IONIC COMPOSITION

Special regulatory mechanisms maintain the levels of certain specific ions in the ECF as well as the level of glucose and other nonionized substances important in metabolism (see Chapters 17 and 19). The feedback of Ca^{2+} on the parathyroids and the calcitonin-secreting cells to adjust their secretion maintains the ionized calcium level of the ECF (see Chapter 21). Magnesium concentration is subject to close regulation, but the mechanisms controlling Mg^{2+} metabolism are incompletely understood.

The mechanisms controlling Na^+ and K^+ content are part of those determining the volume and tonicity of ECF and are discussed above. The level of these ions is also dependent upon the H^+ concentration, and the pH is one of the major factors affecting the anion composition of ECF.

DEFENSE OF H^+ CONCENTRATION

The mystique that has grown up around the subject of acid-base balance makes it necessary to point out that the core of the problem is not ''buffer base'' or ''fixed cation'' or the like but simply the maintenance of the H^+ concentration of the ECF. The mechanisms regulating the composition of the ECF are particularly important as far as this specific ion is concerned because the machinery of the cells is very sensitive to changes in H^+ concentration and because the intracellular H^+ concentration, although not identical with the ECF H^+ concentration, is dependent upon it.

The pH notation is a useful means of expressing H^+ concentrations in the body because the H^+ concentrations happen to be low relative to those of other cations. Thus, the normal Na^+ concentration of arterial plasma that has been equilibrated with red blood cells

Table 40–1. H^+ concentration and pH of body fluids.

| | | H⁺ Concentration | | |
		mEq/L	mol/L	pH
Gastric HCl		150	0.15	0.8
Maximal urine acidity		0.03	3×10^{-5}	4.5
Plasma	Extreme acidosis	0.0001	1×10^{-7}	7.0
	Normal	0.00004	4×10^{-8}	7.4
	Extreme alkalosis	0.00002	2×10^{-8}	7.7
Pancreatic juice		0.00001	1×10^{-8}	8.0

is 145 mEq/L, whereas the H^+ concentration is 0.00004 mEq/L (Table 40–1). The pH, the negative logarithm of 0.00004, is therefore 7.4. Of course, a **decrease** in pH of 1 unit, eg, from 7.0 to 6.0, represents a tenfold increase in H^+ concentration. It is also important to remember that the pH of blood is the pH of **true plasma**—plasma that has been in equilibrium with red cells—because the red cells contain hemoglobin, which is quantitatively one of the most important blood buffers (see Chapter 35).

H^+ Balance

The pH of the arterial plasma is normally 7.40, and that of venous plasma slightly lower. Technically, **acidosis** is present whenever the arterial pH is below 7.40, and **alkalosis** is present whenever it is above 7.40, although variations of up to 0.05 pH units occur without untoward effects. The H^+ concentrations in the ECF that are compatible with life cover an approximately 5-fold range, from 0.00002 mEq/L (pH 7.70) to 0.0001 mEq/L (pH 7.00).

A variety of organic acids are produced during the normal metabolism of neutral carbohydrates, fats, and proteins. These acids are rapidly metabolized, but appreciable quantities of lactic acid, pyruvic acid, and other acids sometimes accumulate in the blood. Oxidation of sulfur-containing amino acids generates H^+ and SO_4^{2-}, and metabolism of phosphorus-containing substances such as nucleoproteins generates H^+ and PO_4^{3-}. The H^+ load from these sources is normally about 100 mEq/d. The CO_2 formed by metabolism in the tissues is in large part hydrated to H_2CO_3 (see Chapter 35), and the total H^+ load from this source is over 12,500 mEq/d. Most of the CO_2 is excreted in the lungs, and only small quantities of the H^+ from this source are excreted by the kidneys. Common sources of extra acid loads are strenuous exercise (lactic acid), diabetic ketosis (acetoacetic and β-hydroxybutyric acid), and ingestion of acidifying salts such as NH_4Cl and $CaCl_2$, which in effect add HCl to the body. Failure of diseased kidneys to excrete the normal acid load is also a cause of acidosis. Fruits are the main dietary source of alkali. They contain Na^+ and K^+ salts of weak organic acids, and the anions of these salts are metabolized to CO_2, leaving $NaHCO_3$ and $KHCO_3$ in the body. $NaHCO_3$ and other alkalinizing salts are sometimes ingested in large amounts, but a more common cause of alkalosis is loss of acid from the body due to vomiting of gastric juice rich in HCl. This is, of course, equivalent to adding alkali to the body.

Buffering

Buffering and the buffer systems in the body are discussed in Chapters 1 and 35. The principal buffers in the ECF are hemoglobin (Hb), protein (Prot), and H_2CO_3:

$$HHb \rightleftharpoons H^+ + Hb^-$$

$$HProt \rightleftharpoons H^+ + Prot^-$$

$$H_2CO_3 \rightleftharpoons H^+ + HCO_3^-$$

The position of H_2CO_3 is unique because it is converted to H_2O and CO_2 and the CO_2 is then excreted in the lungs. The Henderson-Hasselbalch equation for the equilibrium in this system is:

$$pH = pK_{H_2CO_3} + \log \frac{[HCO_3^-]}{[H_2CO_3]}$$

When the symbol $[H_2CO_3]$ stands not for the concentration of carbonic acid alone but for the concentration of carbonic acid plus dissolved CO_2, the normal $[HCO_3^-]/[H_2CO_3]$ ratio is 20 and the pK is 6.1.

$$pH = 6.1 + \log \frac{[HCO_3^-]}{[H_2CO_3]}$$

The amount of carbonic acid and dissolved CO_2 is proportionate to the P_{CO_2}. The plasma HCO_3^- actually equals the total CO_2 of plasma minus the dissolved CO_2, the H_2CO_3, and the carbamino-CO_2, but constants have been derived experimentally to permit writing the Henderson-Hasselbalch equation for the bicarbonate system in plasma in the following special form:

$$pH = 6.10 + \log \frac{[Total\ CO_2]\ -\ aP_{CO_2}}{aP_{CO_2}}$$

When total CO_2 of true plasma ([total CO_2]) is in mmol/L, and P_{CO_2} is in mm Hg, a = 0.0314. This is the clinically applicable form of the equation because the HCO_3^- cannot be measured directly, but the total CO_2 and P_{CO_2} can be measured.

Respiratory Acidosis & Alkalosis

It is apparent from the Henderson-Hasselbalch equation for the bicarbonate system that the primary changes in arterial P_{CO_2} that occur with disorders of respiration change the $[HCO_3^-]/[H_2CO_3]$ ratio and, therefore, the pH. A rise in arterial P_{CO_2} due to decreased ventilation causes **respiratory acidosis.** The CO_2 that is retained is in equilibrium with H_2CO_3, which in turn is in equilibrium with HCO_3^-, so that the plasma HCO_3^- rises and a new equilibrium is reached at a lower pH. This can be indicated graphically on a plot of plasma HCO_3^- concentration versus pH (Fig 40–3). Conversely, a decline in P_{CO_2} causes **respiratory alkalosis.**

The initial changes shown in Fig 40–3 are those which occur independently of any compensatory mechanism, ie, they are those of **uncompensated** respiratory acidosis or alkalosis. In either situation, changes are produced in the kidneys, which then tend to **compensate** for the acidosis or alkalosis, adjusting the pH toward normal.

Renal Compensation

HCO_3^- reabsorption in the renal tubules depends not only upon the plasma HCO_3^- level but also upon the rate of H^+ secretion by the renal tubular cells, since

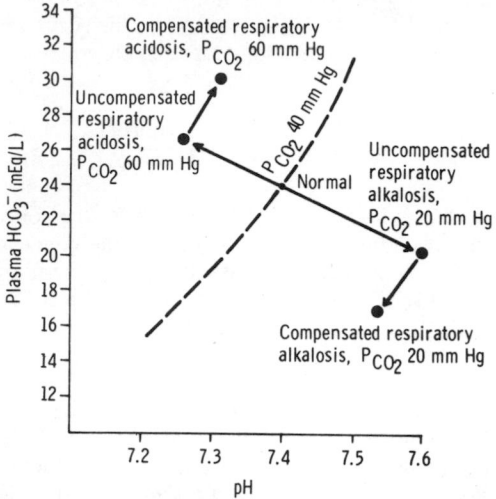

Figure 40–3. Changes in true plasma pH, HCO_3^-, and P_{CO_2} in respiratory acidosis and alkalosis. Note that with this plot the addition of CO_2 moves the point up and to the left along the line indicated by the arrow, and removal of CO_2 moves it down and to the right. On the other hand, addition of stronger acid moves the point down the dashed "iso-CO_2" line to the left, whereas removal of stronger acid (or addition of alkali) moves the point up the iso-CO_2 line to the right. (Based on Davenport HW: *The ABC of Acid-Base Chemistry,* 6th ed. Univ of Chicago Press, 1974.)

HCO_3^- is reabsorbed by exchange for H^+. The rate of H^+ secretion—and hence the rate of HCO_3^- reabsorption—is proportionate to the arterial P_{CO_2}, probably because the greater the amount of CO_2 that is available to form H_2CO_3 in the cells, the greater the amount of H^+ that can be secreted (see Chapter 38). Furthermore, when the P_{CO_2} is high, the interior of most cells becomes more acid (see Chapter 35). In respiratory acidosis, renal tubular H^+ secretion is therefore increased, removing H^+ from the body; and even though the plasma HCO_3^- is elevated, HCO_3^- reabsorption is increased, further raising the plasma HCO_3^-. This "renal compensation for respiratory acidosis" is shown graphically in Fig 40–3. Cl^- excretion is increased, and plasma Cl^- falls as plasma HCO_3^- is increased. Conversely, in respiratory alkalosis, the low P_{CO_2} hinders renal H^+ secretion, HCO_3^- reabsorption is depressed, and HCO_3^- is excreted, further reducing the already low plasma HCO_3^- and lowering the pH toward normal (Fig 40–3).

Metabolic Acidosis

When acids stronger than HHb and the other buffer acids are added to blood, **metabolic acidosis** is produced; and when the free H^+ level falls as a result of addition of alkali or removal of acid, **metabolic alkalosis** results. If, for example, HCl is added, the H^+ is buffered and the Hb^-, $Prot^-$, and HCO_3^- levels in plasma drop. The H_2CO_3 formed is converted to H_2O and CO_2, and the CO_2 is rapidly excreted via the lungs.

The importance of this fact is demonstrated in Fig 40–4. If enough acid were added to halve the HCO_3^- in plasma and CO_2 were not formed and excreted, the pH would fall to approximately 6.0 and death would result. If the H_2CO_3 level were so regulated that it remained constant, the pH would fall only to about 7.1. This is the situation in **uncompensated** metabolic acidosis (Fig 40–5). Actually, the rise in plasma H^+ stimulates respiration, so that the H_2CO_3 level, instead of rising or remaining constant, is reduced. This **respiratory compensation** raises the pH even further. The **renal** compensatory mechanisms then excrete the extra H^+ and return the buffer anion supply to normal.

Renal Compensation

The acid anions that replace HCO_3^- in the plasma in metabolic acidosis are filtered, each with a cation (principally Na^+), thus maintaining electrical neutrality. The renal tubular cells secrete H^+ into the glomerular filtrate; and for each H^+ secreted, 1 Na^+ and 1 HCO_3^- are added to the blood (see Chapter 38). The limiting urinary pH of 4.5 would be reached rapidly and the total amount of H^+ secreted would be small if there were no substances in the urine that "tied up" H^+. However, secreted H^+ reacts with HCO_3^- to form CO_2 and H_2O (bicarbonate reabsorption); with HPO_4^{2-} to form $H_2PO_4^-$ (titratable acidity); and with NH_3 to form NH_4^+. In this way large amounts of H^+ can be secreted, permitting correspondingly large amounts of HCO_3^- to be returned to (in the case of bicarbonate reabsorption) or added to the depleted body stores and large numbers of the cations filtered with the acid anions to be reabsorbed. It is only when the acid load is very large that cations are lost with the

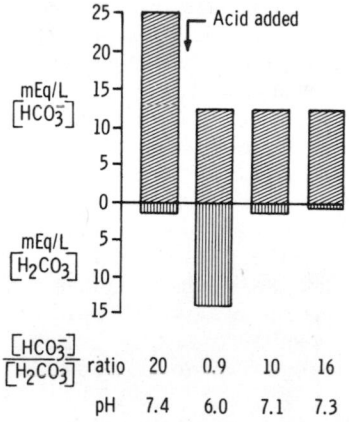

Figure 40–4. Buffering by the H_2CO_3-HCO_3^- system in blood. The bars are drawn as if buffering occurred in separate steps in order to show the effect of the initial reaction, the reduction of H_2CO_3 to its previous value, and its further reduction by the increase in ventilation. In this case, $[H_2CO_3]$ is actually the concentration of H_2CO_3 plus dissolved CO_2 (see text), so that the mEq/L values for it are arbitrary. (Based on Gamble JL: *Chemical Anatomy, Physiology and Pathology of Extracellular Fluid,* 6th ed. Harvard Univ Press, 1954.)

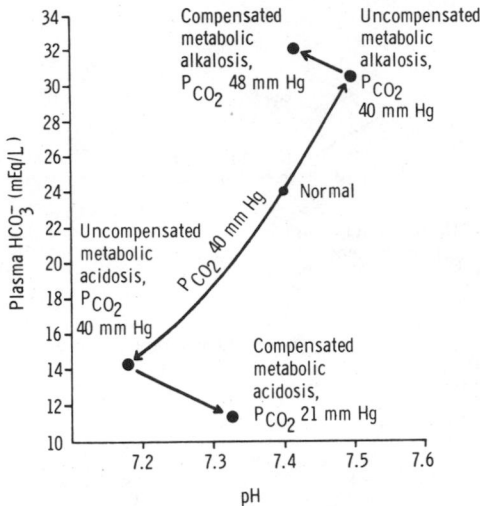

Figure 40–5. Changes in true plasma pH, HCO_3^-, and P_{CO_2} in metabolic acidosis and alkalosis. (Based on Davenport HW: *The ABC of Acid-Base Chemistry*, 6th ed. Univ of Chicago Press, 1974.)

anions, producing diuresis and depletion of body cation stores. In chronic acidosis, NH_3 secretion increases over a period of days (adaptation of NH_3 secretion; see Chapter 38), further improving the renal compensation for acidosis.

The overall reaction in blood when a strong acid such as HCl is added is as follows:

$$NaHCO_3 + HCl \rightarrow NaCl + H_2CO_3$$

For each mole of HCl added, 1 mol of $NaHCO_3$ is lost. The kidney in effect reverses the reaction:

$$NaCl + H_2CO_3 \rightarrow NaHCO_3 + H^+ + Cl^-$$

Of course, HCl is not excreted as such, the H^+ appearing in the urine as titratable acidity and NH_4^+.

In metabolic acidosis, the respiratory compensation tends to inhibit the renal response in the sense that the induced drop in P_{CO_2} hinders acid secretion, but it also decreases the filtered load of HCO_3^- and so its net inhibitory effect is not great.

Metabolic Alkalosis

In metabolic alkalosis, the plasma HCO_3^- and pH rise (Fig 40–5). The respiratory compensation is a decrease in ventilation due to decline in H^+ concentration, which elevates the P_{CO_2}. This brings the pH back toward normal while elevating the plasma HCO_3^- still further. The magnitude of this compensation is limited by the carotid and aortic chemoreceptor mechanisms, which drive the respiratory center if there is any appreciable fall in the arterial P_{O_2}. In metabolic alkalosis, more renal H^+ secretion is expended in reabsorbing the increased filtered load of HCO_3^-; and if the HCO_3^- level in plasma exceeds 28 mEq/L, HCO_3^- appears in

the urine. The rise in P_{CO_2} inhibits the renal compensation by facilitating acid secretion, but its effect is relatively slight.

Clinical Evaluation of Acid-Base Status

In evaluating disturbances of acid-base balance, it is important to know the pH and HCO_3^- content of arterial plasma. The P_{CO_2} is higher and the pH lower in venous plasma because it contains the CO_2 being carried from the tissues to the lungs for excretion (see Chapter 35); but if this is kept in mind in evaluating the results, free-flowing venous blood can be substituted for arterial blood. Reliable pH determinations can be made with a pH meter and a glass pH electrode. The HCO_3^- content of plasma cannot be measured directly, but the total CO_2 content can; and if the pH is known, the P_{CO_2} can be calculated using the special form of the Henderson-Hasselbalch equation discussed above in the section on buffering.

Alternatively, the total CO_2 content and the arterial P_{CO_2} can be measured and the pH calculated. A second alternative is use of the Siggaard-Andersen curve nomogram (see below). In these ways, the precise form of acid-base disturbance and its magnitude can be determined and proper treatment instituted.

The Siggaard-Andersen Curve Nomogram

Use of the Siggaard-Andersen curve nomogram (Fig 40–6) to plot the acid-base characteristics of arterial blood is widespread. This nomogram has log P_{CO_2} on the vertical scale and pH on the horizontal scale. Thus, any point to the left of a vertical line through pH 7.40 indicates acidosis, and any point to the right indicates alkalosis. The position of the point above or below the horizontal line through a P_{CO_2} of 40 mm Hg defines the effective degree of hypoventilation or hyperventilation.

If a solution containing $NaHCO_3$ and no buffers were equilibrated with gas mixtures containing various amounts of CO_2, the pH and P_{CO_2} values at equilibrium would fall along the dashed line on the left in Fig 40–6 or a line parallel to it. If buffers were present, the slope of the line would be greater; and the greater the buffering capacity of the solution, the steeper the line. For normal blood containing 15 g of hemoglobin per dl, the **CO_2 titration line** passes through the 15 g/dl mark on the hemoglobin scale (on the under side of the upper curved scale) and the point where the $P_{CO_2} = 40$ mm Hg and pH = 7.40 lines intersect, as shown in Fig 40–6. When the hemoglobin content of the blood is low, there is significant loss of buffering capacity, and the slope of the CO_2 titration line diminishes. However, blood of course contains buffers in addition to hemoglobin, so that even the line drawn from the zero point on the hemoglobin scale through the normal P_{CO_2}-pH intercept is steeper than the curve for a solution containing no buffers.

The nomogram is very useful clinically. Arterial blood or arterialized capillary blood is drawn anaerobically and its pH measured. The pHs of the same blood after equilibration with each of 2 gas mixtures

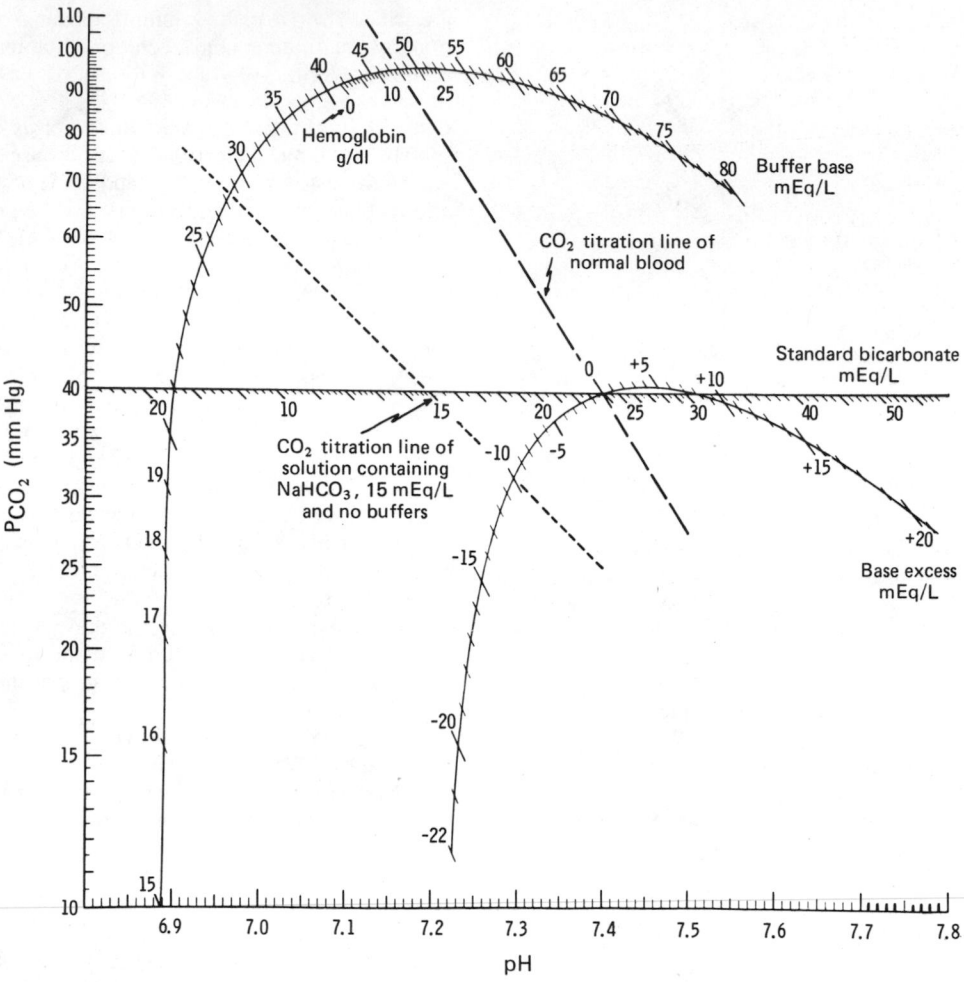

Figure 40–6. Siggaard-Andersen curve nomogram. (Reproduced with the permission of O Siggaard-Andersen and Radiometer, Copenhagen, Denmark.)

Table 40–2. Plasma pH, HCO_3^-, and P_{CO_2} values in various typical disturbances of acid-base balance. In the diabetic acidosis and prolonged vomiting examples, respiratory compensation for primary metabolic acidosis and alkalosis has occurred, and the P_{CO_2} has shifted from 40 mm Hg. In the emphysema and high altitude examples, renal compensation for primary respiratory acidosis and alkalosis has occurred and has made the deviations from normal of the plasma HCO_3^- larger than they would otherwise be. Data from various authors.

		Arterial Plasma		
Condition	pH	HCO_3^- (mEq/L)	P_{CO_2} (mm Hg)	Cause
NORMAL	7.40	24.1	40	
Metabolic	7.26	18.1	40	NH_4Cl ingestion
acidosis	6.94	5.0	23	Diabetic acidosis
Metabolic	7.48	30.1	40	$NaHCO_3$ ingestion
alkalosis	7.54	49.8	58	Prolonged vomiting
Respiratory	7.35	25.0	48	Breathing 7% CO_2
acidosis	7.32	33.5	64	Emphysema
Respiratory	7.50	22.0	27	Voluntary hyperventilation
alkalosis	7.46	18.7	26	Three-week residence at 4000 m altitude

containing different known amounts of CO_2 are also determined. The pH values at the known P_{CO_2} levels are plotted and connected to provide the CO_2 titration line for the blood sample. The pH of the blood sample before equilibration is plotted on this line, and the P_{CO_2} of the sample is read off the vertical scale. The **standard bicarbonate** content of the sample is indicated by the point at which the CO_2 titration line intersects the bicarbonate scale on the $P_{CO_2} = 40$ mm Hg line. The standard bicarbonate is not the actual bicarbonate concentration of the sample but rather what the bicarbonate concentration would be after elimination of any respiratory component. It is a measure of the alkali reserve of the blood, except that it is measured by determining the pH rather than the total CO_2 content of the sample after equilibration. Like the alkali reserve, it is an index of the degree of metabolic acidosis or alkalosis present.

Additional graduations on the upper curved scale of the nomogram (Fig 40–6) are provided for measuring **buffer base** content; the point where the CO_2 calibration line of the arterial blood sample intersects this scale shows the mEq/L of buffer base in the sample. The buffer base is equal to the total amount of buffer anions (principally $Prot^-$, HCO_3^-, and Hb^-; see Chapter 35) that can accept hydrogen ions in the blood. The normal value in an individual with 15 g of hemoglobin per dl of blood is 48 mEq/L.

The point at which the CO_2 calibration line intersects the lower curved scale on the nomogram indicates the **base excess.** This value, which is positive in alkalosis and negative in acidosis, is the amount of acid or base which would restore 1 L of blood to normal acid-base composition at a P_{CO_2} of 40 mm Hg. It should be noted that a base deficiency cannot be completely corrected simply by calculating the difference between the normal standard bicarbonate (24 mEq/L) and the actual standard bicarbonate and administering this amount of $NaHCO_3$ per liter of blood; some of the added HCO_3^- is converted to CO_2 and H_2O, and the CO_2 is lost in the lungs. The actual amount that must be added is roughly 1.2 times the standard bicarbonate deficit, but the lower curved scale on the nomogram, which has been developed empirically by analyzing many blood samples, is more accurate.

Some examples of clinical acid-base disturbances are shown in Table 40–2.

In treating acid-base disturbances, one must, of course, consider not only the blood but all the body fluid compartments. The other fluid compartments have markedly different concentrations of buffers. It has been determined empirically that administration of an amount of acid (in alkalosis) or base (in acidosis) equal to 50% of the body weight in kg times the blood base excess per liter will correct the acid-base disturbance in the whole body. At least when the abnormality is severe, however, it is unwise to attempt such a large correction in a single step; instead, about half the indicated amount should be given, and the arterial blood acid-base values determined again. The amount required for final correction can then be calculated and administered.

Relation Between Potassium Metabolism & Acid-Base Balance

The K^+ and H^+ concentrations of the ECF parallel each other, in part because of the effects of K^+ on renal H^+ secretion (see Chapter 38). K^+ depletion apparently produces an intracellular acidosis, promoting H^+ secretion into the urine. H^+ is thus removed from the body and HCO_3^- reabsorption increased, producing an extracellular alkalosis. Conversely, K^+ excess increases K^+ secretion by the renal tubular cells. Since both H^+ and K^+ are secreted in exchange for Na^+ and compete for the available Na^+ in the tubular fluid, H^+ secretion is inhibited, promoting extracellular acidosis.

References: Section VIII.
Formation & Excretion of Urine

Andreoli TE & others: Questions and replies: Renal mechanisms for urinary concentrating and diluting processes. Am J Physiol 235:F1, 1978.

Brenner BM, Beeuwkes R: The renal circulations. Hosp Pract 13:35, July 1978.

Brenner BM, Boylis C, Deen WM: Transport of molecules across renal glomerular capillaries. Physiol Rev 56:502, 1976.

Brenner BM, Rector FC Jr: *The Kidney.* 2 vols. Saunders, 1976.

Brenner BM, Stein JH (editors): *Sodium and Water Homeostasis.* Churchill-Livingstone, 1978.

Burg M, Stoner L: Renal chloride transport and the mode of action of some diuretics. Annu Rev Physiol 38:150, 1976.

Cannon PJ: The kidney in heart failure. N Engl J Med 296:26, 1977.

Cox M, Sterns RH, Singer I: The defense against hyperkalemia: The roles of insulin and aldosterone. N Engl J Med 299:525, 1978.

Davenport HW: *The ABC of Acid-Base Chemistry,* 6th ed. Univ of Chicago Press, 1974.

DuBose TD, Kokko JP: Renal chloride transport and control of extracellular fluid volume. Cardiovasc Med 2:967, 1977.

Dunn MJ, Hood VL: Prostaglandins and the kidney. Am J Physiol 233:F169, 1977.

Feig PU, McCurdy DK: The hypertonic state. N Engl J Med 297:444, 1977.

Fisher JW (editor): *Kidney Hormones.* Academic Press, 1971.

Gennari FJ, Kassirer JP: Osmotic diuresis. N Engl J Med 291:714, 1974.

Hutch JA: *Anatomy and Physiology of the Bladder, Trigone and Urethra.* Appleton-Century-Crofts, 1972.

Masoro EJ, Siegel PD: *Acid-Base Regulation: Its Physiology, Pathophysiology, and the Interpretation of Blood-Gas Analysis,* 2nd ed. Saunders, 1977.

Mercer PF, Maddox DA, Brenner BM: Current concepts of sodium chloride and water transport by the mammalian nephron. West J Med 120:33, 1974.

Scholander RF: The wonderful net. Sci Am 196:96, April 1957.

Segal S: Disorders of renal amino acid transport. N Engl J Med 294:1044, 1976.

Siggaard-Andersen O: *The New Acid-Base Status of Blood.* Williams & Wilkins, 1965.

Tannen RL: Ammonia metabolism. Am J Physiol 235:F265, 1978.

Waddell WJ, Bates RG: Intracellular pH. Physiol Rev 49:285, 1969.

Wright FS: Regulation of glomerular filtration rate and renal salt excretion by a single-nephron feedback pathway. Cardiovasc Med 3:731, 1978.

Wright FS, Giebisch G: Renal potassium transport: Contributions of individual nephron segments and populations. Am J Physiol 235:F515, 1978.

Appendix

GENERAL REFERENCES

Many large, comprehensive textbooks of physiology are available. The following are among the best of the recently revised volumes:

Brobeck JR (editor): *Best and Taylor's Physiological Basis of Medical Practice,* 9th ed. Williams & Wilkins, 1973.

Guyton AC: *Textbook of Medical Physiology,* 5th ed. Saunders, 1976.

Mountcastle VB (editor): *Medical Physiology,* 13th ed. 2 vols. Mosby, 1974.

Year Book Medical Publishers, Inc., has published a series of monographs on various aspects of physiology. The volumes, which are generally excellent, are collectively equivalent to a comprehensive text on physiology.

Excellent summaries of current research on selected aspects of physiology can be found in the symposia published in *Federation Proceedings* and in the *Annals of the New York Academy of Sciences.* Summary articles appear in *Hospital Practice,* and various types of valuable reviews appear in the *New England Journal of Medicine.* These include articles that review current topics in physiology and biochemistry with the aim of providing up-to-date information for practicing physicians. The most pertinent serial review publications are *Physiological Reviews, Pharmacological Reviews, Recent Progress in Hormone Research* (the proceedings of each annual Laurentian Hormone Conference), *Annual Review of Physiology,* and other volumes of the Annual Review series. The American Physiological Society is currently publishing a *Handbook of Physiology,* separate volumes of which cover all aspects of physiology. The volumes published cover neurophysiology, circulation, respiration, adaptation to the environment, adipose tissue, the alimentary canal, endocrinology, and renal physiology. The articles in them are valuable but extremely detailed reviews. The MTP *International Review of Physiology,* which began to appear in 1974, is now made up of 16 volumes of contributed chapters on all aspects of physiology. The *Biology Data Book,* published in 3 volumes by the Federation of American Societies for Experimental Biology, contains tables and lists that are useful for looking up specific items of information.

NORMAL VALUES & THE STATISTICAL EVALUATION OF DATA

The approximate ranges of values in normal humans for some commonly measured plasma constituents are summarized in the table on the inside back cover. A worldwide attempt is currently being made to convert to a single standard nomenclature by using SI (Système International) units. The system is based on the 7 dimensionally independent physical quantities summarized in Table 1. Units derived from the basic units are summarized in Table 2, and the prefixes used to refer to decimal fractions and multiples of these and other units are listed in Table 3. There are a number of complexities involved in the use of these units—for example, the problem of expressing enzyme units— and they are only slowly making their way into medical literature. In this book, the values in the text are in traditional units, but they are followed in key instances by values in SI units. In addition, values in SI units are listed beside values in more traditional units in the table on the inside back cover.

The accuracy of the methods used for laboratory measurements varies. It is important in evaluating any single measurement to know the possible errors in making the measurement. In the case of chemical determinations on body fluids, these include errors in obtaining the sample and the inherent error of the

Table 1. Basic units

Quantity	Name	Symbol
Length	meter	m
Mass	kilogram	kg
Time	second	s
Electric current	ampere	A
Thermodynamic temperature	kelvin	K
Luminous intensity	candela	cd
Amount of substance	mole	mol

Table 2. Some derived SI units.

Quantity	Unit Name	Unit Symbol
Area	square meter	m^2
Clearance	liter/second	L/s
Concentration		
Mass	kilogram/liter	kg/L
Substance	mole/liter	mol/L
Density	kilogram/liter	kg/L
Electric potential	volt	$V = kg\, m^2/s^3\, A$
Energy	joule	$J = kg\, m^2/s^2$
Force	newton	$N = kg\, m/s^2$
Frequency	hertz	$Hz = 1\ cycle/s$
Pressure	pascal	$Pa = kg/m\, s^2$
Temperature	degree Celsius	$°C = °K - 273.15$
Volume	cubic meter	m^3
	liter	$L = dm^3$

chemical method. However, the values obtained using even the most accurate methods vary from one normal individual to the next as a result of what is usually called **biologic variation.** This variation is due to the fact that in any system as complex as a living organism or tissue there are many variables which affect the particular measurement. Variables such as age, sex, time of day, time since last meal, etc can be controlled. Numerous other variables cannot, and for this reason the values obtained differ from individual to individual.

Table 3. Standard prefixes.

Prefix	Abbreviation	Magnitude
tera-	T	10^{12}
giga-	G	10^9
mega-	M	10^6
kilo-	k	10^3
hecto-	h	10^2
deca-	da	10^1
deci-	d	10^{-1}
centi-	c	10^{-2}
milli-	m	10^{-3}
micro-	μ	10^{-6}
nano-	n, mμ	10^{-9}
pico-	p, $\mu\mu$	10^{-12}
femto-	f	10^{-15}
atto-	a	10^{-18}

These prefixes are applied to SI and other units. For example, a micrometer (μm) is 10^{-6} meter (also called a micron); a picoliter (pl) is 10^{-12} liter; and a kilogram (kg) is 10^3 grams. Also applied to seconds, units, moles, hertz, volts, farads, ohms, curies, equivalents, osmoles, etc.

The magnitude of the normal range for any given physiologic or clinical measurement can be calculated by standard statistical technics if the measurement has been made on a suitable sample of the normal population (preferably more than 20 individuals). It is important to know not only the average value in this sample but also the extent of the deviation of the individual values from the average.

The average, or **arithmetic mean (M),** of the series of values is readily calculated:

$$M = \frac{\Sigma X}{n}$$

where Σ = Sum of
  X = The individual values
  n = Number of individual values in the series

The average deviation is the mean of the deviations of each of the values from the mean. From a mathematical point of view, a better measure of the deviation is the **geometric mean** of the deviations from the mean. This is called the **standard deviation** (σ):

$$\sigma = \sqrt{\frac{\Sigma (M - X)^2}{n-1}}$$

The term $n-1$ rather than n is used in the denominator of this equation because the σ of a sample of the population rather than the σ of the whole population is being calculated. The following form of the equation for σ can be derived algebraically and is convenient for those using a calculator to compute σ:

$$\sigma = \sqrt{\frac{\Sigma X^2 - \frac{(\Sigma X)^2}{n}}{n-1}}$$

Here, ΣX^2 is the sum of the squares of the individual values, and $(\Sigma X)^2$ is the square of the sum of the items, ie, the items added together and then squared.

Another commonly used index of the variation is the **standard error of the mean** (SE, SEM):

$$SE = \frac{\sigma}{\sqrt{n}}$$

Strictly speaking, the SE indicates the reliability of the sample mean as representative of the true mean of the general population from which the sample was drawn.

A **frequency distribution** curve can be constructed from the individual values in the sample by plotting the frequency with which any particular value occurs in the series against the values. If the group of individuals tested was homogeneous, the frequency distribution curve is usually symmetrical (Fig 1), with the highest frequency corresponding to the mean and the width of the curve varying with σ (curve of **normal distribution**). Within an ideal curve of normal distribution, the percentage of observations that fall

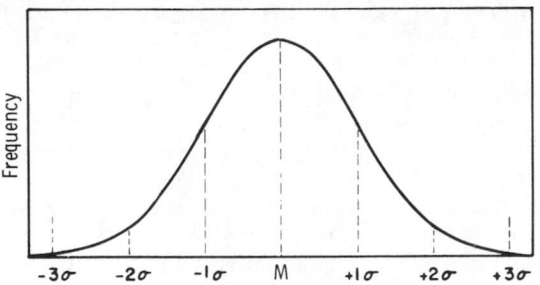

Figure 1. Curve of normal distribution (frequency distribution curve of values from a homogeneous sample of a population).

within various ranges are shown in Table 4. The mean and σ of a representative sample are approximately those of the whole population. It is therefore possible to predict from the mean and σ of the sample the probability that any particular value in the general population is normal. For example, if the difference between such a value and the mean is equal to 1.96 σ, the chances are 1 out of 20 (5 out of 100) that it is normal. Conversely, of course, the chances are 19 out of 20 that it is abnormal. It is unfortunate that data on normal means and σs are not more generally available for the important plasma and urinary constituents in humans.

Table 4. Percentage of values in a population which will fall within various ranges within an ideal curve of normal distribution.

Mean ± 1 σ	68.27%
Mean ± 1.96 σ	95.00%
Mean ± 2 σ	95.45%
Mean ± 3 σ	99.73%

Statistical analysis is also useful in evaluating the significance of the difference between 2 means. In physiologic and clinical research, measurements are often made on a group of animals or patients given a particular treatment. These measurements are compared with similar measurements made on a control group which ideally has been exposed to exactly the same conditions except that the treatment has not been given. If a particular mean value in the treated group is different from the corresponding mean for the control group, the question arises whether the difference is due to the treatment or to chance variation. The probability that the difference represents chance variation can be estimated in many instances by using **"Student's"** t **test.** The value t is the ratio of the difference in the means of 2 series (M_a and M_b) to the uncertainty in these means. The formula used to calculate t is

$$t = \frac{M_a - M_b}{\sqrt{\dfrac{(n_a + n_b)[(n_a - 1)\sigma_a^2 + (n_b - 1)\sigma_b^2]}{n_a n_b (n_a + n_b - 2)}}}$$

where n_a and n_b are the number of individual values in series a and b, respectively. When n_a, = n_b, the equation for t becomes simplified to:

$$t = \frac{M_a - M_b}{\sqrt{(SE_a)^2 + (SE_b)^2}}$$

The higher the value of t, the less the probability that the difference represents chance variation. This probability also decreases as the number of individuals (n) in each group rises because the greater the number of measurements, the smaller the error in the measurements. A mathematical expression of the probability (P) for any value of t at different values of n can be found in tables in most texts on statistics. P is a fraction which expresses the probability that the difference between 2 means was due to chance variation. Thus, for example, if the P value is 0.10, the probability that the difference was due to chance is 10% (1 chance in 10). A P value of < 0.001 means that the chances that the difference was due to random variation are less than 1 in 1000. When the P value is < 0.05, most investigators call the difference "statistically significant," ie, it is concluded that the difference is due to the operation of some factor other than chance— presumably the treatment. The conditions under which it is appropriate to use Student's t test, and the conditions under which other tests should be used to calculate P are discussed in statistics texts.

These elementary statistical methods and many others are available for analyzing data in the research laboratory and the clinic. They provide a valuable objective means of evaluation. Statistical significance does not arbitrarily mean physiologic significance, and the reverse may sometimes be true; but replacement of evaluation by subjective impression with analysis by statistical methods is certainly an important goal in the medical sciences.

References: Appendix

Colton T: *Statistics in Medicine*. Little, Brown, 1974.
The SI for the Health Professions. World Health Organization, 1977.

Winer GJ: *Statistical Principles in Experimental Design*, 2nd ed. McGraw-Hill, 1971.
Zar JH: *Biostatistical Analysis*. Prentice-Hall, 1974.

ABBREVIATIONS & SYMBOLS COMMONLY USED IN PHYSIOLOGY

[ ]: Concentration of

Δ: Change in. (*Example:* ΔV = change in volume.) In steroid nomenclature, Δ followed by a number (eg, Δ^4-) indicates the position of a double bond

σ: Standard deviation

Ia, Ib, II, III, IV nerve fibers: Types of fibers in sensory nerves (see Chapter 2)

μ: Micro, 10^{-6}; see Table 3, above

A (A): Angstrom unit(s) (10^{-10}m, 0.1 nm)

a: atto-, 10^{-18}; see Table 3, above

A⁻: General symbol for anion

A₁, A₂, A₁B, A₂B, B, O: Major blood groups

A, B, and C nerve fibers: Types of fibers in peripheral nerves (see Chapter 2)

Acetyl-CoA: Acetyl-coenzyme A

ACH, Ach: Acetylcholine

ACTH: Adrenocorticotropic hormone

Acyl-CoA: General symbol for an organic compound–coenzyme A ester

ADH: Antidiuretic hormone (vasopressin)

ADP: Adenosine diphosphate

AHG: Antihemophilic globulin

Ala: Alanine

AMP: Adenosine-5-monophosphate

APUD cells: Amine precursor uptake and decarboxylation cells that secrete hormones

Arg: Arginine

   NH₂
   |

Asn, Asp: Asparagine

Asp: Aspartic acid

atm: Atmosphere: 1 atm = 760 torr = mean atmospheric pressure at sea level

ATP: Adenosine triphosphate

A-V difference: Arteriovenous concentration difference of any given substance

AV node: Atrioventricular node

aVR, aVF, aVL: Augmented unipolar electrocardiographic leads

AV valves: Atrioventricular valves of heart

BEI: Butanol-extractable iodine

BER: Basic electrical rhythm

BMR: Basal metabolic rate

BSP: Sulfobromophthalein

BUN: Blood urea nitrogen

c: Centi-, 10^{-2}; see Table 3, above

C: Celsius

C followed by subscript: Clearance; eg, C_{In} = clearance of inulin

C 19 steroids: Steroids containing 19 carbon atoms

C 21 steroids: Steroids containing 21 carbon atoms

cal: The calorie (gram calorie)

Cal: 1000 calories; kilocalorie

cAMP: Cyclic adenosine-3′,5′-monophosphate

CBF: Cerebral blood flow

CBG: Corticosteroid-binding globulin, transcortin

cc: Cubic centimeters

CCK, CCK-PZ: Cholecystokinin-pancreozymin

CFF: Critical fusion frequency

CGP: Chorionic growth hormone–prolactin (same as HCS)

CH₂O: "Free water clearance"

Ci: Curie

CLIP: Corticotropinlike intermediate lobe peptide

CMRO₂: Cerebral metabolic rate for oxygen

CNS: Central nervous system

CoA: Coenzyme A

COHb: Carbonmonoxyhemoglobin

Compound A: 11-Dehydrocorticosterone

Compound B: Corticosterone

Compound E: Cortisone

Compound F: Cortisol

Compound S: 11-Deoxycortisol

COMT: Catechol-O-methyltransferase

cps: Cycles per second, hertz

CR: Conditioned reflex

Cr: Creatinine

CRH, CRF: Corticotropin-releasing hormone

CRO: Cathode-ray oscilloscope

CrP: Creatinine phosphate (phosphocreatine, PC)

CS: Conditioned stimulus

CSF: Cerebrospinal fluid

C terminal: End of peptide or protein having a free –COOH group

CTP: Cytidine triphosphate

CV: Closing volume

CVR: Cerebral vascular resistance

cyclic AMP: Cyclic adenosine-3′,5′-monophosphate

Cys: Half-cystine

CZI: Crystalline zinc insulin

d: Day

D: Geometric isomer of L form of chemical compound

dalton: Unit of mass, equal to one-twelfth the mass of the carbon-12 atom, or about 1.65×10^{-24} g

dB: Decibel

DDAVP: 1-deamino-8D-arginine vasopressin

DDD: Derivative of DDT that inhibits adrenocortical function

DEA, DHEA: Dehydroepiandrosterone

DHT: Dihydrotestosterone

DIT: Diiodotyrosine

DNA: Deoxyribonucleic acid

D/N ratio: Ratio of dextrose (glucose) to nitrogen in the urine

D₂O: Deuterium oxide (heavy water)

DOCA: Desoxycorticosterone acetate

DOMA: 3,4-dihydroxymandelic acid

Dopa: Dihydroxyphenylalanine, L-dopa

DOPAC: 3,4-dihydroxyphenylacetic acid

DOPEG: 3,4-dihydroxyphenylglycol

DOPET: 3,4-dihydroxyphenylethanol

DPG, 2,3-DPG: 2,3-Diphosphoglycerate

DPL: Dipalmitoyl lecithin

DPN: Diphosphopyridine nucleotide

DPNH: Reduced diphosphopyridine nucleotide

DPPC: Dipalmitoylphosphatidylcholine

e: Base for natural logarithms = 2.7182818 . . .

E followed by subscript number: Esophageal electrocardiographic lead, followed by number of cm it is inserted in esophagus

E₁: Estrone

E₂: Estradiol

EACA: Epsilon-aminocaproic acid

ECF: Extracellular fluid

ECG: Electrocardiogram

ECoG: Electrocorticogram

EDTA: Ethylenediaminetetraacetic acid

EEG: Electroencephalogram

EGF: Epidermal growth factor

EJP: Excitatory junction potential

EKG: Electrocardiogram

EMG: Electromyogram

EP: Endogenous pyrogen

EPSP: Excitatory postsynaptic potential

Eq: Equivalent(s)

ERG: Electroretinogram

ERPF: Effective renal plasma flow

ETP: Electron transport particle

f: Femto-, 10^{-15}; see Table 3, above

F: Fahrenheit

FDP: Fibrinogen degradation products

FEV 1'': Forced expiratory volume in 1 s

FFA: Unesterified free fatty acid (also called NEFA, UFA)

FGF: Fibroblast growth factor

FRH, FSH-RH, FRF: FSH-releasing hormone

FSH: Follicle-stimulating hormone

ft: Foot or feet

g, gm: Gram(s)

g: Unit of force; 1 *g* equals the force of gravity on the earth's surface

G: Glucose; also giga-, 10^9; see Table 3, above

GABA: Gamma-aminobutyric acid

GBG: Gonadal steroid–binding globulin

GFR: Glomerular filtration rate

GH: Growth hormone

GIH, GIF: Growth hormone–inhibiting hormone

GIP: Gastric inhibitory peptide

GLI: Glucagonlike immunoreactive factor from gastrointestinal mucosa

$$\overset{\text{NH}_2}{\underset{|}{}}$$

Gln, Glu: Glutamine

Glu: Glutamic acid

Gly: Glycine

G6PD: Glucose-6-phosphate dehydrogenase

GRH, GRF: Growth hormone–releasing hormone

GTP: Guanosine triphosphate

h: Hour(s)

HA: General symbol for an acid

Hb: Deoxygenated hemoglobin

HBE: His bundle electrogram

HbO$_2$: Oxyhemoglobin

HCC, 25-HCC: 25-Hydroxycholecalciferol, an active metabolite of vitamin D$_3$

HCG: Human chorionic gonadotropin

HCS: Human chorionic somatomammotropin

Hct: Hematocrit

HDL: High-density lipoprotein

HGH: Human growth hormone

HIOMT: Hydroxyindole-O-methyltransferase

His: Histidine

HPL: Human placental lactogen (same as HCS)

HS-CoA: Reduced coenzyme A

H substance: Histaminelike capillary vasodilator

5-HT: Serotonin

HVA: Homovanillic acid

Hyl: Hydroxylysine

Hyp: 4-Hydroxyproline

Hz: Hertz, unit of frequency. 1 cycle per second = 1 hertz

IDL: Intermediate-density lipoprotein

IJP: Inhibitory junction potential

Ile, Ileu: Isoleucine

In: Inulin

IPSP: Inhibitory postsynaptic potential

ITP: Inosine triphosphate

IU: International unit(s)

J: Joule (SI unit of energy)

k: Kilo-, 10^3; see Table 3, above

kcal (Cal): Kilocalorie (1000 calories)

K$_E$: Exchangeable body potassium

L: Geometric isomer of D form of chemical compound

LATS: Long-acting thyroid stimulator

LDL: Low-density lipoprotein

Leu: Leucine

LH: Luteinizing hormone

ln: Natural logarithm

log: Logarithm to base 10

LPH: Lipotropin

LRH, LH-RH, LRF: Luteinizing hormone–releasing hormone

LSD: Lysergic acid diethylamide

LTH: Luteotropic hormone (prolactin)

LVET: Left ventricular ejection time

Lys: Lysine

m: Meter(s); also milli-, 10^{-3}; see Table 3, above

M: Molarity (mol/L); also mega-, 10^6; see Table 3, above

MAO: Monoamine oxidase

MBC: Maximal breathing capacity (same as MVV)

Met: Methionine

mho: Unit of conductance; the reciprocal of the ohm

min: Minute(s)

MIT: Monoiodotyrosine

mol: Mole, gram molecular weight

MOPEG: 3-methoxy-4-hydroxyphenylglycol

MRF: Müllerian regression factor

mRNA: Messenger RNA

MSH: Melanocyte-stimulating hormone

MT: 3-Methoxytyramine

MVV: Maximal voluntary ventilation

n: nano-, 10^{-9}; see Table 3, above

N: Normality (of a solution); also newton (SI unit of force)

NAD$^+$: Nicotinamide adenine dinucleotide; same as DPN

NADH: Dihydronicotinamide adenine dinucleotide; same as DPNH

NADP$^+$: Nicotinamide adenine dinucleotide phosphate; same as TPN

NADPH: Dihydronicotinamide adenine dinucleotide phosphate; same as TPNH

Na$_E$: Exchangeable body sodium

NEFA: Unesterified (nonesterified) free fatty acid (same as FFA)

NGF: Nerve growth factor

NPH insulin: Neutral protamine Hagedorn insulin

NPN: Nonprotein nitrogen

NREM sleep: Non–rapid eye movement (spindle) sleep

NSILA: Nonsuppressible insulin-like activity

N terminal: End of peptide or protein having a free $-NH_2$ group

O: The symbol O indicates absence of a sex chromosome, eg, XO as opposed to XX or XY

OGF: Ovarian growth factor

Osm: Osmole(s)

OVLT: Organum vasculosum of the lamina terminalis

p: Pico-, 10^{-12}; see Table 3, above

P followed by subscript: Plasma concentration, eg, P_{Cr} = plasma creatinine concentration; also permeability coefficient, eg, P_{Na^+} = permeability coefficient for Na^+; also pressure (see respiratory symbols, below)

P$_{50}$: Partial pressure of O_2 at which hemoglobin is half saturated with O_2

P$_a$: Pascal (SI unit of pressure)

PAH: Para-aminohippuric acid

PBI: Protein-bound iodine

PEP: Preejection period

P factor: Hypothetical pain-producing substance produced in ischemic muscle

PGO spikes: Ponto-geniculo-occipital spikes in REM sleep

pH: Negative logarithm of the hydrogen ion concentration of a solution

Phe: Phenylalanine

PIH, PIF: Prolactin-inhibiting hormone

pK: Negative logarithm of the equilibrium constant for a chemical reaction

PMN: Polymorphonuclear neutrophilic leukocyte

PMS: Pregnant mare's serum gonadotropin

PRH, PRF: Prolactin-releasing hormone

Pro: Proline

Prot⁻: Protein anion

5-PRPP: 5-Phosphoribosyl pyrophosphate

PTA: Plasma thromboplastin antecedent (clotting factor XI)

PTC: Plasma thromboplastin component (clotting factor IX); also phenylthiocarbamide

PTH: Parathyroid hormone

(pyro)Glu: Pyroglutamic acid

PZI: Protamine zinc insulin

QS₂: Total electrochemical systole

R: General symbol for remainder of a chemical formula, eg, an alcohol is R–OH; also gas constant; also respiratory exchange ratio; also Reynolds' number

RAS: Reticular activating system

rbc: Red blood cell(s)

REF: Renal erythropoietic factor

REM sleep: Rapid eye movement (paradoxical) sleep

Reverse T₃: 3,3′,5′-Triiodothyronine; isomer of triiodothyronine

Rh factor: Rhesus group of red cell agglutinogens

RMV: Respiratory minute volume

RNA: Ribonucleic acid

RPF: Renal plasma flow

RQ: Respiratory quotient

R state: State of heme in hemoglobin that increases O_2 binding

R unit: Unit of resistance in cardiovascular system; mm Hg divided by ml/s

s: Second(s)

SA: Specific activity

SA node: Sinoatrial node

SCUBA: Self-contained underwater breathing apparatus

SDA: Specific dynamic action

SE (SEM): Standard error of the mean

Ser: Serine

Sf units: Svedberg units of flotation

SGOT: Serum glutamic-oxaloacetic transaminase

SH: Sulfhydryl

SI units: Units of the Système International d'Unités

SPCA: Proconvertin (clotting factor VII)

sq cm: Square centimeter(s)

SRIF: Somatotropin release–inhibiting factor; same as GIH

sRNA: Soluble or transfer RNA

STH: Somatotropin, growth hormone

Substance P: Polypeptide found in brain

T: Absolute temperature

T₃: 3,5,3′-Triiodothyronine

T₄: Thyroxine

TBG: Thyroxine-binding globulin

TBPA: Thyroxine-binding prealbumin

TBW: Total body water

TEA: Tetraethylammonium

TETRAC: Tetraiodothyroacetic acid

TF/P: Concentration of a substance in renal tubular fluid divided by its concentration in plasma

Thr: Threonine

Tm: Renal tubular maximum

torr: 1/760 atm = 1.00000014 mm Hg; unit for various pressures in the body

TPN: Triphosphopyridine nucleotide

TPNH: Reduced triphosphopyridine nucleotide

TRH, TRF: Thyrotropin-releasing hormone

tRNA: Transfer RNA; same as sRNA

Trp, Try, Tryp: Tryptophan

TSF: Thrombopoietic stimulating factor, thrombopoietin

TSH: Thyroid-stimulating hormone

TSI: Thyroid-stimulating immunoglobulins

T/S ratio: Thyroid/serum iodide ratio

T state: State of heme in hemoglobin that decreases O_2 binding

TTX: Tetrodotoxin

Tyr: Tyrosine

U: Unit(s)

U followed by subscript: Urine concentration, eg, U_{Cr} = urine creatinine concentration

UDPG: Uridine diphosphoglucose

UFA: Unesterified free fatty acid (same as FFA)

URF: Uterine relaxing factor; relaxin

US: Unconditioned stimulus

UTP: Uridine triphosphate

UWL: Unstirred water layer

V: Urine volume/unit time; volt

V₁, V₂, etc: Unipolar chest electrocardiographic leads

Val: Valine

VF: Unipolar left leg electrocardiographic lead

VIP: Vasoactive intestinal peptide

VL: Left arm unipolar electrocardiographic lead

VLDL: Very low density lipoprotein

VMA: Vanillylmandelic acid (3-methoxy-4-hydroxymandelic acid)

VR: Unipolar right arm electrocardiographic lead

wbc: White blood cell(s)

X chromosome: One of the sex chromosomes in humans

X zone: Inner zone of adrenal cortex in some young mammals

Y chromosome: One of the sex chromosomes in humans

STANDARD RESPIRATORY SYMBOLS
(See Fed Proc 9:602, 1950.)

General Variables

V	Gas volume
$\dot{V}$	Gas volume/unit of time. (Dot over a symbol indicates rate.)
P	Gas pressure
$\bar{P}$	Mean gas pressure
f	Respiratory frequency (breaths/unit of time)
D	Diffusing capacity
F	Fractional concentration in dry gas phase
C	Concentration in blood phase
R	Respiratory exchange ratio = V_{CO_2}/V_{O_2}
Q	Volume of blood
$\dot{Q}$	Volume flow of blood/unit of time

Localization (Subscript letters)

I	Inspired gas
E	Expired gas
A	Alveolar gas
T	Tidal gas
D	Dead space gas
B	Barometric
a	Arterial blood
c	Capillary blood
v	Venous blood

Special Symbols

STPD	Standard temperature and pressure, dry (0 C, 760 mm Hg)
BTPS	Body temperature and pressure, saturated with water vapor
ATPD	Ambient temperature and pressure, dry
ATPS	Ambient temperature and pressure, saturated with water vapor

Molecular Species

Indicated by chemical formula printed as subscript.

Examples

$P_{I_{O_2}}$ = Pressure of oxygen in inspired air
V_D = Dead space gas volume

Equivalents of Metric, United States, and English Measures
(Values rounded off to 2 decimal places.)

Length

1 kilometer = 0.62 mile
1 mile = 5280 feet = 1.61 kilometers
1 meter = 39.37 inches
1 inch = 1/12 foot = 2.54 centimeters

Volume

1 liter = 1.06 US liquid quart
1 US liquid quart = 32 fluid ounces = 1/4 US gallon = 0.95 liter
1 milliliter = 0.03 fluid ounce
1 fluid ounce = 29.57 milliliters
1 US gallon = 0.83 English (Imperial) gallon

Weight

1 kilogram = 2.20 pounds (avoirdupois) = 2.68 pounds (apothecaries')
1 pound (avoirdupois) = 16 ounces = 453.60 grams
1 grain = 65 milligrams

Energy

1 kilogram-meter = 7.25 foot-pounds
1 foot-pound = 0.14 kilogram-meters

Temperature

To convert Celsius degrees into Fahrenheit, multiply by 9/5 and add 32
To convert Fahrenheit degrees into Celsius, subtract 32 and multiply by 5/9

Greek Alphabet

Symbol		Name	Symbol		Name
A	α	alpha	N	ν	nu
B	β	beta	Ξ	ξ	xi
Γ	γ	gamma	O	o	omicron
Δ	δ	delta	Π	π	pi
E	ϵ	epsilon	P	ρ	rho
Z	ζ	zeta	Σ	σ, ς	sigma
H	η	eta	T	τ	tau
Θ	θ	theta	Υ	υ	upsilon
I	ι	iota	Φ	ϕ	phi
K	κ	kappa	X	χ	chi
Λ	λ	lambda	Ψ	ψ	psi
M	μ	mu	Ω	ω	omega

Index

In general, phrases are indexed under the first word in the normal order of speech—eg, *Inborn errors of metabolism, Inhibitory mediator.* Extensive cross-indexing has also been done under major headings—eg, under *Insulin* are listed most of the subjects relating to insulin that are dealt with in the text, and the reader will be able to find specific references by scanning the column under the word. Familiar acronyms are listed as well as the corresponding expanded words and phrases, but only page numbers are given under the former; subheadings are listed under the latter. (See, for example, *ACTH* and *Adrenocorticotropic hormone*.) Acronyms and abbreviations commonly used in physiology are defined on pages 576–578.